STUDENT
SOLUTIONS MANUAL
Laurel Technical Services

ALGEBRA & TRIGONOMETRY

Robert Blitzer

Prentice
Hall

Upper Saddle River, NJ 07458

Editor in Chief: Sally Yagan
Supplement Editor: Dawn Murrin
Special Projects Manager: Barbara A. Murray
Production Editor: Wendy A. Perez
Supplement Cover Manager: Paul Gourhan
Supplement Cover Designer: PM Workshop Inc.
Manufacturing Buyer: Lisa McDowell

© 2001 by Prentice Hall
Upper Saddle River, NJ 07458

Printed in the United States of America

10 9 8 7 6 5 4 3 2

ISBN 0-13-089785-X

Prentice-Hall International (UK) Limited, London
Prentice-Hall of Australia Pty. Limited, Sydney
Prentice-Hall Canada, Inc., Toronto
Prentice-Hall Hispanoamericana, S.A., Mexico
Prentice-Hall of India Private Limited, New Delhi
Pearson Education Asia Pte. Ltd., Singapore
Prentice-Hall of Japan, Inc., Tokyo
Editora Prentice-Hall do Brazil, Ltda., Rio de Janeiro

Table of Contents

Chapter P

Check Point Exercises

1. a. $\left| 1 - \sqrt{2} \right|$

   Because $\sqrt{2} \approx 1.4$, the number inside the absolute value bars is negative. The absolute value of x when $x < 0$ is $-x$. Thus,

   $$\left| 1 - \sqrt{2} \right| = -\left(1 - \sqrt{2} \right) = \sqrt{2} - 1.$$

   b. $\left| \pi - 3 \right|$

   Because $\pi \approx 3.14$, the number inside the absolute value bars is positive. The absolute value of a positive number is the number itself. Thus,
   $\left| \pi - 3 \right| = \pi - 3.$

   c. $\dfrac{|x|}{x}$ if $x > 0$

   If $x > 0$, then $|x| = x$. Thus,

   $$\dfrac{|x|}{x} = \dfrac{x}{x} = 1.$$

2. Because the distance between a and b is given by $|a - b|$, the distance between -4 and 5 is
   $|-4 - 5| = |-9| = 9.$

3. Begin by substituting 100 for x. Because $x = 100$, we will be finding the U.S. population 100 years after 1980, in the year 2080.
   $2.35(100) + 179.5$
   $= 235 + 179.5$
   $= 414.5$
   Thus, in 2080, the population of the United States will be 414.5 million.

4. Simplify: $7(4x - 3y) + 2(5x + y)$.
   Use the distributive property to remove the parentheses. Then, multiply and group like terms. Finally combine like terms.

$7(4x - 3y) + 2(5x + y)$.
$= 7 \cdot 4x - 7 \cdot 3y + 2 \cdot 5x + 2 \cdot y$
$= 28x - 21y + 10x + 2y$
$= (28x + 10x) + (2y - 21y)$
$= 38x - 19y$

Exercise Set P.1

For Exercises 1 and 3:

a. The natural numbers are used for counting, $\{1, 2, 3, 4, 5 \ldots\}$.

b. The whole numbers add 0 to the set of natural numbers, $\{0, 1, 2, 3, 4, 5, \ldots\}$.

c. The integers add the negative of the natural numbers to the set of whole numbers,
$\{\ldots, -5, -4, -3, -2, -1, 0, 1, 2, 3, 4, 5, \ldots\}$.

d. The rational numbers can be expressed as an integer divided by a nonzero integer or a terminating or repeating decimal.

e. The irrational numbers cannot be expressed as a quotient of integers or a terminating or repeating decimal.

1. a. $\sqrt{100}$

   b. $0, \sqrt{100}$

   c. $-9, \ 0, \ \sqrt{100}$

   d. $-9, \ \dfrac{-4}{5}, \ 0, \ 0.25, \ 9.2, \ \sqrt{100}$

   e. $\sqrt{3}$

3. a. $\sqrt{64}$

   b. $0, \sqrt{64}$

   c. $-11, 0, \sqrt{64}$

   d. $-11, \dfrac{-5}{6}, 0, 0.75, \sqrt{64}$

   e. $\sqrt{5}, \pi$

5. 0

7. Answers may vary.

9. True; -13 is to the left of -2 on the number line.

11. True; 4 is to the right of -7 on the number line.

13. True; $-\pi = -\pi$

15. $|300| = 300$

17. $|12 - \pi| = 12 - \pi$

19. $\left|\sqrt{2} - 5\right| = 5 - \sqrt{2}$

21. $\dfrac{-3}{|-3|} = \dfrac{-3}{3} = -1$

23. $|17 - 2| = |15| = 15$

25. $|5 - (-2)| = |7| = 7$

27. $|-4 - (-19)| = |15| = 15$

29. $|-1.4 - (-3.6)| = |2.2| = 2.2$

31. $5x + 7 = 5\,(4) + 7 = 27$

33. $4(x + 3) - 11 = 4[(-5) + 3] - 11$
$$= 4(-2) - 11 = -19$$

35. $\dfrac{5}{9}(F - 32) = \dfrac{5}{9}(77 - 32)$
$$= \dfrac{5}{9}(45)$$
$$= 25$$

37. $\dfrac{5(x + 2)}{2x - 14} = \dfrac{5(10 + 2)}{2(10) - 14}$
$$= \dfrac{5(12)}{6}$$
$$= 5 \cdot 2$$
$$= 10$$

39. $6 + (-4) = (-4) + 6$; commutative property of addition

41. $6 + (2 + 7) = (6 + 2) + 7$; associative property of addition

43. $(2 + 3) + (4 + 5) = (4 + 5) + (2 + 3)$; commutative property of addition

45. $-2 - (-8 + 6) = -16 + 12$; distributive property of multiplication over addition

47. $5(3x + 4) - 4 = 5 \cdot 3x + 5 \cdot 4 - 4$
$$= 15x + 20 - 4$$
$$= 15x + 16$$

49. $5(3x - 2) + 12x = 5 \cdot 3x - 5 \cdot 2 + 12x$
$$= 15x - 10 + 12x$$
$$= 27x - 10$$

51. $7(3y - 5) + 2(4y + 3)$
$$= 7 \cdot 3y - 7 \cdot 5 + 2 \cdot 4y + 2 \cdot 3$$
$$= 21y - 35 + 8y + 6$$
$$= 29y - 29$$

53. $-(-14x) = 14x$

55. $-(2x - 3y - 6) = -2x + 3y + 6$

57. $\dfrac{1}{3}(3x) + [(4y) + (-4y)] = x + 0$
$$= x$$

59. Yes; The order in which you put on your shoes does not matter.

61. Answers may vary.

63. $962x + 18{,}667 = 962(7) + 18{,}667$
$$= 6734 + 18{,}667$$
$$= 25{,}401$$
$1990 + 7 = 1997$
In 1997, the average yearly earnings in the
United States was \$25,401.

65. a. $0.6(220 - a) = 0.6(220) - 0.6(a)$
$$= 132 - 0.6a$$

b.   Let $a = 20$
$0.6(220 - a) = 0.6(220 - 20)$
$$= 0.6(200)$$
$$= 120$$
$132 - 0.6a = 132 - 0.6(20)$
$$= 132 - 12 = 120$$

67.–71. Answers may vary.

73. a.   False; For example, 1.7 is a rational
number and it is not an integer.

b.   False; All whole numbers,
$\{0, 1, 2, 3, \ldots\}$, are also integers.

c.   True; $-7\,5$ is a rational number and it is
not positive.

d.   False; $-\pi$ is an irrational number that is
also negative.

(c) is true.

75. $\sqrt{2} \approx 1.4$
$1.4 < 1.5$
$\sqrt{2} < 1.5$

77.
$-\dfrac{3.14}{2} = -1.57$
$-\dfrac{\pi}{2} \approx -1.571$
$-1.57 > -1.571$
$-\dfrac{3.14}{2} > -\dfrac{\pi}{2}$

Section P.2

Check Point Exercises

1. $(-4)^3 \cdot 2^2 = (-4)(-4)(-4) \cdot 2 \cdot 2$
$$= -64 \cdot 4$$
$$= -256$$

2. a. $2^{-3} = \dfrac{1}{2^3} = \dfrac{1}{2 \cdot 2 \cdot 2} = \dfrac{1}{8}$

b. $\dfrac{1}{6^{-2}} = \dfrac{1}{\frac{1}{6^2}} = 6^2 = 36$

3. a. $3^3 \cdot 3^2 = 3^{3+2} = 3^5 = 243$

b. $2^4 \cdot 2^{-7} = 2^{4+(-7)} = 2^{-3} = \dfrac{1}{2^3} = \dfrac{1}{8}$

c. $x^{-5} \cdot x^{11} = x^{-5+11} = x^6$

4. a. $(3^3)^2 = 3^{3 \cdot 2} = 3^6 = 729$

b. $(y^7)^4 = y^{7 \cdot 4} = y^{28}$

c. $(x^{-4})^2 = x^{-4 \cdot 2} = x^{-8} = \dfrac{1}{x^8}$

5. a. $\dfrac{3^6}{3^4} = 3^{6-4} = 3^2 = 9$

b. $\dfrac{x^5}{x^{12}} = x^{5-12} = x^{-7} = \dfrac{1}{x^7}$

c. $\dfrac{y^2}{y^{-7}} = y^{2-(-7)} = y^{2+7} = y^9$

6. $(-4x)^3 = (-4)^3 x^3 = -64x^3$

7. a. $\left(\dfrac{3}{4}\right)^3 = \dfrac{3^3}{4^3} = \dfrac{27}{64}$

b. $\left(-\dfrac{2}{y}\right)^5 = \dfrac{(-2)^5}{y^5} = \dfrac{-32}{y^5} = -\dfrac{32}{y^5}$

3

8. a. $(2x^3y^6)^4 = (2)^4(x^3)^4(y^6)^4$
         $= (2)^4 x^{3\cdot4} y^{6\cdot4}$
         $= 16x^{12}y^{24}$

    b. $(-6x^2y^5) = (-6)(3)x^2xy^5y3$
         $= -18x^{2+1}y^{5+3}$
         $= -18x^3y^8$

    c. $\dfrac{100x^{12}y^2}{20x^{16}y^{-4}} = \left(\dfrac{100}{20}\right)\left(\dfrac{x^{12}}{x^{16}}\right)\left(\dfrac{y^2}{y^{-4}}\right)$
         $= 5x^{12-16}y^{2-(-4)}$
         $= 5x^{-4}y^6$
         $= \dfrac{5y^6}{x^4}$

    d. $\left(\dfrac{5x}{y^4}\right)^{-2} = \dfrac{5^{-2}x^{-2}}{(y^4)^{-2}}$
         $= \dfrac{5^{-2}x^{-2}}{y^{-8}}$
         $= \dfrac{y^8}{5^2 x^2}$
         $= \dfrac{y^8}{25x^2}$

9. a.   Express 7.4×10^9 in decimal notation by moving the decimal point in 7.4 nine places to the right.
         $7.4 \times 10^9 = 7,400,000,000$

    b.   Express 3.017×10^{-6} in decimal notation by moving the decimal point in 3.017 six places to the left.
         $3.017 \times 10^{-6} = 0.000003017$

10. a.   To express 7,410,000,000 in scientific notation, the decimal point needs to move nine places. The exponent on 10 is positive since 7,410,000,000 is greater than 10.
         $7,410,000,000 = 7.41 \times 10^9$

    b.   To express 0.000000092 in scientific notation, the decimal points needs to move eight places. The exponent on 10

is negative since 0.000000092 is between 0 and 1.
         $0.000000092 = 9.2 \times 10^{-8}$

11. The total distance covered by all runners is the number of people who run in the New York City Marathon, 2×10^4, multiplied by the distance of the Marathon, 26 miles.
    $(2 \times 10^4) \times (26) = (2 \times 26) \times (10^4)$
    $= 52 \times 10^4$
    $= 5.2 \times 10^5$
    Thus, the total distance covered by all runners is 5.2×10^5 miles.

Exercise Set P.2

1. $5^2 \cdot 2 = (5 \cdot 5) \cdot 2 = 25 \cdot 2 = 50$

3. $(-2)^6 = (-2)(-2)(-2)(-2)(-2)(-2) = 64$

5. $-2^6 = -2 \cdot 2 \cdot 2 \cdot 2 \cdot 2 \cdot 2 = -64$

7. $(-3)^0 = 1$

9. $-3^0 = -1$

11. $4^{-3} = \dfrac{1}{4^3} = \dfrac{1}{4 \cdot 4 \cdot 4} = \dfrac{1}{64}$

13. $2^2 \cdot 2^3 = 2^{2+3} = 2^5 = 2 \cdot 2 \cdot 2 \cdot 2 \cdot 2 = 32$

15. $(2^2)^3 = 2^{2\cdot3} = 2^6 = 2 \cdot 2 \cdot 2 \cdot 2 \cdot 2 \cdot 2 = 64$

17. $\dfrac{2^8}{2^4} = 2^{8-4} = 2^4 = 2 \cdot 2 \cdot 2 \cdot 2 = 16$

19. $3^{-3} \cdot 3 = 3^{-3+1} = 3^{-2} = \dfrac{1}{3^2} = \dfrac{1}{3 \cdot 3} = \dfrac{1}{9}$

21. $\dfrac{2^3}{2^7} = 2^{3-7} = 2^{-4} = \dfrac{1}{2^4} = \dfrac{1}{2 \cdot 2 \cdot 2 \cdot 2} = \dfrac{1}{16}$

23. $x^{-2}y = \dfrac{1}{x^2} \cdot y = \dfrac{y}{x^2}$

25. $x^0 y^5 = 1 \cdot y^5 = y^5$

27. $x^3 \cdot x^7 = x^{3+7} = x^{10}$

29. $x^{-5} \cdot x^{10} = x^{-5+10} = x^5$

31. $(x^3)^7 = x^{3 \cdot 7} = x^{21}$

33. $(x^{-5})^3 = x^{-5 \cdot 3} = x^{-15} = \dfrac{1}{x^{15}}$

35. $\dfrac{x^{14}}{x^7} = x^{14-7} = x^7$

37. $\dfrac{x^{14}}{x^{-7}} = x^{14-(-7)} = x^{14+7} = x^{21}$

39. $(8x^3)^2 = 8^2(x^3)^2 = 8^2 x^{3 \cdot 2} = 64x^6$

41. $\left(-\dfrac{4}{x}\right)^3 = \dfrac{(-4)^3}{x^3} = -\dfrac{64}{x^3}$

43. $(-3x^2 y^5)^2 = (-3)^2 (x^2)^2 \cdot (y^5)^2$
$$= 9x^{2 \cdot 2} y^{5 \cdot 2}$$
$$= 9x^4 y^{10}$$

45. $(3x^4)(2x^7) = 3 \cdot 2 x^4 \cdot x^7 = 6x^{4+7} = 6x^{11}$

47. $(-9x^3 y)(-2x^6 y^4) = (-9)(-2)x^3 x^6 yy^4$
$$= 18x^{3+6} y^{1+4}$$
$$= 18x^9 y^5$$

49. $\dfrac{8x^{20}}{2x^4} = \left(\dfrac{8}{2}\right)\left(\dfrac{x^{20}}{x^4}\right) = 4x^{20-4} = 4x^{16}$

51. $\dfrac{25a^{13} \cdot b^4}{-5a^2 \cdot b^3} = \left(\dfrac{25}{-5}\right)\left(\dfrac{a^{13}}{a^2}\right)\left(\dfrac{b^4}{b^3}\right)$
$$= -5a^{13-2} b^{4-3}$$
$$= -5a^{11} b$$

53. $\dfrac{14b^7}{7b^{14}} = \left(\dfrac{14}{7}\right)\left(\dfrac{b^7}{b^{14}}\right) = 2 \cdot b^{7-14} = 2b^{-7} = \dfrac{2}{b^7}$

55. $(4x^3)^{-2} = (4^{-2})(x^3)^{-2}$
$$= 4^{-2} x^{-6}$$
$$= \dfrac{1}{4^2 x^6}$$
$$= \dfrac{1}{16x^6}$$

57. $\dfrac{24x^3 \cdot y^5}{32x^7 y^{-9}} = \dfrac{3}{4} x^{3-7} y^{5-(-9)}$
$$= \dfrac{3}{4} x^{-4} y^{14}$$
$$= \dfrac{3y^{14}}{4x^4}$$

59. $\left(\dfrac{5x^3}{y}\right)^{-2} = \dfrac{5^{-2} x^{3 \cdot (-2)}}{y^{-2}}$
$$= \dfrac{5^{-2} \cdot x^{-6}}{y^{-2}}$$
$$= \dfrac{y^2}{5^2 \cdot x^6}$$
$$= \dfrac{y^2}{25x^6}$$

61. $4.7 \times 10^3 = 4700$

63. $4 \times 10^6 = 4,000,000$

65. $7.86 \times 10^{-4} = 0.000786$

67. $3.18 \times 10^{-6} = 0.00000318$

69. $3600 = 3.6 \times 10^3$

71. $220,000,000 = 2.2 \times 10^8$

73. $0.027 = 2.7 \times 10^{-2}$

75. $0.000763 = 7.63 \times 10^{-4}$

77. $(2 \times 10^3)(3 \times 10^2) = (2 \times 3) \times (10^3 \times 10^2)$
$$= 6 \times 10^{3+2}$$
$$= 6 \times 10^5$$
$$= 600,000$$

79. $(4.1 \times 10^2)(3 \times 10^{-4}) = (4.1 \times 3) \times (10^2 \times 10^{-4})$
$$= 12.3 \times 10^{2+(-4)}$$
$$= 12.3 \times 10^{-2}$$
$$= 0.123$$

81. $\dfrac{12 \times 10^6}{4 \times 10^2} = \left(\dfrac{12}{4}\right) \times \left(\dfrac{10^6}{10^2}\right)$
$$= 3 \times 10^{6-2}$$
$$= 3 \times 10^4$$
$$= 30,000$$

83. $\dfrac{6.3 \times 10^3}{3 \times 10^5} = \left(\dfrac{6.3}{3}\right) \times \left(\dfrac{10^3}{10^5}\right)$
$$= 2.1 \times 10^{3-5} = 2.1 \times 10^{-2}$$
$$= 0.021$$

85. $1,694,000$ million $= (1.694 \times 10^6)(1 \times 10^6)$
$$= 1.694 \times 10^{6+6}$$
$$= 1.694 \times 10^{12}$$

87. 60 billion $= (6.0 \times 10)\left(1 \times 10^9\right) = 6.0 \times 10^{10}$

89. $(2.7 \times 10^8)(120) = (2.7 \times 10^8)(1.2 \times 10^2)$
$$= (2.7 \times 1.2) \times (10^8 \times 10^2)$$
$$= 3.24 \times 10^{8+2}$$
$$= 3.24 \times 10^{10}$$

91.–97. Answers may vary.

99. $1 - (2^{-1} + 2^{-2}) = 1 - \left(\dfrac{1}{2} + \dfrac{1}{2^2}\right)$
$$= 1 - \left(\dfrac{1}{2} + \dfrac{1}{4}\right)$$
$$= 1 - \left(\dfrac{3}{4}\right)$$
$$= \dfrac{1}{4}$$

Section P.3

Check Point Exercises

1. a. Since $\sqrt{a^2} = |a|$,
$$\sqrt{3^2} = 3.$$

b. $\sqrt{5x} \cdot \sqrt{10x} = \sqrt{5x \cdot 10x}$
$$= \sqrt{50x^2}$$
$$= \sqrt{25x^2 \cdot 2}$$
$$= \sqrt{25x^2}\sqrt{2}$$
$$= \sqrt{25}\sqrt{x^2}\sqrt{2}$$
$$= 5|x|\sqrt{2}$$

2. a. $\sqrt{\dfrac{25}{16}} = \dfrac{\sqrt{25}}{\sqrt{16}} = \dfrac{5}{4}$

b. $\dfrac{\sqrt{150x^3}}{\sqrt{2x}} = \sqrt{\dfrac{150x^3}{2x}} = \sqrt{75x^2}$
$$= \sqrt{25x^2}\sqrt{3}$$
$$= \sqrt{25}\sqrt{x^2}\sqrt{3}$$
$$= 5|x|\sqrt{3}$$

3. a. $8\sqrt{13} + 9\sqrt{13} = (8+9)\sqrt{3}$
$$= 17\sqrt{13}$$

b. $\sqrt{17x} - 20\sqrt{17x}$
$$= 1\sqrt{17x} - 20\sqrt{17x}$$
$$= (1-20)\sqrt{17x}$$
$$= -19\sqrt{17x}$$

4. a. $5\sqrt{27} + \sqrt{12}$
$$= 5\sqrt{9 \cdot 3} + \sqrt{4 \cdot 3}$$
$$= 5 \cdot 3\sqrt{3} + 2\sqrt{3}$$
$$= 15\sqrt{3} + 2\sqrt{3}$$
$$= (15+2)\sqrt{3}$$
$$= 17\sqrt{3}$$

b.
$$6\sqrt{18x} - 4\sqrt{8x}$$
$$= 6\sqrt{9 \cdot 2x} - 4\sqrt{4 \cdot 2x}$$
$$= 6 \cdot 3\sqrt{2x} - 4 \cdot 2\sqrt{2x}$$
$$= 18\sqrt{2x} - 8\sqrt{2x}$$
$$= (18 - 8)\sqrt{2x}$$
$$= 10\sqrt{2x}$$

5. a. If we multiply numerator and denominator by $\sqrt{3}$, the denominator becomes $\sqrt{3} \cdot \sqrt{3} = \sqrt{9} = 3$. Therefore, multiply by 1, choosing $\dfrac{\sqrt{3}}{\sqrt{3}}$ for 1.

$$\frac{5}{\sqrt{3}} = \frac{5}{\sqrt{3}} \cdot \frac{\sqrt{3}}{\sqrt{3}} = \frac{5\sqrt{3}}{\sqrt{9}} = \frac{5\sqrt{3}}{3}$$

b. The *smallest* number that will produce a perfect square in the denominator of $\dfrac{6}{\sqrt{12}}$ is $\sqrt{3}$ because $\sqrt{12} \cdot \sqrt{3} = \sqrt{36} = 6$. So multiply by 1, choosing $\dfrac{\sqrt{3}}{\sqrt{3}}$ for 1.

$$\frac{6}{\sqrt{12}} = \frac{6}{\sqrt{12}} \cdot \frac{\sqrt{3}}{\sqrt{3}} = \frac{6\sqrt{3}}{\sqrt{36}} = \frac{6\sqrt{3}}{6} = \sqrt{3}$$

6. The denominator will not contain a radical if multiplied by $4 - \sqrt{5}$. Therefore, multiply by 1, choosing $\dfrac{4 - \sqrt{5}}{4 - \sqrt{5}}$ for 1.

$$\frac{8}{4 + \sqrt{5}} = \frac{8}{4 + \sqrt{5}} \cdot \frac{4 - \sqrt{5}}{4 - \sqrt{5}}$$
$$= \frac{8(4 - \sqrt{5})}{4^2 - (\sqrt{5})^2}$$
$$= \frac{8(4 - \sqrt{5})}{16 - 5}$$
$$= \frac{8(4 - \sqrt{5})}{11} \text{ or } \frac{32 - 8\sqrt{5}}{11}$$

7. a. $\sqrt[3]{40} = \sqrt[3]{8 \cdot 5} = \sqrt[3]{8} \cdot \sqrt[3]{5} = 2\sqrt[3]{5}$

b.
$$\sqrt[5]{8} \cdot \sqrt[5]{8} = \sqrt[5]{8 \cdot 8}$$
$$= \sqrt[5]{64}$$
$$= \sqrt[5]{32} \cdot \sqrt[5]{2}$$
$$= 2\sqrt[5]{2}$$
$$5_2$$

c. $\sqrt[3]{\dfrac{125}{27}} = \dfrac{\sqrt[3]{125}}{\sqrt[3]{27}} = \dfrac{5}{3}$

8. $3\sqrt[3]{81} - 4\sqrt[3]{3}$
$$= 3\sqrt[3]{27 \cdot 3} - 4\sqrt[3]{3}$$
$$= 3 \cdot 3\sqrt[3]{3} - 4\sqrt[3]{3}$$
$$= 9\sqrt[3]{3} - 4\sqrt[3]{3}$$
$$= (9 - 4)\sqrt[3]{3}$$
$$= 5\sqrt[3]{3}$$

9. a. $81^{\frac{1}{2}} = \sqrt{81} = 9$

b. $27^{\frac{1}{3}} = \sqrt[3]{27} = 3$

c. $32^{-\frac{1}{5}} = \dfrac{1}{32^{\frac{1}{5}}} = \dfrac{1}{\sqrt[5]{32}} = \dfrac{1}{2}$

10. a. $4^{\frac{3}{2}} = (\sqrt{4})^3 = 2^3 = 8$

b. $32^{-\frac{2}{5}} = \dfrac{1}{32^{\frac{2}{5}}} = \dfrac{1}{(\sqrt[5]{32})^2} = \dfrac{1}{2^2} = \dfrac{1}{4}$

11. a. $\left(2x^{\frac{4}{3}}\right)\left(5x^{\frac{8}{3}}\right)$
$$= 2 \cdot 5x^{\frac{4}{3}} - x^{\frac{8}{3}}$$
$$= 10x^{(\frac{4}{3}) + (\frac{8}{3})}$$
$$= 10x^{\frac{12}{3}}$$
$$= 10x^4$$

b. $\dfrac{20x^4}{5x^{\frac{3}{2}}} = \left(\dfrac{20}{5}\right)\left(\dfrac{x^4}{x^{\frac{3}{2}}}\right)$
$$= 4x^{4 - (\frac{3}{2})}$$
$$= 4x^{(\frac{8}{2}) - (\frac{3}{2})}$$
$$= 4x^{\frac{5}{2}}$$

12. $\sqrt[6]{x^3} = x^{3/6} = x^{1/2} = \sqrt{x}$

Exercise Set P.3

1. $\sqrt{36} = \sqrt{6^2} = 6$

3. $\sqrt{-36}$ is not a real number.

5. $\sqrt{(-13)^2} = |-13| = 13$

7. $\sqrt{50} = \sqrt{25 \cdot 2} = \sqrt{25}\sqrt{2} = 5\sqrt{2}$

9. $\sqrt{45x^2} = \sqrt{9x^2 \cdot 5}$
$= \sqrt{9x^2}\sqrt{5}$
$= \sqrt{9}\sqrt{x^2}\sqrt{5}$
$= 3|x|\sqrt{5}$

11. $\sqrt{2x} \cdot \sqrt{6x} = \sqrt{2x \cdot 6x}$
$= \sqrt{12x^2}$
$= \sqrt{4x^2 \cdot 3}$
$= \sqrt{4x^2}\sqrt{3}$
$= \sqrt{4}\sqrt{x^2}\sqrt{3}$
$= 2|x|\sqrt{3}$

13. $\sqrt{x^3} = \sqrt{x^2 \cdot x} = |x|\sqrt{x}$

15. $\sqrt{2x^2} \cdot \sqrt{6x} = \sqrt{2x^2 \cdot 6x}$
$= \sqrt{12x^3}$
$= \sqrt{4x^2}\sqrt{x}$
$= 2|x|\sqrt{3x}$

17. $\sqrt{\dfrac{1}{81}} = \dfrac{\sqrt{1}}{\sqrt{81}} = \dfrac{1}{9}$

19. $\sqrt{\dfrac{49}{16}} = \dfrac{\sqrt{49}}{\sqrt{16}} = \dfrac{7}{4}$

21. $\dfrac{\sqrt{48x^3}}{\sqrt{3x}} = \sqrt{\dfrac{48x^3}{3x}} = \sqrt{16x^2} = 4|x|$

23. $\dfrac{\sqrt{150x^4}}{\sqrt{3x}} = \sqrt{\dfrac{150x^4}{3x}}$
$= \sqrt{50x^3}$
$= \sqrt{25x^2}\sqrt{2x}$
$= 5|x|\sqrt{2x}$

25. $7\sqrt{3} + 6\sqrt{3} = (7+6)\sqrt{3} = 13\sqrt{3}$

27. $6\sqrt{17x} - 8\sqrt{17x} = (6-8)\sqrt{17x} = -2\sqrt{17x}$

29. $\sqrt{8} + 3\sqrt{2} = \sqrt{4 \cdot 2} + 3\sqrt{2}$
$= 2\sqrt{2} + 3\sqrt{2}$
$= (2+3)\sqrt{2}$
$= 5\sqrt{2}$

31. $\sqrt{50x} - \sqrt{8x} = \sqrt{25 \cdot 2x} - \sqrt{4 \cdot 2x}$
$= 5\sqrt{2x} - 2\sqrt{2x}$
$= (5-2)\sqrt{2x}$
$= 3\sqrt{2x}$

33. $3\sqrt{18} + 5\sqrt{50} = 3\sqrt{9 \cdot 2} + 5\sqrt{25 \cdot 2}$
$= 3 \cdot 3\sqrt{2} + 5 \cdot 5\sqrt{2}$
$= 9\sqrt{2} + 25\sqrt{2}$
$= (9+25)\sqrt{2}$
$= 34\sqrt{2}$

35. $\dfrac{1}{\sqrt{7}} = \dfrac{1}{\sqrt{7}} \cdot \dfrac{\sqrt{7}}{\sqrt{7}} = \dfrac{\sqrt{7}}{7}$

37. $\dfrac{\sqrt{2}}{\sqrt{5}} = \dfrac{\sqrt{2}}{\sqrt{5}} \cdot \dfrac{\sqrt{5}}{\sqrt{5}} = \dfrac{\sqrt{10}}{5}$

39. $\dfrac{13}{3+\sqrt{11}} = \dfrac{13}{3+\sqrt{11}} \cdot \dfrac{3-\sqrt{11}}{3-\sqrt{11}}$
$= \dfrac{13(3-\sqrt{11})}{3^2 - (\sqrt{11})^2}$
$= \dfrac{13(3-\sqrt{11})}{9-11}$
$= \dfrac{13(3-\sqrt{11})}{-2}$

41. $\dfrac{7}{\sqrt{5}-2} = \dfrac{7}{\sqrt{5}-2} \cdot \dfrac{\sqrt{5}+2}{\sqrt{5}+2}$

$= \dfrac{7(\sqrt{5}+2)}{(\sqrt{5})^2 - 2^2}$

$= \dfrac{7(\sqrt{5}+2)}{5-4}$

$= 7(\sqrt{5}+2)$

43. $\dfrac{6}{\sqrt{5}+\sqrt{3}} = \dfrac{6}{\sqrt{5}+\sqrt{3}} \cdot \dfrac{\sqrt{5}-\sqrt{3}}{\sqrt{5}-\sqrt{3}}$

$= \dfrac{6(\sqrt{5}-\sqrt{3})}{(\sqrt{5})^2 - (\sqrt{3})^2}$

$= \dfrac{6(\sqrt{5}-\sqrt{3})}{5-3}$

$= \dfrac{6(\sqrt{5}-\sqrt{3})}{2}$

$= 3(\sqrt{5}-\sqrt{3})$

45. $\sqrt[3]{125} = \sqrt[3]{5^3} = 5$

47. $\sqrt[3]{-8} = \sqrt[3]{(-2)^3} = -2$

49. $\sqrt[4]{-16}$ is not a real number.

51. $\sqrt[4]{(-3)^4} = |-3| = 3$

53. $\sqrt[5]{(-3)^5} = -3$

55. $\sqrt[3]{32} = \sqrt[3]{8 \cdot 4} = \sqrt[3]{8}\sqrt[3]{4} = 2 \cdot \sqrt[3]{4}$

57. $\sqrt[3]{x^4} = \sqrt[3]{x^3 \cdot x} = x \cdot \sqrt[3]{x}$

59. $\sqrt[3]{9} \cdot \sqrt[3]{6} = \sqrt[3]{54} = \sqrt[3]{27 \cdot 2} = \sqrt[3]{27}\sqrt[3]{2} = 3\sqrt[3]{2}$

61. $\dfrac{\sqrt[5]{64x^6}}{\sqrt[5]{2x}} = \sqrt[5]{\dfrac{64x^6}{2x}} = \sqrt[5]{32x^5} = 2x$

63. $36^{1/2} = \sqrt{36} = 6$

65. $8^{1/3} = \sqrt[3]{8} = 2$

67. $125^{2/3} = \left(\sqrt[3]{125}\right)^2 = 5^2 = 25$

69. $32^{-4/5} = \dfrac{1}{32^{4/5}} = \dfrac{1}{2^4} = \dfrac{1}{16}$

71. $\left(7x^{1/3}\right)\left(2x^{1/4}\right) = 7 \cdot 2x^{1/3} \cdot x^{1/4}$

$= 14 \cdot x^{1/3+1/4}$

$= 14x^{7/12}$

73. $\dfrac{20x^{1/2}}{5x^{1/4}} = \left(\dfrac{20}{5}\right)\left(\dfrac{x^{1/2}}{x^{1/4}}\right)$

$= 4 \cdot x^{1/2-1/4}$

$= 4x^{1/4}$

75. $\left(x^{2/3}\right)^3 = x^{2/3 \cdot 3} = x^2$

77. $(25x^4y^6)^{1/2} = 25^{1/2}x^{4 \cdot 1/2}y^{6 \cdot 1/2} = 5x^2|y|^3$

79. $\sqrt[4]{5^2} = 5^{2/4} = 5^{1/2} = \sqrt{5}$

81. $\sqrt[3]{x^6} = x^{6/3} = x^2$

83. $\sqrt[6]{x^4} = x^{4/6} = |x|^{2/3}$

85. $2\sqrt{5L}$ with $L = 40$ gives

$2\sqrt{5 \cdot 40} = 2\sqrt{200}$

$= 2\sqrt{100 \cdot 2}$

$= 2 \cdot 10\sqrt{2}$

$= 20\sqrt{2}$

The speed of the car prior to the accident was $20\sqrt{2}$ miles per hour.

87.
$$\frac{w}{h} = \frac{2}{\sqrt{5}-1}$$
$$= \frac{2}{\sqrt{5}-1} \cdot \frac{\sqrt{5}+1}{\sqrt{5}+1}$$
$$= \frac{2(\sqrt{5}+1)}{(\sqrt{5})^2 - 1^2}$$
$$= \frac{2(\sqrt{5}+1)}{5-1}$$
$$= \frac{2(\sqrt{5}+1)}{4}$$
$$= \frac{\sqrt{5}+1}{2}$$
$$\approx 1.62$$

89.
$$\frac{7\sqrt{2 \cdot 2 \cdot 3}}{6} = \frac{7\sqrt{2^2 \cdot 3}}{6}$$
$$= \frac{7\sqrt{2^2}\sqrt{3}}{6}$$
$$= \frac{7 \cdot 2\sqrt{3}}{6}$$
$$= \frac{7}{3}\sqrt{3}$$

91.
$$0.07d^{3/2} = 0.07 \cdot 9^{3/2}$$
$$= 0.07(\sqrt{9})^3$$
$$= 0.07 \cdot 3^3$$
$$= 0.07 \cdot 27$$
$$= 1.89$$

The duration of a storm whose diameter is 9 miles is 1.89 hours.

93.–97. Answers may vary.

99. $60.19x^{0.025}$

x	$60.19x^{0.025}$	x	$60.19x^{0.025x}$
1	60.19	17	64.61
2	61.24	18	64.70
3	61.87	19	64.79
4	62.31	20	64.87
5	62.66	21	64.95
6	62.95	22	65.03
7	63.19	23	65.10
8	63.40	24	65.17
9	63.59	25	65.23
10	63.76	26	65.30
11	63.91	27	65.36
12	64.05	28	65.42
13	64.18	29	65.48
14	64.30	30	65.53
15	64.41	31	65.59
16	64.51		

At the beginning of 1990, the expected lifespan was 64.95 years. During 1990, the lifespan of African American men first exceeded 65 years. At the beginning of 1991, the expected lifespan was 65.03 years.

101. a. False; $(-8)^{1/3} = \sqrt[3]{-8} = -2$, which is a real number.

b. False; $\sqrt{x^2 + y^2} \neq \sqrt{(x+y)^2} = x + y$, if $x + y \geq 0$.

c. False; $\frac{1}{2} = 8^{-1/3} \neq -2$

d. True; $2^1 = 2^{1/2}2^{1/2} = 2$

(d) is true.

103. $\sqrt{\square \cdot x^{\square}} = 5 \cdot x^7$

$\left(\square \cdot x^{\square}\right)^{1/2} = 5 \cdot x^7$

Square both sides.

$\square \cdot x^{\square} = 25 \cdot x^{14}$

Let $\square = 25$ and $\square = 14$.

105. a. $3^{1/2} \boxed{} 3^{1/3}$

Square both sides. $3 \boxed{} 3^{2/3} = 9^{1/3}$

Raise to the third power on both sides.

$3^3 = 27 \boxed{>} \left(9^{1/3}\right)^3 = 9$

b. $\sqrt{7} + \sqrt{18} \boxed{} \sqrt{7 + 18}$

$\sqrt{7} + \sqrt{18} \boxed{} \sqrt{7 + 18} = \sqrt{25} = 5$

Square both sides.

$(\sqrt{7} + \sqrt{18})^2 = 7 + 2\sqrt{126} + 18$

$= 25 + 3\sqrt{14} \boxed{>} 25$

Section P.4

Check Point Exercises

1. a. $(-17x^3 + 4x^2 - 11x - 5) + (16x^3 - 3x^2 + 3x - 15)$

$= (-17x^3 + 16x^3) + (4x^2 - 3x^2) + (-11x + 3x) + (-5 - 15)$

$= -x^3 + x^2 - 8x - 20$

b. $(13x^3 - 9x^2 - 7x + 1) - (7x^3 + 2x^2 - 5x + 9)$

$= (13x^3 - 9x^2 - 7x + 1) + (7x^3 - 2x^2 + 5x - 9)$

$= (13x^3 + 7x^3) + (-9x^2 - 2x^2) + (-7x + 5x) + (1 - 9)$

$= 20x^3 - 11x^2 - 2x - 8$

2. $(5x - 2)(3x^2 - 5x + 4)$

$= 5x(3x^2 - 5x + 4) - 2(3x^2 - 5x + 4)$

$= 5x \cdot 3x^2 - 5x \cdot 5x + 5x \cdot 4 - 2 \cdot 3x^2 + 2 \cdot 5x - 2 \cdot 4$

$= 15x^3 - 25x^2 + 20x - 6x^2 + 10x - 8$

$= 15x^3 - 31x^2 + 30x - 8$

3. $(7x - 5)(4x - 3) = 7x \cdot 4x + 7x(-3) + (-5)4x + (-5)(-3)$

$$= 28x^2 - 21x - 20x + 15$$
$$= 28x^2 - 41x + 15$$

4. a. Use the special-product formula shown.

$$(A + B)(A - B) = A^2 - B^2$$
$$(7x + 8)(7x - 8) = (7x)^2 - (8)^2$$
$$= 49x^2 - 64$$

b. Use the special-product formula shown.

$$(A + B)(A - B) = A^2 - B^2$$
$$(2y^3 - 5)(2y^3 + 5) = (2y^3 + 5)(2y^3 - 5) = (2y^3)^2 - (5)^2 = 4y^6 - 25$$

5. a. Use the special-product formula shown.

$$(A + B)^2 = A^2 + 2AB + B^2$$
$$(x + 10)^2 = x^2 + 2 \cdot x \cdot 10 + 10^2$$
$$= x^2 + 20x + 100$$

b. Use the special-product formula shown.

$$(A + B)^2 = A^2 + 2AB + B^2$$
$$(5x + 4)^2 = (5x)^2 + 2(5x)(4) + 4^2$$
$$= 25x^2 + 40x + 16$$

6. a. Use the special-product formula shown.

$$(A - B)^2 = A^2 - 2AB + B^2$$
$$(x - 9)^2 = x^2 - 2 \cdot x \cdot 9 + 9^2$$
$$= x^2 - 18x + 81$$

b. Use the special-product formula shown.

$$(A - B)^2 = A^2 - 2AB + B^2$$
$$(7x - 3)^2 = (7x)^2 - 2(7x)(3) + 3^2$$
$$= 49x^2 - 42x + 9$$

7. $(x^3 - 4x^2 y + 5xy^2 - y^3) - (x^3 - 6x^2 y + y^3)$

$$= (x^3 - 4x^2 y + 5xy^2 - y^3) + (-x^3 + 6x^2 y - y^3)$$
$$= (x^3 - x^3) + (-4x^2 y + 6x^2 y) + (5xy^2) + (-y^3 - y^3)$$
$$= 2x^2 y + 5xy^2 - 2y^3$$

8. a. $(7x - 6y)(3x - y) = (7x)(3x) + (7x)(-y) + (-6y)(3x) + (-6y)(-y)$
$$= 21x^2 - 7xy - 18xy + 6y^2$$
$$= 21x^2 - 25xy + 6y^2$$

b. $(x^2 + 5y)^2 = (x^2)^2 + 2(x^2)(5y) + (5y)^2$
$$= x^4 + 10x^2y + 25y^2$$

Exercise Set P.4

1. Yes; $2x + 3x^2 - 5 = 3x^2 + 2x - 5$

3. No; The form of a polynomial involves addition and subtraction, not division.

5. $3x^2$ has degree 2
$-5x$ has degree 1
4 has degree 0
$3x^2 - 5x + 4$ has degree 2.

7. x^2 has degree 2
$-4x^3$ has degree 3
$9x$ has degree 1
$-12x^4$ has degree 4
63 has degree 0
$x^2 - 4x^3 + 9x - 12x^4 + 63$ has degree 4.

9. $(-6x^3 + 5x^2 - 8x + 9) + (17x^3 + 2x^2 - 4x - 13) = (-6x^3 + 17x^3) + (5x^2 + 2x^2) + (-8x - 4x) + (9 - 13)$
$$= 11x^3 + 7x^2 - 12x - 4$$
The degree is 3.

11. $(17x^3 - 5x^2 + 4x - 3) - (5x^3 - 9x^2 - 8x + 11) = (17x^3 - 5x^2 + 4x - 3) + (-5x^3 + 9x^2 + 8x - 11)$
$$= (17x^3 - 5x^3) + (-5x^2 + 9x^2) + (4x + 8x) + (-3 - 11)$$
$$= 12x^3 + 4x^2 + 12x - 14$$
The degree is 3.

13. $(5x^2 - 7x - 8) + (2x^2 - 3x + 7) - (x^2 - 4x - 3) = (5x^2 - 7x - 8) + (2x^2 - 3x + 7) + (-x^2 + 4x + 3)$
$$= (5x^2 + 2x^2 - x^2) + (-7x - 3x + 4x) + (-8 + 7 + 3)$$
$$= 6x^2 - 6x + 2$$
The degree is 2.

15. $(x + 1)(x^2 - x + 1) = x(x^2) - x \cdot x + x \cdot 1 + 1(x^2) - 1 \cdot x + 1 \cdot 1$
$$= x^3 - x^2 + x + x^2 - x + 1$$
$$= x^3 + 1$$

17. $(2x - 3)(x^2 - 3x + 5) = (2x)(x^2) + (2x)(-3x) + (2x)(5) + (-3)(x^2) + (-3)(-3x) + (-3)(5)$
$$= 2x^3 - 6x^2 + 10x - 3x^2 + 9x - 15$$
$$= 2x^3 - 9x^2 + 19x - 15$$

19. $(x + 7)(x + 3) = x^2 + 3x + 7x + 21 = x^2 + 10x + 21$

21. $(x - 5)(x + 3) = x^2 + 3x - 5x - 15 = x^2 - 2x - 15$

23. $(3x + 5)(2x + 1) = (3x)(2x) + 3x(1) + 5(2x) + 5 = 6x^2 + 3x + 10x + 5 = 6x^2 + 13x + 5$

25. $(2x - 3)(5x + 3) = (2x)(5x) + (2x)(3) + (-3)(5x) + (-3)(3)$
$$= 10x^2 + 6x - 15x - 9$$
$$= 10x^2 - 9x - 9$$

27. $(5x^2 - 4)(3x^2 - 7) = (5x^2)(3x^2) + (5x^2)(-7) + (-4)(3x^2) + (-4)(-7)$
$$= 15x^4 - 35x^2 - 12x^2 + 28$$
$$= 15x^4 - 47x^2 + 28$$

29. $(x + 3)(x - 3) = x^2 - 3^2$
$$= x^2 - 9$$

31. $(3x + 2)(3x - 2) = (3x)^2 - 2^2$
$$= 9x^2 - 4$$

33. $(5 - 7x)(5 + 7x) = 5^2 - (7x)^2$
$$= 25 - 49x^2$$

35. $(4x^2 + 5x)(4x^2 - 5x) = (4x^2)^2 - (5x)^2$
$$= 16x^4 - 25x^2$$

37. $(x + 2)^2 = x^2 + 2 \cdot x \cdot 2 + 2^2 = x^2 + 4x + 4$

39. $(2x + 3)^2 = (2x)^2 + 2(2x)(3) + 3^2$
$$= 4x^2 + 12x + 9$$

41. $(x - 3)^2 = x^2 - 2 \cdot x \cdot 3 + 3^2 = x^2 - 6x + 9$

43. $(4x^2 - 1)^2$
$$= (4x^2)^2 - 2(4x^2)(1) + 1^2$$
$$= 16x^4 - 8x^2 + 1$$

45. $(7-2x)^2 = 7^2 - 2(7)(2x) + (2x)^2$
$$= 49 - 28x + 4x^2$$
$$= 4x^2 - 28x + 49$$

47. $(x+1)^3 = x^3 + 3 \cdot x^2 \cdot 1 + 3x \cdot 1^2 + 1^3$
$$= x^3 + 3x^2 + 3x + 1$$

49. $(2x+3)^3$
$$= (2x)^3 + 3 \cdot (2x)^2 \cdot 3 + 3(2x) \cdot 3^2 + 3^3$$
$$= 8x^3 + 36x^2 + 54x + 27$$

51. $(x-3)^3 = x^3 - 3 \cdot x^3 \cdot 3 + 3 \cdot x \cdot 3^2 - 3^3$
$$= x^3 - 9x^2 + 27x - 27$$

53. $(3x-4)^3 = (3x)^3 - 3(3x)^2 \cdot 4 + 3(3x) \cdot 4^2 - 4^3$
$$= 27x^3 - 108x^2 + 144x - 64$$

55. $(5x^2y - 3xy) + (2x^2y - xy) = (5x^2y + 2x^2y) + (-3xy - xy)$
$$= (5+2)x^2y + (-3-1)xy$$
$$= 7x^2y - 4xy \text{ is of degree 3.}$$

57. $(4x^2y + 8xy + 11) + (-2x^2y + 5xy + 2) = (4x^2y - 2x^2y) + (8xy + 5xy) + (11+2)$
$$= (4-2)x^2y + (8+5)xy + 13$$
$$= 2x^2y + 13xy + 13 \text{ is of degree 3.}$$

59. $(x^3 + 7xy - 5y^2) - (6x^3 - xy + 4y^2) = (x^3 + 7xy - 5y^2)$
$$= (x^3 - 6x^3) + (7xy + xy) + (-5y^2 - 4y^2)$$
$$= (1-6)x^3 + (7+1)xy + (-5-4)y^2$$
$$= -5x^3 + 8xy - 9y^2 \text{ is of degree 3.}$$

61. $(3x^4y^2 + 5x^3y - 3y) - (2x^4y^2 - 3x^3y - 4y + 6x) = (3x^4y^2 + 5x^3y - 3y) + (-2x^4y^2 + 3x^3y + 4y - 6x)$
$$= (3x^4y^2 - 2x^4y^2) + (5x^3y + 3x^3y) + (-3y + 4y) - 6x$$
$$= (3-2)x^4y^2 + (5+3)x^3y + (-3+4)y - 6x$$
$$= x^4y^2 + 8x^3y + y - 6x \text{ is of degree 6.}$$

63. $(x+5y)(7x+3y) = x(7x) + x(3y) + (5y)(7x) + (5y)(3y)$
$$= 7x^2 + 3xy + 35xy + 15y^2$$
$$= 7x^2 + 38xy + 15y^2$$

65. $(x - 3y)(2x + 7y) = x(2x) + x(7y) + (-3y)(2x) + (-3y)(7y)$
$$= 2x^2 + 7xy - 6xy - 21y^2$$
$$= 2x^2 + xy - 21y^2$$

67. $(3xy - 1)(5xy + 2) = (3xy)(5xy) + (3xy)(2) + (-1)(5xy) + (-1)(2)$
$$= 15x^2y^2 + 6xy - 5xy - 2$$
$$= 15x^2y^2 + xy - 2$$

69. $(7x + 5y)^2 = (7x)^2 + 2(7x)(5y) + (5y)^2 = 49x^2 + 70xy + 25y^2$

71. $(x^2y^2 - 3)^2 = (x^2y^2)^2 - 2(x^2y^2)(3) + 3^2 = x^4y^4 - 6x^2y^2 + 9$

73. $(x - y)(x^2 + xy + y^2) = x(x^2) + x(xy) + x(y^2) + (-y)(x^2) + (-y)(xy) + (-y)(y^2)$
$$= x^3 + x^2y + xy^2 - x^2y - xy^2 - y^3$$
$$= x^3 - y^3$$

75. $(3x + 5y)(3x - 5y) = (3x)^2 - (5y)^2 = 9x^2 - 25y^2$

77. $0.018x^2 - 0.757x + 9.047$ when $x = 40$ yields
$0.018(40)^2 - 0.757(40) + 9.047 = 28.8 - 30.28 + 9.047 = 7.567$
A person earning \$40,000 feels underpaid \$7567.

79. Let $A = 20$
$-0.02A^2 + 2A + 22$
$= -0.02(20)^2 + 2(20) + 22$
$= -8 + 40 + 22$
$= 54$
Let $A = 50$
$-0.02A^2 + 2A + 22$
$= -0.02(50)^2 + 2(50) + 22$
$= -50 + 100 + 22$
$= 72$
Let $A = 80$
$-0.02A^2 + 2A + 22$
$= -0.02(80)^2 + 2(80) + 22$
$= -128 + 160 + 22$
$= 54$
Performance increases as enthusiasm goes from 1 to 50, then performance decreases as enthusiasm goes from 50 to 100.

81. Number of people still ill t weeks after January 1 = (Number of people who catch cold t weeks after January 1) − (Number of people who recover t weeks after January 1)

$$= (5t - 3t^2 + t^3) - \left(t - t^2 + \frac{1}{3}t^3 \right)$$

$$= (5t - 3t^2 + t^3) + \left(-t + t^2 - \frac{1}{3}t^3 \right)$$

$$= (5t - t) + (-3t^2 + t^2) + \left(t^3 - \frac{1}{3}t^3 \right)$$

$$= 4t - 2t^2 + \frac{2}{3}t^3$$

83. $(x+3)(x+9) - (x+1)(x+5)$

$$= (x^2 + 9x + 3x + 27) - (x^2 + 5x + x + 5)$$

$$= (x^2 + 12x + 27) - (x^2 + 6x + 5)$$

$$= (x^2 + 12x + 27) + (-x^2 - 6x - 6)$$

$$= (x^2 - x^2) + (12x - 6x) + (27 - 5)$$

$$= 6x + 22$$

85.–91. Answers may vary.

93.

x	$-3.08x^2 + 40.35x + 305.89$	# of aggravated assaults in US per 100,000	x	$-3.08x^2 + 40.35x + 305.89$	# of aggravated assaults in US per 100,000
0	305.89	306 in 1986	8	431.57	432 in 1994
1	343.16	343 in 1987	9	419.56	420 in 1995
2	374.27	374 in 1988	10	401.39	401 in 1996
3	399.22	399 in 1989	11	377.06	377 in 1997
4	418.01	418 in 1990	12	346.57	347 in 1998
5	430.64	431 in 1991	13	309.92	310 in 1999
6	437.11	437 in 1992	14	267.11	267 in 2000
7	437.42	437 in 1993			

The number of aggravated assaults in US per 100,000 was the greatest during 1992 and 1993.

95. $[(7x+5)+4y][(7x+5)-4y] = (7x+5)^2 - 4y^2$
$$= (7x)^2 + 2(7x)(5) + 5^2 - 16y^2$$
$$= 49x^2 + 70x + 25 - 16y^2$$

97. $(x+y)(x-y)(x^2+y^2) = (x^2-y^2)(x^2+y^2)$
$$= (x^2)^2 - (y^2)^2$$
$$= x^4 - y^4$$

Section P.5

Check Point Exercises

1. **a.** $10x^3 - 4x^2$
    $$= 2x^2(5x) - 2x^2(2)$$
    $$= 2x^2(5x-2)$$

    b. $2x(x-7) + 3(x-7)$
    $$= (x-7)(2x+3)$$

2. $x^3 + 5x^2 - 2x - 10$
    $$= (x^3 + 5x^2) - (2x + 10)$$
    $$= x^2(x+5) - 2(x+5)$$
    $$= (x+5)(x^2-2)$$

3. **a.** Find two numbers whose product is 40 and whose sum is 13. The required integers are 8 and 5. Thus,
    $$x^2 + 13x + 40 = (x+5)(x+8) \text{ or } (x+8)(x+5)$$

    b. Find two numbers whose product is –14 and whose sum is –5. The required integers are –7 and 2. Thus,
    $$x^2 - 5x - 14 = (x-7)(x+2) \text{ or } (x+2)(x-7).$$

4. Find two First terms whose product is $6x^2$.
    $$6x^2 + 19x - 7 \stackrel{?}{=} (6x \quad)(x \quad)$$
    $$6x^2 + 19x - 7 = (3x \quad)(2x \quad)$$

    Find two Last terms whose product is –7.
    The possible factors are 1(–7) and –1(7).

Try various combinations of these factors to find the factorization in which the sum of the Outside and Inside products is $19x$.

Possible Factors of $6x^2 + 19x - 7$	Sum of Outside and Inside Products (Should Equal $19x$)
$(6x+1)(x-7)$	$-42x + x = -41x$
$(6x-7)(x+1)$	$6x - 7x = -x$
$(6x-1)(x+7)$	$42x - x = 41x$
$(6x+7)(x-1)$	$-6x + 7x = x$
$(3x+1)(2x-7)$	$-21x + 2x = -19x$
$(3x-7)(2x+1)$	$3x - 14x = -11x$
$(3x-1)(2x+7)$	$21x - 2x = 19x$
$(3x+7)(2x-1)$	$-3x + 14x = 11x$

Thus, $6x^2 + 19x - 7 = (3x-1)(2x+7)$ or $(2x+7)(3x-1)$.

5. Express each term as the square of some monomial. Then use the formula for factoring $A^2 - B^2$.

   a. $x^2 - 81 = x^2 - 9^2 = (x+9)(x-9)$

   b. $36x^2 - 25 = (6x)^2 - 5^2 = (6x+5)(6x-5)$

6. Express $81x^4 - 16$ as the difference of two squares and use the formula for factoring $A^2 - B^2$.
   $$81x^4 - 16 = (9x^2)^2 - 4^2 = (9x^2 + 4)(9x^2 - 4)$$

   The factor $9x^2 - 4$ is the difference of two squares and can be factored. Express $9x^2 - 4$ as the difference of two squares and again use the formula for factoring $A^2 - B^2$.
   $$(9x^2 + 4)(9x^2 - 4) = (9x^2 + 4)\left[(3x)^2 - 2^2\right] = (9x^2 + 4)(3x + 2)(3x - 2)$$

   Thus, factored completely,
   $$81x^4 - 16 = (9x^2 + 4)(3x + 2)(3x - 2).$$

7. **a.** $x^2 + 14x + 49 = x^2 + 2 \cdot x \cdot 7 + 7^2 = (x+7)^2$

   b.   Since $16x^2 = (4x)^2$ and $49 = 7^2$, check to see if the middle term can be expressed as twice the product of $4x$ and 7. Since $2 \cdot 4x \cdot 7 = 56x$, $16x^2 - 56x + 49$ is a perfect square trinomial. Thus,
   $$16x^2 - 56x + 49 = (4x)^2 - 2 \cdot 4x \cdot 7 + 7^2$$
   $$= (4x - 7)^2$$

8. a. $x^3 + 1 = x^3 + 1^3$
$$= (x+1)(x^2 - x \cdot 1 + 1^2)$$
$$= (x+1)(x^2 - x + 1)$$

b. $125x^3 - 8 = (5x)^3 - 2^3$
$$= (5x-2)\left[(5x)^2 + (5x)(2) + 2^2\right]$$
$$= (5x-2)(25x^2 + 10x + 4]$$

9. a. Factor out the greatest common factor.
$$2x^3 - 24x^2 + 72x = 2x(x^2 - 12x + 36)$$

Factor the perfect square trinomial.
$$2x(x^2 - 12x + 36) = 2x(x-6)^2$$
Thus, $2x^3 - 24x^2 + 72x = 2x(x-6)^2$.

b. Group the terms with common factors and factor each group.
$$x^3 - 4x^2 - 9x + 36 = (x^3 - 4x^2) - (9x - 36)$$
$$= x^2(x-4) - 9(x-4)$$

Factor out the common binomial factor and factor completely by factoring $x^2 - 9$ as the difference of two squares.
$$x^2(x-4) - 9(x-4) = (x-4)(x^2 - 9)$$
$$= (x-4)(x+3)(x-3)$$
Thus, $x^3 - 4x^2 - 9x + 36 = (x-4)(x+3)(x-3)$.

Exercise Set P.5

1. $18x + 27 = 9 \cdot 2x + 9 \cdot 3$
$$= 9(2x + 3)$$

3. $3x^2 + 6x = 3x \cdot x + 3x \cdot 2$
$$= 3x(x + 2)$$

5. $9x^4 - 18x^3 + 27x^2$
$$= 9x^2(x^2) + 9x^2(-2x) + 9x^2(3)$$
$$= 9x^2(x^2 - 2x + 3)$$

7. $x(x+5) + 3(x+5) = (x+5)(x+3)$

9. $x^2(x-3) + 12(x-3) = (x-3)(x^2+12)$

11. $x^3 - 2x^2 + 5x - 10 = x^2(x-2) + 5(x-2)$
$$= (x^2 + 5)(x-2)$$

13. $x^3 - x^2 + 2x - 2 = x^2(x-1) + 2(x-1)$
$$= (x-1)(x^2+2)$$

15. $3x^3 - 2x^2 - 6x + 4 = x^2(3x-2) - 2(3x-2)$
$$= (3x-2)(x^2-2)$$

17. $x^2 + 5x + 6 = (x+2)(x+3)$

19. $x^2 - 2x - 15 = (x-5)(x+3)$

21. $x^2 - 8x + 15 = (x-5)(x-3)$

23. $3x^2 - x - 2 = (3x+2)(x-1)$

25. $3x^2 - 25x - 28 = (3x-28)(x+1)$

27. $6x^2 - 11x + 4 = (2x-1)(3x-4)$

29. $4x^2 + 16x + 15 = (2x+3)(2x+5)$

31. $x^2 - 100 = x^2 - 10^2 = (x+10)(x-10)$

33. $36x^2 - 49 = (6x)^2 - 7^2 = (6x+7)(6x-7)$

35. $9x^2 - 25y^2 = (3x)^2 - (5y)^2$
$$= (3x+5y)(3x-5y)$$

37. $x^4 - 16 = (x^2)^2 - 4^2$
$$= (x^2+4)(x^2-4)$$
$$= (x^2+4)(x+2)(x-2)$$

39. $16x^4 - 81 = (4x^2)^2 - 9^2$
$$= (4x^2+9)(4x^2-9)$$
$$= (4x^2+9)[(2x)^2 - 3^2]$$
$$= (4x^2+9)(2x+3)(2x-3)$$

41. $x^2 + 2x + 1 = x^2 + 2 \cdot x \cdot 1 + 1^2 = (x+1)^2$

43. $x^2 - 14x + 49 = x^2 - 2 \cdot x \cdot 7 + 7^2$
$$= (x-7)^2$$

45. $4x^2 + 4x + 1 = (2x)^2 + 2 \cdot 2x \cdot 1 + 1^2$
$$= (2x+1)^2$$

47. $9x^2 - 6x + 1 = (3x)^2 - 2 \cdot 3x \cdot 1 + 1^2$
$$= (3x-1)^2$$

49. $x^3 + 27 = x^3 + 3^3$
$$= (x+3)(x^2 - x \cdot 3 + 3^2)$$
$$= (x+3)(x^2 - 3x + 9)$$

51. $x^3 - 64 = x^3 - 4^3$
$$= (x-4)(x^2 + x \cdot 4 + 4^2)$$
$$= (x-4)(x^2 + 4x + 16)$$

53. $8x^3 - 1 = (2x)^3 - 1^3$
$$= (2x-1)[(2x)^2 + (2x)(1) + 1^2]$$
$$= (2x-1)(4x^2 + 2x + 1)$$

55. $64x^3 + 27 = (4x)^3 + 3^3$
$$= (4x+3)[(4x)^2 - (4x)(3) + 3^2]$$
$$= (4x+3)(16x^2 - 12x + 9)$$

57. $3x^3 - 3x = 3x(x^2-1) = 3x(x+1)(x-1)$

59. $4x^2 - 4x - 24 = 4(x^2 - x - 6)$
$$= 4(x+2)(x-3)$$

61. $2x^4 - 162 = 2(x^4 - 81)$
$$= 2[(x^2)^2 - 9^2]$$
$$= 2(x^2+9)(x^2-9)$$
$$= 2(x^2+9)(x^2 - 3^2)$$
$$= 2(x^2+9)(x+3)(x-3)$$

63. $x^3 + 2x^2 - 9x - 18 = (x^3 + 2x^2) - (9x + 18)$
$$= x^2(x+2) - 9(x+2)$$
$$= (x^2-9)(x+2)$$
$$= (x^2 - 3^2)(x+2)$$
$$= (x-3)(x+3)(x+2)$$

65. $2x^2 - 2x - 112 = 2(x^2 - x - 56)$
$$= 2(x-8)(x+7)$$

67. $x^3 - 4x = x(x^2 - 4)$
$\qquad = x(x^2 - 2^2)$
$\qquad = x(x - 2)(x + 2)$

69. $x^2 + 64$ is prime.

71. $x^3 + 2x^2 - 4x - 8 = (x^3 + 2x^2) + (-4x - 8)$
$\qquad = x^2(x + 2) - 4(x + 2)$
$\qquad = (x^2 - 4)(x + 2)$
$\qquad = (x^2 - 2^2)(x + 2)$
$\qquad = (x - 2)(x + 2)(x + 2)$
$\qquad = (x - 2)(x + 2)^2$

73. $y^5 - 81y = y(y^4 - 81)$
$\qquad = y[(y^2)^2 - 9^2]$
$\qquad = y(y^2 + 9)(y^2 - 9)$
$\qquad = y(y^2 + 9)(y^2 - 3^2)$
$\qquad = y(y^2 + 9)(y + 3)(y - 3)$

75. $20y^4 - 45y^2 = 5y^2(4y^2 - 9)$
$\qquad = 5y^2[(2y)^2 - 3^2]$
$\qquad = 5y^2(2y + 3)(2y - 3)$

77. $-16t^2 + 16t + 32 = -16(t^2 - t - 2)$
$\qquad = -16(t - 2)(t + 1)$

79. $(3x)(3x) - 2 \cdot 2 = (3x)^2 - 2^2$
$\qquad = (3x + 2)(3x - 2)$

81.–87. Answers may vary.

89. a. False; $x^3 + 1 = (x + 1)(x^2 - x + 1)$

    b. False; this is not a product.

    c. False; $(x - 4)^3 = x^3 - 12x^2 + 48x - 64$

    d. True

    (d) is true.

91. $-x^2 - 4x + 5 = -(x^2 + 4x - 5)$
$\qquad = -(x + 5)(x - 1)$

93. $x^4 - y^4 - 2x^3y + 2xy^3$
$\qquad = (x^4 - y^4 + (-2x^3y + 2xy^3)$
$\qquad = [(x^2)^2 - (y^2)^2] - 2xy(x^2 - y^2)$
$\qquad = (x^2 - y^2)(x^2 + y^2) - 2xy(x^2 - y^2)$
$\qquad = (x^2 - y^2)(x^2 + y^2 - 2xy)$
$\qquad = (x - y)(x + y)(x - y)^2$
$\qquad = (x - y)^3(x + y)$

95. For the polynomial $x^2 + 4x + b$ to be factorable, b needs to be any product of two integers whose sum is 4. So if $x^2 + 4x + b$ equals
$\qquad x(x + 4)$ then $b = 0$
$\qquad (x + 1)(x + 3)$ then $b = 3$
$\qquad (x + 2)^2$ then $b = 4$
$\qquad (x - 1)(x + 5)$ then $b = -5$
$\qquad (x - 2)(x + 6)$ then $b = -12$
In fact, given any positive integer c and $c + 4$, we can set $b = -c \cdot (c + 4)$. Then $x^2 + 4x + b$ is factorable.
So $b = 0, 3, 4, -c(c + 4)$, where $c > 0$ is an integer.

Section P.6

Check Point Exercises

1. a. The denominator would equal zero if $x = -5$, so -5 must be excluded from the domain.

    b. $x^2 - 36 = (x + 6)(x - 6)$
The denominator would equal zero if $x = -6$ or $x = 6$, so -6 and 6 must both be excluded from the domain.

2. a. $\dfrac{x^3 + 3x^2}{x+3} = \dfrac{x^2(x+3)}{x+3}$ Because the denominator is $x + 3,\ x \neq -3$

$$= \dfrac{x^2(x+3)}{x+3}$$

$$= x^2,\ x \neq -3$$

b. $\dfrac{x^2 - 1}{x^2 + 2x + 1} = \dfrac{(x+1)(x-1)}{(x+1)(x+1)}$ Because the denominator is $(x+1)(x-1),\ x \neq -1$ and $x \neq 1$.

$$= \dfrac{(x+1)(x-1)}{(x+1)(x+1)}$$

$$= \dfrac{x-1}{x+1},\ x \neq -1 \text{ and } x \neq 1$$

3. $\dfrac{x+3}{x^2 - 4} \cdot \dfrac{x^2 - x - 6}{x^2 + 6x + 9}$

$$= \dfrac{x+3}{(x+2)(x-2)} \cdot \dfrac{(x-3)(x+2)}{(x+3)(x+3)}$$

Because the denominator has factors of $x + 2,\ x - 2,$ and $x + 3,\ x \neq -2,\ x \neq 2,$ and $x \neq -3$.

$$= \dfrac{x+3}{(x+2)(x-2)} \cdot \dfrac{(x-3)(x+2)}{(x+3)(x+3)}$$

$$= \dfrac{x-3}{(x-2)(x+3)},\ x \neq -2,\ x \neq 2,\ x \neq -3$$

4. $\dfrac{x^2 - 2x + 1}{x^3 + x} \div \dfrac{x^2 + x - 2}{3x^2 + 3}$

$$= \dfrac{x^2 - 2x + 1}{x^3 + x} \cdot \dfrac{3x^2 + 3}{x^2 + x - 2}$$

$$= \dfrac{(x-1)(x-1)}{x(x^2+1)} \cdot \dfrac{3(x^2+1)}{(x+2)(x-1)}$$

For nonzero denominators, $x \neq 0,\ x \neq -2,\ x \neq 1$.

$$= \dfrac{3(x-1)}{x(x+2)},\ x \neq 0,\ x \neq -2,\ x \neq 1$$

5. $\dfrac{x}{x+1} - \dfrac{3x+2}{x+1}$

$$= \dfrac{x - (3x+2)}{x+1}$$

$$= \dfrac{x - 3x - 2}{x+1}$$

$$= \dfrac{-2x - 2}{x+1}$$

$$= \dfrac{-2(x+1)}{x+1}$$

For a nonzero denominator, $x \neq -1$.

$$= \dfrac{-2(x+1)}{x+1}$$

$$= -2,\ x \neq -1$$

6. $\dfrac{3}{x+1} + \dfrac{5}{x-1}$

$= \dfrac{3x(x-1)+5(x+1)}{(x+1)(x-1)}$

$= \dfrac{3x-3+5x+5}{(x+1)(x-1)}$

$= \dfrac{8x+2}{(x+1)(x-1)}$

$= \dfrac{2(4x+1)}{(x+1)(x-1)}$ For a nonzero denominator, $x \neq -1$ and $x \neq 1$.

$= \dfrac{2(4x+1)}{(x+1)(x-1)},\ x \neq -1,\ x \neq 1$

7. Factor each denominator completely.

$x^2 - 6x + 9 = (x-3)^2$

$x^2 - 9 = (x+3)(x-3)$

List the factors of the first denominator.

$x-3,\ x-3$

Add any unlisted factors from the second denominator.

$x-3,\ x-3,\ x+3$

The least common denominator is the product of all factors in the final list.

$(x-3)(x-3)(x+3)$ or $(x-3)^2(x+3)$
is the least common denominator.

8. Find the least common denominator.

$x^2 - 10x + 25 = (x-5)^2$
$2x - 10 = 2(x-5)$
The least common denominator is $2(x-5)(x-5)$.
Write all rational expressions in terms of the least common denominator.

$\dfrac{x}{x^2-10x+25} - \dfrac{x-4}{2x-10}$

$= \dfrac{x}{(x-5)(x-5)} - \dfrac{x-4}{2(x-5)}$

$= \dfrac{2x}{2(x-5)(x-5)} - \dfrac{(x-4)(x-5)}{2(x-5)(x-5)}$

Add numerators, putting this sum over the least common denominator.

$$= \frac{2x - (x-4)(x-5)}{2(x-5)(x-5)}$$

$$= \frac{2x - (x^2 - 5x - 4x + 20)}{2(x-5)(x-5)}$$

$$= \frac{2x - x^2 + 5x + 4x - 20}{2(x-5)(x-5)}$$

$$= \frac{2x - x^2 + 5x + 4x - 20}{2(x-5)(x-5)}$$

$$= \frac{-x^2 + 11x - 20}{2(x-5)(x-5)}$$

$$= \frac{-x^2 + 11x - 20}{2(x-5)^2}, \; x \neq 5$$

9. $\dfrac{\frac{1}{x} - \frac{3}{2}}{\frac{1}{x} + \frac{3}{4}} = \dfrac{\frac{2}{2x} - \frac{3x}{2x}}{\frac{4}{4x} + \frac{3x}{4x}}, \; x \neq 0$

$$= \frac{\frac{2-3x}{2x}}{\frac{4+3x}{4x}}, \; x \neq \frac{-4}{3}$$

$$= \frac{2-3x}{2x} \div \frac{4+3x}{4x}$$

$$= \frac{2-3x}{2x} \cdot \frac{4x}{4+3x}$$

$$= \frac{2-3x}{4+3x} \cdot \frac{4}{2}$$

$$= \frac{2-3x}{4+3x} \cdot \frac{2}{1}$$

$$= \frac{2(2-3x)}{4+3x}, \; x \neq 0 \text{ and } x \neq \frac{-4}{3}$$

Exercise Set P.6

1. $\dfrac{7}{x-3}, \; x \neq 3$

3. $\dfrac{x+5}{x^2-25} = \dfrac{x+5}{(x+5)(x-5)}, \; x \neq 5, -5$

5. $\dfrac{x-1}{x^2 + 11x + 10} = \dfrac{x-1}{(x+1)(x+10)}, \; x \neq -1, -10$

7. $\dfrac{3x-9}{x^2 - 6x + 9} = \dfrac{3(x-3)}{(x-3)(x-3)}$

$$= \frac{3}{x-3}, \; x \neq 3$$

9. $\dfrac{x^2 - 12x + 36}{4x - 24} = \dfrac{(x-6)(x-6)}{4(x-6)} = \dfrac{x-6}{4}.$

$x \neq 6$

11. $\dfrac{y^2 + 7y - 18}{y^2 - 3y + 2} = \dfrac{(y+9)(y-2)}{(y-2)(y-1)} = \dfrac{y+9}{y-1},$

$y \neq 1, 2$

13. $\dfrac{x^2 + 12x + 36}{x^2 - 36} = \dfrac{(x+6)^2}{(x+6)(x-6)} = \dfrac{x+6}{x-6},$

$x \neq 6, -6$

15. $\dfrac{x-2}{3x+9} \cdot \dfrac{2x+6}{2x-4} = \dfrac{x-2}{3(x+3)} \cdot \dfrac{2(x+3)}{2(x-2)}$

$$= \frac{2}{6} = \frac{1}{3}, \; x \neq 2, -3$$

17. $\dfrac{x^2-9}{x^2} \cdot \dfrac{x^2 - 3x}{x^2 + x - 12}$

$$= \frac{(x-3)(x+3)}{x^2} \cdot \frac{x(x-3)}{(x+4)(x-3)}$$

$$= \frac{(x-3)(x+3)}{x(x+4)}, \; x \neq 0, -4, 3$$

19. $\dfrac{x^2 - 5x + 6}{x^2 - 2x - 3} \cdot \dfrac{x^2 - 1}{x^2 - 4}$

$$= \frac{(x-3)(x-2)}{(x-3)(x+1)} \cdot \frac{(x+1)(x-1)}{(x-2)(x+2)}$$

$$= \frac{x-1}{x+2}, \; x \neq -2, -1, 2, 3$$

21. $\dfrac{x^3 - 8}{x^2 - 4} \cdot \dfrac{x+2}{3x} = \dfrac{(x-2)(x^2 + 2x + 4)}{(x-2)(x+2)} \cdot \dfrac{x+2}{3x}$

$$= \frac{x^2 + 2x + 4}{3x}, \; x \neq -2, 0, 2$$

23. $\dfrac{x+1}{3} \div \dfrac{3x+3}{7} = \dfrac{x+1}{3} \div \dfrac{3(x+1)}{7}$

$\qquad = \dfrac{x+1}{3} \cdot \dfrac{7}{3(x+1)}$

$\qquad = \dfrac{7}{9}, \ x \ne -1$

25. $\dfrac{x^2-4}{x} \div \dfrac{x+2}{x-2} = \dfrac{(x-2)(x+2)}{x} \div \dfrac{x+2}{x-2}$

$\qquad = \dfrac{(x-2)(x+2)}{x} \cdot \dfrac{x-2}{x+2}$

$\qquad = \dfrac{(x-2)^2}{x}, \ x \ne 0, -2, 2$

27. $\dfrac{4x^2+10}{x-3} \div \dfrac{6x^2+15}{x^2-9}$

$= \dfrac{2(2x^2+5)}{x-3} \div \dfrac{3(2x^2+5)}{(x-3)(x+3)}$

$= \dfrac{2(2x^2+5)}{x-3} \cdot \dfrac{(x-3)(x+3)}{3(2x^2+5)}$

$= \dfrac{2(x+3)}{3}, \ x \ne 3, \ -3$

29. $\dfrac{x^2-25}{2x-2} \div \dfrac{x^2+10x+25}{x^2+4x-5}$

$= \dfrac{(x-5)(x+5)}{2(x-1)} \div \dfrac{(x+5)^2}{(x+5)(x-1)}$

$= \dfrac{(x-5)(x+5)}{2(x-1)} \cdot \dfrac{(x+5)(x-1)}{(x+5)^2}$

$= \dfrac{x-5}{2}, \ x \ne 1, -5$

31. $\dfrac{4x+1}{6x+5} + \dfrac{8x+9}{6x+5} = \dfrac{4x+1+8x+9}{6x+5}$

$\qquad = \dfrac{12x+10}{6x+5}$

$\qquad = \dfrac{2(6x+5)}{6x+5} = 2, \ x \ne -\dfrac{5}{6}$

33. $\dfrac{x^2-2x}{x^2+3x} + \dfrac{x^2+x}{x^2+3x} = \dfrac{x^2-2x+x^2+x}{x^2+3x}$

$\qquad = \dfrac{2x^2-x}{x^2+3x}$

$\qquad = \dfrac{x(2x-1)}{x(x+3)}$

$\qquad = \dfrac{2x-1}{x+3}, \ x \ne 0, -3$

35. $\dfrac{4x-10}{x-2} - \dfrac{x-4}{x-2} = \dfrac{4x-10-(x-4)}{x-2}$

$\qquad = \dfrac{4x-10-x+4}{x-2}$

$\qquad = \dfrac{3x-6}{x-2}$

$\qquad = \dfrac{3(x-2)}{x-2}$

$\qquad = 3, \ x \ne 2$

37. $\dfrac{x^2+3x}{x^2+x-12} - \dfrac{x^2-12}{x^2+x-12}$

$= \dfrac{x^2+3x-(x^2-12)}{x^2+x-12}$

$= \dfrac{x^2+3x-x^2+12}{x^2+x-12}$

$= \dfrac{3x+12}{x^2+x-12}$

$= \dfrac{3(x+4)}{(x+4)(x-3)}$

$= \dfrac{3}{x-3}, \ x \ne 3, -4$

39. $\dfrac{3}{x+4} + \dfrac{6}{x+5} = \dfrac{3(x+5)+6(x+4)}{(x+4)(x+5)}$

$\qquad = \dfrac{3x+15+6x+24}{(x+4)(x+5)}$

$\qquad = \dfrac{9x+39}{(x+4)(x+5)}, \ x \ne -4, -5$

41. $\dfrac{3}{x+1} - \dfrac{3}{x} = \dfrac{3x-3(x+1)}{x(x+1)}$

$\qquad = \dfrac{3x-3x-3}{x(x+1)} = -\dfrac{3}{x(x+1)}, \ x \ne -1, 0$

43. $\dfrac{2x}{x+2}+\dfrac{x+2}{x-2}=\dfrac{2x(x-2)+(x+2)(x+2)}{(x+2)(x-2)}$

$=\dfrac{2x^2-4x+x^2+4x+4}{(x+2)(x-2)}$

$=\dfrac{3x^2+4}{(x+2)(x-2)},\ x\neq-2,2$

45. $\dfrac{x+5}{x-5}+\dfrac{x-5}{x+5}$

$=\dfrac{(x+5)(x+5)+(x-5)(x-5)}{(x-5)(x+5)}$

$=\dfrac{x^2+10x+25+x^2-10x+25}{(x-5)(x+5)}$

$=\dfrac{2x^2+50}{(x-5)(x+5)},\ x\neq-5,5$

47. $\dfrac{4}{x^2+6x+9}+\dfrac{4}{x+3}=\dfrac{4}{(x+3)^2}+\dfrac{4}{x+3}$

$=\dfrac{4+4(x+3)}{(x+3)^2}=\dfrac{4+4x+12}{(x+3)^2}=\dfrac{4x+16}{(x+3)^2},$

$x\neq-3$

49. $\dfrac{3x}{x^2+3x-10}-\dfrac{2x}{x^2+x-6}$

$=\dfrac{3x}{(x+5)(x-2)}-\dfrac{2x}{(x+3)(x-2)}$

$=\dfrac{3x(x+3)-2x(x+5)}{(x+5)(x-2)(x+3)}$

$=\dfrac{3x^2+9x-2x^2-10x}{(x+5)(x-2)(x+3)}$

$=\dfrac{x^2-x}{(x+5)(x-2)(x+3)},\ x\neq-5,2,-3$

51. $\dfrac{\frac{x}{3}-1}{x-3}=\dfrac{3\left[\frac{x}{3}-1\right]}{3[x-3]}=\dfrac{x-3}{3(x-3)}=\dfrac{1}{3},\ x\neq3$

53. $\dfrac{1+\frac{1}{x}}{3-\frac{1}{x}}=\dfrac{x\left[1+\frac{1}{x}\right]}{x\left[3-\frac{1}{x}\right]}=\dfrac{x+1}{3x-1},\ x\neq0,\ \dfrac{1}{3}$

55. $\dfrac{\frac{1}{x}+\frac{1}{y}}{x+y}=\dfrac{xy\left[\frac{1}{x}+\frac{1}{y}\right]}{xy[x+y]}=\dfrac{y+x}{xy(x+y)}=\dfrac{1}{xy},$

$x\neq0,\ y\neq0,\ x\neq-y$

57. $\dfrac{x-\frac{x}{x+3}}{x+2}=\dfrac{(x+3)\left[x-\frac{x}{x+3}\right]}{(x+3)(x+2)}=\dfrac{x(x+3)-x}{(x+3)(x+2)}$

$=\dfrac{x^2+3x-x}{(x+3)(x+2)}=\dfrac{x^2+2x}{(x+3)(x+2)}$

$=\dfrac{x(x+2)}{(x+3)(x+2)}=\dfrac{x}{x+3},\ x\neq-2,-3$

59. $\dfrac{\frac{3}{x-2}-\frac{4}{x+2}}{\frac{7}{x^2-4}}=\dfrac{\frac{3}{x-2}-\frac{4}{x+2}}{\frac{7}{(x-2)(x+2)}}$

$=\dfrac{\left[\frac{3}{x-2}-\frac{4}{x+2}\right](x-2)(x+2)}{\left[\frac{7}{(x-2)(x+2)}\right](x-2)(x+2)}$

$=\dfrac{3(x+2)-4(x-2)}{7}$

$=\dfrac{3x+6-4x+8}{7}=\dfrac{-x+14}{7}$

$=-\dfrac{x-14}{7}\ \ x\neq-2,2$

61. Adjust the polynomial that describes the total yearly cost to millions of dollars by multiplying the polynomial by 1000:
$540t^2+12,640t+107,100$.
The average cost per person (in dollars) is
$$\dfrac{540t^2+12,640t+107,100}{-0.14t^2+0.51t+31.6}$$

63. a. $\dfrac{130x}{100-x}$ is equal to

1. $\dfrac{130\cdot40}{100-40}=\dfrac{130\cdot40}{60}=86.67,$
   when $x=40$

2. $\dfrac{130\cdot80}{100-80}=\dfrac{130\cdot80}{20}=520,$
   when $x=80$

3. $\dfrac{130\cdot90}{100-90}=\dfrac{130\cdot90}{10}=1170,$
   when $x=90$

It costs \$86,670,000 to inoculate 40% of the population against this strain of flu, and \$520,000,000 to inoculate 80% of the population, and \$1,170,000,000 to inoculate 90% of the population.

b. For $x=100$, the function is not defined.

c. As x approaches close to 100, the value of the function increases rapidly. So it costs an astronomical amount of money to inoculate almost all of the people, and it is impossible to inoculate 100% of the population.

65. $\dfrac{2d}{\frac{d}{r_1}+\frac{d}{r_2}}=\dfrac{2d}{\frac{d}{r_1}+\frac{d}{r_2}}\cdot\dfrac{r_1r_2}{r_1r_2}$

$=\dfrac{2dr_1r_2}{dr_2+dr_1}$

$=\dfrac{d(2r_1r_2)}{d(r_2+r_1)}$

$=\dfrac{2r_1r_2}{r_1+r_2},$

Let $r_1=30$ and $r_2=20$. The average speed is $\dfrac{2(30)(20)}{30+20}=\dfrac{1200}{50}=24$ miles per hour.

The reason that the average speed is not $\dfrac{30+20}{2}=25$ is that the average of speeds is defined by

$\dfrac{\text{total distance travelled}}{\text{total time}}$, not by

$\dfrac{\text{sum of every speed}}{\text{number of the speeds being added}}.$

67.–77. Answers may vary.

79.

t	$f(t)$	Amount paid per recipient of Medicaid in $	t	$f(t)$	Amount paid per recipient of Medicaid in $
8	1105.87	1105 in 1988	15	412.84	412.84 in 1995
9	968.29	968.29 in 1989	16	364.54	364.54 in 1996
10	837.74	837.74 in 1990	17	323.94	323.94 in 1997
11	721.97	721.97 in 1991	18	289.60	289.60 in 1998
12	623.00	623.00 in 1992	19	260.36	260.36 in 1999
13	539.89	539.89 in 1993	20	235.29	235.29 in 2000
14	470.60	470.60 in 1994			

where $f(t) = \dfrac{413.48t^2 + 185.72t + 24,031.95}{0.004t^4 + 0.02t^3 + 0.01t^2 - 0.24t + 21.66}$

In 1990, the amount paid per recipient fell below \$900.

81.

$$\frac{3x}{x-5} + \frac{\Box}{5-x} = \frac{7x+1}{x-5}$$

$$\frac{3x}{x-5} + \frac{\Box}{-1(x-5)} = \frac{7x+1}{x-5}$$

$$\frac{3x - \Box}{x-5} = \frac{7x+1}{x-5}$$

$$3x - \Box = 7x+1$$

$$\Box = -4x - 1$$

83. It cubes x, $x \neq 0$.

Section P.7

Check Point Exercises

1. a. $(5-2i) + (3+3i)$

     $= 5 - 2i + 3 + 3i$

     $= (5+3) + (-2+3)i$

     $= 8 + i$

b. $(2+6i) - (12-4i)$

     $= 2 + 6i - 12 + 4i$

     $= (2-12) + (6+4)i$

     $= -10 + 10i$

2. a. $7i(2-9i) = 7i(2) - 7i(9i)$
$$= 14i - 63i^2$$
$$= 14i - 63(-1)$$
$$= 63 + 14i$$

b. $(5+4i)(6-7i) = 30 - 35i + 24i - 28i^2$
$$= 30 - 35i + 24i - 28(-1)$$
$$= 30 + 28 - 35i + 24i$$
$$= 58 - 11i$$

3. The complex conjugate of the denominator, $4 - 2i$, is $4 + 2i$, so multiply the numerator and denominator by $4 + 2i$.

$$\frac{5+4i}{4-2i} = \frac{(5+4i)}{(4-2i)} \cdot \frac{(4+2i)}{(4+2i)}$$
$$= \frac{20 + 10i + 16i + 8i^2}{4^2 + 2^2}$$
$$= \frac{20 + 26i + 8(-1)}{20}$$
$$= \frac{12 + 26i}{20}$$
$$= \frac{12}{20} + \frac{26}{20}i$$
$$= \frac{3}{5} + \frac{13}{10}i$$

4. a. $\sqrt{-27} + \sqrt{-48} = i\sqrt{27} + i\sqrt{48}$
$$= i\sqrt{9 \cdot 3} + i\sqrt{16 \cdot 3}$$
$$= 3i\sqrt{3} + 4i\sqrt{3}$$
$$= 7i\sqrt{3}$$

b. $(-2 + \sqrt{-3})^2 = (-2 + i\sqrt{3})^2$
$$= (-2)^2 + 2(-2)(i\sqrt{3}) + (i\sqrt{3})^2$$
$$= 4 - 4i\sqrt{3} + 3i^2$$
$$= 4 - 4i\sqrt{3} + 3(-1)$$
$$= 1 - 4i\sqrt{3}$$

c. $\dfrac{-14 + \sqrt{-12}}{2} = \dfrac{-14 + i\sqrt{12}}{2}$
$$= \frac{-14 + 2i\sqrt{3}}{2}$$
$$= \frac{-14}{2} + \frac{2i\sqrt{3}}{2}$$
$$= -7 + i\sqrt{3}$$

Exercise Set P.7

1. $(7 + 2i) + (1 - 4i) = 7 + 2i + 1 - 4i$
$$= 7 + 1 + 2i - 4i$$
$$= 8 - 2i$$

3. $(3 + 2i) - (5 - 7i) = 3 - 5 + 2i + 7i$
$$= 3 + 2i - 5 + 7i$$
$$= -2 + 9i$$

5. $6 - (-5 + 4i) - (-13 - 11i)$
$$= 6 + 5 - 4i + 13 + 11i$$
$$= 24 + 7i$$

7. $8i - (14 - 9i) = 8i - 14 + 9i$
$$= -14 + 8i + 9i$$
$$= -14 + 17i$$

9. $-3i(7i - 5) = -21i^2 + 15i$
$$= -21(-1) + 15i$$
$$= 21 + 15i$$

11. $(-5 + 4i)(3 + 7i) = -15 - 35i + 12i + 28i^2$
$$= -15 - 35i + 12i + 28(-1)$$
$$= -43 - 23i$$

13. $(7 - 5i)(-2 - 3i) = -14 - 21i + 10i + 15i^2$
$$= -14 - 15 - 11i$$
$$= -29 - 11i$$

15. $(3 + 5i)(3 - 5i) = 9 - 25i^2 = 9 + 25 = 34$

17. $(-5 + 3i)(-5 - 3i) = 25 - 9i^2 = 25 + 9 = 34$

19. $(2 + 3i)^2 = 4 + 12i + 9i^2$
$$= 4 + 12i - 9$$
$$= -5 + 12i$$

21. $\dfrac{2}{3-i} = \dfrac{2}{3-i} \cdot \dfrac{3+i}{3+i}$

$\qquad = \dfrac{2(3+i)}{9+1}$

$\qquad = \dfrac{2(3+i)}{10}$

$\qquad = \dfrac{3+i}{5}$

$\qquad = \dfrac{3}{5} + \dfrac{1}{5}i$

23. $\dfrac{2i}{1+i} = \dfrac{2i}{1+i} \cdot \dfrac{1-i}{1-i} = \dfrac{2i-2i^2}{1+1} = \dfrac{2+2i}{2} = 1+i$

25. $\dfrac{8i}{4-3i} = \dfrac{8i}{4-3i} \cdot \dfrac{4+3i}{4+3i}$

$\qquad = \dfrac{32i+24i^2}{16+9}$

$\qquad = \dfrac{-24+32i}{25}$

$\qquad = -\dfrac{24}{25} + \dfrac{32}{25}i$

27. $\dfrac{2+3i}{2+i} = \dfrac{2+3i}{2+i} \cdot \dfrac{2-i}{2-i}$

$\qquad = \dfrac{4+4i-3i^2}{4+1}$

$\qquad = \dfrac{7+4i}{5}$

$\qquad = \dfrac{7}{5} + \dfrac{4}{5}i$

29. $\sqrt{-64} - \sqrt{-25} = i\sqrt{64} - i\sqrt{25}$

$\qquad\qquad\qquad\quad = 8i - 5i = 3i$

31. $5\sqrt{-16} + 3\sqrt{-81} = 5(4i) + 3(9i)$

$\qquad\qquad\qquad\quad = 20i + 27i = 47i$

33. $\left(-2 + \sqrt{-4}\right)^2 = (-2 + 2i)^2$

$\qquad\qquad\qquad = 4 - 8i + 4i^2$

$\qquad\qquad\qquad = 4 - 8i - 4$

$\qquad\qquad\qquad = -8i$

35. $\left(-3 - \sqrt{-7}\right)^2 = \left(-3 - i\sqrt{7}\right)^2$

$\qquad\qquad\qquad = 9 + 6i\sqrt{7} + i^2(7)$

$\qquad\qquad\qquad = 9 - 7 + 6i\sqrt{7}$

$\qquad\qquad\qquad = 2 + 6i\sqrt{7}$

37. $\dfrac{-8 + \sqrt{-32}}{24} = \dfrac{-8 + i\sqrt{32}}{24}$

$\qquad\qquad\qquad = \dfrac{-8 + i\sqrt{16 \cdot 2}}{24}$

$\qquad\qquad\qquad = \dfrac{-8 + 4i\sqrt{2}}{24}$

$\qquad\qquad\qquad = -\dfrac{1}{3} + \dfrac{\sqrt{2}}{6}i$

39. $\dfrac{-6 - \sqrt{-12}}{48} = \dfrac{-6 - i\sqrt{12}}{48}$

$\qquad\qquad\qquad = \dfrac{-6 - i\sqrt{4 \cdot 3}}{48}$

$\qquad\qquad\qquad = \dfrac{-6 - 2i\sqrt{3}}{48}$

$\qquad\qquad\qquad = -\dfrac{1}{8} - \dfrac{\sqrt{3}}{24}i$

41. $\sqrt{-8}\left(\sqrt{-3} - \sqrt{5}\right) = i\sqrt{8}(i\sqrt{3} - \sqrt{5})$

$\qquad\qquad\qquad = 2i\sqrt{2}\left(i\sqrt{3} - \sqrt{5}\right)$

$\qquad\qquad\qquad = -2\sqrt{6} - 2i\sqrt{10}$

43. $\left(3\sqrt{-5}\right)\left(-4\sqrt{-12}\right) = \left(3i\sqrt{5}\right)\left(-8i\sqrt{3}\right)$

$\qquad\qquad\qquad = -24i^2\sqrt{15}$

$\qquad\qquad\qquad = 24\sqrt{15}$

45.–51. Answers may vary.

53. a. False; all irrational numbers are complex numbers.

b. False; $(3 + 7i)(3 - 7i) = 9 + 49 = 58$ is a real number.

c. False; $\dfrac{7 + 3i}{5 + 3i} = \dfrac{7 + 3i}{5 + 3i} \cdot \dfrac{5 - 3i}{5 - 3i}$

$= \dfrac{44 - 6i}{34} = \dfrac{22}{17} - \dfrac{3}{17} i$

d. True; $(x + yi)(x - yi) = x^2 - (yi)^2 = x^2 + y^2$

(d) is true.

55. $\dfrac{4}{(2 + i)(3 - i)} = \dfrac{4}{6 + i - i^2}$

$= \dfrac{4}{6 + i + 1}$

$= \dfrac{4}{7 + i}$

$= \dfrac{4}{7 + i} \cdot \dfrac{7 - i}{7 - i}$

$= \dfrac{4(7 - i)}{49 + 1}$

$= \dfrac{28 - 4i}{50}$

$= \dfrac{28}{50} - \dfrac{4}{50} i$

$= \dfrac{14}{25} - \dfrac{2}{25} i$

57. $x^2 - 2x + 2$ for $x = 1 + i$

$\begin{aligned}
x^2 - 2x + 2 &= (1 + i)^2 - 2(1 + i) + 2 \\
&= 1 + 2i - 1 - 2 - 2i + 2 \\
&= 0
\end{aligned}$

Section P.8

Check Point Exercises

1.

2.

x	$y = 2x - 4$	Ordered Pair (x, y)
-1	$y = 2(-1) - 4 = -2 - 4 = -6$	$(-1, -6)$
0	$y = 2(0) - 4 = 0 - 4 = -4$	$(0, -4)$
1	$y = 2(1) - 4 = 2 - 4 = -2$	$(1, -2)$
2	$y = 2(2) - 4 = 4 - 4 = 0$	$(2, 0)$
3	$y = 2(3) - 4 = 6 - 4 = 2$	$(3, 2)$

3. The minimum x-value is -100 and the maximum x-value is 100. The distance between consecutive tick marks is 50. The minimum y-value is -100 and the maximum y-value is 100. The distance between consecutive tick marks is 10.

4. Letting $(x_1, y_1) = (2, -2)$ and $(x_2, y_2) = (5, 2)$, we obtain

$$d = \sqrt{(x_2 - x_1)^2 + (y_2 - y_1)^2}$$
$$= \sqrt{(5 - 2)^2 + (2 - (-2))^2}$$
$$= \sqrt{(5 - 2)^2 + (2 + 2)^2}$$
$$= \sqrt{3^2 + 4^2}$$
$$= \sqrt{9 + 16}$$
$$= \sqrt{25}$$
$$= 5$$

The distance between the given points is 5 units.

5. To find the coordinates of the midpoint, we average the coordinates of the endpoints.

$$\text{Midpoint} = \left(\frac{1+7}{2}, \frac{2+(-3)}{2} \right)$$
$$= \left(\frac{8}{2}, \frac{-1}{2} \right)$$
$$= \left(4, -\frac{1}{2} \right)$$

6. Minimum sales correspond to the lowest point on the graph. The coordinates of this point are approximately (1991, 800). This means that in 1991 ticket sales reached a minimum. The sales for that year were about $800 million.

Exercise Set P.8

1.

3.

5.

7.

9.

11.

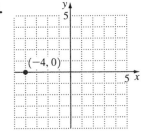

$x = -3, \ y = 7$
$x = -2, \ y = 2$
$x = -1, \ y = -1$
$x = 0, \ y = -2$
$x = 1, \ y = -1$
$x = 2, \ y = 2$
$x = 3, \ y = 7$

13.

$x = -3, \ y = -5$
$x = -2, \ y = -4$
$x = -1, \ y = -3$
$x = 0, \ y = -2$
$x = 1, \ y = -1$
$x = 2, \ y = 0$
$x = 3, \ y = 1$

15.

$x = -3, \ y = -5$
$x = -2, \ y = -3$
$x = -1, \ y = -1$
$x = 0, \ y = 1$
$x = 1, \ y = 3$
$x = 2, \ y = 5$
$x = 3, \ y = 7$

17.

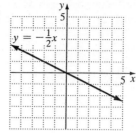

$x = -3, \ y = \dfrac{3}{2}$
$x = -2, \ y = 1$
$x = -1, \ y = \dfrac{1}{2}$
$x = 0, \ y = 0$
$x = 1, \ y = -\dfrac{1}{2}$
$x = 2, \ y = -1$
$x = 3, \ y = -\dfrac{3}{2}$

19.

$x = -3, \ y = -27$
$x = -2, \ y = -8$
$x = -1, \ y = -1$
$x = 0, \ y = 0$
$x = 1, \ y = 1$
$x = 2, \ y = 8$
$x = 3, \ y = 27$

21.

$x = -3, \ y = 3$
$x = -2, \ y = 2$
$x = -1, \ y = 1$
$x = 0, \ y = 0$
$x = 1, \ y = 1$
$x = 2, \ y = 2$
$x = 3, \ y = 3$

23. (c); *x*-axis tick marks –5, –4, –3, –2, –1, 0, 1, 2, 3, 4, 5; *y*-axis tick marks are the same.

25. (b); *x*-axis tick marks –20, –10, 0, 10, 20, 30, 40, 50, 60, 70, 80; *y*-axis tick marks –30, –20, –10, 0, 10, 20, 30, 40, 50, 60, 70

27. a. 2; The graph intersects the *x*-axis at (2, 0).

    b. –4; The graph intersects the *y*-axis at (0,–4).

29. a. 1, –2; The graph intersects the *x*-axis at (1, 0) and (–2, 0).

    b. 2; The graph intersects the *y*-axis at (0, 2).

31. a. –1; The graph intersects the *x*-axis at (–1, 0).

    b. None; The graph does not intersect the *y*-axis.

33. a.

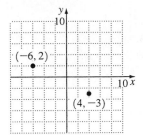

    b. $\sqrt{[4-(-6)]^2 + [-3-2]^2} = \sqrt{100+25}$
$$= \sqrt{125}$$
$$= 5\sqrt{5}$$

    c. $\left(\dfrac{4-6}{2}, \dfrac{-3+2}{2}\right) = \left(\dfrac{-2}{2}, \dfrac{-1}{2}\right)$
$$= \left(-1, \ -\dfrac{1}{2}\right)$$

35. a.

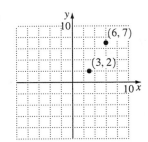

    b. $\sqrt{(3-6)^2 + (2-7)^2} = \sqrt{9+25} = \sqrt{34}$

    c. $\left(\dfrac{3+6}{2}, \dfrac{2+7}{2}\right) = \left(\dfrac{9}{2}, \dfrac{9}{2}\right)$

37. a.

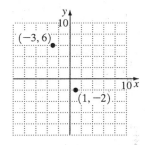

b. $\sqrt{[1-(-3)]^2+(-2-6)^2} = \sqrt{16+64}$
$$= \sqrt{80}$$
$$= 4\sqrt{5}$$

c. $\left(\dfrac{1-3}{2},\ \dfrac{-2+6}{2}\right) = (-1,\ 2)$

39. The point on the graph is about (1970, 5).
The unemployment rate in 1970 was about 5%.

41. The maximum point is about (1982, 9.7).
Therefore the maximum rate of 9.7% was in 1982.

43. (1970, 61)
In 1970, the population of US for people under 16 was about 61 million.

45. (1990, 60)
In 1990, the population of US for people under 16 was about 60 million.

47. a. The maximum height of the graph, i.e., from where the ball was dropped, is (0, 1250). Therefore, the height of the building is 1250 ft.

b. The point on the graph which represents when the ball hit the ground is (8.8, 0). Therefore, the ball hit the ground after 8.8 seconds.

49.–53. Answers may vary.

55. Exercise 11

Exercise 13

Exercise 15

Exercise 17

Exercise 19

57. $y = x^2 + 10$

a.

b.

c.

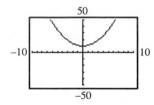

(c) gives a complete graph.

59. $y = \sqrt{x + 18}$

a.

b.

c.

(b) gives a complete graph.

61. a. False; (x, y) can be in quadrant III.

   b. False; when $x = 2$ and $y = 5$,
   $3y - 2x = 3(5) - 2(2) = 11.$

   c. False; if a point is on the x-axis, $y = 0$.

   d. True; all of the above are false.

   (d) is true.

63. a. $d_1 = $ distance from (x, y) to $\left(\dfrac{x_1 + x_2}{2}, \dfrac{y_1 + y_2}{2} \right)$

$d_2 = $ distance from $\left(\dfrac{x_1 + x_2}{2}, \dfrac{y_1 + y_2}{2} \right)$ to $\left(x_2 y_2 \right)$

$d_1 = \sqrt{\left(x_1 - \dfrac{x_1 + x_2}{2} \right)^2 + \left(y_1 - \dfrac{y_1 + y_2}{2} \right)^2}$

$d_1 = \sqrt{\left(\dfrac{2x_1 - x_1 - x_2}{2} \right)^2 + \left(\dfrac{2y_1 - y_1 - y_2}{2} \right)^2}$

$d_1 = \sqrt{\left(\dfrac{x_1 - x_2}{2} \right)^2 + \left(\dfrac{y_1 - y_2}{2} \right)^2}$

$d_1 = \sqrt{\dfrac{x_1^2 - 2x_1 x_2 + x_2^2}{4} + \dfrac{y_1^2 - 2y_1 y_2 + y_2^2}{4}}$

$d_1 = \dfrac{1}{2} \sqrt{x_1^2 - 2x_1 x_2 + x_2^2 + y_1^2 - 2y_1 y_2 + y_2^2}$

$d_2 = \sqrt{\left(x_2 - \dfrac{x_1 + x_2}{2} \right)^2 + \left(y_2 - \dfrac{y_1 + y_2}{2} \right)^2}$

$d_2 = \sqrt{\left(\dfrac{2x_2 - x_1 - x_2}{2} \right)^2 + \left(\dfrac{2y_2 - y_1 - y_2}{2} \right)^2}$

$d_2 = \sqrt{\left(\dfrac{x_2 - x_1}{2} \right)^2 + \left(\dfrac{y_2 - y_1}{2} \right)^2}$

$d_2 = \sqrt{\dfrac{x_2^2 - 2x_1 x_2 + x_1^2}{4} + \dfrac{y_2^2 - 2y_1 y_2 + y_1^2}{4}}$

$d_2 = \dfrac{1}{2} \sqrt{x_1^2 - 2x_1 x_2 + x_2^2 + y_1^2 - 2y_1 y_2 + y_2^2}$

$d_1 = d_2$

b. $d_1 + d_2 = \sqrt{x_1^2 - 2x_1 x_2 + x_2^2 + y_1^2 - 2y_1 y_2 + y_2^2}$

distance from $\left(x_1 y_1 \right)$ to $\left(x_2, y_2 \right)$

$d_3 = \sqrt{\left(x_1 - x_2 \right)^2 + \left(y_1 - y_2 \right)^2}$

$d_3 = \sqrt{x_1^2 - 2x_1 x_2 + x_2^2 + y_1^2 - 2y_1 y_2 + y_2^2}$

$d_1 + d_2 = d_3$

Review Exercises

1. a. $\sqrt{81}$

  b. $0,\ \sqrt{81}$

  c. $-17,\ 0,\ \sqrt{81}$

  d. $-17,\ -\dfrac{9}{13},\ 0,\ 0.75,\ \sqrt{81}$

  e. $\sqrt{2},\ \pi$

2. $|-103| = 103$

3. $\left|\sqrt{2} - 1\right| = \sqrt{2} - 1$

4. $\left|3 - \sqrt{17}\right| = \sqrt{17} - 3$ since $\sqrt{17}$ is greater than 3.

5. $|4 - (-17)| = |4 + 17| = |21| = 21$

6. $\dfrac{5}{9}(F - 32) = \dfrac{5}{9}(68 - 32) = \dfrac{5}{9}(36) = 20$

7. $\dfrac{8(x + 5)}{3x + 8} = \dfrac{8(2 + 5)}{3 \cdot 2 + 8} = \dfrac{8 \cdot 7}{6 + 8} = \dfrac{56}{14} = 4$

8. $3 + 17 = 17 + 3$;
commutative property of addition.

9. $(6 \cdot 3) \cdot 9 = 6 \cdot (3 \cdot 9)$;
associative property of multiplication.

10. $\sqrt{3}(\sqrt{5} + \sqrt{3}) = \sqrt{15} + 3$;
distributive property of multiplication over addition.

11. $(6 \cdot 9) \cdot 2 = 2 \cdot (6 \cdot 9)$;
commutative property of multiplication.

12. $\sqrt{3}(\sqrt{5} + \sqrt{3}) = (\sqrt{5} + \sqrt{3})\sqrt{3}$;
commutative property of multiplication.

13. $(3 \cdot 7) + (4 \cdot 7) = (4 \cdot 7) + (3 \cdot 7)$;
commutative property of addition.

14. $3(7x - 5y) - 2(4y - x + 1)$
$= 21x - 15y - 8y + 2x - 2$
$= (21x + 2x) + (-15y - 8y) - 2$
$= 23x - 23y - 2$

15. $\dfrac{1}{5}(5x) + [(3y) + (-3y)] - (-x) = x + x = 2x$

16. $(-3)^3(-2)^2 = (-27) \cdot (4) = -108$

17. $2^{-4} + 4^{-1} = \dfrac{1}{2^4} + \dfrac{1}{4}$
$= \dfrac{1}{16} + \dfrac{1}{4}$
$= \dfrac{1}{16} + \dfrac{4}{16}$
$= \dfrac{5}{16}$

18. $5^{-3} \cdot 5 = 5^{-3}5^1 = 5^{-3+1} = 5^{-2} = \dfrac{1}{5^2} = \dfrac{1}{25}$

19. $\dfrac{3^3}{3^6} = 3^{3-6} = 3^{-3} = \dfrac{1}{3^3} = \dfrac{1}{27}$

20. $(-2x^4y^3)^3 = (-2)^3(x^4)^3(y^3)^3$
$= (-2)^3 x^{4 \cdot 3} y^{3 \cdot 3}$
$= -8x^{12}y^9$

21. $(-5x^3y^2)(-2x^{-11}y^{-2})$
$= (-5)(-2)x^3x^{-11}y^2y^{-2}$
$= 10 \cdot x^{3-11}y^{2-2}$
$= 10x^{-8}y^0$
$= \dfrac{10}{x^8}$

22. $(2x^3)^{-4} = (2)^{-4}(x^3)^{-4}$
$= 2^{-4}x^{-12}$
$= \dfrac{1}{2^4x^{12}}$
$= \dfrac{1}{16x^{12}}$

23. $\dfrac{7x^5 y^6}{28x^{15} y^{-2}} = \left(\dfrac{7}{28}\right)(x^{5-15})(y^{6-(-2)})$

$\qquad = \dfrac{1}{4} x^{-10} y^8$

$\qquad = \dfrac{y^8}{4x^{10}}$

24. $3.74 \times 10^4 = 37,400$

25. $7.45 \times 10^{-5} = 0.0000745$

26. $3,590,000 = 3.59 \times 10^6$

27. $0.00725 = 7.25 \times 10^{-3}$

28. $(3 \times 10^3)(1.3 \times 10^2) = (3 \times 1.3) \times (10^3 \times 10^2)$

$\qquad\qquad = 3.9 \times 10^5$

29. $\dfrac{6.9 \times 10^3}{3 \times 10^5} = \left(\dfrac{6.9}{3}\right) \times 10^{3-5}$

$\qquad\qquad = 2.3 \times 10^{-2}$

30. $\dfrac{10^9}{10^6} - 10^{9-6} = 10^3$

It would take 10^3 or 1000 years to accumulate \$1 billion.

31. $(2.7 \times 10^8) \times (150)$

$= (2.7 \times 10^8) \times (1.5 \times 10^2)$

$= (2.7 \times 1.5) \times (10^8 \times 10^2)$

$= 4.05 \times 10^{10}$

The total annual spending on movies is $\$4.05 \times 10^{10}$.

32. $\sqrt{300} = \sqrt{100 \cdot 3} = \sqrt{100} \cdot \sqrt{3} = 10\sqrt{3}$

33. $\sqrt{12x^2} = \sqrt{4x^2 \cdot 3} = \sqrt{4x^2} \cdot \sqrt{3} = 2|x|\sqrt{3}$

34. $\sqrt{10x} \cdot \sqrt{2x} = \sqrt{20x^2}$

$\qquad\qquad = \sqrt{4x^2 \cdot 5}$

$\qquad\qquad = \sqrt{4x^2} \cdot \sqrt{5}$

$\qquad\qquad = 2|x|\sqrt{5}$

35. $\sqrt{r^3} = \sqrt{r^2 \cdot r} = |r|\sqrt{r}$

36. $\sqrt{\dfrac{121}{4}} = \dfrac{\sqrt{121}}{\sqrt{4}} = \dfrac{11}{2}$

37. $\dfrac{\sqrt{96x^3}}{\sqrt{2x}} = \sqrt{\dfrac{96x^3}{2x}}$

$\qquad = \sqrt{48x^2}$

$\qquad = \sqrt{16x^2 \cdot 3}$

$\qquad = \sqrt{16x^2} \cdot \sqrt{3}$

$\qquad = 4|x|\sqrt{3}$

38. $7\sqrt{5} + 13\sqrt{5} = (7+13)\sqrt{5} = 20\sqrt{5}$

39. $2\sqrt{50} + 3\sqrt{8} = 2\sqrt{25 \cdot 2} + 3\sqrt{4 \cdot 2}$

$\qquad\qquad = 2 \cdot 5\sqrt{2} + 3 \cdot 2\sqrt{2}$

$\qquad\qquad = 10\sqrt{2} + 6\sqrt{2}$

$\qquad\qquad = 16\sqrt{2}$

40. $4\sqrt{72} - 2\sqrt{48} = 4\sqrt{36 \cdot 2} - 2\sqrt{16 \cdot 3}$

$\qquad\qquad = 4 \cdot 6\sqrt{2} - 2 \cdot 4\sqrt{3}$

$\qquad\qquad = 24\sqrt{2} - 8\sqrt{3}$

41. $\dfrac{30}{\sqrt{5}} = \dfrac{30}{\sqrt{5}} \cdot \dfrac{\sqrt{5}}{\sqrt{5}} = \dfrac{30\sqrt{5}}{5} = 6\sqrt{5}$

42. $\dfrac{\sqrt{2}}{\sqrt{3}} = \dfrac{\sqrt{2}}{\sqrt{3}} \cdot \dfrac{\sqrt{3}}{\sqrt{3}} = \dfrac{\sqrt{6}}{3}$

43. $\dfrac{5}{6+\sqrt{3}} = \dfrac{5}{6+\sqrt{3}} \cdot \dfrac{6-\sqrt{3}}{6-\sqrt{3}}$

$\qquad = \dfrac{5(6-\sqrt{3})}{36-3}$

$\qquad = \dfrac{5(6-\sqrt{3})}{33}$

44.

$$\frac{14}{\sqrt{7}-\sqrt{5}} = \frac{14}{\sqrt{7}-\sqrt{5}} \cdot \frac{\sqrt{7}+\sqrt{5}}{\sqrt{7}+\sqrt{5}}$$

$$= \frac{14(\sqrt{7}+\sqrt{5})}{7-5}$$

$$= \frac{14(\sqrt{7}+\sqrt{5})}{2}$$

$$= 7(\sqrt{7}+\sqrt{5})$$

45. $\sqrt[3]{125} = 5$

46. $\sqrt[5]{-32} = -2$

47. $\sqrt[4]{-125}$ is not a real number.

48. $\sqrt[4]{(-5)^4} = \sqrt[4]{625} = \sqrt[4]{5^4} = 5$

49. $\sqrt[3]{81} = \sqrt[3]{27 \cdot 3} = \sqrt[3]{27} \cdot \sqrt[3]{3} = 3\sqrt[3]{3}$

50. $\sqrt[3]{y^5} = \sqrt[3]{y^3 y^2} = y\sqrt[3]{y^2}$

51. $\sqrt[4]{8} \cdot \sqrt[4]{10} = \sqrt[4]{80} = \sqrt[4]{16 \cdot 5} = \sqrt[4]{16} \cdot \sqrt[4]{5} = 2\sqrt[4]{5}$

52.

$$4\sqrt[3]{16} + 5\sqrt[3]{2} = 4\sqrt[3]{8 \cdot 2} + 5\sqrt[3]{2}$$

$$= 4 \cdot 2\sqrt[3]{2} + 5\sqrt[3]{2}$$

$$= 8\sqrt[3]{2} + 5\sqrt[3]{2}$$

$$= 13\sqrt[3]{2}$$

53. $\dfrac{\sqrt[4]{32x^5}}{\sqrt[4]{16x}} = \sqrt[4]{\dfrac{32x^5}{16x}} = \sqrt[4]{2x^4} = |x|\sqrt[4]{2}$

54. $16^{1/2} = \sqrt{16} = 4$

55. $25^{-1/2} = \dfrac{1}{25^{1/2}} = \dfrac{1}{\sqrt{25}} = \dfrac{1}{5}$

56. $125^{1/3} = \sqrt[3]{125} = 5$

57. $27^{-1/3} = \dfrac{1}{27^{1/3}} = \dfrac{1}{\sqrt[3]{27}} = \dfrac{1}{3}$

58. $64^{2/3} = (\sqrt[3]{64})^2 = 4^2 = 16$

59. $27^{-4/3} = \dfrac{1}{27^{4/3}} = \dfrac{1}{(\sqrt[3]{27})^4} = \dfrac{1}{3^4} = \dfrac{1}{81}$

60. $(5x^{2/3})(4x^{1/4}) = 5 \cdot 4x^{2/3+1/4} = 20x^{11/12}$

61. $\dfrac{15x^{3/4}}{5x^{1/2}} = \left(\dfrac{15}{5}\right)x^{3/4-1/2} = 3x^{1/4}$

62.

$$(125 \cdot x^6)^{2/3} = (\sqrt[3]{125x^6})^2$$

$$= (5x^2)^2$$

$$= 25x^4$$

63. $\sqrt[6]{y^3} = (y^3)^{1/6} = y^{3 \cdot 1/6} = y^{1/2}$

64. $(-6x^3 + 7x^2 - 9x + 3) + (14x^3 + 3x^2 - 11x - 7) = (-6x^3 + 14x^3) + (7x^2 + 3x^2) + (-9x - 11x) + (3 - 7)$
$$= 8x^3 + 10x^2 - 20x - 4$$
The degree is 3.

65. $(13x^4 - 8x^3 + 2x^2) - (5x^4 - 3x^3 + 2x^2 - 6) = (13x^4 - 8x^3 + 2x^2) + (-5x^4 + 3x^3 - 2x^2 + 6)$
$$= (13x^4 - 5x^4) + (-8x^3 + 3x^3) + (2x^2 - 2x^2) + 6$$
$$= 8x^4 - 5x^3 + 6$$
The degree is 4.

66. $(3x - 2)(4x^2 + 3x - 5) = (3x)(4x^2) + (3x)(3x) + (3x)(-5) + (-2)(4x^2) + (-2)(3x) + (-2)(-5)$
$$= 12x^3 + 9x^2 - 15x - 8x^2 - 6x + 10$$
$$= 12x^3 + x^2 - 21x + 10$$

67. $(3x - 5)(2x + 1) = (3x)(2x) + (3x)(1) + (-5)(2x) + (-5)(1)$
$$= 6x^2 + 3x - 10x - 5$$
$$= 6x^2 - 7x - 5$$

68. $(4x + 5)(4x - 5) = (4x^2) - 5^2 = 16x^2 - 25$

69. $(2x + 5)^2 = (2x)^2 + 2(2x) \cdot 5 + 5^2 = 4x^2 + 20x + 25$

70. $(3x - 4)^2 = (3x)^2 - 2(3x) \cdot 4 + (-4)^2 = 9x^2 \quad 24x + 16$

71. $(2x + 1)^3 = (2x)^3 + 3(2x)^2(1) + 3(2x)(1)^2 + 1^3 = 8x^3 + 12x^2 + 6x + 1$

72. $(5x - 2)^3 = (5x)^3 - 3(5x)^2(2) + 3(5x)(2)^2 - 2^3 = 125x^3 - 150x^2 + 60x - 8$

73. $(7x^2 - 8xy + y^2) + (-8x^2 - 9xy - 4y^2) = (7x^2 - 8x^2) + (-8xy - 9xy) + (y^2 - 4y^2)$
$$= -x^2 - 17xy - 3y^2$$
The degree is 2.

74. $(13x^3y^2 - 5x^2y - 9x^2) - (-11x^3y^2 - 6x^2y + 3x^2 - 4)$
$$= (13x^3y^2 - 5x^2y - 9x^2) + (11x^3y^2 + 6x^2y - 3x^2 + 4)$$
$$= (13x^3y^2 + 11x^3y^2) + (-5x^2y + 6x^2y) + (-9x^2 - 3x^2) + 4$$
$$= 24x^3y^2 + x^2y - 12x^2 + 4$$
The degree is 5.

75. $(x + 7y)(3x - 5y) = x(3x) + (x)(-5y) + (7y)(3x) + (7y)(-5y)$
$$= 3x^2 - 5xy + 21xy - 35y^2$$
$$= 3x^2 + 16xy - 35y^2$$

76. $(3x - 5y)^2 = (3x)^2 - 2(3x)(5y) + (-5y)^2$
$$= 9x^2 - 30xy + 25y^2$$

77. $(3x^2 + 2y)^2 = (3x^2)^2 + 2(3x^2)(2y) + (2y)^2$
$$= 9x^4 + 12x^2y + 4y^2$$

78. $(7x + 4y)(7x - 4y) = (7x)^2 - (4y)^2$
$$= 49x^2 - 16y^2$$

79. $(a - b)(a^2 + ab + b^2)$
$= a(a^2) + a(ab) + a(b^2) + (-b)(a^2)$
$+(-b)(ab) + (-b)(b^2)$
$= a^3 + a^2b + ab^2 - a^2b - ab^2 - b^3$
$= a^3 - b^3$

80. $15x^3 + 3x^2 = 3x^2 \cdot 5x + 3x^2 \cdot 1$
$$= 3x^2(5x + 1)$$

81. $x^2 - 11x + 28 = (x - 4)(x - 7)$

82. $15x^2 - x - 2 = (3x + 1)(5x - 2)$

83. $64 - x^2 = 8^2 - x^2 = (8 - x)(8 + x)$

84. $x^2 + 16$ is prime.

85. $3x^4 - 9x^3 - 30x^2 = 3x^2(x^2 - 3x - 10)$
$$= 3x^2(x - 5)(x + 2)$$

86. $20x^7 - 36x^3 = 4x^3(5x^4 - 9)$

87. $x^3 - 3x^2 - 9x + 27 = x^2(x - 3) - 9(x - 3)$
$$= (x^2 - 9)(x - 3)$$
$$= (x + 3)(x - 3)(x - 3)$$
$$= (x + 3)(x - 3)^2$$

88. $16x^2 - 40x + 25 = (4x - 5)(4x - 5)$
$$= (4x - 5)^2$$

89. $x^4 - 16 = (x^2)^2 - 4^2$
$$= (x^2 + 4)(x^2 - 4)$$
$$= (x^2 + 4)(x + 2)(x - 2)$$

90. $y^3 - 8 = y^3 - 2^3 = (y - 2)(y^2 + 2y + 4)$

91. $x^3 + 64 = x^3 + 4^3 = (x + 4)(x^2 - 4x + 16)$

92. $3x^4 - 12x^2 = 3x^2(x^2 - 4)$
$$= 3x^2(x - 2)(x + 2)$$

93. $27x^3 - 125 = (3x)^3 - 5^3$
$$= (3x - 5)[(3x)^2 + (3x)(5) + 5^2]$$
$$= (3x - 5)(9x^2 + 15x + 25)$$

94. $x^5 - x = x(x^4 - 1)$
$$= x(x^2 - 1)(x^2 + 1)$$
$$= x(x - 1)(x + 1)(x^2 + 1)$$

95. $x^3 + 5x^2 - 2x - 10 = x^2(x + 5) - 2(x + 5)$
$$= (x^2 - 2)(x + 5)$$

96. $\dfrac{x^3 + 2x^2}{x + 2} = \dfrac{x^2(x + 2)}{x + 2} = x^2, x \neq -2$

97. $\dfrac{x^2 + 3x - 18}{x^2 - 36} = \dfrac{(x + 6)(x - 3)}{(x + 6)(x - 6)} = \dfrac{x - 3}{x - 6},$
$x \neq -6, 6$

98. $\dfrac{x^2 + 2x}{x^2 + 4x + 4} = \dfrac{x(x + 2)}{(x + 2)^2} = \dfrac{x}{x + 2},$
$x \neq -2$

99. $\dfrac{x^2 + 6x + 9}{x^2 - 4} \cdot \dfrac{x + 3}{x - 2} = \dfrac{(x + 3)^2}{(x - 2)(x + 2)} \cdot \dfrac{x + 3}{x - 2}$
$$= \dfrac{(x + 3)^3}{(x - 2)^2(x + 2)},$$
$x \neq 2, -2$

100.

$$\frac{6x+2}{x^2-1} \div \frac{3x^2+x}{x-1}$$

$$= \frac{2(3x+1)}{(x-1)(x+1)} \div \frac{x(3x+1)}{x-1}$$

$$= \frac{2(3x+1)}{(x-1)(x+1)} \cdot \frac{x-1}{x(3x+1)}$$

$$= \frac{2}{x(x+1)},$$

$$x \neq 0,\ 1,\ -1,\ -\frac{1}{3}$$

101.

$$\frac{x^2-5x-24}{x^2-x-12} \div \frac{x^2-10x+16}{x^2+x-6}$$

$$= \frac{(x-8)(x+3)}{(x-4)(x+3)} \div \frac{(x-2)(x-8)}{(x+3)(x-2)}$$

$$= \frac{x-8}{x-4} \cdot \frac{x+3}{x-8}$$

$$= \frac{x+3}{x-4},$$

$$x \neq -3, 4, 2, 8$$

102.

$$\frac{2x-7}{x^2-9} - \frac{x-10}{x^2-9} = \frac{2x-7-(x-10)}{x^2-9}$$

$$= \frac{x+3}{(x+3)(x-3)}$$

$$= \frac{1}{x-3},$$

$$x \neq 3, -3$$

103.

$$\frac{3x}{x+2} + \frac{x}{x-2} = \frac{3x}{x+2} \cdot \frac{x-2}{x-2} + \frac{x}{x-2} \cdot \frac{x+2}{x+2}$$

$$= \frac{3x^2-6x+x^2+2x}{(x+2)(x-2)}$$

$$= \frac{4x^2-4x}{(x+2)(x-2)}$$

$$= \frac{4x(x-1)}{(x+2)(x-2)},$$

$$x \neq 2, -2$$

104.

$$\frac{x}{x^2-9} + \frac{x}{x^2-5x+6}$$

$$= \frac{x}{(x-3)(x+3)} + \frac{x}{(x-2)(x-3)}$$

$$= \frac{x}{(x-3)(x+3)} \cdot \frac{x-2}{x-2}$$

$$+ \frac{x}{(x-2)(x-3)} \cdot \frac{x+3}{x+3}$$

$$= \frac{x(x-2)+x(x+3)}{(x-3)(x+3)(x-2)}$$

$$= \frac{2x^2+x}{(x-3)(x+3)(x-2)}$$

$$= \frac{x(2x+1)}{(x-3)(x+3)(x-2)}$$

$$x \neq 3, -3, 2$$

105.

$$\frac{4x-1}{2x^2+5x-3} - \frac{x+3}{6x^2+x-2}$$

$$= \frac{4x-1}{(2x-1)(x+3)} - \frac{x+3}{(2x-1)(3x+2)}$$

$$- \frac{4x-1}{(2x-1)(x+3)} \cdot \frac{3x+2}{3x+2}$$

$$- \frac{x+3}{(2x-1)(3x+2)} \cdot \frac{x+3}{x+3}$$

$$= \frac{12x^2+8x-3x-2-x^2-6x-9}{(2x-1)(x+3)(3x+2)}$$

$$= \frac{11x^2-x-11}{(2x-1)(x+3)(3x+2)},$$

$$x \neq \frac{1}{2},\ -3,\ -\frac{2}{3}$$

106.

$$\frac{\frac{1}{x}-\frac{1}{2}}{\frac{1}{3}-\frac{x}{6}} = \frac{\frac{1}{x}-\frac{1}{2}}{\frac{1}{3}-\frac{x}{6}} \cdot \frac{6x}{6x}$$

$$= \frac{6-3x}{2x-x^2}$$

$$= \frac{-3(x-2)}{-x(x-2)}$$

$$= \frac{3}{x},$$

$$x \neq 0, 2$$

107.
$$\frac{3+\frac{12}{x}}{1-\frac{16}{x^2}} = \frac{3+\frac{12}{x}}{1-\frac{16}{x^2}} \cdot \frac{x^2}{x^2}$$
$$= \frac{3x^2 + 12x}{x^2 - 16}$$
$$= \frac{3x(x+4)}{(x+4)(x-4)}$$
$$= \frac{3x}{x-4},$$
$$x \neq 0, 4, -4$$

108.
$$\frac{3-\frac{1}{x+3}}{3+\frac{1}{x+3}} = \frac{3-\frac{1}{x+3}}{3+\frac{1}{x+3}} \cdot \frac{x+3}{x+3}$$
$$= \frac{3(x+3)-1}{3(x+3)+1}$$
$$= \frac{3x+9-1}{3x+9+1}$$
$$= \frac{3x+8}{3x+10},$$
$$x \neq -3, -\frac{10}{3}$$

109. $(8-3i)-(17-7i) = 8 - 3i - 17 + 7i$
$$= -9 + 4i$$

110. $4i(3i-2) = (4i)(3i) + (4i)(-2)$
$$= 12i^2 - 8i$$
$$= -12 - 8i$$

111. $(7-5i)(2+3i)$
$$= 7 \cdot 2 + 7(3i) + (-5i)(2) + (-5i)(3i)$$
$$= 14 + 21i - 10i + 15$$
$$= 29 + 11i$$

112. $(3-4i)^2 = 3^2 + 2 \cdot 3(-4i) + (-4i)^2$
$$= 9 - 24i - 16$$
$$= -7 - 24i$$

113. $(7+8i)(7-8i) = 7^2 + 8^2 = 49 + 64 = 113$

114.
$$\frac{6}{5+i} = \frac{6}{5+i} \cdot \frac{5-i}{5-i}$$
$$= \frac{6(5-i)}{25+1}$$
$$= \frac{6(5-i)}{26}$$
$$= \frac{3(5-i)}{13} = \frac{15}{13} - \frac{3}{13}i$$

115.
$$\frac{3+4i}{4-2i} = \frac{3+4i}{4-2i} \cdot \frac{4+2i}{4+2i}$$
$$= \frac{12 + 6i + 16i + 8i^2}{4^2 + 2^2}$$
$$= \frac{12 + 22i - 8}{16 + 4}$$
$$= \frac{4 + 22i}{20}$$
$$= \frac{1}{5} + \frac{11}{10}i$$

116. $\sqrt{-32} - \sqrt{-18} = i\sqrt{32} - i\sqrt{18}$
$$= i\sqrt{16 \cdot 2} - i\sqrt{9 \cdot 2}$$
$$= 4i\sqrt{2} - 3i\sqrt{2}$$
$$= (4i - 3i)\sqrt{2}$$
$$= i\sqrt{2}$$

117. $(-2+\sqrt{-100})^2 = (-2 + i\sqrt{100})^2$
$$= (-2 + 10i)^2$$
$$= 4 - 40i + (10i)^2$$
$$= 4 - 40i - 100$$
$$= -96 - 40i$$

118.
$$\frac{4+\sqrt{-8}}{2} = \frac{4 + i\sqrt{8}}{2} = \frac{4 + 2i\sqrt{2}}{2} = 2 + i\sqrt{2}$$

119. $y = 2x - 2$

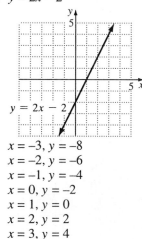

$x = -3, y = -8$
$x = -2, y = -6$
$x = -1, y = -4$
$x = 0, y = -2$
$x = 1, y = 0$
$x = 2, y = 2$
$x = 3, y = 4$

120. $y = x^2 - 3$

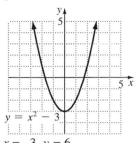

$x = -3, y = 6$
$x = -2, y = 1$
$x = -1, y = -2$
$x = 0, y = -3$
$x = 1, y = -2$
$x = 2, y = 1$
$x = 3, y = 6$

121. $y = x$

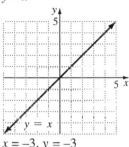

$x = -3, y = -3$
$x = 2, y = -2$
$x = -1, y = -1$
$x = 0, y = 0$
$x = 1, y = 1$
$x = 2, y = 2$
$x = 3, y = 3$

122. A portion of Cartesian coordinate plane with minimum x-value equal to -20, maximum x-value equal to 40, x-scale equal to 10 and with minimum y-value equal to -5, maximum y-value equal to 5, and y-scale equal to 1.

123. x-intercept: -2; The graph intersects the x-axis at $(-2, 0)$.
y-intercept: 2; The graph intersects the y-axis at $(0, 2)$.

124. x-intercepts: $2, -2$; The graph intersects the x-axis at $(-2, 0)$ and $(2, 0)$.
y-intercept: -4; The graph intercepts the y-axis at $(0, -4)$.

125. x-intercept: 5; The graph intersects the x-axis at $(5, 0)$.
y-intercept: None; The graph does not intersect the y-axis.

126. a.

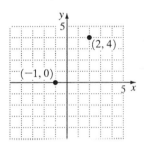

b.
$$\sqrt{[2-(-1)]^2 + (4-0)^2} = \sqrt{3^2 + 4^2}$$
$$= \sqrt{9+16}$$
$$= \sqrt{25}$$
$$= 5$$

c. $\left(\dfrac{-1+2}{2}, \dfrac{0+4}{2} \right) = \left(\dfrac{1}{2}, 2 \right)$

127. a.

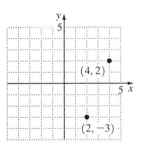

b.
$$\sqrt{(4-2)^2 + [2-(-3)]^2} = \sqrt{4+25}$$
$$= \sqrt{29}$$

c. $\left(\dfrac{2+4}{2}, \dfrac{-3+2}{2} \right) = \left(3, -\dfrac{1}{2} \right)$

128. a. 1991 because the maximum point is at (1991, 100). The number of applicants for 1991 is 100,000.

b. (1990, 30). The number of medical school applicants in 1990 is about 30,000.

c. The coordinates of A are approximately (1998, 70). In 1998 there were about 70,000 law school applicants.

Chapter P Test

1. -7, $-\dfrac{4}{5}$, 0, 0.25, $\sqrt{4}$, $\dfrac{22}{7}$ are rational numbers.

2. $3(2 + 5) = 3(5 + 2)$; commutative property of addition

3. $6(7 + 4) = 6 \cdot 7 + 6 \cdot 4$ distributive property of multiplication over addition

4. $0.00076 = 7.6 \times 10^{-4}$

5. $9(10x - 2y) - 5(x - 4y + 3)$
$= 90x - 18y - 5x + 20y - 15$
$= 85x + 2y - 15$

6. $\dfrac{30x^3 y^4}{6x^9 y^{-4}} = 5x^{3-9} y^{4-(-4)} = 5x^{-6} y^8 = \dfrac{5y^8}{x^6}$

7. $\sqrt{6r}\sqrt{3r} = \sqrt{18r^2} = \sqrt{9r^2 \cdot 2} = 3|r|\sqrt{2}$

8. $4\sqrt{50} - 3\sqrt{18} = 4\sqrt{25 \cdot 2} - 3\sqrt{9 \cdot 2}$
$= 4 \cdot 5\sqrt{2} - 3 \cdot 3\sqrt{2}$
$= 20\sqrt{2} - 9\sqrt{2}$
$= 11\sqrt{2}$

9. $\dfrac{3}{5 + \sqrt{2}} = \dfrac{3}{5 + \sqrt{2}} \cdot \dfrac{5 - \sqrt{2}}{5 - \sqrt{2}}$
$= \dfrac{3(5 - \sqrt{2})}{25 - 2}$
$= \dfrac{3(5 - \sqrt{2})}{23}$

10. $\sqrt[3]{16x^4} = \sqrt[3]{8x^3 \cdot 2x}$
$= \sqrt[3]{8x^3} \cdot \sqrt[3]{2x}$
$= 2x\sqrt[3]{2x}$

11. $\dfrac{x^2 + 2x - 3}{x^2 - 3x + 2} = \dfrac{(x+3)(x-1)}{(x-2)(x-1)} = \dfrac{x+3}{x-2}$,
$x \neq 2, 1$

12. $27^{-5/3} = \dfrac{1}{27^{5/3}} = \dfrac{1}{\left(\sqrt[3]{27}\right)^5} = \dfrac{1}{3^5} = \dfrac{1}{243}$

13. $(2x - 5)(x^2 - 4x + 3)$
$= 2x^3 - 8x^2 + 6x - 5x^2 + 20x - 15$
$= 2x^3 - 13x^2 + 26x - 15$

14. $(5x + 3y)^2 = (5x)^2 + 2(5x)(3y) + (3y)^2$
$= 25x^2 + 30xy + 9y^2$

15. $x^2 - 9x + 18 = (x - 3)(x - 6)$

16. $x^3 + 2x^2 + 3x + 6 = x^2(x + 2) + 3(x + 2)$
$= (x^2 + 3)(x + 2)$

17. $25x^2 - 9 = (5x)^2 - 3^2 = (5x - 3)(5x + 3)$

18. $36x^2 - 84x + 49 = (6x)^2 - 2(6x) \cdot 7 + 7^2$
$= (6x - 7)^2$

19. $y^3 - 125 = y^3 - 5^3 = (y - 5)(y^2 + 5y + 25)$

20. $\dfrac{2x + 8}{x - 3} \div \dfrac{x^2 + 5x + 4}{x^2 - 9}$
$= \dfrac{2(x + 4)}{x - 3} \div \dfrac{(x + 1)(x + 4)}{(x - 3)(x + 3)}$
$= \dfrac{2(x + 4)}{x - 3} \cdot \dfrac{(x - 3)(x + 3)}{(x + 1)(x + 4)}$
$= \dfrac{2(x + 3)}{x + 1}$,
$x \neq 3, -1, -4, -3$

21. $\dfrac{x}{x+3} + \dfrac{5}{x-3}$

$= \dfrac{x}{x+3} \cdot \dfrac{x-3}{x-3} + \dfrac{5}{x-3} \cdot \dfrac{x+3}{x+3}$

$= \dfrac{x(x-3) + 5(x+3)}{(x+3)(x-3)}$

$= \dfrac{x^2 - 3x + 5x + 15}{(x+3)(x-3)}$

$= \dfrac{x^2 + 2x + 15}{(x+3)(x-3)}, \quad x \neq 3, \ -3$

22. $\dfrac{2x+3}{x^2 - 7x + 12} - \dfrac{2}{x-3}$

$= \dfrac{2x+3}{(x-3)(x-4)} - \dfrac{2}{x-3}$

$= \dfrac{2x+3}{(x-3)(x-4)} - \dfrac{2}{x-3} \cdot \dfrac{x-4}{x-4}$

$= \dfrac{2x + 3 - 2(x-4)}{(x-3)(x-4)}$

$= \dfrac{2x + 3 - 2(x-4)}{(x-3)(x-4)}$

$= \dfrac{2x + 3 - 2x + 8}{(x-3)(x-4)}$

$= \dfrac{11}{(x-3)(x-4)},$

$x \neq 3, \ 4$

23. $\dfrac{\frac{1}{x} - \frac{1}{3}}{\frac{1}{x}} = \dfrac{\frac{1}{x} - \frac{1}{3}}{\frac{1}{x}} \cdot \dfrac{3x}{3x} = \dfrac{3-x}{3},$

$x \neq 0$

24. $(6 - 7i)(2 + 5i) = 12 + 30i - 14i - 35i^2$

$\qquad = 12 + 16i + 35$

$\qquad = 47 + 16i$

25. $\dfrac{5}{2-i} = \dfrac{5}{2-i} \cdot \dfrac{2+i}{2+i}$

$\qquad = \dfrac{5(2+i)}{4+i}$

$\qquad - \dfrac{5(2+i)}{5}$

$\qquad = 2 + i$

26. $2\sqrt{-49} + 3\sqrt{-64} = 2(7i) + 3(8i)$

$\qquad\qquad\qquad\quad = 14i + 24i$

$\qquad\qquad\qquad\quad = 38i$

27.

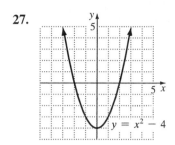

$y = x^2 - 4$

$x = -3, y = 5$
$x = -2, y = 0$
$x = -1, y = -3$
$x = 0, y = 4$
$x = 1, y = -3$
$x = 2, y = 0$
$x = 3, y = 5$

28. $(2, 9)$ and $(6, 3)$

$\sqrt{(6-2)^2 + (3-9)^2} = \sqrt{16 + 36}$

$\qquad\qquad\qquad\qquad = \sqrt{52}$

$\qquad\qquad\qquad\qquad = \sqrt{4 \cdot 13}$

$\qquad\qquad\qquad\qquad = 2\sqrt{13}$

Chapter 1

Check Point Exercises

1.
$$5x - 8 = 72$$
$$5x - 8 + 8 = 72 + 8$$
$$5x = 80$$
$$\frac{5x}{5} = \frac{80}{5}$$
$$x = 16$$

Check:
$$5x - 8 = 72$$
$$5(16) - 8 \overset{?}{=} 72$$
$$80 - 8 \overset{?}{=} 72$$
$$72 = 72$$
The solution set is $\{16\}$.

2.
$$4(2x + 1) - 29 = 3(2x - 5)$$
$$8x + 4 - 29 = 6x - 15$$
$$8x - 25 = 6x - 15$$
$$8x - 25 - 6x = 6x - 15 - 6x$$
$$2x - 25 = -15$$
$$2x - 25 + 25 = -15 + 25$$
$$2x = 10$$
$$\frac{2x}{2} = \frac{10}{2}$$
$$x = 5$$

Check:
$$4(2x + 1) - 29 \overset{?}{=} 3(2x - 5)$$
$$4[2(5) + 1] - 29 \overset{?}{=} 3[2(5) - 5]$$
$$4(10 + 1) - 29 \overset{?}{=} 3(10 - 5)$$
$$4(11) - 29 \overset{?}{=} 3(5)$$
$$44 - 29 \overset{?}{=} 15$$
$$15 \overset{?}{=} 15$$
The solution set is $\{5\}$.

3.
$$\frac{x}{4} = \frac{2x}{3} + \frac{5}{6}$$
$$12 \cdot \frac{x}{4} = 12\left(\frac{2x}{3} + \frac{5}{6}\right)$$
$$12 \cdot \frac{x}{4} = 12 \cdot \frac{2x}{3} + 12 \cdot \frac{5}{6}$$
$$3x = 8x + 10$$
$$3x - 8x = 8x + 10 - 8x$$
$$-5x = 10$$
$$\frac{-5x}{-5} = \frac{10}{-5}$$
$$x = -2$$

Check:
$$\frac{x}{4} = \frac{2x}{3} + \frac{5}{6}$$
$$\frac{-2}{4} \overset{?}{=} \frac{2(-2)}{3} + \frac{5}{6}$$
$$\frac{-1}{2} \overset{?}{=} \frac{-4}{3} + \frac{5}{6}$$
$$\frac{-1}{2} = \frac{-1}{2}$$
The solution set is $\{-2\}$.

4.
$$\frac{5}{2x} = \frac{17}{18} - \frac{1}{3x}, \ x \neq 0$$
$$18x \cdot \frac{5}{2x} = 18x\left(\frac{17}{18} - \frac{1}{3x}\right)$$
$$18 \cdot \frac{5}{2x} = 18x \cdot \frac{17}{18} - 18x \cdot \frac{1}{3x}$$
$$45 = 17x - 6$$
$$45 + 6 = 17x - 6 + 6$$
$$51 = 17x$$
$$\frac{51}{17} = \frac{17x}{17}$$
$$3 = x$$
The solution set is $\{3\}$.

5.

$$\frac{x}{x-2} = \frac{2}{x-2} - \frac{2}{3}, x \neq 2$$

$$3(x-2) \cdot \frac{x}{x-2} = 3(x-2)\left[\frac{2}{x-2} - \frac{2}{3}\right]$$

$$3(x-2) \cdot \frac{x}{x-2} = (3x-2) \cdot \frac{2}{x-2} - 3(x-2) \cdot \frac{2}{3}$$

$$3x = 6 - (x-2) \cdot 2$$
$$3x = 6 - 2(x-2)$$
$$3x = 6 - 2x + 4$$
$$3x = 10 - 2x$$
$$3x + 2x = 10 - 2x + 2x$$
$$5x = 10$$
$$\frac{5x}{5} = \frac{10}{5}$$
$$x = 2$$

The solution set is the empty set, $\varnothing$.

6. $2(x+1) = 2x + 2$
$2x + 2 = 2x + 2$
The given equation is an identity.

Exercise Set 1.1

1. $5x - 8 = 72$
$5x = 80$
$x = 16$
The solution set is $\{16\}$.

Check:
$5x - 8 = 72$
$5(16) - 8 \stackrel{?}{=} 72$
$80 - 8 \stackrel{?}{=} 72$
$72 = 72$

3. $11x - (6x - 5) = 40$
$11x - 6x + 5 = 40$
$5x + 5 = 40$
$5x = 35$
$x = 7$
The solution set is $\{7\}$.

Check:
$11x - (6x - 5) = 40$
$11(7) - [6(7) - 5] \stackrel{?}{=} 40$
$77 - (42 - 5) \stackrel{?}{=} 40$
$77 - 37 \stackrel{?}{=} 40$
$40 = 40$

5. $2x - 7 = 6 + x$
$x - 7 = 6$
$x = 13$
The solution set is $\{13\}$.

Check:
$2x - 7 = 6 + x$
$2(13) - 7 \stackrel{?}{=} 6 + 13$
$26 - 7 \stackrel{?}{=} 19$
$19 = 19$

7. $7x + 4 = x + 16$
$6x + 4 = 16$
$6x = 12$
$x = 2$
The solution set is $\{2\}$.

Check:
$7x + 4 = x + 16$
$7(2) + 4 \stackrel{?}{=} 2 + 16$
$14 + 4 = 18$
$18 = 18$

9. $3(x - 2) + 7 = 2(x + 5)$
$3x - 6 + 7 = 2x + 10$
$3x + 1 = 2x + 10$
$x + 1 = 10$
$x = 9$
The solution set is $\{9\}$.

Check:
$3(x - 2) + 7 = 2(x + 5)$
$3(9 - 2) + 7 \stackrel{?}{=} 2(9 + 5)$
$3(7) + 7 \stackrel{?}{=} 2(14)$
$21 + 7 = 28$
$28 = 28$

11. $3(x - 4) - 4(x - 3) = x + 3 - (x - 2)$
$3x - 12 - 4x + 12 = x + 3 - x + 2$
$-x = 5$
$x = -5$
The solution set is $\{-5\}$.

Check:
$3(x - 4) - 4(x - 3) = x + 3 - (x - 2)$
$3(-5 - 4) - 4(-5 - 3) \stackrel{?}{=} -5 + 3 - (5 - 2)$
$3(-9) - 4(-8) \stackrel{?}{=} -2 - (-7)$
$-27 + 32 = -2 + 7$
$5 = 5$

13. $16 = 3(x - 1) - (x - 7)$
$16 = 3x - 3 - x + 7$
$16 = 2x + 4$
$12 = 2x$
$6 = x$
$x = 6$
The solution set is $\{6\}$.

Check:
$16 = 3(x - 1) - (x - 7)$
$16 \stackrel{?}{=} 3(6 - 1) - (6 - 7)$
$16 \stackrel{?}{=} 3(5) - (-1)$
$16 = 15 + 1$
$16 = 16$

15. $25 - [2 + 5y - 3(y + 2)] = -3(2y - 5) - [5(y - 1) - 3y + 3]$
$25 - [2 + 5y - 3y - 6] = -6y + 15 - [5y - 5 - 3y + 3]$
$25 - [2y - 4] = -6y + 15 - [2y - 2]$
$25 - 2y + 4 = -6y + 15 - 2y + 2$
$-2y + 29 = -8y + 17$
$6y = -12$
$y = -2$
The solution set is $\{-2\}$.

Check:
$25 - [2 + 5y - 3(y + 2)] = -3(2y - 5) - [5(y - 1) - 3y + 3]$
$25 - [2 + 5(-2) - 3(-2 + 2)] \stackrel{?}{=} -3[2(-2) - 5] - [5(-2 - 1) - 3(-2) + 3]$
$25 - [2 - 10 - 3(0)] \stackrel{?}{=} -3(-4 - 5) - [5(-3) + 6 + 3]$
$25 + 8 \stackrel{?}{=} 27 - (-6)$
$33 = 33$

17. $\dfrac{x}{3} = \dfrac{x}{2} - 2$
$6\left[\dfrac{x}{3} = \dfrac{x}{2} - 2\right]$
$2x = 3x - 12$
$12 = 3x - 2x$
$x = 12$
The solution set is $\{12\}$.

19. $20 - \dfrac{x}{3} = \dfrac{x}{2}$

$6\left[20 - \dfrac{x}{3} = \dfrac{x}{2}\right]$

$120 - 2x = 3x$

$120 = 3x + 2x$

$120 = 5x$

$x = \dfrac{120}{5}$

$x = 24$

The solution set is $\{24\}$.

21. $\dfrac{3x}{5} = \dfrac{2x}{3} + 1$

$15\left[\dfrac{3x}{5} = \dfrac{2x}{3} + 1\right]$

$9x = 10x + 15$

$9x - 10x = 15$

$-x = 15$

$x = -15$

The solution set is $\{-15\}$.

23. $\dfrac{3x}{5} - x = \dfrac{x}{10} - \dfrac{5}{2}$

$10\left[\dfrac{3x}{5} - x = \dfrac{x}{10} - \dfrac{5}{2}\right]$

$6x - 10x = x - 25$

$-4x - x = -25$

$-5x = -25$

$x = 5$

The solution set is $\{5\}$.

25. $\dfrac{x+3}{6} = \dfrac{3}{8} + \dfrac{x-5}{4}$

$24\left[\dfrac{x+3}{6} = \dfrac{3}{8} + \dfrac{x-5}{4}\right]$

$4x + 12 = 9 + 6x - 30$

$4x - 6x = -21 - 12$

$-2x = -33$

$x = \dfrac{33}{2}$

The solution set is $\left\{\dfrac{33}{2}\right\}$.

27. $\dfrac{x}{4} = 2 + \dfrac{x-3}{3}$

$12\left[\dfrac{x}{4} = 2 + \dfrac{x-3}{3}\right]$

$3x = 24 + 4x - 12$

$3x - 4x = 12$

$-x = 12$

$x = -12$

The solution set is $\{-12\}$.

29. $\dfrac{x+1}{3} - 5 - \dfrac{x+2}{7}$

$21\left[\dfrac{x+1}{3} = 5 - \dfrac{x+2}{7}\right]$

$7x + 7 = 105 - 3x - 6$

$7x + 3x = 99 - 7$

$10x = 92$

$x = \dfrac{92}{10}$

$x = \dfrac{46}{5}$

The solution set is $\left\{\dfrac{46}{5}\right\}$.

31. a. $\dfrac{4}{x} = \dfrac{3}{2x} + 3 \ (x \neq 0)$

b. $\dfrac{4}{x} = \dfrac{5}{2x} + 3$

$8 = 5 + 6x$

$3 = 6x$

$\dfrac{1}{2} = x$

The solution set is $\left\{\dfrac{1}{2}\right\}$.

33. a. $\dfrac{2}{x} + 3 = \dfrac{5}{2x} + \dfrac{13}{4} \ (x \neq 0)$

b. $\dfrac{2}{x} + 3 = \dfrac{5}{2x} + \dfrac{13}{4}$

$8 + 12x = 10 + 13x$

$-x = 2$

$x = -2$

The solution set is $\{-2\}$.

35. a. $\dfrac{2}{3x} + \dfrac{1}{4} = \dfrac{11}{6x} - \dfrac{1}{3}$ $(x \neq 0)$

b. $\dfrac{2}{3x} + \dfrac{1}{4} = \dfrac{11}{6x} - \dfrac{1}{3}$
$8 + 3x = 22 - 4x$
$7x = 14$
$x = 2$
The solution set is $\{2\}$.

37. a. $\dfrac{x-2}{2x} + 1 = \dfrac{x+1}{x}$ $(x \neq 0)$

b. $\dfrac{x-2}{2x} + 1 = \dfrac{x+1}{x}$
$x - 2 + 2x = 2x + 2$
$x - 2 = 2$
$x = 4$
The solution set is $\{4\}$.

39. a. $\dfrac{1}{x-1} + 5 = \dfrac{11}{x-1}$ $(x \neq 1)$

b. $\dfrac{1}{x-1} + 5 = \dfrac{11}{x-1}$
$1 + 5(x-1) = 11$
$1 + 5x - 5 = 11$
$5x - 4 = 11$
$5x = 15$
$x = 3$
The solution set is $\{3\}$.

41. a. $\dfrac{8x}{x+1} = 4 - \dfrac{8}{x+1}$ $(x \neq -1)$

b. $\dfrac{8x}{x+1} = 4 - \dfrac{8}{x+1}$
$8x = 4(x+1) - 8$
$8x = 4x + 4 - 8$
$4x = -4$
$x = -1 \Rightarrow$ no solution
The solution set is the empty set, $\varnothing$.

43. a. $\dfrac{3}{2x-2} + \dfrac{1}{2} = \dfrac{2}{x-1}$ $(x \neq 1)$

b. $\dfrac{3}{2x-2} + \dfrac{1}{2} = \dfrac{2}{x-1}$
$\dfrac{3}{2(x-1)} + \dfrac{1}{2} = \dfrac{2}{x-1}$
$3 + 1(x-1) = 4$
$3 + x - 1 = 4$
$x = 2$
The solution set is $\{2\}$.

45. a. $\dfrac{3}{x+2} + \dfrac{2}{x-2} = \dfrac{8}{(x+2)(x-2)}$

b. $\dfrac{3}{x+2} + \dfrac{2}{x-2} = \dfrac{8}{(x+2)(x-2)}$
$(x \neq 2, \ x \neq -2)$
$3(x-2) + 2(x+2) = 8$
$3x - 6 + 2x + 4 = 8$
$5x = 10$
$x = 2 \Rightarrow$ no solution
The solution set is the empty set, $\varnothing$.

47. a. $\dfrac{2}{x+1} - \dfrac{1}{x-1} = \dfrac{2x}{x^2-1}$ $(x \neq 1, \ x \neq -1)$

b. $\dfrac{2}{x+1} - \dfrac{1}{x-1} = \dfrac{2x}{x^2-1}$
$\dfrac{2}{x+1} - \dfrac{1}{x-1} = \dfrac{2x}{(x+1)(x-1)}$
$2(x-1) - 1(x+1) = 2x$
$2x - 2 - x - 1 = 2x$
$-x = 3$
$x = -3$
The solution set is $\{-3\}$.

49. a. $\dfrac{1}{x-4} - \dfrac{5}{x+2} = \dfrac{6}{x^2-2x-8}$

b. $\dfrac{1}{x-4} - \dfrac{5}{x+2} = \dfrac{6}{x^2-2x-8}$
$\dfrac{1}{x-4} - \dfrac{5}{x+2} = \dfrac{6}{(x-4)(x+2)}$
$(x \neq 4, \ x \neq -2)$
$1(x+2) - 5(x-4) = 6$
$x + 2 - 5x + 20 = 6$
$-4x = -16$
$x = 4 \Rightarrow$ no solution
The solution set is the empty set, $\varnothing$.

51. $4(x - 7) = 4x - 28$
$4x - 28 = 4x - 28$
The given equation is an identity.

53. $2x + 3 = 2x - 3$
$3 = -3$
The given equation is an inconsistent equation.

55. $4x + 5x = 8x$
$9x = 8x$
$x = 0$
The given equation is a conditional equation.

57. $\dfrac{2x}{x - 3} = \dfrac{6}{x - 3} + 4$
$2x = 6 + 4(x - 3)$
$2x = 6 + 4x - 12$
$-2x = -6$
$x = 3 \Rightarrow$ no solution
The given equation is an inconsistent equation.

59. $\dfrac{x + 5}{2} - 4 = \dfrac{2x - 1}{3}$
$3(x + 5) - 24 = 2(2x - 1)$
$3x + 15 - 24 = 4x - 2$
$-x = 7$
$x = -7$
The solution set is $\{-7\}$.

61. $\dfrac{2}{x - 2} = 3 + \dfrac{x}{x - 2}$
$2 = 3(x - 2) + x$
$2 = 3x - 6 + x$
$-4x = -8$
$x = 2 \Rightarrow$ no solution
The solution set is the empty set, $\varnothing$.

63. $8x - (3x + 2) + 10 = 3x$
$8x - 3x - 2 + 10 = 3x$
$2x = -8$
$x = -4$
The solution set is $\{-4\}$.

65. $\dfrac{2}{x} + \dfrac{1}{2} = \dfrac{3}{4}$
$8 + 2x = 3x$
$-x = -8$
$x = 8$
The solution set is $\{8\}$.

67. $\dfrac{4}{x - 2} + \dfrac{3}{x + 5} = \dfrac{7}{(x + 5)(x - 2)}$
$4(x + 5) + 3(x - 2) = 7$
$4x + 20 + 3x - 6 = 7$
$7x = -7$
$x = -1$
The solution set is $\{-1\}$.

69. a. Let $d = 500{,}000$.
$d = 5000c - 525{,}000$
$500{,}000 = 5000c - 525{,}000$
$1{,}025{,}000 = 5000c$
$205 = c$
In 1990, the average cholesterol level was 205 milligrams per deciliter.

b. Let $c = 180$.
$d = 5000c - 525{,}000$
$d = 5000(180) - 525{,}000$
$d = 375{,}000$
$500{,}000 - 375{,}000 = 125{,}000$
125,000 lives could be saved.

71. $p = 15 + \dfrac{15d}{33}$
$201 = 15 + \dfrac{15d}{33}$
$186 = \dfrac{15d}{33}$
$15d = 6138$
$d = 409\dfrac{1}{5}$ feet

Ferreras descended to $409\dfrac{1}{5}$ feet.

73.–83. Answers may vary.

85. Graph $y_1 = 9x + 3 - 3x$
$y_2 = 2(3x + 1)$

The given equation is an inconsistent equation.

87. Graph $y_1 = \dfrac{2x-1}{3} - \dfrac{x-5}{6}$
$y_2 = \dfrac{x-3}{4}$

The given equation is a conditional equation.
The solution set is $\{-5\}$.

89. $ax + b = c$
$ax = c - b$
$x = \dfrac{c-b}{a}$

91. Answers may vary.

93. $\dfrac{4x-b}{x-5} = 3$
$4x - b = 3(x - 5)$
The solution set will be $\varnothing$ if $x = 5$.
$4(5) - b = 3(5-5)$
$20 - b = 0$
$20 = b$
$b = 20$

Section 1.2

Check Point Exercises

1.
$$D = 0.2F - 1$$
$$19 = 0.2F - 1$$
$$19 + 1 = 0.2F - 1 + 1$$
$$20 = 0.2F$$
$$\dfrac{20}{0.2} = \dfrac{0.2F}{0.2}$$
$$100 = F$$
The daily fat intake for women in America is 100 grams.

2. Let x = the number (in millions) of copies of the Bee Gees album sold. Let $x + 5$ = the number (in millions) of copies the Morissette album sold.
Then $x + x + 5 = 27$
$$2x + 5 = 27$$
$$2x + 5 - 5 = 27 - 5$$
$$2x = 22$$
$$\dfrac{2x}{2} = \dfrac{22}{2}$$
$$x = 11$$
There were 11 million copies of the Bee Gees album sold, and $11 + 5 = 16$ million copies of the Morisette album sold.

3. Let x = the number of hours of use.
Then $440 + 1.75x = 540$.
$$440 + 1.75x - 440 = 540 - 440$$
$$1.75x = 100$$
$$\dfrac{1.75x}{1.75} = \dfrac{100}{1.75}$$
$$x \approx 57$$
You are allowed 57 hours of use.

4. Let x = the amount invested at 9%.
Let $25,000 - x$ = the amount invested at 12%.
Then $0.09x + 0.12(25,000 - x) = 2550$.
$$0.09x + 3000 - 0.12x = 2550$$
$$-0.03x + 3000 - 3000 = 2550 - 3000$$
$$-0.03x = -450$$
$$\dfrac{-0.03x}{-0.03} = \dfrac{-450}{-0.03}$$
$$x = 15,000$$
\$15,000 should be invested at 9% and \$10,000 at 12%.

5. Let x = the width of the swimming pool.
Let $3x$ = the length of the swimming pool.
Then $2 \cdot 3x + 2 \cdot x = 320$

$$6x + 2x = 320$$
$$8x = 320$$
$$\frac{8x}{8} = \frac{320}{8}$$
$$x = 4$$
$$3x = 120$$

The length of the pool is 120 feet; its width is 40 feet.

6.
$$y = mx + b$$
$$y - b = mx + b - b$$
$$y - b = mx$$
$$\frac{y - b}{x} = \frac{mx}{x}$$
$$\frac{y - b}{x} = m$$
$$m = \frac{y - b}{x}$$

Exercise Set 1.2

1. $x + 9$

3. $20 - x$

5. $8 - 5x$

7. $15 \div x$

9. $2x + 20$

11. $7x - 30$

13. $4(x + 12)$

15. $x + 40 = 450$
$x = 410$
The solution set is $\{410\}$.

17. $5x - 7 = 123$
$5x = 130$
$x = 26$
The solution set is $\{26\}$.

19. $9x = 3x + 30$
$6x = 30$
$x = 5$
The solution set is $\{5\}$.

21.
$$R = 143 - 0.65A$$
$$117 = 143 - 0.65A$$
$$-0.65A = -26$$
$$A = 40$$
She is 40 years old. Find 117 on the vertical axis and follow it over to the Female graph.

23.
$$y = 2.5x + 198.73$$
$$273.73 = 2.5x + 198.73$$
$$75 = 2.5x$$
$$x = 30$$
30 years after 1980 or in 2010 the winning predicted speed will be 273.73.

25.
$$f = 0.432h - 10.44$$
$$16 = 0.432h - 10.44$$
$$26.44 = 0.432h$$
$$h \approx 61.2 \text{ inches}$$
Yes, the skeleton could be the missing woman's since the height (about 61.2 inches) is greater than 5 feet.

27. Let x = Sosa homeruns
$x + 4$ = McGwire homeruns
$x + x + 4 = 136$
$2x + 4 = 136$
$2x = 132$
$x = 66$
Sosa hit 66 homeruns.
McGwire hit 70 homeruns.

29. Let x = losing score
$x + 1$ = winning score
$x + x + 1 = 39$
$2x + 1 = 39$
$2x = 38$
$x = 19$
The losing score was 19.
The winning score was 20.

31. Let x = Sweden
$2x + 14$ = United States
$$x + 2x + 14 = 54.5$$
$$3x + 14 = 54.5$$
$$3x = 40.5$$
$$x = 13.5$$
Sweden = 13.5%
United States = 41%

33. Let x = number of miles
$$200 + 0.15x = 320$$
$$0.15x = 120$$
$$x = 800$$
You can travel 800 miles.

35. Let x = number of months
$$7 + 1.5x = 16$$
$$1.5x = 9$$
$$x = 6$$
After 6 months, a baby girl weighs 16 pounds.

37. Let x = the weight of unpeeled bananas.
$\frac{7}{8}x$ = weight of peeled bananas
$$x = \frac{7}{8}x + \frac{7}{8}$$
$$\frac{1}{8}x = \frac{7}{8}$$
$$x = 7$$
The banana with peel weighs 7 ounces.

39. a. with book: $21 + 0.5x$
without book: $1.25x$

b. $\begin{aligned} 21 + 0.5x &= 1.25x \\ 21 &= 0.75x \\ x &= 28 \end{aligned}$
If the bus is used 28 times, the costs are the same.

41. Let x = amount at 9%
$25000 - x$ = amount at 12%
$$0.09x + 0.12(25000 - x) = 2250$$
$$0.09x + 3000 - 0.12x = 2250$$
$$-0.03x = -750$$
$$x = 25,000$$
$25,000 at 9%
$0 at 12%

43. Let x = width
$2x + 6$ = length
$$2x + 2(2x + 6) = 228$$
$$2x + 4x + 12 = 228$$
$$6x + 12 = 228$$
$$6x = 216$$
$$x = 36$$
$$2(36) + 6 = 78$$
The dimensions are 78 feet by 36 feet.

45. Let x = height
$3x$ = length
$$4(3x) + 3x = 60$$
$$12x + 3x = 60$$
$$15x = 60$$
$$x = 4$$
$$3(4) = 12$$
The length is 12 feet, the height is 4 feet.

47. Let x = number of hours
$35x$ = labor cost
$$35x + 63 = 448$$
$$35x = 385$$
$$x = 11$$
It took 11 hours.

49. Let x = original price
$$x - .35x = 81.90$$
$$.65x = 81.90$$
$$x = 126$$
Before the reduction, it cost $126.

51. Let x = original price
$$x + .065x = 788.10$$
$$1.065x = 788.10$$
$$x = 740$$
Before taxes, the price was $740.

53. Let x = dealer's cost
$$x + 0.25x = 584$$
$$1.25x = 584$$
$$x = 467.20$$
The dealer's cost is $467.20.

55. Let x = inches over 5 feet
$$100 + 5x = 135$$
$$5x = 35$$
$$x = 7$$
A height of 5 feet 7 inches corresponds to 135 pounds.

57. $A = lw$

$w = \dfrac{A}{l}$;

area of rectangle

59. $A = \dfrac{1}{2}bh$

$2A = bh$

$b = \dfrac{2A}{h}$;

area of triangle

61. $I = Prt$

$P = \dfrac{I}{rt}$;

interest

63. $E = mc^2$

$m = \dfrac{E}{c^2}$;

energy

65. $T = D + pm$

$T - D = pm$

$p = \dfrac{(T - D)}{m}$

67. $A = \dfrac{1}{2}h(a + b)$

$2A = h(a + b)$

$\dfrac{2A}{h} = a + b$

$\dfrac{2A}{h} - b = a$;

area of trapezoid

69. $S = P + Prt$

$S - P = Prt$

$\dfrac{S - P}{Pt} = r$;

interest

71. $B = \dfrac{F}{S - V}$

$B(S - V) = F$

$S - V = \dfrac{F}{B}$

$S = \dfrac{F}{B} + V$

73.–75. Answers may vary.

77. a. $y = 3.82 + 0.3x$

b.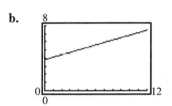

c. The trace feature shows x to be about 8 when $y = 6.22$. $1980 + 8 = 1988$

d. $6.22 = 3.82 + 0.3x$

$2.4 = 0.3x$

$x = 8$

$1980 + 8 = 1988$

79. Let x = student population of one school

$1000 - x$ = student population of the other school

$0.1x + 0.9(1000 - x) = .42(1000)$

$0.1x + 900 - 0.9x = 420$

$-0.8x + 900 = 420$

$-0.8x = -480$

$x = 600$

The school with 10% African Americans has 600 students. The other has 400 students.

81. Let x = woman's age

$3x$ = Coburn's age

$3x + 20 = 2(x + 20)$

$3x + 20 = 2x + 40$

$x + 20 = 40$

$x = 20$

Coburn is 60 years old the woman is 20 years old.

83. Let x = mother's amount

$2x$ = boy's amount

$\dfrac{x}{2}$ = girl's amount

$$x + 2x + \dfrac{x}{2} = 14,000$$

$$\dfrac{7}{2}x = 14,000$$

$$x = \$4,000$$

The mother got \$4000, the boy got \$8000, and the girl got \$2000.

Section 1.3

Check Point Exercises

1. a. $3x^2 - 9x = 0$

$3x(x - 3) = 0$

$3x = 0$ or $x - 3 = 0$

$x = 0$ $x = 3$

The solution set is $\{0, 3\}$.

b. $2x^2 + x = 1$

$2x^2 + x - 1 = 0$

$(2x - 1)(x + 1) = 0$

$2x - 1 = 0$ or $x + 1 = 0$

$2x = 1$ $x = -1$

$x = \dfrac{1}{2}$

The solution set is $\left\{-1, \dfrac{1}{2}\right\}$.

2. a. $3x^2 = 21$

$\dfrac{3x^2}{3} = \dfrac{21}{3}$

$x^2 = 7$

$x = \pm\sqrt{7}$

The solution set is $\left\{-\sqrt{7}, \sqrt{7}\right\}$.

b. $(x + 5)^2 = 11$

$x + 5 = \pm\sqrt{11}$

$x = -5 \pm \sqrt{11}$

The solution set is

$\left\{-5 + \sqrt{11}, -5 - \sqrt{11}\right\}$.

3. Add $\left(\dfrac{14}{2}\right)^2 = 49$.

$$x^2 - 14x + 7^2 = x^2 - 14x + 49 = (x - 7)^2$$

4. $x^2 - 2x - 2 = 0$

$x^2 - 2x - 2 + 2 = 0 + 2$

$x^2 - 2x = 2$

$x^2 - 2x + 1 = 2 + 1$

$(x - 1)^2 = 3$

$x - 1 = \pm\sqrt{3}$

$x = 1 \pm \sqrt{3}$

The solution set is $\left\{1 + \sqrt{3}, 1 - \sqrt{3}\right\}$.

5. $2x^2 + 2x - 1 = 0$

$a = 2, \ b = 2, \ c = -1$

$$x = \dfrac{-b \pm \sqrt{b^2 - 4ac}}{2a}$$

$$= \dfrac{-2 \pm \sqrt{2^2 - 4(2)(-1)}}{2(2)}$$

$$= \dfrac{-2 \pm \sqrt{4 + 8}}{4}$$

$$= \dfrac{-2 \pm \sqrt{12}}{4}$$

$$= \dfrac{-2 \pm 2\sqrt{3}}{4}$$

$$= \dfrac{2(-1 \pm \sqrt{3})}{4}$$

$$= \dfrac{-1 \pm \sqrt{3}}{2}$$

The solution set is $\left\{\dfrac{-1 + \sqrt{3}}{2}, \dfrac{-1 - \sqrt{3}}{2}\right\}$.

6. $x^2 - 2x + 2 = 0$

$a = 1, \ b = -2, \ c = 2$

$$x = \frac{-b \pm \sqrt{b^2 - 4ac}}{2a}$$

$$= \frac{-(-2) \pm \sqrt{(-2)^2 - 4(1)(2)}}{2(1)}$$

$$= \frac{2 + \sqrt{-4}}{2}$$

$$= \frac{2 + 2i}{2}$$

$$= \frac{2(1+i)}{2}$$

$$= 1 + i$$

The solution set is $\{1 + i, \ 1 - i\}$.

7. $3x^2 - 2x + 5 = 0$

$a = 3, \ b = -2, \ c = 5$

$b^2 - 4ac = (-2)^2 - 4 \cdot 3 \cdot 5 = 4 - 60 = -56$

The discriminant is -56. The equation has two complex imaginary solutions.

8. $P = -10x^2 + 475x + 3500$

$7250 = -10x^2 + 475x + 3500$

$= 10x^2 + 475x - 3750 = 0$

$a = -10, \ b = 475, \ c = -3750$

$$x = \frac{-b \pm \sqrt{b^2 - 4ac}}{2a}$$

$$= \frac{-475 \pm \sqrt{(475)^2 - 4(-10)(-3750)}}{2(-10)}$$

$$= \frac{-475 \pm \sqrt{75,625}}{-20}$$

$x = \dfrac{-475 + \sqrt{75,625}}{-20}$ or $x = \dfrac{-475 - \sqrt{75,625}}{-20}$

$\quad = 10 \qquad\qquad\qquad\quad = 37.5$

It will take 10 years.

9. $w^2 + 9^2 = 15^2$

$w^2 + 81 = 225$

$w^2 = 144$

$w = \pm\sqrt{144}$

$w = \pm 12$

The width of the television is 12 inches.

Exercise Set 1.3

1. $x^2 - 3x - 10 = 0$

$(x + 2)(x - 5) = 0$

$x + 2 = 0 \quad \text{or} \quad x - 5 = 0$

$x = -2 \qquad \text{or} \qquad x = 5$

The solution set is $\{-2, 5\}$.

3. $x^2 = 8x - 15$

$x^2 - 8x + 15 = 0$

$(x - 3)(x - 5) = 0$

$x - 3 = 0 \quad \text{or} \quad x - 5 = 0$

$x = 3 \qquad \text{or} \qquad x = 5$

The solution set is $\{3, 5\}$.

5. $6x^2 + 11x - 10 = 0$

$(2x + 5)(3x - 2) = 0$

$2x + 5 = 0 \quad \text{or} \quad 3x - 2 = 0$

$2x = -5 \qquad\qquad 3x = 2$

$x = -\dfrac{5}{2} \quad \text{or} \quad x = \dfrac{2}{3}$

The solution set is $\left\{-\dfrac{5}{2}, \dfrac{2}{3}\right\}$.

7. $3x^2 - 2x = 8$

$3x^2 - 2x - 8 = 0$

$(3x + 4)(x - 2) = 0$

$3x + 4 = 0 \quad \text{or} \quad x - 2 = 0$

$3x = -4$

$x = -\dfrac{4}{3} \quad \text{or} \quad x = 2$

The solution set is $\left\{-\dfrac{4}{3}, 2\right\}$.

9. $3x^2 + 12x = 0$

$3x(x + 4) = 0$

$3x = 0 \quad \text{or} \quad x + 4 = 0$

$x = 0 \quad \text{or} \quad x = -4$

The solution set is $\{-4, 0\}$.

11. $2x(x-3) = 5x^2 - 7x$

    $2x^2 - 6x - 5x^2 + 7x = 0$

    $-3x^2 + x = 0$

    $x(-3x + 1) = 0$

    $x = 0$ or $-3x + 1 = 0$

    $ -3x = -1$

    $ x = \frac{1}{3}$

    The solution set is $\left\{0, \frac{1}{3}\right\}$.

13. $7 - 7x = (3x + 2)(x - 1)$

    $7 - 7x = 3x^2 - x - 2$

    $7 - 7x - 3x^2 + x + 2 = 0$

    $-3x^2 - 6x + 9 = 0$

    $-3(x + 3)(x - 1) = 0$

    $x + 3 = 0$ or $x - 1 = 0$

    $x = -3$ or $x = 1$

    The solution set is $\{-3, 1\}$.

15. $3x^2 = 27$

    $x^2 = 9$

    $x = \pm\sqrt{9} = \pm 3$

    The solution set is $\{-3, 3\}$.

17. $5x^2 + 1 = 51$

    $5x^2 = 50$

    $x^2 = 10$

    $x = \pm\sqrt{10}$

    The solution set is $\left\{-\sqrt{10}, \sqrt{10}\right\}$.

19. $(x + 2)^2 = 25$

    $x + 2 = \pm\sqrt{25} = \pm 5$

    $x = -2 \pm 5$

    The solution set is $\{-7, 3\}$.

21. $(3x + 2)^2 = 9$

    $3x + 2 = \pm\sqrt{9} = \pm 3$

    $3x + 2 = -3$ or $3x + 2 = 3$

    $3x = -5$ $3x = 1$

    $x = -\frac{5}{3}$ or $x = \frac{1}{3}$

    The solution set is $\left\{-\frac{5}{3}, \frac{1}{3}\right\}$.

23. $(5x - 1)^2 = 7$

    $5x - 1 = \pm\sqrt{7}$

    $5x = 1 \pm \sqrt{7}$

    $x = \frac{1 \pm \sqrt{7}}{5}$

    The solution set is $\left\{\frac{1 - \sqrt{7}}{5}, \frac{1 + \sqrt{7}}{5}\right\}$.

25. $(3x - 4)^2 = 8$

    $3x - 4 = \pm\sqrt{8} = \pm 2\sqrt{2}$

    $3x = 4 \pm 2\sqrt{2}$

    $x = \frac{4 \pm 2\sqrt{2}}{3}$

    The solution set is $\left\{\frac{4 - 2\sqrt{2}}{3}, \frac{4 + 2\sqrt{2}}{3}\right\}$.

27. $x^2 + 12x$

    $\left(\frac{12}{2}\right)^2 = 6^2 = 36$

    $x^2 + 12x + 36 = (x + 6)^2$

29. $x^2 - 10x$

    $\left(\frac{10}{2}\right)^2 = 5^2 = 25$

    $x^2 - 10x + 25 = (x - 5)^2$

31. $x^2 + 3x$

    $\left(\frac{3}{2}\right)^2 = \frac{9}{4}$

    $x^2 + 3x + \frac{9}{4} = \left(x + \frac{3}{2}\right)^2$

33. $x^2 - 7x$

    $\left(\frac{7}{2}\right)^2 = \frac{49}{4}$

    $x^2 - 7x + \frac{49}{4} = \left(x - \frac{7}{2}\right)^2$

35. $x^2 - \dfrac{2}{3}x$

$$\left(\dfrac{\frac{2}{3}}{2}\right)^2 = \left(\dfrac{1}{3}\right)^2 = \dfrac{1}{9}$$

$$x^2 - \dfrac{2}{3}x + \dfrac{1}{9} = \left(x - \dfrac{1}{3}\right)^2$$

37. $x^2 - \dfrac{1}{3}x$

$$\left(\dfrac{\frac{1}{3}}{2}\right)^2 = \left(\dfrac{1}{6}\right)^2 = \dfrac{1}{36}$$

$$x^2 - \dfrac{1}{3}x + \dfrac{1}{36} = \left(x - \dfrac{1}{6}\right)^2$$

39.
$$x^2 + 6x = 7$$
$$x^2 + 6x + 9 = 7 + 9$$
$$(x + 3)^2 = 16$$
$$x + 3 = \pm 4$$
$$x = -3 + 4$$
The solution set is $\{-7, 1\}$.

41.
$$x^2 - 2x = 2$$
$$x^2 - 2x + 1 = 2 + 1$$
$$(x - 1)^2 = 3$$
$$x - 1 = \pm\sqrt{3}$$
$$x = 1 \pm \sqrt{3}$$
The solution set is $\left\{1 + \sqrt{3},\ 1 - \sqrt{3}\right\}$.

43. $x^2 - 6x - 11 = 0$
$$x^2 - 6x = 11$$
$$x^2 - 6x + 9 = 11 + 9$$
$$(x - 3)^2 = 20$$
$$x - 3 = \pm\sqrt{20}$$
$$x = 3 \pm 2\sqrt{5}$$
The solution set is $\left\{3 + 2\sqrt{5},\ 3 - 2\sqrt{5}\right\}$.

45. $x^2 + 4x + 1 = 0$
$$x^2 + 4x = -1$$
$$x^2 + 4x + 4 = -1 + 4$$
$$(x + 2)^2 = 3$$
$$x + 2 = \pm\sqrt{3}$$
$$x = -2 \pm \sqrt{3}$$
The solution set is $\left\{-2 + \sqrt{3},\ -2 - \sqrt{3}\right\}$.

47. $x^2 + 3x - 1 = 0$
$$x^2 + 3x = 1$$
$$x^2 + 3x + \dfrac{9}{4} = 1 + \dfrac{9}{4}$$
$$\left(x + \dfrac{3}{2}\right)^2 = \dfrac{13}{4}$$
$$x + \dfrac{3}{2} = \pm\dfrac{\sqrt{13}}{2}$$
$$x = \dfrac{-3 \pm \sqrt{13}}{2}$$
The solution set is $\left\{\dfrac{-3 + \sqrt{13}}{2},\ \dfrac{-3 - \sqrt{13}}{2}\right\}$.

49. $2x^2 - 7x + 3 = 0$
$$x^2 - \dfrac{7}{2}x + \dfrac{3}{2} = 0$$
$$x^2 - \dfrac{7}{2}x = \dfrac{-3}{2}$$
$$x^2 - \dfrac{7}{2}x + \dfrac{49}{16} = -\dfrac{3}{2} + \dfrac{49}{16}$$
$$\left(x - \dfrac{7}{4}\right)^2 = \dfrac{25}{16}$$
$$x - \dfrac{7}{4} = \pm\dfrac{5}{4}$$
$$x = \dfrac{7}{4} \pm \dfrac{5}{4}$$
The solution set is $\left\{\dfrac{1}{2},\ 3\right\}$.

51. $4x^2 - 4x - 1 = 0$

$$4x^2 - 4x - 1 = 0$$

$$x^2 - x - \frac{1}{4} = 0$$

$$x^2 - x = \frac{1}{4}$$

$$x^2 - x + \frac{1}{4} = \frac{1}{4} + \frac{1}{4}$$

$$\left(x - \frac{1}{2}\right)^2 = \frac{2}{4}$$

$$x - \frac{1}{2} = \frac{\pm\sqrt{2}}{2}$$

$$x = \frac{1 \pm \sqrt{2}}{2}$$

The solution set is $\left\{\dfrac{1+\sqrt{2}}{2}, \ \dfrac{1-\sqrt{2}}{2}\right\}$.

53. $3x^2 - 2x - 2 = 0$

$$x^2 - \frac{2}{3}x - \frac{2}{3} = 0$$

$$x^2 - \frac{2}{3}x = \frac{2}{3}$$

$$x^2 - \frac{2}{3}x + \frac{1}{9} = \frac{2}{3} + \frac{1}{9}$$

$$\left(x - \frac{1}{3}\right)^2 = \frac{7}{9}$$

$$x - \frac{1}{3} = \frac{\pm\sqrt{7}}{3}$$

$$x = \frac{1 \pm \sqrt{7}}{3}$$

The solution set is $\left\{\dfrac{1+\sqrt{7}}{3}, \ \dfrac{1-\sqrt{7}}{3}\right\}$.

55. $x^2 + 8x + 15 = 0$

$$x = \frac{-8 \pm \sqrt{8^2 - 4(1)(15)}}{2(1)}$$

$$x = \frac{-8 \pm \sqrt{64 - 60}}{2}$$

$$x = \frac{-8 \pm \sqrt{4}}{2}$$

$$x = \frac{-8 \pm 2}{2}$$

The solution set is $\{-5, \ -3\}$.

57. $x^2 + 5x + 3 = 0$

$$x = \frac{-5 \pm \sqrt{5^2 - 4(1)(3)}}{2(1)}$$

$$x = \frac{-5 \pm \sqrt{25 - 12}}{2}$$

$$x = \frac{-5 \pm \sqrt{13}}{2}$$

The solution set is $\left\{\dfrac{-5+\sqrt{13}}{2}, \ \dfrac{-5-\sqrt{13}}{2}\right\}$.

59. $3x^2 - 3x - 4 = 0$

$$x = \frac{3 \pm \sqrt{(-3)^2 - 4(3)(-4)}}{2(3)}$$

$$x = \frac{3 \pm \sqrt{9 + 48}}{6}$$

$$x = \frac{3 \pm \sqrt{57}}{6}$$

The solution set is $\left\{\dfrac{3+\sqrt{57}}{6}, \ \dfrac{3-\sqrt{57}}{6}\right\}$.

61.
$$4x^2 = 2x + 7$$
$$4x^2 - 2x - 7 = 0$$

$$x = \frac{2 \pm \sqrt{(-2)^2 - 4(4)(-7)}}{2(4)}$$

$$x = \frac{2 \pm \sqrt{4 + 112}}{8}$$

$$x = \frac{2 \pm \sqrt{116}}{8}$$

$$x = \frac{2 \pm 2\sqrt{29}}{8}$$

$$x = \frac{1 \pm \sqrt{29}}{4}$$

The solution set is $\left\{ \dfrac{1 + \sqrt{29}}{4}, \ \dfrac{1 - \sqrt{29}}{4} \right\}$.

63. $x^2 - 6x + 10 = 0$

$$x = \frac{6 + \sqrt{(-6)^2 - 4(1)(10)}}{2(1)}$$

$$x = \frac{6 \pm \sqrt{36 - 40}}{2}$$

$$x = \frac{6 \pm \sqrt{-4}}{2}$$

$$x = \frac{6 \pm 2i}{2}$$

$$x = 3 \pm i$$

The solution set is $\{3 + i, \ 3 - i\}$.

65. $x^2 - 4x - 5 = 0$
$$(-4)^2 - 4(1)(-5)$$
$$= 16 + 20$$
$$= 36; \ 2 \text{ unequal real solutions}$$

67. $2x^2 - 11x + 3 = 0$
$$(-11)^2 - 4(2)(3)$$
$$= 121 - 24$$
$$= 97; \ 2 \text{ unequal real solutions}$$

69. $x^2 - 2x + 1 = 0$
$$(-2)^2 - 4(1)(1)$$
$$= 4 - 4$$
$$= 0; \ 1 \text{ real solution}$$

71. $x^2 - 3x - 7 = 0$
$$(-3)^2 - 4(1)(-7)$$
$$= 9 + 28$$
$$= 37; \ 2 \text{ unequal real solutions}$$

73.
$$2x^2 - x = 1$$
$$2x^2 - x - 1 = 0$$
$$(2x + 1)(x - 1) = 0$$
$$2x + 1 = 0 \text{ or } x - 1 = 0$$
$$2x = -1$$
$$x = -\frac{1}{2} \text{ or } x = 1$$
The solution set is $\left\{ -\dfrac{1}{2}, \ 1 \right\}$.

75.
$$5x^2 + 2 = 11x$$
$$5x^2 - 11x + 2 = 0$$
$$(5x - 1)(x - 2) = 0$$
$$5x - 1 = 0 \text{ or } x - 2 = 0$$
$$5x = 1$$
$$x = \frac{1}{5} \text{ or } x = 2$$
The solution set is $\left\{ \dfrac{1}{5}, \ 2 \right\}$.

77. $3x^2 = 60$
$$x^2 = 20$$
$$x = \pm\sqrt{20}$$
$$x = \pm 2\sqrt{5}$$
The solution set is $\left\{ -2\sqrt{5}, \ 2\sqrt{5} \right\}$.

79.
$$x^2 - 2x = 1$$
$$x^2 - 2x + 1 = 1 + 1$$
$$(x - 1)^2 = 2$$
$$x - 1 = \pm\sqrt{2}$$
$$x = 1 \pm \sqrt{2}$$
The solution set is $\left\{ 1 + \sqrt{2}, \ 1 - \sqrt{2} \right\}$.

81. $(2x + 3)(x + 4) = 1$

$2x^2 + 8x + 3x + 12 = 1$

$2x^2 + 11x + 11 = 0$

$$x = \frac{-11 \pm \sqrt{11^2 - 4(2)(11)}}{2(2)}$$

$$x = \frac{-11 \pm \sqrt{121 - 88}}{4}$$

$$x = \frac{-11 \pm \sqrt{33}}{4}$$

The solution set is

$$\left\{ \frac{-11 + \sqrt{33}}{4}, \ \frac{-11 - \sqrt{33}}{4} \right\}.$$

83. $(3x - 4)^2 = 16$

$3x - 4 = \pm\sqrt{16}$

$3x - 4 = \pm 4$

$3x = 4 \pm 4$

$3x = 8 \text{ or } 3x = 0$

$x = \dfrac{8}{3} \text{ or } x = 0$

The solution set is $\left\{ 0, \ \dfrac{8}{3} \right\}$.

85. $3x^2 - 12x + 12 = 0$

$x^2 - 4x + 4 = 0$

$(x - 2)(x - 2) = 0$

$x - 2 = 0$

$x = 2$

The solution set is $\{2\}$.

87. $4x^2 - 16 = 0$

$4x^2 = 16$

$x^2 = 4$

$x = \pm 2$

The solution set is $\{-2, \ 2\}$.

89. $x^2 - 6x + 13 = 0$

$x^2 - 6x = -13$

$x^2 - 6x + 9 = -13 + 9$

$(x - 3)^2 = -4$

$x - 3 = \pm 2i$

$x = 3 \pm 2i$

The solution set is $\{3 + 2i, \ 3 - 2i\}$.

91. $x^2 = 4x - 7$

$x^2 - 4x = -7$

$x^2 - 4x + 4 = -7 + 4$

$(x - 2)^2 = -3$

$x - 2 = \pm i\sqrt{3}$

$x = 2 \pm i\sqrt{3}$

The solution set is $\left\{ 2 + i\sqrt{3}, \ 2 - i\sqrt{3} \right\}$.

93. $2x^2 - 7x = 0$

$x(2x - 7) = 0$

$x = 0 \text{ or } 2x - 7 = 0$

$2x = 7$

$x = 0 \text{ or } x = \dfrac{7}{2}$

The solution set is $\left\{ 0, \ \dfrac{7}{2} \right\}$.

95.
$$45 = 0.0075x^2 - 0.2676x + 14.8$$
$$0 = 0.0075x^2 - 0.2676x - 30.2$$
$$x = \frac{0.2676 \pm \sqrt{(-0.2676)^2 - 4(0.0075)(-30.2)}}{2(0.0075)}$$
$$x = \frac{0.2676 \pm \sqrt{0.07160976 + 0.906}}{0.015}$$
$$x = \frac{0.2676 \pm \sqrt{0.97760976}}{0.015}$$
$$x = \frac{0.2676 \pm 0.9887415031}{0.015}$$
$$x \approx \frac{1.2563}{0.015} \text{ or } x \approx \frac{-0.7211}{0.015}$$
$$\Rightarrow x \approx 83.76 \text{ or } -48.1$$
$$\Rightarrow 1940 + 84 = 2024$$
Fuel efficiency reached 45 miles per gallon in 2024.

97.
$$4.1 = 0.4x^2 + 0.5$$
$$3.6 = 0.4x^2$$
$$x^2 = 9$$
$$x = \pm 3$$
$$1996 + 3 = 1999$$
In 1999 4.1 million Americans use modems. The formula gives a number that is slightly larger than the actual number of users. The formula describes the number of users very well.

99.
$$690,515 = 29,035t^2 + 429,200$$
$$29,035t^2 = 261,315$$
$$t^2 = 9$$
$$t = \pm 3$$
$$1983 + 3 = 1986$$
It occurred in 1986.

101.
$$740 = 2x^2 + 22x + 320$$
$$0 = 2x^2 + 22x - 420$$
$$0 = x^2 + 11x - 210$$
$$x = \frac{-11 \pm \sqrt{11^2 - 4(1)(-210)}}{2(1)}$$
$$x = \frac{-11 \pm \sqrt{121 + 840}}{2}$$
$$x = \frac{-11 \pm \sqrt{961}}{2}$$
$$x = \frac{-11 \pm 31}{2}$$
$$x = \frac{-42}{2}, \frac{20}{2}$$
$$x = -21, \ 10$$
$1980 + 10 = 1990$; actual number: 739,980; The formula describes very well.

103.
$$330 = -1.65x^2 + 51.8x + 111.44$$
$$0 = -1.65x^2 + 51.8x - 218.56$$
$$x = \frac{-51.8 \pm \sqrt{51.8^2 - 4(-1.65)(-218.56)}}{2(-1.65)}$$
$$x = \frac{-51.8 \pm \sqrt{2683.24 - 1442.496}}{-3.3}$$
$$x = \frac{-51.8 \pm \sqrt{1240.744}}{-3.3}$$
$$x \approx \frac{-51.8 \pm 35.22}{-3.3}$$
$$x \approx \frac{-16.58}{-3.3}, \frac{-87.024}{-3.3}$$
$$x \approx 5.024, \ 26.37$$
$1990 + 5.024 \approx 1995$; actual number: 340,000; The formula is fairly close.

105.
$$90^2 + 90^2 = x^2$$
$$8100 + 8100 = x^2$$
$$16200 = x^2$$
$$x \approx \pm 127.28$$
The distance is 127.28 feet.

107. $15^2 + 8^2 = x^2$

$225 + 64 = x^2$

$289 = x^2$

$x = \pm 17$

$17 \times 2 = 34$

The total length is 34 feet.

109. Let x = width

$x + 5$ = length

$x(x + 5) = 300$

$x^2 + 5x = 300$

$x^2 + 5x - 300 = 0$

$(x + 20)(x - 15) = 0$

$x + 20 = 0 \quad x - 15 = 0$

$x = -20 \qquad x = 15$

The width is 15 feet, the length is 20 feet.

111. $x(x)(2) = 200$

$2x^2 = 200$

$x^2 = 100$

$x = \pm 10$

The length and width are 10 inches.

113.–119. Answers may vary.

121. Exercises 55 and 57

Exercises 59 and 61

Exercise 63

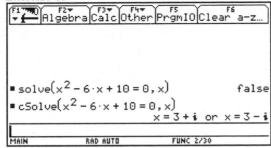

123. **a.** False;
$$(2x-3)^2 = 25$$
$$2x-3 = \pm 5$$

     b. False;
Consider $x^2 = 0$, then $x = 0$ is the only distinct solution.

     c. True

     d. False;
$$ax^2 + c = 0$$
$$x = \frac{0 \pm \sqrt{0 - 4ac}}{2a} = \frac{2i\sqrt{ac}}{2a} = \frac{i\sqrt{ac}}{u}$$

     (c) is true.

125. $(x+3)(x-5) = 0$
$$x^2 - 5x + 3x - 15 = 0$$
$$x^2 - 2x - 15 = 0$$

127. $19 = -2x^2 + 36x$
$$-2x^2 + 36x - 19 = 0$$
$$36^2 - 4(-2)(-19)$$
$$1296 - 152$$
1144; it is possible, the applicant should be hired.

Section 1.4

Check Point Exercises

1. $4x^4 = 12x^2$

$$4x^4 - 12x^2 = 0$$

$$4x^2\left(x^2 - 3\right) = 0$$

$4x^2 = 0$ or $x^2 - 3 = 0$

$\quad x^2 = 0 \qquad\qquad x^2 = 3$

$\quad x = \pm\sqrt{0} \qquad\quad x = \pm\sqrt{3}$

$\quad x = 0 \qquad\qquad\quad x = \pm\sqrt{3}$

The solution set is $\left\{-\sqrt{3},\ 0,\ \sqrt{3}\right\}$.

2. $2x^3 + 3x^2 = 8x + 12$

$$x^2(2x + 3) - 4(2x + 3) = 10$$

$$(2x + 3)(x^2 - 4) = 0$$

$2x + 3 = 0$ or $x^2 - 4 = 0$

$\quad 2x = -3 \qquad\qquad x^2 = 4$

$\quad x = -\dfrac{3}{2} \qquad\qquad x = \pm 2$

The solution set is $\left\{-2,\ -\dfrac{3}{2},\ 2\right\}$.

3. $\sqrt{6x + 7} - x = 2$

$$\sqrt{6x + 7} = x + 2$$

$$6x + 7 = (x + 2)^2$$

$$6x + 7 = x^2 + 4x + 4$$

$$0 = x^2 - 2x - 3$$

$$0 = (x - 3)(x + 1)$$

$x - 3 = 0$ or $x + 1 = 0$

$\quad x = 3 \qquad\qquad x = -1$

Check 3:

$$\sqrt{6(3) + 7} - 3 \stackrel{?}{=} 2$$

$$\sqrt{18 + 7} - 3 \stackrel{?}{=} 2$$

$$\sqrt{25} - 3 \stackrel{?}{=} 2$$

$$5 - 3 \stackrel{?}{=} 2$$

$$2 = 2$$

Check 1:

$$\sqrt{6(-1) + 7} - (-1) \stackrel{?}{=} 2$$

$$\sqrt{-6 + 7} + 1 \stackrel{?}{=} 2$$

$$\sqrt{1} + 1 \stackrel{?}{=} 2$$

$$1 + 1 \stackrel{?}{=} 2$$

$$2 = 2$$

The solution set is $\{-1,\ 3\}$.

4. $\sqrt{x + 5} - \sqrt{x - 3} = 2$

$$\sqrt{x + 5} = \sqrt{x - 3} + 2$$

$$x + 5 = \left(\sqrt{x - 3} + 2\right)^2$$

$$x + 5 = x - 3 + 4\sqrt{x - 3} + 4$$

$$x + 5 = x + 1 + 4\sqrt{x - 3}$$

$$4 = 4\sqrt{x - 3}$$

$$1 = \sqrt{x - 3}$$

$$1 = x - 3$$

$$4 = x$$

$x - 3 = 0$ or $x + 1 = 0$

$\quad x = 3 \qquad\qquad x = -1$

Check:

$$\sqrt{4 + 5} - \sqrt{4 - 3} \stackrel{?}{=} 2$$

$$\sqrt{9} - \sqrt{1} \stackrel{?}{=} 2$$

$$3 - 1 \stackrel{?}{=} 2$$

$$2 = 2$$

The solution set is $\{4\}$.

5. $5x^{3/2} - 25 = 0$

$$5x^{3/2} = 25$$

$$x^{3/2} = 5$$

$$x = 5^{2/3}$$

Check:

$$5\left(5^{2/3}\right)^{3/2} - 25 \stackrel{?}{=} 0$$

$$5(5) - 25 \stackrel{?}{=} 0$$

$$0 = 0$$

The solution set is $\left\{5^{2/3}\right\}$.

6. $\quad x^4 - 5x^2 + 6 = 0$

$\left(x^2\right)^2 - 5x^2 + 6 = 0$

Let $t = x^2$.

$t^2 - 5t + 6 = 0$

$(t-3)(t-2) = 0$

$t - 3 = 0 \quad$ or $\quad t - 2 = 0$

$\qquad t = 3 \quad$ or $\qquad t = 2$

$\qquad x^2 = 3 \quad$ or $\qquad x^2 = 2$

$\qquad x = \pm\sqrt{3} \quad$ or $\qquad x = \pm\sqrt{2}$

The solution set is $\left\{-\sqrt{3},\ \sqrt{3},\ -\sqrt{2},\ \sqrt{2}\right\}$.

7. $\quad 3x^{2/3} - 11x^{1/3} - 4 = 0$

Let $t = x^{1/3}$.

$3t^2 - 11t - 4 = 0$

$(3t+1)(t-4) = 0$

$3t + 1 = 0 \quad$ or $\quad t - 4 = 0$

$3t = -1$

$t = -\dfrac{1}{3} \qquad\qquad t = 4$

$x^{1/3} = -\dfrac{1}{3} \qquad\qquad x^{1/3} = 4$

$x = \left(-\dfrac{1}{3}\right)^3 \qquad x = 4^3$

$x = -\dfrac{1}{27} \qquad\qquad x = 64$

The solution set is $\left\{-\dfrac{1}{27},\ 64\right\}$.

8. $\quad |2x - 1| = 5$

$2x - 1 = 5 \quad$ or $\quad 2x - 1 = -5$

$2x = 6 \qquad\qquad 2x = -4$

$x = 3 \qquad\qquad x = -2$

The solution set is $\{-2, 3\}$.

Exercise Set 1.4

1. $\qquad 3x^4 - 48x^2 = 0$

$3x^2(x^2 - 16) = 0$

$3x^2(x+4)(x-4) = 0$

$3x^2 = 0 \quad x + 4 = 0 \quad x - 4 = 0$

$x^2 = 0 \qquad x = -4 \qquad x = 4$

$x = 0$

The solution set is $\{0, -4, 4\}$.

3. $\qquad 2x^4 = 16x$

$2x^4 - 16x = 0$

$2x\left(x^3 - 8\right) = 0$

$2x = 0 \quad x^3 - 8 = 0$

$\qquad\qquad x^3 = 8$

$x = 0 \qquad\qquad x = 2$

The solution set is $\{0, 2\}$.

5. $\qquad 3x^3 + 2x^2 = 12x + 8$

$3x^3 + 2x^2 - 12x - 8 = 0$

$x^2(3x+2) - 4(3x+2) = 0$

$\qquad (3x+2)(x^2 - 4) = 0$

$3x + 2 = 0 \qquad x^2 - 4 = 0$

$3x = -2 \qquad\qquad x^2 = 4$

$x = -\dfrac{2}{3} \qquad\qquad x = \pm 2$

The solution set is $\left\{-\dfrac{2}{3},\ 2,\ -2\right\}$.

7. $\qquad\qquad 2x - 3 = 8x^3 - 12x^2$

$8x^3 - 12x^2 - 2x + 3 = 0$

$4x^2(2x - 3) - (2x - 3) = 0$

$\qquad (2x-3)(4x^2 - 1) = 0$

$2x - 3 = 0 \qquad 4x^2 - 1 = 0$

$2x = 3 \qquad\qquad 4x^2 = 1$

$\qquad\qquad\qquad x^2 = \dfrac{1}{4}$

$x = \dfrac{3}{2} \qquad\qquad x = \pm\dfrac{1}{2}$

The solution set is $\left\{\dfrac{3}{2}, \dfrac{1}{2}, -\dfrac{1}{2}\right\}$.

9.
$$4y^3 - 2 = y - 8y^2$$
$$4y^3 + 8y^2 - y - 2 = 0$$
$$4y^2(y+2) - (y+2) = 0$$
$$(y+2)(4y^2 - 1) = 0$$
$$y + 2 = 0 \quad 4y^2 - 1 = 0$$
$$4y^2 = 1$$
$$y^2 = \frac{1}{4}$$
$$y = -2 \qquad y = \pm\frac{1}{2}$$

The solution set is $\left\{-2, \dfrac{1}{2}, -\dfrac{1}{2}\right\}$.

11.
$$\sqrt{3x + 18} = x$$
$$3x + 18 = x^2$$
$$x^2 - 3x - 18 = 0$$
$$(x + 3)(x - 6) = 0$$
$$x + 3 = 0 \quad x - 6 = 0$$
$$x = -3 \qquad x = 6$$
$$\sqrt{3(-3) + 18} = -3 \quad \sqrt{3(6) + 18} = 6$$
$$\sqrt{-9 + 18} = -3 \quad \sqrt{18 + 18} = 6$$
$$\sqrt{9} = -3 \text{ False} \quad \sqrt{36} = 6$$

The solution set is $\{6\}$.

13.
$$\sqrt{x + 3} = x - 3$$
$$x + 3 = x^2 - 6x + 9$$
$$x^2 - 7x + 6 = 0$$
$$(x - 1)(x - 6) = 0$$
$$x - 1 = 0 \quad x - 6 = 0$$
$$x = 1 \qquad x = 6$$
$$\sqrt{1 + 3} = 1 - 3 \qquad \sqrt{6 + 3} = 6 - 3$$
$$\sqrt{4} = -2 \quad \text{False} \quad \sqrt{9} = 3$$

The solution set is $\{6\}$.

15.
$$\sqrt{2x + 13} = x + 7$$
$$2x + 13 = (x + 7)^2$$
$$2x + 13 = x^2 + 14x + 49$$
$$x^2 + 12x + 36 = 0$$
$$(x + 6)^2 = 0$$
$$x + 6 = 0$$
$$x = -6$$
$$\sqrt{2(-6) + 13} = -6 + 7$$
$$\sqrt{-12 + 13} = 1$$
$$\sqrt{1} = 1$$

The solution set is $\{-6\}$.

17.
$$x - \sqrt{2x + 5} = 5$$
$$x - 5 = \sqrt{2x + 5}$$
$$(x - 5)^2 = 2x + 5$$
$$x^2 - 10x + 25 = 2x + 5$$
$$x^2 - 12x + 20 = 0$$
$$(x - 2)(x - 10) = 0$$
$$x - 2 = 0 \quad x - 10 = 0$$
$$x = 2 \qquad x = 10$$
$$2 - \sqrt{2(2) + 5} = 5 \quad 10 - \sqrt{2(10) + 5} = 5$$
$$2 - \sqrt{9} = 5 \qquad 10 - \sqrt{25} = 5$$
$$2 - 3 = 5 \quad \text{False} \qquad 10 - 5 = 5$$

The solution set is $\{10\}$.

19.
$$\sqrt{3x} + 10 = x + 4$$
$$\sqrt{3x} = x - 6$$
$$3x = (x - 6)^2$$
$$3x = x^2 - 12x + 36$$
$$x^2 - 15x + 36 = 0$$
$$(x - 12)(x - 3) = 0$$
$$x - 12 = 0 \quad x - 3 = 0$$
$$x = 12 \qquad x = 3$$
$$\sqrt{3(12)} + 10 = 12 + 4 \quad \sqrt{3(3)} + 10 = 3 + 4$$
$$\sqrt{36} + 10 = 16 \qquad \sqrt{9} + 10 = 7$$
$$6 + 10 = 16 \qquad 3 + 10 = 7 \text{ False}$$

The solution set is $\{12\}$.

21.
$$\sqrt{x+8}-\sqrt{x-4}=2$$
$$\sqrt{x+8}=\sqrt{x-4}+2$$
$$x+8=(\sqrt{x-4}+2)^2$$
$$x+8=x-4+4\sqrt{x-4}+4$$
$$x+8=x+4\sqrt{x-4}$$
$$8=4\sqrt{x-4}$$
$$2=\sqrt{x-4}$$
$$4=x-4$$
$$x=8$$
$$\sqrt{8+8}-\sqrt{8-4}=2$$
$$\sqrt{16}-\sqrt{4}=2$$
$$4-2=2$$
The solution set is $\{8\}$.

23.
$$\sqrt{x-5}-\sqrt{x-8}=3$$
$$\sqrt{x-5}=\sqrt{x-8}+3$$
$$x-5=(\sqrt{x-8}+3)^2$$
$$x-5=x-8+6\sqrt{x-8}+9$$
$$x-5=x+1+6\sqrt{x-8}$$
$$-6=6\sqrt{x-8}$$
$$-1=\sqrt{x-8}$$
$$1=x-8$$
$$x=9$$
$$\sqrt{9-5}-\sqrt{9-8}=3$$
$$\sqrt{4}-\sqrt{1}=3$$
$$2-1=3 \text{ False}$$
The solution set is the empty set, $\varnothing$.

25.
$$\sqrt{2x+3}+\sqrt{x-2}=2$$
$$\sqrt{2x+3}=2-\sqrt{x-2}$$
$$2x+3=(2-\sqrt{x-2})^2$$
$$2x+3=4-4\sqrt{x-2}+x-2$$
$$x+1=-4\sqrt{x-2}$$
$$(x+1)^2=16(x-2)$$
$$x^2+2x+1=16x-32$$
$$x^2-14x+33=0$$
$$(x-11)(x-3)=0$$
$$x-11=0 \quad x-3=0$$
$$x=11 \qquad x=3$$

$$\sqrt{2(11)+3}+\sqrt{11-2}=2$$
$$\sqrt{22+3}+\sqrt{9}=2$$
$$5+3=2 \text{ False}$$
$$\sqrt{2(3)+3}+\sqrt{3-2}=2$$
$$\sqrt{6+3}+\sqrt{1}=2$$
$$3+1=2 \text{ False}$$
The solution set is the empty set, $\varnothing$.

27.
$$\sqrt{3\sqrt{x+1}}=\sqrt{3x-5}$$
$$3\sqrt{x+1}=3x-5$$
$$9(x+1)=9x^2-30x+25$$
$$9x^2-39x+16=0$$
$$x=\frac{39\pm\sqrt{945}}{18}=\frac{13\pm\sqrt{105}}{6}$$
Check proposed solutions.

The solution set is $\left\{\dfrac{13+\sqrt{105}}{6}\right\}$.

29.
$$x^{3/2}=8$$
$$(x^{3/2})^{2/3}=8^{2/3}$$
$$x=\sqrt[3]{8}^2$$
$$x=2^2$$
$$x=4$$
$$4^{3/2}=8$$
$$\sqrt{4}^3=8$$
$$2^3=8$$
The solution set is $\{4\}$.

31.
$$(x-4)^{3/2}=27$$
$$((x-4)^{3/2})^{2/3}=27^{2/3}$$
$$x-4=\sqrt[3]{27}^2$$
$$x-4=3^2$$
$$x-4=9$$
$$x=13$$
$$(13-4)^{3/2}=27$$
$$9^{3/2}=27$$
$$\sqrt{9}^3=27$$
$$3^3=27$$
The solution set is $\{13\}$.

33. $6x^{5/2} - 12 = 0$

$$6x^{5/2} = 12$$
$$x^{5/2} = 2$$
$$(x^{5/2})^{2/5} = 2^{2/5}$$
$$x = \sqrt[5]{2^2}$$
$$x = \sqrt[5]{4}$$
$$6(\sqrt[5]{4})^{5/2} - 12 = 0$$
$$6(4^{1/5})^{5/2} - 12 = 0$$
$$6(4^{1/2}) - 12 = 0$$
$$6(2) - 12 = 0$$

The solution set is $\left\{\sqrt[5]{4}\right\}$.

35. $(x^2 - x - 4)^{3/4} - 2 = 6$

$$(x^2 - x - 4)^{3/4} = 8$$
$$((x^2 - x - 4)^{3/4})^{4/3} = 8^{4/3}$$
$$x^2 - x - 4 = \sqrt[3]{8}^4$$
$$x^2 - x - 4 = 2^4$$
$$x^2 - x - 4 = 16$$
$$x^2 - x - 20 = 0$$
$$(x - 5)(x + 4) = 0$$
$$x - 5 = 0 \quad x + 4 = 0$$
$$x = 5 \qquad x = -4$$
$$(5^2 - 5 - 4)^{3/4} - 2 = 6$$
$$(25 - 9)^{3/4} - 2 = 6$$
$$16^{3/4} - 2 = 6$$
$$\sqrt[4]{16}^3 - 2 = 6$$
$$2^3 - 2 = 6$$
$$8 - 2 = 6$$
$$((-4)^2 - (-4) - 4)^{3/4} - 2 = 6$$
$$(16 + 4 - 4)^{3/4} - 2 = 6$$
$$16^{3/4} - 2 = 6$$
$$\sqrt[4]{16}^3 - 2 = 6$$
$$2^3 - 2 = 6$$
$$8 - 2 = 6$$

The solution set is $\{5, -4\}$.

37. $x^4 - 5x^2 + 4 = 0$ let $t = x^2$

$$t^2 - 5t + 4 = 0$$
$$(t - 1)(t - 4) = 0$$
$$t - 1 = 0 \quad t - 4 = 0$$
$$t = 1 \qquad t = 4$$
$$x^2 = 1 \qquad x^2 = 4$$
$$x = \pm 1 \qquad x = \pm 2$$

The solution set is $\{1, -1, 2, -2\}$

39. $9x^4 = 25x^2 - 16$

$$9x^4 - 25x^2 + 16 = 0 \text{ let } t = x^2$$
$$9t^2 - 25t + 16 = 0$$
$$(9t - 16)(t - 1) = 0$$
$$9t - 16 = 0$$
$$9t = 16$$
$$t = \frac{16}{9} \quad t - 1 = 0$$
$$\qquad\qquad t = 1$$
$$x^2 = \frac{16}{9} \quad x^2 = 1$$
$$\qquad\qquad x = \pm 1$$
$$x = \pm\frac{4}{3}$$

The solution set is $\left\{1, -1, \frac{4}{3}, -\frac{4}{3}\right\}$.

41. $x^6 + 8x^3 + 15 = 0$ let $t = x^3$

$$t^2 + 8t + 15 = 0$$
$$(t + 5)(t + 3) = 0$$
$$t + 5 = 0 \qquad t + 3 = 0$$
$$t = -5 \qquad\qquad t = -3$$
$$x^3 = -5 \qquad x^3 = -3$$
$$x = -\sqrt[3]{5} \qquad x = -\sqrt[3]{3}$$

The solution set is $\left\{-\sqrt[3]{5}, -\sqrt[3]{5}\right\}$.

43. $5x^6 + x^3 = 18$ let $t = x^3$

$5t^2 + t - 18 = 0$

$(5t - 9)(t + 2) = 0$

$5t - 9 = 0$

$5t = 9$

$t = \dfrac{9}{5}$ $t + 2 = 0$

           $t = -2$

$x^3 = \dfrac{9}{5}$ $x^3 = -2$

           $x = -\sqrt[3]{2}$

$x = \sqrt[3]{\dfrac{9}{5}}$

The solution set is $\left\{ \sqrt[3]{\dfrac{9}{5}}, -\sqrt[3]{2} \right\}$.

45. $x^{2/3} - x^{1/3} - 6 = 0$ let $t = x^{1/3}$

$t^2 - t - 6 = 0$

$(t - 3)(t + 2) = 0$

$t - 3 = 0$ $t + 2 = 0$

$t = 3$ $t = -2$

$x^{1/3} = 3$ $x^{1/3} = -2$

$x = 3^3$ $x = (-2)^3$

$x = 27$ $x = -8$

The solution set is $\{27, -8\}$.

47. $x^{3/2} - 2x^{3/4} + 1 = 0$ let $t = x^{3/4}$

$t^2 - 2t + 1 = 0$

$(t - 1)(t - 1) = 0$

$t - 1 = 0$

$t = 1$

$x^{3/4} = 1$

$x = 1^{4/3}$

$x = 1$

The solution set is $\{1\}$.

49. $2x - 3x^{1/2} + 1 = 0$ let $t = x^{1/2}$

$2t^2 - 3t + 1 = 0$

$(2t - 1)(t - 1) = 0$

$2t - 1 = 0$ $t - 1 = 0$

$2t = 1$

$t = \dfrac{1}{2}$ $t = 1$

$x^{1/2} = \dfrac{1}{2}$ $x^{1/2} = 1$

$x = \left(\dfrac{1}{2}\right)^2$ $x - 1^2$

$x = \dfrac{1}{4}$ $x = 1$

The solution set is $\left\{ \dfrac{1}{4}, 1 \right\}$.

51. $(x - 5)^2 - 4(x - 5) - 21 = 0$ let $t = x - 5$

$t^2 - 4t - 21 = 0$

$(t + 3)(t - 7) = 0$

$t + 3 = 0$ $t - 7 = 0$

$t = -3$ $t = 7$

$x - 5 = -3$ $x - 5 - 7$

$x = 2$ $x = 12$

The solution set is $\{2, 12\}$.

53. $\left(x^2 - x\right)^2 - 14\left(x^2 - x\right) + 24 = 0$

Let $t = x^2 - x$.

$t^2 - 14t + 24 = 0$

$(t - 2)(t - 12) = 0$

$t = 2$ or $t = 12$

$x^2 - x = 2$ or $x^2 - x = 12$

$x^2 - x - 2 = 0$ $x^2 - x - 12 = 0$

$(x - 2)(x + 1) = 0$ $(x - 4)(x + 3) = 0$

The solution set is $\{-3, -1, 2, 4\}$.

55. $\left(y - \dfrac{8}{y}\right)^2 + 5\left(y - \dfrac{8}{y}\right) - 14 = 0$

Let $t = y - \dfrac{8}{y}$.

$t^2 + 5t - 14 = 0$
$(t + 7)(t - 2) = 0$
$t = -7$ or $t = 2$

$y - \dfrac{8}{y} = -7 \qquad$ or $\quad y - \dfrac{8}{y} = 2$

$y^2 + 7y - 8 = 0 \qquad\qquad y^2 - 2y - 8 = 0$

$(y + 8)(y - 1) = 0 \qquad (y - 4)(y + 2) = 0$

The solution set is $\{-8, -2, 1, 4\}$.

57. $|x| = 8$

$x = 8, x = -8$
The solution set is $\{8, -8\}$.

59. $|x - 2| = 7$

$x - 2 = 7 \quad x - 2 = -7$
$x = 9 \qquad x = -5$
The solution set is $\{9, -5\}$.

61. $|2x - 1| = 5$

$2x - 1 = 5 \quad 2x - 1 = -5$
$2x = 6 \qquad 2x = -4$
$x = 3 \qquad x = -2$
The solution set is $\{3, -2\}$.

63. $x + 2\sqrt{x} - 3 = 0$ let $t = \sqrt{x}$

$t^2 + 2t - 3 = 0$
$(t - 1)(t + 3) = 0$
$t - 1 = 0 \quad t + 3 = 0$
$t = 1 \qquad t = -3$
$\sqrt{x} = 1 \quad \sqrt{x} = -3$
$x = 1 \qquad x = 9$
The solution set is $\{1\}$.

65. $(x + 4)^{3/2} = 8$

$x + 4 = 8^{2/3}$

$x + 4 = \sqrt[3]{8}^2$

$x + 4 = 2^2$

$x + 4 = 4$

$x = 0$

The solution set is $\{0\}$.

67. $\sqrt{4x + 15} - 2x = 0$

$\sqrt{4x + 15} = 2x$

$4x + 15 = 4x^2$

$4x^2 - 4x - 15 = 0$

$(2x - 5)(2x + 3) = 0$

$2x - 5 = 0 \quad 2x + 3 = 0$

$2x = 5 \qquad 2x = -3$

$x = \dfrac{5}{2} \qquad x = \dfrac{-3}{2}$

The solution set is $\left\{\dfrac{5}{2}\right\}$.

69. $|x^2 + 2x - 36| = 12$

$x^2 + 2x - 36 = 12 \quad x^2 + 2x - 36 = -12$

$x^2 + 2x - 48 = 0 \qquad x^2 + 2x - 24 = 0$

$(x - 6)(x + 8) = 0 \qquad (x + 6)(x - 4) = 0$

$x - 6 = 0 \quad x + 8 = 0 \quad x + 6 = 0 \quad x - 4 = 0$

$x = 6 \qquad x = -8 \qquad x = -6 \qquad x = 4$

The solution set is $\{6, -8, -6, 4\}$.

71. $x^3 - 2x^2 = x - 2$

$x^3 - 2x^2 - x + 2 = 0$

$x^2(x - 2) - (x - 2) = 0$

$(x - 2)(x^2 - 1) = 0$

$x - 2 = 0 \quad x^2 - 1 = 0$

$x = 2 \qquad x^2 = 1$

$x = \pm 1$

The solution set is $\{1, -1, 2\}$

73. $N = 5000\sqrt{100 - x}$

$40000 = 5000\sqrt{100 - x}$

$8 = \sqrt{100 - x}$

$64 = 100 - x$

$x = 36$

They will survive to 36 years old.

75.
$$N = 1220\sqrt[3]{x + 42} + 4900$$
$$9780 = 1220\sqrt[3]{x + 42} + 4900$$
$$4880 = 1220\sqrt[3]{x + 42}$$
$$4 = \sqrt[3]{x + 42}$$
$$64 = x + 42$$
$$x = 22$$
$$1930 + 22 = 1952$$
9780 aides were assigned in 1952.

77. $T = \dfrac{T_0}{\sqrt{1 - \dfrac{v^2}{c^2}}}$

$$4 = \frac{2}{\sqrt{1 - \dfrac{v^2}{c^2}}}$$

$$\sqrt{1 - \frac{v^2}{c^2}} = \frac{2}{4}$$

$$\sqrt{1 - \frac{v^2}{(186,000)^2}} = \frac{1}{2}$$

$$1 - \frac{v^2}{(186,000)^2} = \frac{1}{4}$$

$$-\frac{v^2}{(186,000)^2} = -\frac{3}{4}$$

$$v^2 = \frac{3}{4}(186,000)^2$$

$$v \approx 161,081$$

The ship is traveling about 161,081 miles/second.

79. a. $p = 30 - \sqrt{0.01(0) + 1}$

$p = 29$

There will be no demand for CD sets at a price of $29.

b. $27.76 = 30 - \sqrt{0.01x + 1}$

$$\left(\sqrt{0.01x + 1}\right)^2 = (2.24)^2$$

$0.01x + 1 = 5.0176$

$x = 401.76 \approx 402$

402 CD sets will sell weekly.

81. a.

$$\sqrt{6^2 + x^2} + \sqrt{3^2 + (12-x)^2} = 15$$
$$\sqrt{36 + x^2} = 15 - \sqrt{9 + 144 - 24x + x^2}$$
$$36 + x^2 = 225 - 30\sqrt{153 - 24x + x^2} + x^2 - 24x + 153$$
$$30\sqrt{x^2 - 24x + 153} = -24x + 342$$
$$5\sqrt{x^2 - 24x + 153} = -4x + 157$$
$$25(x^2 - 24x + 153) = 16x^2 - 456x + 3249$$
$$25x^2 - 600x + 3825 = 16x^2 - 456x + 3249$$
$$9x^2 - 144x + 576 = 0$$
$$x^2 - 16x + 64 = 0$$
$$(x-8)(x-8) = 0$$
$$x = 8$$

b.   You may either position the roads $1\frac{5}{7}$ miles from A and $10\frac{2}{7}$ miles from B *or* directly below B..

83.–89.   Answers may vary.

91. $-x^4 + 4x^3 - 4x^2 = 0$

$x = 0, 2$
$$-(0)^4 + 4(0)^3 - 4(0) = 0$$
$$0 + 0 - 0 = 0$$
$$-2^4 + 4(2)^3 - 4(2)^2 = 0$$
$$-16 + 4(8) - 4(4) = 0$$
$$-16 + 32 - 16 = 0$$
The solution set is $\{0, 2\}$.

93. $\sqrt{2x+13} - x - 5 = 0$

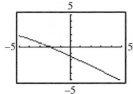

$x = -2$

$\sqrt{2(-2)+13} - (-2) - 5 = 0$

$\sqrt{-4+13} + 2 - 5 = 0$

$\sqrt{9} - 3 = 0$

$3 - 3 = 0$

The solution set is $\{-2\}$.

95.

Tracing along the curve shows the point $(36, 40{,}000)$ on the graph.

97. **a.** False;

$$\left(\sqrt{y+4} + \sqrt{y-1}\right)^2 \neq y + 4 + y - 1$$

b. False; if $t = (x^2 - 2x)^3$, the original equation can be written as $t^3 - 5t + 6 = 0$, not a quadratic form.

c. False; the other value may be a solution.

d. True

(d) is true

99. $5 - \dfrac{2}{x} = \sqrt{5 - \dfrac{2}{x}}$

$$\begin{array}{ccc}
 & \text{or} & \\
5 - \dfrac{2}{x} = 0 & & 5 - \dfrac{2}{x} = 1 \\
5 = \dfrac{2}{x} & & -\dfrac{2}{x} = -4 \\
5x = 2 & & -4x = -2 \\
x = \dfrac{2}{5} & & x = \dfrac{1}{2}
\end{array}$$

The solution set is $\left\{\dfrac{2}{5}, \dfrac{15}{2}\right\}$.

101. $x^{5/6} + x^{2/3} - 2x^{1/2} = 0$

$x^{1/2}(x^{2/6} + x^{1/6} - 2) = 0$ let $t = x^{1/6}$

$x^{1/2}(t^2 + t - 2) = 0$

$x^{1/2} = 0 \quad t^2 + t - 2 = 0$

$(t - 1)(t + 2) = 0$

$t - 1 = 0 \quad t + 2 = 0$

$t = 1 \qquad t = -2$

$x^{1/6} = 1 \qquad x^{1/6} = -2$

$x = 1^6 \qquad x = (-2)^6$

$x = 0 \quad x = 1 \qquad x = 64$

The solution set is $\{0, 1, 64\}$.

Section 1.5

Check Point Exercises

1. a.

b.

c.

2. a. $[-2, \ 5) = \left\{ x \middle| -2 \le x < 5 \right\}$

b. $[1, \ 3.5] = \left\{ x \middle| 1 \le x \le 3.5 \right\}$

c. $[-\infty, \ -1) = \left\{ x \middle| x < -1 \right\}$

3. $2 - 3x \le 5$

$-3x \le 3$

$x \ge -1$

The solution set is $\left\{ x \middle| x \ge -1 \right\}$ or $[-1, \ \infty)$.

4. $6 - 3x \le 5x - 2$

$8 - 3x \le 5x$

$8 \le 8x$

$1 \le x$

$x \ge 1$

The solution set is $\left\{ x \middle| x \ge 1 \right\}$ or $[1, \ \infty)$.

5. $1 \le 2x + 3 < 11$

$-2 \le 2x < 8$

$-1 \le x < 4$

The solution set is $\left\{ x \middle| -1 \le x < 4 \right\}$ or $[-1, \ 4)$.

6. $|x - 2| < 5$

$-5 < x - 2 < 5$

$-3 < x < 7$

The solution set is $\left\{ x \middle| -3 < x < 7 \right\}$ or $(-3, \ 7)$.

7. $|2x - 5| \ge 3$

$2x - 5 \le -3 \quad \text{or} \quad 2x - 5 \ge 3$

$2x \le 2 \quad \text{or} \qquad 2x \ge 8$

$x \le 1 \quad \text{or} \qquad x \ge 4$

The solution set is $\left\{ x \middle| x \le 1 \text{ or } x \ge 4 \right\}$, that is, all x in $(-\infty, 1]$ or $[4, \infty)$.

8. Let x = the number of miles driven in a week.

$260 < 80 + 0.25x$

$180 < 0.25x$

$720 < x$

Driving more than 720 miles in a week makes Basic the better deal.

Exercise Set 1.5

1.

3.

5.

-3

7.

4

9.

2 5

11.

-1 4

13. $1 < x \le 6$

1 6

15. $-5 \le x < 2$

-5 2

17. $-3 \le x \le 1$

-3 1

19. $x > 2$

2

21. $x \ge 3$

-3

23. $x < 3$

3

25. $x < 5.5$

5.5

27. $5x + 11 < 26$
$5x < 15$
$x < 3$
The solution set is $\left\{ x \mid x < 3 \right\}$, or $(-\infty, 3)$.

3

29. $3x - 7 \ge 13$
$3x \ge 20$
$x \ge \dfrac{20}{3}$

The solution set is $\left\{ x \mid x > \dfrac{20}{3} \right\}$, or

$\left[\dfrac{20}{3}, \infty \right)$.

$\dfrac{20}{3}$

31. $-9x \ge 36$
$x \le -4$
The solution set is $\left\{ x \mid x \le -4 \right\}$, or $(-\infty, -4]$.

-4

33. $8x - 11 \le 3x - 13$
$8x - 3x \le -13 + 11$
$5x \le -2$
$x \le -\dfrac{2}{5}$

The solution set is $\left\{ x \mid x \le -\dfrac{2}{5} \right\}$, or

$\left(-\infty, -\dfrac{2}{5} \right]$.

$-\dfrac{2}{5}$

35. $4(x + 1) + 2 \ge 3x + 6$
$4x + 4 + 2 \ge 3x + 6$
$4x + 6 \ge 3x + 6$
$4x - 3x \ge 6 - 6$
$x \ge 0$
The solution set is $\left\{ x \mid x > 0 \right\}$, or $[0, \infty)$.

0

37. $2x - 11 < -3(x + 2)$
$2x - 11 < -3x - 6$
$5x < 5$
$x < 1$
The solution set is $\left\{ x \mid x < 1 \right\}$, or $(-\infty, 1)$.

1

39. $1 - (x + 3) \geq 4 - 2x$
$1 - x - 3 \geq 4 - 2x$
$-x - 2 \geq 4 - 2x$
$x \geq 6$
The solution set is $\{x \mid x \geq 6\}$, or $[6, \infty)$.

41. $\dfrac{x}{4} - \dfrac{3}{5} \leq \dfrac{x}{2} + 1$

$-\dfrac{8}{5} \leq \dfrac{x}{4}$

$x \geq -\dfrac{32}{5}$

The solution set is $\left\{ x \mid x \geq -\dfrac{32}{5} \right\}$, or

$\left[-\dfrac{32}{5}, \infty \right)$.

43. $1 - \dfrac{x}{2} > 4$

$-\dfrac{x}{2} > 3$
$x < -6$
The solution set is $\{x \mid x, -6\}$, or $(-\infty, -6)$.

45. $\dfrac{x - 4}{6} \geq \dfrac{x - 2}{9} + \dfrac{5}{18}$
$3(x - 4) \geq 2(x - 2) + 5$
$3x - 12 \geq 2x - 4 + 5$
$\quad\quad x \geq 13$
The solution set is $\{x \mid x \geq 13\}$, or $(13, \infty)$.

47. $4(3x - 2) - 3x < 3(1 + 3x) - 7$
$12x - 8 - 3x < 3 + 9x - 7$
$9x - 8 < -4 + 9x$
$-8 < -4$
True for all x

The solution set is $\{x \mid x$ is any real number$\}$,
or $(-\infty, \infty)$.

49. $6 < x + 3 < 8$
$6 - 3 < x + 3 - 3 < 8 - 3$
$3 < x < 5$
The solution set is $\{x \mid 3 < x < 5\}$, or $(3, 5)$.

51. $-3 \leq x - 2 < 1$
$-1 \leq x < 3$
The solution set is $\{x \mid -1 \leq x < 3\}$, or
$[-1, 3)$.

53. $-11 < 2x - 1 \leq -5$
$-10 < 2x \leq -4$
$-5 < x \leq -2$
The solution set is $\{x \mid -5 < x \leq -2\}$, or
$(-5, -2]$.

55. $-3 \leq \dfrac{2}{3}x - 5 < -1$

$2 \leq \dfrac{2}{3}x < 4$

$3 \leq x < 6$
The solution set is $\{x \mid 3 \leq x < 6\}$, or $[3, 6)$.

57. $|x| < 3$
$-3 < x < 3$
The solution set is $\{x \mid -3 < x < 3\}$, or
$(-3, 3)$.

59. $|x - 1| \le 2$

$-2 \le x - 1 \le 2$

$-1 \le x \le 3$

The solution set is $\{x| -1 \le x \le 3\}$, or

$[-1, 3]$.

61. $|2x - 6| < 8$

$-8 < 2x - 6 < 8$

$-2 < 2x < 14$

$-1 < x < 7$

The solution set is $\{x| -1 < x < 7\}$, or

$(-1, 7)$.

63. $|2(x - 1) + 4| \le 8$

$-8 \le 2(x - 1) + 4 \le 8$

$-8 \le 2x - 2 + 4 \le 8$

$-8 \le 2x + 2 \le 8$

$-10 \le 2x \le 6$

$-5 \le x \le 3$

The solution set is $\{x| -5 \le x \le 3\}$, or

$[-5, 3]$

65. $\left|\dfrac{2y + 6}{3}\right| < 2$

$-2 < \dfrac{2y + 6}{3} < 2$

$-6 < 2y + 6 < 6$

$-12 < 2y < 0$

$-6 < y < 0$

The solution set is $\{x| -6 < y < 0\}$, or

$(-6, 0)$.

67. $|x| > 3$

$x > 3$ or $x < -3$

The solution set is $\{x| x > 3 \text{ or } x < -3\}$, that

is, $(-\infty, -3)$ or $(3, \infty)$.

69. $|x - 1| \ge 2$

$x - 1 \ge 2$ or $x - 1 \le -2$

$x \ge 3$ $x \le -1$

The solution set is $\{x| x \le -1 \text{ or } x \ge 3\}$, that

is, $(-\infty, -1]$ or $[3, \infty)$.

71. $|3x - 8| > 7$

$3x - 8 > 7$ or $3x - 8 < -7$

$3x > 15$ $3x < 1$

$x > 5$ $x < \dfrac{1}{3}$

The solution set is $\left\{x\middle| x < \dfrac{1}{3} \text{ or } x > 5\right\}$, that

is, $\left(-\infty, \dfrac{1}{3}\right)$ or $(5, \infty)$.

73. $\left|\dfrac{2x + 2}{4}\right| \ge 2$

$\dfrac{2x + 2}{4} \ge 2$ or $\dfrac{2x + 2}{4} \le -2$

$2x + 2 \ge 8$ $2x + 2 \le -8$

$2x \ge 6$ $2x \le -10$

$x \ge 3$ $x \le -5$

The solution set is $\{x| x \le -5 \text{ or } x \ge 3\}$, that

is, $(-\infty, -5]$ or $[3, \infty)$.

75. $\left|3 - \dfrac{2}{3}x\right| > 5$

$3 - \dfrac{2}{3}x > 5$ or $3 - \dfrac{2}{3}x < -5$

$-\dfrac{2}{3}x > 2$ $-\dfrac{2}{3}x < -8$

$x < -3$ $x > 12$

The solution set is $\{x| x < -3 \text{ or } x > 12\}$, that

is, $(-\infty, -3)$ or $(12, \infty)$.

77. $3|x-1|+2 \geq 8$

$3|x-1| \geq 6$

$|x-1| \geq 2$

$x-1 \geq 2$ or $x-1 \leq -2$

$x \geq 3$ $x \leq -1$

The solution set is $\{x|\ x \leq 1 \text{ or } x \geq 3\}$, that is,

$(-\infty,-1] \text{ or } [3,\infty)$.

79. $3 < |2x-1|$

$2x-1 > 3$ or $2x-1 < -3$

$2x > 4$ $2x < -2$

$x > 2$ $x < -1$

The solution set is $\{x|\ x < -1 \text{ or } x > 2\}$, that is, $(-\infty,-1) \text{ or } (2,\infty)$.

81. $12 < \left|-2x+\dfrac{6}{7}\right| + \dfrac{3}{7}$

$\dfrac{81}{7} < \left|-2x+\dfrac{6}{7}\right|$

$-2x+\dfrac{6}{7} > \dfrac{81}{7}$ or $-2x+\dfrac{6}{7} < -\dfrac{81}{7}$

$-2x > \dfrac{75}{7}$ $-2x < -\dfrac{87}{7}$

$x < -\dfrac{75}{14}$ $x > \dfrac{87}{14}$

The solution set is $\left\{x\middle|\ x < -\dfrac{75}{14} \text{ or } x > \dfrac{87}{14}\right\}$,

that is, $\left(-\infty,-\dfrac{75}{14}\right) \text{ or } \left(\dfrac{87}{14},\infty\right)$.

83. $4 + \left|3-\dfrac{x}{3}\right| \geq 9$

$\left|3-\dfrac{x}{3}\right| \geq 5$

$3-\dfrac{x}{3} \geq 5$ or $3-\dfrac{x}{3} \leq -5$

$-\dfrac{x}{3} \geq 2$ $-\dfrac{x}{3} \leq -8$

$x \leq -6$ $x \geq 24$

The solution set is $\{x|\ x \leq -6 \text{ or } x \geq 24\}$,

that is, $(-\infty,-6] \text{ or } [24,\infty)$.

85. Raleigh, NC, Seattle, San Francisco, Austin, TX

87. San Diego

89. Austin, TX, Washington, DC, Lexington-Fayette, KY, Minneapolis, Boston, Arlington, TX

91. $11 \leq 3x-4 \leq 56$

$15 \leq 3x \leq 60$

$5 \leq x \leq 20$

This inequality includes 5.0 million, 17.5 million, and 17.6 million. The disorders are severe cognitive impairment, substance abuse disorders, and depressive: manic, major depression.

93. $y = 30x + 113$

$623 < 30x + 113$

$510 < 30x$

$17 < x$

$x > 17$

$1996 + 17 = 2013$

Liposuctions exceed 623 thousand in 2013.

95. $C = 18x + 250$

$322 < 18x + 250 < 412$

$72 < 18x < 162$

$4 < x < 9$

$2000 + 4 = 2004; 2000 + 9 = 2009$

Cost ranges from 322 to 412 billion dollars between 2004 and 2009.

97. Let x = number of checks
$$8 + 0.05x > 2 + 0.08x$$
$$6 > 0.03x$$
$$200 > x$$
The number of checks that should be written is 199 checks or fewer.

99. a.
$$\frac{86 + 88 + x}{3} \geq 90$$
$$\frac{174 + x}{3} \geq 90$$
$$174 + x \geq 270$$
$$x \geq 96$$
You must get at least a 96.

b.
$$\frac{86 + 88 + x}{3} < 80$$
$$\frac{174 + x}{3} < 80$$
$$174 + x < 240$$
$$x < 66$$
This will happen if you get a grade less than 66.

101. Cost = $65,000 + 20x$
Revenue = $85x$
$$85x - (65,000 + 20x) > 0$$
$$65x > 65,000$$
$$x > 1000$$
The company should manufacture and sell 1001 or more pairs of shoes.

103.–111. Answers may vary.

113.

$x < -3$

115.

The graph of the left side of the inequality is always greater than the right side, therefore all real numbers are part of the solution.
$$2x + 3 > 3(2x - 4) - 4x$$
$$2x + 3 > 6x - 12 - 4x$$
$$2x + 3 > 2x - 12$$
$$0 > -15$$
You get a true statement with no variable.

117. a. False; $|2x - 3| > -7$ is true for any x because the absolute value is 0 or positive.

b. False; $2x > 6$, $x > 3$
3.1 is a real number that satisfies the inequality.

c. True; $|x - 4| > 0$ is not satisfied only when $x = 4$. Since 4 is rational, all irrational numbers satisfy the inequality.

d. False

(c) is true.

119. $(-10, -8)$

Section 1.6

Check Point Exercises

1. $x^2 + 2x - 3 < 0$
    Solve $x^2 + 2x - 3 = 0$.
    $(x-1)(x+3) = 0$
    $x - 1 = 0$ or $x + 3 = 0$
    $x = 1$ or $x = -3$
    The boundary points are 1 and –3.
    The test intervals are
    $(-\infty, -3)$, $(-3, 1)$, and $(1, \infty)$.

    Test –5: $(-5)^2 + 2(-5) - 3 < 0$
    $\qquad\qquad 25 - 10 - 3 < 0$
    $\qquad\qquad\qquad\qquad 12 < 0$ False
    Test 0: $0^2 + 2(0) - 3 < 0$
    $\qquad\qquad\qquad -3 = 0$ True
    Test 2: $2^2 + 2(2) - 3 < 0$
    $\qquad\qquad 4 + 4 - 3 < 0$
    $\qquad\qquad\qquad\quad 5 < 0$ False
    The solution set is (–3, 1).

    $\xleftarrow{\quad\overset{(}{-3}\;\rule[0.5ex]{3em}{1pt}\;\overset{)}{1}\quad}\rightarrow$

2. $\qquad x^2 - x \geq 20$
    $x^2 - x - 20 \geq 0$
    Solve $x^2 - x - 20 = 0$.
    $(x-5)(x+4) = 0$
    $x - 5 = 0$ or $x + 4 = 0$
    $x = 5$ or $4 = -4$
    The boundary points are –4 and 5.
    The test intervals are
    $(-\infty, -4]$, $[-4, 5]$, and $[5, \infty)$.
    Test –5: $(-5)^2 - (5) \geq 20$
    $\qquad\qquad 25 + 5 \geq 20$
    $\qquad\qquad\qquad 30 \geq 20$ True

Test 0: $0^2 - 0 \geq 20$
$\qquad\qquad 0 \geq 20$ False
Test 6: $6^2 - 6 \geq 20$
$\qquad\qquad 36 - 6 \geq 20$
$\qquad\qquad\qquad 30 \geq 20$ True
The solution set is $(-\infty, -4]$ or $[5, \infty)$.

$\xleftarrow{\quad\overset{]}{-4}\;\rule[0.5ex]{3em}{1pt}\;\overset{[}{5}\quad}\rightarrow$

3. $\dfrac{x-5}{x+2} > 0$
    $x - 5 = 0 \quad x + 2 = 0$
    $\qquad x = 5 \qquad x = -2$
    The boundary points are –2 and 5.
    The test intervals are
    $(-\infty, -2)$, $(-2, 5)$, and $(5, \infty)$.
    Test –3: $\dfrac{-3-5}{-3+2} > 0$
    $\qquad\qquad \dfrac{-8}{-1} > 0$ True
    Test 0: $\dfrac{0-5}{0+2} > 0$
    $\qquad\qquad \dfrac{-5}{2} > 0$ False
    Test 6: $\dfrac{6-5}{6+2} > 0$
    $\qquad\qquad \dfrac{1}{8} > 0$ True
    The solution set is $(-\infty, -2)$ or $(5, \infty)$.

4.
$$\frac{2x}{x+1} \le 1$$

$$\frac{2x}{x+1} - 1 \le 0$$

$$\frac{2x - x - 1}{x+1} \le 0$$

$$\frac{x-1}{x+1} \le 0$$

$$x - 1 = 0 \quad x + 1 = 0$$

$$x = 1 \qquad x = -1$$

The boundary points are -1 and 1.
The test intervals are
$(-\infty, -1), (-1, 1],$ and $[1, \infty)$.

Test -2: $\dfrac{2(2)}{-2+1} \le 1$

$$\frac{-4}{-1} \le 1$$

$$4 \le 1 \text{ False}$$

Test 0: $\dfrac{2(0)}{0+1} \le 1$

$$0 \le 1 \text{ True}$$

Test 2: $\dfrac{2(2)}{2+1} \le 1$

$$\frac{4}{3} \le 1 \text{ False}$$

The solution set is $(-1, 1]$.

5.
$$-16t^2 + 80t > 64$$

$$-16t^2 + 80t - 64 > 0$$

$$t^2 - 5t + 4 < 0$$

Solve $\quad t^2 - 5t + 4 = 0$

$$(t-4)(t-1) = 0$$

$$t - 4 = 0 \quad \text{or} \quad t - 1 = 0$$

$$t = 4 \quad \text{or} \qquad t = 1$$

The boundary points are 1 and 4.
Note that the object is at ground level when
$s = 0$.

$$0 = 16t^2 + 80t$$

$$0 = -16t(t-5)$$

$$t = 0 \quad \text{or} \quad t = 5$$

The test intervals are $(0, 1), (1, 4),$ and $(4, 5)$.

Test $\dfrac{1}{2}$: $-16\left(\dfrac{1}{2}\right)^2 + 80\left(\dfrac{1}{2}\right) > 64$

$$-4 + 40 > 64$$

$$36 > 64 \text{ False}$$

Test 2: $-16(2)^2 + 80(2) > 64$

$$-64 + 160 > 64$$

$$96 > 64 \text{ True}$$

Test $\dfrac{9}{2}$: $-16\left(\dfrac{9}{2}\right)^2 + 80\left(\dfrac{9}{2}\right) > 64$

$$-324 + 360 > 64$$

$$36 > 64 \text{ False}$$

The object will be more than 64 feet above
the ground between 1 and 4 seconds,
excluding $t = 1$ and $t = 4$.

Exercise Set 1.6

1. $(x-4)(x+2) > 0$
$x = 4$ or $x = -2$

T	F	T
-2		4

Test -3: $(-3-4)(-3+2) > 0$

$$7 > 0 \text{ True}$$

Test 0: $(0-4)(0+2) > 0$

$$-8 > 0 \text{ False}$$

Test 5: $(5-4)(5+2) > 0$

$$7 > 0 \text{ True}$$

$(-\infty, -2)$ or $(4, \infty)$

3. $(x-7)(x+3) \le 0$
$x = 7$ or $x = -3$

F	T	F
-3		7

Test -4: $(-4-7)(-4+3) \le 0$

$$11 \le 0 \text{ False}$$

Test 0: $(0-7)(0+3) \le 0$

$$-21 \le 0 \text{ True}$$

Test 8: $(8-7)(8+3) \le 0$

$$11 \le 0 \text{ False}$$

The solution set is $[-3, 7]$.

5. $x^2 - 5x + 4 > 0$
$(x - 4)(x - 1) > 0$
$x = 4$ or $x = 1$

T	F	T
	1	4

Test 0: $0^2 - 5(0) + 4 > 0$
$\qquad 4 > 0$ True
Test 2: $2^2 - 5(2) + 4 > 0$
$\qquad -2 > 0$ False
Test 5: $5^2 - 5(5) + 4 > 0$
$\qquad 4 > 0$ True
The solution set is $(-\infty, \ 1)$ or $(4, \ \infty)$.

```
◄─────)───────(─────►
      1       4
```

7. $x^2 + 5x + 4 > 0$
$(x + 1)(x + 4) > 0$
$x = -1$ or $x = -4$

T	F	T
-4	-1	

Test -5: $(-5)^2 + 5(-5) + 4 > 0$
$\qquad 4 > 0$ True
Test -3: $(-3)^2 + 5(-3) + 4 > 0$
$\qquad -2 > 0$ False
Test 0: $0^2 + 5(0) + 4 > 0$
$\qquad 4 > 0$ True
The solution set is $(-\infty, \ -4)$ or $(-1, \ \infty)$.

```
◄─────)───────(─────►
     -4        1
```

9. $x^2 - 6x + 9 < 0$
$(x - 3)(x - 3) < 0$
$\qquad x = 0$

F	F
3	

Test 0: $0^2 - 6(0) + 9 < 0$
$\qquad 9 < 0$ False
Test 4: $4^2 - 6(4) + 9 < 0$
$\qquad 1 < 0$ False
The solution set is the empty set, $\varnothing$.

```
◄──────────────────►
```

11. $x^2 - 6x + 8 \le 0$
$(x - 4)(x - 2) \le 0$
$x = 4$ or $x = 2$

F	T	F
2	4	

Test 0: $0^2 - 6(0) + 8 \le 0$
$\qquad 8 \le 0$ False
Test 3: $3^2 - 6(3) + 8 \le 0$
$\qquad -1 \le 0$ True
Test 5: $5^2 - 6(5) + 8 \le 0$
$\qquad 3 \le 0$ False
The solution set is [2, 4].

```
◄─────[═══════]─────►
      2       4
```

13. $3x^2 + 10x - 8 \le 0$
$(3x - 2)(x + 4) \le 0$
$x = \dfrac{2}{3}$ or $x = -4$

F	T	F
-4	$\frac{2}{3}$	

Test -5: $3(-5)^2 + 10(-5) - 8 \le 0$
$\qquad 17 \le 0$ False
Test 0: $3(0)^2 + 10(0) - 8 \le 0$
$\qquad 8 \le 0$ True
Test 1: $3(1)^2 + 10(1) - 8 \le 0$
$\qquad 5 \le 0$ False
The solution set is $\left[-4, \ \dfrac{2}{3} \right]$.

```
◄─────[═══════]─────►
     -4       2/3
```

15.
$$2x^2 + x < 15$$
$$2x^2 + x - 15 < 0$$
$$(2x - 5)(x + 3) < 0$$
$$2x - 5 = 0 \quad \text{or} \quad x + 3 = 0$$
$$2x = 5$$
$$x = \frac{5}{2} \quad \text{or} \quad x = -3$$

F	T	F
	-3	$\frac{5}{2}$

Test -4: $2(-4)^2 + (-4) < 15$
$$28 < 15 \text{ False}$$
Test 0: $2(0)^2 + 0 < 15$
$$0 < 15 \text{ True}$$
Test 3: $2(3)^2 + 3 < 15$
$$21 < 15 \text{ False}$$

The solution set is $\left(-3, \ \frac{5}{2}\right)$.

17.
$$4x^2 + 7x < -3$$
$$4x^2 + 7x + 3 < 0$$
$$(4x + 3)(x + 1) < 0$$
$$4x + 3 = 0 \quad \text{or} \quad x + 1 = 0$$
$$4x - 3 = 0$$
$$x = -\frac{3}{4} \quad \text{or} \quad x = -1$$

F	T	F
	-1	$-\frac{3}{4}$

Test -2: $4(-2)^2 + 7(-2) < -3$
$$2 < -3 \text{ False}$$

Test $-\frac{7}{8}$: $4\left(-\frac{7}{8}\right)^2 + 7\left(-\frac{7}{8}\right) < -3$
$$\frac{49}{16} - \frac{49}{8} < -3$$
$$-\frac{49}{16} < -3 \text{ True}$$
Test 0: $4(0)^2 + 7(0) < -3$
$$0 < -3 \text{ False}$$

The solution set is $\left(-1, \ -\frac{3}{4}\right)$.

19.
$$5x \le 2 - 3x^2$$
$$3x^2 + 5x - 2 \le 0$$
$$(3x - 1)(x + 2) \le 0$$
$$3x - 1 = 0 \text{ or } x + 2 = 0$$
$$3x = 1$$
$$3x - 1 = 0 \quad \text{or} \quad x + 2 = 0$$
$$3x = 1$$
$$x = \frac{1}{3} \quad \text{or} \quad x = -2$$

F	T	F
	-2	$\frac{1}{3}$

Test -3: $5(-3) \le 2 - 3(-3)^2$
$$-15 \le -25 \text{ False}$$
Test 0: $5(0) \le 2 - 3(0)^2$
$$0 \le 2 \text{ True}$$
Test 1: $5(1) \le 2 - 3(1)^2$
$$5 \le -1 \text{ False}$$

Ths solution set is $\left[-2, \frac{1}{3}\right]$.

21. $x^2 - 4x \geq 0$

$x(x - 4) \geq 0$

$x = 0$ or $x - 4 = 0$

$\qquad\qquad x = 4$

T		F		T
	0		4	

Test -1: $(-1)^2 - 4(-1) \geq 0$

$\qquad\qquad 5 \geq 0$ True

Test 1: $(1)^2 - 4(1) \geq 0$

$\qquad\qquad -3 \geq 0$ False

$\qquad\quad 0 \leq 2$ True

Test 5: $5^2 - 4(5) \geq 0$

$\qquad\qquad 5 \geq 0$ True

The solution set is $(-\infty, \ 0]$ or $[4, \ \infty)$.

23. $2x^2 + 3x > 0$

$x(2x + 3) > 0$

$x = 0$ or $x = -\dfrac{3}{2}$

T		F		T
	$-\frac{3}{2}$		0	

Test -2: $2(-2)^2 + 3(-2) > 0$

$\qquad\qquad 2 > 0$ True

Test -1: $2(-1)^2 + 3(-1) > 0$

$\qquad\qquad -1 > 0$ False

Test 1: $2(1)^2 + 3(1) > 0$

$\qquad\qquad 5 > 0$ True

The solution set is $\left(-\infty, \ -\dfrac{3}{2}\right)$ or $(0, \ \infty)$.

25. $-x^2 + x \geq 0$

$x^2 - x \leq 0$

$x(x - 1) \leq 0$

$x = 0$ or $x = 1$

F		T		F
	0		1	

Test -1: $-(-1)^2 + (-1) \geq 0$

$\qquad\qquad -2 \geq 0$ False

Test $\dfrac{1}{2}$: $-\left(\dfrac{1}{2}\right)^2 + \left(\dfrac{1}{2}\right) \geq 0$

$\qquad\qquad \dfrac{1}{4} \geq 0$ True

Test 2: $-(2)^2 + 2 \geq 0$

$\qquad\qquad -2 \geq 0$ False

The solution set is $[0, 1]$.

27. $\dfrac{x - 4}{x + 3} > 0$

$x - 4 = 0 \quad x + 3 = 0$

$\quad x = 4 \qquad x = -3$

T		F		T
	-3		4	

Test -4: $\dfrac{-4 - 4}{-4 + 3} > 0$

$\qquad\qquad \dfrac{-8}{-1} > 0$

$\qquad\qquad 8 > 0$ True

Test 0: $\dfrac{0 - 4}{0 + 3} > 0$

$\qquad\qquad -\dfrac{4}{3} > 0$ False

Test 5: $\dfrac{5 - 4}{5 + 3} > 0$

$\qquad\qquad \dfrac{1}{8} > 0$ True

The solution set is $(-\infty, \ -3)$ or $(4, \ \infty)$.

29. $\dfrac{x+3}{x+4} < 0$

$x = -3$ or $x = -4$

F	T	F

-4 -3

Test -5: $\dfrac{-5+3}{-5+4} < 0$

$\qquad\qquad 2 < 0$ False

Test $-\dfrac{7}{2}$: $\dfrac{-\frac{7}{2}+3}{-\frac{7}{2}+4} < 0$

$\qquad\qquad\qquad -1 < 0$ True

Test 0: $\dfrac{0+3}{0+4} < 0$

$\qquad\qquad \dfrac{3}{4} < 0$ False

The solution set is $(-4, -3)$.

$-4 \qquad\qquad -3$

31. $\dfrac{-x+2}{x-4} \ge 0$

$x = 2$ or $x = 4$

F	T	F

$2 \qquad\qquad 4$

Test 0: $\dfrac{0+2}{0-4} \ge 0$

$\qquad\qquad -\dfrac{1}{2} \ge 0$ False

Test 3: $\dfrac{-3+2}{3-4} \ge 0$

$\qquad\qquad 1 \ge 0$ True

Test 5: $\dfrac{-5+2}{5-4} \ge 0$

$\qquad\qquad -3 \ge 0$ False

The solution set is $[2, 4)$.

$2 \qquad\qquad 4$

33. $\dfrac{4-2x}{3x+4} \le 0$

$x = 2$ or $x = -\dfrac{4}{3}$

T	F	T

$-\dfrac{4}{3} \qquad\qquad 2$

Test -2: $\dfrac{4-2(-2)}{3(-2)+4} \le 0$

$\qquad\qquad\qquad -4 \le 0$ True

Test 0: $\dfrac{4-2(0)}{3(0)+4} \le 0$

$\qquad\qquad\qquad 1 \le 0$ False

Test 3: $\dfrac{4-2(3)}{3(3)+4} \le 0$

$\qquad\qquad\qquad \dfrac{-2}{13} \le 0$ True

The solution set is $\left(-\infty, \dfrac{-4}{3}\right)$ or $[2, \ \infty)$.

$-\dfrac{4}{3} \qquad\qquad 2$

35. $\dfrac{x}{x-3} > 0$

$x = 0$ or $x = 3$

T	F	T

$0 \qquad\qquad 3$

Test -1: $\dfrac{-1}{-1-3} > 0$

$\qquad\qquad \dfrac{1}{4} > 0$ True

Test 2: $\dfrac{2}{2-3} > 0$

$\qquad\qquad -2 > 0$ False

Test 4: $\dfrac{4}{4-3} > 0$

$\qquad\qquad 4 > 0$ True

The solution set is $(-\infty, \ 0)$ or $(3, \ \infty)$.

$0 \qquad\qquad 3$

37.

$$\frac{x+1}{x+3} < 0$$

$$\frac{x+1}{x+3} - 2 < 0$$

$$\frac{x+1-2(x+3)}{x+3} < 0$$

$$\frac{x+1-2x-6}{x+3} < 0$$

$$\frac{-x-5}{x+3} < 0$$

$$x = \text{ or } x = -3$$

T		F		T
	-5		-3	

Test -6: $\dfrac{-6+1}{-6+3} < 2$

$$\frac{5}{3} < 2 \text{ True}$$

Test -4: $\dfrac{-4+1}{-4+3} < 2$

$$3 < 2 \text{ False}$$

Test 0: $\dfrac{0+1}{0+3} < 2$

$$\frac{1}{3} < 2 \text{ True}$$

The solution set is $(-\infty, -5)$ or $(-3, \infty)$.

39.

$$\frac{x+4}{2x-1} \le 3$$

$$\frac{x+4}{2x-1} - 3 \le 0$$

$$\frac{x+4-3(2x-1)}{2x-1} \le 0$$

$$\frac{x+4-6x+3}{2x-1} \le 0$$

$$\frac{-5x+7}{2x-1} \le 0$$

$$x = \frac{7}{5} \text{ or } x = \frac{1}{2}$$

T		F		T
	$\frac{1}{2}$		$\frac{7}{5}$	

Test 0: $\dfrac{0+4}{2(0)-1} \le 3$

$$-4 \le 3 \text{ True}$$

Test 1: $\dfrac{1+4}{2(1)-1} \le 3$

$$5 \le 3 \text{ False}$$

Test 2: $\dfrac{2+4}{2(2)-1} \le 3$

$$2 \le 3 \text{ True}$$

The solution set is $\left(-\infty, \frac{1}{2}\right)$ or $\left[\frac{7}{5}, \infty\right)$.

41.

$$\frac{x-2}{x+2} \le 2$$

$$\frac{x-2}{x+2} - 2 \le 0$$

$$\frac{x-2-2(x+2)}{x+2} \le 0$$

$$\frac{x-2-2x-4}{x+2} \le 0$$

$$\frac{-x-6}{x+2} \le 0$$

$$x = -6 \quad \text{or} \quad x = -2$$

T	F	T
-6		-2

Test -7: $\dfrac{-7-2}{-7+2} \le 2$

$$\frac{9}{5} \le 2 \text{ True}$$

Test -3: $\dfrac{-3-2}{-3+2} \le 2$

$$5 \le 2 \text{ False}$$

Test 0: $\dfrac{0-2}{0+2} \le 2$

$$-1 \le 2 \text{ True}$$

The solution set is $(-\infty, -6]$ or $(-2, \infty)$.

43. $S = -16t^2 + v_0 t + s_0$

$$96 < -16t^2 + 80t + 0$$

$$0 < -16t^2 + 80t - 96$$

$$0 < -16(t^2 - 5t + 6)$$

$$0 < -16(t-3)(t-2)$$

F	T	F
	2	3

$$2 < t < 3$$

The projectile's height will exceed 96 feet between 2 and 3 seconds exclusive.

45. $S = -16t^2 + v_0 t + s_0$

$$96 < -16t^2 + 64t + 80$$

$$0 < -16t^2 + 64t - 16$$

$$0 < -16(t^2 - 4t + 1)$$

$$t = \frac{4 \pm \sqrt{(-4)^2 - 4(1)(1)}}{2}$$

$$t = \frac{4 \pm 2\sqrt{3}}{2}$$

$$t = 2 \pm \sqrt{3}$$

F	T	F
	$2-\sqrt{3}$	$2+\sqrt{3}$

$$2 + \sqrt{3} - \left(2 - \sqrt{3}\right) = 2\sqrt{3} \approx 3.46$$

The ball is higher than 96 feet for about 3.46 seconds.

47. $H = \dfrac{15}{8}x^2 - 30x + 200$

a. $H = \dfrac{15}{8}(0)^2 - 30(0) + 200$

$H = 200$ beats per minute

b. $110 < \dfrac{15}{8}x^2 - 30x + 200$

$880 < 15x^2 - 240x + 1600$

$0 < x^2 - 16x + 48$

$0 < (x-12)(x-4)$

$x = 12$ or $x = 4$

T		F		T
	4		12	

Test 0:

$110 < \dfrac{15}{8}(0)^2 - 30(0) + 200$

$110 < 200$ True

Test 8: $110 < \dfrac{15}{8}(8)^2 - 30(8) + 200$

$110 < 80$ False

Test 16: $110 < \dfrac{15}{8}(16)^2 - 30(16) + 200$

$110 < 200$ True

Heart rate exceeds 110 beats per minute up to 4 minutes after work-out.

49. $y = -0.22x^2 + 4.32x + 26$

$41.3 > -0.22x^2 + 4.32x + 26$

$0 > -0.22x^2 + 4.32x - 15.3$

$0 > -22x^2 + 432x - 1530$

$0 < 11x^2 - 216x + 765$

$x = \dfrac{216 \pm \sqrt{(-216)^2 - 4(11)(765)}}{2(11)}$

$x = \dfrac{216 \pm \sqrt{46656 - 33660}}{22}$

$x = \dfrac{216 \pm \sqrt{12996}}{22}$

$x = \dfrac{216 \pm 114}{22}$

$x = 15,\ 4\dfrac{7}{11}$

T		F		T
	$4\frac{7}{11}$		15	

Test 0: $41.3 > -0.22(0)^2 + 4.32(0) + 26$

$41.3 > 26$ True

Test 5: $41.3 > -0.22(5)^2 + 4.32(5) + 26$

$41.3 > 42.1$ False

Test 16: $41.3 > -0.22(16)^2 + 4.32(16) + 26$

$41.3 > 38.8$ True

$1986 + 15 = 2001$

After 2001 the number of visitors will be less than 41.3 million.

51. $C = \dfrac{4p}{100 - p}$

$6 > \dfrac{4p}{100 - p}$

$600 - 6p > 4p$

$600 > 10p$

$60 > p$

Less than 60% can be removed.

53. Answers may vary.

55. Graph $y_1 = x^2 + 3x - 10$ in a standard viewing window. The graph is above the x-axis, or zero, for $x < -5$ and $x > 2$.

The solution set is $(-\infty, -5]$ or $(2, \infty)$.

57. Graph $y_1 = \dfrac{x - 4}{x - 1}$ in a standard viewing window. The graph is below the x-axis for $1 < x \le 4$.

The solution set is $\{1, 4\}$.

59. Graph $y_1 = \dfrac{1}{x + 1}$ and $y_2 = \dfrac{2}{x + 4}$ in a standard viewing window. y_1 is below y_2 for $-4 < x < -1$.

The solution set is $(-4, -1]$ or $(2, \infty)$.

61. $N = 14W^3 - 17W^2 - 6W + 34$

We want $46 < 14W^3 - 17W^2 - 6W + 34$.

Graph $y_1 = 14x^3 - 17x^2 - 6x + 34$ and $y_2 = 46$ for $1.5 \le x \le 3.5$. The graph of y_1 is above y_2 for approximately $x > 1.74$.

$(1.7, 3.5]$.

The abdominal width is from 1.7 mm to 3.5 mm.

63. Answers may vary.

65. Because any non-zero number squared is positive, the solution is all real numbers except 2.

67. Because any number squared is positive, the solution is the empty set, $\varnothing$.

69. a. The solution set is all real numbers.

     b. The solution set is the empty set, $\varnothing$.

     c. $4x^2 - 8x + 7 > 0$

$$x = \dfrac{8 \pm \sqrt{(-8)^2 - 4(4)(7)}}{2(4)}$$

$$x = \dfrac{8 \pm \sqrt{64 - 112}}{8}$$

$$x = \dfrac{8 \pm \sqrt{-48}}{8} \Rightarrow \text{imaginary}$$

no critical values

Test 0: $4(0)^2 - 8(0) + 7 > 0$

$ 7 > 0$ True

The inequality is true for all numbers.

Chapter 1 Review Exercises

1. $2x - 5 = 7$
$2x = 12$
$x = 6$
$2(6) - 5 = 7$
$12 - 5 = 7$
The solution set is $\{6\}$.

2. $5x + 20 = 3x$
$2x = -20$
$x = -10$
$5(-10) + 20 = 3(-10)$
$-50 + 20 = -30$
The solution set is $\{-10\}$.

3. $7(x - 4) = x + 2$
$7x - 28 = x + 2$
$6x = 30$
$x = 5$
$7(5 - 4) = 5 + 2$
$7(1) = 7$
The solution set is $\{5\}$.

4. $1 - 2(6 - x) = 3x + 2$
$1 - 12 + 2x = 3x + 2$
$-11 - x = 2$
$-x = 13$
$x = -13$
$1 - 2[6 - (-13)] = 3(-13) + 2$
$1 - 2(19) = -39 + 2$
$1 - 38 = -37$
The solution set is $\{-13\}$.

5. $2(x - 4) + 3(x + 5) = 2x - 2$
$2x - 8 + 3x + 15 = 2x - 2$
$5x + 7 = 2x - 2$
$3x = -9$
$x = -3$
$2(-3 - 4) + 3(-3 + 5) = 2(-3) - 2$
$2(-7) + 3(2) = -6 - 2$
$-14 + 6 = -8$
The solution set is $\{-3\}$.

6. $2x - 4(5x + 1) = 3x + 17$
$2x - 20x - 4 = 3x + 17$
$-18x - 4 = 3x + 17$
$-21x = 21$
$x = -1$
$2(-1) - 4(5(-1) + 1) = 3(-1) + 17$
$-2 - 4(-4) = -3 + 17$
$-2 + 16 = 14$
The solution set is $\{-1\}$.

7. $\dfrac{2x}{3} = \dfrac{x}{6} + 1$
$2(2x) = x + 6$
$4x = x + 6$
$3x = 6$
$x = 2$
$\dfrac{2(2)}{3} = \dfrac{2}{6} + 1$
$\dfrac{4}{3} = \dfrac{1}{3} + \dfrac{3}{3}$
$\dfrac{4}{3} = \dfrac{4}{3}$
The solution set is $\{2\}$.

8. $\dfrac{x}{2} - \dfrac{1}{10} = \dfrac{x}{5} + \dfrac{1}{2}$
$5x - 1 = 2x + 5$
$3x = 6$
$x = 2$
$\dfrac{2}{2} - \dfrac{1}{10} = \dfrac{2}{5} + \dfrac{1}{2}$
$1 - \dfrac{1}{10} = \dfrac{4}{10} + \dfrac{5}{10}$
$\dfrac{9}{10} = \dfrac{9}{10}$
The solution set is $\{2\}$.

9.

$$\frac{2x}{3} = 6 - \frac{x}{4}$$

$$4(2x) = 12(6) - 3x$$

$$8x = 72 - 3x$$

$$11x = 72$$

$$x = \frac{72}{11}$$

$$\frac{2\left(\frac{72}{11}\right)}{3} = 6 - \frac{\frac{72}{11}}{4}$$

$$\frac{\frac{144}{11}}{3} = 6 - \frac{72}{11} \cdot \frac{1}{4}$$

$$\frac{144}{11} \cdot \frac{1}{3} = 6 - \frac{18}{11}$$

$$\frac{48}{11} = \frac{66}{11} - \frac{18}{11}$$

$$\frac{48}{11} = \frac{48}{11}$$

The solution set is $\left\{\dfrac{72}{11}\right\}$.

10.

$$\frac{x}{4} = 2 + \frac{x-3}{3}$$

$$3x = 12(2) + 4(x - 3)$$

$$3x = 24 + 4x - 12$$

$$-x = 12$$

$$x = -12$$

$$\frac{-12}{4} = 2 + \frac{-12 - 3}{3}$$

$$-3 = 2 + \frac{-15}{3}$$

$$-3 = 2 - 5$$

The solution set is $\{-12\}$.

11.

$$\frac{3x+1}{3} - \frac{13}{2} = \frac{1-x}{4}$$

$$4(3x+1) - 6(13) = 3(1 - x)$$

$$12x + 4 - 78 = 3 - 3x$$

$$12x - 74 = 3 - 3x$$

$$15x = 77$$

$$x = \frac{77}{15}$$

$$\frac{3\left(\frac{77}{15}\right) + 1}{3} - \frac{13}{2} = \frac{1 - \frac{77}{15}}{4}$$

$$\frac{\frac{77}{5} + 1}{3} - \frac{13}{2} = \frac{\frac{-62}{15}}{4}$$

$$\frac{82}{5} \cdot \frac{1}{3} - \frac{13}{2} = \frac{-62}{15} \cdot \frac{1}{4}$$

$$\frac{82}{15} - \frac{13}{2} = \frac{-31}{30}$$

$$\frac{164}{30} - \frac{195}{30} = \frac{-31}{30}$$

The solution set is $\left\{\dfrac{77}{15}\right\}$.

12. a. $x \neq 0$

    b.

$$\frac{9}{4} - \frac{1}{2x} = \frac{4}{x}$$

$$9x - 2 = 16$$

$$9x = 18$$

$$x = 2$$

The solution set is $\{2\}$.

13. a. $x \neq 5$

    b.

$$\frac{7}{x-5} + 2 = \frac{x+2}{x-5}$$

$$7 + 2(x - 5) = x + 2$$

$$7 + 2x - 10 = x + 2$$

$$2x - 3 = x + 2$$

$$x = 5$$

The solution set is the empty set, $\varnothing$.

14. **a.** $x \neq 1, x \neq -1$

    b.

    $$\frac{1}{x-1} - \frac{1}{x+1} = \frac{2}{x^2 - 1}$$

    $$\frac{1}{x-1} - \frac{1}{x+1} = \frac{2}{(x+1)(x-1)}$$

    $$x + 1 - (x - 1) = 2$$

    $$x + 1 - x + 1 = 2$$

    $$2 = 2$$

    The solution set is all real numbers except 1 and −1.

15. **a.** $x \neq -2, x \neq 4$

    b.

    $$\frac{4}{x+2} + \frac{2}{x-4} = \frac{30}{(x+2)(x-4)}$$

    $$4(x-4) + 2(x+2) = 30$$

    $$4x - 16 + 2x + 4 = 30$$

    $$6x - 12 = 30$$

    $$6x = 42$$

    $$x = 7$$

    The solution set is $\{7\}$.

16. $\dfrac{1}{x+5} = 0$

    $$1 = 0$$

    The given equation is an inconsistent equation.

17. $7x + 13 = 4x - 10 + 3x + 23$

    $$7x + 13 = 7x + 13$$

    $$13 = 13$$

    The given equation is an identity.

18. $7x + 13 = 3x - 10 + 2x + 23$

    $$7x + 13 = 5x + 13$$

    $$2x = 0$$

    $$x = 0$$

    The given equation is a conditional equation.

19. $4080 = 420x + 720$

    $$3360 = 420x$$

    $$x = 8$$

    $$1989 + 8 = 1997$$

    Losses amounted to \$4080 million in 1997.

20. $47,587 = 1321.7(x - 1980) + 21,153$

    $$26,434 = 1321.7(x - 1980)$$

    $$20 = x - 1980$$

    $$x = 2000$$

    The median income was \$47,587 in 2000.

21.   Let x = number of times bus is used
    $1.50x$ = fare without coupon book
    $25 + .0.25x$ = fare with coupon book
    $$1.50x = 25 + 0.25x$$
    $$1.25x = 25$$
    $$x = 20$$
    The bus must be used 20 times.

22.   Let x = number of unhealthy days per year in New York
    $5x + 29$ = number of unhealthy days per year in Los Angeles.
    $$x + 5x + 29 = 185$$
    $$6x + 29 = 185$$
    $$6x = 156$$
    $$x = 26$$
    $$5x = 29 = 159$$
    There are 26 unhealthy days per year in New York and 159 in Los Angeles.

23.   Let x = amount at 8%
    $10,000 - x$ = amount at 12%
    $$0.08x + 0.12(10,000 - x) = 950$$
    $$0.08x + 1200 - 0.12x = 950$$
    $$-0.04x = -250$$
    $$x = \$6250$$
    Invest \$6250 at 8%, \$3750 at 12%.

24.   Let x = width of field
    $2x + 14$ = length of field
    $$2x + 2(2x + 14) = 346$$
    $$2x + 4x + 28 = 346$$
    $$6x = 318$$
    $$x = 53$$
    $$2(53) + 14 = 120$$
    The width is 53 meters, the length is 120 meters.

25.   Let x = amount sold
    $$300 + 0.05x = 800$$
    $$0.05x = 500$$
    $$x = 10,000$$
    \$10,000 in sales must be sold.

26. Let x = price before reduction
$$x - 0.45x = 247.50$$
$$0.55x = 247.50$$
$$x = 450$$
The price before reduction was \$450.

27. Let x = number of concerts over 50
$$2627 = 2987 - 8x$$
$$8x = 360$$
$$x = 45$$
$$50 + 45 = 95$$
95 concerts should be given.

28. $V = \dfrac{1}{3} Bh$
$$3V = Bh$$
$$h = \dfrac{3V}{B}$$

29. $F = f(1 - M)$
$$F = f - fM$$
$$F - f = -fM$$
$$M = \dfrac{F - f}{-f}$$
$$M = \dfrac{f - F}{f}$$

30. $2x^2 + 15x = 8$
$$2x^2 + 15x - 8 = 0$$
$$(2x - 1)(x + 8) = 0$$
$$2x - 1 = 0 \quad x + 8 = 0$$
$$x = \dfrac{1}{2} \text{ or } x = -8$$

The solution set is $\left\{ \dfrac{1}{2}, -8 \right\}$.

31. $5x^2 + 20x = 0$
$$5x(x + 4) = 0$$
$$5x = 0 \quad x + 4 = 0$$
$$x = 0 \text{ or } x = -4$$
The solution set is $\{0, -4\}$.

32. $2x^2 - 3 = 125$
$$2x^2 = 128$$
$$x^2 = 64$$
$$x = \pm 8$$
The solution set is $\{8, -8\}$.

33. $(3x - 4)^2 = 18$
$$3x - 4 = \pm\sqrt{18}$$
$$3x = 4 \pm 3\sqrt{2}$$
$$x = \dfrac{4 \pm 3\sqrt{2}}{3}$$

The solution set is $\left\{ \dfrac{4 + 3\sqrt{2}}{3}, \dfrac{4 - 3\sqrt{2}}{3} \right\}$.

34. $x^2 + 20x$
$$\left(\dfrac{20}{2} \right)^2 = 10^2 = 100$$
$$x^2 + 20x + 100 = (x + 10)^2$$

35. $x^2 - 3x$
$$\left(\dfrac{3}{2} \right)^2 = \dfrac{9}{4}$$
$$x^2 - 3x + \dfrac{9}{4} = \left(x - \dfrac{3}{2} \right)^2$$

36. $x^2 - 12x = -27$
$$x^2 - 12x + 36 = -27 + 36$$
$$(x - 6)^2 = 9$$
$$x - 6 = \pm 3$$
$$x = 6 \pm 3$$
$$x = 9, \ 3$$
The solution set is $\{9, 3\}$.

37. $3x^2 - 12x + 11 = 0$

$$x^2 - 4x = -\frac{11}{3}$$

$$x^2 - 4x + 4 = -\frac{11}{3} + 4$$

$$(x-2)^2 = \frac{1}{3}$$

$$x - 2 = \pm\sqrt{\frac{1}{3}}$$

$$x = 2 \pm \frac{\sqrt{3}}{3}$$

The solution set is $\left\{2 + \dfrac{\sqrt{3}}{3}, 2 - \dfrac{\sqrt{3}}{3}\right\}$.

38. $\qquad x^2 = 2x + 4$

$$x^2 - 2x - 4 = 0$$

$$x = \frac{2 \pm \sqrt{(-2)^2 - 4(1)(-4)}}{2(1)}$$

$$x = \frac{2 \pm \sqrt{4 + 16}}{2}$$

$$x = \frac{2 \pm \sqrt{20}}{2}$$

$$x = \frac{2 \pm 2\sqrt{5}}{2}$$

$$x = 1 \pm \sqrt{5}$$

The solution set is $\left\{1 + \sqrt{5}, 1 - \sqrt{5}\right\}$.

39. $x^2 - 2x + 19 = 0$

$$x = \frac{2 \pm \sqrt{(-2)^2 - 4(1)(19)}}{2(1)}$$

$$x = \frac{2 \pm \sqrt{4 - 76}}{2}$$

$$x = \frac{2 \pm \sqrt{-72}}{2}$$

$$x = \frac{2 \pm 6i\sqrt{2}}{2}$$

$$x = 1 \pm 3i\sqrt{2}$$

The solution set is $\left\{1 + 3i\sqrt{2}, 1 - 3i\sqrt{2}\right\}$.

40. $\qquad 2x^2 = 3 - 4x$

$$2x^2 + 4x - 3 = 0$$

$$x = \frac{-4 \pm \sqrt{4^2 - 4(2)(-3)}}{2(2)}$$

$$x = \frac{-4 \pm \sqrt{16 + 24}}{4}$$

$$x = \frac{-4 \pm \sqrt{40}}{4}$$

$$x = \frac{-4 \pm 2\sqrt{10}}{4}$$

$$x = \frac{-2 \pm \sqrt{10}}{2}$$

The solution set is $\left\{\dfrac{-2 + \sqrt{10}}{2}, \dfrac{-2 - \sqrt{10}}{2}\right\}$.

41. $x^2 - 4x + 13 = 0$

$$(-4)^2 - 4(1)(13)$$
$$= 16 - 52$$
$$= -36;\ 2 \text{ complex imaginary solutions}$$

42. $9x^2 = 2 - 3x$

$$9x^2 + 3x - 2 = 0$$

$$3^2 - 4(9)(-2)$$
$$= 9 + 72$$
$$= 81;\ 2 \text{ unequal real solutions}$$

43. $2x^2 - 11x + 5 = 0$

$$(2x - 1)(x - 5) = 0$$
$$2x - 1 = 0 \quad x - 5 = 0$$
$$x = \frac{1}{2} \text{ or } x = 5$$

The solution set is $\left\{5, \dfrac{1}{2}\right\}$.

44.
$$(3x+5)(x-3)=5$$
$$3x^2+5x-9x-15=5$$
$$3x^2-4x-20=0$$
$$x=\frac{4\pm\sqrt{(-4)^2-4(3)(-20)}}{2(3)}$$
$$x=\frac{4\pm\sqrt{16+240}}{6}$$
$$x=\frac{4\pm\sqrt{256}}{6}$$
$$x=\frac{4\pm16}{6}$$
$$x=\frac{20}{6},\frac{-12}{6}$$
$$x=\frac{10}{3},-2$$

The solution set is $\left\{-2,\dfrac{10}{3}\right\}$.

45. $3x^2-7x+1=0$
$$x=\frac{7\pm\sqrt{(-7)^2-4(3)(1)}}{2(3)}$$
$$x=\frac{7\pm\sqrt{49-12}}{6}$$
$$x=\frac{7\pm\sqrt{37}}{6}$$

The solution set is $\left\{\dfrac{7+\sqrt{37}}{6},\dfrac{7-\sqrt{37}}{6}\right\}$.

46. $x^2-9=0$
$$x^2=9$$
$$x=\pm3$$
The solution set is $\{-3,3\}$.

47. $(x-3)^2-25=0$
$$(x-3)^2=25$$
$$x-3=\pm5$$
$$x=3\pm5$$
$$x=8,-2$$
The solution set is $\{8,-2\}$.

48. $3x^2-x+2=0$
$$x=\frac{1\pm\sqrt{(-1)^2-4(3)(2)}}{2(3)}$$
$$x=\frac{1\pm\sqrt{1-24}}{6}$$
$$x=\frac{1\pm\sqrt{-23}}{6}$$
$$x=\frac{1\pm i\sqrt{23}}{6}$$

The solution set is $\left\{\dfrac{1+i\sqrt{23}}{6},\dfrac{1-i\sqrt{23}}{6}\right\}$.

49.
$$W=3t^2$$
$$1200=3t^2$$
$$400=t^2$$
$$t=\pm20$$
Discard negative time; it will weigh 1200 grams in 20 weeks.

50. $N=0.337x^2-2.265x+3.962$
$$10.9=0.337x^2-2.265x+3.962$$
$$0=0.337x^2-2.265x-6.938$$
$$x=\frac{2.265\pm\sqrt{(-2.265)^2-4(0.337)(-6.938)}}{2(0.337)}$$
$$x=\frac{2.265\pm\sqrt{5.130225+9.352424}}{0.674}$$
$$x=\frac{2.265\pm\sqrt{14.482649}}{0.674}$$
$$x\approx\frac{2.265\pm3.8056}{0.674}$$
$$\approx\frac{6.0706}{0.674},\frac{-1.5406}{0.674}$$
Discard negative value;
$$x\approx9$$
10.9 million Amercians owned mountain bikes in 1989.

51. Let x = height
$$x(15 + x) = 324$$
$$15x + x^2 = 324$$
$$x^2 + 15x - 324 = 0$$
$$(x + 27)(x - 12) = 0$$
$$x = -27 \text{ or } x = 12$$
$$12 + 15 = 27$$
Disregard a negative length. The dimensions are 12 ft by 27 ft.

52. Let x = height of building
$2x$ = shadow height
$$x^2 + (2x)^2 = 300^2$$
$$x^2 + 4x^2 = 90,000$$
$$5x^2 = 90,000$$
$$x^2 = 18,000$$
$$x \approx \pm 134.164$$
Discard negative height.
The building is approximately 134.16 meters high.

53. $2x^4 = 50x^2$
$$2x^4 - 50x^2 = 0$$
$$2x^2\left(x^2 - 25\right) = 0$$
$$x = 0$$
$$x = \pm 5$$
The solution set is $\{-5, 0, 5\}$.

54. $2x^3 - x^2 - 18x + 9 = 0$
$$x^2(2x - 1) - 9(2x - 1) = 0$$
$$\left(x^2 - 9\right)(2x - 1) = 0$$
$$x = \pm 3, \ x = \frac{1}{2}$$
The solution set is $\left\{-3, \frac{1}{2}, 3\right\}$.

55. $\sqrt{2x - 3} + x = 3$
$$\sqrt{2x - 3} = 3 - x$$
$$2x - 3 = 9 - 6x + x^2$$
$$x^2 - 8x + 12 = 0$$
$$x^2 - 8x = -12$$
$$x^2 - 8x + 16 = -12 + 16$$
$$(x - 4)^2 = 4$$
$$x - 4 = \pm 2$$
$$x = 4 + 2$$
$$x = 6, 2$$
The solution set is $\{2\}$.

56. $\sqrt{x - 4} + \sqrt{x + 1} = 5$
$$\sqrt{x - 4} = 5 - \sqrt{x + 1}$$
$$x - 4 = 25 - 10\sqrt{x + 1} + (x + 1)$$
$$x - 4 = 26 + x - 10\sqrt{x + 1}$$
$$-30 = -10\sqrt{x + 1}$$
$$3 = \sqrt{x + 1}$$
$$9 = x + 1$$
$$x = 8$$
The solution set is $\{8\}$.

57. $3x^{3/4} - 24 = 0$
$$3x^{3/4} = 24$$
$$x^{3/4} = 8$$
$$x = 8^{4/3}$$
$$x = 16$$
The solution set is $\{16\}$.

58. $(x - 7)^{3/2} = 125$
$$x - 7 = 125^{2/3}$$
$$x - 7 = \sqrt[3]{125}^{\,2}$$
$$x - 7 = 5^2$$
$$x - 7 = 25$$
$$x = 32$$
The solution set is $\{32\}$.

59. $x^4 - 5x^2 + 4 = 0$

Let $t = x^2$

$t^2 - 5t + 4 = 0$

$(t - 4)(t - 1) = 0$

$t = 4 \quad$ or $\quad t = 1$

$x^2 = 4 \qquad x^2 = 1$

$x = \pm 2 \qquad x = \pm 1$

The solution set is $\{-2, -1, 1, 2\}$.

60. $x^{1/2} + 3x^{1/4} - 10 = 0$

Let $t = x^{1/4}$

$t^2 + 3t - 10 = 0$

$(t + 5)(t - 2) = 0$

$t = -5$ or $t = 2$

$x^{1/4} = -5 \quad$ or $\quad x^{1/4} = 2$

$x = 625 \qquad x = 16$

The solution set is $\{16\}$.

61. $|2x + 1| = 7$

$2x + 1 = 7$ or $2x + 1 = -7$

$2x = 6 \qquad\qquad 2x = -8$

$x = 3 \quad$ or $\quad x = -4$

The solution set is $\{-4, 3\}$.

62. $2|x - 3| - 7 = 10$

$2|x - 3| = 17$

$|x - 3| = \dfrac{17}{2}$

$x - 3 = \dfrac{17}{2}$ or $x - 3 = -\dfrac{17}{2}$

$x = \dfrac{23}{2} \quad$ or $x = -\dfrac{11}{2}$

The solution set is $\left\{-\dfrac{11}{2}, \dfrac{23}{2}\right\}$.

63. $3x^{4/3} - 5x^{2/3} + 2 = 0$

Let $t = x^{2/3}$

$3t^2 - 5t + 2 = 0$

$(3t - 2)(t - 1) = 0$

$t = \dfrac{2}{3} \qquad$ or $\quad t = 1$

$x^{2/3} = \dfrac{2}{3} \qquad\qquad x^{2/3} = 1$

$x = \pm\left(\dfrac{2}{3}\right)^{3/2} \qquad x = \pm 1^{3/2}$

$x = \pm\dfrac{2\sqrt{6}}{9} \qquad\qquad x = \pm 1$

The solution set is $\left\{-1, \ -\dfrac{2\sqrt{6}}{9}, \ \dfrac{2\sqrt{6}}{9}, \ 1\right\}$.

64. $2\sqrt{x-1} = x$

$4(x - 1) = x^2$

$4x - 4 = x^2$

$x^2 - 4x + 4 = 0$

$(x - 2)^2 = 0$

$x = 2$

The solution set is $\{2\}$.

65. $|2x - 5| - 3 = 0$

$|2x - 5| = 3$

$2x - 5 = 3$ or $2x - 5 = -3$

$2x = 8 \qquad\qquad 2x = 2$

$x = 4 \qquad\qquad x = 1$

The solution set is $\{4, 1\}$.

66. $x^3 + 2x^2 - 9x - 18 = 0$

$x^2(x + 2) - 9(x + 2) = 0$

$(x^2 - 9)(x + 2) = 0$

$x + 2 = 0 \quad$ or $\quad x^2 - 9 = 0$

$x = -2 \qquad\qquad x = -3, 3$

The solution set is $\{-3, -2, 3\}$.

67.
$$D = \sqrt{2H}$$
$$50 = \sqrt{2H}$$
$$2500 = 2H$$
$$H = 1250$$
The mountain is 1250 feet high.

68.
5

69.

1

70.

−3   0

71. $-2 < x \le 3$

−2   3

72. $-1.5 \le x \le 2$

−1.5   2

73. $x > -1$

−1

74. $-6x + 3 \le 15$
$$-6x \le 12$$
$$x \ge 2$$

2

The solution set is $[-2, \infty)$.

75. $6x - 9 \ge -4x - 3$
$$10x \ge 6$$
$$x \ge \frac{3}{5}$$

$\frac{3}{5}$

The solution set is $\left[\frac{3}{5}, \infty\right)$.

76. $\frac{x}{3} - \frac{3}{4} - 1 > \frac{x}{2}$
$$12\left(\frac{x}{3} - \frac{3}{4} - 1\right) > 12\left(\frac{x}{2}\right)$$
$$4x - 9 - 12 > 6x$$
$$-21 > 2x$$
$$-\frac{21}{2} > x$$

$-\frac{21}{2}$

The solution set is $\left(-\infty, -\frac{21}{2}\right)$.

77. $6x + 5 > -2(x - 3) - 25$
$$6x + 5 > -2x + 6 - 25$$
$$8x + 5 > -19$$
$$8x > -24$$
$$x > -3$$

−3

The solution set is $(-3, \infty)$.

78. $3(2x - 1) - 2(x - 4) \ge 7 + 2(3 + 4x)$
$$6x - 3 - 2x + 8 \ge 7 + 6 + 8x$$
$$4x + 5 \ge 8x + 13$$
$$-4x \ge 8$$
$$x \le -2$$

−2

The solution set is $[-\infty, -2)$.

79. $7 < 2x + 3 \le 9$
$$4 < 2x \le 6$$
$$2 < x \le 3$$
$$(2, 3]$$

2   5

The solution set is $[2, 3)$.

80. $|2x + 3| \le 15$
$$-15 \le 2x + 3 \le 15$$
$$-18 \le 2x \le 12$$
$$-9 \le x \le 6$$

−9   6

The solution set is $[-9, 6]$.

81. $\left|\dfrac{2x+6}{3}\right| > 2$

$\dfrac{2x+6}{3} > 2 \qquad \dfrac{2x+6}{3} < -2$

$2x+6 > 6 \qquad 2x+6 < -6$

$\quad 2x > 0 \qquad\qquad 2x < -12$

$\qquad x > 0 \qquad\qquad x < -6$

The solution set is $(-\infty, -6)$ or $(0, \infty)$.

82. $|2x+5| - 7 \geq -6$

$\quad |2x+5| \geq 1$

$2x+5 \geq 1$ or $2x+5 \leq -1$

$\quad 2x \geq -4 \qquad\quad 2x \leq -6$

$\quad x \geq -2 \quad$ or $\quad x \leq -3$

The solution set is $(-\infty, -3]$ or $[-2, \infty)$.

83. $437 \leq 4x - 7 \leq 1229$

$444 \leq 4x \leq 1236$

$111 \leq x \leq 309$

Canada, Former Soviet Union

84. $|x - 320| > 80$

$x - 320 > 80 \quad$ or $\quad x - 320 < -80$

$x > 400 \qquad$ or $\qquad x < 240$

Australia, Canada, United States

85. $|h - 6.5| \leq 1$

$-1 \leq h - 6.5 \leq 1$

$5.5 \leq h \leq 7.5$

Most people sleep between 5.5 and 7.5 hours.

86. $15 \leq \dfrac{5}{9}(F - 32) \leq 35$

$27 \leq F - 32 \leq 63$

$59 \leq F \leq 95$

The range is between 59° and 95°, inclusively.

87. Option 1: $11 + 0.06x$

Option 2: $4 + 0.20x$

$11 + 0.06x < 4 + 0.20x$

$\quad -0.14x < -7$

$\qquad\quad x > 50$

More than 50 checks should be written.

88. Let x = number of years since 1984.

turntables: $1,644 - 82x$

CD players: $284 + 496x$

$284 + 496x > 1644 - 82x$

$578x > 1360$

$x > 2.3529$

$1984 + 2.35 = 1986.35$

The first year was 1986.

89. $2x^2 + 7x \leq 4$

$2x^2 + 7x - 4 \leq 0$

$(2x - 1)(x + 4) \leq 0$

$x = -4 \quad$ or $\quad x = \dfrac{1}{2}$

$$2(-5)^2 + 7(-5) \leq 4$$

Test -5: $\qquad 50 - 35 \leq 4$

$\qquad\qquad\qquad 15 \leq 4 \quad$ False

Test 0: $\quad 2(0)^2 + 7(0) \leq 4$

$\qquad\qquad\qquad 0 \leq 4 \quad$ True

$\qquad\qquad 2(1)^2 + 7(1) \leq 4$

Test 1: $\qquad 2 + 7 \leq 4$

$\qquad\qquad\qquad 9 \leq 4 \quad$ False

The solution set is $\left[-4, \dfrac{1}{2}\right]$.

90. $2x^2 > 6x - 3$

$2x^2 - 6x + 3 > 0$

$x = \dfrac{6 \pm \sqrt{(-6)^2 - 4(2)(3)}}{2(2)}$

$x = \dfrac{6 \pm 2\sqrt{3}}{4}$

$x = \dfrac{3 \pm \sqrt{3}}{2}$

T	F	T
	$\frac{3-\sqrt{3}}{2}$	$\frac{3+\sqrt{3}}{2}$

Test 0: $2(0)^2 > 6(0) - 4$

$0 > -3$ True

Test 1: $2(1)^2 > 6(1) - 3$

$2 > 3$ True

Test 3: $2(3)^2 > 6(3) - 3$

$18 > 15$ True

The solution set is $\left(-\infty, \dfrac{3 - \sqrt{3}}{2}\right)$ or

$\left(\dfrac{3 + \sqrt{3}}{2}, \infty\right)$.

91. $\dfrac{x - 6}{x + 2} > 0$

$x - 6 = 0$ or $x + 2 = 0$

$x = 6$ or $x = -2$

T	F	T
	-2	6

Test -3: $\dfrac{-3 - 6}{-3 + 2} > 0$

$9 > 0$ True

Test 0: $\dfrac{0 - 6}{0 + 2} > 0$

$-3 > 0$ False

Test 7: $\dfrac{7 - 6}{7 + 2} > 0$

$\dfrac{1}{9} > 0$ True

The solution set is $(-\infty, -2)$ or $(6, \infty)$.

92. $\dfrac{x + 3}{x - 4} \le 5$

$\dfrac{x + 3 - 5(x - 4)}{x - 4} \le 0$

$\dfrac{x + 3 - 5x + 20}{x - 4} \le 0$

$\dfrac{23 - 4x}{x - 4} \le 0$

$x = 4$ or $x = \dfrac{23}{4}$

T	F	T
	4	$\frac{23}{4}$

Test 0: $\dfrac{0 + 3}{0 - 4} \le 5$

$-\dfrac{3}{4} \le 5$ True

Test 5: $\dfrac{5 + 3}{5 - 4} \le 5$

$8 \le 5$ False

Test 6: $\dfrac{6 + 3}{6 - 4} \le 5$

$\dfrac{9}{2} \le 5$ True

The solution set is $(-\infty, 4)$ or $\left[\dfrac{23}{4}, \infty\right)$.

93. $s = -16t^2 + v_0 t + s_0$

$32 < -16t^2 + 48t + 0$

$0 < -16t^2 + 48t - 32$

$0 < -16(t^2 - 3t + 2)$

$0 < -16(t-2)(t-1)$

	F		T		F
		1		2	

The projectile's height exceeds 32 feet during the time period from 1 to 2 seconds.

Chapter 1 Test

1. $7(x-2) = 4(x+1) - 21$

$7x - 14 = 4x + 4 - 21$

$7x - 14 = 4x - 17$

$3x = -3$

$x = -1$

The solution set is $\{-1\}$.

2. $\dfrac{2x-3}{4} = \dfrac{x-4}{2} - \dfrac{x+1}{4}$

$2x - 3 = 2(x-4) - (x+1)$

$2x - 3 = 2x - 8 - x - 1$

$2x - 3 = x - 9$

$x = -6$

The solution set is $\{-6\}$.

3. $\dfrac{2}{x-3} - \dfrac{4}{x+3} = \dfrac{8}{(x-3)(x+3)}$

$2(x+3) - 4(x-3) = 8$

$2x + 6 - 4x + 12 = 8$

$-2x + 18 = 8$

$-2x = -10$

$x = 5$

The solution set is $\{5\}$.

4. $2x^2 - 3x - 2 = 0$

$(2x+1)(x-2) = 0$

$2x + 1 = 0$ or $x - 2 = 0$

$x = -\dfrac{1}{2}$ or $x = 2$

The solution set is $\left\{-\dfrac{1}{2}, 2\right\}$.

5. $(3x-1)^2 = 75$

$3x - 1 = \pm\sqrt{75}$

$3x = 1 \pm 5\sqrt{3}$

$x = \dfrac{1 \pm 5\sqrt{3}}{3}$

The solution set is $\left\{\dfrac{1-5\sqrt{3}}{3}, \dfrac{1+5\sqrt{3}}{3}\right\}$.

6. $x(x-2) = 4$

$x^2 - 2x - 4 = 0$

$x = \dfrac{2 \pm \sqrt{(-2)^2 - 4(1)(-4)}}{2}$

$x = \dfrac{2 \pm 2\sqrt{5}}{2}$

$x = 1 \pm \sqrt{5}$

The solution set is $\left\{1-\sqrt{5}, 1+\sqrt{5}\right\}$.

7. $4x^2 = 8x - 5$

$4x^2 - 8x + 5 = 0$

$x = \dfrac{8 \pm \sqrt{(-8)^2 - 4(4)(5)}}{2(4)}$

$x = \dfrac{8 \pm \sqrt{-16}}{8}$

$x = \dfrac{8 \pm 4i}{8}$

$x = \dfrac{2 \pm i}{2}$

The solution set is $\left\{\dfrac{2-i}{2}, \dfrac{2+i}{2}\right\}$.

8. $x^3 - 4x^2 - x + 4 = 0$

$x^2(x-4) - 1(x-4) = 0$

$(x^2 - 1)(x-4) = 0$

$(x-1)(x+1)(x-4) = 0$

$x = 1$ or $x = -1$ or $x = 4$

The solution set is $\{-1, 1, 4\}$.

9. $\sqrt{x-3}+5=x$

$\sqrt{x-3}=x-5$

$x-3=x^2-10x+25$

$x^2-11x+28=0$

$x=\dfrac{11\pm\sqrt{11^2-4(1)(28)}}{2(1)}$

$x=\dfrac{11\pm\sqrt{121-112}}{2}$

$x=\dfrac{11\pm\sqrt{9}}{2}$

$x=\dfrac{11\pm3}{2}$

$x=7$ or $x=4$

The solution set is $\{7\}$.

10. $\sqrt{x+4}+\sqrt{x-1}=5$

$\sqrt{x+4}=5-\sqrt{x-1}$

$x+4=25-10\sqrt{x-1}+(x-1)$

$x+4=25-10\sqrt{x-1}+x-1$

$-20=-10\sqrt{x-1}$

$2=\sqrt{x-1}$

$4=x-1$

$x=5$

The solution set is $\{5\}$.

11. $5x^{3/2}-10=0$

$5x^{3/2}=10$

$x^{3/2}=2$

$x=2^{2/3}$

$x=\sqrt[3]{4}$

The solution set is $\left\{\sqrt[3]{4}\right\}$.

12. $x^{2/3}-9x^{1/3}+8=0$ let $t=x^{1/3}$

$t^2-9t+8=0$

$(t-1)(t-8)=0$

$t=1\qquad t=8$

$x^{1/3}=1\quad x^{1/3}=8$

$x=1\qquad x=512$

The solution set is $\{1,512\}$.

13. $\left|\dfrac{2}{3}x-6\right|=2$

$\dfrac{2}{3}x-6=2\qquad \dfrac{2}{3}x-6=-2$

$\dfrac{2}{3}x=8\qquad\quad \dfrac{2}{3}x=4$

$x=12\qquad\qquad x=6$

The solution set is $\{6,12\}$.

14. $3(x+4)\geq 5x-12$

$3x+12\geq 5x-12$

$-2x\geq -24$

$x\leq 12$

The solution set is $(-\infty,\ 12]$.

15. $\dfrac{x}{6}+\dfrac{1}{8}\leq\dfrac{x}{2}-\dfrac{3}{4}$

$4x+3\leq 12x-18$

$-8x\leq -21$

$x\geq\dfrac{21}{8}$

The solution set is $\left[\dfrac{21}{8},\infty\right)$.

16. $-3\leq\dfrac{2x+5}{3}<6$

$-9\leq 2x+5<18$

$-14\leq 2x<13$

$-7\leq x<\dfrac{13}{2}$

The solution set is $\left[-7,\dfrac{13}{2}\right)$.

17. $|3x + 2| \geq 3$

$3x + 2 \geq 3$ or $3x + 2 \leq -3$

$3x \geq 1$ $3x \leq -5$

$x \geq \dfrac{1}{3}$ $x \leq -\dfrac{5}{3}$

The solution set is $\left(-\infty, -\dfrac{5}{3}\right]$ or $\left[\dfrac{1}{3}, \infty\right)$.

$-\dfrac{5}{3}$ $\dfrac{1}{3}$

18. $x^2 < x + 12$

$x^2 - x - 12 < 0$

$(x - 4)(x + 3) < 0$

$x = 4$ or $x = -3$

F		T		F
	-3		4	

Test -4: $(-4)^2 < -4 + 12$

           $16 < 8$ False

Test 0: $0^2 < 0 + 12$

        $0 < 12$ True

Test 5: $5^2 < 5 + 12$

        $25 < 17$ False

The solution set is $(-3, 4)$.

-3 4

19. $\dfrac{2x + 1}{x - 3} > 3$

$\dfrac{2x + 1 - 3(x - 3)}{x - 3} > 0$

$\dfrac{2x + 1 - 3x + 9}{x - 3} > 0$

$\dfrac{10 - x}{x - 3} > 0$

$x = 3$ or $x = 10$

F		T		F
	3		10	

Test 0: $\dfrac{2(0) + 1}{0 - 3} > 3$

        $-\dfrac{1}{3} > 3$ False

Test 4: $\dfrac{2(4) + 1}{4 - 3} > 3$

          $9 > 3$ True

Test 11: $\dfrac{2(11) + 1}{11 - 3} \geq 3$

        $\dfrac{23}{8} > 3$ False

The solution set is $[3, 10)$.

3 10

20. a. $B = \dfrac{2}{5}w + \dfrac{1}{125}n$

      $125B = 125\left(\dfrac{2}{5}w + \dfrac{1}{125}n\right)$

      $125B = 50w + n$

      $125B - 50w = n$

      $n = 125B - 50w$

b. $n - 125(512) - 50(800)$

    $n = 24{,}000$

    An employee must work 24,000 years!

21. let x = years after 1980

$2795 + 89x$ = Arizona population

$3071 + 43x$ = South Carolina population

$2795 + 89x = 3071 + 43x$

       $46x = 276$

         $x = 6$

$1980 + 6 = 1986$

The populations were the same in 1986.

22. $4080 = 420x + 720$

$3360 = 420x$

   $x = 8$

$1989 + 8 = 1997$

Losses amounted to $4080 million in 1997.

23. Let x = original salary

$1.09x = 45{,}780$

$x = 42{,}000$

The therapist's salary was $42,000.

24. let x = amount at 9%
$6000 - x$ = amount at 6%
$$0.09(x) + 0.06(6000 - x) = 480$$
$$0.09x + 360 - 0.06x = 480$$
$$0.03x = 120$$
$$x = 4000$$
$4000 was invested at 9%; $2000 at 6%.

25. $24^2 + x^2 = 26^2$
$$576 + x^2 = 676$$
$$x^2 = 100$$
$$x = \pm 10$$
The wire should be attached 10 feet up the pole.

26. $\dfrac{76 + 80 + 72 + x}{4} \geq 80$
$$76 + 80 + 72 + x \geq 320$$
$$228 + x \geq 320$$
$$x \geq 92$$
The student must earn at least a 92.

27. Option 1: $20
Option 2: $5 + 0.15x$
$$5 + 0.15x < 20$$
$$0.15x < 15$$
$$x < 100$$
Less than 100 hours make the second option a better deal.

Chapter 2

Section 2.1

Check Point Exercises

1. a. $m = \dfrac{-2-4}{-4-(-3)} = \dfrac{-6}{-1} = 6$

b. $m = \dfrac{5-(-2)}{-1-4} = \dfrac{7}{-5} = -\dfrac{7}{5}$

2.
$$y - y_1 = m(x - x_1)$$
$$y - (-5) = 6(x - 2)$$
$$y + 5 = 6x - 12$$
$$y = 6x - 17$$

3. $m = \dfrac{-6-(-1)}{-1-(-2)} = \dfrac{-5}{1} = -5$,

so the slope is –5. Using the point (–2, –1), we get the point slope equation:
$$y - y_1 = m(x - x_1)$$
$$y - (-1) = -5[x - (-2)]$$
$$y + 1 = 5(x + 2). \text{ Solve the equation for } y:$$
$$y + 1 = -5x - 10$$
$$y = -5x - 11.$$

4. The slope m is $\frac{3}{5}$ and the y-intercept is 1, so one point on the line is (1, 0). We can find a second point on the line by using the slope $m = \frac{3}{5} = \frac{\text{Rise}}{\text{Run}}$: starting at the point (0, 1), move 3 units up and 5 units to the right, to obtain the point (5, 4).

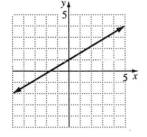

5. All points on the graph of $x = -1$ have a value of x that is always –1. For example, we could plot the points (–1, –2) and (–1, 3) and connect them.

6.
$$3x + 6y - 12 = 0$$
$$6y = -3x + 12$$
$$y = \dfrac{-3}{6}x + \dfrac{12}{6}$$
$$y = -\dfrac{1}{2}x + 2$$

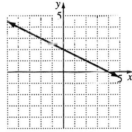

The slope is $-\dfrac{1}{2}$ and the y-intercept is 2.

7. Using the points (10, 203.3) and (20, 226.5), we obtain a slope of

$$m = \frac{\text{change in } y}{\text{change in } x}$$

$$= \frac{226.5 - 203.3}{20 - 10} = \frac{23.2}{10} = 2.32.$$

Using the point (10, 203.3), the point slope equation of the line is given by:

$$y - y_1 = m(x - x_1)$$
$$y - 203.3 = 2.32(x - 10)$$
$$y - 203.3 = 2.32x - 23.2$$
$$y = 2.32x + 180.1.$$

The linear equation that models U.S. population, y, in millions, x years after 1960 is $y = 2.32x + 180.1$. To estimate the U.S. population in 2020, note that 2020 is $x = 60$ years after 1960, so substitute 60 for x and compute y. $y = 2.32(60) + 180.1 = 319.3$

Our equation predicts that the U.S. population in the year 2020 will be 319.3 million.

Exercise Set 2.1

1. $m = \dfrac{10 - 7}{8 - 4} = \dfrac{3}{4}$; rises

3. $m = \dfrac{2 - 1}{2 - (-2)} = \dfrac{1}{4}$; rises

5. $m = \dfrac{2 - (-2)}{3 - 4} = \dfrac{0}{-1} = 0$; horizontal

7. $m = \dfrac{-1 - 4}{-1 - (-2)} = \dfrac{-5}{1} = -5$; falls

9. $m = \dfrac{-2 - 3}{5 - 5} = \dfrac{-5}{0}$ undefined; vertical

11. $m = 2$, $x_1 = 3$, $y_1 = 5$;
    point-slope form: $y - 5 = 2(x - 3)$;
    slope-intercept form: $y - 5 = 2x - 6$
    $$y = 2x - 1$$

13. $m = 6$, $x_1 = -2$, $y_1 = 5$;
    point-slope form: $y - 5 = 6(x + 2)$;
    slope-intercept form: $y - 5 = 6x + 12$
    $$y = 6x + 17$$

15. $m = -3$, $x_1 = -2$, $y_1 = -3$;
    point-slope form: $y + 3 = -3(x + 2)$;
    slope-intercept form: $y + 3 = -3x - 6$
    $$y = -3x - 9$$

17. $m = -4$, $x_1 = -4$, $y_1 = 0$;
    point-slope form: $y - 0 = -4(x + 4)$;
    slope-intercept form: $y = -4(x + 4)$
    $$y = -4x - 16$$

19. $m = -1$, $x_1 = \dfrac{-1}{2}$, $y_1 = -2$;

    point-slope form: $y + 2 = -1\left(x + \dfrac{1}{2}\right)$;

    slope-intercept form: $y + 2 = -x - \dfrac{1}{2}$

    $$y = -x - \dfrac{5}{2}$$

21. $m = \dfrac{1}{2}$, $x_1 = 0$, $y_1 = 0$;

    point-slope form: $y - 0 = \dfrac{1}{2}(x - 0)$;

    slope-intercept form: $y = \dfrac{1}{2}x$

23. $m = -\dfrac{2}{3}$, $x_1 = 6$, $y_1 = -2$;

    point-slope form: $y + 2 = -\dfrac{2}{3}(x - 6)$;

    slope-intercept form: $y + 2 = -\dfrac{2}{3}x + 4$

    $$y = -\dfrac{2}{3}x + 2$$

25. $m = \dfrac{10 - 2}{5 - 1} = \dfrac{8}{4} = 2$;
    point-slope form: $y - 2 = 2(x - 1)$ using $(x_1, y_1) = (1, 2)$, or $y - 10 = 2(x - 5)$ using $(x_1, y_1) = (5, 10)$; slope-intercept form:
    $y - 2 = 2x - 2$ or
    $y - 10 = 2x - 10$,
    $$y = 2x$$

27. $m = \dfrac{3-0}{0-(-3)} = \dfrac{3}{3} = 1$;

point-slope form: $y - 0 = 1(x + 3)$ using
$(x_1, y_1) = (-3, 0)$, or $y - 3 = 1(x - 0)$ using
$(x_1, y_1) = (0, 3)$; slope-intercept form:
$y = x + 3$

29. $m = \dfrac{4-(-1)}{2-(-3)} = \dfrac{5}{5} = 1$;

point-slope form: $y + 1 = 1(x + 3)$ using
$(x_1, y_1) = (-3, -1)$, or $y - 4 = 1(x - 2)$ using
$(x_1, y_1) = (2, 4)$; slope-intercept form:
$y + 1 = x + 3$ or
$y - 4 = x - 2$
$\qquad y = x + 2$

31. $m = \dfrac{6-(-2)}{3-(-3)} = \dfrac{8}{6} = \dfrac{4}{3}$;

point-slope form: $y + 2 = \dfrac{4}{3}(x + 3)$ using

$(x_1, y_1) = (-3, -2)$, or $y - 6 = \dfrac{4}{3}(x - 3)$

using $(x_1, y_1) = (3, 6)$; slope-intercept form:

$y + 2 = \dfrac{4}{3x} + 4$ or

$y - 6 = \dfrac{4}{3}x - 4,$

$\qquad y = \dfrac{4}{3}x + 2$

33. $m = \dfrac{-1-(-1)}{4-(-3)} = \dfrac{0}{7} = 0$;

point-slope form: $y + 1 = 0(x + 3)$ using
$(x_1, y_1) = (-3, -1)$, or $y + 1 = 0(x - 4)$ using
$(x_1, y_1) = (4, -1)$; slope-intercept form:
$y + 1 = 0,$ so
$\qquad y = -1$

35. $m = \dfrac{0-4}{-2-2} = \dfrac{-4}{-4} = 1$;

point-slope form: $y - 4 = 1(x - 2)$ using
$(x_1, y_1) = (2, 4)$, or $y - 0 = 1(x + 2)$ using

$(x_1, y_1) = (-2, 0)$; slope-intercept form:
$y - 9 = x - 2,$ or
$\qquad y = x + 2$

37. $m = \dfrac{4-0}{0-\left(-\frac{1}{2}\right)} = \dfrac{4}{\frac{1}{2}} = 8$;

point-slope form: $y - 4 = 8(x - 0)$ using
$(x_1, y_1) = (0, 4)$, or $y - 0 = 8\left(x + \frac{1}{2}\right)$ using

$(x_1, y_1) = \left(-\frac{1}{2}, 0\right)$; or $y - 0 = 8\left(x + \frac{1}{2}\right)$

slope-intercept form: $y - 4 = 8x$ or
$\qquad\qquad y = 8x + 4$

39. $m = 2; b = 1$

41. $m = -2; b = 1$

43. $m = \dfrac{3}{4}; b = -2$

45. $m = -\dfrac{3}{5}; \; b = 7$

47.

49.

51.

53. **a.** $3x + y - 5 = 0$
$$y - 5 = -3x$$
$$y = -3x + 5$$

b. $m = -3; \; b = 5$

c.

55. **a.** $2x + 3y - 18 = 0$
$$2x - 18 = -3y$$
$$-3y = 2x - 18$$
$$y = \dfrac{2}{-3}x - \dfrac{18}{-3}$$
$$y = -\dfrac{2}{3}x + 6$$

b. $m = -\dfrac{2}{3}; \; b = 6$

c.

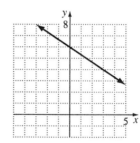

57. **a.** $8x - 4y - 12 = 0$
$$8x - 12 = 4y$$
$$4y = 8x - 12$$
$$y = \dfrac{8}{4}x - \dfrac{12}{4}$$
$$y = 2x - 3$$

b. $m = 2; \; b = -3$

c.

59. a. $3x - 9 = 0$
$$3x = 9$$
$$x = 3$$

b. m is undefined since the line is vertical; no y-intercept since all x values are 3.

c.

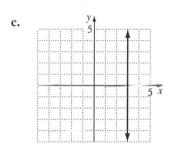

61. Answers may vary. The equation $y = 80$ is a reasonable approximation to model the data, since the data are almost constant.

63. In 2030, it will be $x = 70$ years after 1960, and $y = 2.35(70) + 179.5 = 344$ million U.S. people are predicted.
In 2040, it will be $x = 80$ years after 1960, and $y = 2.35(80) + 179.5 = 367.5$ million U.S. people are predicted.
In 2050, it will be $x = 90$ years after 1960, and $y = 2.35(90) + 179.5 = 391$ million U.S. people are predicted.
The equation models the projections well, but is slightly lower than the projections.

65. $m = \dfrac{5493.7 - 4459.2}{7 - 3} = \dfrac{1034.5}{4} = 258.625;$
point-slope form:
$y - 4459.2 = 258.625(x - 3)$ using $(x_1, y_1) = (3, 4459.2)$; slope-intercept form:
$$y - 4459.2 = 258.625x - 775.875$$
$$y = 258.625x + 3683.325;$$
2020 is 30 years after 1990, so
$y = 258.625(30) + 3683.325 = 11442.075;$
Consumers in the US are expected to spend about \$11,442.075 billion in the year 2020.

67. $m = \dfrac{55 - 19}{2000 - 20,000}$
$$= \dfrac{36}{-18,000}$$
$$= -\dfrac{1}{500}$$
$$= -0.002;$$
$y - 55 = -0.002(x - 2000)$ using $(x_1, y_1) = (2000, 55);$
slope-intercept equation:
$$y - 55 = 0.002x + 4$$
$$y = -0.002x + 59$$
When $y = 50$: $50 = -0.002x + 59$
$$-9 = -0.002x$$
$$x = 4500$$
4500 shirts can be sold for \$50 each.

69. It appears that the regression line passes through the points $(2, 9.5)$ and $(12, 3)$.
$$m = \dfrac{3 - 9.5}{12 - 2} = \dfrac{-6.5}{10} = -0.65;$$
point-slope form: $y - 3 = -0.65(x - 12)$ using $(x_1, y_1) = (12, 3);$
slope-intercept form: $y - 3 = -0.65x + 7.8$
$$y = -0.65x + 10.8$$
When $x = 7$; $y = -0.65(7) + 10.8 = 6.25;$
A person with 7 years education is predicted to have a score of about 6.25.

71.–77. Answers may vary.

79. Two points are $(0, 6)$ and $(10, -24)$.
$$m = \dfrac{-24 - 6}{10 - 0} = \dfrac{-30}{10} = -3.$$
Check: $y = mx + b$: $y = -3x + 6$.

81. Two points are $(0, -2)$ and $(10, 5.5)$.
$$m = \frac{5.5 - (-2)}{10 - 0} = \frac{7.5}{10} = 0.75 \text{ or } \frac{3}{4}.$$
Check: $y = mx + b$: $y = \dfrac{3}{4}x - 2$.

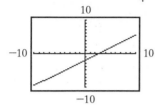

83. a. False; if $m = 0$, the graph does not rise.

b. False; the product of their slopes is -16.

c. True; the point $(6, 0)$ satisfies the equation. Write the equation in slope-intercept form,
$y = -\dfrac{5}{6} + 5$, so the slope $m = -\dfrac{5}{6}$.

d. False; the graph of $y = 7$ is a horizontal line through $(0, 7)$.

(c) is true

85. a. m_1, m_3, m_2, m_4

b. b_2, b_1, b_4, b_3

Section 2.2

Check Point Exercises

1. Since the line is to pass through the point $(2, 5)$, in the point-slope formula we have $x_1 = -2$ and $y_1 = 5$. Also since the line is to be parallel to the line $y = 3x + 1$, the two lines must have the same slope $m = 3$.
point-slope form: $y - 5 = 3(x + 2)$
slope-intercept form:
$y - 5 = 3x + 6$, $y = 3x + 11$

2. $x + 3y - 12 = 0$
$$3y = -x + 12$$
$$y = -\frac{1}{3}x + 4$$
The given line has slope $m = \frac{-1}{3}$, so any line perpendicular to it has a slope that is the negative reciprocal of $\frac{-1}{3}$, or 3.

3. $h = 0$, $k = 0$, $r = 4$;
$$(x - 0)^2 + (y - 0)^2 = 4^2$$
$$x^2 + y^2 = 16$$

4. $h = 5$, $k = -6$, $r = 10$;
$$(x - 5)^2 + [y - (-6)]^2 = 10^2$$
$$(x - 5)^2 + (y + 6)^2 = 100$$

5. $(x + 3)^2 + (y - 1)^2 = 4$
$$[x - (-3)]^2 + (y - 1)^2 = 2^2$$
So in the standard form of the circle's equation $(x - h)^2 + (y - k)^2 = r^2$, we have $h = -3$, $k = 1$, $r = 2$.
center: $(h, k) = (-3, 1)$
radius: $r = 2$

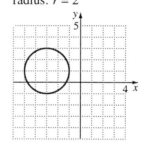

6.
$$x^2 + y^2 + 4x - 4y - 1 = 0$$
$$\left(x^2 + 4x \quad\right) + \left(y^2 - 4y \quad\right) = 0$$
$$\left(x^2 + 4x + 4\right) + \left(y^2 + 4y + 4\right) = 1 + 4 + 4$$
$$(x+2)^2 + (y-2)^2 = 9$$
$$[x - (-x)]^2 + (y-2)^2 = 3^2$$

So in the standard form of the circle's equation $(x-h)^2 + (y-k)^2 = r^2$, we have $h = -2$, $k = 2$, $r = 3$.

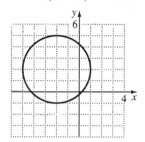

Exercise Set 2.2

1. a. 5

   b. $-\dfrac{1}{5}$

3. a. -7

   b. $\dfrac{1}{7}$

5. a. $\dfrac{1}{2}$

   b. -2

7. a. $-\dfrac{2}{5}$

   b. $\dfrac{5}{2}$

9. a. -4

   b. $\dfrac{1}{4}$

11. a. $-\dfrac{1}{2}$

   b. 2

13. a. $\dfrac{2}{3}$

   b. $-\dfrac{3}{2}$

15. a. undefined

   b. 0

17. L has slope 2 because it is parellel to $y = 2x$, and passes through (4, 2).
point-slope form: $y - 2 = 2(x - 4)$
slope-intercept form: $y - 2 = 2x - 8$
$$y = 2x - 6$$

19. L has slope $-\dfrac{1}{2}$ because it is perpendicular to $y = 2x$, and passes through (2, 4).
point-slope form: $y - 4 = -\dfrac{1}{2}(x - 2)$
slope-intercept form: $y - 4 = -\dfrac{1}{2}x + 1$
$$y = -\dfrac{1}{2}x + 5$$

21. $m = -4$ since the line is parallel to $y = -4x + 3$; $x_1 = -8$, $y_1 = -10$;
point-slope form: $\quad y + 10 = -4(x + 8)$
slope-intercept form: $y + 10 = -4x - 32$
$$y = -4x - 42$$

23. $m = -5$ since the line is perpendicular to $y = \dfrac{1}{5}x + 6$; $x_1 = 2$, $y_1 = -3$;
point-slope form: $y + 3 = -5(x - 2)$
slope-intercept form: $y + 3 = -5x + 10$
$$y = -5x + 7$$

25. $2x - 3y - 7 = 0$
$$-3y = -2x + 7$$
$$y = \frac{2}{3}x - \frac{7}{3}$$

The slope of the given line is $\frac{2}{3}$, so $m = \frac{2}{3}$
since the lines are parallel.

point-slope form: $y - 2 = \frac{2}{3}(x + 2)$

slope-intercept form: $y = \frac{2}{3}x + \frac{10}{3}$

27. $x - 2y - 3 = 0$
$$-2y = -x + 3$$
$$y = \frac{1}{2}x - \frac{3}{2}$$

The slope of the given line is $\frac{1}{2}$, so
$m = -2$ since the lines are perpendicular.
point-slope form: $y + 7 = -2(x - 4)$
slope-intercept form: $y + 7 = -2x + 8$
$$y = -2x + 1$$

29. $(x - 0)^2 + (y - 0)^2 = 7^2$
$$x^2 + y^2 = 49$$

31. $(x - 3)^2 + (y - 2)^2 = 5^2$
$$(x - 3)^2 + (y - 2)^2 = 25$$

33. $[x - (-1)]^2 + (y - 4)^2 = 2^2$
$$(x + 1)^2 + (y - 4)^2 = 4$$

35. $[x - (-3)]^2 + [y - (-1)]^2 = (\sqrt{3})^2$
$$(x + 3)^2 + (y + 1)^2 = 3$$

37. $[x - (-4)]^2 + (y - 0)^2 = 10^2$
$$(x + 4)^2 + (y - 0)^2 = 100$$

39.
$$x^2 + y^2 = 16$$
$$(x - 0)^2 + (y - 0)^2 = y^2$$
$h = 0, k = 0, r = 4;$
center $= (0, 0)$
radius $= 4$

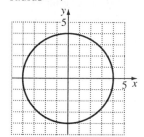

41. $(x - 3)^2 + (y - 1)^2 = 36$
$$(x - 3)^2 + (y - 1)^2 = 6^2$$
$h = 3, k = 1, r = 6;$
center $= (3, 1)$
radius $= 6$

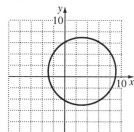

43. $(x + 3)^2 + (y - 2)^2 = 4$
$$[x - (-3)]^2 + (y - 2)^2 = 2^2$$
$h = -3, k = 2, r = 2$
center $= (-3, 2)$
radius $= 2$

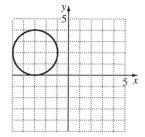

45. $\quad (x+2)^2 + (y+2)^2 = 4$

$[x-(-2)]^2 + [y-(-2)]^2 = 2^2$

$h = -2,\ k = -2,\ r = 2$

center $= (-2, -2)$

radius $= 2$

47. $\quad x^2 + y^2 + 6x + 2y + 6 = 0$

$\left(x^2 + 6x\right) + \left(y^2 + 2y\right) = -6$

$\left(x^2 + 6x + 9\right) + \left(y^2 + 2y + 1\right) = 9 + 1 - 6$

$(x+3)^2 + (y+1)^2 = 4$

$[x-(-3)]^2 + [9-(-1)]^2 = 2^2$

center $= (-3, -1)$

radius $= 2$

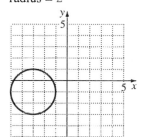

49. $\quad x^2 + y^2 - 10x - 6y - 30 = 0$

$\left(x^2 - 10x\right) + \left(y^2 - 6y\right) = 30$

$\left(x^2 - 10x + 25\right) + \left(y^2 - 6y + 9\right) = 25 + 9 + 30$

$(x-5)^2 + (y-3)^2 = 64$

$(x-5)^2 + (y-3)^2 = 8^2$

center $= (5, 3)$

radius $= 8$

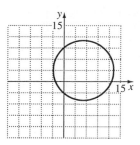

51. $\quad x^2 + y^2 + 8x - 2y - 8 = 0$

$\left(x^2 + 8x\right) + \left(y^2 - 2y\right) = 8$

$\left(x^2 + 8x + 16\right) + \left(y^2 - 2y + 1\right) = 16 + 1 + 8$

$(x+4)^2 + (y-1)^2 = 25$

$[x-(-4)]^2 + (y-1)^2 = 5^2$

center $= (-4, 1)$

radius $= 5$

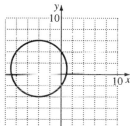

53. $\quad x^2 - 2x + y^2 - 15 = 0$

$\left(x^2 - 2x\right) + y^2 = 15$

$\left(x^2 - 2x + 1\right) + (y-0)^2 = 1 + 0 + 15$

$(x-1)^2 + (y-0)^2 = 16$

$(x-1)^2 + (y-0)^2 = 4^2$

center $= (1, 0)$

radius $= 4$

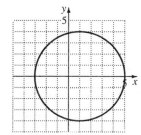

55. a. $m = \dfrac{17-14}{2010-1995} = \dfrac{3}{15} = \dfrac{1}{5}$

b. $m = \dfrac{12-10}{2010-1995} = \dfrac{2}{15}$

c. No, the lines are not parallel since
$\dfrac{1}{5} \neq \dfrac{2}{15}$. Since $\dfrac{3}{15} > \dfrac{2}{15}$, the number of
women living alone is growing at a
faster rate than the number of men
living alone, if the projections are
correct.

57. a. For the smaller circle, the equation is
$(x-0)^2 + (y-0)^2 = 38^2$, or
$x^2 + y^2 = 1444$. Thus, the left portion
of the inequality can be written as
$x^2 + y^2 \geq 1444$.

b. For the larger circle, the equation is
$(x-0)^2 + (y-0)^2 = 52^2$, or
$x^2 + y^2 = 2704$. Thus, the right portion
of the inequailty can be written as
$x^2 + y^2 \leq 2704$.

59.–67. Answers may vary.

69.

71.

73. The line passing through (0, 0) and (6, –2)
has slope $m = \dfrac{-2-0}{`6-0} = \dfrac{-2}{6} = -\dfrac{1}{3}$ and

equation $y = -\dfrac{1}{3}x$. The line perpendicular
to it has slope 3 and since it passes through
(–3, 0), its equation in point-slope form is
$y - 0 = 3(x + 3)$ and in slope-intercept form
is $y = 3x + 9$.

75. standard form: $(x-3)^2 + (y+5)^2 = r^2$.
Substitute $x = -2$ and $y = 1$:
$$(-2-3)^2 + (1+5)^2 = r^2$$
$$(-5)^2 + 6^2 = r^2$$
$$25 + 36 = r^2$$
$$61 = r^2$$
$$(x-3)^2 + (y+5)^2 = 61$$
general form:
$$\left(x^2 - 6x + 9\right) + \left(y^2 + 10y + 25\right) = 61$$
$$x^2 + y^2 - 6x + 10y + 34 = 61$$
$$x^2 + y^2 - 6x + 10y = 27$$

77. Both circles have center (2, –3). The smaller
circle has radius 5 and the larger circle has
radius 6. The smaller circle is inside of the
larger circle. The area between them is given
by
$$\pi(6)^2 - \pi(5)^2 = 36\pi - 25\pi$$
$$= 11\pi$$
$$\approx 34.56 \text{ square units.}$$

Section 2.3

Check Point Exercises

1. The domain is the set of all first
components: {20, 30, 100, 200}. The range
is the set of all second components: { 157.4,
231.8, 752.6, 1496.6}.

2. a. The relation is not a function since the
two ordered pairs (5, 6) and (5, 8) have
the same first component but different
second components.

b. The relation is a function since two
ordered pairs have the same first
component and different second
components.

3. a. $2x + y = 6$
$$y = -2x + 6$$
For each value of x, there is one and only one value for y, so the equation defines y as a function of x.

b. $x^2 + y^2 = 1$
$$y^2 = 1 - x^2$$
$$y = \pm\sqrt{1 - x^2}$$
Since there are values of x (all values between -1 and 1 exclusive) that give more than one value for y (for example, if $x = 0$, then $y = \pm\sqrt{1 - 0^2} = \pm 1$), the equation does not define y as a function of x.

4. a. $f(-5) = (-5)^2 - 2(-5) + 7$
$$= 25 - (-10) + 7$$
$$= 42$$

b. $f(x + 4) = (x + 4)^2 - 2(x + 4) + 7$
$$= x^2 + 8x + 16 - 2x - 8 + 7$$
$$= x^2 + 6x + 15$$

c. $f(-x) = (-x)^2 - 2(-x) + 7$
$$= x^2 - (-2x) + 7$$
$$= x^2 + 2x + 7$$

5. a. Since $-5 < 0$, we use the first line of the piece wise function:
$$f(-5) = (-5)^2 + 3 = 25 + 3 = 28.$$

b. Since $6 > 0$, we use the second line of the piece wise function:
$$f(6) = 5(6) + 3 = 30 + 3 = 33.$$

6. a. The function $f(x) = x^2 + 3x - 17$ contains neither division nor an even root. The domain of f is the set of all real numbers.

b. The denominator equals zero when $x = 7$ or $x = -7$, so we must exclude these values. Thus, the domain of g is $\{x \mid x \neq -7,\ x \neq 7\}$.

c. Since $h(x) = \sqrt{9x - 27}$ contains an even root, the quantity under the radical must be greater than or equal to 0.
$$9x - 27 \geq 0$$
$$9x \geq 27$$
$$x \geq 3$$
Thus, the domain of h is $\{x \mid x \geq 3\}$, or the interval $[3, \infty)$.

7. $f(x) = 0.0075x^2 - 0.2672x + 14.8$
$$f(50) = 0.0075(50)^2 - 0.2672(50) + 14.8$$
$$= 20.19$$
Since 50 represents the number of years after 1940, this means that in 1990, U.S. automobiles averaged approximately 20.19 miles per gallon of gasoline.

Exercise Set 2.3

1. The relation is a function since no two ordered pairs have the same first component and different second components. The domain is {1, 3, 5} and the range is {2, 4, 5}.

3. The relation is not a function since the two ordered pairs (3, 4) and (3, 5) have the same first component but different second components (the same could be said for the ordered pairs (4, 4) and (4, 5)). The domain is {3, 4} and the range is {4, 5}.

5. The relation is a function since there are no same first components with different second components. The domain is {$-3, -2, -1, 0$} and the range is {$-3, -2, -1, 0$}.

7. The relation is not a function since there are ordered pairs with the same first component and different second components. The domain is {1} and the range is {4, 5, 6}.

9. $x + y = 16$
$$y = 16 - x$$
Since only one value of y can be obtained for each value of x, y is a function of x.

11. $x^2 + y = 16$

$\qquad y = 16 - x^2$

Since only one value of y can be obtained for each value of x, y is a function of x.

13. $x^2 + y^2 = 16$

$\qquad y^2 = 16 - x^2$

$\qquad y = \pm\sqrt{16 - x^2}$

If $x = 0$, $y = \pm 4$.

Since two values, $y = 4$ and $y = -4$, can be obtained for one value of x, y is not a function of x.

15. $x = y^2$

$\qquad y = \pm\sqrt{x}$

If $x = 1$, $y = \pm 1$.

Since two values, $y = 1$ and $y = -1$, can be obtained for $x = 1$, y is not a function of x.

17. $y = \sqrt{x + 4}$

Since only one value of y can be obtained for each value of x, y is a function of x.

19. $x + y^3 = 8$

$\qquad y^3 = 8 - x$

$\qquad y = \sqrt[3]{8 - x}$

Since only one value of y can be obtained for each value of x, y is a function of x.

21. a. $f(6) = 4(6) + 5 = 29$

b. $f(x + 1) = 4(x + 1) + 5 = 4x + 9$

c. $f(-x) = 4(-x) + 5 = -4x + 5$

23. a. $g(-1) = (-1)^2 + 2(-1) + 3$

$\qquad\qquad = 1 - 2 + 3$

$\qquad\qquad = 2$

b. $g(x + 5) = (x + 5)^2 + 2(x + 5) + 3$

$\qquad\qquad = x^2 + 10x + 25 + 2x + 10 + 3$

$\qquad\qquad = x^2 + 12x + 38$

c. $g(-x) = (-x)^2 + 2(-x) + 3$

$\qquad\qquad = x^2 - 2x + 3$

25. a. $h(2) = 2^4 - 2^2 + 1$

$\qquad\qquad = 16 - 4 + 1$

$\qquad\qquad = 13$

b. $h(-1) = (-1)^4 - (-1)^2 + 1$

$\qquad\qquad = 1 - 1 + 1$

$\qquad\qquad = 1$

c. $h(-x) = (-x)^4 - (-x)^2 + 1 = x^4 - x^2 + 1$

d. $h(3a) = (3a)^4 - (3a)^2 + 1$

$\qquad\qquad = 81a^4 - 9a^2 + 1$

27. a. $f(-6) = \sqrt{-6 + 6} + 3 = \sqrt{0} + 3 = 3$

b. $f(10) = \sqrt{10 + 6} + 3$

$\qquad\qquad = \sqrt{16} + 3$

$\qquad\qquad = 4 + 3$

$\qquad\qquad = 7$

c. $f(x - 6) = \sqrt{x - 6 + 6} + 3 = \sqrt{x} + 3$

29. a. $f(2) = \dfrac{4(2)^2 - 1}{2^2} = \dfrac{15}{4}$

b. $f(-2) = \dfrac{4(-2)^2 - 1}{(-2)^2} = \dfrac{15}{4}$

c. $f(-x) = \dfrac{4(-x)^2 - 1}{(-x)^2} = \dfrac{4x^2 - 1}{x^2}$

31. a. $f(6) = \dfrac{6}{|6|} = 1$

b. $f(-6) = \dfrac{-6}{|-6|} = \dfrac{-6}{6} = -1$

c. $f(r^2) = \dfrac{r^2}{|r^2|} = \dfrac{r^2}{r^2} = 1$

33. a. $f(a) = 4a$

  b. $f(a + h) = 4(a + h) = 4a + 4h$

  c. $\dfrac{f(a+h)-f(a)}{h} = \dfrac{4a + 4h - 4a}{h}$
  $$= \dfrac{4h}{h}$$
  $$= 4, \ h \neq 0$$

  d. $f(a) + f(h) = 4a + 4h$

35. a. $f(a) = 3a + 7$

  b. $f(a + h) = 3(a + h) + 7 = 3a + 3h + 7$

  c. $\dfrac{f(a+h)-f(a)}{h} = \dfrac{3a + 3h + 7 - (3a + 7)}{h}$
  $$= \dfrac{3h}{h}$$
  $$= 3, \ h \neq 0$$

  d. $f(a) + f(h) = 3a + 7 + 3h + 7$
  $$= 3a + 3h + 14$$

37. a. $f(a) = -5a - 3$

  b. $f(a + h) = -5(a + h) - 3 = -5a - 5h - 3$

  c. $\dfrac{f(a+h)-f(a)}{h}$
  $$= \dfrac{-5a - 5h - 3 - (-5a - 3)}{h}$$
  $$= \dfrac{-5h}{h}$$
  $$= -5, \ h \neq 0$$

  d. $f(a) + f(h) = (-5a - 3) + (-5h - 3)$
  $$= -5a - 5h - 6$$

39. a. $f(a) = a^2$

  b. $f(a + h) = (a + h)^2 = a^2 + 2ah + h^2$

c. $\dfrac{f(a+h)-f(a)}{h} = \dfrac{a^2 + 2ah + h^2 - a^2}{h}$
  $$= \dfrac{2ah + h^2}{h}$$
  $$= 2a + h, \ h \neq 0$$

  d. $f(a) + f(h) = a^2 + h^2$

41. a. $f(a) = 6$

  b. $f(a + h) = 6$

  c. $\dfrac{f(a+h)-f(a)}{h} = \dfrac{6-6}{h} = 0, \ h \neq 0$

  d. $f(a) + f(h) = 6 + 6 = 12$

43. a. $f(a) = \dfrac{1}{a}$

  b. $f(a + h) = \dfrac{1}{a + h}$

  c. $\dfrac{f(a+h)-f(a)}{h} = \dfrac{\frac{1}{a+h} - \frac{1}{a}}{h}$
  $$= \dfrac{\frac{a-(a+h)}{a(a+h)}}{h}$$
  $$= \dfrac{-h}{a(a+h)} \cdot \dfrac{1}{h}$$
  $$= -\dfrac{1}{a(a + h)}, \ h \neq 0$$

  d. $f(a) + f(h) = \dfrac{1}{a} + \dfrac{1}{h} = \dfrac{h+a}{ah}$

45. a. $f(-2) = 3(-2) + 5 = -1$

  b. $f(0) = 4(0) + 7 = 7$

  c. $f(3) = 4(3) + 7 = 19$

47. a. $g(0) = 0 + 3 = 3$

  b. $g(-6) = -(-6 + 3) = -(-3) = 3$

  c. $g(-3) = -3 + 3 = 0$

49. a. $h(5) = \dfrac{5^2 - 9}{5 - 3} = \dfrac{25 - 9}{2} = \dfrac{16}{2} = 8$

b. $h(0) = \dfrac{0^2 - 9}{0 - 3} = \dfrac{-9}{-3} = 3$

c. $h(3) = 6$

51. Since the function is defined and equal to a real number for all real numbers, the domain is $(-\infty, \infty)$.

53. The denominator equals zero when $x = 4$. The domain is $\{x | x \neq 4\}$.

55. Factor the denominator:
$$h(x) = \dfrac{7x}{(x - 4)(x + 4)}$$
The denominator equals zero when $x = 4$ or $x = -4$. The domain is $\{x | x \neq -4 \text{ and } x \neq 4\}$.

57. The denominator is zero when $x = -3$ or $x = 7$. The domain is 3 $\{x | x \neq -3 \text{ and } x \neq 7\}$.

59. Factor the denominator.
$$H(r) = \dfrac{4}{(r + 8)(r + 3)}$$
The denominator equals zero when $r = -8$ or $r = -3$. The domain is $\{x | x \neq -8 \text{ and } x \neq -3\}$.

61. The denominator is never equal to zero. Since the function is defined and equal to a real number for all real numbers, the domain is $(-\infty, \infty)$.

63. We want $\sqrt{x - 3}$ to equal a real number.
$x - 3 \geq 0$
$x \geq 3$
The domain is $[3, \infty)$.

65. We want $\sqrt{x - 3}$ to equal a positive real number.
$x - 3 > 0$
$x > 3$
The domain is $(3, \infty)$.

67. We want $\sqrt{5x + 35}$ to equal a real number.
$5x + 35 \geq 0$
$5x \geq -35$
$x \geq -7$
The domain is $[-7, \infty)$.

69. We want $\sqrt{24 - 2x}$ to equal a real number.
$24 - 2x \geq 0$
$-2x \geq -24$
$x \leq 12$
The domain is $(-\infty, 12]$.

71. We want $\sqrt{x^2 - 5x - 14}$ to equal a real number.
$x^2 - 5x - 14 \geq 0$
Solve $x^2 - 5x - 14 = 0$
$(x + 2)(x - 7) = 0$
$x = -2$ or $x = 7$
The test intervals are $(-\infty, -2)$, $(-2, 7)$, $(7, \infty)$. Using a representative number from each test interval, the solution is $(-\infty, -2]$ or $[7, \infty)$.

73. Answers may vary.

75. $f(16) = 0.07(16) + 4.1 = 5.22$
There were 5.22 million women enrolled in U.S. colleges in the year 2000.

77. $f(20) - g(20)$
$= (0.07(20) + 4.1) - (0.01(20) + 3.9)$
$= 5.5 - 4.1$
$= 1.4$
There will be 1.4 million more women than men enrolled in U.S. colleges in the year 2004.

79. $f(0) = 6.5(0) + 200 = 200$
There were 200 thousand lawyers in the United States in 1951.

81. $f(50) = 26.2(50) - 252 = 1058$
There will be 1058 thousand or 1,058,000 lawyers in the United States in the year 2001.

83. $f(0) = 1.5(0) + 7 = 7$
$f(2) = 1.5(2) + 7 = 10$
$f(4) = 1.5(4) + 7 = 13$
$f(6) = 1.5(6) + 7 = 16$
$f(0) = 7$ represents the point $(0, 7)$ on the graph. It means that the average infant girl weighs 7 pounds at birth.
$f(2) = 10$ represents the point $(2, 10)$ on the graph. It means that an average infant girl weighs 10 pounds at age 2 months.
$f(4) = 13$ represents the point $(4, 13)$ on the graph. It means that an average infant girl weighs 13 pounds at age 4 months.
$f(6) = 16$ represents the point $(6, 16)$ on the graph. It means that an average infant girl weighs 16 pounds at age 6 months.

85. $f(10) = 0.89(10)^2 - 1.93(10) + 3306.27$
$\quad\quad = 3375.97$
In 1984, 3375.97 calories per person were consumed each day in the United States.

87. $f(15) - f(10) = 3477.57 - 3375.97 = 101.6$
Between 1984 and 1989, the number of calories per person consumed each day in the United States increased by 101.6.

89. a. $f(15) = 0.0005(15)^2 + 0.025(15) + 8.8 = 9.3$
In 1955, an average of 10.3 thousand miles were driven per car in the United States each year.

b. $f(50) = 0.0202(50)^2 - 1.58(50) + 39.2 = 10.7$
In 1990, an average of 10.7 thousand miles were driven per car in the United States each year.

91. $V(x) = 17,900 - 2100x$
$V(4) = 17,900 - 2100(4) = 9500$
The value of the car after 4 years is $9500.

93.–97. Answers may vary.

99.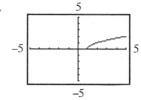

The domain is $[1, \infty)$. Algebraically, $\sqrt{x-1}$ must equal a real number.
$x - 1 \geq 0$
$\quad x \geq 1$

101.

The domain is $(-\infty, 5]$. Algebraically, $\sqrt{15-3x}$ must equal a real number.

$$15 - 3x \geq 0$$
$$-3x \geq -15$$
$$x \leq 5$$

103. Answers may vary.

105. Answers may vary.

Section 2.4

Check Point Exercises

1.

x	$f(x) = x^2 - 2$	(x, y) or $(x, f(x))$
-3	$f(-3) = (-3)^2 - 2 = 7$	$(-3, 7)$
-2	$f(-2) = (-2)^2 - 2 = 2$	$(-2, 2)$
-1	$f(-1) = (-1)^2 - 2 = -1$	$(-1, -1)$
0	$f(0) = 0^2 - 2 = -2$	$(0, -2)$
1	$f(1) = 1^2 - 2 = -1$	$(1, -1)$
2	$f(2) = 2^2 - 2 = 2$	$(2, 2)$
3	$f(3) = 3^2 - 2 = 7$	$(3, 7)$

2. $f(4) = 1$
domain: $[0, 6)$
range: $(-2, 2]$

3. y is a function of x for the graphs in (a) and (b).

126

4. The function is increasing on the interval $(-\infty, -1)$, decreasing on the interval $(-1, 1)$, and increasing on the interval $(1, \infty)$.

5. a. $f(-x) = (-x)^2 + 6 = x^2 + 6 = f(x)$
The function is even.

   b. $g(-x) = 7(-x)^3 - (-x) = -7x^3 + x = -f(x)$
The function is odd.

   c. $h(-x) = (-x)^5 + 1 = -x^5 + 1$
The function is neither even nor odd.

6. a. f is increasing on the interval $(0, 3)$. The concentration of the drug in the body increases during the first three hours after an injection.

   b. f is decreasing on the interval $(3, 13)$. The concentration of the drug in the body decreases between the third and thirteenth hours after injection.

   c. The drug's maximum concentration is 0.05 milligrams per 100 milliliters at 3 hours after the injection.

   d. By the end of the 13 hours, there is no more of the drug in the body.

Exercise Set 2.4

1. $(-3, 11), (-2, 6), (-1, 3), (0, 2), (1, 3), (2, 6), (3, 11)$

domain: $(-\infty, \infty)$
range: $[2, \infty)$

3. $(0, -1), (1, 0), (4, 1), (9, 2)$

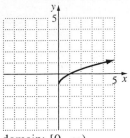

domain: $[0, \infty)$
range: $[-1, \infty)$

5. $(1, 0), (2, 1), (5, 2), (10, 3)$

domain: $[1, \infty)$
range: $[0, \infty)$

7. $(-3, 2), (-2, 1), (-1, 0), (0, -1), (1, 0), (2, 1),$ $(3, 2)$

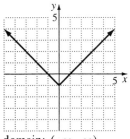

domain: $(-\infty, \infty)$
range: $[-1, \infty)$

9. $(-3, 4), (-2, 3), (-1, 2), (0, 1), (1, 0), (2, 1),$ $(3, 2)$

domain: $(-\infty, \infty)$
range: $[0, \infty)$

11. $(-3, 5), (-2, 5), (-1, 5), (0, 5), (1, 5), (2, 5),$ $(3, 5)$

domain: $(-\infty, \infty)$
range: $\{5\}$

13. $(-2, -10), (-1, -3), (0, -2), (1, -1), (2, 6)$

domain: $(-\infty, \infty)$
range: $(-\infty, \infty)$

15. a. domain: $(-\infty, \infty)$

    b. range: $[-4, \infty)$

    c. x-intercepts: -3 and 1

    d. y-intercept: -3

17. **a.** domain: $(-\infty, \infty)$

    b. range: $[1, \infty)$

    c. x-intercept: none

    d. y-intercept: 1

    e. $f(-1) = 2$ and $f(3) = 4$

19. **a.** domain: $[0, 5)$

    b. range: $[-1, 5)$

    c. x-intercept: 2

    d. y-intercept: -1

    e. $f(3) = 1$

21. **a.** domain: $[0, \infty)$

    b. range: $[1, \infty)$

    c. x-intercept: none

    d. y-intercept: 1

    e. $f(4) = 3$

23. **a.** domain: $[-2, 6]$

    b. range: $[-2, 6]$

    c. x-intercept: 4

    d. y-intercept: 4

    e. $f(-1) = 5$

25. **a.** domain: $(-\infty, \infty)$

    b. range: $(-\infty, -2]$

    c. x-intercept: none

    d. y-intercept: -2

    e. $f(-4) = -5$ and $f(4) = -2$

27. **a.** domain: $(-\infty, \infty)$

    b. range: $(0, \infty)$

    c. x-intercept: none

    d. y-intercept: 1

29. **a.** domain: $\{-5, -2, 0, 1, 3\}$

    b. range: $\{2\}$

    c. x-intercept: none

    d. y-intercept: 2

31. function

33. function

35. not a function

37. function

39. **a.** increasing: $(-1, \infty)$

    b. decreasing: $(-\infty, -1)$

    c. constant: none

41. **a.** increasing: $(0, \infty)$

    b. decreasing: none

    c. constant: none

43. **a.** increasing: none

    b. decreasing: $(-2, 6)$

    c. constant: none

45. **a.** increasing: $(-\infty, -1)$

    b. decreasing: none

    c. constant: $(-1, \infty)$

47. a. increasing: $(-\infty,\ 0)$ or $(1.5,\ 3)$

b. decreasing: $(0,\ 1.5)$ or $(3,\ \infty)$

c. constant: none

49. a. increasing: $(-2, 4)$

b. decreasing: none

c. constant: $(-\infty,\ -2)$ or $(4,\ \infty)$

51. $f(x) = x^3 + x$
$f(-x) = (-x)^3 + (-x)$
$f(-x) = -x^3 - x = -(x^3 + x)$
$f(-x) = -f(x)$, odd function

53. $g(x) = x^2 + x$
$g(-x) = (-x)^2 + (-x)$
$g(-x) = x^2 - x$, neither

55. $h(x) = x^2 - x^4$
$h(-x) = (-x)^2 - (-x)^4$
$h(-x) = x^2 - x^4$
$h(-x) = h(x)$, even function

57. $f(x) = x^2 - x^4 + 1$
$f(-x) = (-x)^2 - (-x)^4 + 1$
$f(-x) = x^2 - x^4 + 1$
$f(-x) = f(x)$, even function

59. $f(x) = \dfrac{1}{5}x^6 - 3x^2$
$f(-x) = \dfrac{1}{5}(-x)^6 - 3(-x)^2$
$f(-x) = \dfrac{1}{5}x^6 - 3x^2$
$f(-x) = f(x)$, even function

61. $f(x) = x\sqrt{1 - x^2}$
$f(-x) = -x\sqrt{1 - (-x)^2}$
$f(-x) = -x\sqrt{1 - x^2}$
$\qquad = -\left(x\sqrt{1 - x^2}\right)$
$f(-x) = -f(x)$, odd function

63. The graph is symmetric with respect to the y-axis. The function is even.

65. The graph is symmetric with respect to the origin. The function is odd.

67. identity function

69. square root function

71. standard cubic function

73. $f(1.06) = 1$

75. $f\left(\dfrac{1}{3}\right) = 0$

77. $f(-2.3) = -3$

79. $f(1989) \approx 294$ billion dollars. This is the maximum function value.

81. Defense spending is increasing from 1988 to 1989, from 1991 to 1992 and from 1996 to 1997.

83. a. Increasing: $(45, 74)$
Decreasing: $(16, 45)$
The number of accidents occurring per 50 million miles driven increases with age starting at age 45, while it decreases with age starting at age 16.

b. $x = 45$ and $f(45) = 190$
The fewest number of accidents per 50 million miles driven occurs at age 45.

c. $f(16) = f(74) = 526.4$ so the range is $[190, 526.4]$.
Between the ages of 16 and 74, the number of accidents per 50 million miles driven is between 190 and 526.4.

85.

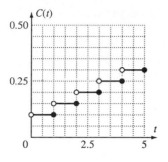

87.–95. Answers may vary.

97.

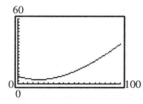

    b. The number of doctor visits decreases during childhood and then increases as you get older.

    c. The minimum is (20.29, 3.99), which means that the minimum number of doctor visits, about 4, occurs at around age 20.

99.

    Increasing: $(-\infty,\ 1)$ or $(3,\ \infty)$
    Decreasing: $(1, 3)$

101.

    Increasing: $(2,\ \infty)$
    Decreasing: $(-\infty,\ -2)$
    Constant: $(-2, 2)$

103.

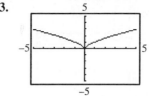

Increasing: $(0,\ \infty)$
Decreasing: $(-\infty,\ 0)$

105. a.

    b.

    c. Increasing: $(0, \infty)$
        Decreasing: $(-\infty, 0)$

    d. $f(x) = x^n$ is increasing from $(-\infty, \infty)$ when n is odd.

    e.

    As n increases the steepness increases.

107. Answers may vary.

109. Answers may vary.

111.

Weight at least	Cost
0 oz.	$0.33
1	0.55
2	0.77
3	0.99
4	1.21

Section 2.5

Check Point Exercises

1. Shift up vertically 3 units.

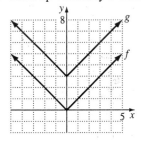

2. Shift horizontally to the right 4 units.

3. Shift horizontally to the right 1 unit and vertically down 2 units.

4. Reflect about the *x*-axis.

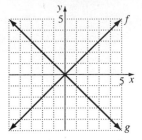

5. Reflect about the *y*-axis.

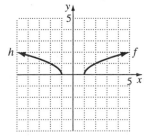

6. Vertically stretch the graph.

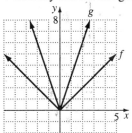

7. Vertically shrink the graph.

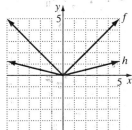

8. Shift horizontally to the right 2 units, reflect across the *x*-axis, and shift vertically up 3 units.

9. a. $(f+g)(x) = f(x) + g(x)$
$$= 3x^2 + 4x - 1 + 2x + 7$$
$$(f+g)(x) = 3x^2 + 6x + 6$$

b. $(f+g)(4) = 3(4)^2 + 6(4) + 6 = 78$

10. a. $(f+g)(x) = f(x) + g(x)$
$$= \sqrt{x-3} + \sqrt{x+1}$$

b. Domain of *f*:
$$x - 3 \geq 0$$
$$x \geq 3$$
$$[3, \infty)$$
Domain of g:
$$x + 1 \geq 0$$
$$x \geq -1$$
$$[-1, \infty)$$
The domain of $f + g$ is the set of all real numbers that are common to the domain of *f* and the domain of *g*. Thus, the domain of $f + g$ is $[3, \infty)$.

11. a. $(f-g)(x) = f(x) - g(x)$
$$= x - 5 - \left(x^2 - 1\right)$$
$$= x - 5 - x^2 - 1$$
$$= -x^2 + x - 4$$

b. $(fg)(x) = (x-5)\left(x^2 - 1\right)$
$$= x\left(x^2 - 1\right) - 5\left(x^2 - 1\right)$$
$$= x^3 - x - 5x^2 + 5$$
$$= x^3 - 5x^2 - x + 5$$

c. $\left(\dfrac{f}{g}\right)(x) = \dfrac{f(x)}{g(x)}$
$$= \frac{x-5}{x^2 - 1}, \ x \neq \pm 1$$

Exercise Set 2.5

1.

3.

5.

7.

133

9.

11.

13.

15.

17.

19.

21.

23.

25.

27.

29.

31.

33.

35.

37.

39.

41.

43.

45.

47.

49.

51.

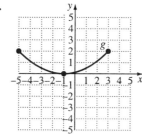

53. a. $(f+g)(x) = 2x^2 + 3x + 2$

    b. $(f+g)(4) = 2(4)^2 + 3(4) + 2$

           $= 32 + 12 + 2$

           $= 46$

55. a. $(f+g)(x) = \sqrt{x-6} + \sqrt{x+2}$

    b. Domain: $[6, \ \infty)$.

57. $(f+g)(x) = 3x + 2$

Domain: $(-\infty, \ \infty)$

$(f-g)(x) = f(x) - g(x)$

           $= (2x+3) - (x-1)$

           $= x + 4$

Domain: $(-\infty, \ \infty)$

$(fg)(x) = f(x) \cdot g(x)$

         $= (2x+3) \cdot (x-1)$

         $= 2x^2 + x - 3$

Domain: $(-\infty, \ \infty)$

$\left(\dfrac{f}{g}\right)(x) = \dfrac{f(x)}{g(x)} = \dfrac{2x+3}{x-1}$

Domain: $\{x | x \neq 1\}$

59. $(f+g)(x) = 3x^2 + x - 5$

Domain: $(-\infty, \ \infty)$

$(f-g)(x) = -3x^2 + x - 5$

Domain: $(-\infty, \ \infty)$

$(fg)(x) = (x-5)(3x^2) = 3x^3 - 15x^2$

Domain: $(-\infty, \ \infty)$

$\left(\dfrac{f}{g}\right)(x) = \dfrac{x-5}{3x^2}$

Domain: $\{x | x \neq 0\}$

61. $(f+g)(x) = 2x^2 - 2$

Domain: $(-\infty, \infty)$

$(f-g)(x) = 2x^2 - 2x - 4$

Domain: $(-\infty, \infty)$

$(fg)(x) = (2x^2 - x - 3)(x+1)$

           $= 2x^3 + x^2 - 4x - 3$

Domain: $(-\infty, \infty)$

$\left(\dfrac{f}{g}\right)(x) = \dfrac{2x^2 - x - 3}{x+1}$

           $= \dfrac{(2x-3)(x+1)}{(x+1)} = 2x - 3$

Domain: $\{x | x \neq -1\}$

63. $(f+g)(x) = \sqrt{x} + x - 4$

Domain: $[0, \ \infty)$

$(f-g)(x) = \sqrt{x} - x + 4$

Domain: $[0, \ \infty)$

$(fg)(x) = \sqrt{x}(x-4)$

Domain: $[0, \ \infty)$

$\left(\dfrac{f}{g}\right)(x) = \dfrac{\sqrt{x}}{x-4}$

Domain: $\{x | x \geq 0 \text{ and } x \neq 4\}$

65. $(f+g)(x) = 2 + \dfrac{1}{x} + \dfrac{1}{x} = 2 + \dfrac{2}{x} = \dfrac{2x+2}{x}$

Domain: $\{x | x \neq 0\}$

$(f-g)(x) = 2 + \dfrac{1}{x} - \dfrac{1}{x} = 2$

Domain: $\{x | x \neq 0\}$

$(fg)(x) = \left(2 + \dfrac{1}{x}\right) \cdot \dfrac{1}{x} = \dfrac{2}{x} + \dfrac{1}{x^2} = \dfrac{2x+1}{x^2}$

Domain: $\{x | x \neq 0\}$

$\left(\dfrac{f}{g}\right)(x) = \dfrac{2 + \frac{1}{x}}{\frac{1}{x}} = \left(2 + \dfrac{1}{x}\right) \cdot x = 2x + 1$

Domain: $\{x | x \neq 0\}$

67. $(f+g)(x) = \sqrt{x+4} + \sqrt{x-1}$

Domain: $[1, \infty)$

$(f-g)(x) = \sqrt{x+4} - \sqrt{x-1}$

Domain: $[1, \infty)$

$(fg)(x) = \sqrt{x+4} \cdot \sqrt{x-1} = \sqrt{x^2 + 3x - 4}$

Domain: $[1, \infty)$

$\left(\dfrac{f}{g}\right)(x) = \dfrac{\sqrt{x+4}}{\sqrt{x-1}}$

Domain: $(1, \infty)$

69. $f + g$ represents the total world population in year x.

71. $f(2000) \approx 1.5$ billion people
$g(2000) \approx 6$ billion people
$(f+g)(2000) = f(2000) + g(2000)$
$\qquad\qquad\qquad \approx 1.5 + 6.0$
$\qquad\qquad\qquad = 7.5$ billion people.

73. $(R-C)(20,000)$
$= 65(20,000) - (600,000 + 45(20,000))$
$= -200,000$
The company lost \$200,000 since costs exceeded revenues.
$(R-C)(30,000)$
$= 65(30,000) - (600,000 + 45(30,000))$
$= 0$

The company broke even since revenues equaled cost.
$(R-C)(40,000)$
$= 65(40,000) - (600,000 + 45(40,000))$
$= 200,000$
The company made a profit of \$200,000.

75.

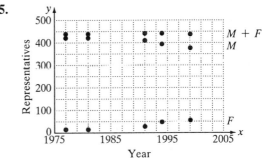

$f(x) = 435$
There is a total of 435 members of the House of Representatives.

77.–83. Answers may vary.

85. a.

    b.

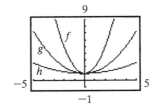

    c.   Answers may vary.

    d.   Answers may vary.

    e.   Answers may vary.

87. $g(x) = -(x+4)^2$

89. $g(x) = -\sqrt{x-2} + 2$

91. $(-a, b)$

93. $(a+3, b)$

Section 2.6

Check Point Exercises

1. a. $(f \circ g)(x) = f(g(x)) = 5g(x) + 6$
$$= 5\left(x^2 - 1\right) + 6$$
$$= 5x^2 - 5 + 6$$
$$= 5x^2 + 1$$

  b. $(g \circ f)(x) = g(f(x)) = (f(x))^2 - 1$
$$= (5x + 6)^2 - 1$$
$$= 25x^2 + 60x + 36 - 1$$
$$= 25x^2 + 60x + 35$$

2. $f(g(x)) = 7g(x) = 7\left(\dfrac{x}{7}\right) = x$

   $g(f(x)) = \dfrac{f(x)}{7} = \dfrac{7x}{7} = x$

   f and *g* are inverses.

3. $f(g(x)) = 4g(x) - 7$
$$= 4\left(\frac{x+7}{4}\right) - 7$$
$$= x + 7 - 7$$
$$= x$$

   $g(f(x)) = \dfrac{f(x) + 7}{4}$
$$= \frac{4x - 7 + 7}{4}$$
$$= \frac{4x}{4}$$
$$= x$$

   f and *g* are inverses.

4. $f(x) = 2x + 7$
$$y = 2x + 7$$
$$x = 2y + 7$$
$$x - 7 = 2y$$
$$\frac{x-7}{2} = y$$
$$f^{-1}(x) = \frac{x-7}{2}$$

5. $f(x) = 4x^3 - 1$
$$y = 4x^3 - 1$$
$$x = 4y^3 - 1$$
$$x + 1 = 4y^3$$
$$\frac{x+1}{4} = y^3$$
$$\sqrt[3]{\frac{x+1}{4}} = y$$
$$f^{-1}(x) = \sqrt[3]{\frac{x+1}{4}}$$

6. (b) and **(c)** have inverse functions.

7.

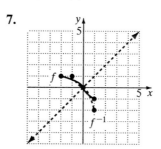

Exercise Set 2.6

1. $f(x) = 2x;\ g(x) = x + 7$

   a. $(f \circ g)(x) = 2(x + 7) = 2x + 14$

   b. $(g \circ f)(x) = 2x + 7$

   c. $(f \circ g)(2) = 2(2) + 14 = 18$

3. $f(x) = x + 4;\ g(x) = 2x + 1$

   a. $(f \circ g)(x) = (2x + 1) + 4 = 2x + 5$

   b. $(g \circ f)(x) = 2(x + 4) + 1 = 2x + 9$

   c. $(f \circ g)(2) = 2(2) + 5 = 9$

5. $f(x) = 4x - 3$; $g(x) = 5x^2 - 2$

   a. $(f \circ g)(x) = 4(5x^2 - 2) - 3$
$$= 20x^2 - 11$$

   b. $(g \circ f)(x) = 5(4x - 3)^2 - 2$
$$= 5(16x^2 - 24x + 9) - 2$$
$$= 80x^2 - 120x + 43$$

   c. $(f \circ g)(2) = 20(2)^2 - 11 = 69$

7. $f(x) = x^2 + 2$; $g(x) = x^2 - 2$

   a. $(f \circ g)(x) = (x^2 - 2)^2 + 2$
$$= x^4 - 4x^2 + 4 + 2$$
$$= x^4 - 4x^2 + 6$$

   b. $(g \circ f)(x) = (x^2 + 2)^2 - 2$
$$= x^4 + 4x^2 + 4 - 2$$
$$= x^4 + 4x^2 + 2$$

   c. $(f \circ g)(2) = 2^4 - 4(2)^2 + 6 = 6$

9. $f(x) = \sqrt{x}$; $g(x) = x - 1$

   a. $(f \circ g)(x) = \sqrt{x - 1}$

   b. $(g \circ f)(x) = \sqrt{x} - 1$

   c. $(f \circ g)(2) = \sqrt{2 - 1} = \sqrt{1} = 1$

11. $f(x) = 2x - 3$; $g(x) = \dfrac{x + 3}{2}$

   a. $(f \circ g)(x) = 2\left(\dfrac{x + 3}{2}\right) - 3$
$$= x + 3 - 3$$
$$= x$$

   b. $(g \circ f)(x) = \dfrac{(2x - 3) + 3}{2} = \dfrac{2x}{2} = x$

   c. $(f \circ g)(2) = 2$

13. $f(x) = \dfrac{1}{x}$; $g(x) = \dfrac{1}{x}$

   a. $(f \circ g)(x) = \dfrac{1}{\frac{1}{x}} = 1 \cdot \dfrac{x}{1} = x$

   b. $(g \circ f)(x) = \dfrac{1}{\frac{1}{x}} = 1 \cdot \dfrac{x}{1} = x$

   c. $(f \circ g)(2) = 2$

15. $f(x) = 4x$; $g(x) = \dfrac{x}{4}$

$$f(g(x)) = 4\left(\dfrac{x}{4}\right) = x$$
$$g(f(x)) = \dfrac{4x}{4} = x$$
f and g are inverses.

17. $f(x) = 3x + 8$; $g(x) = \dfrac{x - 8}{3}$

$$f(g(x)) = 3\left(\dfrac{x - 8}{3}\right) + 8 = x - 8 + 8 = x$$
$$g(f(x)) = \dfrac{(3x + 8) - 8}{3} = \dfrac{3x}{3} = x$$
f and g are inverses.

19. $f(x) = 5x - 9$; $g(x) = \dfrac{x + 5}{9}$

$$f(g(x)) = 5\left(\dfrac{x + 5}{9}\right) - 9$$
$$= \dfrac{5x + 25}{9} - 9$$
$$= \dfrac{5x - 56}{9}$$
$$g(f(x)) = \dfrac{5x - 9 + 5}{9} = \dfrac{5x - 4}{9}$$
f and g are not inverses.

21. $f(x) = \dfrac{3}{x-4}; \ g(x) = \dfrac{3}{x} + 4$

$f(g(x)) = \dfrac{3}{\frac{3}{x}+4-4} = \dfrac{3}{\frac{3}{x}} = x$

$g(f(x)) = \dfrac{3}{\frac{3}{x-4}} + 4$

$\qquad = 3 \cdot \left(\dfrac{x-4}{3}\right) + 4$

$\qquad = x - 4 + 4$

$\qquad = x$

f and g are inverses.

23. $f(x) = -x; g(x) = -x$

$f(g(x)) = -(-x) = x$

$g(f(x)) = -(-x) = x$

f and g are inverses.

25. a. $f(x) = x + 3$

$\qquad y = x + 3$

$\qquad x = y + 3$

$\qquad y = x - 3$

$\qquad f^{-1}(x) = x - 3$

b. $f(f^{-1}(x)) = x - 3 + 3 = x$

$\qquad f^{-1}(f(x)) = x + 3 - 3 = x$

27. a. $f(x) = 2x$

$\qquad y = 2x$

$\qquad x = 2y$

$\qquad y = \dfrac{x}{2}$

$\qquad f^{-1}(x) = \dfrac{x}{2}$

b. $f(f^{-1}(x)) = 2\left(\dfrac{x}{2}\right) = x$

$\qquad f^{-1}(f(x)) = \dfrac{2x}{2} = x$

29. a. $f(x) = 2x + 3$

$\qquad y = 2x + 3$

$\qquad x = 2y + 3$

$\qquad x - 3 = 2y$

$\qquad y = \dfrac{x-3}{2}$

$\qquad f^{-1}(x) = \dfrac{x-3}{2}$

b. $f(f^{-1}(x)) = 2\left(\dfrac{x-3}{2}\right) + 3$

$\qquad = x - 3 + 3$

$\qquad = x$

$\qquad f^{-1}(f(x)) = \dfrac{2x+3-3}{2} = \dfrac{2x}{2} = x$

31. a. $f(x) = x^3 + 2$

$\qquad y = x^3 + 2$

$\qquad x = y^3 + 2$

$\qquad x - 2 = y^3$

$\qquad y = \sqrt[3]{x-2}$

$\qquad f^{-1}(x) = \sqrt[3]{x-2}$

b. $f(f^{-1}(x)) = \left(\sqrt[3]{x-2}\right)^3 + 2$

$\qquad = x - 2 + 2$

$\qquad = x$

$\qquad f^{-1}(f(x)) = \sqrt[3]{x^3 + 2 - 2} = \sqrt[3]{x^3} = x$

33. a. $f(x) = (x+2)^3$

$\qquad y = (x+2)^3$

$\qquad x = (y+2)^3$

$\qquad \sqrt[3]{x} = y + 2$

$\qquad y = \sqrt[3]{x} - 2$

$\qquad f^{-1}(x) = \sqrt[3]{x} - 2$

b. $f(f^{-1}(x)) = \left(\sqrt[3]{x} - 2 + 2\right)^3 = \left(\sqrt[3]{x}\right)^3 = x$

$\qquad f^{-1}(f(x)) = \sqrt[3]{(x+2)^3} - 2$

$\qquad = x + 2 - 2$

$\qquad = x$

35. a.
$$f(x) = \frac{1}{x}$$
$$y = \frac{1}{x}$$
$$x = \frac{1}{y}$$
$$xy = 1$$
$$y = \frac{1}{x}$$
$$f^{-1}(x) = \frac{1}{x}$$

b. $f(f^{-1}(x)) = \dfrac{1}{\frac{1}{x}} = x$

$f^{-1}(f(x)) = \dfrac{1}{\frac{1}{x}} = x$

37. a.
$$f(x) = \sqrt{x}$$
$$y = \sqrt{x}$$
$$x = \sqrt{y}$$
$$y = x^2$$
$$f^{-1}(x) = x^2, \quad x \geq 0$$

b. $f(f^{-1}(x)) = \sqrt{x^2} = |x| = x$ for $x \geq 0$.
$f^{-1}(f(x)) = (\sqrt{x})^2 = x$

39. a.
$$f(x) = x^2 + 1, \text{ for } x \geq 0$$
$$y = x^2 + 1$$
$$x = y^2 + 1, \text{ for } y \geq 0$$
$$x - 1 = y^2$$
$$y = \sqrt{x-1} \text{ since } y \geq 0$$
$$f^{-1}(x) = \sqrt{x-1}$$

b. $f(f^{-1}(x)) = (\sqrt{x-1})^2 + 1$
$$= x - 1 + 1$$
$$= x$$
$f^{-1}(f(x)) = \sqrt{x^2 + 1 - 1} = \sqrt{x^2} = x$
for $x \geq 0$.

41. a.
$$f(x) = \frac{2x+1}{x-3}$$
$$y = \frac{2x+1}{x-3}$$
$$x = \frac{2y+1}{y-3}$$
$$x(y-3) = 2y + 1$$
$$xy - 3x = 2y + 1$$
$$xy - 2y = 3x + 1$$
$$y(x-2) = 3x + 1$$
$$y = \frac{3x+1}{x-2}$$
$$f^{-1}(x) = \frac{3x+1}{x-2}$$

b. $f(f^{-1}(x)) = \dfrac{2\left(\frac{3x+1}{x-2}\right)+1}{\frac{3x+1}{x-2}-3}$

$$= \frac{2(3x+1)+x-2}{3x+1-3(x-2)} = \frac{6x+2+x-2}{3x+1-3x+6}$$

$$= \frac{7x}{7} = x$$

$f^{-1}(f(x)) = \dfrac{3\left(\frac{2x+1}{x-3}\right)+1}{\frac{2x+1}{x-3}-2}$

$$= \frac{3(2x+1)+x-3}{2x+1-2(x-3)}$$

$$= \frac{6x+3+x-3}{2x+1-2x+6} = \frac{7x}{7} = x$$

43. a.
$$f(x) = \sqrt[3]{x-4} + 3$$
$$y = \sqrt[3]{x-4} + 3$$
$$x = \sqrt[3]{y-4} + 3$$
$$x - 3 = \sqrt[3]{y-4}$$
$$(x-3)^3 = y - 4$$
$$y = (x-3)^3 + 4$$
$$f^{-1}(x) = (x-3)^3 + 4$$

b. $f(f^{-1}(x)) = \sqrt[3]{(x-3)^3 + 4 - 4} + 3$
$$= \sqrt[3]{(x-3)^3} + 3$$
$$= x - 3 + 3 = x$$
$f^{-1}(f(x)) = \left(\sqrt[3]{x-4} + 3 - 3\right)^3 + 4$
$$= \left(\sqrt[3]{x-4}\right)^3 + 4 = x - 4 + 4 = x$$

45. The function is not one-to-one, so it does not have an inverse function.

47. The function is not one-to-one, so it does not have an inverse function.

49. The function is one-to-one, so it does have an inverse function.

51.

53.

55. a. *f* gives the price of the computer after a $400 discount. *g* gives the price of the computer after a 25% discount.

b. $(f \circ g)(x) = 0.75x - 400$

This models the price of a computer after first a 25% discount and then a $400 discount.

c. $(g \circ f)(x) = 0.75(x - 400)$

This models the price of a computer after first a $400 discount and then a 25% discount.

d. The function $f \circ g$ models the greater discount, since the 25% discount is taken on the regular price first.

e. $f(x) = x - 400$
$y = x - 400$
$x = y - 400$
$y = x + 400$
$f^{-1}(x) = x + 400$

If *x* is the discount price of the computer, then $f^{-1}(x)$ is the regular price.

57. a. *f* is a one-to-one function.

b. $f^{-1}(0.25)$ is the number of people in a room for a 25% probability of two people sharing a birthday. $f^{-1}(0.5)$ is the number of people in a room for a 50% probability of two people sharing a birthday. $f^{-1}(0.7)$ is the number of people in a room for a 70% probability of two people sharing a birthday.

59. No. The graph does not pass the horizontal line test, so it is not one-to-one. This means that the average age at which U.S. women marry has been the same during more than one year.

61.–67. Answers may vary.

69.

one-to-one

71.

not one-to-one

73.

not one-to-one

75.

not one-to-one

77.

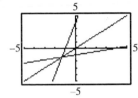

f and *g* are inverses.

79.

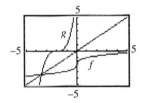

f and *g* are inverses.

81. Answers may vary.

83.

$$f(x) = \frac{3x - 2}{5x - 3}$$

$$y = \frac{3x - 2}{5x - 3}$$

$$x = \frac{3y - 2}{5y - 3}$$

$$x(5y - 3) = 3y - 2$$

$$5xy - 3x = 3y - 2$$

$$5xy - 3y = 3x - 2$$

$$y(5x - 3) = 3x - 2$$

$$y = \frac{3x - 2}{5x - 3}$$

$$f^{-1}(x) = \frac{3x - 2}{5x - 3}$$

Note: An alternative approach is to show that $(f \circ f)(x) = x$.

Review Exercises

1. $m = \dfrac{1 - 2}{5 - 3} = \dfrac{-1}{2} = -\dfrac{1}{2}$; falls

2. $m = \dfrac{-4 - (-2)}{3 - (-1)} = \dfrac{-2}{-2} = 1$; rises

3. $m = \dfrac{\frac{1}{4} - \frac{1}{4}}{6 - (-3)} = \dfrac{0}{9} = 0$; horizontal

4. $m = \dfrac{10 - 5}{-2 - (-2)} = \dfrac{5}{0}$ undefined; vertical

5. point-slope form: $y - 2 = -6(x + 3)$
slope-intercept form: $y = -6x - 16$

6. $m = \dfrac{2 - 6}{-1 - 1} = \dfrac{-4}{-2} = 2$
point-slope form: $y - 6 = 2(x - 1)$
or $y - 2 = 2(x + 1)$
slope-intercept form: $y = 2x + 4$

7. slope: $\dfrac{2}{5}$; y-intercept: -1

8. slope: -4; y-intercept: 5

9. $2x + 3y + 6 = 0$

$$3y = -2x - 6$$

$$y = -\dfrac{2}{3}x - 2$$

slope: $-\dfrac{2}{3}$; y-intercept: -2

10. $2y - 8 = 0$

$$2y = 8$$

$$y = 4$$

slope: 0; y-intercept: 4

11. a. $m = \dfrac{12.1 - 16}{30 - 0} = \dfrac{-3.9}{30} = -0.13$

$$y - 16 = -0.13(x - 0)$$

or $y - 12.1 = -0.13(x - 30)$

b. $y = -0.13x + 16$

c. In 1970: $y = -0.13(70) + 16$
$y = 6.9$
The average surfboard length in 1970 was 6.9 feet.
In 1980: $y = -0.13(80) + 16$
$y = 5.6$
The average surfboard length in 1980 was 5.6 feet.

d. In 2000: $y = -0.13(100) + 16$
$y = 3$
In 2000, the equation predicts the surfboard length to be 3 feet, which is not reasonable.

12. a. Answers may vary.

b. Answers may vary.

c. Answers may vary.

13. $3x + y - 9 = 0$
$$y = -3x + 9$$
$m = -3$
point-slope form: $y + 7 = -3(x - 4)$
slope-intercept form: $y = -3x + 12 - 7$
$$y = -3x + 5$$

14. perpendicular to $y = \frac{1}{3}x + 4$

$m = -3$
point-slope form:
$y - 6 = -3(x + 3)$
slope-intercept form:
$y = -3x - 9 + 6$
$y = -3x - 3$

15. $x^2 + y^2 = 3^2$
$x^2 + y^2 = 9$

16. $(x - (-2))^2 + (y - 4)^2 = 6^2$
$(x + 2)^2 + (y - 4)^2 = 36$

17. center: (0, 0); radius: 1

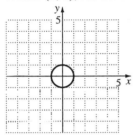

18. center: (−2, 3); radius: 3

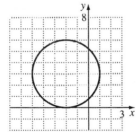

19.
$$x^2 + y^2 - 4x + 2y - 4 = 0$$
$$x^2 - 4x + y^2 + 2y = 4$$
$$(x^2 - 4x + 4) + (y^2 + 2y + 1) = 4 + 4 + 1$$
$$(x - 2)^2 + (y + 1)^2 = 9$$
center: (2, −1); radius: 3

20. function
domain: {2, 3, 5}
range: {7}

21. function
domain: {1, 2, 13}
range: {10, 500, π}

22. not a function
domain: {12, 14}
range: {13, 15, 19}

23. $2x + y = 8$
$\qquad y = -2x + 8$
Since only one value of y can be obtained for each value of x, y is a function of x.

24. $3x^2 + y = 14$
$\qquad y = -3x^2 + 14$
Since only one value of y can be obtained for each value of x, y is a function of x.

25. $2x + y^2 = 6$
$\qquad y^2 = -2x + 6$
$\qquad y = \pm\sqrt{-2x + 6}$
Since more than one value of y can be obtained from some values of x, y is not a function of x.

26. $f(x) = 5 - 7x$

 a. $f(4) = 5 - 7(4) = -23$

 b. $f(x + 3) = 5 - 7(x + 3)$
 $= 5 - 7x - 21$
 $= -7x - 16$

 c. $f(-x) = 5 - 7(-x) = 5 + 7x$

27. $g(x) = 3x^2 - 5x + 2$

 a. $g(0) = 3(0)^2 - 5(0) + 2 = 2$

 b. $g(-2) = 3(-2)^2 - 5(-2) + 2$
 $= 12 + 10 + 2$
 $= 24$

 c. $g(x - 1) = 3(x - 1)^2 - 5(x - 1) + 2$
 $= 3(x^2 - 2x + 1) - 5x + 5 + 2$
 $= 3x^2 - 11x + 10$

 d. $g(-x) = 3(-x)^2 - 5(-x) + 2$
 $= 3x^2 + 5x + 2$

28. $f(x) = 4x - 3$

 a. $f(a) = 4a - 3$

 b. $f(a + h) = 4(a + h) - 3 = 4a + 4h - 3$

 c.
$$\frac{f(a + h) - f(a)}{h}$$
$$= \frac{(4a + 4h - 3) - (4a - 3)}{h}$$
$$= \frac{4h}{h} = 4, \ h \neq 0$$

 d. $f(a) + f(h) = 4a - 3 + 4h - 3$
 $= 4a + 4h - 6$

29. a. $g(13) = \sqrt{13 - 4} = \sqrt{9} = 3$

 b. $g(0) = 4 - 0 = 4$

 c. $g(-3) = 4 - (-3) = 7$

30. a. $f(-2) = \dfrac{(-2)^2 - 1}{-2 - 1} = \dfrac{3}{-3} = -1$

 b. $f(1) = 12$

 c. $f(2) = \dfrac{2^2 - 1}{2 - 1} = \dfrac{3}{1} = 3$

31. domain: $(-\infty, \ \infty)$

32. The denominator is zero when $x = 7$. The domain is $\{x | x \neq 7\}$.

33. We want $\sqrt{8 - 2x}$ to equal a real number.
$8 - 2x \geq 0$
$-2x \geq -8$
$x \leq 4$
The domain is $(-\infty, \ 4]$.

34. The denominator is zero when $x = 1$ or $x = -1$. The domain is $\{x | x \neq -1 \text{ and } x \neq 1\}$.

35. The denominator is zero when $x = 5$. We also want $\sqrt{x - 2}$ to equal a real number.
$x - 2 \geq 0$
 $x \geq 2$
The domain is: $\{x | x \geq 2 \text{ and } x \neq 5\}$.

36. $f(6) = -0.46(6)^2 + 3.66(6) + 20.08 = 25.48$
In 1996, there were 25.48 million participants in the Federal Food Stamp program.

37. Ordered pairs: $(-1, 9)$, $(0, 4)$, $(1, 1)$, $(2, 0)$, $(3, 1)$, $(4, 4)$.

domain: $(-\infty, \ \infty)$
range: $[0, \ \infty)$

38. Ordered pairs: $(-1, 3)$, $(0, 2)$, $(1, 1)$, $(2, 0)$, $(3, 1)$, $(4, 2)$.

domain: $(-\infty, \infty)$
range: $[0, \infty)$

39. a. domain: $[-3, 5)$

   b. range: $[-5, 0]$

   c. x-intercept: -3

   d. y-intercept: -2

   e. increasing: $(-2, \ 0)$ or $(3, \ 5)$
       decreasing: $(-3, \ -2)$ or $(0, \ 3)$

   f. $f(-2) = -3$ and $f(3) = -5$

40. a. domain: $(-\infty, \infty)$

   b. range: $(-\infty, \infty)$

   c. x-intercepts: -2 and 3

   d. y-intercept: 3

   e. increasing: $(-5, 0)$
       decreasing: $(-\infty, \ -5)$ or $(0, \ \infty)$

   f. $f(-2) = 0$ and $f(6) = -3$

41. a. domain: $(-\infty, \infty)$

   b. range: $[-2, 2]$

   c. x-intercept: 0

   d. y-intercept: 0

   e. increasing: $(-2, 2)$
       constant: $(-\infty, \ -2)$ or $(2, \ \infty)$

   f. $f(-9) = -2$ and $f(14) = 2$

42. not a function

43. function

44. function

45. not a function

46. $f(x) = x^3 - 5x$
$$f(-x) = (-x)^3 - 5(-x)$$
$$= -x^3 + 5x$$
$$= -f(x)$$
The function is odd. The function is symmetric with respect to the origin.

47. $f(x) = x^4 - 2x^2 + 1$
$$f(-x) = (-x)^4 - 2(-x)^2 + 1$$
$$= x^4 - 2x^2 + 1$$
$$= f(x)$$
The function is even. The function is symmetric with respect to the y-axis.

48. $f(x) = 2x\sqrt{1 - x^2}$

$f(-x) = 2(-x)\sqrt{1 - (-x)^2}$

$\qquad = -2x\sqrt{1 - x^2}$

$\qquad = -f(x)$

The function is odd. The function is symmetric with respect to the origin.

49. a. Yes, the vulture's height is a function of time since the graph passes the vertical line test.

b. Decreasing: (3, 12)
The vulture descended.

c. Constant: (0, 3) and (12, 17)
The vulture's height held steady during the first 3 seconds and the vulture was on the ground for 5 seconds.

d. Increasing: (17, 30)
The vulture was ascending.

50.

51.

52.

53.

54.

55.

56.

57.

58.

59.

60.

61.

62.

63.

64.

149

65.

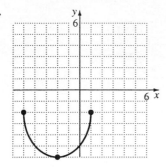

66. $f(x) = 3x - 1; \ g(x) = x - 5$
$(f + g)(x) = 4x - 6$
Domain: $(-\infty, \ \infty)$
$(f - g)(x) = (3x - 1) - (x - 5) = 2x + 4$
Domain: $(-\infty, \ \infty)$
$(fg)(x) = (3x - 1)(x - 5) = 3x^2 - 16x + 5$
Domain: $(-\infty, \ \infty)$
$\left(\dfrac{f}{g}\right)(x) = \dfrac{3x - 1}{x - 5}$
Domain: $\{x | x \neq 5\}$

67. $f(x) = x^2 + x + 1; \ g(x) = x^2 - 1$
$(f + g)(x) = 2x^2 + x$
Domain: $(-\infty, \ \infty)$
$(f - g)(x) = (x^2 + x + 1) - (x^2 - 1) = x + 2$
Domain: $(-\infty, \ \infty)$
$(fg)(x) = (x^2 + x + 1)(x^2 - 1)$
$\qquad = x^4 + x^3 - x - 1$
$\left(\dfrac{f}{g}\right)(x) = \dfrac{x^2 + x + 1}{x^2 - 1}$
Domain: $\{x | x \neq -1 \text{ and } x \neq 1\}$

68. $f(x) = \sqrt{x + 7}; \ g(x) = \sqrt{x - 2}$
$(f + g)(x) = \sqrt{x + 7} + \sqrt{x - 2}$
Domain: $[2, \ \infty)$
$(f - g)(x) = \sqrt{x + 7} - \sqrt{x - 2}$
Domain: $[2, \ \infty)$
$(fg)(x) = \sqrt{x + 7} \cdot \sqrt{x - 2}$
$\qquad = \sqrt{x^2 + 5x - 14}$
Domain: $[2, \ \infty)$

$\left(\dfrac{f}{g}\right)(x) = \dfrac{\sqrt{x + 7}}{\sqrt{x - 2}}$
Domain: $(2, \ \infty)$

69. $f(x) = x^2 + 3; \ g(x) = 4x - 1$

   a. $(f \circ g)(x) = (4x - 1)^2 + 3$
$\qquad\qquad\quad = 16x^2 - 8x + 4$

   b. $(g \circ f)(x) = 4(x^2 + 3) - 1$
$\qquad\qquad\quad = 4x^2 + 11$

   c. $(f \circ g)(3) = 16(3)^2 - 8(3) + 4 = 124$

70. $f(x) = \sqrt{x}; \ g(x) = x + 1$

   a. $(f \circ g)(x) = \sqrt{x + 1}$

   b. $(g \circ f)(x) = \sqrt{x} + 1$

   c. $(f \circ g)(3) = \sqrt{3 + 1} = \sqrt{4} = 2$

71. $f(x) = \dfrac{3}{5}x + \dfrac{1}{2}; \ g(x) = \dfrac{5}{3}x - 2$
$f(g(x)) = \dfrac{3}{5}\left(\dfrac{5}{3}x - 2\right) + \dfrac{1}{2}$
$\qquad\quad = x - \dfrac{6}{5} + \dfrac{1}{2}$
$\qquad\quad = x - \dfrac{7}{10}$
$g(f(x)) = \dfrac{5}{3}\left(\dfrac{3}{5}x + \dfrac{1}{2}\right) - 2$
$\qquad\quad = x + \dfrac{5}{6} - 2$
$\qquad\quad = x - \dfrac{7}{6}$
f and g are not inverses.

72. $f(x) = 2 - 5x; \ g(x) = \dfrac{2-x}{5}$

$$f(g(x)) = 2 - 5\left(\dfrac{2-x}{5}\right)$$
$$= 2 - (2 - x)$$
$$= x$$
$$g(f(x)) = \dfrac{2 - (2 - 5x)}{5} = \dfrac{5x}{5} = x$$

f and g are inverses.

73. a. $\quad f(x) = 4x - 3$
$$y = 4x - 3$$
$$x = 4y - 3$$
$$y = \dfrac{x+3}{4}$$
$$f^{-1}(x) = \dfrac{x+3}{4}$$

   b. $\quad f(f^{-1}(x)) = 4\left(\dfrac{x+3}{4}\right) - 3$
$$= x + 3 - 3$$
$$= x$$
$$f^{-1}(f(x)) = \dfrac{(4x-3)+3}{4} = \dfrac{4x}{4} = x$$

74. a. $\quad f(x) = \sqrt{x+2}$
$$y = \sqrt{x+2}$$
$$x = \sqrt{y+2}$$
$$x^2 = y + 2$$
$$y = x^2 - 2$$
$$f^{-1}(x) = x^2 - 2 \text{ for } x \geq 0$$

   b. $\quad f(f^{-1}(x)) = \sqrt{x^2 - 2 + 2}$
$$= \sqrt{x^2}$$
$$= |x|$$
$$= x \text{ for } x \geq 0$$
$$f^{-1}(f(x)) = \left(\sqrt{x+2}\right)^2 - 2$$
$$= x + 2 - 2$$
$$= x$$

75. a. $\quad f(x) = 8x^3 + 1$
$$y = 8x^3 + 1$$
$$x = 8y^3 + 1$$
$$\dfrac{x-1}{8} = y^3$$
$$y = \sqrt[3]{\dfrac{x-1}{8}}$$
$$f^{-1}(x) = \sqrt[3]{\dfrac{x-1}{8}}$$

   b. $\quad f(f^{-1}(x)) = 8\left(\sqrt[3]{\dfrac{x-1}{8}}\right)^3 + 1$
$$= 8\left(\dfrac{x-1}{8}\right) + 1$$
$$= x - 1 + 1$$
$$= x$$
$$f^{-1}(f(x)) = \sqrt[3]{\dfrac{8x^3 + 1 - 1}{8}}$$
$$= \sqrt[3]{\dfrac{8x^3}{8}}$$
$$= \sqrt[3]{x^3}$$
$$= x$$

76. The inverse function exists.

77. The inverse function does not exist since it does not pass the horizontal line test.

78. The inverse function exists.

79. The inverse function does not exist since it does not pass the horizontal line test.

80.

Chapter 2 Test

1. $m = \dfrac{-8-1}{-1-2} = \dfrac{-9}{-3} = 3$
   point-slope form: $y - 1 = 3(x - 2)$
   or $y + 8 = 3(x + 1)$
   slope-intercept form: $y = 3x - 5$

2. $y = -\dfrac{1}{4}x + 5$ so $m = 4$
   point-slope form: $y - 6 = 4(x + 4)$
   slope-intercept form: $y = 4x + 22$

3. **a.** $(4, 401.1)$; $(9, 475.6)$
   $m = \dfrac{475.6 - 401.1}{9 - 4} = \dfrac{74.5}{5} = 14.9$
   point-slope form:
   $y - 401.1 = 14.9(x - 4)$ or
   $y - 475.6 = 14.9(x - 9)$
   slope-intercept form: $y = 14.9x + 341.5$

   b. When $x = 20$,
   $y = 14.9(20) + 341.5 = 639.5$
   The predicted average weekly earnings
   for U.S. workers in 2005 is $639.50

4. $x^2 + y^2 + 4x - 6y - 3 = 0$
   $(x^2 + 4x + 4) + (y^2 - 6y + 9) = 3 + 4 + 9$
   $(x + 2)^2 + (y - 3)^2 = 16$
   center: $(-2, 3)$; radius: 4

5. (b), (c), and (d) are not functions.

6. $f(x) = x^2 - 2x + 5$
   $f(x - 1) = (x - 1)^2 - 2(x - 1) + 5$
   $= x^2 - 2x + 1 - 2x + 2 + 5$
   $= x^2 - 4x + 8$

7. $g(-1) = 3 - (-1) = 4$
   $g(7) = \sqrt{7 - 3} = \sqrt{4} = 2$

8. We want $\sqrt{12 - 3x}$ to equal a real number.
   $12 - 3x \geq 0$
   $-3x \geq -12$
   $x \leq 4$
   domain: $(-\infty, 4]$

9. $f(10) = 0.79(10)^2 - 2(10) - 4$
   $= 79 - 20 - 4$
   $= 55$
   There are 55 board feet in a 16-foot log
   whose average diameter is 10 inches.

10. **a.** $f(4) - f(-3) = 3 - (-2) = 5$
    b. domain: $(-5, 6]$
    c. range: $[-4, 5]$
    d. increasing: $(-1, 2)$
    e. decreasing: $(-5, -1)$ or $(2, 6)$
    f. x-intercepts: -4, 1, and 5.
    g. y-intercept: -3

11. $f(x) = x^4 - x^2$
    $f(-x) = (-x)^4 - (-x)^2 = x^4 - x^2 = f(x)$
    $f(-x) = f(x)$, so the function $f(x)$ is even and
    is symmetric with respect to the y-axis. The
    graph in the figure is symmetric with respect
    to the origin.

12. The graph of f is shifted 3 to the right to
    obtain the graph of g. Then the graph of g is
    stretched by a factor of 2 and reflected about
    the x-axis to obtain the graph of h.

13.

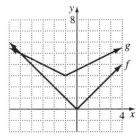

14. $(f - g)(x) = (x^2 + 3x - 4) - (5x - 2)$

$\qquad = x^2 - 2x - 2$

15. $\left(\dfrac{f}{g}\right)(x) = \dfrac{x^2 + 3x - 4}{5x - 2}$

domain: $\left\{x \middle| x \neq \dfrac{2}{5}\right\}$

16. $(f \circ g)(x) = (5x - 2)^2 + 3(5x - 2) - 4$

$\qquad = 25x^2 - 20x + 4 + 15x - 6 - 4$

$\qquad = 25x^2 - 5x - 6$

17. $(g \circ f)(x) = 5(x^2 + 3x - 4) - 2$

$\qquad = 5x^2 + 15x - 22$

18. $g(2) = 5(2) - 2 = 8$

$f(g(2)) = f(8)$

$\qquad = 8^2 + 3(8) - 4$

$\qquad = 64 + 24 - 4$

$\qquad = 84$

19. $f(x) = \sqrt{x - 2}$

$y = \sqrt{x - 2}$

$x = \sqrt{y - 2}$

$x^2 = y - 2$

$y = x^2 + 2$

$f^{-1}(x) = x^2 + 2$ for $x \geq 0$

$f(f^{-1}(x)) = \sqrt{x^2 + 2 - 2}$

$\qquad = \sqrt{x^2}$

$\qquad = |x|$

$\qquad = x$ for $x \geq 0$

$f^{-1}(f(x)) = \left(\sqrt{x - 2}\right)^2 + 2$

$\qquad = x - 2 + 2$

$\qquad = x$

20. a. The graph of f passes the horizontal line test.

    b. $f(80) = 2000$

    c. $f^{-1}(2000)$ is the income, in thousands of dollars, for those who give \$2000 to charity.

21.

    a. f is not one-to-one since it fails the horizontal line test.

    b. f is neither even or odd since it shows no y-axis symmetry or symmetry about the origin.

    c. range: $[-\infty, \ \infty)$

    d. increasing: $(-\infty, \ -5)$ or $(3, \ \infty)$

    e. decreasing: $(-5, \ 3)$

Cumulative Review Exercises (Chapters P–2)

1. $\dfrac{4x^2y}{2x^5y^{-3}} = \dfrac{2y^4}{x^3}$

2. $\dfrac{5}{4\sqrt{2}} = \dfrac{5}{4\sqrt{2}} \cdot \dfrac{\sqrt{2}}{\sqrt{2}} = \dfrac{5\sqrt{2}}{8}$

3. $x^3 - 4x^2 + 2x - 8 = x^2(x-4) + 2(x-4)$
$$= (x-4)(x^2+2)$$

4. $\dfrac{x-3}{x+4} + \dfrac{x}{x-2} = \dfrac{(x-3)(x-2) + x(x+4)}{(x+4)(x-2)}$
$$= \dfrac{x^2 - 5x + 6 + x^2 + 4x}{(x+4)(x-2)}$$
$$= \dfrac{2x^2 - x + 6}{(x+4)(x-2)}$$

5. $\dfrac{4+\frac{2}{x}}{4-\frac{2}{x}} = \dfrac{\left(4+\frac{2}{x}\right)\cdot x}{\left(4-\frac{2}{x}\right)\cdot x}$
$$= \dfrac{4x+2}{4x-2}$$
$$= \dfrac{2(2x+1)}{2(2x-1)}$$
$$= \dfrac{2x+1}{2x-1}$$

6. $(x+3)(x-4) = 8$
$x^2 - x - 12 = 8$
$x^2 - x - 20 = 0$
$(x+4)(x-5) = 0$
$x+4=0 \quad \text{or} \quad x-5=0$
$x=-4 \quad \text{or} \quad\quad x=5$

7. $3(4x-1) = 4 - 6(x-3)$
$12x - 3 = 4 - 6x + 18$
$18x = 25$
$x = \dfrac{25}{18}$

8. $\sqrt{x} + 2 = x$
$\sqrt{x} = x - 2$
$(\sqrt{x})^2 = (x-2)^2$
$x = x^2 - 4x + 4$
$0 = x^2 - 5x + 4$
$0 = (x-1)(x-4)$
$x - 1 = 0 \quad \text{or} \quad x - 4 = 0$
$x = 1 \quad \text{or} \quad\quad x = 4$
A check of the solutions shows that $x = 1$ is an extraneous solution. The only solution is $x = 4$.

9. $x^{2/3} - x^{1/3} - 6 = 0$
Let $u = x^{1/3}$. Then $u^2 = x^{2/3}$.
$u^2 - u - 6 = 0$
$(u+2)(u-3) = 0$
$u = -2 \quad \text{or} \quad\quad u = 3$
$x^{1/3} = -2 \quad \text{or} \quad x^{1/3} = 3$
$x = (-2)^3 \quad \text{or} \quad\quad x = 3^3$
$x = -8 \quad \text{or} \quad\quad x = 27$

10. $\dfrac{x}{2} - 3 \le \dfrac{x}{4} + 2$
$4 \cdot \left(\dfrac{x}{2} - 3\right) \le 4 \cdot \left(\dfrac{x}{4} + 2\right)$
$2x - 12 \le x + 8$
$x \le 20;$
The solution set is $(-\infty, \ 20]$.

11.
$$\frac{x+3}{x-2} \le 2$$

$$\frac{x+3}{x-2} - 2 \le 0$$

$$\frac{x+3-2(x-2)}{x-2} \le 0$$

$$\frac{-x+7}{x-2} \le 0$$

Critical numbers:

$-x+7=0 \quad x-2=0$

$\quad\quad x=7 \quad\quad x=2$

0 1 2 3 4 5 6 7 8 9 10

Test Interval	Representative Number	Substitute into $\frac{x+3}{x-2} \le 2$	Conclusion
$(-\infty,\ 2)$	0	$\frac{0+3}{0-2} \overset{?}{\le} 2$ $-\frac{3}{2} \le 2$ True	$(-\infty,\ 2)$ belongs to the solution set.
$(2, 7)$	3	$\frac{3+3}{3-2} \overset{?}{\le} 2$ $6 \le 2$ False	$(2, 7)$ does not belong to the solution set.
$(7,\ \infty)$	8	$\frac{8+3}{8-2} \overset{?}{\le} 2$ $\frac{11}{6} \le 2$ True	$(7,\ \infty)$ belongs to the solution set.

Solution: $(-\infty,\ 2)$ or $[7,\ \infty)$

12. $y = -\frac{1}{4}x + \frac{1}{3}$, so $m = 4$.

point-slope form: $y - 5 = 4(x + 2)$

slope-intercept form: $y = 4x + 13$

13.

14.
$$f(x) = 2 + \sqrt{x-3}$$
$$y = 2 + \sqrt{x-3}$$
$$x = 2 + \sqrt{y-3}$$
$$x - 2 = \sqrt{y-3}$$
$$(x-2)^2 = y - 3$$
$$y = (x-2)^2 + 3$$
$$f^{-1}(x) = (x-2)^2 + 3$$

15.
$$f(x) = 3 - x^2$$
$$f(x-2) = 3 - (x-2)^2$$
$$= 3 - (x^2 - 4x + 4)$$
$$= 3 - x^2 + 4x - 4$$
$$= -x^2 + 4x - 1$$

16.
$$G = \frac{a}{1-r}$$
$$G - Gr = a$$
$$Gr = G - a$$
$$r = \frac{G-a}{G}$$

17. width $= w$
length $= 2w + 2$
$$2(2w + 2) + 2w = 22$$
$$4w + 4 + 2w = 22$$
$$6w = 18$$
$$w = 3$$
$$2w + 2 = 8$$
The garden is 3 feet by 8 feet.

18. New wage
$= $ Old wage $+$ (Percent raise)$\times$(Old wage)
Let $x = $ your salary prior to the raise (old wage)
$$19,610 = x + 0.06x$$
$$19,610 = 1.06x$$
$$x = \frac{19,610}{1.06}$$
$$x = 18,500$$
Your salary prior to the raise was $18,500.

19. Let $x = $ your score on the final.
Then,
$$\frac{61 + 95 + 71 + 83 + 80 + x + x}{7} = 80$$
$$\frac{390 + 2x}{7} = 80$$
$$390 + 2x = 560$$
$$2x = 170$$
$$x = 85$$
You must make an 85 on the final exam to have an average score of 80.

20.
$$f(x) = -16x^2 + 80x$$
$$f(3) = -16(3)^2 + 80(3)$$
$$= -144 + 240$$
$$= 96$$
A rock thrown with an initial velocity of 80 feet per second will have a height of 96 feet at a time of 3 seconds after it was thrown.

Chapter 3

Check Point Exercises

1. $f(x) = -(x-1)^2 + 4$
   The vertex is (1, 4).
   $0 = -(x-1)^2 + 4$
   $(x-1)^2 = 4$
   $x - 1 = \pm 2$
   $x = 3$ or $x = -1$
   The x-intercepts are 3 and –1.
   $f(0) = -(0-1)^2 + 4 = 3$
   The y-intercept is 3.

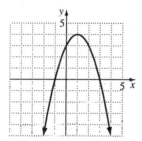

2. $f(x) = (x-2)^2 + 1$
   The vertex is (2, 1).
   $0 = (x-2)^2 + 1$
   $(x-2)^2 = -1$
   No x-intercepts.
   $f(0) = (0-2)^2 + 1 = 5$
   The y-intercept is 5.

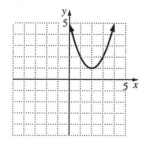

3. $f(x) = x^2 - 2x - 3$
   $x = -\dfrac{b}{2a} = -\dfrac{-2}{2} = 1$
   $f(1) = 1^2 - 2(1) - 3 = -4$
   $x^2 - 2x - 3 = 0$
   $(x-3)(x+1) = 0$
   $x = 3$ or $x = -1$
   The x-intercepts are 3 and –1.
   $f(0) = 0^2 - 2(0) - 3 = -3$
   The y-intercept is –3.

4. $x = -\dfrac{b}{2a} = -\dfrac{-36}{2(0.4)} = 45$
   $f(45) = 0.4(45)^2 - 36(45) + 1000 = 190$
   The age of a driver having the least number of accidents is 45. The minimum number of accidents is 190 per 50 million miles driven.

Exercise Set 3.1

1. vertex: (1, 1)
   $h(x) = (x-1)^2 + 1$

3. vertex: (1, –1)
   $j(x) = (x-1)^2 - 1$

5. The graph is $f(x) = x^2$ translated down one.
   $h(x) = x^2 - 1$

7. The point (1, 0) is on the graph and
   $g(1) = 0$. $g(x) = x^2 - 2x + 1$

9. $f(x) = 2(x-3)^2 + 1$
$h = 3, k = 1$
The vertex is at (3, 1).

11. $f(x) = -2(x+1)^2 + 5$
$h = -1, k = 5$
The vertex is at (–1, 5).

13. $f(x) = 2x^2 - 8x + 3$
$x = \dfrac{-b}{2a} = \dfrac{8}{4} = 2$
$f(2) = 2(2)^2 - 8(2) + 3$
$= 8 - 16 + 3 = -5$
The vertex is at (2, –5).

15. $f(x) = -x^2 - 2x + 8$
$x = \dfrac{-b}{2a} = \dfrac{2}{-2} = -1$
$f(-1) = -(-1)^2 - 2(-1) + 8$
$= -1 + 2 + 8 = 9$
The vertex is at (–1, 9).

17. $f(x) = (x-4)^2 - 1$
vertex: (4, –1)
x-intercepts:
$0 = (x-4)^2 - 1$
$1 = (x-4)^2$
$\pm 1 = x - 4$
$x = 3$ or $x = 5$
y-intercept:
$f(0) = (0-4)^2 - 1 = 15$
The axis of symmetry is $x = 4$.

19. $f(x) = (x-1)^2 + 2$
vertex: (1, 2)
x-intercepts:
$0 = (x-1)^2 + 2$
$(x-1)^2 = -2$
$x - 1 = \pm\sqrt{-2}$
$x = 1 \pm i\sqrt{2}$
No x-intercepts.
y-intercept:
$f(0) = (0-1)^2 + 2 = 3$
The axis of symmetry is $x = 1$.

21. $y - 1 = (x-3)^2$
$y = (x-3)^2 + 1$
vertex: (3, 1)
x-intercepts:
$0 = (x-3)^2 + 1$
$(x-3)^2 = -1$
$x - 3 = \pm i$
$x = 3 \pm i$
No x-intercepts.
y-intercept: 10
$y = (0-3)^2 + 1 = 10$
The axis of symmetry is $x = 3$.

23. $y = 2(x+2)^2 - 1$

vertex: $(-2, -1)$

x-intercepts:

$0 = 2(x+2)^2 - 1$

$2(x+2)^2 = 1$

$(x+2)^2 = \frac{1}{2}$

$x + 2 = \pm\frac{1}{\sqrt{2}}$

$x = -2 \pm \frac{1}{\sqrt{2}} = -2 \pm \frac{\sqrt{2}}{2}$

y-intercept:

$y = 2(0+2)^2 - 1 = 7$

The axis of symmetry is $x = -2$.

25. $f(x) = 4 - (x-1)^2$

$f(x) = -(x-1)^2 + 4$

vertex: $(1, 4)$

x-intercepts:

$0 = -(x-1)^2 + 4$

$(x-1)^2 = 4$

$x - 1 = \pm 2$

$x = -1$ or $x = 3$

y-intercept:

$f(x) = -(0-1)^2 + 4 = 3$

The axis of symmetry is $x = 1$.

27. $f(x) = x^2 - 2x - 3$

$f(x) = \left(x^2 - 2x + 1\right) - 3 - 1$

$f(x) = (x-1)^2 - 4$

vertex: $(1, -4)$

x-intercepts:

$0 = (x-1)^2 - 4$

$(x-1)^2 = 4$

$x - 1 = \pm 2$

$x = -1$ or $x = 3$

y-intercept: -3

$f(0) = 0^2 - 2(0) - 3 = -3$

The axis of symmetry is $x = 1$.

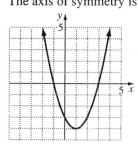

29. $f(x) = x^2 + 3x - 10$

$f(x) = \left(x^2 + 3x + \dfrac{9}{4}\right) - 10 - \dfrac{9}{4}$

$f(x) = \left(x + \dfrac{3}{2}\right)^2 - \dfrac{49}{4}$

vertex: $\left(-\dfrac{3}{2}, -\dfrac{49}{4}\right)$

x-intercepts:

$0 = \left(x + \dfrac{3}{2}\right)^2 - \dfrac{49}{4}$

$\left(x + \dfrac{3}{2}\right)^2 = \dfrac{49}{4}$

$x + \dfrac{3}{2} = \pm\dfrac{7}{2}$

$x = -\dfrac{3}{2} \pm \dfrac{7}{2}$

$x = 2$ or $x = -5$

y-intercept:

$f(x) = 0^2 + 3(0) - 10 = -10$

The axis of symmetry is $x = -\dfrac{3}{2}$.

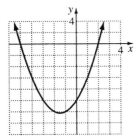

31. $y = 2x - x^2 + 3$

$y = -x^2 + 2x + 3$

$y = -\left(x^2 - 2x + 1\right) + 3 + 1$

$y = -(x - 1)^2 + 4$

vertex: $(1, 4)$

x-intercepts:

$0 = -(x - 1)^2 + 4$

$(x - 1)^2 = 4$

$x - 1 = \pm 2$

$x = -1$ or $x = 3$

y-intercept:

$f(0) = 2(0) - (0)^2 + 3 = 3$

The axis of symmetry is $x = 1$.

33. $y = 2x - x^2 - 2$

$y = -x^2 + 2x - 2$

$y = -\left(x^2 - 2x + 1\right) - 2 + 1$

$y = -(x - 1)^2 - 1$

vertex: $(1, -1)$

x-intercepts:

$0 = -(x - 1)^2 - 1$

$(x - 1)^2 = -1$

$x - 1 = \pm i$

$x = 1 \pm i$

No x-intercepts.

y-intercept:

$y = 2(0) - (0)^2 - 2 = -2$

The axis of symmetry is $x = 1$.

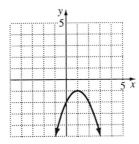

35. $f(x) = 3x^2 - 12x - 1$

$a = 3$. The parabola opens upward and has a minimum value.

$x = \dfrac{-b}{2a} = \dfrac{12}{6} = 2$

$f(2) = 3(2)^2 - 12(2) - 1$
$= 12 - 24 - 1 = -13$

The minimum point is $(2, -13)$.

37. $f(x) = -4x^2 + 8x - 3$

$a = -4$. The parabola opens downward and has a maximum value.

$x = \dfrac{-b}{2a} = \dfrac{-8}{-8} = 1$

$f(1) = -4(1)^2 + 8(1) - 3$
$= -4 + 8 - 3 = 1$

The maximum point is $(1, 1)$.

39. $f(x) = 5x^2 - 5x$

$a = 5$. The parabola opens upward and has a minimum value.

$x = \dfrac{-b}{2a} = \dfrac{5}{10} = \dfrac{1}{2}$

$f\left(\dfrac{1}{2}\right) = 5\left(\dfrac{1}{2}\right)^2 - 5\left(\dfrac{1}{2}\right)$

$= \dfrac{5}{4} - \dfrac{5}{2} = \dfrac{5}{4} - \dfrac{10}{4} = \dfrac{-5}{4}$

The minimum point is $\left(\dfrac{1}{2}, \dfrac{-5}{4}\right)$.

41. $c(t) = -3.1t^2 + 51.4t + 4024.5$

$a = -3.1, \; b = 51.4$

$x = -\dfrac{b}{2a} = -\dfrac{51.4}{-6.2} \approx 8.3$ years

$1960 + 8.3 = 1968.3 \Rightarrow 1968$
Year: 1968

$c(8.3) = -3.1(8.3)^2 + 51.4(8.3) + 4021.5$
$= +213.559 + 426.62 + 4024.5$
$= 4237.561 \approx 4238$

The consumption is 4238 cigarettes per person.

43. $y = -16x^2 + 64x + 80$

$x = \dfrac{-b}{2a} = \dfrac{-64}{-32} = 2$

$y = -16(2)^2 + 64(2) + 80$
$= -64 + 128 + 80 = 144$

The maximum height of 144 feet is reached in 2 seconds.

45. The maximum point on the graph appears to be about 2100 in 1994. Hence, the vertex is approximately $(9, 2100)$.

47. $A(x) = x(120 - 2x)$

$= 12x - 2x^2$

$a = -2, \; b = 120$

$x = \dfrac{-b}{2a} = \dfrac{-120}{-4} = 30$

length $= 120 - 2x = 120 - 2(30)$
$= 120 - 60 = 60$

width: 30 ft
length: 60 ft

$A(30) = 120(30) - 2(30)^2$
$= 1800$

The maximum area is 1800 ft^2.

49.-55. Answers may vary.

57. $y = 2x^2 - 82x + 720$

a.

You can only see a little of the parabola.

b. $a = 2; \; b = -82$

$x = -\dfrac{b}{2a} = -\dfrac{-82}{4} = 20.5$

$y = 2(20.5)^2 - 82(20.5) + 720$
$= 840.5 - 1681 + 720$
$= -120.5$

vertex: $(20.5, -120.5)$

c. Answers may vary.

d. Answers may vary.

59. $y = -4x^2 + 20x + 160$

$x = \dfrac{-b}{2a} = \dfrac{-20}{-8} = 2.5$

$y = -4(2.5)^2 + 20(2.5) + 160$

$= -2.5 + 50 + 160 = 185$

The vertex is at (2.5, 185).

61. $y = 0.01x^2 + 0.6x + 100$

$x = \dfrac{-b}{2a} = \dfrac{-0.6}{0.02} = -30$

$y = 0.01(-30)^2 + 0.6(-30) + 100$

$= 9 - 18 + 100 = 91$

The vertex is at (-30, 91).

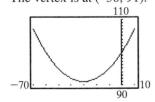

63. $y = 0.011x^2 - 0.097x + 4.1$

vertex: about (4.41, 3.89)

The minimum number of people in the U.S. holding more than one job was 3.89 million in 1974.

65. a. True; all quadratic functions have a minimum value or a maximum value.

b. False;

$f(x) = 2(x - 5)^2 - 1$

vertex = (5, -1)

c. False;

$f(x) = -2(x + 4)^2 - 8$

The parabola is opening concave downward, with a vertex <u>below</u> the *x*-axis, at (-4, -8). No *x*-intercepts exist.

d. False;

$f(x) = -x^2 + x + 1$

$x = -\dfrac{b}{2a} = -\dfrac{1}{2(-1)} = \dfrac{1}{2}$

$f\left(\dfrac{1}{2}\right) = -\left(\dfrac{1}{2}\right)^2 + \left(\dfrac{1}{2}\right) + 1 = \dfrac{3}{2} - \dfrac{1}{4} = \dfrac{5}{4}$

Maximum value of *y* is $\dfrac{5}{4}$.

(a) is true.

67. $f(x) = 3(x + 2)^2 - 5$; (-1, -2)

axis: $x = -2$

(-1, -2) is one unit right of (-2, -2). One unit left of (-2, -2) is (-3, -2).

point: (-3, -2)

69. $3x + 4y = 100$

$4y = 1000 - 3x$

$y = 250 - 0.75x$

$A(x) = x(250 - 0.75x)$

$= 250x - 0.75x^2$

$x = \dfrac{-b}{2a} = \dfrac{-250}{-1.5} = 166\dfrac{2}{3}$

$y = 250 - 0.75\left(166\dfrac{2}{3}\right) = 125$

The dimensions are $x = 166\dfrac{2}{3}$ ft, $y = 125$ ft.

The maximum area is about 20,833 ft^2.

Section 3.2

Check Point Exercises

1. Since *n* is even and $a_n > 0$, the graph rises to the left and to the right.

2. Since *n* is odd and the leading coefficient is negative, the function falls to the right. Since the ratio cannot be negative, the model won't be appropriate.

3. The graph does not show the function's end behavior. Since $a_n > 0$ and n is odd, the graph should fall to the left.

4. $f(x) = x^3 + 2x^2 - 4x - 8$

$$0 = x^2(x + 2) - 4(x + 2)$$
$$0 = (x + 2)(x^2 - 4)$$
$$0 = (x + 2)^2(x - 2)$$
$x = 2$ or $x = -2$
The zeros are 2 and -2.

5. $f(x) = x^4 - 4x^2$

$$x^4 - 4x^2 = 0$$
$$x^2(x^2 - 4) = 0$$
$$x^2(x + 2)(x - 2) = 0$$
$x = 0$ or $x = -2$ or $x = 2$
The zeros are 0, -2, and 2.

6. $f(x) = x^3 - 3x^2$

Since $a_n > 0$ and n is odd, the graph falls to the left and rises to the right.
$$x^3 - 3x^2 = 0$$
$$x^2(x - 3) = 0$$
$x = 0$ or $x = 3$
The x-intercepts are 0 and 3.
$$f(0) = 0^3 - 3(0)^2 = 0$$
The y-intercept is 0.
$$f(-x) = (-x)^3 - 3(-x)^2 = -x^3 - 3x^2$$
No symmetry.

Exercise Set 3.2

1. polynomial function;
degree: 3

3. polynomial function;
degree: 5

5. not a polynomial function

7. not a polynomial function

9. not a polynomial function

11. polynomial function

13. Not a polynomial function because graph is not continuous.

15. (c)

17. (b)

19. (a)

21. $f(x) = 5x^3 + 7x^2 - x + 9$
Since $a_n > 0$ and n is odd, the graph of $f(x)$ falls to the left and rises to the right.

23. $f(x) = 5x^4 + 7x^2 - x + 9$
Since $a_n > 0$ and n is even, the graph of $f(x)$ rises to the left and to the right.

25. $f(x) = -5x^4 + 7x^2 - x + 9$
Since $a_n < 0$ and n is even, the graph of $f(x)$ falls to the left and to the right.

27. $f(x) = 2(x - 5)(x + 4)^2$
x = 5 has multiplicity 1;
The graph crosses the x-axis.
$x = -4$ has multiplicity 2;
The graph touches the x-axis and turns around.

29. $f(x) = 4(x - 3)(x + 6)^3$
x = 3 has multiplicity 1;
The graph crosses the x-axis.
$x = -6$ has multiplicity 3;
The graph crosses the x-axis.

31. $f(x) = x^3 - 2x^2 + x$

$\qquad = x\left(x^2 - 2x + 1\right)$

$\qquad = x(x-1)^2$

$x = 0$ has multiplicity 1;
The graph crosses the x-axis.
$x = 1$ has multiplicity 2;
The graph touches the x-axis and turns around.

33. $f(x) = x^3 + 7x^2 - 4x - 28$

$\qquad = x^2(x+7) - 4(x+7)$

$\qquad = \left(x^2 - 4\right)(x+7)$

$\qquad = (x-2)(x+2)(x+7)$

$x = 2, x = -2$ and $x = -7$ have multiplicity 1;
The graph crosses the x-axis.

35. $f(x) = x^3 + 2x^2 - x - 2$

a. Since $a_n > 0$ and n is odd, $f(x)$ rises to the right and falls to the left.

b. $\quad x^3 + 2x^2 - x - 2 = 0$

$\quad x^2(x+2) - (x+2) = 0$

$\quad (x+2)(x^2 - 1) = 0$

$\quad (x+2)(x-1)(x+1) = 0$

$\quad x = -2, x = 1, x = -1$

The zeros at -2, -1, and 1 have odd multiplicity so $f(x)$ crosses the x-axis at these points.

c. $\quad f(0) = (0)^3 + 2(0)^2 - 0 - 2$

$\qquad = -2$

The y-intercept is -2.

d. $\quad f(-x) = (-x) + 2(-x)^2 - (-x) - 2$

$\qquad\quad = -x^3 + 2x^2 + x - 2$

$\quad -f(x) = -x^3 - 2x^2 + x + 2$

The graph has neither origin symmetry or y-axis symmetry.

e. The graph has 2 turning points and $2 \le 3 - 1$.

37. $f(x) = x^4 - 9x^2$

a. Since $a_n > 0$ and n is even, $f(x)$ rises to the left and the right.

b. $\qquad x^4 - 9x^2 = 0$

$\qquad x^2\left(x^2 - 9\right) = 0$

$\qquad x^2(x-3)(x+3) = 0$

$\qquad x = 0, x = 3, x = -3$

The zeros at -3 and 3 have odd multiplicity, so $f(x)$ crosses the x-axis at these points. The root at 0 has even multiplicity, so $f(x)$ touches the x-axis at 0.

c. $\quad f(0) = (0)^4 - 9(0)^2 = 0$

The y-intercept is 0.

d. $\quad f(-x) = x^4 - 9x^2$

$\qquad f(-x) = f(x)$

The graph has y-axis symmetry.

e. The graph has 3 turning points and $3 \le 4 - 1$.

39. $f(x) = -x^4 + 16x^2$

   a. Since $a_n < 0$ and n is even, $f(x)$ falls to the left and the right.

   b. $\qquad -x^4 + 16x^2 = 0$
$$x^2\left(-x^2 + 16\right) = 0$$
$$x^2(4 - x)(4 + x) = 0$$
$$x = 0,\ x = 4,\ x = -4$$
The zeros at –4 and 4 have odd multiplicity, so $f(x)$ crosses the x-axis at these points. The root at 0 has even multiplicity, so $f(x)$ touches the x-axis at 0.

   c. $f(0) = (0)^4 - 9(0)^2 = 0$
The y-intercept is 0.

   d. $f(-x) = -x^4 + 16x^2$
$f(-x) = f(x)$
The graph has y-axis symmetry.

   e. The graph has 3 turning points and $3 \le 4 - 1$.

41. $f(x) = x^4 - 2x^3 + x^2$

   a. Since $a_n > 0$ and n is even, $f(x)$ rises to the left and the right.

   b. $\qquad x^4 - 2x^3 + x^2 = 0$
$$x^2\left(x^2 - 2x + 1\right) = 0$$
$$x^2(x - 1)(x - 1) = 0$$
$$x = 0,\ x = 1$$
The zeros at 1 and 0 have even multiplicity, so $f(x)$ touches the x-axis at 0 and 1.

   c. $f(0) = (0)^4 - 2(0)^3 + (0)^2 = 0$
The y-intercept is 0.

   d. $f(-x) = x^4 + 2x^3 + x^2$
The graph has neither y-axis nor origin symmetry.

   e. The graph has 3 turning points and $3 \le 4 - 1$.

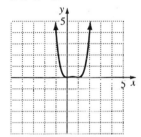

43. $f(x) = -2x^4 + 4x^3$

a. Since $a_n < 0$ and n is even, $f(x)$ falls to the left and the right.

b. $-2x^4 + 4x^3 = 0$
$x^3(-2x + 4) = 0$
$x = 0, x = 2$
The zeros at 0 and 1 have odd multiplicity, so $f(x)$ crosses the x-axis at these points. At 0 the multiplicity is greater than 1, so the function will also flatten out.

c. $f(0) = -2(0)^4 + 4(0)^3 = 0$
The y-intercept is 0.

d. $f(-x) = -2x^4 - 4x^3$
The graph has neither y-axis nor origin symmetry.

e. The graph has 1 turning point and $1 \le 4 - 1$.

45. $f(x) = 6x^3 - 9x - x^5$

a. Since $a_n < 0$ and n is odd, $f(x)$ rises to the left and falls to the right.

b. $-x^5 + 6x^3 - 9x = 0$
$-x(x^4 - 6x^2 + 9) = 0$
$-x(x^2 - 3)(x^2 - 3) = 0$
$x = 0, x = \pm\sqrt{3}$

The root at 0 has odd multiplicity so $f(x)$ crosses the x-axis at (0, 0). The zeros at $-\sqrt{3}$ and $\sqrt{3}$ have even multiplicity so $f(x)$ touches the x-axis at $\sqrt{3}$ and $-\sqrt{3}$.

c. $f(0) = -(0)^5 + 6(0)^3 - 9(0) = 0$
The y-intercept is 0.

d. $f(-x) = x^5 - 6x^3 + 9x$
$f(-x) = -f(x)$
The graph has origin symmetry.

e. The graph has 4 turning point and $4 \le 5 - 1$.

47. $f(x) = 3x^2 - x^3$

a. Since $a_n < 0$ and n is odd, $f(x)$ rises to the left and falls to the right.

b. $-x^3 + 3x^2 = 0$
$-x^2(x - 3) = 0$
$x = 0, x = 3$
The zero at 3 has odd multiplicity so $f(x)$ crosses the x-axis at that point. The root at 0 has even multiplicity so $f(x)$ touches the axis at (0, 0).

c. $f(0) = -(0)^3 + 3(0)^2 = 0$
The y-intercept is 0.

d. $f(-x) = x^3 + 3x^2$
The graph has neither y-axis nor origin symmetry.

e. The graph has 2 turning point and $2 \leq 3 - 1$.

49. $f(x) = -3(x-1)^2 (x^2 - 4)$

a. Since $a_n < 0$ and n is even, $f(x)$ falls to the left and the right.

b. $-3(x-1)^2 (x^2 - 4) = 0$

$x = 1, x = -2, x = 2$

The zeros at -2 and 2 have odd multiplicity, so $f(x)$ crosses the x-axis at these points. The root at 1 has even multiplicity, so $f(x)$ touches the x-axis at $(1, 0)$.

c. $f(0) = -3(0-1)^2 (0^2 - 4)^3$
$= -3(1)(-4) = 12$
The y-intercept is 12.

d. $f(-x) = -3(-x-1)^2 (x^2 - 4)$

The graph has neither x-axis nor origin symmetry.

e. The graph has 3 turning point and $3 \leq 4 - 1$.

51. a. Leading coefficient test suggests the elk population will decline and eventually will die off.

b.

c.

The population reaches extinction at the end of 5 years.

53. a. $F(x) = -0.87x^3 + 0.35x^2 + 81.62x + 7684.94$

$2005 - 1987 = 18$

$F(18) = -0.87(18)^3 + 0.35(18)^2$
$+ 81.62(18) + 7684.94$
$= -5073.84 + 113.4$
$+ 1469.16 + 7684.94$
$= 4193.66$

There are about 4194 larceny thefts.

b. No. Since $a_n < 0$ and n is odd, the graph of $F(x)$ falls to the right. Eventually the function would predict a negative number of larceny thefts, which is impossible.

55. $H(x) = -0.001183x^4 + 0.05495x^3$
$\quad -0.8523x^2 + 9.054x + 6.748$

a. $H(10) = -0.001183(10)^4$
$\quad +0.05495(10)^3 - 0.8523(10)^2$
$\quad +9.054(10) + 6.748$
$\quad = -11.83 + 54.95 - 85.23$
$\quad +90.54 + 6.748$
$\quad = 55.178$ years

b. No. $a_n < 0$ and n is even; the graph falls to the right and would eventually give $H(x) < x$.

57.–71. Answers may vary.

73.

75.

77.

79. a. False; $f(x)$ falls to the left and rises to the right.

b. False

c. True; There are many 3rd degree polynomials with the same three x-intercepts.

d. False; a function with origin symmetry either falls to the left and rises to the right, or rises to the left and falls to the right.

(c) is true.

81. Answers may vary.

Section 3.3

Check Point Exercises

1.
$$\begin{array}{r} x+5 \\ x+9\overline{\smash{)}x^2+14x+45} \\ \underline{x^2+9x} \\ 5x+45 \\ \underline{5x+45} \\ 0 \end{array}$$

The answer is $x + 5$.

2.
$$\begin{array}{r} 2x^2+3x-2 \\ x-3\overline{\smash{)}2x^3-3x^2-11x+7} \\ \underline{2x^3-6x^2} \\ 3x^2-11x \\ \underline{3x^2-9x} \\ -2x+7 \\ \underline{-2x+6} \\ 1 \end{array}$$

The answer is $2x^2 + 3x - 2 + \dfrac{1}{x-3}$.

3.
$$\begin{array}{r} 2x^2+7x+14 \\ x^2-2x\overline{\smash{)}2x^4+3x^3+0x^2-7x-10} \\ \underline{2x^4-4x^3} \\ 7x^3+0x^2 \\ \underline{7x^3-14x^2} \\ 14x^2-7x \\ \underline{14x^2-28x} \\ 21x-10 \end{array}$$

The answer is $2x^2 + 7x + 14 + \dfrac{21x-10}{x^2-2x}$.

4.

$$\begin{array}{r|rrrr} -2 & 1 & 0 & -7 & -6 \\ & & -2 & 4 & 6 \\ \hline & 1 & -2 & -3 & 0 \end{array}$$

The answer is $x^2 - 2x - 3$.

5.

$$\begin{array}{r|rrrr} -4 & 3 & 4 & -5 & 3 \\ & & -12 & 32 & -108 \\ \hline & 3 & -8 & 27 & -105 \end{array}$$

$f(-4) = -105$

6.

$$\begin{array}{r|rrrr} -1 & 15 & 14 & -3 & -2 \\ & & -15 & 1 & 2 \\ \hline & 15 & -1 & -2 & 0 \end{array}$$

$15x^2 - x - 2 = 0$

$(3x + 1)(5x - 2) = 0$

$x = -\dfrac{1}{3}$ or $x = \dfrac{2}{5}$

The solution set is $\left\{-1, -\dfrac{1}{3}, \dfrac{2}{5}\right\}$.

Exercise Set 3.3

1.

$$\begin{array}{r} x + 3 \\ x + 5 \overline{\smash{)}x^2 + 8x + 15} \\ \underline{x^2 + 5x} \\ 3x + 15 \\ \underline{3x + 15} \\ 0 \end{array}$$

The answer is $x + 3$.

3.

$$\begin{array}{r} x^2 + 3x + 1 \\ x + 2 \overline{\smash{)}x^3 + 5x^2 + 7x + 2} \\ \underline{x^3 + 2x^2} \\ 3x^2 + 7x \\ \underline{3x^2 + 6x} \\ x + 2 \\ \underline{x + 2} \\ 0 \end{array}$$

The answer is $x^2 + 3x + 1$.

5.

$$\begin{array}{r} 2x^2 + 3x + 5 \\ 3x - 1 \overline{\smash{)}6x^3 + 7x^2 + 12x - 5} \\ \underline{6x^3 - 2x^2} \\ 9x^2 + 12x \\ \underline{9x^2 - 3x} \\ 15x - 5 \\ \underline{15x - 5} \\ 0 \end{array}$$

The answer is $2x^2 + 3x + 5$.

7.

$$\begin{array}{r} 4x + 3 + \dfrac{2}{3x - 2} \\ 3x - 2 \overline{\smash{)}12x^2 + x - 4} \\ \underline{12x^2 - 8x} \\ 9x - 4 \\ \underline{9x - 6} \\ 2 \end{array}$$

The answer is $4x + 3 + \dfrac{2}{3x - 2}$.

9.

$$\begin{array}{r} 2x^2 + x + 6 - \dfrac{38}{x + 3} \\ x + 3 \overline{\smash{)}2x^3 + 7x^2 + 9x - 20} \\ \underline{2x^3 + 6x^2} \\ x^2 + 9x \\ \underline{x^2 + 3x} \\ 6x - 20 \\ \underline{6x + 18} \\ -38 \end{array}$$

The answer is $2x^2 + x + 6 - \dfrac{38}{x + 3}$.

$$4x^3 + 16x^2 + 60x + 246 + \frac{984}{x-4}$$

11. $x - 4 \overline{\smash{\big)}4x^4 - 4x^2 + 6x}$

$$\underline{4x^4 - 16x^3}$$
$$16x^3 - 4x^2$$
$$\underline{16x^3 - 64x^2}$$
$$60x^2 + 6x$$
$$\underline{60x^2 - 240x}$$
$$246x$$
$$\underline{246x - 984}$$
$$984$$

The answer is

$$4x^3 + 16x^2 + 60x + 246 + \frac{984}{x-4}.$$

13. $3x^2 - x - 3 \overline{\smash{\big)}6x^3 + 13x^2 - 11x - 15}$ with quotient $2x + 5$

$$\underline{6x^3 - 2x^2 - 6x}$$
$$15x^2 - 5x - 15$$
$$\underline{15x^2 - 5x - 15}$$
$$0$$

The answer is $2x + 5$.

15. $3x^2 + 1 \overline{\smash{\big)}18x^4 + 9x^3 + 3x^2}$ with quotient $6x^2 + 3x - 1$

$$\underline{18x^4 + 6x^2}$$
$$9x^3 - 3x^2$$
$$\underline{9x^3 + 3x}$$
$$-3x^2 - 3x$$
$$\underline{-3x^2 - 1}$$
$$-3x + 1$$

The answer is $6x^2 + 3x - 1 - \dfrac{3x-1}{3x^2+1}$.

17. $\left(2x^2 + x - 10\right) \div (x - 2)$

2	2	1	−10
		4	10
	2	5	0

The answer is $2x + 5$.

19. $\left(3x^2 + 7x - 20\right) \div (x + 5)$

−5	3	7	−20
		−15	40
	3	−8	20

The answer is $3x - 8 + \dfrac{20}{x+5}$.

21. $\left(4x^3 - 3x^2 + 3x - 1\right) \div (x - 1)$

1	4	−3	3	−1
		4	1	4
	4	1	4	3

The answer is $4x^2 + x + 4 + \dfrac{3}{x-1}$.

23. $\left(6x^5 - 2x^3 + 4x^2 - 3x + 1\right) \div (x - 2)$

2	6	0	−2	4	−3	1
		12	24	44	96	186
	6	12	22	48	93	187

The answer is

$$6x^4 + 12x^3 + 22x^2 + 48x + 93 + \frac{187}{x-2}.$$

25. $\left(x^2 - 5x - 5x^3 + x^4\right) \div (5 + x) \Rightarrow$

$\left(x^4 - 5x^3 + x^2 - 5x\right) \div (x + 5)$

$$
\begin{array}{r|rrrrr}
-5 & 1 & -5 & 1 & -5 & 0 \\
   &   & -5 & 50 & -255 & 1300 \\
\hline
   & 1 & -10 & 51 & -260 & 1300
\end{array}
$$

The answer is

$x^3 - 10x^2 + 51x - 260 + \dfrac{1300}{x+5}$.

27. $\dfrac{x^5 + x^3 - 2}{x - 1}$

$$
\begin{array}{r|rrrrrr}
1 & 1 & 0 & 1 & 0 & 0 & -2 \\
  &   & 1 & 1 & 2 & 2 & 2 \\
\hline
  & 1 & 1 & 2 & 2 & 2 & 0
\end{array}
$$

The answer is $x^4 + x^3 + 2x^2 + 2x + 2$.

29. $\dfrac{x^4 - 256}{x - 4}$

$$
\begin{array}{r|rrrrr}
4 & 1 & 0 & 0 & 0 & -256 \\
  &   & 4 & 16 & 64 & 256 \\
\hline
  & 1 & 4 & 16 & 64 & 0
\end{array}
$$

The answer is $x^3 + 4x^2 + 16x + 64$.

31. $\dfrac{2x^5 - 3x^4 + x^3 - x^2 + 2x - 1}{x + 2}$

$$
\begin{array}{r|rrrrrr}
-2 & 2 & -3 & 1 & -1 & 2 & -1 \\
   &   & -4 & 14 & -30 & 62 & -128 \\
\hline
   & 2 & -7 & 15 & -31 & 64 & -129
\end{array}
$$

The answswer is

$2x^4 - 7x^3 + 15x^2 - 31x + 64 - \dfrac{129}{x+2}$.

33. $f(x) = 2x^3 - 11x^2 + 7x - 5$

$$
\begin{array}{r|rrrr}
4 & 2 & -11 & 7 & -5 \\
  &   & 8 & -12 & -20 \\
\hline
  & 2 & -3 & -5 & -25
\end{array}
$$

$f(4) = -25$

35. $f(x) = 7x^4 - 3x^3 + 6x + 9$

$$
\begin{array}{r|rrrrr}
-5 & 7 & -3 & 0 & 6 & 9 \\
   &   & -35 & 190 & -950 & 4720 \\
\hline
   & 7 & -38 & 190 & -944 & 4729
\end{array}
$$

$f(-5) = 4729$

37. Dividend: $x^3 - 4x^2 + x + 6$
Divisor: $x + 1$

$$
\begin{array}{r|rrrr}
-1 & 1 & -4 & 1 & 6 \\
   &   & -1 & 5 & -6 \\
\hline
   & 1 & -5 & 6 & 0
\end{array}
$$

The answer is $x^2 - 5x + 6$.

$(x + 1)(x^2 - 5x + 6) = 0$
$(x + 1)(x - 2)(x - 3) = 0$
$x = -1, x = 2, x = 3$
The solution set is $\{-1, 2, 3\}$.

39. $2x^3 - 5x^2 + x + 2 = 0$

$$
\begin{array}{r|rrrr}
2 & 2 & -5 & 1 & 2 \\
  &   & 4 & -2 & -2 \\
\hline
  & 2 & -1 & -1 & 0
\end{array}
$$

$(x - 2)(2x^2 - x - 1) = 0$
$(x - 2)(2x + 1)(x - 1) = 0$
$x = 2, \ x = -\dfrac{1}{2}, x = 1$

The solution set is $\left\{-\dfrac{1}{2}, 1, 2\right\}$.

41. $12x^3 + 16x^2 - 5x - 3 = 0$

$$
\begin{array}{r|rrrr}
-\frac{3}{2} & 12 & 16 & -5 & -3 \\
 & & -18 & 3 & 3 \\
\hline
 & 12 & -2 & -2 & 0
\end{array}
$$

$\left(x + \frac{3}{2}\right)(12x^2 - 2x - 2) = 0$

$\left(x + \frac{3}{2}\right)2(6x^2 - x - 1) = 0$

$\left(x + \frac{3}{2}\right)2(3x + 1)(2x - 1) = 0$

$x = -\frac{3}{2}, \ x = -\frac{1}{3}, \ x = \frac{1}{2}$

The solution set is $\left\{-\frac{3}{2}, -\frac{1}{3}, \frac{1}{2}\right\}$.

43.
$$
\begin{array}{r}
x^3 + 5x^2 - 9x - 45 \\
2x+5\overline{)2x^4 + 15x^3 + 7x^2 - 135x - 225} \\
\underline{2x^4 + 5x^3} \\
10x^3 + 7x^2 \\
\underline{10x^3 + 25x^2} \\
-18x^2 - 135x \\
\underline{-18x^2 - 45x} \\
-90x - 225 \\
\underline{-90x - 225}
\end{array}
$$

Width: $x^3 + 5x^2 - 9x - 45$

45. a.
$$
\begin{array}{r}
1 + \dfrac{5}{x+20} \\
x+20\overline{)x + 25} \\
\underline{x + 20} \\
5
\end{array}
$$

b.

x	0	5	10	25	50	75
$\dfrac{x+25}{x+20}$	1.25	1.2	1.17	1.11	1.07	1.05

c. Answers may vary.

47.–53. Answers may vary.

55.

The division is not correct.

$$
\begin{array}{r|rrrr}
1 & 2 & -3 & -3 & 4 \\
 & & 2 & -1 & -4 \\
\hline
 & 2 & -1 & -4 & 0
\end{array}
$$

Quotient: $2x^2 - x - 4$

57.

The division is correct.

59.
$$
\begin{array}{r}
5x^2 + 2x - 4 \\
4x+3\overline{)20x^3 + 23x^2 - 10x + k} \\
\underline{20x^3 + 15x^2} \\
8x^2 - 10 \\
\underline{8x^2 + 6x} \\
-16x + k \\
\underline{-16x - 12}
\end{array}
$$

To get a remainder of zero, k must equal -12.
$k = -12$

61.
$$x^n+1 \overline{) x^{3n} \qquad +1}$$
quotient: $x^{2n}-x^n+1$

$$\underline{x^{3n}+x^{2n}}$$
$$-x^{2n}$$
$$\underline{-x^{2n}-x^n}$$
$$x^n+1$$
$$\underline{x^n+1}$$
$$0$$

Section 3.4

Check Point Exercises

1. p: $\pm1,\ \pm2,\ \pm3,\ \pm6$
q: ±1

$\dfrac{p}{q}$: $\pm1,\ \pm2,\ \pm3,\ \pm6$

are the possible rational zeros.

2. p: $\pm1,\ \pm3$
q: $\pm1,\ \pm2,\ \pm4$

$\dfrac{p}{q}$: $\pm1,\ \pm3,\ \pm\dfrac{1}{2},\ \pm\dfrac{1}{4},\ \pm\dfrac{3}{2},\ \pm\dfrac{3}{4}$

are the possible rational zeros.

3. $\pm1,\ \pm2,\ \pm4,\ \pm5,\ \pm10,\ \pm20$ are possible rational zeros

1	1	8	11	−20
		1	9	20
	1	9	20	0

1 is a zero.
$$x^2+9x+20=0$$
$$(x+4)(x+5)=0$$
$$x=-4 \quad \text{or} \quad x=-5$$
The solution set is $\{1,-4,-5\}$.

4. $\pm1,\ \pm13$ are possible rational zeros.

1	1	−6	22	−30	13
		1	−5	17	−13
	1	−5	17	−13	0

1 is a zero.

1	1	5	17	−13
		1	−4	13
	1	−4	13	0

1 is a double root.
$$x^2-4x+13=0$$
$$x=\frac{4\pm\sqrt{16-52}}{2}=\frac{4\pm\sqrt{-36}}{2}=2+3i$$
The solution set is $\{1,\ 2+3i,\ 2-3i\}$.

5. $f(x)=x^4-14x^3+71x^2-154x+120$
$f(x)=x^4+14x^3+71x^2+154x+120$
Since $f(x)$ has 4 changes of sign, there are 4, 2, or 0 positive real zeros.
Since $f(-x)$ has no changes of sign, there are no negative real zeros.

Exercise Set 3.4

1. $f(x)=x^3+x^2-4x-4$
p: $\pm1,\pm2,\pm4$
q: ±1
$\dfrac{p}{q}$: $\pm1,\pm2,\pm4$

3. $f(x)=3x^4-11x^3-x^2+19x+6$
p: $\pm1,\pm2,\pm3,\pm6$
q: $\pm1,\pm3$
$\dfrac{p}{q}$: $\pm1,\pm2,\pm3,\pm6,\pm\dfrac{1}{3},\pm\dfrac{2}{3}$

5. $f(x) = 4x^4 - x^3 + 5x^2 - 2x - 6$

    $p: \pm 1, \pm 2, \pm 3, \pm 6$

    $q: \pm 1, \pm 2, \pm 4$

    $\dfrac{p}{q}: \pm 1, \pm 2, \pm 3, \pm 6, \pm\dfrac{1}{2}, \pm\dfrac{1}{4}, \pm\dfrac{3}{2}, \pm\dfrac{3}{4}$

7. $f(x) = x^5 - x^4 - 7x^3 + 7x^2 - 12x - 12$

    $p: \pm 1, \pm 2, \pm 3 \pm 4 \pm 6 \pm 12$

    $q: \pm 1$

    $\dfrac{p}{q}: \pm 1, \pm 2, \pm 3 \pm 4 \pm 6 \pm 12$

9. $f(x) = x^3 + x^2 - 4x - 4$

    a. $p: \pm 1, \pm 2, \pm 4$

        $q: \pm 1$

        $\dfrac{p}{q}: \pm 1, \pm 2, \pm 4$

    b.
    $$\begin{array}{r|rrrr} 2 & 1 & 1 & -4 & -4 \\ & & 2 & 6 & 4 \\ \hline & 1 & 3 & 2 & 0 \end{array}$$

    2 is a zero.

    c. $x^3 + x^2 - 4x - 4 = 0$

        $(x - 2)(x^2 + 3x + 2) = 0$

        $(x - 2)(x + 2)(x + 1) = 0$

        $x - 2 = 0 \quad x + 2 = 0 \quad x + 1 = 0$

        $x = 2, \ x = -2, \ x = -1$

        The solution set is $\{2, -2, -1\}$.

11. $f(x) = 2x^3 - 3x^2 - 11x + 6$

    a. $p: \pm 1, \pm 2, \pm 3, \pm 6$

        $q: \pm 1, \pm 2$

        $\dfrac{p}{q}: \pm 1, \pm 2, \pm 3, \pm 6, \pm\dfrac{1}{2}, \pm\dfrac{3}{2}$

    b.
    $$\begin{array}{r|rrrr} 3 & 2 & -3 & -11 & 6 \\ & & 6 & 9 & -6 \\ \hline & 2 & 3 & -2 & 0 \end{array}$$

    3 is a zero.

    c. $2x^3 - 3x^2 - 11x + 6 = 0$

        $(x - 3)(2x^2 + 3x - 2) = 0$

        $(x - 3)(2x - 1)(x + 2) = 0$

        $x = 3, \ x = \dfrac{1}{2}, \ x = -2$

        The solution set is $\left\{3, \dfrac{1}{2}, -2\right\}$.

13. $f(x) = 3x^3 + 7x^2 - 22x - 8$

    a. $p: \pm 1, \pm 2, \pm 4, \pm 8$

        $q: \pm 1, \pm 3$

        $\dfrac{p}{q}: \pm 1, \pm 2, \pm 4, \pm 8, \pm\dfrac{1}{3}, \pm\dfrac{2}{3}, \pm\dfrac{4}{3}, \pm\dfrac{8}{3}$

    b.
    $$\begin{array}{r|rrrr} 4 & 3 & 7 & -22 & -8 \\ & & 12 & 76 & 216 \\ \hline & 3 & 19 & 54 & 208 \end{array}$$

    4 is not a zero.

    $$\begin{array}{r|rrrr} 2 & 3 & 7 & -22 & -8 \\ & & 6 & 26 & 8 \\ \hline & 3 & 13 & 4 & 0 \end{array}$$

    2 is a zero.

    c. $3x^3 + 7x^2 - 22x - 8 = 0$

        $(x - 2)(3x^2 + 13x + 4) = 0$

        $(x - 2)(3x + 1)(x + 4) = 0$

        $x = 2, \ x = -\dfrac{1}{3}, \ x = -4$

        The solution set is $\left\{2, -\dfrac{1}{3}, -4\right\}$.

15. $x^3 - 2x^2 - 11x + 12 = 0$

  a. p: $\pm 1, \pm 2, \pm 3, \pm 4, \pm 6, \pm 12$
      q: ± 1

      $\dfrac{p}{q}$: $\pm 1, \pm 2, \pm 3, \pm 4, \pm 6, \pm 12$

  b.

3	1	−2	−11	12
		3	3	−24
	1	1	−8	−12

     3 is not a zero.

4	1	−2	−11	12
		4	8	−12
	1	2	−3	0

     4 is a zero.

  c. $x^3 - 2x^2 - 11x + 12$
      $(x - 4)(x^2 + 2x - 3) = 0$
      $(x - 4)(x + 3)(x - 1) = 0$
      $x - 4 = 0 \quad x + 3 = 0 \quad x - 1 = 0$
      $x = 4 \qquad x = -3 \qquad x = 1$
      The solution set is $\{-3, 1, 4\}$.

17. $x^3 - 10x - 12 = 0$

  a. p: $\pm 1, \pm 2, \pm 3, \pm 4, \pm 6, \pm 12$
      q: ± 1

      $\dfrac{p}{q}$: $\pm 1, \pm 2, \pm 3, \pm 4, \pm 6, \pm 12$

  b.

−2	1	0	−10	−12
		−2	4	12
	1	−2	−6	0

     −2 is a zero.

  c. $x^3 - 10x - 12 = 0$
      $(x + 2)(x^2 - 2x - 6) = 0$

      $x = \dfrac{2 \pm \sqrt{4 + 24}}{2} = \dfrac{2 \pm \sqrt{28}}{2}$

      $= \dfrac{2 \pm 2\sqrt{7}}{2} = 1 \pm \sqrt{7}$

      The solution set is $\left\{-2, 1 + \sqrt{7}, 1 - \sqrt{7}\right\}$.

19. $6x^3 + 25x^2 - 24x + 5 = 0$

  a. p: $\pm 1, \pm 5$
      q: $\pm 1, \pm 2, \pm 3, \pm 6$

      $\dfrac{p}{q}$: $\pm 1, \pm 5, \pm \dfrac{1}{2}, \pm \dfrac{5}{2}, \pm \dfrac{1}{3}, \pm \dfrac{5}{3}, \pm \dfrac{1}{6}, \pm \dfrac{5}{6}$

  b.

−5	6	25	−24	5
		−30	25	−5
	6	−5	1	0

     −5 is a zero.

  c. $6x^3 + 25x^2 - 24x + 5 = 0$
      $(x + 5)(6x^2 - 5x + 1) = 0$
      $(x + 5)(2x - 1)(3x - 1) = 0$
      $x + 5 = 0 \quad 2x - 1 = 0 \quad 3x - 1 = 0$

      $x = -5, \qquad x = \dfrac{1}{2}, \qquad x = \dfrac{1}{3}$

      The solution set is $\left\{-5, \dfrac{1}{2}, \dfrac{1}{3}\right\}$.

21. $x^4 - 2x^3 - 5x^2 + 8x + 4 = 0$

    a. $p: \pm 1, \pm 2, \pm 4$

       $q: \pm 1$

       $\dfrac{p}{q}: \pm 1, \pm 2, \pm 4$

    b.

$$\begin{array}{r|rrrrr} 2 & 1 & -2 & -5 & 8 & 4 \\ & & 2 & 0 & -10 & -4 \\ \hline & 1 & 0 & -5 & -2 & 0 \end{array}$$

       2 is a zero.

    c. $x^4 - 2x^3 - 5x^2 + 8x + 4 = 0$

       $(x-2)(x^3 - 5x - 2) = 0$

$$\begin{array}{r|rrrr} -2 & 1 & 0 & -5 & -2 \\ & & -2 & 4 & 2 \\ \hline & 1 & -2 & -1 & 0 \end{array}$$

       -2 is a zero of $x^3 - 5x - 2 = 0$.

       $(x-2)(x+2)\left(x^2 - 2x - 1\right) = 0$

       $x = \dfrac{2 \pm \sqrt{4+4}}{2} = \dfrac{2 \pm \sqrt{8}}{2} = \dfrac{2 \pm 2\sqrt{2}}{2}$

       $= 1 \pm \sqrt{2}$

       The solution set is

       $\left\{-2, 2, 1 + \sqrt{2}, 1 - \sqrt{2}\right\}$.

23. $f(x) = x^3 + 2x^2 + 5x + 4$

Since $f(x)$ has no sign variations, no positive real roots exist.

$f(-x) = -x^3 + 2x^2 - 5x + 4$

Since $f(-x)$ has 3 sign variations, 3 or 1 negative real roots exist.

25. $f(x) = 5x^3 - 3x^2 + 3x - 1$

Since $f(x)$ has 3 sign variations, 3 or 1 positive real roots exist.

$f(-x) = -5x^3 - 3x^2 - 3x - 1$

Since $f(-x)$ has no sign variations, no negative real roots exist.

27. $f(x) = 2x^4 - 5x^3 - x^2 - 6x + 4$

Since $f(x)$ has 2 sign variations, 2 or 0 positive real roots exist.

$f(-x) = 2x^4 + 5x^3 - x^2 + 6x + 4$

Since $f(-x)$ has 2 sign variations, 2 or 0 negative real roots exist.

29. $f(x) = x^3 - 4x^2 - 7x + 10$

$p: \pm 1, \pm 2, \pm 5, \pm 10$

$q: \pm 1$

$\dfrac{p}{q}: \pm 1, \pm 2, \pm 5, \pm 10$

Since $f(x)$ has 2 sign variations, 0 or 2 positive real zeros exist.

$f(-x) = -x^3 - 4x^2 + 7x + 10$

Since $f(-x)$ has 1 sign variation, exactly one negative real zeros exists.

$$\begin{array}{r|rrrr} -2 & 1 & -4 & -7 & 10 \\ & & -2 & 12 & -10 \\ \hline & 1 & -6 & 5 & 0 \end{array}$$

-2 is a zero.

$f(x) = (x+2)\left(x^2 - 6x + 5\right)$

$ = (x+2)(x-5)(x-1)$

$x = -2, x = 5, x = 1$

The solution set is $\{-2, 5, 1\}$.

31. $2x^3 - x^2 - 9x - 4 = 0$

$p: \pm 1, \pm 2, \pm 4$

$q: \pm 1, \pm 2$

$\dfrac{p}{q}: \pm 1, \pm 2, \pm 4 \pm \dfrac{1}{2}$

1 positive real root exists.

$f(-x) = -2x^3 - x^2 + 9x - 4$ 2 or no negative real roots exist.

$$
\begin{array}{r|rrrr}
-\frac{1}{2} & 2 & -1 & -9 & -4 \\
 & & -1 & 1 & 4 \\
\hline
 & 2 & -2 & -8 & 0 \\
\end{array}
$$

$-\dfrac{1}{2}$ is a root.

$\left(x + \dfrac{1}{2}\right)\left(2x^2 - 2x - 8\right) = 0$

$2\left(x + \dfrac{1}{2}\right)\left(x^2 - x - 4\right) = 0$

$x = \dfrac{1 \pm \sqrt{1 + 16}}{2} = \dfrac{1 \pm \sqrt{17}}{2}$

The solution set is

$\left\{ -\dfrac{1}{2}, \dfrac{1 + \sqrt{17}}{2}, \dfrac{1}{2} \dfrac{\sqrt{17}}{2} \right\}.$

33. $x^4 - 3x^3 - 20x^2 - 24x - 8 = 0$

$p: \pm 1, \pm 2, \pm 4, \pm 8$

$q: \pm 1$

$\dfrac{p}{q}: \pm 1, \pm 2, \pm 4 \pm 8$

1 positive real root exists.
3 or 1 negative real roots exist.

$$
\begin{array}{r|rrrrr}
-1 & 1 & -3 & -20 & -24 & -8 \\
 & & -1 & 4 & 16 & 8 \\
\hline
 & 1 & -4 & -16 & -8 & 0 \\
\end{array}
$$

$(x + 1)\left(x^3 - 4x^2 - 16x - 8\right) = 0$

$$
\begin{array}{r|rrrr}
-2 & 1 & -4 & -16 & -8 \\
 & & -2 & 12 & 8 \\
\hline
 & 1 & -6 & -4 & 0 \\
\end{array}
$$

$(x + 1)(x + 2)\left(x^2 - 6x - 4\right) = 0$

$x = \dfrac{6 \pm \sqrt{36 + 16}}{2} = \dfrac{6 \pm \sqrt{52}}{2}$

$= \dfrac{6 \pm 2\sqrt{13}}{2} = \dfrac{3 \pm \sqrt{13}}{2}$

The solution set is

$\left\{ -1, -2, 3 \pm \sqrt{13}, 3 - \sqrt{13} \right\}.$

35. $f(x) = 3x^4 - 11x^3 - x^2 + 19x + 6$

$p: \pm 1, \pm 2, \pm 3, \pm 6$

$q: \pm 1, \pm 3$

$\dfrac{p}{q}: \pm 1, \pm 2, \pm 3, \pm 6, \pm \dfrac{1}{3}, \pm \dfrac{2}{3}$

2 or no positive real zeros exists.

$f(-x) = 3x^4 + 11x^3 - x^2 - 19x + 6$

2 or no negative real zeros exist.

$$
\begin{array}{r|rrrrr}
-1 & 3 & -11 & -1 & 19 & 6 \\
 & & -3 & 14 & -13 & -6 \\
\hline
 & 3 & -14 & 13 & 6 & 0 \\
\end{array}
$$

$f(x) = (x + 1)\left(3x^3 - 14x^2 + 13x + 6\right)$

$$
\begin{array}{r|rrrr}
2 & 3 & -14 & 13 & 6 \\
 & & 6 & -16 & -6 \\
\hline
 & 3 & -8 & -3 & 0 \\
\end{array}
$$

$f(x) = (x + 1)(x - 2)\left(3x^2 - 8x - 3\right)$

$ = (x + 1)(x - 2)(3x + 1)(x - 3)$

$x = -1, \; x = 2 \; x = -\dfrac{1}{3}, \; x = 3$

The solution set is $\left\{ -1, 2, -\dfrac{1}{3}, 3 \right\}.$

37. $4x^4 - x^3 + 5x^2 - 2x - 6 = 0$

$p: \pm 1, \pm 2, \pm 3, \pm 6$

$q: \pm 1, \pm 2, \pm 4$

$\dfrac{p}{q}: \pm 1, \pm 2, \pm 3, \pm 6, \pm \dfrac{1}{2}, \pm \dfrac{3}{2}, \pm \dfrac{1}{4}, \pm \dfrac{3}{4}$

3 or 1 positive real roots exists.

1 negative real root exists.

1	4	−1	5	−2	−6
		4	3	8	6
	4	3	8	6	0

$(x - 1)(4x^3 + 3x^2 + 8x + 6) = 0$

$4x^3 + 3x^2 + 8x + 6 = 0$ has no positive real roots.

$-\frac{3}{4}$	4	3	8	6
		−3	0	−6
	4	0	8	0

$(x - 1)\left(x + \dfrac{3}{4} \right)(4x^2 + 8) = 0$

$4(x - 1)\left(x + \dfrac{3}{4} \right)(x^2 + 2) = 0$

$x^2 + 2 = 0$

$x^2 = -2$

$x = \pm i\sqrt{2}$

The solution set is $\left\{ 1, -\dfrac{3}{4}, i\sqrt{2}, -i\sqrt{2} \right\}$.

39. $2x^5 + 7x^4 - 18x^2 - 8x + 8 = 0$

$p: \pm 1, \pm 2, \pm 4, \pm 8$

$q: \pm 1, \pm 2$

$\dfrac{p}{q}: \pm 1, \pm 2, \pm 4, \pm 8, \pm \dfrac{1}{2}$

2 or no positive real roots exists.

3 or 1 negative real root exist.

−2	2	7	0	−18	−8	8
		−4	−6	12	12	−8
	2	3	−6	−6	4	0

$(x + 2)(2x^4 + 3x^3 - 6x^2 - 6x + 4) = 0$

$4x^3 + 3x^2 + 8x + 6 = 0$ has no positive real roots.

−2	2	3	−6	−6	4
		−4	2	8	−4
	2	−1	−4	2	0

$(x + 2)^2 (2x^3 - x^2 - 4x + 2)$

$\frac{1}{2}$	2	−1	−4	2
		1	0	2
	2	0	−4	0

$(x + 2)^2 \left(x - \dfrac{1}{2} \right)(2x^2 - 4) = 0$

$2(x + 2)^2 \left(x - \dfrac{1}{2} \right)(x^2 - 2) = 0$

$x^2 - 2 = 0$

$x^2 = 2$

$x = \pm\sqrt{2}$

The solution set is $\left\{ -2, \dfrac{1}{2}, \sqrt{2}, -\sqrt{2} \right\}$.

41. a. $f(x) = 6.2$
  $x = 3$, $x \approx 4.2$

  b. degree: 4
  leading coefficient: negative

43. $14W^3 - 17W^2 - 16W + 34 = 211$
  $14W^3 - 17W^2 - 16W - 177 = 0$
  p: $\pm 1, \pm 3, \pm 59, \pm 177$
  q: $\pm 1, \pm 2, \pm 7, \pm 14$

$$\begin{array}{r|rrrr} 3 & 14 & -17 & -16 & -177 \\ & & 42 & 75 & 177 \\ \hline & 14 & 25 & 59 & 0 \end{array}$$

  $(x - 3)(14x^2 + 25x + 59) = 0$
  $b^2 - 4ac = 625 - 3304 < 0$
  $W = 3$ mm
  The abdominal width is 3 millimeters.

45. $V = lwh$
  $72 = (h + 7)(2h)(h)$
  $72 = 2h^2(h + 7)$
  $2h^3 + 14h^2 - 72 = 0$
  $h^3 + 7h^2 - 36 = 0$

$$\begin{array}{r|rrrr} 2 & 1 & 7 & 0 & -36 \\ & & 2 & 18 & 36 \\ \hline & 1 & 9 & 18 & 0 \end{array}$$

  $(h - 2)(h^2 + 9h + 18) = 0$
  $(h - 2)(h + 3)(h + 6) = 0$
  $h = 2$ $h = -3$ $h = -6$
  $h = -3$ and $h = -6$ do not make sense.
  $h = 2$
  $h + 7 = 9$
  $2h = 4$
  The dimensions are 2 in. by 9 in. by 4 in.

47.–53. Answers may vary.

55. $6x^3 - 19x^2 + 16x - 4 = 0$
  p: $\pm 1, \pm 2, \pm 4$
  q: $\pm 1, \pm 2, \pm 3, \pm 6$
  $\dfrac{p}{q}$: $\pm 1, \pm 2, \pm 4, \pm\dfrac{1}{2}, \pm\dfrac{1}{3}, \pm\dfrac{2}{3}, \pm\dfrac{4}{3}, \pm\dfrac{1}{6}$

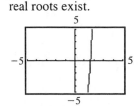

  From the graph, we see that the solutions are
  $\dfrac{1}{2}, \dfrac{2}{3}$ and 2.

57. $4x^4 + 4x^3 + 7x^2 - x - 2 = 0$
  p: $\pm 1, \pm 2$
  q: $\pm 1, \pm 2, \pm 4$
  $\dfrac{p}{q}$: $\pm 1, \pm 2, \pm\dfrac{1}{2}, \pm\dfrac{1}{4}$

  From the graph, we see that the solutions are
  $-\dfrac{1}{2}$ and $\dfrac{1}{2}$.

59. $f(x) = x^5 - x^4 + x^3 - x^2 + x - 8$
  $f(x)$ has 5 sign variations, so either 5, 3, or 1
  positive real roots exist.
  $f(-x) = -x^5 - x^4 - x^3 - x^2 - x - 8$
  $f(-x)$ has no sign variations, so no negative
  real roots exist.

61. a. False; the equation has 0 sign variations, so no positive roots exist.

b. False; Descartes's Rule gives the possible number of roots.

c. False; Every polynomial equation of degree 3 has at least one <u>real</u> root.

d. True

(d) is true.

63. $(2x+1)(x+5)(x+2) - 3x(x+5) = 208$

$(2x^2 + 11x + 5)(x+2) - 3x^2 - 15x = 208$

$2x^3 + 4x^2 + 11x^2 + 22x + 5x$
$+10 - 3x^2 - 15x = 208$

$2x^3 + 15x^2 + 27x - 3x^2 - 15x - 198 = 0$

$2x^3 + 12x^2 + 12x - 198 = 0$

$2(x^3 + 6x^2 + 6x - 99) = 0$

$$
\begin{array}{r|rrrr}
3 & 1 & 6 & 6 & -99 \\
  &   & 3 & 27 & 99 \\
\hline
  & 1 & 9 & 33 & 0
\end{array}
$$

$x^2 + 9x + 33 = 0$

$b^2 - 4ac = -51$

$x = 3$ in.

Section 3.5

Check Point Exercises

1.
$$
\begin{array}{r|rrrr}
-7 & 2 & 11 & -7 & -6 \\
   &   & -14 & 21 & -98 \\
\hline
   & 2 & -3 & 14 & -104
\end{array}
$$

The signs alternate.

$$
\begin{array}{r|rrrr}
2 & 2 & 11 & -7 & -6 \\
  &   & 4 & 30 & 46 \\
\hline
  & 2 & 15 & 23 & 40
\end{array}
$$

All the numbers are nonnegative. Thus, -7 is a lower bound and 2 is an upper bound.

2. $f(-3) = 3(-3)^3 - 10(-3) + 9 = -42$

$f(-2) = 3(-2)^3 - 10(-2) + 9 = 5$

The sign change shows there is a zero between -3 and -2.

3. $(x - 2 + i)(x - 2 - i) = x^2 - 2x - ix - 2x + 4$
$+ 2i + ix - 2i - i^2 = x^2 - 4x + 5$

$$
\require{enclose}
\begin{array}{r}
x^2 - 4x - 21 \\
x^2 - 4x + 5 \enclose{longdiv}{x^4 - 8x^3 + 0x^2 + 64x - 105} \\
\underline{x^4 - 4x^3 + 5x^2} \\
-4x^3 - 5x^2 + 64x \\
\underline{-4x^3 + 16x^2 - 20x} \\
-21x^2 + 84x - 105 \\
\underline{-21x^2 + 84x - 105} \\
0
\end{array}
$$

$x^2 - 4x - 21 = 0$

$(x - 7)(x + 3) = 0$

$x = 7$ or $x = -3$

The solution set is $\{-3, 7, 2 + i, 2 - i\}$.

4. a. $x^4 - 4x^2 - 5 = (x^2 - 5)(x^2 + 1)$

b. $(x + \sqrt{5})(x - \sqrt{5})(x^2 + 1)$

c $(x + \sqrt{5})(x - \sqrt{5})(x + i)(x - i)$

5. $(x + 3)(x - i)(x + i) = (x + 3)(x^2 + 1)$

$f(x) = a_n(x + 3)(x^2 + 1)$

$f(1) = a_n(1 + 3)(1^2 + 1) = 8a_n = 8$

$a_n = 1$

$f(x) = (x + 3)(x^2 + 1)$ or $x^3 + 3x^2 + x + 3$

Exercise Set 3.5

1. $x^4 - 5x^3 + 11x^2 + 33x - 18 = 0$

$$
\begin{array}{r|rrrrr}
-4 & 1 & -5 & 11 & 33 & -18 \\
   &   & -4 & 36 & -188 & 620 \\
\hline
   & 1 & -9 & 47 & -155 & 602
\end{array}
$$

Since signs alternate, -4 is a lower bound.

$$\begin{array}{c|ccccc} 7 & 1 & -5 & 11 & 33 & -18 \\ & & 7 & 14 & 175 & 1456 \\ \hline & 1 & 2 & 25 & 208 & 1438 \end{array}$$

Since no sign is negative, 7 is an upper bound.

3. $2x^3 + 5x^2 - 8x - 7 = 0$

$$\begin{array}{c|cccc} -4 & 2 & 5 & -8 & 7 \\ & & -8 & 12 & -16 \\ \hline & 2 & -3 & 4 & -9 \end{array}$$

Since signs alternate, -4 is a lower bound.

$$\begin{array}{c|cccc} 2 & 2 & 5 & -8 & 7 \\ & & 4 & 18 & 20 \\ \hline & 2 & 9 & 10 & 27 \end{array}$$

Since no sign is negative, 2 is an upper bound.

5. $x^4 + 3x^3 + 2x^2 - 5x + 12 = 0$

a. $p: \pm 1, \pm 2, \pm 3, \pm 4, \pm 6, \pm 12$
   $q: \pm 1$

   $\dfrac{p}{q}: \pm 1, \pm 2, \pm 3, \pm 4, +6, \pm 12$

b.
$$\begin{array}{c|ccccc} 1 & 1 & 3 & 2 & -5 & 12 \\ & & 1 & 4 & 6 & 1 \\ \hline & 1 & 4 & 6 & 1 & 13 \end{array}$$

1 is not a root.
1 is an upper bound.

c. Eliminate all positive possible rational roots.

d.
$$\begin{array}{c|ccccc} -3 & 1 & 3 & 2 & -5 & 12 \\ & & -3 & 0 & -6 & 33 \\ \hline & 1 & 0 & 2 & -11 & 45 \end{array}$$

-3 is not a root.
-3 is a lower bound.

e. Eliminate $-3, -4, -6$ and -12.

7. $f(x) = x^3 - x - 1$
   $f(1) = -1$
   $f(2) = 5$
   $f(1.3) = -0.103$
   $f(1.4) = 0.344$
   $f(1.35) = 0.11038$
   To the nearest tenth, the zero is 1.3.

9. $f(x) = 2x^4 - 4x^2 + 1$
   $f(-1) = -1$
   $f(0) = 1$
   $f(-0.5) = 0.125$
   $f(-0.6) = -0.1808$
   $f(-0.55) = -0.027$
   To the nearest tenth, the zero is -0.5.

11. $f(x) = x^3 + x^2 - 2x + 1$
   $f(-3) = -11$
   $f(-2) = 1$
   $f(-2.2) = -0.408$
   $f(-2.1) = 0.349$
   $f(-2.15) = -0.0159$
   To the nearest tenth, the zero is -2.1.

13. $f(x) = 3x^3 - 10x + 9$
   $f(-3) = -42$
   $f(-2) = 5$
   $f(-2.1) = 2.217$
   $f(-2.2) = -0.944$
   $f(-2.15) = 0.68488$
   To the nearest tenth, the zero is -2.2.

15. $x = -2i$, so $x = 2i$ also.
   $(x + 2i)(x - 2i) = x^2 + 4$

$$\require{enclose}\begin{array}{r} x - 2 \\ x^2 + 4 \enclose{longdiv}{x^3 + 4x - 2x^2 - 8} \\ \underline{x^3 + 4x } \\ -2x^2 - 8 \\ \underline{-2x^2 - 8} \\ 0 \end{array}$$

   $x - 2 = 0$
   $x = 2$
   Solution: $\{\ 2i, 2i, 2\}$

17. $x = (1 + i)$, so $x = (1 - i)$ also.

$(x - 1 - i)(x - 1 + i)$

$= x^2 - x + ix - x + 1 - i - ix + i - i^2$

$= x^2 - 2x + 2$

$$
\begin{array}{r}
3x - 1 \\
x^2 - 2x + 2 \overline{\smash{\big)}\ 3x^3 - 7x^2 + 8x - 2} \\
\underline{3x^3 - 6x^2 + 6x} \\
-x^2 + 2x - 2 \\
\underline{-x^2 + 2x - 2} \\
0
\end{array}
$$

$3x - 1 = 0$

$x = \dfrac{1}{3}$

Solution: $\left\{ 1 - i, \ 1 + i, \ \dfrac{1}{3} \right\}$

19. $x = 2 - i$, so $x = 2 + i$ also.

$(x - 2 + i)(x - 2 - i)$

$= x^2 - 2x - ix - 2x + 4 + 2i + ix - 2i - i^2$

$= x^2 - 4x + 5$

$$
\begin{array}{r}
x^2 + 4x + 5 \\
x^2 - 4x + 5 \overline{\smash{\big)}\ x^4 + 0x^3 - 6x^2 + 0x + 25} \\
\underline{x^4 - 4x^3 + 5x^2} \\
4x^3 - 11x^2 + \ 0x \\
\underline{4x^3 - 16x^2 + 20x} \\
5x^2 - 20x + 25 \\
\underline{5x^2 - 20x + 25} \\
0
\end{array}
$$

$x^2 + 4x + 5 = 0$

$x = \dfrac{-4 \pm \sqrt{16 - 4(5)}}{2} = \dfrac{-4 \pm \sqrt{-4}}{2}$

$= \dfrac{-4 \pm 2i}{2} = -2 \pm i$

The solution set is

$\{2 - i, \ 2 + i, \ -2 + i, \ -2 - i\}$,

21. $x = 2 - i$, so $x = 2 + i$ also.

$(x - 2 + i)(x - 2 - i)$

$= x^2 - 2x - xi - 2x + 4 + 2i + ix - 2i - i^2$

$= x^2 - 4x + 5$

$$
\begin{array}{r}
x^2 - 4x + 5 \\
x^2 - 4x + 5 \overline{\smash{\big)}\ x^4 - 8x^3 + 0x^2 + 64x - 105} \\
\underline{x^4 - 4x^3 + 5x^2} \\
-4x^3 - 5x^2 + 64x \\
\underline{-4x^3 + 16x^2 - 20x} \\
-21x^2 + \ 84x - 105 \\
\underline{-21x^2 + \ 84x - 105} \\
0
\end{array}
$$

$x^2 - 4x - 21 = 0$

$(x - 7)(x + 3) = 0$

$x = 7, \ x = -3$

The solution set is $\{2 + i, \ 2 - i, \ -3, \ 7\}$.

23. $x^4 - x^2 - 20$

   a. $\left(x^2 - 5 \right)\left(x^2 + 4 \right)$

   b. $\left(x + \sqrt{5} \right)\left(x - \sqrt{5} \right)\left(x^2 + 4 \right)$

   c. $\left(x + \sqrt{5} \right)\left(x - \sqrt{5} \right)(x + 2i)(x - 2i)$

25. $x^4 + x^2 - 6$

   a. $\left(x^2 - 2 \right)\left(x^2 + 3 \right)$

   b. $\left(x + \sqrt{2} \right)\left(x - \sqrt{2} \right)\left(x^2 + 3 \right)$

   c. $\left(x + \sqrt{2} \right)\left(x - \sqrt{2} \right)\left(x + i\sqrt{3} \right)\left(x - i\sqrt{3} \right)$

27. $x^4 - 2x^3 + x^2 - 8x - 12$

a.

$$x^2 + 4 \overline{\smash{\big)}\, x^4 - 2x^3 + x^2 + 8x - 12} \quad \frac{x^2 - 2x - 3}{}$$

$$\frac{x^4 \qquad\quad -4x^2}{}$$

$$-2x^3 - 3x^2 + 8x$$

$$\frac{-2x^3 \qquad\quad -8x}{}$$

$$-3x^2 - 12$$

$$\frac{-3x^2 - 12}{}$$

$$\left(x^2 - 2x - 3\right)\left(x^2 + 4\right)$$

$$(x - 3)\ (x + 1)\left(x^2 + 4\right)$$

b. $(x - 3)\ (x + 1)\left(x^2 + 4\right)$

c. $(x - 3)\ (x + 1)\ (x + 2i)\ (x - 2i)$

29. $(x - 1)\ (x + 5i)\ (x - 5i)$

$$= (x - 1)\left(x^2 + 25\right)$$

$$= x^3 + 25x - x^2 - 25$$

$$= x^3 - x^2 + 25x - 25$$

$$f(x) = a_n\left(x^3 - x^2 + 25x - 25\right)$$

$$f(-1) = a_n(-1 - 1 - 25 - 25)$$

$$-104 = a_n(-52)$$

$$a_n = 2$$

$$f(x) = 2\left(x^3 - x^2 + 25x - 25\right)$$

$$f(x) = 2x^3 - 2x^2 + 50x - 50$$

31. $(x + 5)(x - 4 - 3i)(x - 4 + 3i)$

$$= (x + 5)\left(x^2 - 4x + 3ix - 4x + 16 - 12i\right.$$

$$\left. -3ix + 12i - 9i^2\right)$$

$$= (x + 5)\left(x^2 - 8x + 25\right)$$

$$= \left(x^3 - 8x^2 + 25x + 5x^2 - 40x + 125\right)$$

$$= x^3 - 3x^2 - 15x + 125$$

$$f(x) = a_n(x^3 - 3x^2 - 15x + 125)$$

$$f(2) = a_n\left(2^3 - 3(2)^2 - 15(2) + 125\right)$$

$$91 = a_n(91)$$

$$a_n = 1$$

$$f(x) = 1\left(x^3 - 3x^2 - 15x + 125\right)$$

$$f(x) = x^3 - 3x^2 - 15x + 125$$

33. $(x - i)(x + i)(x - 3i)(x + 3i)$

$$= \left(x^2 - i^2\right)\left(x^2 - 9i^2\right)$$

$$= \left(x^2 + 1\right)\left(x^2 + 9\right)$$

$$= x^4 + 10x^2 + 9$$

$$f(x) = a_n(x^4 + 10x^2 + 9)$$

$$f(-1) = a_n((-1)^4 + 10(-1)^2 + 9)$$

$$20 = a_n(20)$$

$$a_n = 1$$

$$f(x) = x^4 + 10x^2 + 9$$

35. $(x + 2)\ (x - 5)\ (x - 3 + 2i)\ (x - 3 - 2i)$

$$= \left(x^2 - 3x - 10\right)$$

$$\left(x^2 - 3x - 2ix - 3x + 9 + 6i + 2ix - 6i - 4i^2\right)$$

$$= \left(x^2 - 3x - 10\right)\left(x^2 - 6x + 13\right)$$

$$= x^4 - 6x + 13x^2 - 3x^3 + 18x^2$$

$$- 39x - 10x^2 + 60x - 130$$

$$= x^4 - 9x^3 + 21x^2 + 21x - 130$$

$$f(x) = a_n\left(x^4 - 9x^3 + 21x^2 + 21x - 130\right)$$

$$f(1) = a_n(1 - 9 + 21 + 21 - 130)$$

$$-96 = a_n(-96)$$

$$a_n = 1$$

$$f(x) = x^4 - 9x^3 + 21x^2 + 21x - 130$$

37. $f(x) = x^3 - x^2 + 25x - 25$

p: $\pm 1, \pm 5, \pm 25$

q: ± 1

$\dfrac{p}{q}$: $\pm 1, \pm 5, \pm 25$

$$
\begin{array}{c|cccc}
1 & 1 & -1 & 25 & -25 \\
  &   & 1 & 0 & 25 \\
\hline
  & 1 & 0 & 25 & 0
\end{array}
$$

$x = 1$

$x^2 + 25 = 0$

$x^2 = -25$

$x = \pm\sqrt{-25} = \pm 5i$

$f(x) = (x - 1)(x - 5i)(x + 5i)$

39. $f(x) = x^3 - 8x^2 + 25x - 26$

p: $\pm 1, \pm 2, \pm 13, \pm 26$

q: ± 1

p: $\pm 1, \pm 2, \pm 13, \pm 26$

q:

$$
\begin{array}{c|cccc}
2 & 1 & -8 & 25 & -26 \\
  &   & 2 & -12 & 26 \\
\hline
  & 1 & -6 & 13 & 0
\end{array}
$$

$x = 2$

$x^2 - 6x + 13 = 0$

$x = \dfrac{6 \pm \sqrt{36 - 52}}{2} = \dfrac{6 \pm \sqrt{-16}}{2}$

$= \dfrac{6 \pm 4i}{2} = 3 \pm 2i$

$f(x) = (x - 2)(x - 3 + 2i)(x - 3 - 2i)$

41. $f(x) = x^4 + 37x^2 + 36$

$x^4 + 37x^2 + 36 = 0$

$\left(x^2 + 36\right)\left(x^2 + 1\right) = 0$

$x^2 = -36 \qquad x^2 = -1$

$x = \pm 6i \qquad x = \pm i$

$f(x) = (x - 6i)(x + 6i)(x - i)(x + i)$

43. $f(x) = 16x^4 + 36x^3 + 16x^2 + x - 30$

p: $\pm 1, \pm 2, \pm 3, \pm 5, \pm 6, \pm 10, \pm 15, \pm 30$

q: $\pm 1, \pm 2, \pm 4, \pm 8, \pm 16$

$\dfrac{p}{q}$: $\pm 1, \pm 2, \pm 3, \pm 5, \pm 6, \pm 10, \pm 15, \pm 30,$

$\pm\dfrac{1}{2}, \pm\dfrac{3}{2}, \pm\dfrac{5}{2}, \pm\dfrac{15}{2}, \pm\dfrac{1}{4}, \pm\dfrac{3}{4}, \pm\dfrac{5}{4},$

$\pm\dfrac{15}{4}, \pm\dfrac{30}{4}, \pm\dfrac{1}{8}, \pm\dfrac{3}{8}, \pm\dfrac{5}{8}, \pm\dfrac{15}{8},$

$\pm\dfrac{30}{8}, \pm\dfrac{1}{16}, \pm\dfrac{3}{16}, \pm\dfrac{5}{16}, \pm\dfrac{15}{16}$

$$
\begin{array}{c|ccccc}
-2 & 16 & 36 & 16 & 1 & -30 \\
   &   & -32 & -8 & -16 & 30 \\
\hline
   & 16 & 4 & 8 & -15 & 0
\end{array}
$$

$x = -2$

$0 = 16x^3 + 4x^2 + 8x - 15$

$$
\begin{array}{c|cccc}
\frac{3}{4} & 16 & 4 & 8 & -15 \\
   &   & 12 & 12 & 15 \\
\hline
   & 16 & 16 & 20 & 0
\end{array}
$$

$x = \dfrac{3}{4}$

$16x^2 + 16x + 20 = 0$

$x = \dfrac{-16 \pm \sqrt{-1024}}{32} = \dfrac{-16 \pm 32i}{32}$

$x = -\dfrac{1}{2} \pm i$

$f(x)$
$= (x + 2)(4x - 3)(2x + 1 - 2i)(2x + 1 + 2i)$

45. about 2.5 years

47. Answers may vary.

49. $27x + 163 = 458$

$$27x = 295$$
$$x = 10.9$$

According to the linear model, spending will reach \$458 billion, 10.9 or almost 11 years after 1995, just before 2006.

$$1.2x^2 + 15.2x + 181.4 = 458$$

$$1.2x^2 + 15.2x - 276.6 = 0$$

$$x = \frac{-15.2 \pm \sqrt{231.04 + 1327.68}}{2.4}$$

$$\approx \frac{-15.2 \pm 39.48}{2.4}$$

$$x \approx -22.78 \text{ or } x \approx 10.12$$

According to quadratic model, spending will reach \$458 billion 10.12 years after 1995, in 2005.

$$0.08x^3 - 0.06x^2 + 20.08x + 178.32 = 458$$

$$0.08x^3 - 0.06x^2 + 20.08x - 279.68 = 0$$

$$0.08(10.1)^3 - 0.06(10.1)^2 + 20.08(10.1) - 279.68$$
$$= -0.56852$$

$$0.08(10.2)^3 - 0.06(10.2)^2 + 20.08(10.2) - 279.68$$
$$= 3.79$$

There is a solution between 10.1 and 10.2. According to the third-degree polynomial model, spending will reach \$458 billion, just over 10 years after 1995, in 2005. The third-degree polynomial model is best.

51.–53. Answers may vary.

55. $f(x) = 2x^3 + x^2 - 14x - 7$

-3	2	1	-14	-7
		-6	15	-3
	2	-5	1	-10

3	2	1	-14	-7
		6	21	21
	2	7	7	14

-3 is a lower bound; 3 is an upper bound.

57. $f(x) = -0.00002x^3 + 0.008x^2 - 0.3x + 6.95$

a. $f(x) = -0.00002x^3 + 0.008x^2 - 0.3x + 6.95$

The graph suggests that people visit a physician more often as they age.

b. $f(x) = -0.00002x^3 + 0.008x^2 - 0.3x + 6.95$

$$13.43 = -0.00002x^3 + 0.008x^2 - 0.3x + 6.95$$

$$0 = -0.00002x^3 + 0.008x^2 - 0.3x - 6.48$$

$$x = 60 \Rightarrow 60 \text{ years of age}$$

c. Use Trace to find the value of the function at $y = 13.43$.

59. $f(x) = 3x^5 - 2x^4 + 6x^3 - 4x^2 - 24x + 16$

3 real zeros
2 nonreal complex zeros

61. $f(x) = x^6 - 64$

2 real zeros
4 nonreal complex zeros

63. Because the polynomial has no obvious changes of direction but the graph is obviously not linear, the smallest degree is 3.

65.–67. Answers may vary.

Section 3.6

Check Point Exercises

1. a. $x - 5 = 0$
$x = 5$
$\{x \mid x \neq 5\}$

b. $x^2 - 25 = 0$
$x^2 = 25$
$x = \pm 5$
$\{x \mid x \neq 5, x \neq 5\}$

c. The denominator cannot equal zero. All real numbers.

2. a. $x^2 - 1 = 0$
$x^2 = 1$
$x = 1, \quad x = -1$

b. $g(x) = \dfrac{x-1}{x^2-1} = \dfrac{x-1}{(x-1)(x+1)} = \dfrac{1}{x+1}$
$x = -1$

c. The denominator cannot equal zero. No vertical asymptotes

3. a. Since $n = m, \ y = \dfrac{9}{3} = 3$ is a horizontal asymptote.

b. Since $n < m, \ y = 0$ is a horizontal asymptote.

c. Since $n > m$, there is no horizontal asymptote.

4. $f(x) = \dfrac{3x}{x-2}$
$f(-x) = \dfrac{3(-x)}{-x-2} = \dfrac{3x}{x+2}$
no symmetry
$f(0) = \dfrac{3(0)}{0-2} = 0$
The y-intercept is 0.
$3x = 0$
$x = 0$
The x-intercept is 0.
Vertical asymptote:
$x - 2 = 0$
$x = 2$
Horizontal asymptote:
$y = \dfrac{3}{1} = 3$

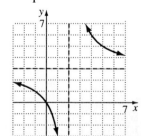

5. $f(x) = \dfrac{2x^2}{x^2 - 9}$

$f(-x) = \dfrac{2(-x)^2}{(-x)^2 - 9} = \dfrac{2x^2}{x^2 - 9} = f(x)$

The y-axis symmetry.

$f(0) = \dfrac{2(0)^2}{0^2 - 9} = 0$

The y-intercept is 0.

$2x^2 = 0$

$x = 0$

The x-intercept is 0.

vertical asymptotes:

$x^2 - 9 = 0$

$x = 3, \quad x = -3$

horizontal asymptote:

$y = \dfrac{2}{1} = 2$

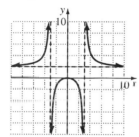

6. $f(x) = \dfrac{x^4}{x^2 + 2}$

$f(-x) = \dfrac{(-x)^4}{(-x)^2 + 2} = \dfrac{x^4}{x^2 + 2} = f(x)$

y-axis symmetry

$f(0) = \dfrac{0^4}{0^2 + 2} = 0$

The y-intercept is 0.

$x^4 = 0$

$x = 0$

The x-intercept is 0.

vertical asymptotes:

$x^2 + 2 = 0$

$x^2 = -2$

no vertical asymptotes

horizontal asymptote:
Since $n > m$, there is no horizontal asymptote.

7.

$$
\begin{array}{r|rrr}
2 & 2 & -5 & 7 \\
  &   & 4 & -2 \\
\hline
  & 2 & -1 & 5
\end{array}
$$

the equation of the slant asymptote is $y = 2x - 1$.

8. a. $\overline{C}(1000) = \dfrac{30(1000) + 300,000}{1000} = \$330$

When 1000 pairs of shoes are produced, it costs \$330 to produce each pair.

$\overline{C}(10,000) = \dfrac{30(10,000) + 300,000}{10,000} = \$60$

When 10,000 pairs of shoes are produced, it costs \$60 to produce each pair.

$\overline{C}(100,000) = \dfrac{30(100,000) + 300,000}{100,000} = \$33$

When 100,000 pairs of shoes are produced, it cost \$33 to produce each pair.

These are the average costs per pair of shoes for producing 1000, 10,000, and 100,000 pairs per week.

b. horizontal asymptote:

$y = \dfrac{30}{1} = 30$

The cost per pair of shoes approaches \$30 as more shoes are produced.

Exercise Set 3.6

1. $f(x) = \dfrac{5x}{x-4}$

$\{x | x \neq 4\}$

3. $g(x) = \dfrac{3x^2}{(x-5)(x+4)}$

$\{x | x \neq 5, x \neq -4\}$

5. $h(x) = \dfrac{x+7}{x^2-49}$

$x^2 - 49 = (x-7)(x+7)$

$\{x | x \neq 7, x \neq -7\}$

7. $f(x) = \dfrac{x+7}{x^2+49}$

all real numbers

9. $-\infty$

11. $-\infty$

13. 0

15. $+\infty$

17. $-\infty$

19. 1

21. $f(x) = \dfrac{x}{x+4}$

$x + 4 = 0$

$x = -4$

vertical asymptote: $x = 0, \ x - -4$

23. $g(x) = \dfrac{x+3}{x(x+4)}$

$x(x+4) = 0$

$x = 0, x = -4$

vertical asymptotes: $x = 0, x = -4$

25. $h(x) = \dfrac{x}{x(x+4)} = \dfrac{1}{x+4}$

$x + 4 = 0$

$x = -4$

vertical asymptote: $x = -4$

27. $r(x) = \dfrac{x}{x^2+4}$

$x^2 + 4$ has no real zeros

There are no vertical asymptotes.

29. $f(x) = \dfrac{12x}{3x^2+1}$

$n < m$

horizontal asymptote: $y = 0$

31. $g(x) = \dfrac{12x^2}{3x^2+1}$

$n = m$,

horizontal asymptote: $y = \dfrac{12}{3} = 4$

33. $h(x) = \dfrac{12x^3}{3x^2+1}$

$n > m$

no horizontal asymptote

35. $f(x) = \dfrac{-2x+1}{3x+5}$

$n = m$

horizontal asymptote: $y = -\dfrac{2}{3}$

37. $f(x) = \dfrac{4x}{x-2}$

$f(-x) = \dfrac{4(-x)}{(-x)-2} = \dfrac{4x}{x+2}$

$f(-x) \neq f(x), f(-x) \neq -f(x)$

no symmetry

y-intercept: $y = \dfrac{4(0)}{0-2} = 0$

x-intercept: $4x = 0$

$x = 0$

vertical asymptote:

$\quad x - 2 = 0$

$\qquad x = 2$

horizontal asymptote:

$n = m$, so $y = \dfrac{4}{1} = 4$

39. $f(x) = \dfrac{2x}{x^2-4}$

$f(-x) = \dfrac{2(-x)}{(-x)^2-4} = -\dfrac{2x}{x^2-4} = -f(x)$

Origin symmetry

y-intercept: $\dfrac{2(0)}{0^2-4} = \dfrac{0}{-4} = 0$

x-intercept:

$2x = 0$

$x = 0$

vertical asymptotes:

$x^2 - 4 = 0$

$x = \pm 2$

horizontal asymptote:
$n < m$ so $y = 0$

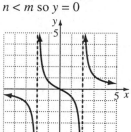

41. $f(x) = \dfrac{2x^2}{x^2-1}$

$f(-x) = \dfrac{2(-x)^2}{(-x)^2-1} = \dfrac{2x^2}{x^2-1} = f(x)$

y-axis symmetry

y-intercept: $y = \dfrac{2(0)^2}{0^2-1} = \dfrac{0}{1} = 0$

x-intercept:

$2x^2 = 0$

$x = 0$

vertical asymptote:

$x^2 - 1 = 0$

$x^2 = 1$

$x = \pm 1$

horizontal asymptote:

$n = m$, so $y = \dfrac{2}{1} = 2$

43. $f(x) = \dfrac{-x}{x+1}$

$f(-x) = \dfrac{-(-x)}{(-x)+1} = \dfrac{x}{-x+1}$

$f(-x) \ne f(x), f(-x) \ne -f(x)$

no symmetry

y-intercept: $y = \dfrac{-(0)}{0+1} = \dfrac{0}{1} = 0$

x-intercept:

$-x = 0$

$x = 0$

vertical asymptote:

$x + 1 = 0$

$x = -1$

horizontal asymptote:

$n = m$, so $y = \dfrac{-1}{1} = -1$

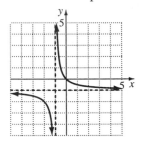

45. $f(x) = -\dfrac{1}{x^2 - 4}$

$f(-x) = -\dfrac{1}{(-x)^2 - 4} = -\dfrac{1}{x^2 - 4} = f(x)$

y-axis symmetry

y-intercept: $y = -\dfrac{1}{0^2 - 4} = \dfrac{1}{4}$

x-intercept: $-1 \ne 0$

no x-intercept

vertical asymptotes:

$x^2 - 4 = 0$

$x^2 = 4$

$x = \pm 2$

horizontal asymptote:

$n < m$ or $y = 0$

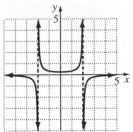

47. $f(x) = \dfrac{2}{x^2 + x - 2}$

$f(-x) = -\dfrac{2}{(-x)^2 - x - 2} = \dfrac{2}{x^2 - x - 2}$

$f(-x) \ne f(x), f(-x) \ne -f(x)$

no symmetry

y-intercept: $y = \dfrac{2}{0^2 + 0 - 2} = \dfrac{2}{-2} = -1$

x-intercept: none

vertical asymptotes:

$x^2 + x - 2 = 0$

$(x + 2)(x - 1) = 0$

$x = -2, x = 1$

horizontal asymptote:

$n < m$ so $y = 0$

49. $f(x) = \dfrac{2x^2}{x^2 + 4}$

$f(-x) = \dfrac{2(-x)^2}{(-x)^2 + 4} = \dfrac{2x^2}{x^2 + 4} = f(x)$

y axis symmetry

y-intercept: $\quad y = \dfrac{2(0)^2}{0^2 + 4} = 0$

x-intercept: $2x^2 = 0$
$x = 0$
vertical asymptote: none
horizontal asymptote:

$n = m,$ so $y = \dfrac{2}{1} = 2$

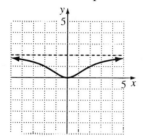

51. $f(x) = \dfrac{x + 2}{x^2 + x - 6}$

$f(-x) = \dfrac{-x + 2}{(-x)^2 - (-x) - 6} = \dfrac{-x + 2}{x^2 + x - 6}$

$f(-x) \neq f(x), f(-x) \neq -f(x)$
no symmetry

y-intercept: $\quad y = \dfrac{0 + 2}{0^2 + 0 - 6} = -\dfrac{2}{6} = -\dfrac{1}{3}$

x-intercept:
$x + 2 = 0$
$x = -2$
vertical asymptotes:
$x^2 + x - 6 = 0$
$(x + 3)(x - 2)$
$x = -3, x = 2$

horizontal asymptote:
$n < m,$ so $y = 0$

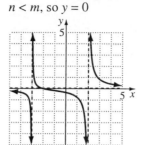

53. $f(x) = \dfrac{x^4}{x^2 + 2}$

$f(-x) = \dfrac{(-x)^4}{(-x)^2 + 2} = \dfrac{x^4}{x^2 + 2} = f(x)$

y-axis symmetry

y-intercept: $\quad y = \dfrac{0^4}{0^2 + 2} = 0$

x-intercept: $x^4 = 0$
$x = 0$
vertical asymptote: none
horizontal asymptote:
$n > m,$ so none

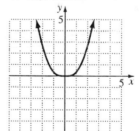

55. $f(x) = \dfrac{x^2 + x - 12}{x^2 - 4}$

$f(-x) = \dfrac{(-x)^2 - x - 12}{(-x)^2 - 4} = \dfrac{x^2 - x - 12}{x^2 - 4}$

$f(-x) \neq f(x), f(-x) \neq -f(x)$

no symmetry

y-intercept: $y = \dfrac{0^2 + 0 - 12}{0^2 - 4} = 3$

x-intercept: $x^2 + x - 12 = 0$
$\qquad\qquad (x - 3)(x + 4) = 0$
$\qquad\qquad\qquad\qquad x = 3, x = -4$

vertical asymptotes:
$\qquad x^2 - 4 = 0$
$(x - 2)(x + 2) = 0$
$\qquad\qquad x = 2, x = -2$

horizontal asymptote:

$n = m$, so $y = \dfrac{1}{1} = 1$

57. $f(x) = \dfrac{3x^2 + x - 4}{2x^2 - 5x}$

$f(-x) = \dfrac{3(-x)^2 - x - 4}{2(-x)^2 + 5x} = \dfrac{3x^2 - x - 4}{2x^2 + 5x}$

$f(-x) \neq f(x), f(-x) \neq -f(x)$

no symmetry

y-intercept: $y = \dfrac{3(0)^2 + 0 - 4}{2(0)^2 - 5(0)} = \dfrac{-4}{0}$

no y-intercept
x-intercepts:
$\qquad 3x^2 + x - 4 = 0$
$(3x + 4)(x - 1) = 0$
$\qquad 3x + 4 = 0 \quad x - 1 = 0$
$\qquad\qquad 3x = -4$
$\qquad\qquad\qquad x = -\dfrac{4}{3}, x = 1$

vertical asymptotes:
$2x^2 - 5x = 0$
$x(2x - 5) = 0$
$x = 0, 2x = 5$
$\qquad\qquad x = \dfrac{5}{2}$

horizontal asymptote:

$n = m$, so $y = \dfrac{3}{2}$

59. a. Slant asymptote:

$f(x) = x - \dfrac{1}{x}$

$y = x$

b. $f(x) = \dfrac{x^2 - 1}{x}$

$f(-x) = \dfrac{(-x)^2 - 1}{(-x)} = \dfrac{x^2 - 1}{-x} = -f(x)$

Origin symmetry

y-intercept: $y = \dfrac{0^2 - 1}{0} = \dfrac{-1}{0}$

no y-intercept
x-intercepts:
$x^2 - 1 = 0$
$x = \pm 1$

vertical asymptote: $x = 0$
horizontal asymptote:
$n < m$, so none exist.

61. a. Slant asymptote:

$$f(x) = x + \frac{1}{x}$$

$$y = x$$

b. $f(x) = \dfrac{x^2 + 1}{x}$

$$f(-x) = \frac{(-x)^2 + 1}{-x} = \frac{x^2 + 1}{-x} = -f(x)$$

Origin symmetry

y-intercept: $y = \dfrac{0^2 + 1}{0} = \dfrac{1}{0}$

no y-intercept

x-intercept:

$$x^2 + 1 = 0$$

$$x^2 = -1$$

no x-intercept

vertical asymptote: $x = 0$

horizontal asymptote:

$n > m$, so none exist.

b. $f(x) = \dfrac{x^2 + x - 6}{x - 3}$

$$f(-x) = \frac{(-x)^2 + (-x) - 6}{-x - 3} = \frac{x^2 - x - 6}{-x - 3}$$

$f(-x) \neq g(x),\ g(-x) \neq -g(x)$

No symmetry

y-intercept: $y = \dfrac{0^2 + 0 - 6}{0 - 3} = \dfrac{-6}{-3} = 2$

x-intercept:

$$x^2 + x - 6 = 0$$

$$(x + 3)(x - 2) = 0$$

$$x = -3 \text{ and } x = 2$$

vertical asymptote:

$$x - 3 = 0$$

$$x = 3$$

horizontal asymptote:

$n > m$, so none exist.

63. a. Slant asymptote:

$$f(x) = x + 4 + \frac{6}{x - 3}$$

$$y = x + 4$$

65. $f(x) = \dfrac{x^3 + 1}{x^2 + 2x}$

   a. slant asymptote:

$$\begin{array}{r} x - 2 \\ x^2 + 2x \overline{\smash{\big)}\, x^3 + 1} \\ \underline{x^3 + 2x^2 } \\ -2x^2 \\ \underline{-2x^2 + 4x } \\ -4x + 1 \end{array}$$

$$y = x - 2$$

   b.

$$f(-x) = \dfrac{(-x)^3 + 1}{(-x)^2 + 2(-x)} = \dfrac{-x^3 + 1}{x^2 - 2x}$$

$$f(-x) \neq f(x), \quad f(-x) \neq -f(x)$$

no symmetry

y-intercept: $y = \dfrac{0^3 + 1}{0^2 + 2(0)} = \dfrac{1}{0}$

no y-intercept

x-intercept: $x^3 + 1 = 0$

$$x^3 = -1$$

$$x = -1$$

vertical asymptotes:

$$x^2 + 2x = 0$$

$$x(x + 2) = 0$$

$$x = 0, \quad x = -2$$

horizontal asymptote:

$n > m$, so none

67. a. $\overline{C}(x) = \dfrac{20(x) + 20,000}{x}$

$\overline{C}(100) = \dfrac{20(100) + 20,000}{100} = \$220$

$\overline{C}(1000) = \dfrac{20(1000) + 20,000}{1000} = \$40$

$\overline{C}(10,000) = \dfrac{20(10,000) + 20,000}{10,000}$

$= \$22$

$\overline{C}(100,000) = \dfrac{20(100,000) + 20,000}{100,000}$

$= \$20.20$

  b. $n = m$, so $y = \dfrac{20}{1} = 20$ is the horizontal

asymptote.
$20 is the minimum average cost of producing a canoe. As more canoes are manufactured, the average cost approaches $20.

69. a. $C(p) = \dfrac{60,000p}{100 - p}$

$C(85) - C(80)$

$= \dfrac{60,000(85)}{100 - 85} - \dfrac{60,000(80)}{100 - 80}$

$= \$100,000$

  b. No; the model indicates that no amount of money can remove 100% of the pollutants since $C(p)$ increases without bound as p approaches 100.

71. a. $F(t) = \dfrac{80}{t^2 + t + 1}$

$F(0) = \dfrac{80}{0^2 + 4(0) + 1} = 80$

When the dessert is placed in the icebox, its temperature is 80°F.

b. $F(1) = \dfrac{80}{1^2 + 4(1) + 1} = \dfrac{80}{6} \approx 13.3°F$

$F(2) = \dfrac{80}{2^2 + 4(2) + 1} = \dfrac{80}{13} \approx 6.2°F$

$F(3) = \dfrac{80}{3^2 + 4(3) + 1} = \dfrac{80}{22} \approx 3.6°F$

$F(4) = \dfrac{80}{4^2 + 4(4) + 1} = \dfrac{80}{33} \approx 2.4°F$

$F(5) = \dfrac{80}{5^2 + 4(5) + 1} = \dfrac{80}{46} \approx 1.7°F$

c. $n < m$, so $y = 0$.
The temperature will approach but not reach 0°F.

d.

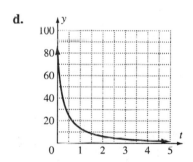

73. a. after 1 day: 35 words
after 5 days: about 12 words
after 15 days: about 7 words

b. $N(t) = \dfrac{5t + 30}{t},\ t \ge 1$

$N(1) = \dfrac{5 + 30}{t} = 35$ words

This is the same as the estimate for the graph.

$N(5) = \dfrac{25 + 30}{5} = 11$ words

This is a little less than the estimate from the graph.

$N(15) = 7$ words
This is the same as the estimate from the graph.

c. The graph indicates that the students will remember 5 words over a long period of time.

d. $n = m$, so $y = \dfrac{5}{1} = 5$

The horizontal asymptote indicates that the students will remember 5 words over a long period of time.

75.–83. Answers may very.

85.

87.

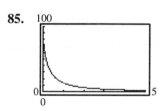

The graph approaches the horizontal asymptote faster and the vertical asymptote slower as n increases.

89. $f(x) = \dfrac{x^2 - 4x + 3}{x - 2}$

$g(x) = \dfrac{x^2 - 5x + 6}{x - 2}$

$g(x)$ is the graph of a line where $f(x)$ is the graph of a rational function with a slant asymptote.
In $g(x)$, $x - 2$ is a factor of $x^2 - 5x + 6$.

91. a. False

   b. False; the graph of a rational function may not have a y-intercept when the y-axis is a vertical asymptote.

   c. False; the graph can have 1 or no horizontal asymptotes.

   d. True; the function is undefined for x values at a vertical asymptote.

   (d) is true.

93.–95. Answers may very.

Section 3.7

Check Point Exercises

1. a. $L = kN$

   b. $L = 4N$

   c. $L = 4(17) = 68$

   Sain's moustache grew to 68 inches.

2. a. $W = kL$

   b. $75 = k(6)$

   $k = \dfrac{75}{6}$

   c. $W = kL$

   $W = \left(\dfrac{75}{6}\right)L = \dfrac{75L}{6}$

   d. $W = \dfrac{75(16)}{6} = 200$

   A 16-foot canoe weighs 200 pounds.

3. $P = kD$

   $25 = k(60)$

   $k = \dfrac{25}{60} = \dfrac{5}{12}$

   $P = \dfrac{5}{12}D$

   $P = \dfrac{5}{12}(330) = 137.5$

   The pressure will be 137.5 pounds per square inch.

4. $d = kv^2$

   $200 = k(60)^2$

   $k = \dfrac{200}{3600} = \dfrac{1}{18}$

   $d = \dfrac{1}{18}v^2$

   $d = \dfrac{1}{18}(100)^2 \approx 556$

   About 556 feet are required.

5. $P = \dfrac{k}{v}$

   $12 = \dfrac{k}{8}$

   $k = 96$

   $P = \dfrac{96}{v}$

   $p = \dfrac{96}{22} \approx 4.36$

   The new pressure is about 4.36 pounds per square inch.

6. $M = \dfrac{kP}{W}$

$32 = \dfrac{k16}{4}$

$k = 8$

$M = \dfrac{8P}{W}$

$M = \dfrac{8(24)}{8} = 24$

It will take 24 minutes.

7. $V = khr^2$

$120\pi = k(10)(6)^2$

$k = \dfrac{120\pi}{360} = \dfrac{\pi}{3}$

$V = \dfrac{\pi hr^2}{3}$

$V = \dfrac{\pi(2)(12)^2}{3} = 96\pi$

The volume of the cone is 96π cubic feet.

Exercise Set 3.7

1. $g = kh$

3. $a = kb^2$

5. $r = \dfrac{k}{t}$

7. $a = \dfrac{k}{b^3}$

9. $r = \dfrac{ks}{v}$

11. $s = kgt^2$

13. $y = kx$

$75 = k \cdot 3$

$k = 25$

15. $y = kx^2$

$45 = k \cdot 3^2$

$9k = 45$

$k = 5$

17. $W = \dfrac{k}{r}$

$500 = \dfrac{k}{10}$

$k = 5000$

19. $A = \dfrac{kB}{C}$

$9 = \dfrac{k \cdot 12}{4}$

$k = 9 \cdot \dfrac{4}{12}$

$k = 3$

21. $a = kbc$

$72 = k \cdot 18 \cdot 2$

$36k = 72$

$k = 2$

23. $y = kx$

$35 = k \cdot 5$

$k = 7$

$y = 7x$

$y = 7 \cdot 12$

$y = 84$

25. $y = \dfrac{k}{x}$

$10 = \dfrac{k}{5}$

$k = 50$

$y = \dfrac{50}{x}$

$y = \dfrac{50}{2}$

$y = 25$

27. $y = \dfrac{kx}{z^2}$

$20 = \dfrac{k \cdot 50}{5^2} = \dfrac{50k}{25} = 2k$

$20 = 2k$

$k = 10$

$y = \dfrac{10x}{z^2}$

$y = \dfrac{10 \cdot 3}{6^2} = \dfrac{30}{36} = \dfrac{5}{6}$

$y = \dfrac{5}{6}$

29. $y = hxz$

$25 = k \cdot 2 \cdot 5$

$k = \dfrac{25}{10} = 2.5$

$y = 2.5xz$

$y = 2.5(8)(12)$

$y = 240$

31. a. $L = kW$

  b. $L = 0.02W$

  c. $L = 0.02(52)$
  $= 1.04$
  Your fingernail length will be
  1.04 inches.

33. $C = kM$

$400 = k \cdot 3000$

$k = \dfrac{400}{3000} = \dfrac{2}{15}$

$C = \dfrac{2}{15}M$

$C = \dfrac{2}{15} \cdot 450 = 60$

The cost is \$60.

35. $s = kM$

$1502.2 = k(2.03)$

$k = 740$

$s = 740M$

$s = 740(3.3)$

$\quad = 2442$

The Blackbird's speed is 2442 miles per hour.

37. $W = kh^3$

$170 = k \cdot 70^3$

$343,000k = 170$

$k = \dfrac{17}{34,300}$

$W = \dfrac{17}{34,300}h^3$

$W = \dfrac{17}{34,300}(107)^3$

$W \approx 607$

Mr. Wadlow weighed approximately 607 pounds.

39. $t = \dfrac{k}{r}$

$1.5 = \dfrac{k}{20}$

$k = 30$

$t = \dfrac{30}{r}$

$t = \dfrac{30}{60} = 0.5$

It will take half an hour.

41. $v = \dfrac{k}{p}$

$32 = \dfrac{k}{8}$

$k = 256$

$v = \dfrac{256}{p}$

$40 = \dfrac{256}{p}$

$40p = 256$

$p = 6.4$

The pressure is 6.4 pounds.

43.

$$i = \frac{kw}{h}$$

$$21 = \frac{k \cdot 150}{70}$$

$$1470 = 150k$$

$$k = 9.8$$

$$i = \frac{9.8w}{h}$$

$$i = \frac{9.8(240)}{74} \approx 31.78$$

index: about 32

This person is not in the desirable range.

45.

$$I = \frac{k}{d^2}$$

$$25 = \frac{k}{4^2}$$

$$k = 400$$

$$I = \frac{400}{d^2}$$

$$I = \frac{400}{6^2} \approx 11.11$$

The illumination is about 11.11 foot-candles.

47.

$$e = kmv^2$$

$$36 = k \cdot 8 \cdot 3^2$$

$$72k = 36$$

$$k = 0.5$$

$$e = 0.5mv^2$$

$$e = 0.5(4)6^2 = 72$$

The kinetic energy is 72 ergs.

49.

$$\frac{c}{p} = \frac{kp_1 \cdot p_2}{d^2}$$

$$158,233 = \frac{k(2538)(1818)}{(108)^2}$$

$$k \approx 400$$

$$c = \frac{(400)(1225)(2970)}{(3403)^2}$$

$$c \approx 126$$

About 126 phone calls per day are made.

51.–57. Answers may vary.

59.

$$p = kv^2$$

$$p = k(2v)^2$$

$$p = k \cdot 4v^2$$

$$p = 4kv^2$$

The destructive power is four times as much.

61.

$$h = \frac{kv^2}{r}$$

$$3h = \frac{3kv^2}{r} = \frac{kv^2}{\frac{r}{3}}$$

Reduce the resistance by a factor of $\frac{1}{3}$.

Review Exercises

1. $f(x) = -2(x-1)^2 + 3$

axis of symmetry: $x = 1$

2. $g(x) = (x+4)^2 - 2$

axis of symmetry: $x = -4$

3. $f(x) = -x^2 + 2x + 3$

$\qquad = -\left(x^2 - 2x + 1\right) + 3 + 1$

$\quad f(x) = -(x-1)^2 + 4$

axis of symmetry: $x = 1$

4. $f(x) = 2x^2 - 4x - 6$

$\quad f(x) = 2\left(x^2 - 2x + 1\right) - 6 - 2$

$\qquad 2(x-1)^2 - 8$

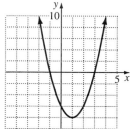

axis of symmetry: $x = 1$

5. $f(x) = 104.5x^2 - 1501.5x + 6016$

$\quad x = \dfrac{1501.5}{209} \approx 7.2$

7.2 hours of sleep

$\quad f(7.2) = 104.5(7.2)^2 - 1501.5(7.2) \approx 622$

622 is the minimum death rate.

6. $s(t) = -16t^2 + 64t + 80$

$\quad t = -\dfrac{b}{2a} = -\dfrac{64}{2(-16)} = 2$

It reaches its maximum height after 2 seconds.

$\quad s(2) = -16(2)^2 + 64(2) + 80 = 144$

The maximum height is 144 feet.

7. $f(x) = -x^3 + 12x^2 - x$

The graph rises to the left and falls to the right and goes through the origin, so graph (c) is the best match.

8. $g(x) = x^6 - 6x^4 + 9x^2$

The graph rises to the left and rises to the right, so graph (b) is the best match.

9. $h(x) = x^5 - 5x^3 + 4x$

The graph falls to the left and rises to the right and crosses the y-axis at zero, so graph (a) is the best match.

10. $r(x) = x^3 + 1$

$r(x)$ falls to the left and rises to the right and does not go through the origin, so graph (d) is the best match.

11. $f(x) = -0.0013x^3 + 0.78x^2 - 1.43x + 18.1$

Because the degree is odd and the leading coefficient is negative, the graph falls to the right. Therefore, the model indicates that the percentage of families below the poverty level will eventually be negative, which is impossible.

12. $N(t) = -\dfrac{3}{4}t^4 + 3t^3 + 5$

Since the degree is even and the leading coefficient is negative, the graph falls to the right. Therefore, the model indicates a patient will eventually have a negative number of viral bodies, which is impossible.

13. $f(x) = -2(x-1)(x+2)^2(x+5)^3$

$x = 1$, multiplicity 1, the graph crosses the x-axis

$x = -2$, multiplicity 2, the graph touches the x-axis

$x = -5$, multiplicity 5, the graph crosses the x-axis

14. $f(x) = x^3 - 5x^2 - 25x + 125$

$\qquad = x^2(x - 5) - 25(x - 5)$

$\qquad = (x^2 - 25)(x - 5)$

$\qquad = (x + 5)(x - 5)^2$

$x = -5$, multiplicity 1, the graph crosses the x-axis

$x = 5$, multiplicity 2, the graph touches the x-axis

15. $f(x) = x^3 - x^2 - 9x + 9$

  a. Since n is odd and $a_n > 0$, the graph falls to the left and rises to the right.

  b. $f(-x) = (-x)^3 - (-x)^2 - 9(-x) + 9$

$\qquad\qquad = -x^3 - x^2 + 9x + 9$

$\qquad f(-x) \neq f(x), f(-x) \neq -f(x)$

$\qquad$ no symmetry

  c. $f(x) = (x - 3)(x + 3)(x - 1)$

$\qquad$ zeros: $3, -3, 1$

16. $f(x) = 4x - x^3$

  a. Since n is odd and $a_n < 0$, the graph rises to the left and falls to the right.

  b. $f(-x) = -4x + x^3$

$\qquad f(-x) = -f(x)$

$\qquad$ origin symmetry

  c. $f(x) = x(x^2 - 4) = x(x - 2)(x + 2)$

$\qquad$ zeros: $x = 0, 2, -2$

17. $f(x) = 2x^3 + 3x^2 - 8x - 12$

  a. Since h is odd and $a_n > 0$, the graph falls to the left and rises to the right.

  b. $f(-x) = -2x^3 + 3x^2 + 8x - 12$

$\qquad f(-x) \neq f(x), \; f(-x) = -f(x)$

$\qquad$ no symmetry

  c. $f(x) = (x - 2)(x + 2)(2x + 3)$

$\qquad$ zeros: $x = 2, \; 2, -\dfrac{3}{2}$

18. $g(x) = -x^4 + 25x^2$

   a. The graph falls to the left and to the right.

   b. $f(-x) = -(-x)^4 + 25(-x)^2$
$$= -x^4 + 25x^2 = f(x)$$
     y-axis symmetry

   c. $\quad -x^4 + 25x^2 = 0$
$$-x^2\left(x^2 - 25\right) = 0$$
$$-x^2(x - 5)(x + 5) = 0$$
     zeros: $x = -5, 0, 5$

19. $f(x) = -x^4 + 6x^3 - 9x^2$

   a. The graph falls to the left and to the right.

   b. $f(-x) = -(-x)^4 + 6(-x)^3 - 9(-x)$
$$= -x^4 - 6x^3 - 9x^2 \, f(-x) \neq f(x)$$
     $f(-x) \neq -f(x)$
     no symmetry

   c. $\quad = -x^2\left(x^2 - 6x + 9\right) = 0$
$$-x^2(x - 3)(x - 3) = 0$$
     zeros: $x = 0, 3$

20. $f(x) = 3x^4 - 15x^3$

   a. The graph rises to the left and to the right.

   b. $f(-x) = 3(-x)^4 - 15(-x)^2 = 3x^4 + 15x^3$
     $f(-x) \neq f(x), \ f(-x) \neq -f(x)$
     no symmetry

   c $\quad 3x^4 - 15x^3 = 0$
$$3x^3(x - 5) = 0$$
     zeros: $x = 0, 5$

21.
$$
\begin{array}{r}
4x^2 - 7x + 5 \\
x+1\overline{)\,4x^3 - 3x^2 - 2x + 1} \\
\underline{4x^3 + 4x^2} \\
-7x^2 - 2x \\
\underline{-7x^2 - 7x} \\
5x + 1 \\
\underline{5x + 5} \\
-4
\end{array}
$$

Quotient: $4x^2 - 7x + 5 - \dfrac{4}{x+1}$

22.
$$
\begin{array}{r}
2x^2 - 4x + 1 \\
5x-3\overline{)\,10x^3 - 26x^2 + 17x - 13} \\
\underline{10x^3 + 6x^2} \\
-20x^2 + 17x \\
\underline{-20x^2 + 12x} \\
5x - 13 \\
\underline{5x - 3} \\
-10
\end{array}
$$

Quotient: $2x^2 - 4x + 1 - \dfrac{10}{5x - 3}$

23.
$$2x^2 + 1 \overline{\smash{\big)}\ 4x^4 + 6x^3 + 3x - 1} \quad \frac{2x^2 + 3x - 1}{}$$

$$\underline{4x^2 + 2x^2}$$
$$6x^3 - 2x^2 + 3x$$
$$\underline{6x^2 + 3x}$$
$$-2x^2 - 1$$
$$\underline{-2x^2 - 1}$$
$$0$$

24. $(3x^4 + 11x^3 - 20x^3 + 7x + 35) \div (x + 5)$

$$\begin{array}{r|rrrrr} -5 & 3 & 11 & -20 & 7 & 35 \\ & & -15 & 20 & 0 & -35 \\ \hline & 3 & -4 & 0 & 7 & 0 \end{array}$$

Quotient: $3x^3 - 4x^2 + 7$

25. $(3x^4 - 2x^2 - 10x) \div (x - 2)$

$$\begin{array}{r|rrrrr} 2 & 3 & 0 & -2 & -10 & 0 \\ & & 6 & 12 & 20 & 20 \\ \hline & 3 & 6 & 10 & 10 & 20 \end{array}$$

Quotient: $3x^3 + 6x^2 + 10x + 10 + \dfrac{20}{x - 2}$

26. $f(x) = 2x^3 - 7x^2 + 9x - 3$

$$\begin{array}{r|rrrr} -13 & 2 & -7 & 9 & -3 \\ & & -26 & 429 & -5694 \\ \hline & 2 & -33 & 438 & -5697 \end{array}$$

Quotient: $f(-13) = -5697$

27. $f(x) = 2x^3 + x^2 - 13x + 6$

$$\begin{array}{r|rrrr} 2 & 2 & 1 & -13 & 6 \\ & & 4 & 10 & -6 \\ \hline & 2 & 5 & -3 & 0 \end{array}$$

$$f(x) = (x - 2)(2x^2 + 5x - 3)$$
$$= (x - 2)(2x - 1)(x + 3)$$

Zeros: $x = 2, \dfrac{1}{2}, -3$

28. $x^3 - 17x + 4 = 0$

$$\begin{array}{r|rrrr} 4 & 1 & 0 & -17 & 4 \\ & & 4 & 16 & -4 \\ \hline & 1 & 4 & -1 & 0 \end{array}$$

$$(x - 4)\left(x^2 + 4x - 1\right) = 0$$
$$x = \frac{-4 \pm \sqrt{16 + 4}}{2} = \frac{-4 \pm 2\sqrt{5}}{2} = -2 \pm \sqrt{5}$$

The solution set is $\left\{4, -2 \pm \sqrt{5}, -2 - \sqrt{5}\right\}$.

29. $f(x) = x^4 - 6x^3 + 14x^2 - 14x + 5$

$p:\ \pm 1,\ \pm 5$

$q:\ \pm 1$

$\dfrac{p}{q}:\ \pm 1,\ \pm 5$

30. $f(x) = 3x^5 - 2x^4 - 15x^3 + 10x^2 + 12x - 8$

$p:\ \pm 1, \pm 2, \pm 4, \pm 8$

$q:\ \pm 1, \pm 3$

$\dfrac{p}{q}:\ \pm 1, \pm 2, \pm 4, \pm 8, \pm \dfrac{8}{3}, \pm \dfrac{4}{3}, \pm \dfrac{2}{3}, \pm \dfrac{1}{3}$

31. $f(x) = 3x^4 - 2x^3 - 8x + 5$

f(*x*) has 2 sign variations, so *f*(*x*) = 0 has 2 or 0 positive solutions.

$f(-x) = 3x^4 + 2x^3 + x + 5$

f(–*x*) has no sign variations, so *f*(*x*) = 0 has no negative solutions.

32. $f(x) = 2x^5 - 3x^3 - 5x^2 + 3x - 1$

f(*x*) has 3 sign variations, so *f*(*x*) = 0 has 3 or 1 positive real roots.

$f(-x) = -2x^5 + 3x^3 - 5x^2 - 3x - 1$

f(–*x*) has 2 sign variations, so *f*(*x*) = 0 has 2 or 0 negative solutions.

33. $f(x) = f(-x) = 2x^4 + 6x^2 + 8$
No sign variations exist for either $f(x)$ or
$f(-x)$, so no real roots exist.

34. $f(x) = x^3 + 3x^2 - 4$

    a. $p: \pm 1, \pm 2, \pm 4$
        $q: \pm 1$
        $\dfrac{p}{q}: \pm 1, \pm 2, \pm 4$

    b.   1 sign variation $\Rightarrow$ 1 positive real zero
        $f(-x) = -x^3 + 3x^2 - 4$
        2 sign variations $\Rightarrow$ 2 or no negative
        real zeros

    c.

$$\begin{array}{r|rrrr} 1 & 1 & 3 & 0 & -4 \\ & & 1 & 4 & 4 \\ \hline & 1 & 4 & 4 & 0 \end{array}$$

        1 is a zero.

    d. $(x - 1)(x^2 + 4x + 4) = 0$
        $(x - 1)(x + 2)^2 = 0$
        $x = 1$ or $x = -2$
        The solution set is $\{1, -2\}$.

35. $f(x) = 6x^3 + x^2 - 4x + 1$

    a. $p: \pm 1$
        $q: \pm 1, \pm 2, \pm 3, \pm 6$
        $\dfrac{p}{q}: \pm 1, \pm \dfrac{1}{2}, \pm \dfrac{1}{3}, \pm \dfrac{1}{6}$

    b. $f(x) = 6x^3 + x^2 - 4x + 1$
        2 sign variations $\Rightarrow$ 2 or 0 positive real
        zeros.
        $f(-x) = -6x^3 + x^2 + 4x + 1$
        1 sign variation $\Rightarrow$ 1 negative real zero.

    c.

$$\begin{array}{r|rrrr} -1 & 6 & 1 & -4 & 1 \\ & & -6 & 5 & -1 \\ \hline & 6 & -5 & 1 & 0 \end{array}$$

        -1 is a zero.

    d. $6x^3 + x^2 - 4x + 1 = 0$
        $(x + 1)(6x^2 - 5x + 1) = 0$
        $(x + 1)(3x - 1)(2x - 1) = 0$
        $x = -1$ or $x = \dfrac{1}{3}$ or $x = \dfrac{1}{2}$
        The solution set is $\left\{-1, \dfrac{1}{3}, \dfrac{1}{2}\right\}$.

36. $f(x) = 8x^3 - 36x^2 + 46x - 15$

    a. $p: \pm 1, \pm 3, \pm 5, \pm 15$
        $q: \pm 1, \pm 2, \pm 4, \pm 8$
        $\dfrac{p}{q}: \pm 1, \pm 3, \pm 5, \pm 15, \pm \dfrac{1}{2}, \pm \dfrac{1}{4}, \pm \dfrac{1}{8},$
        $\pm \dfrac{3}{2}, \pm \dfrac{3}{4}, \pm \dfrac{3}{8}, \pm \dfrac{5}{2}, \pm \dfrac{5}{4},$
        $\pm \dfrac{5}{8}, \pm \dfrac{15}{2}, \pm \dfrac{15}{4}, \pm \dfrac{15}{8}$

    b. $f(x) = 8x^3 - 36x^2 + 46x - 15$
        3 sign variations $\Rightarrow$ 3 or 1 positive real
        solutions.
        $f(-x) = -8x^3 - 36x^2 - 46x - 15$
        0 sign variations $\Rightarrow$ no negative real
        solutions.

    c.

$$\begin{array}{r|rrrr} \frac{1}{2} & 8 & -36 & 46 & -15 \\ & & 4 & -16 & 15 \\ \hline & 8 & -32 & 30 & 0 \end{array}$$

        $\dfrac{1}{2}$ is a zero.

d. $8x^3 - 36x^2 + 46x - 15 = 0$

$\left(x - \dfrac{1}{2}\right)(8x^2 - 32x + 30) = 0$

$2\left(x - \dfrac{1}{2}\right)(4x^2 - 16x + 15) = 0$

$2\left(x - \dfrac{1}{2}\right)(2x - 5)(2x - 3) = 0$

$x = \dfrac{1}{2}$ or $x = \dfrac{5}{2}$ or $x = \dfrac{3}{2}$

The solution set is $\left\{\dfrac{1}{2}, \dfrac{3}{2}, \dfrac{5}{2}\right\}$.

37. $f(x) = x^4 - x^3 - 7x^2 + x + 6$

a. $p: \pm 1, \pm 2, \pm 3, \pm 6$
$q: \pm 1$

$\dfrac{p}{q}: \pm 1, \pm 2, \pm 3, \pm 6$

b. $f(x) = x^4 - x^3 - 7x^2 + x + 6$
2 sign variations $\Rightarrow$ 2 or zero positive real solutions.
$f(-x) = x^4 + x^3 - 7x^2 - x + 6$
2 sign variations $\rightarrow$ 2 or zero negative real solutions.

c.

$$\begin{array}{r|rrrrr}
-2 & 1 & -1 & -7 & 1 & 6 \\
   &   & -2 & 6 & 2 & -6 \\
\hline
   & 1 & -3 & -1 & 3 & 0
\end{array}$$

-2 is a zero.

d. $x^4 - x^3 - 7x^2 + x + 6 = 0$
$(x + 2)(x^3 - 3x^2 - x + 3) = 0$
$(x + 2)[x^2(x - 3) - (x - 3)] = 0$
$(x + 2)(x - 3)(x^2 - 1) = 0$
$(x + 2)(x - 3)(x - 1)(x + 1) = 0$
$x = -2$ or $x = 3$ or $x = 1$ or $x = -1$
The solution set is $\{-2, -1, 1, 3\}$.

38. $4x^4 + 7x^2 - 2 = 0$

a. $p: \pm 1, \pm 2$
$q: \pm 1, \pm 2, \pm 4$

$\dfrac{p}{q}: \pm 1, \pm 2, \pm \dfrac{1}{2}, \pm \dfrac{1}{4}$

b.   1 sign variation $\Rightarrow$ 1 positive real root
$f(-x) = 4x^4 + 7x^2 - 2$
1 sign variation $\Rightarrow$ 1 negative real root

c.

$$\begin{array}{r|rrrrr}
\dfrac{1}{2} & 4 & 0 & 7 & 0 & -2 \\
            &   & 2 & 1 & 4 & 2 \\
\hline
            & 4 & 2 & 8 & 4 & 0
\end{array}$$

$(2x - 1)\left(4x^3 + 2x^2 + 8x + 4\right) = 0$

$\dfrac{1}{2}$ is a zero.

d.

$$\begin{array}{r|rrrr}
-\dfrac{1}{2} & 4 & 2 & 8 & 4 \\
             &   & -2 & 0 & -4 \\
\hline
             & 4 & 0 & 8 & 0
\end{array}$$

$(2x - 1)(2x + 1)(4x^2 + 8) = 0$
$4(2x - 1)(2x + 1)(x^2 + 2) = 0$
$x^2 = -2$
$x = \pm i\sqrt{2}$
The solution set is $\left\{\dfrac{1}{2}, -\dfrac{1}{2}, i\sqrt{2}, -i\sqrt{2}\right\}$.

39. $f(x) = 2x^4 + x^3 - 9x^2 - 4x + 4$

a. $p: \pm 1, \pm 2, \pm 4$
$q: \pm 1, \pm 2$

$\dfrac{p}{q} = \pm 1, \ \pm 2, \ \pm 4, \ \pm \dfrac{1}{2}$

b. 2 sign variations $\Rightarrow$ 2 or no positive zeros
$f(-x) = 2x^4 - x^3 - 9x^2 + 4x + 4$
2 sign variations $\Rightarrow$ 2 or no negative zeros

c.

2	2	1	−9	−4	4
		4	10	2	−4
	2	5	1	−2	0

2 is a zero.

d. $f(x) = (x - 2)\left(2x^3 + 5x^2 + x - 2\right)$

−2	2	5	1	−2
		−4	−2	2
	2	1	−1	0

$f(x) = (x - 2)(x + 2)(2x^2 + x - 1)$
$\quad\quad = (x - 2)(x + 2)(2x - 1)(x + 1)$
$x = 2, \ -2, \ \dfrac{1}{2}, \ -1$

The solution set is $\left\{ 2, \ -2, \ \dfrac{1}{2}, \ -1 \right\}$.

40. $2x^4 - 7x^3 - 5x^2 + 28x - 12 = 0$

−2	2	−7	−5	28	−12
		−4	22	−34	12
	2	−11	17	−6	0

−2 is a root and a lower bound.

6	2	−7	−5	28	−12
		12	30	150	1068
	2	5	25	178	1056

6 is an upper bound, but not a zero.
$p: \pm 1, \pm 2, \pm 3, \pm 4, +6, \pm 12$
$q: \pm 1, \pm 2$

$\dfrac{p}{q}: \pm 1, \pm 2, \pm 3, \pm 4, \pm 6, \pm 12, \pm \dfrac{1}{2}, \pm \dfrac{3}{2}$

Possible roots are: $\pm 1, \pm 2, 3, 4, \ \pm \dfrac{1}{2}, \pm \dfrac{3}{2}$

41. $2x^4 - x^3 - 5x^2 + 10x + 12 = 0$

a. $p: \pm 1, \pm 2, \pm 3, \pm 4, \pm 6, \pm 12$
$q: \pm 1, \pm 2$

$\dfrac{p}{q}: \pm 1, \pm 2, \pm 3, \pm 4, \pm 6, \pm 12, \pm \dfrac{1}{2}, \pm \dfrac{3}{2}$

b.

2	2	−1	−5	10	12
		4	6	2	24
	2	3	1	12	36

2 is not a root but is an upper bound.

c.

−2	2	−1	−5	10	12
		−4	10	−10	0
	2	−5	5	0	12

−2 is not a root but is a lower bound.

d. Possible roots are $\pm 1, \ \pm \dfrac{1}{2}$, and $\pm \dfrac{3}{2}$.

42. $f(x) = x^3 - 2x - 1$
$f(1) = (1)^3 - 2(1) - 1 = -2$
$f(2) = (2)^3 - 2(2) - 1 = 3$
Continue to use the Intermediate Value Theorem:
$f(1.5) = -0.625$
$f(1.6) = -0.104$
$f(1.7) = 0.513$
$f(1.65) = 0.192125$
$x \approx 1.6$

43. $f(x) = 3x^3 + 2x^2 - 8x + 7$

$f(-3) = 3(-3)^3 + 2(-3)^2 - 8(-3) + 7 = -32$

$f(-2) = 3(-2)^3 + 2(-2)^2 - 8(-2) + 7 = 7$

Continue to use the Intermediate Value
Theorem:

$f(-2.4) = -3.752$

$f(-2.3) = -0.521$

$f(-2.2) = 2.336$

$f(-2.25) = 0.953125$

$x \approx -2.3$

44. $(x - 6 - 5i)(x - 6 + 5i)$

$= x^2 - 6x - 6x + 36 - 25i^2$

$= x^2 - 12x + 61$

$$\begin{array}{r}
4x + 1 \\
x^2 - 12x + 61 \overline{\smash{\big)}\ 4x^3 - 47x^2 + 232x + 61} \\
\underline{4x^3 - 48x^2 + 244x} \\
x^2 - 12x + 61 \\
\underline{x^2 - 12x + 61} \\
0
\end{array}$$

$4x + 1 = 0$

$x = -\dfrac{1}{4}$

The solution set is $\left\{ -\dfrac{1}{4},\ 6 \pm 5i,\ 6 - 5i \right\}$.

45. $(x - 1 + 3i)(x - 1 - 3i) = x^2 - 2x + 1 - 9i^2$

$= x^2 - 2x + 10$

$$\begin{array}{r}
x^2 - 2x + 2 \\
x^2 - 2x + 10 \overline{\smash{\big)}\ x^4 - 4x^3 + 16x^2 - 24x + 20} \\
\underline{x^4 - 2x^3 + 10x^2} \\
-2x^3 + 6x^2 - 24x \\
\underline{-2x^3 + 4x^2 - 20x} \\
2x^2 - 4x + 20 \\
\underline{2x^2 - 4x + 20} \\
0
\end{array}$$

$x^2 - 2x + 2 = 0$

$x = \dfrac{2 \pm \sqrt{4 - 4(1)(2)}}{2}$

$x = \dfrac{2 \pm 2i}{2} = 1 \pm i$

The solution set is
$\{1 + 3i,\ 1 - 3i,\ 1 + i,\ 1 - i\}$.

46. $(x - 4 - 7i)(x - 4 + 7i) = x^2 - 8x + 16 + 49$

$= x^2 - 8x + 65$

$$\begin{array}{r}
2x^2 - x - 1 \\
x^2 - 8x + 65 \overline{\smash{\big)}\ 2x^4 - 17x^3 + 137x^2 - 57x - 65} \\
\underline{2x^4 - 16x^3 + 130x^2} \\
-x^3 + 7x^2 - 57x \\
\underline{-x^3 + 8x^2 - 65x} \\
-x^2 + 8x - 65 \\
\underline{-x^2 + 8x - 65} \\
0
\end{array}$$

$2x^2 - x - 1 = 0$

$x = \dfrac{1 \pm \sqrt{1 - 4(2)(-1)}}{4}$

$x = \dfrac{1 \pm 3}{4}$

$x = 1,\ -\dfrac{1}{2}$

The solution set is $\left\{ -\dfrac{1}{2},\ 1,\ 4 \pm 7i,\ 7i \right\}$.

47. $f(x) = a_n(x - 2)(x - 2 + 3i)(x - 2 - 3i)$

$f(x) = a_n(x - 2)\left(x^2 - 4x + 13\right)$

$f(1) = a_n(1 - 2)\left[1^2 - 4(1) + 13\right]$

$-10 = -10a_n$

$a_n = 1$

$f(x) = 1(x - 2)\left(x^2 - 4x + 13\right)$

$f(x) = x^3 - 4x^2 + 13x - 2x^2 + 8x - 26$

$f(x) = x^3 - 6x^2 + 21x - 26$

48. $f(x) = a_n(x - i)(x + i)(x + 3)^2$

$f(x) = a_n\left(x^2 + 1\right)\left(x^2 + 6x + 9\right)$

$f(-1) = a_n\left[(-1)^2 + 1\right]\left[(-1)^2 + 6(-1) + 9\right]$

$16 = 8a_n$

$a_n = 2$

$f(x) = 2\left(x^2 + 1\right)\left(x^2 + 6x + 9\right)$

$f(x) = 2\left(x^4 + 6x^3 + 9x^2 + x^2 + 6x + 9\right)$

$f(x) = 2x^4 + 12x^3 + 20x^2 + 12x + 18$

49. $f(x) = a_n(x+2)(x-3)(x-1-3i)(x-1+3i)$
$f(x) = a_n\left(x^2 - x - 6\right)\left(x^2 - 2x + 10\right)$
$f(x) = a_n\left(\begin{array}{c} x^4 - 2x^3 + 10x^2 - x^3 + \\ 2x^2 - 10x - 6x^2 + 12x - 60 \end{array}\right)$
$f(x) = a_n\left(x^4 - 3x^3 + 6x^2 + 2x - 60\right)$
$f(2) = a_n\left[(2)^4 - 3(2)^3 + 6(2)^2 + 2(2) - 60\right]$
$-40 = -40a_n$
$a_n = 1$
$f(x) = x^4 - 3x^3 + 6x^2 + 2x - 60$

50. $f(x) = 2x^4 + 3x^3 + 3x - 2$
$p: \pm 1, \pm 2$
$q: \pm 1, \pm 2$
$\dfrac{p}{q}: \pm 1, \pm 2, \pm \dfrac{1}{2}$

$$\begin{array}{r|rrrrr} -2 & 2 & 3 & 0 & 3 & -2 \\ & & -4 & 2 & -4 & 2 \\ \hline & 2 & -1 & 2 & -1 & 0 \end{array}$$

$2x^4 + 3x^3 + 3x - 2 = 0$
$(x+2)(2x^3 - x^2 + 2x - 1) = 0$
$(x+2)[x^2(2x-1) + (2x-1)] = 0$
$(x+2)(2x-1)(x^2+1) = 0$
$x = -2,\ x = \dfrac{1}{2}$ or $x = \pm i$

The zeros are -2, $\dfrac{1}{2}$, $\pm i$.
$f(x) = (x-i)(x+i)(x+2)\left(x - \dfrac{1}{2}\right)$

51. $g(x) = x^4 - 6x^3 + x^2 + 24x + 16$
$p: \pm 1, \pm 2, \pm 4, \pm 8, \pm 16$
$q: \pm 1$
$\dfrac{p}{q}: \pm 1, \pm 2, \pm 4, \pm 8, \pm 16$

$$\begin{array}{r|rrrrr} -1 & 1 & -6 & 1 & 24 & 16 \\ & & -1 & 7 & -8 & -16 \\ \hline & 1 & -7 & 8 & 16 & 0 \end{array}$$

$x^4 - 6x^3 + x^2 + 24x + 16 = 0$
$(x+1)(x^3 - 7x^2 + 8x + 16) = 0$

$$\begin{array}{r|rrrr} -1 & 1 & -7 & 8 & 16 \\ & & -1 & 8 & -16 \\ \hline & 1 & -8 & 16 & 0 \end{array}$$

$(x+1)^2(x^2 - 8x + 16) = 0$
$(x+1)^2(x-4)^2 = 0$
$x = -1$ or $x = 4$
$g(x) = (x+1)^2(x-4)^2$

52. 4 real zeros, one with multiplicity two

53. 3 real zeros; 2 nonreal complex zeros

54. 2 real zeros, one with multiplicity two; 2 nonreal complex zeros

55. 1 real zero; 4 nonreal complex zeros

56. $f(x) = \dfrac{2x}{x^2 - 9}$

Symmetry: $f(-x) = -\dfrac{2x}{x^2 - 9} = -f(x)$

origin symmetry

x-intercept:

$0 = \dfrac{2x}{x^2 - 9}$

$2x = 0$

$x = 0$

y-intercept: $y = \dfrac{2(0)}{0^2 - 9} = 0$

Vertical asymptote:

$x^2 - 9 = 0$

$(x - 3)(x + 3) = 0$

$x = 3$ and $x = -3$

Horizontal asymptote:

$n < m$, so $y = 0$

57. $g(x) = \dfrac{2x - 4}{x + 3}$

Symmetry: $g(-x) = \dfrac{-2x - 4}{x + 3}$

$g(-x) \neq g(x)$, $g(-x) \neq -g(x)$

No symmetry

x-intercept:

$2x - 4 = 0$

$x = 2$

y-intercept: $y = \dfrac{2(0) - 4}{(0) + 3} = -\dfrac{4}{3}$

Vertical asymptote:

$x + 3 = 0$

$x = -3$

Horizontal asymptote:

$n = m$, so $y = \dfrac{2}{1} = 2$

58. $h(x) = \dfrac{x^2 - 3x - 4}{x^2 - x - 6}$

Symmetry: $h(-x) = \dfrac{x^2 + 3x - 4}{x^2 + x - 6}$

$h(-x) \neq h(x)$, $h(-x) \neq -h(x)$

No symmetry

x-intercepts:

$x^2 - 3x - 4 = 0$

$(x - 4)(x + 1)$

$x = 4 \quad x = -1$

y-intercept: $y = \dfrac{0^2 - 3(0) - 4}{0^2 - 0 - 6} = \dfrac{2}{3}$

Vertical asymptotes:

$x^2 - x - 6 = 0$

$(x - 3)(x + 2) = 0$

$x = 3, -2$

Horizontal asymptote:

$n = m$, so $y = \dfrac{1}{1} = 1$

59. $r(x) = \dfrac{x^2 + 4x + 3}{(x + 2)^2}$

Symmetry: $r(-x) = \dfrac{x^2 - 4x + 3}{(-x + 2)^2}$

$r(-x) \neq r(x)$, $r(-x) \neq -r(x)$
No symmetry
x-intercepts:
$\quad x^2 + 4x + 3 = 0$
$\quad (x + 3)(x + 1) = 0$
$\quad x = -3, -1$

y-intercept: $y = \dfrac{0^2 + 4(0) + 3}{(0 + 2)^2} = \dfrac{3}{4}$

Vertical asymptote:
$x + 2 = 0$
$x = -2$
Horizontal asymptote:
$n = m$, so $y = \dfrac{1}{1} = 1$

60. $y = \dfrac{x^2}{x + 1}$

Symmetry: $f(-x) = \dfrac{x^2}{-x + 1}$

$f(-x) \neq f(x)$, $f(-x) \neq -f(x)$
No symmetry
x-intercept:
$\quad x^2 = 0$
$\quad x = 0$

y-intercept: $y = \dfrac{0^2}{0 + 1} = 0$

Vertical asymptote:
$x + 1 = 0$
$x = -1$
$n > m$, no horizontal asymptote.

Slant asymptote:

$y = x - 1 + \dfrac{1}{x + 1}$

$y = x - 1$

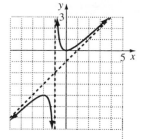

61. $y = \dfrac{x^2 + 2x - 3}{x - 3}$

Symmetry: $f(-x) = \dfrac{x^2 - 2x - 3}{-x - 3}$

$f(-x) \neq f(x)$, $f(-x) \neq -f(x)$
No symmetry
x-intercepts:
$\quad x^2 + 2x - 3 = 0$
$\quad (x + 3)(x - 1) = 0$
$\quad x = -3, 1$

y-intercept: $y = \dfrac{0^2 + 2(0) - 3}{0 - 3} = \dfrac{-3}{-3} = 1$

Vertical asymptote:
$x - 3 = 0$
$x = 3$
Horizontal asymptote:
$n > m$, so no horizontal asymptote.
slant asymptote:

$y = x + 5 + \dfrac{12}{x - 3}$

$y = x + 5$

62. $f(x) = \dfrac{-2x^3}{x^2+1}$

Symmetry: $f(-x) = \dfrac{2}{x^2+1} = -f(x)$

Origin symmetry

x-intercept:

$-2x^3 = 0$

$x = 0$

y-intercept: $y = \dfrac{-2(0)^3}{0^2+1} = \dfrac{0}{1} = 0$

Vertical asymptote:

$x^2 + 1 = 0$

$x^2 = -1$

No vertical asymptote.

Horizontal asymptote:

$n > m$, so no horizontal asymptote.

Slant asymptote:

$f(x) = -2x + \dfrac{2x}{x^2+1}$

$y = -2x$

63. $g(x) = \dfrac{4x^2 - 16x + 16}{2x - 3}$

Symmetry: $g(-x) = \dfrac{4x^2 + 16x + 16}{-2x - 3}$

$g(-x) \neq g(x)$, $g(-x) \neq -g(x)$

No symmetry

x-intercept:

$4x^2 - 16x + 16 = 0$

$4(x-2)^2 = 0$

$x = 2$

y-intercept:

$y = \dfrac{4(0)^2 - 16(0) + 16}{2(0) - 3} = -\dfrac{16}{3}$

Vertical asymptote:

$2x - 3 = 0$

$x = \dfrac{3}{2}$

Horizontal asymptote:

$n > m$, so no horizontal asymptote.

Slant asymptote:

$g(x) = 2x - 5 + \dfrac{1}{2x - 3}$

$y = 2x - 5$

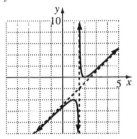

64. $\overline{C}(x) = \dfrac{25x + 50,000}{x}$

a. $\overline{C}(50) = \dfrac{25(50) + 50,000}{50} = 1025$

When 50 calculators are manufactured, it costs \$1025 to manufacture each.

$\overline{C}(100) = \dfrac{25(100) + 50,000}{100} = 525$

When 100 calculators are manufactured, it costs \$525 to manufacture each.

$\overline{C}(1000) = \dfrac{25(1000) + 50,000}{1000} = 75$

When 1,000 calculators are manufactured, it costs \$75 to manufacture each.

$\overline{C}(100,000) = \dfrac{25(100,000) + 50,000}{100,000} = 25.5$

When 100,000 calculators are manufactured, it costs \$25.50 to manufacture each.

b. $n = m$, so $y = \dfrac{25}{1} = 25$ is the horizontal asymptote. Minimum costs will approach \$25.

65. a. $C(90) - C(50) = \dfrac{200(90)}{100 - 90} - \dfrac{200(50)}{100 - 50}$

$C(90) - C(50) = 1800 - 200$

$C(90) - C(50) = 1600$

The difference in cost of removing 90% versus 50% of the contaminants is 16 million dollars.

b. $x = 100$; No amount of money can remove 100% of the contaminants, since $C(x)$ increases without bound as x approaches 100.

66. $F(x) = \dfrac{30(4 + 5x)}{1 + 0.05x}$

$n = m$, so $y = \dfrac{150}{0.05} = 3000$

The number of fish available in the pond approaches 3,000,000.

67. $P(x) = \dfrac{72{,}900}{100x^2 + 729}$

$n < m$ so $y = 0$

As the number of years of education increases the percentage rate of unemployment approaches zero.

68. Since $C(p)$ increases without bound as P approaches 100, the politician will not be able to keep the promise to seize 100% of illegal drugs as they enter the country.

69. $b = ke$

$98 = k \cdot 1400$

$k = 0.07$

$b = 0.07e$

$b = 0.07(2200) = \$154$

70. $d = kt^2$

$144 = k(3)^2$

$k = 16$

$d = 16t^2$

$d = 16(10)^2 = 1{,}600$ ft

71. $t = \dfrac{k}{r}$

$4 = \dfrac{k}{50}$

$k = 200$

$t = \dfrac{200}{r}$

$t = \dfrac{200}{40} = 5$ hours

72. $l = \dfrac{k}{d^2}$

$28 = \dfrac{k}{8^2}$

$k = 1792$

$l = \dfrac{1792}{d^2}$

$l = \dfrac{1792}{4^2} = 112$ decibels

73. $t = \dfrac{kc}{w}$

$10 = \dfrac{k \cdot 30}{6}$

$10 = 5h$

$h = 2$

$t = \dfrac{2c}{w}$

$t = \dfrac{2(40)}{5} = 16$ hours

74. $V = khB$

$175 = k \cdot 15 \cdot 35$

$k = \dfrac{1}{3}$

$V = \dfrac{1}{3}hB$

$V = \dfrac{1}{3} \cdot 20 \cdot 120 = 800$ ft^3

Chapter 3 Test

1. $f(x) = (x+1)^2 + 4$
vertex: $(-1, 4)$
axis of symmetry: $x = -1$
x-intercepts:
$(x+1)^2 + 4 = 0$
$x^2 + 2x + 5 = 0$
$x = \dfrac{-2 \pm \sqrt{4 - 20}}{2} = -1 \pm 2i$
no x-intercepts
y intercept.
$f(0) = (0+1)^2 + 4 = 5$

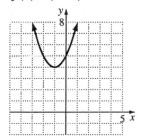

2. $f(x) - x^2 - 2x - 3$
$x = \dfrac{-b}{2a} = \dfrac{2}{2} = 1$
$f(1) = 1^2 - 2(1) - 3 = -4$
vertex: $(1, -4)$
axis of symmetry $x = 1$
x-intercepts:
$x^2 - 2x - 3 = 0$
$(x-3)(x+1) = 0$
$x = 3$ or $x = -1$
y-intercept:
$f(0) = 0^2 - 2(0) - 3 = -3$

3. $f(x) = -2x^2 - 12x - 16$
Since the coefficient of x^2 is negative, the graph of $f(x)$ opens down and $f(x)$ has a maximum point.
$x = \dfrac{-b}{2a} = \dfrac{12}{2(-2)} = -3$
$f(-3) = -2(-3)^2 - 12(-3) - 16$
$\qquad = -18 + 36 - 16 = 2$
maximum point: $(-3, 2)$

4. $f(x) = x^2 + 46x - 360$
$x = -\dfrac{b}{2a} = \dfrac{-46}{-2} = 23$
23 VCRs will maximize profit.
$f(23) = -(23)^2 + 46(23) - 360 = 169$
Maximum daily profit = \$16,900.

5. a. $\qquad\qquad f(x) = x^3 - 5x^2 - 4x + 20$
$x^3 - 5x^2 - 4x + 20 = 0$
$x^2(x - 5) - 4(x - 5) = 0$
$(x - 5)(x - 2)(x + 2) = 0$
$x = 5, 2, -2$
The solution set is $\{5, 2, -2\}$.

b. The degree of the polynomial is odd and the leading coefficient is positive. Thus the graph falls to the left and rises to the right.

6. $f(x) = x^5 - x$
Since the degree of the polynomial is odd and the leading coefficient is positive, the graph of f should fall to the left and rise to the right. The x-intercepts should be -1 and 1.

7. a. The integral root appears to be 2.

   b.

$$
\begin{array}{r|rrrr}
2 & 6 & -19 & 16 & -4 \\
  &   & 12 & -14 & 4 \\
\hline
  & 6 & -7 & 2 & 0
\end{array}
$$

$$6x^2 - 7x + 2 = 0$$
$$(3x - 2)(2x - 1) = 0$$
$$x = \frac{2}{3} \text{ or } x = \frac{1}{2}$$

The other two roots are $\frac{1}{2}$ and $\frac{2}{3}$.

8. $2x^3 + 11x^2 - 7x - 6 = 0$
p: ±1, ±2, ±3, ±6
q: ±1, ±2
$\frac{p}{q}$: $\pm 1, \pm 2, \pm 3, \pm 6, \pm \frac{1}{2}, \pm \frac{3}{2}$

9. $f(x) = 3x^5 - 2x^4 - 2x^2 + x - 1$
$f(x)$ has 3 sign variations.
$f(-x) = -3x^5 - 2x^4 - 2x^2 - x - 1$
$f(-x)$ has no sign variations.
There are 3 or 1 positive real solutions and no negative real solutions.

10. $x^3 + 6x^2 - x - 30 = 0$
p: ±1, ±2, ±3, ±5, ±6, ±10, ±15, ±30
q: ±1
$\frac{p}{q}$: $\pm 1, \pm 2, \pm 3, \pm 5, \pm 6, \pm 10, \pm 15, \pm 30$

$$
\begin{array}{r|rrrr}
-5 & 1 & 6 & -1 & -30 \\
   &   & -5 & -5 & 30 \\
\hline
   & 1 & 1 & -6 & 0
\end{array}
$$

$$x^3 + 6x^2 - x - 30 = 0$$
$$(x + 5)(x^2 + x - 6) = 0$$
$$(x + 5)(x + 3)(x - 2) = 0$$
$$x = -5 \text{ or } x = -3 \text{ or } x = 2$$
The solution set is {−5, −3, 2}.

11. $f(x) = 2x^4 - x^3 - 13x^2 + 5x + 15$

   a. p: ±1, ±3, ±5, ±15
      q: ±1, ±2
      $\frac{p}{q}$: $\pm 1, \pm 3, \pm 5, \pm 15, \pm \frac{1}{2}, \pm \frac{3}{2}, \pm \frac{5}{2}, \pm \frac{15}{2}$

   b.

$$
\begin{array}{r|rrrrr}
-1 & 2 & -1 & -13 & 5 & 15 \\
   &   & -2 & 3 & 10 & -15 \\
\hline
   & 2 & -3 & -10 & 15 & 0
\end{array}
$$

$$(x + 1)(2x^3 - 3x^2 - 10x + 15) = 0$$
$$(x + 1)[x^2(2x - 3) - 5(2x - 3)] = 0$$
$$(x + 1)(2x - 3)(x^2 - 5) = 0$$
$$x = -1 \text{ or } x = \frac{3}{2} \text{ or } x = \pm\sqrt{5}$$

The solution set is $\left\{-1, \frac{3}{2}, \sqrt{5}, -\sqrt{5}\right\}$.

12. $3x^4 + 4x^3 - 7x^2 - 2x - 3 = 0$

$$
\begin{array}{r|rrrrr}
-3 & 3 & 4 & -7 & -2 & -3 \\
   &   & -9 & 15 & -24 & 78 \\
\hline
   & 3 & -5 & 8 & -26 & 75
\end{array}
$$

−3 is a lower bound.

$$
\begin{array}{r|rrrrr}
2 & 3 & 4 & -7 & -2 & -3 \\
  &   & 6 & 20 & 26 & 48 \\
\hline
  & 3 & 10 & 13 & 24 & 45
\end{array}
$$

2 is an upper bound.

13. $(x-1+i)(x-1-i) = x^2 - 2x + 2$

$$
\begin{array}{r}
x^2 - 5x + 6 \\
x^2 - 2x + 2 \overline{\smash{)}\; x^4 - 7x^3 + 18x^2 - 22x + 12} \\
\underline{x^4 - 2x^3 + 2x^2} \\
-5x^3 + 16x^2 - 22x \\
\underline{-5x^3 + 10x^2 - 10x} \\
6x^2 - 12x + 12 \\
\underline{6x^2 - 12x + 12} \\
0
\end{array}
$$

$x^2 - 5x + 6 = 0$
$(x-3)(x-2) = 0$
$x = 3$ or $x = 2$
The solution set is $\{2, 3, 1 + i\}$.

14. $f(x)$ has zeros at -2 and 1. The zero at -2 has multiplicity of 2.
$$x^3 + 3x^2 - 4 = (x-1)(x+2)^2$$

15. $f(x) = \dfrac{x}{x^2 - 16}$

domain: $\{x \mid x \neq 4, x \neq -4\}$

Symmetry: $f(-x) = \dfrac{-x}{x^2 - 16} = -f(x)$

y-axis symmetry
x-intercept: $x = 0$

y-intercept: $y = \dfrac{0}{0^2 - 16} = 0$

Vertical asymptotes:
$x^2 - 16 = 0$
$(x-4)(x+4) = 0$
$x = 4, -4$
Horizontal asymptote:
$n < m$, so $y = 0$ is the horizontal asymptote.

16. $f(x) = \dfrac{x^2 - 9}{x - 2}$

domain: $\{x \mid x \neq 2\}$

Symmetry: $f(-x) = \dfrac{x^2 - 9}{-x - 2}$

$f(-x) \neq f(x), f(-x) \neq -f(x)$
No symmetry
x-intercepts:
$x^2 - 9 = 0$
$(x - 3)(x + 3) = 0$
$x = 3, -3$

y-intercept: $y = \dfrac{0^2 - 9}{0 - 2} = \dfrac{9}{2}$

Vertical asymptote:
$x - 2 = 0$
$x = 2$
Horizontal asymptote:
$n > m$, so no horizontal asymptote exists.

Slant asymptote: $f(x) = x + 2 - \dfrac{5}{x - 2}$

$y = x + 2$

17. $f(x) = \dfrac{x+1}{x^2 + 2x - 3}$

$x^2 + 2x - 3 = (x+3)(x-1)$

domain: $\{x \mid x = -3, x \neq 1\}$

Symmetry: $f(-x) = \dfrac{-x+1}{x^2 - 2x - 3}$

$f(-x) \neq f(x), f(-x) \neq -f(x)$

No symmetry

x-intercept:

$x + 1 = 0$

$x = -1$

y-intercept: $y = \dfrac{0+1}{0^2 + 2(0) - 3} = -\dfrac{1}{3}$

Vertical asymptotes:

$x^2 + 2x - 3 = 0$

$(x+3)(x-1) = 0$

$x - 3, 1$

Horizontal asymptote:

$n < m$, so $y = 0$ is the horizontal asymptote.

18. $f(x) = \dfrac{4x^2}{x^2 + 3}$

domain: all real numbers

Symmetry: $f(-x) = \dfrac{4x^2}{x^2 + 3} = f(x)$

y-axis symmetry

x-intercept:

$4x^2 = 0$

$x = 0$

y-intercept: $y = \dfrac{4(0)^2}{0^2 + 3} = 0$

Vertical asymptote:

$x^2 + 3 = 0$

$x^2 = -3$

No vertical asymptote.

Horizontal asymptote:

$n = m$, so $y = \dfrac{4}{1} = 4$ is the horizontal asymptote.

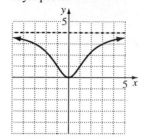

19. a. When $x = 0$, $y = 50$
50 deer were introduced into the habitat.

b. When $x = 10$, $y = 150$
After 10 years, there are 150 deer.

c. $y = 225$
The deer population will approach a maximum of 225 deer.

20. $I = \dfrac{k}{d^2}$

$20 = \dfrac{k}{d^2}$

$k = 4500$

$I = \dfrac{4500}{d^2}$

$I = \dfrac{4500}{10^2} = 45$ foot-candles

Cumulative Review Exercises (Chapters P–3)

1. $\dfrac{1}{2 - \sqrt{3}} \cdot \dfrac{2 + \sqrt{3}}{2 + \sqrt{3}} = \dfrac{2 + \sqrt{3}}{4 - 3} = 2 + \sqrt{3}$

2. $3\left(x^2 - 3x + 1\right) - 2\left(3x^2 + x - 4\right)$

$= 3x^2 - 9x + 3 - 6x^2 - 2x + 8$

$= -3x^2 - 11x + 11$

3. $3\sqrt{8} + 5\sqrt{50} - 4\sqrt{32}$

$\quad = 3\sqrt{4 \cdot 2} + 5\sqrt{25 \cdot 2} - 4\sqrt{16 \cdot 2}$

$\quad = 3 \cdot 2\sqrt{2} + 5 \cdot 5\sqrt{2} - 4 \cdot 4\sqrt{2}$

$\quad = 6\sqrt{2} + 25\sqrt{2} - 16\sqrt{2}$

$\quad = 15\sqrt{2}$

4. $x^7 - x^5 = x^5\left(x^2 - 1\right)$

$\qquad\qquad = x^5(x-1)(x+1)$

5. $12x - 11 = 3$

$\qquad 2x - 1 = 3$

$\qquad\quad 2x = 4$

$\qquad\qquad x = 2$

$\qquad 2x - 1 = -3$

$\qquad\quad 2x = -2$

$\qquad\qquad x = -1$

The solution set is $\{2, -1\}$.

6. $3x^2 - 5x + 1 = 0$

$\quad x = \dfrac{5 \pm \sqrt{25 - 12}}{6} = \dfrac{5 \pm \sqrt{13}}{6}$

The solution set is $\left\{\dfrac{5 + \sqrt{13}}{6}, \dfrac{5 - \sqrt{13}}{6}\right\}$.

7. $9 + \dfrac{3}{x} = \dfrac{2}{x^2}$

$\qquad 9x^2 + 3x = 2$

$\qquad 9x^2 + 3x - 2 = 0$

$\qquad (3x - 1)(3x + 2) = 0$

$\qquad 3x - 1 = 0 \qquad 3x + 2 = 0$

$\qquad\quad x = \dfrac{1}{3} \qquad \text{or} \qquad x = -\dfrac{2}{3}$

The solution set is $\left\{\dfrac{1}{3}, -\dfrac{2}{3}\right\}$.

8. $x^3 + 2x^2 - 5x - 6 = 0$

$\quad p: \pm 1, \pm 2, \pm 3, \pm 6$

$\quad q: \pm 1$

$\quad \dfrac{p}{q}: \pm 1, \pm 2, \pm 3, \pm 6$

$$
\begin{array}{r|rrrr}
-3 & 1 & 2 & -5 & -6 \\
   &   & -3 & 3 & 6 \\
\hline
   & 1 & -1 & -2 & 0
\end{array}
$$

$\quad x^3 + 2x^2 - 5x - 6 = 0$

$\quad (x + 3)(x^2 - x - 2) = 0$

$\quad (x + 3)(x + 1)(x - 2) = 0$

$\quad x = -3 \text{ or } x = -1 \text{ or } x = 2$

The solution set is $\{-3, -1, 2\}$.

9. $|2x - 5| > 3$

$\quad 2x - 5 > 3$

$\qquad 2x > 8$

$\qquad\quad x > 4$

$\quad 2x - 5 < -3$

$\qquad 2x < 2$

$\qquad\quad x < 1$

$\quad (-\infty, \ 1) \text{ or } (4, \ \infty)$

10. $\qquad\qquad 3x^2 > 2x + 5$

$\qquad 3x^2 - 2x - 5 > 0$

$\qquad 3x^2 - 2x - 5 = 0$

$\qquad (3x - 5)(x + 1) = 0$

$\qquad x = \dfrac{5}{3} \text{ or } x = -1$

Test intervals are $(-\infty, -1)$,

$\left(-1, \dfrac{5}{3}\right), \left(\dfrac{5}{3}, \infty\right)$.

Testing points, the solution is

$(-\infty, \ -1) \text{ or } \left(\dfrac{5}{3}, \ \infty\right)$.

11. $x^2 + y^2 - 2x + 4y - 4 = 0$

$x^2 - 2x + 1 + y^2 + 4y + 4 = 4 + 1 + 4$

$(x-1)^2 + (y+2)^2 = 9$

center: $(1, -2)$

radius: 3

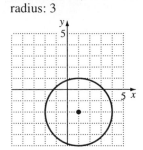

12. $V = C(1-t)$

$\dfrac{V}{C} = 1 - t$

$\dfrac{V}{C} - 1 = -t$

$t = 1 - \dfrac{V}{C}$

13. $f(x) = \sqrt{45 - 9x}$

$45 - 9x \geq 0$

$45 \geq 9x$

$5 \geq x$

Domain: $(-\infty, 5]$

14. $(f - g)(x) = x^2 + 2x - 5 - (4x - 1)$

$= x^2 + 2x - 5 - 4x + 1$

$= x^2 - 2x - 4$

15. $(f \circ g)(x) = (4x - 1)^2 + 2(4x - 1) - 5$

$= 16x^2 - 8x + 1 + 8x - 2 - 5$

$= 16x^2 - 6$

16. $g(f(-3))$

$f(-3) = (-3)^2 + 2(-3) - 5$

$= 9 - 6 - 5 = -2$

$g(-2) = 4(-2) - 1 = -8 - 1 = -9$

17. $f(x) = x^3 - 4x^2 - x + 4$

a. $x^3 - 4x^2 - x + 4 = 0$

$x^2(x - 4) - (x - 4) = 0$

$\left(x^2 - 1\right)(x - 4) = 0$

$(x - 1)(x + 1)(x - 4) = 0$

$x = -1, 1, 4$

The solution set is $\{-1, 1, 4\}$.

b. The graph falls to the left and rises to the right.

18. $f(x) = x^2 + 2x - 8$

$x = \dfrac{-b}{2a} = \dfrac{-2}{2} = -1$

$f(-1) = (-1)^2 + 2(-1) - 8$

$= 1 - 2 - 8 = -9$

vertex: $(-1, -9)$

x-intercepts:

$x^2 + 2x - 8 = 0$

$(x + 4)(x - 2) = 0$

$x = -4 \text{ or } x = 2$

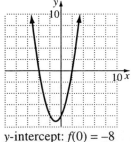

y-intercept: $f(0) = -8$

19. $f(x) = x^2(x - 3)$

zeros: $x = 0$ (multiplicity 2) and $x = 3$

y-intercept: $y = 0$

$f(x) = x^3 - 3x^2$

$n = 3$, $a_n = 0$ so the graph falls to the left and rises to the right.

20. $f(x) = \dfrac{x - 1}{x - 2}$

vertical asymptote: $x = 2$

horizontal asymptote: $y = 1$

x-intercept: $x = 1$

y-intercept: $y = \dfrac{1}{2}$

Chapter 4

Section 4.1

Check Point Exercises

1. Substitute 60 for x and evaluate the function at 60. $f(60) = 13.49(0.967)^{-60} - 1 \approx 1$
   Thus, one O-ring is expected to fail at a temperature of 60°F.

2. Begin by setting up a table of coordinates.

x	$f(x) = 3^x$
-3	$f(-3) = 3^{-3} = \frac{1}{27}$
-2	$f(-2) = 3^{-2} = \frac{1}{9}$
-1	$f(-1) = 3^{-1} = \frac{1}{3}$
0	$f(0) = 3^0 = 1$
1	$f(1) = 3^1 = 3$
2	$f(2) = 3^2 = 9$
3	$f(3) = 3^3 = 27$

   Plot these points, connecting them with a continuous curve.

   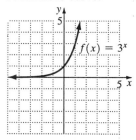

3. Note that the function $g(x) = 3^{x-1}$ has the general form $g(x) = b^{x+c}$ where $c = -1$.
   Because $c < 0$, we graph $g(x) = 3^{x-1}$ by shifting the graph of $f(x) = 3^x$ one unit to the right. Construct a table showing some of the coordinates for f and g.

x	$f(x) = 3^x$	$g(x) = 3^{x-1}$
-2	$3^{-2} = \frac{1}{9}$	$3^{-2-1} = 3^{-3} = \frac{1}{27}$
-1	$3^{-1} = \frac{1}{3}$	$3^{-1-1} = 3^{-2} = \frac{1}{9}$
0	$3^0 = 1$	$3^{0-1} = 3^{-1} = \frac{1}{3}$
1	$3^1 = 3$	$3^{1-1} = 3^0 = 1$
2	$3^2 = 9$	$3^{2-1} = 3^1 = 3$

4. Note that the function $g(x) = 2^x + 1$ has the general form $g(x) = b^x + c$ where $c = 1$.
   Because $c > 0$, we graph $g(x) = 2^x + 1$ by shifting the graph of $f(x) = 2^x$ up one unit. Construct a table showing some of the coordinates for f and g.

x	$f(x) - 2^x$	$g(x) = 2^x + 1$
-2	$2^{-2} = \frac{1}{4}$	$2^{-2} + 1 = \frac{1}{4} + 1 = \frac{5}{4}$
-1	$2^{-1} = \frac{1}{2}$	$2^{-1} + 1 = \frac{1}{2} + 1 = \frac{3}{2}$
0	$2^0 = 1$	$2^0 + 1 = 1 + 1 = 2$
1	$2^1 = 2$	$2^1 + 1 = 2 + 1 = 3$
2	$2^2 = 4$	$2^2 + 1 = 4 + 1 = 5$

   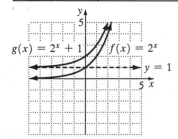

5. Because 2050 is 51 years after 1999, substitute 51 for x.

$f(51) = 6e^{0.013(51)} = 6e^{0.663} \approx 11.64$.

The world population is 2050 will be approximately 11.64 billion.

6. a. $A = 10,000\left(1 + \dfrac{0.08}{4}\right)^{4 \cdot 5} \approx 14,859.47$

The balance in this account after 5 years is \$14,859.47.

b. $A = 10,000e^{0.08(5)} \approx 14,918.25$

The balance in this account after 5 years is \$14,918.25.

Exercise Set 4.1

1. $2^{3.4} \approx 10.556$

3. $3^{\sqrt{5}} \approx 11.665$

5. $4^{-1.5} = 0.125$

7. $e^{2.3} \approx 9.974$

9. $e^{-0.95} \approx 0.387$

11.

x	$f(x) = 4^x$
-2	$4^{-2} = \frac{1}{16}$
-1	$4^{-1} = \frac{1}{4}$
0	$4^0 = 1$
1	$4^1 = 4$
2	$4^2 = 16$

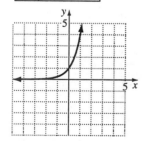

13.

x	$g(x) = \left(\frac{3}{2}\right)^x$
-2	$\left(\frac{3}{2}\right)^{-2} = \frac{4}{9}$
-1	$\left(\frac{3}{2}\right)^{-1} = \frac{2}{3}$
0	$\left(\frac{3}{2}\right)^0 = 1$
1	$\left(\frac{3}{2}\right)^1 = \frac{3}{2}$
2	$\left(\frac{3}{2}\right)^2 = \frac{9}{4}$

15.

x	$h(x) = \left(\frac{1}{2}\right)^x$
-2	$\left(\frac{1}{2}\right)^{-2} = 4$
-1	$\left(\frac{1}{2}\right)^{-1} = 2$
0	$\left(\frac{1}{2}\right)^0 = 1$
1	$\left(\frac{1}{2}\right)^1 = \frac{1}{2}$
2	$\left(\frac{1}{2}\right)^2 = \frac{1}{4}$

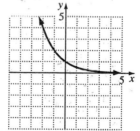

17.

x	$f(x) = (0.6)^x$
-2	$(0.6)^{-2} = 2.\overline{7}$
-1	$(0.6)^{-1} = 1.\overline{6}$
0	$(0.6)^0 = 1$
1	$(0.6)^1 = 0.6$
2	$(0.6)^2 = 0.36$

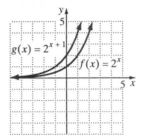

19. This is the graph of $f(x) = 3^x$ reflected about the x-axis and about the y-axis, so the function is $H(x) = -3^{-x}$.

21. This is the graph of $f(x) = 3^x$ reflected about the x-axis, so the function is $F(x) = -3^x$.

23. This is the graph of $f(x) = 3^x$ shifted one unit downward, so the function is $h(x) = 3^x - 1$.

25. The graph of $g(x) = 2^{x+1}$ can be obtained by shifting the graph of $f(x) = 2^x$ one unit to the left.

x	$g(x) = 2^{x+1}$
-2	$2^{-2+1} = 2^{-1} = \frac{1}{2}$
-1	$2^{-1+1} = 2^0 = 1$
0	$2^{0+1} = 2^1 = 2$
1	$2^{1+1} = 2^2 = 4$
2	$2^{2+1} = 2^3 = 8$

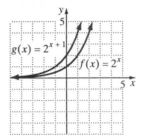

27. The graph of $g(x) = 2^x - 1$ can be obtained by shifting the graph of $f(x) = 2^x$ downward one unit.

x	$g(x) = 2^x - 1$
-2	$2^{-2} - 1 = \frac{1}{4} - 1 = -\frac{3}{4}$
-1	$2^{-1} - 1 = \frac{1}{2} - 1 = -\frac{1}{2}$
0	$2^0 - 1 = 1 - 1 = 0$
1	$2^1 - 1 = 2 - 1 = 1$
2	$2^2 - 1 = 4 - 1 = 3$

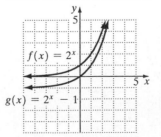

29. The graph of $h(x) = 2^{x+1} - 1$ can be obtained by shifting the graph of $f(x) = 2^x$ one unit to the left and one unit downward.

x	$h(x) = 2^{x+1} - 1$
-2	$2^{-2+1} - 1 = 2^{-1} - 1 = \frac{1}{2} - 1 = -\frac{1}{2}$
-1	$2^{-1+1} - 1 = 2^0 - 1 = 1 - 1 = 0$
0	$2^{0+1} - 1 = 2^1 - 1 = 2 - 1 = 1$
1	$2^{1+1} - 1 = 2^2 - 1 = 4 - 1 = 3$
2	$2^{2+1} - 1 = 2^3 - 1 = 8 - 1 = 7$

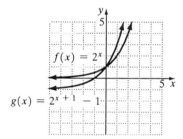

31. The graph of $g(x) = -2^x$ can be obtained by reflecting the graph of $f(x) = 2^x$ about the x-axis.

x	$g(x) = -2^x$
-2	$-2^{-2} = -\frac{1}{4}$
-1	$-2^{-1} = -\frac{1}{2}$
0	$-2^0 = -1$
1	$-2^1 = -2$
2	$-2^2 = -4$

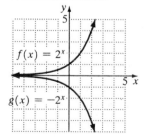

33. The graph of $g(x) = 2 \cdot 2^x$ can be obtained by vertically stretching the graph of $f(x) = 2^x$ by a factor of two.

x	$g(x) = 2 \cdot 2^x$
-2	$2 \cdot 2^{-2} = 2 \cdot \frac{1}{4} = \frac{1}{2}$
-1	$2 \cdot 2^{-1} = 2 \cdot \frac{1}{2} = 1$
0	$2 \cdot 2^0 = 2 \cdot 1 = 2$
1	$2 \cdot 2^1 = 2 \cdot 2 = 4$
2	$2 \cdot 2^2 = 2 \cdot 4 = 8$

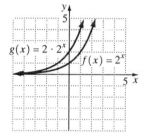

35. a. $A = 10,000\left(1 + \dfrac{0.055}{2}\right)^{2(5)}$

$\approx 13,116.51$

b. $A = 10,000\left(1 + \dfrac{0.055}{12}\right)^{12(5)}$

$\approx 13,157.04$

c. $A = 10,000e^{0.055(5)}$

$\approx 13,165.31$

37. $A = 12,000\left(1 + \dfrac{0.07}{12}\right)^{12(3)}$

$\approx 14,795.11$ (7% yield)

$A = 12,000e^{0.0685(3)}$

$\approx 14,737.67$ (6.85% yield)

Investing \$12,000 for 3 years at 7% compounded monthly yields the greatest return.

223

39. a. $f(0) = 67.38(1.026)^0 = 67.38$
   67.38 million
   b. $f(27) = 67.38(1.026)^{27}$
   ≈ 134.7441 million
   c. $f(54) = 67.38(1.026)^{254}$
   ≈ 269.4564 million
   d. $f(81) = 67.38(1.026)^{81}$
   ≈ 538.8492 million
   e. The population appears to double every 27 years.

41. $f(25) = \dfrac{0.9}{1 + 271(0.885)^{25}} \approx 0.0653$
   This means that only 6.5% of 25-year-olds have some coronary heart disease.

43. $\$65,000(1 + 0.06)^{10} \approx 116,405.10$
   The house will be worth \$116,405.10.

45. $2^{1.7} \approx 3.249009585$
   $2^{1.73} \approx 3.317278183$
   $2^{1.732} \approx 3.321880096$
   $2^{1.73205} \approx 3.321995226$
   $2^{1.7320508} \approx 3.321997068$

   $2^{\sqrt{3}} \approx 3.321997085$

   The closer the exponent is to $\sqrt{3}$, the closer the value is to $2^{\sqrt{3}}$.

47. $f(11) = 24,000e^{0.21(11)} \approx 241,786.1917$
   The number of AIDS cases among IV drug users in 2000 will be about 241,786.

49. a. $24\left(1 + \dfrac{0.05}{12}\right)^{12(374)}$
   $\approx \$3,052,428,614.31$
   b. $24e^{0.05(374)} \approx \$3,173,350,575.95$

51. a. $N(0) = \dfrac{30,000}{1 + 20e^{-1.5(0)}} = 1428.57$
   About 1429 people became ill.

   b. $N(3) = \dfrac{30,000}{1 + 20e^{-1.5(3)}} \approx 24,546.30$
   About 24,546 people were ill by the end of the third week.

c. The growth of the epidemic is limited by the size of the population. The horizontal asymptote shows that the epidemic will grow to the limiting size of the population, so that the entire population will eventually become ill.

53.–57. Answers may vary.

59.

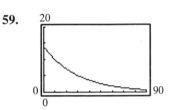

When $x = 31$, $y \approx 3.77$. NASA would not have launched the *Challenger*, since nearly 4 O-rings are expected to fail.

61. a. $A = 10,000\left(1 + \dfrac{0.05}{4}\right)^{4(t)}$

   $A = 10,000\left(1 + \dfrac{0.045}{12}\right)^{12(t)}$

   b. 5% compounded quarterly offers the better return.

63. a. False; even continuous compounding has a limit on the amount over a fixed interval of time.

   b. False; $f(x) = 3^{-x}$ reflects the graph of $y = 3^x$ about the y-axis while $f(x) = -3^x$ reflects the graph of $y = 3^x$ about the x-axis.

   c. False; $e \approx 2.718$, but e is irrational.

   d. True;
   $$f(x) = \left(\frac{1}{3}\right)^x = \left(3^{-1}\right)^x = (3)^{-x} = g(x).$$

   (d) is true.

65. $y = 3^x$ is (d). y increases as x increases, but not as quickly as $y = 5^x$. $y = 5^x$ is (c).

$y = \left(\frac{1}{3}\right)^x$ is (a). $y = \left(\frac{1}{3}\right)^x$ is the same as $y = 3^{-x}$, so it is (d) reflected about the y-axis.

$y = \left(\frac{1}{5}\right)^x$ is (b). $y = \left(\frac{1}{5}\right)^x$ is the same as $y = 5^{-x}$, so it is (c) reflected about the y-axis.

Section 4.2

Check Point Exercises

1. a. $3 = \log_7 x$ means $7^3 = x$.

b. $2 = \log_b 25$ means $b^2 = 25$.

c. $\log_4 26 = y$ means $4^y = 26$.

2. a. $2^5 = x$ means $5 = \log_2 x$.

b. $b^3 = 27$ means $3 = \log_b 27$.

c. $e^y = 33$ means $y = \log_e 33$.

3. a. Question: 10 to what power gives 100?
$\log_{10} 100 = 2$ because $10^2 = 100$.

b. Question: 3 to what power gives 3?
$\log_3 3 = 1$ because $3^1 = 3$.

c. Question: 36 to what power gives 6?
$\log_{36} 6 = \frac{1}{2}$ because $36^{1/2} = \sqrt{36} = 6$.

4. a. Because $\log_b b = 1$, we conclude $\log_9 9 = 1$.

b. Because $\log_b 1 = 0$, we conclude $\log_8 1 = 0$.

5. a. Because $\log_b b^x = x$, we conclude $\log_7 7^8 = 8$.

b. Because $b^{\log_b x} = x$, we conclude $3^{\log_3 17} = 17$.

6. First, set up a table of coordinates for $f(x) = 3^x$.

x	-2	-1	0	1	2	3
$f(x) = 3^x$	$\frac{1}{9}$	$\frac{1}{3}$	1	3	9	27

Reversing these coordinates gives the coordinates for the inverse function $g(x) = \log_3 x$.

x	$\frac{1}{9}$	$\frac{1}{3}$	1	3	9	27
$g(x) = \log_3 x$	-2	-1	0	1	2	3

The graph of the inverse can also be drawn by reflecting the graph of $f(x) = 3^x$ about the line $y = x$.

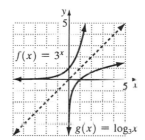

7. The domain of h consists of all x for which $x - 5 > 0$. Solving this inequality for x, we obtain $x > 5$. Thus, the domain of h is $(5, \infty)$.

8. Substitute the boy's age, 10, for x and evaluate the function at 10.
$f(10) = 29 + 48.8 \ \log(10 + 1)$
$\qquad = 29 + 48.8 \ \log(11)$
$\qquad \approx 80$
Thus, a 10-year-old boy is approximately 80% of his adult height.

9. Because $I = 10,000 \ I_0$,
$R = \log \dfrac{10,000 I_0}{I_0}$
$\quad = \log \ 10,000$
$\quad = 4$
The earthquake registered 4.0 on the Richter scale.

10. a. The domain of f consists of all x for which $4 - x > 0$. Solving this inequality for x, we obtain $x < 4$. Thus, the domain of f is $(-\infty, 4)$

b. The domain of g consists of all x for which $x^2 > 0$. Solving this inequality for x, we obtain $x < 0$ or $x > 0$. Thus the domain of g is $(-\infty, 0)$ or $(0, \infty)$.

11. a. Because $\ln e^x = x$, we conclude $\ln e^{25x} = 25x$.

b. Because $e^{\ln x} = x$, we conclude $e^{\ln \sqrt{x}} = \sqrt{x}$.

12. Substitute 197 for P, the population in thousands. $W = 0.35 \ln 197 + 2.74 \approx 4.6$ The average walking speed in Jackson, Mississippi is approximately 4.6 feet per second.

Exercise Set 4.2

1. $2^4 = 16$

3. $3^2 = x$

5. $b^5 = 32$

7. $6^y = 216$

9. $\log_2 8 = 3$

11. $\log_2 \dfrac{1}{16} = -4$

13. $\log_8 2 = \dfrac{1}{3}$

15. $\log_{13} x = 2$

17. $\log_b 1000 = 3$

19. $\log_7 200 = y$

21. $\log_4 16 = 2$ because $4^2 = 16$.

23. $\log_2 64 = 6$ because $2^6 = 64$.

25. $\log_7 \sqrt{7} = \dfrac{1}{2}$ because $7^{\frac{1}{2}} = \sqrt{7}$.

27. $\log_2 \dfrac{1}{8} = -3$ because $2^{-3} = \dfrac{1}{8}$.

29. $\log_{64} 8 = \dfrac{1}{2}$ because $64^{\frac{1}{2}} = \sqrt{64} = 8$.

31. Because $\log_b b = 1$, we conclude $\log_5 5 = 1$.

33. Because $\log_b 1 = 0$, we conclude $\log_4 1 = 0$.

35. Because $\log_b b^x = x$, we conclude $\log_5 5^7 = 7$.

37. Because $b^{\log_b x} = x$, we conclude $8^{\log_8 19} = 19$.

39. First, set up a table of coordinates for $f(x) = 4^x$.

x	-2	-1	0	1	2	3
$f(x) = 4x$	$\frac{1}{16}$	$\frac{1}{4}$	1	4	16	64

Reversing these coordinates gives the coordinates for the inverse function $g(x) = \log_4 x$.

x	$\frac{1}{16}$	$\frac{1}{4}$	1	4	16	64
$g(x) = \log_{4x}$	-2	-1	0	1	2	3

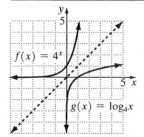

41. First, set up a table of coordinates for

$$f(x) = \left(\frac{1}{2}\right)^x .$$

x	-2	-1	0	1	2	3
$f(x) = \left(\frac{1}{2}\right)^x$	4	2	1	$\frac{1}{2}$	$\frac{1}{4}$	$\frac{1}{8}$

Reversing these coordinates gives the coordinates for the inverse function $g(x) = \log_{1/2} x$.

x	4	2	1	$\frac{1}{2}$	$\frac{1}{4}$	$\frac{1}{8}$
$g(x) = \log_{1/2} x$	-2	-1	0	1	2	3

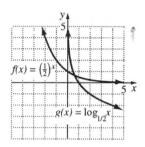

43. This is the graph of $f(x) = \log_3 x$ reflected about the x-axis and shifted up one unit, so the function is $H(x) = 1 - \log_3 x$.

45. This is the graph of $f(x) = \log_3 x$ shifted down one unit, so the function is $h(x) = \log_3 x - 1$.

47. This is the graph of $f(x) = \log_3 x$ shifted right one unit, so the function is $g(x) = \log_3(x-1)$.

49.

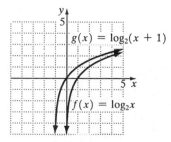

x-intercept: (0,0)
vertical asymptote: $x = -1$

51.

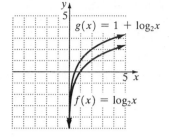

x-intercept: (0.5,0)
vertical asymptote: $x = 0$

53.

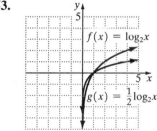

x-intercept: (1,0)
vertical asymptote: $x = 0$

55. The domain of f consists of all x for which $x + 4 > 0$. Solving this inequality for x, we obtain $x > -4$. Thus, the domain of f is $(-4, \infty)$.

57. The domain of f consists of all x for which $2 - x > 0$. Solving this inequality for x, we obtain $x < 2$. Thus, the domain of f is $(-\infty, 2)$.

59. The domain of f consists of all x for which $(x - 2)^2 > 0$. Solving this inequality for x, we obtain $x < 2$ or $x > 2$. Thus, the domain of f is $(-\infty, 2)$ or $(2, -\infty)$.

61. $\log 100 = \log_{10} 100 = 2$
because $10^2 = 100$.

63. Because $\log 10^x = x$, we conclude $\log 10^7 = 7$.

65. Because $10^{\log x} = x$, we conclude $10^{\log 33} = 33$.

67. $\ln 1 = 0$ because $e^0 = 1$.

69. Because $\ln e^x = x$, we
conclude $\ln e^6 = 6$.

71. $\ln \dfrac{1}{e^6} = \ln e^{-6}$

Because $\ln e^x = x$ we conclude

$\ln e^{-6} = -6$, so $\ln \dfrac{1}{e^6} = -6$.

73. Because $e^{\ln x} = x$, we conclude
$e^{\ln 125} = 125$.

75. Because $\ln e^x = x$, we conclude
$\ln e^{9x} = 9x$.

77. Because $e^{\ln x} = x$, we conclude
$e^{\ln 5x^2} = 5x^2$.

79. Because $10^{\log x} = x$, we conclude
$10^{\log \sqrt{x}} = \sqrt{x}$.

81. $f(13) = 62 + 35\log(13-4) \approx 95.4$
She is approximately 95.4% of her adult
height.

83. $f(16) = 2.05 + 1.3\ln(16) \approx 5.65$ billion
Approximately $5.65 billion was spent in
2000.

85. $D = 10\log\left[10^{12}(6.3\times10^6)\right] \approx 188$
Yes, the sound can rupture the human
eardrum.

87. a. $f(0) = 88-15\ln(0 + 1) = 88$
The average score on the original exam
was 88.

b. $f(2) = 88-15\ln(2 + 1) = 71.5$
$f(4) = 88-15\ln(4 + 1) = 63.9$
$f(6) = 88-15\ln(6 + 1) = 58.8$
$f(8) = 88-15\ln(8 + 1) = 55$
$f(10) = 88-15\ln(10 + 1) = 52$
$f(12) = 88-15\ln(12 + 1) = 49.5$

The average score after 2 months was
about 71.5, after 4 months was about
63.9, after 6 months was about 58.8,
after 8 months was about 55, after 10
months was about 52, and after one year
was about 49.5.

c.

Material retention decreases as time
passes.

89.–95. Answers may vary.

97.

$g(x)$ is $f(x)$ shifted 3 units left.

99.

$g(x)$ is $f(x)$ reflected about the x-axis.

101.

The score falls below 65 after 9 months.

103.

$$y = \ln x, \ y = \sqrt{x}, \ y = x,$$
$$y = x^2, \ y = e^x, \ y = x^x$$

105. $\dfrac{\log_3 81 - \log_\pi 1}{\log_{2\sqrt{2}} 8 - \log 0.001} = \dfrac{4 - 0}{2 - (-3)} = \dfrac{4}{5}$

107. $\log_4 60 < \log_4 64 = 3$ so $\log_4 60 < 3$.
$\log_3 40 > \log_3 27 = 3$ so $\log_3 40 > 3$.
So $\log_4 60 < 3 < \log_3 40$.
Thus, $\log_3 > \log_4 60$.

Section 4.3

Check Point Exercises

1. a. $\log_6(10 \cdot 9) = \log_6 10 + \log_6 9$

   b. $\log(100x) = \log 100 + \log x$
$$= 2 + \log x$$

2. a. $\log_8\left(\dfrac{23}{x}\right) = \log_8 23 - \log_8 x$

   b. $\ln\left(\dfrac{e^5}{11}\right) = \ln e^5 - \ln 11$
$$= 5 - \ln 11$$

3. a. $\log_6 8^9 = 9 \log_6 8$

   b. $\ln \sqrt[3]{x} = \ln x^{1/3}$
$$= \dfrac{1}{3} \ln x$$

4. a. $\log_b x^4 \sqrt[3]{y}$
$$= \log_6 x^4 y^{1/3}$$
$$= \log_b x^4 + \log_b y^{1/3}$$
$$= 4 \log_b x + \dfrac{1}{3} \log_b y$$

   b. $\log_5 \dfrac{\sqrt{x}}{25y^3}$
$$= \log_5 \dfrac{x^{1/2}}{25y^3}$$
$$= \log_5 x^{1/2} - \log_5 25y^3$$
$$= \log_5 x^{1/2} - \left(\log_5 25 + \log_5 y^3\right)$$
$$= \dfrac{1}{2} \log_5 x - \left(\log_5 25 + 3 \log_5 y\right)$$
$$= \dfrac{1}{2} \log_5 x - \log_5 25 - 3 \log_5 y$$
$$= \dfrac{1}{2} \log_5 x - 2 - 3 \log_5 y$$

5. a. $\log 25 + \log 4 = \log(25 \cdot 4)$
$$= \log 100$$
$$= 2$$

   b. $\log(7x + 6) - \log x = \log \dfrac{7x + 6}{x}$

6. a. $\ln x^2 + \dfrac{1}{3} \ln(x + 5)$
$$= \ln x^2 + \ln(x + 5)^{1/3}$$
$$= \ln x^2 (x + 5)^{1/3}$$
$$= \ln x^2 \sqrt[3]{x + 5}$$

   b. $2 \log(x - 3) - \log x$
$$= \log(x - 3)^2 - \log x$$
$$= \log \dfrac{(x - 3)^2}{x}$$

7. $\log_7 2506 = \dfrac{\log 2506}{\log 7}$
$$\approx 4.02$$

8. $\log_7 2506 = \dfrac{\ln 2506}{\ln 7}$
$$\approx 4.02$$

9. $y = \log_3 x = \dfrac{\ln x}{\ln 3}$

$y = \log_{15} x = \dfrac{\ln x}{\ln 15}$

Using a [0, 10, 1] by [–3, 3, 1] viewing rectangle, the graphs are:

Exercise Set 4.3

1. $\log_5(12 \cdot 3) = \log_5 12 + \log_5 3$

3. $\log_7(7x) = \log_7 7 + \log_7 x$
$= 1 + \log_7 x$

5. $\log(1000x) = \log 1000 + \log x$
$= 3 + \log x$

7. $\log_7\left(\dfrac{7}{x}\right) = \log_7 7 - \log_7 x$
$= 1 - \log_7 x$

9. $\log\left(\dfrac{x}{100}\right) = \log x - \log 100$
$= \log_x - 2$

11. $\log_4\left(\dfrac{64}{y}\right) = \log_4 64 - \log_4 y$
$= 3 - \log_4 y$

13. $\ln\left(\dfrac{e^2}{5}\right) = \ln e^2 - \ln 5$
$= 2 \ln e - \ln 5$
$= 2 - \ln 5$

15. $\log_b x^3 = 3\log_b x$

17. $\log N^{-b} = -b \log N$

19. $\ln \sqrt[5]{x} = \ln x^{(1/5)}$
$= \dfrac{1}{5} \ln x$

21. $\log_b x^2 y = \log_b x^2 + \log_b y$
$= 2\log_b x + \log_b y$

23. $\log_4\left(\dfrac{\sqrt{x}}{64}\right) = \log_4 x^{1/2} - \log_4 64$
$= \dfrac{1}{2}\log_4 x - 3$

25. $\log_6\left(\dfrac{36}{\sqrt{x+1}}\right) = \log_6 36 - \log_6(x+1)^{1/2}$
$= 2 - \dfrac{1}{2}\log_6(x+1)$

27. $\log_b\left(\dfrac{x^2 y}{z^2}\right) = \log_b\left(x^2 y\right) - \log_b z^2$
$= \log_b x^2 + \log_b y - \log_b z^2$
$= 2\log_b x + \log_b y - 2\log_b z$

29. $\log \sqrt{100x} = \log(100x)^{1/2}$
$= \dfrac{1}{2}\log(100x)$
$= \dfrac{1}{2}(\log 100 + \log x)$
$= \dfrac{1}{2}(2 + \log x)$
$= 1 + \dfrac{1}{2}\log x$

31. $\log \sqrt[3]{\dfrac{x}{y}} = \log\left(\dfrac{x}{y}\right)^{1/3}$
$= \dfrac{1}{3}\left[\log\left(\dfrac{x}{y}\right)\right]$
$= \dfrac{1}{3}(\log x - \log y)$
$= \dfrac{1}{3}\log x - \dfrac{1}{3}\log y$

33. $\log 5 + \log 2 = \log(5 \cdot 2)$
$$= \log 10$$
$$= 1$$

35. $\ln x + \ln 7 = \ln(7x)$

37. $\log_2 96 - \log_2 3 = \log_2\left(\dfrac{96}{3}\right)$
$$= \log_2 32$$
$$= 5$$

39. $\log(2x+5) - \log x = \log\left(\dfrac{2x+5}{x}\right)$

41. $\log x + 3\log y = \log x + \log y^3$
$$= \log(xy^3)$$

43. $\dfrac{1}{2}\ln x + \ln y = \ln x^{1/2} + \ln y$
$$= \ln\left(x^{\frac{1}{2}}y\right) \text{ or } \ln\left(\sqrt{x}\,y\right)$$

45. $2\log_b x + 3\log_b y = \log_b x^2 + \log_b y^3$
$$= \log_b(x^2 y^3)$$

47. $5\ln x - 2\ln y = \ln x^5 - \ln y^2$
$$= \ln\left(\dfrac{x^5}{y^2}\right)$$

49. $3\ln x - \dfrac{1}{3}\ln y = \ln x^3 - \ln y^{1/3}$
$$= \ln\left(\dfrac{x^3}{y^{1/3}}\right) \text{ or } \ln\left(\dfrac{x^3}{\sqrt[3]{y}}\right)$$

51. $4\ln(x+6) - 3\ln x = \ln(x+6)^4 - \ln x^3$
$$= \ln\dfrac{(x+6)^4}{x^3}$$

53. $\log_5 13 = \dfrac{\log 13}{\log 5} \approx 1.5937$

55. $\log_{14} 87.5 = \dfrac{\ln 87.5}{\ln 14} \approx 1.6944$

57. $\log_{0.1} 17 = \dfrac{\log 17}{\log 0.1} \approx -1.2304$

59. $\log_\pi 63 = \dfrac{\ln 63}{\ln \pi} \approx 3.6193$

61. a. $D = 10\log\left(\dfrac{I}{I_0}\right)$

b. $D_1 = 10\log\left(\dfrac{100I}{I_0}\right)$
$$= 10\log(100I - I_0)$$
$$= 10\log 100 + 10\log I - 10\log I_0$$
$$= 10(2) + 10\log I - 10\log I_0$$
$$= 20 + 10\log\left(\dfrac{I}{I_0}\right)$$

This is 20 more than the loudness level of the softer sound. This means that the 100 times louder sound will be 20 decibels louder.

63.–69. Answers may vary.

71. a. $y = \log_3 x = \dfrac{\ln x}{\ln 3}$

b.

To obtain the graph of $y = 2 + \log_3 x$, shift the graph of $y = \log_3 x$ two units upward. To obtain the graph of $y = \log_3(x + 2)$, shift the graph of $y = \log_3 x$ two units left. To obtain the graph of $y = -\log_3 x$, reflect the graph of $y = \log_3 x$ about the x-axis.

73.
$$\log_3 x = \frac{\log x}{\log 3};$$

$$\log_{25} x = \frac{\log x}{\log 25};$$

$$\log_{100} x = \frac{\log x}{\log 100}$$

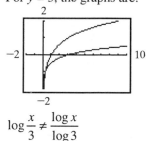

a. top graph: $y = \log_{100} x$
bottom graph: $y = \log_3 x$

b. top graph: $y = \log_3 x$
bottom graph: $y = \log_{100} x$

c. Comparing graphs of $\log_b x$ for $b > 1$, the graph of the equation with the largest b will be on the top in the interval $(0, 1)$ and on the bottom in the interval $(1, \infty)$.

75. a. Values of y may vary.
b. For $y = 3$, the graphs are:

$$\log \frac{x}{3} \neq \frac{\log x}{\log 3}$$

77. a. Values of y may vary.
b. For $y = 6$, the graphs are:

$$\ln(6x) \neq (\ln x)(\ln 6)$$

79. a. False;
$$\log_7 49 - \log_7 7 = \log_7 \frac{49}{7} = \log_7 7 = 1;$$

$$\frac{\log_7 49}{\log_7 7} = \frac{2}{1} = 2$$

b. False;
$$3\log_b x + 3\log_b y = \log_b (xy)^3$$
$$\neq \log_b \left(x^3 + y^3 \right)$$

c. False;
$$\log_b (xy)^5 = 5\log_b (xy)$$
$$= 5(\log_b x + \log_b y)$$
$$\neq (\log_b x + \log_b y)^5$$

d. True;
$$\ln \sqrt{2} = \ln 2^{1/2}$$
$$= \frac{1}{2} \ln 2 = \frac{\ln 2}{2}$$

(d) is true.

81. $\log_7 9 = \dfrac{\log 9}{\log 7} = \dfrac{\log 3^2}{\log 7} = \dfrac{2\log 3}{\log 7}$
$$= \frac{2A}{B}$$

Section 4.4

Check Point Exercises

1. $5^x = 134$
$\ln 5^x = \ln 134$
$x \ln 5 = \ln 134$
$$x = \frac{\ln 134}{\ln 5} \approx 3.04$$

The solution set is $\left\{ \dfrac{\ln 134}{\ln 5} \right\}$, approximately 3.04.

2. $7e^{2x} = 63$

$\qquad e^{2x} = 9$

$\quad \ln e^{2x} = \ln 9$

$\qquad 2x = \ln 9$

$\qquad x = \dfrac{\ln 9}{2} \approx 1.10$

The solution set is $\left\{ \dfrac{\ln 9}{2} \right\}$,

approximately 1.10.

3. $6^{3x-4} - 7 = 2081$

$\qquad 6^{3x-4} = 2088$

$\quad \ln 6^{3x-4} = \ln 2088$

$\quad (3x - 4)\ln 6 = \ln 2088$

$3x \ln 6 - 4 \ln 6 = \ln 2088$

$\qquad 3x \ln 6 = \ln 2088 + 4 \ln 6$

$\qquad x = \dfrac{\ln 2088 + 4 \ln 6}{3 \ln 6} \approx 2.76$

The solution set is $\left\{ \dfrac{\ln 2088 + 4 \ln 6}{3 \ln 6} \right\}$,

approximately 2.76.

4. $e^{2x} - 8e^{x} + 7 = 0$

$\left(e^{x} - 7\right)\left(e^{x} - 1\right) = 0$

$e^{x} - 7 = 0 \quad$ or $\quad e^{x} - 1 = 0$

$\qquad e^{x} = 7 \qquad\qquad e^{x} = 1$

$\quad \ln e^{x} = \ln 7 \qquad \ln e^{x} = \ln 1$

$\qquad x = \ln 7 \qquad\qquad x = 0$

The solution set is $\{0, \ln 7\}$. The solutions
are 0 and (approximately) 1.95.

5. $\log_2(x - 4) = 3$

$\quad 2^3 = x - 4$

$\quad 8 = x - 4$

$\quad 12 = x$

Check:

$\quad \log_2(x - 4) = 3$

$\log_2(12 - 4) \overset{?}{=} 3$

$\qquad \log_2 8 \overset{?}{=} 3$

$\qquad\qquad 3 = 3$

The solution set is $\{12\}$.

6. $\log x + \log(x - 3) = 1$

$\qquad \log x(x - 3) = 1$

$\qquad 10^1 = x(x - 3)$

$\qquad 10 = x^2 - 3x$

$\qquad 0 = x^2 - 3x - 10$

$\qquad 0 = (x - 5)(x + 2)$

$x - 5 = 0 \quad$ or $\quad x + 2 = 0$

$\quad x = 5 \quad$ or $\qquad x = -2$

Check

Checking 5:

$\log x + \log(x - 3) = 1$

$\log 5 + \log(5 - 3) \overset{?}{=} 1$

$\quad \log 5 + \log 2 \overset{?}{=} 1$

$\qquad \log(5 \cdot 2) \overset{?}{=} 1$

$\qquad\quad \log 10 \overset{?}{=} 1$

$\qquad\qquad\quad 1 = 1$

Checking -2:

$\log x + \log(x - 3) = 1$

$\log(-2) + \log(-2 - 3) \overset{?}{=} 1$

Negative numbers do not have logarithms so
-2 does not check.

The solution set is $\{5\}$.

7 $4 \ln 3x = 8$

$\quad \ln 3x = 2$

$\quad e^{\ln 3x} = e^2$

$\qquad 3x = e^2$

$\qquad x = \dfrac{e^2}{3} \approx 2.46$

Check

$\qquad 4 \ln 3x = 8$

$4 \ln 3\left(\dfrac{e^2}{3}\right) \overset{?}{=} 8$

$\quad 4 \ln e^2 \overset{?}{=} 8$

$\qquad\quad 8 = 8$

The solution set is $\left\{ \dfrac{e^2}{3} \right\}$,

approximately 2.46.

8. For a risk of 7%, let $R = 7$ in

$$R = 6e^{12.77x}$$

$$6e^{12.77x} = 7$$

$$e^{12.77x} = \frac{7}{6}$$

$$\ln e^{12.77x} = \ln\left(\frac{7}{6}\right)$$

$$12.77x = \ln\left(\frac{7}{6}\right)$$

$$x = \frac{\ln\left(\frac{7}{6}\right)}{12.77} \approx 0.01$$

For a blood alcohol concentration of 0.01, the risk of a car accident is 7%.

9. $A = P\left(1 + \frac{r}{n}\right)^{nt}$

$$3600 = 1000\left(1 + \frac{0.08}{4}\right)^{4t}$$

$$1000\left(1 - \frac{0.08}{4}\right)^{4t} = 3600$$

$$1000(1 + 0.02)^{4t} = 3600$$

$$1000(1.02)^{4t} = 3600$$

$$(1.02)^{4t} = \ln 3.6$$

$$4t\ln(1.02) = \ln 3.6$$

$$t = \frac{\ln 3.6}{4\ln 1.02}$$

$$\approx 16.2$$

After approximately 16.2 years, the $1000 will grow to an accumulated value of $3600.

10.
$$N = 461.87 + 299.4\ln x$$
$$2000 = 461.87 + 299.4\ln x$$
$$461.87 + 299.4\ln x = 2000$$
$$299.4\ln x = 1538.13$$
$$\ln x = \frac{1538.13}{299.4}$$
$$e^{\ln x} = e^{1538.13/299.4}$$
$$x = e^{1538.13/299.4}$$
$$\approx 170$$

Approximately 170 years after 1979, in 2149, there will be 2 million U.S. workers in the environmental industry.

Exercise Set 4.4

1. $10^x = 3.91$

$$\ln 10^x = \ln 3.91$$

$$x\ln 10 = \ln 3.91$$

$$x = \frac{\ln 3.91}{\ln 10} \approx 0.59$$

The solution set is $\left\{\frac{\ln 3.91}{\ln 10}\right\}$, approximately 0.59.

3. $e^x = 5.7$

$$\ln e^x = 5.7$$

$$x = \ln 5.7 \approx 1.74$$

The solution set is $\{\ln 5.7\}$, approximately 1.74.

5. $5^x = 17$

$$\ln 5^x = \ln 17$$

$$x\ln 5 = \ln 17$$

$$x = \frac{\ln 17}{\ln 5} \approx 1.76$$

The solution set is $\left\{\frac{\ln 17}{\ln 5}\right\}$, approximately 1.76.

7. $5e^x = 23$

$$e^x = \frac{23}{5}$$

$$\ln e^x = \ln\frac{23}{5}$$

$$x = \ln\frac{23}{5} \approx 1.53$$

The solution set is $\left\{\ln\frac{23}{5}\right\}$, approximately 1.53.

9. $3e^{5x} = 1977$

$e^{5x} = 659$

$\ln e^{5x} = \ln 659$

$x = \dfrac{\ln 659}{5} \approx 1.30$

The solution set is $\left\{ \dfrac{\ln 659}{5} \right\}$, approximately 1.30.

11. $e^{1-5x} = 793$

$\ln e^{1-5x} = \ln 793$

$(1 - 5x)(\ln e) = \ln 793$

$1 - 5x = \ln 793$

$5x = 1 - \ln 793$

$x = \dfrac{1 - \ln 793}{5} \approx -1.14$

The solution set is $\left\{ \dfrac{1 - \ln 793}{5} \right\}$, approximately -1.14.

13. $e^{5x-3} - 2 = 10,476$

$e^{5x-3} = 10,478$

$\ln e^{5x-3} = \ln 10,478$

$(5x - 3)\ln e = \ln 10,478$

$5x - 3 = \ln 10,478$

$5x = \ln 10,478 + 3$

$x = \dfrac{\ln 10,478 + 3}{5} \approx 2.45$

The solution set is $\left\{ \dfrac{\ln 10,478 + 3}{5} \right\}$, approximately 2.45.

15. $7^{x+2} = 410$

$\ln 7^{x+2} = \ln 410$

$(x + 2)\ln 7 = \ln 410$

$x + 2 = \dfrac{\ln 410}{\ln 7}$

$x = \dfrac{\ln 410}{\ln 7} - 2 \approx 1.09$

The solution set is $\left\{ \dfrac{\ln 410}{\ln 7} - 2 \right\}$, approximately 1.09.

17. $7^{0.3x} = 813$

$\ln 7^{0.3x} = \ln 813$

$0.3x \ln 7 = \ln 813$

$x = \dfrac{\ln 813}{0.3 \ln 7} \approx 11.48$

The solution set is $\left\{ \dfrac{\ln 813}{0.3 \ln 7} \right\}$, approximately 11.48.

19. $e^{2x} - 3e^x + 2 = 0$

$\left(e^x - 2 \right)\left(e^x - 1 \right) = 0$

$e^x - 2 = 0$ or $e^x - 1 = 0$

$\qquad e^x = 2 \qquad\qquad e^x = 1$

$\ln e^x = \ln 2 \qquad \ln e^x = \ln 1$

$\quad x = \ln 2 \qquad\qquad x = 0$

The solution set is $\{0, \ln 2\}$. The solutions are 0 and (approximately) 0.69.

21. $e^{4x} + 5e^{2x} - 24 = 0$

$\left(e^{2x} + 8 \right)\left(e^{2x} - 3 \right) = 0$

$e^{2x} + 8 = 0$ or $e^{2x} - 3 = 0$

$\quad e^{2x} = -8 \qquad\qquad e^{2x} = 3$

$\ln e^{2x} = \ln(-8) \qquad \ln e^{2x} = \ln 3$

$\quad 2x = \ln(-8) \qquad\quad 2x = \ln 3$

$\ln(-8)$ does not exist $\qquad x = \dfrac{\ln 3}{2}$

$x = \dfrac{\ln 3}{2} \approx 0.55$

The solution set is $\left\{ \dfrac{\ln 3}{2} \right\}$, approximately 0.55.

23. $\log_3 x = 4$

$x = 3^4$

$x = 81$

The solution set is $\{81\}$.

25. $\log_4(x + 5) = 3$

$x + 5 = 4^3$

$x + 5 = 64$

$x = 59$

The solution set is $\{59\}$.

27. $\log_3(x-4) = -3$

$$x - 4 = 3^{-3}$$
$$x - 4 = \frac{1}{27}$$
$$x = \frac{109}{27}$$

The solution set is $\left\{\dfrac{109}{27}\right\}$.

29. $\log_4(3x+2) = 3$

$$3x + 2 = 4^3$$
$$3x + 2 = 64$$
$$3x = 62$$
$$x = \frac{62}{3}$$

The solution set is $\left\{\dfrac{62}{3}\right\}$.

31. $\log_5 x + \log_5(4x-1) = 1$

$$\log_5\left(4x^2 - x\right) = 1$$
$$4x^2 - x = 5$$
$$4x^2 - x - 5 = 0$$
$$(4x-5)(x+1) = 0$$
$$x = \frac{5}{4} \text{ or } x = -1$$

$x = -1$ does not check because $\log_5(-1)$ does not exist.

The solution set is $\left\{\dfrac{5}{4}\right\}$.

33. $\log_3(x-5) + \log_3(x+3) = 2$

$$\log_3\left[(x-5)(x+3)\right] = 2$$
$$(x-5)(x+3) = 3^2$$
$$x^2 - 2x - 15 = 9$$
$$x^2 - 2x - 24 = 0$$
$$(x-6)(x+4) = 0$$
$$x = 6 \text{ or } x = -4$$

$x = -4$ does not check because $\log_3(-4-5)$ does not exist.
The solution set is $\{6\}$.

35. $\log_2(x+2) - \log_2(x-5) = 3$

$$\log_2\left(\frac{x+2}{x-5}\right) = 3$$
$$\frac{x+2}{x-5} = 2^3$$
$$\frac{x+2}{x-5} = 8$$
$$x + 2 = 8(x-5)$$
$$x + 2 = 8x - 40$$
$$7x = 42$$
$$x = 6$$

The solution set is $\{6\}$.

37. $\ln x = 2$

$$e^{\ln x} = e^2$$
$$x = e^2 \approx 7.39$$

The solution set is $\left\{e^2\right\}$, approximately 7.39.

39. $5\ln 2x = 20$

$$\ln 2x = 4$$
$$e^{\ln 2x} = e^4$$
$$2x = e^4$$
$$x = \frac{e^4}{2} \approx 27.30$$

The solution set is $\left\{\dfrac{e^4}{2}\right\}$, approximately 27.30.

41. $6 + 2\ln x = 5$

$$2\ln x = -1$$
$$\ln x = -\frac{1}{2}$$
$$e^{\ln x} = e^{-1/2}$$
$$x = e^{-1/2} \approx 0.61$$

The solution set is $\left\{e^{-1/2}\right\}$, approximately 0.61.

43. $\ln\sqrt{x+3} = 1$

$e^{\ln\sqrt{x+3}} = e^1$

$\sqrt{x+3} = e$

$x + 3 = e^2$

$x = e^2 - 3 \approx 4.39$

The solution set is $\{e^2 - 3\}$, approximately 4.39.

45. $100 = 6e^{12.77x}$

$e^{12.77x} = \dfrac{50}{3}$

$\ln e^{12.77x} = \ln\left(\dfrac{50}{3}\right)$

$12.77x = \ln\left(\dfrac{50}{3}\right)$

$x = \dfrac{\ln\left(\frac{50}{3}\right)}{12.77} \approx 0.22$

A blood alcohol level of about 0.22 corresponds to a 100% risk of a car accident.

47. a. In 1994, $t = 0$.

$A = 18.2e^{0.001(0)}$

$A = 18.2$ million

In 1994, the population was 18.2 million.

b. $18.5 = 18.2e^{0.001t}$

$e^{0.001t} = \dfrac{18.5}{18.2}$

$\ln e^{0.001t} = \ln\left(\dfrac{18.5}{18.2}\right)$

$0.001t = \ln\left(\dfrac{18.5}{18.2}\right)$

$t = \dfrac{\ln\left(\dfrac{18.5}{18.2}\right)}{0.001} \approx 16$

The population will reach 18.5 million about 16 years after 1994, in 2010.

49. $20{,}000 = 12{,}500\left(1 + \dfrac{0.0575}{4}\right)^{4t}$

$12{,}500(1.014375)^{4t} = 20{,}000$

$(1.014375)^{4t} = 1.6$

$\ln(1.014375)^{4t} = \ln 1.6$

$4t \ln(1.014375) = \ln 1.6$

$t = \dfrac{\ln 1.6}{4\ln 1.014375} \approx 8$

8 years

51. $1400 = 1000\left(1 + \dfrac{r}{360}\right)^{360 \cdot 2}$

$\left(1 + \dfrac{r}{360}\right)^{720} = 1.4$

$\ln\left(1 + \dfrac{r}{360}\right)^{720} = \ln 1.4$

$720\ln\left(1 + \dfrac{r}{360}\right) = \ln 1.4$

$\ln\left(1 + \dfrac{r}{360}\right) = \dfrac{\ln 1.4}{720}$

$e^{\ln(1 + r/360)} = e^{(\ln 1.4)/720}$

$1 + \dfrac{r}{360} = e^{(\ln 1.4)/720} - 1$

$r = 360(e^{(\ln 1.4)/720}) - 1$

≈ 0.168

16.8%

53. accumulated amount $= 2(8000) = 16{,}000$

$16{,}000 = 800e^{0.08t}$

$e^{0.08t} = 2$

$\ln e^{0.08t} = \ln 2$

$0.08t = \ln 2$

$t = \dfrac{\ln 2}{0.08} \approx 9$

15.7%

55. accumulated amount $= 3(2350) = 7050$

$$7050 = 2350e^{r \cdot 7}$$
$$e^{7r} = 3$$
$$\ln e^{7r} = \ln 3$$
$$7r = \ln 3$$
$$r = \frac{\ln 3}{7} \approx 0.157$$

15.7%

57. $25,000 = 15,557 + 5259 \ln x$
$$5259 \ln x = 9443$$
$$\ln x = \frac{9443}{5259}$$
$$e^{\ln x} = e^{9443/5259}$$
$$x = e^{9443/5259} \approx 6$$

The average cost was \$25,000 6 years after 1989, in 1995.

59. $30 \log_2 x = 45$
$$\log_2 x = 1.5$$
$$x = 2^{1.5} \approx 2.8$$

Only half the students recall the important features of the lecture after 2.8 days.

61. $2.4 = -\log x$
$$\log x = -2.4$$
$$x = 10^{-2.4} \approx 0.004$$

The hydrogen ion concentration was $10^{-2.4}$, approximately 0.004 moles per liter.

63.–65. Answers may vary.

67.

The intersection point is $(2, 8)$.
Verify $x = 2$:
$$2^{x+1} = 8$$
$$2^2 + 1 \overset{?}{=} 8$$
$$2^3 \overset{?}{=} 8$$
$$8 = 8$$
The solution set is $\{2\}$.

69.

The intersection point is $(4, 2)$.
Verify $x = 4$:
$$\log_3(4x - 7) = 2$$
$$\log_3(4 \cdot 4 - 7) = 2$$
$$\log_3 9 \overset{?}{=} 2$$
$$9 \overset{?}{=} 3^2$$
$$9 = 9$$
The solution set is $\{4\}$.

71.

The intersection point is $(2, 1)$.
Verify $x = 2$:
$$\log(x + 3) + \log x = 1$$
$$\log(2 + 3) + \log 2 \overset{?}{=} 1$$
$$\log 5 + \log 2 \overset{?}{=} 1$$
$$\log 10 \overset{?}{=} 1$$
$$10 \overset{?}{=} 10^1$$
$$10 = 10$$
The solution set is $\{2\}$.

73.

There are 2 points of intersection, approximately
$(-1.391606, 0.21678798)$ and
$(1.6855579, 6.3711158)$.
Verify $x \approx -1.391606$:
$$3x = 2x + 3$$
$$3^{-1.391606} \stackrel{?}{=} 2(-1.391606) + 3$$
$$0.2167879803 \approx 0.216788$$
Verify $x \approx 1.6855579$:
$$3^x = 2x + 3$$
$$3^{1.6855579} \stackrel{?}{=} 2(1.6855579) + 3$$
$$6.37111582 \approx 6.371158$$
The solution set is $\{-1.391606, 1.6855579\}$.

75.

As the distance from the eye increases, barometric air pressure increases, leveling off at about 30 inches of mercury.

77.

When $P = 70$, $t \approx 7.9$, so it will take about 7.9 minutes.
Verify:
$$70 \stackrel{?}{=} 145e^{-0.092(7.9)}$$
$$70 \approx 70.10076749$$
The runner's pulse will be 70 beats per minute after about 7.9 minutes.

79. a. False; $\log(x + 3) = 2$ means $x + 3 = 10^2$

    b. False; $\log(7x + 3) - \log(2x + 5) = 4$
       means $\log \dfrac{7x + 3}{2x + 5} = 4$ which means
$$\frac{7x + 3}{2x + 5} = 10^4$$

    c. True; $x = \dfrac{1}{k}\ln y$
$$kx = \ln y$$
$$e^{kx} = e^{\ln y}$$
$$e^{kx} = y$$

    d. False; The equation $x^{10} = 5.71$ has no variable in an exponent so is not an exponential equation.

    (c) is true

81.
$$(\ln x)^2 = \ln x^2$$
$$(\ln x)^2 = 2\ln x$$
$$(\ln x)^2 - 2\ln x = 0$$
$$\ln x(\ln x - 2) = 0$$
$$\ln x = 0 \quad \text{or} \quad \ln x - 2 = 0$$
$$x = 1 \qquad\qquad \ln x = 2$$
$$\qquad\qquad\qquad e^{\ln x} = e^2$$
$$\qquad\qquad\qquad x = e$$
The solution set is $\left\{1, e^2\right\}$.
Check with graphing utility:

There are two points of intersection: $(1, 0)$ and approximately $(7.3890561, 4)$. Since $e^2 \approx 7.3890566099$, the graph verifies $x = 1$ and $x = e^2$, so the solution set is $\left\{1, e^2\right\}$ as determined algebraically.

83. $\ln(\ln x) = 0$

$e^{\ln(\ln x)} = e^0$

$\ln x = 1$

$e^{\ln x} = e^1$

$x = e$

The solution set is $\{e\}$.

Check by direct substitution:

$\ln(\ln x) = 0$

$\ln(\ln e) \overset{?}{=} 0$

$\ln(1) \overset{?}{=} 0$

$0 = 0$

Section 4.5

Check Point Exercises

1. a. Use the exponential growth model
$A = A_0 e^{kt}$ with 1980 corresponding to $t = 0$ when the population was 491 million:

$A = 491 e^{kt}$

Substitute $t = 1990 - 1980 = 10$ when the population was 643 million, so $A = 643$, to find k.

$643 = 491 e^{k \cdot 10}$

$e^{10k} = \dfrac{643}{491}$

$\ln e^{10k} = \ln\left(\dfrac{643}{491}\right)$

$10k = \ln\left(\dfrac{643}{491}\right)$

$k = \dfrac{\ln\left(\frac{643}{491}\right)}{10} \approx 0.027$

So the exponential growth function is
$A = 491 e^{0.027t}$.

b. Substitute 1000 for A in the model from part (a) and solve for t.

$1000 = 491 e^{0.027t}$

$e^{0.027t} = \dfrac{1000}{491}$

$\ln e^{0.027t} = \ln\left(\dfrac{1000}{491}\right)$

$0.027t = \ln\left(\dfrac{1000}{491}\right)$

$t = \dfrac{\ln\left(\frac{1000}{491}\right)}{0.027} \approx 26$

The population will reach 1000 million, or one billion, about 26 years after 1980, in 2006.

2. a. In the exponential decay model
$A = A_0 e^{kt}$, substitute $\dfrac{A_0}{2}$ for A since the amount present after 28 years is half the original amount.

$\dfrac{A_0}{2} = A_0 e^{k \cdot 28}$

$e^{28k} = \dfrac{1}{2}$

$\ln e^{28k} = \ln \dfrac{1}{2}$

$28k = \ln \dfrac{1}{2}$

$k = \dfrac{\ln^{1/2}}{28} \approx -0.0248$

So the exponential decay model is
$A = A_0 e^{-0.0248t}$

b. Substitute 60 for A_0 and 10 for A in the model from part (a) and solve for t.

$10 = 60 e^{-0.0248t}$

$e^{-0.0248t} = \dfrac{1}{6}$

$\ln e^{-0.0248t} = \ln \dfrac{1}{6}$

$-0.0248t = \ln \dfrac{1}{6}$

$t = \dfrac{\ln \frac{1}{6}}{-0.0248} \approx 72$

The strontium-90 will decay to a level of 10 grams about 72 years after the accident.

3. a. The time prior to learning trials corresponds to $t = 0$.

$$f(0) = \frac{0.8}{1 + e^{-0.2(0)}} = 0.4$$

The proportion of correct responses prior to learning trials was 0.4.

b. Substitute 10 for t in the model:

$$f(10) = \frac{0.8}{1 + e^{-0.2(10)}} \approx 0.7$$

The proportion of correct responses after 10 learning trials was 0.7.

c. In the logistic growth model,

$$f(t) = \frac{c}{1 + ae^{-bt}},$$ the constant c

represents the limiting size that $f(t)$ can attain. The limiting size of the proportion of correct responses as continued learning trials take place is 0.8.

4. $y = ab^x$ is equivalent to $y = ae^{(\ln b)x}$.

For $y = 4(7.8)^x$, $a = 4$, $b = 7.8$.

Thus, $y = 4(7.8)^x$ is equivalent to

$y = 4e^{(\ln 7.8)x}$ in terms of a natural logarithm. Rounded to three decimal places, the model is approximately equivalent to

$y = 4e^{2.054x}$.

Exercise Set 4.5

1. 1970 corresponds to $t = 0$.

$A = 208e^{0.008(0)} = 208$ million

In 1970, the population was 208 million.

3. $300 = 208e^{0.008t}$

$$\frac{75}{52} = e^{0.008t}$$

$$\ln \frac{75}{52} = \ln e^{0.008t}$$

$$\ln \frac{75}{52} = 0.008t$$

$$t = \frac{\ln \frac{75}{52}}{0.008} \approx 46$$

The population will be 300 million about 46 years after 1970, in 2016.

5. In the exponential growth model,

$A = A_0 e^{kt}$, k represents the growth rate. The population was increasing by about 2.6% each year.

7. $1624 = 574e^{0.026t}$

$$\frac{116}{41} = e^{0.026t}$$

$$\ln \frac{116}{41} = \ln e^{0.026t}$$

$$\ln \frac{116}{41} = 0.026t$$

$$t = \frac{\ln \frac{116}{41}}{0.026} \approx 40$$

The population will be 1624 million about 40 years after 1974, in 2014.

9. The time of purchase corresponds to $t = 0$.

$V = 140e^{0.068(0)} = 140$

The purchase price was $140,000.

11. $200 = 140e^{0.068t}$

$$\frac{10}{7} = e^{0.068t}$$

$$\ln \frac{10}{7} = \ln e^{0.068t}$$

$$\ln \frac{10}{7} = 0.068t$$

$$t = \frac{\ln \frac{10}{7}}{0.068} \approx 5$$

The house will be worth $200,000 about 5 years after 2000, in 2005.

13. $t = 7$ corresponds to $A = 680$.

Substitute these values to find k.

$$680 = 200e^{k(7)}$$

$$\frac{17}{5} = e^{7k}$$

$$\ln \frac{17}{5} = \ln e^{7k}$$

$$\ln \frac{17}{5} = 7k$$

$$k = \frac{\ln \frac{17}{5}}{7} \approx 0.175$$

The exponential growth function is
$A = 200e^{0.175t}$
$k = 0.175$ corresponds to a 17.5% increase each year.

15. $A = 16e^{-0.000121(5715)} \approx 8.01$
In 5715 years, 8.01 grams of carbon-14 will be present.

17. After 10 seconds, $\dfrac{16}{2}$ or 8 grams;

After 20 seconds, $\dfrac{8}{2}$ or 4 grams;

After 30 seconds, $\dfrac{4}{2}$ or 2 grams;

After 40 seconds, $\dfrac{2}{2}$ or 1 gram;

After 50 seconds, $\dfrac{1}{2}$ or 0.5 gram.

19. For an original amount of A_0, for the amount remaining is $A = 0.15A_0$.
$$0.15A_0 = A_0 e^{-0.000121t}$$
$$0.15 = e^{-0.000121t}$$
$$\ln 0.15 = \ln e^{-0.000121t}$$
$$\ln 0.15 = -0.000121t$$
$$t = \ln \frac{0.15}{-0.000121} \approx 15{,}679$$
The paintings were about 15,679 years old.

21. a. Half the original anount corresponds to an amount remaining of $A = \dfrac{1}{2}A_0$. This amount corresponds to $t = 1.31$.
$$\frac{1}{2}A_0 = A_0 e^{1.31k}$$
$$\frac{1}{2} = e^{1.31k}$$
$$\ln \frac{1}{2} = \ln e^{1.31k}$$
$$k = \frac{\ln \frac{1}{2}}{1.31} \approx -0.52912$$
The dacay model is given by
$$A = A_0 e^{-0.52912t}$$

b. $0.945A_0 = A_0 e^{-0.52912t}$
$$0.945 = e^{-0.52912t}$$
$$\ln 0.945 = -0.52912t$$
$$t = \frac{\ln 0.945}{-0.52912} \approx 0.107$$
The bones of the dinosaur were about 0.107 billion, or 107 million years old.

23. The doubling of the original population corresponds to $A = 2A_0$
$$2A_0 = A_0 e^{kt}$$
$$2 = e^{kt}$$
$$\ln 2 = \ln e^{kt}$$
$$\ln 2 = kt$$
$$t = \frac{\ln 2}{k}$$

25. $t = \dfrac{\ln 2}{0.011} \approx 63$
It will take China about 63 years to double its population.

27. a. When the epidemic began, $t = 0$.
$$f(0) = \frac{100{,}000}{1 + 5000e^0} \approx 20$$
Twenty people became ill when the epidemic began.

b. $f(4) = \dfrac{100{,}000}{1 + 5{,}000e^{-4}} \approx 1080$
About 1080 people were ill at the end of the fourth week.

c. In the logistic growth model,
$$f(t) = \frac{c}{1 + ae^{-bt}},$$
the constant c represents the limiting size that $f(t)$ can attain. The limiting size of the population that becomes ill is 100,000 people.

29. $P(20) = \dfrac{0.9}{1 + 271e^{-0.122(20)}} \approx 0.037$
The probability that a 20-year-old has some coronary heart disease is about 3.7%.

31.

$$0.5 = \frac{1.9}{1 + 271e^{-0.122t}}$$

$$0.5\left(1 + 271e^{-0.122t}\right) = 0.9$$

$$1 + 271e^{-0.122t} = 1.8$$

$$271e^{-0.122t} = 0.8$$

$$e^{-0.122t} = \frac{0.8}{271}$$

$$\ln e^{-0.122t} = \ln \frac{0.8}{271}$$

$$-0.122t = \ln \frac{0.8}{271}$$

$$t = \frac{\ln \frac{0.8}{271}}{-0.122} \approx 48$$

The probability of some coronary heart disease is 0.5 at about age 48.

33. $y = 100(4.6)^x$ is equivalent to
$y = 100e^{(\ln 4.6)x}$;
Using $\ln 4.6 \approx 1.526$,
$y = 100e^{1.526x}$.

35. $y = 2.5(0.7)^x$ is equivalent to
$y = 2.5e^{(\ln 0.7)x}$;
Using $\ln 0.7 \approx -0.357$,
$y = 2.5e^{-0.357x}$.

37.–45. Answers may vary.

47. $y = 51.75985638 + 109.7788574 \ln x$
The correlation coefficient,
$r = 0.8974781617$, is somewhat close to 1, indicating that the model is a good fit.

49. $y = 98.06189365x^{0.4398361087}$
The correlation coefficient, $r = 0.9546621296$, is close to 1, indicating that the model is a good fit.

51.

The probability of coronary heart disease starts increasing at a more rapid rate at about age 20. At about age 60, the rate of increase starts to slow down.

53. linear model:
$y = 74.52833333x + 214.7694444$
$r = 0.973863504$

quadratic model:
$y = -4.438852814x^2 + 118.9168615x + 133.390$
$R^2 = 0.9656802033$

exponential model:
$y = 271.7360257(1.151326831)^x$
$r = 0.9601071451$

logarithmic model:
$y = 192.4568631 + 277.6625633 \ln x$
$r = 0.9529069638$

The linear model best fits the data; Answers for prediction may vary.

55.
$$140 = 70 + (210 - 70)e^{-k(30)}$$
$$70 = (140)e^{-30k}$$
$$0.5 = e^{-30k}$$
$$\ln 0.5 = \ln e^{-30k}$$
$$\ln 0.5 = -30k$$
$$k = \frac{\ln 0.5}{-30} \approx 0.023$$
$$T = 70 + (210 - 70)e^{-0.023(40)} \approx 126°$$

Substitute $t = 40$ in the model
$T = C + (T_0 - C)e^{-0.023t}$

Review Exercises

1. This is the graph of $f(x) = 4^x$ reflected about the y-axis, so the function is $g(x) = 4^{-x}$.

2. This is the graph of $f(x) = 4^x$ reflected about the x-axis and about the y-axis, so the function is $h(x) = -4^{-x}$.

3. This is the graph of $f(x) = 4^x$ reflected about the x-axis and about the y-axis then shifted upward 3 units, so the function is $r(x) = -4^{-x} + 3$.

4. This is the graph of $f(x) = 4^x$.

5.

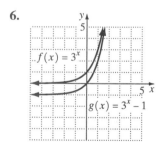

x	$f(x) = 2x$	$g(x) = 2^{x-1}$
-2	$2^{-2} = \frac{1}{4}$	$2^{-2-1} = 2^{-3} = \frac{1}{8}$
-1	$2^{-1} = \frac{1}{2}$	$2^{-1-1} = 2^{-2} = \frac{1}{2}$
0	$2^0 = 1$	$2^{0-1} = 2^{-1} = \frac{1}{2}$
1	$2^1 = 2$	$2^{1-1} = 2^0 = 1$
2	$2^2 = 4$	$2^{2-1} = 2^1 = 2$

The graph of $g(x)$ shifts the graph of $f(x)$ one unit to the right.

6.

x	$f(x) = 3^x$	$g(x) = 3^x - 1$
-2	$3^{-2} = \frac{1}{9}$	$3^{-2} - 1 = \frac{1}{9} - 1 = -\frac{8}{9}$
-1	$3^{-1} = \frac{1}{3}$	$3^{-1} - 1 = \frac{1}{3} - 1 = -\frac{2}{3}$
0	$3^0 = 1$	$3^0 - 1 = 1 - 1 = 0$
1	$3^1 = 3$	$3^1 - 1 = 3 - 1 = 2$
2	$3^2 = 9$	$3^2 - 1 = 9 - 1 = 8$

The graph of $g(x)$ shifts the graph of $f(x)$ one unit downward.

7.

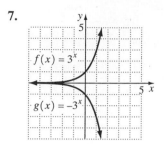

x	$f(x) = 3^x$	$g(x) = -3x$
-2	$3^{-2} = \frac{1}{9}$	$-3^{-2} = -\frac{1}{9}$
-1	$3^{-1} = \frac{1}{3}$	$-3^{-1} = -\frac{1}{3}$
0	$3^0 = 1$	$-3^0 = -1$
1	$3^1 = 3$	$-3^1 = -3$
2	$3^2 = 9$	$-3^2 = -9$

The graph of $g(x)$ reflects the graph of $f(x)$ about the x-axis.

8.

x	$f(x) = \left(\frac{1}{2}\right)^x$	$g(x) = \left(\frac{1}{2}\right)^{-x}$
-2	$\left(\frac{1}{2}\right)^{-2} = 4$	$\left(\frac{1}{2}\right)^{-(-2)} = \left(\frac{1}{2}\right)^2 = \frac{1}{4}$
-1	$\left(\frac{1}{2}\right)^{-1} = 2$	$\left(\frac{1}{2}\right)^{-1(-1)} = \left(\frac{1}{2}\right)^1 = \frac{1}{2}$
0	$\left(\frac{1}{2}\right)^0 = 1$	$\left(\frac{1}{2}\right)^{-(0)} = \left(\frac{1}{2}\right)^0 = 1$
1	$\left(\frac{1}{2}\right)^1 = \frac{1}{2}$	$\left(\frac{1}{2}\right)^{-1(1)} = \left(\frac{1}{2}\right)^{-1} = 2$
2	$\left(\frac{1}{2}\right)^2 = \frac{1}{4}$	$\left(\frac{1}{2}\right)^{-2(2)} = \left(\frac{1}{2}\right)^{-2} = 4$

The graph of $g(x)$ reflects the graph of $f(x)$ about the y-axis.

9. 5.5% compounded semiannually:

$$A = 5000\left(1 + \frac{0.055}{2}\right)^{2\cdot5} \approx 6558.26$$

5.25% compounded monthly:

$$A = 5000\left(1 + \frac{0.0525}{12}\right)^{12\cdot5} \approx 6497.16$$

5.5% compounded semiannually yields the greater return.

10. 7% compounded monthly:

$$A = 14,000\left(1 + \frac{0.07}{12}\right)^{12\cdot10} \approx 28,135.26$$

6.85% compounded continuously:

$$A = 14,000e^{0.0685(10)} \approx 27,772.81$$

7% compounded monthly yields the greater return.

11. a. When first taken out of the microwave, the temperature of the coffee was 200°.

b. After 20 minutes, the temperature of the coffee was about 120°.

$$T = 70 + 130e^{-0.04855(20)} \approx 119.23$$

Using a calculator, the temperature is about 119°.

c. The coffee will cool to about 70°; The temperature of the room is 70°.

12. $49^{1/2} = 7$

13. $4^3 = x$

14. $3^y = 81$

15. $\log_6 216 = 3$

16. $\log_b 625 = 4$

17. $\log_{13} 874 = y$

18. $\log_4 64 = 3$ because $4^3 = 64$.

19. $\log_5 \frac{1}{25} = -2$ because $5^{-2} = \frac{1}{25}$.

20. $\log_3(-9)$ cannot be evaluated since $\log_b x$ is defined only for $x > 0$.

21. $\log_{16} 4 = \frac{1}{2}$ because $16^{1/2} = \sqrt{16} = 4$.

22. Because $\log_b b = 1$, we conclude $\log_{17} 17 = 1$.

23. Because $\log_b b^x = x$, we conclude $\log_3 3^8 = 8$.

24. Because $\ln e^x = x$, we conclude $e^5 = 5$.

25. Because $\log_b = 1$, we conclude $\log_8 8 = 1$. So, $\log_3(\log_8 8) = \log_3 1$. Because $\log_b 1 = 0$ we conclude $\log_3 1 = 0$. Therefore, $\log_3(\log_8 8) = 0$.

26.

27.

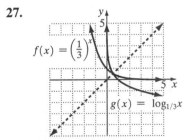

28. This is the graph of $f(x) = \log x$ reflected about the y-axis, so the function is $g(x) = \log(-x)$.

29. This is the graph of $f(x) = \log x$ shifted left 2 units, reflected about the y-axis, then shifted upward one unit, so the function is $r(x) = 1 + \log(2 - x)$.

30. This is the graph of $f(x) = \log x$ shifted left 2 units then reflected about the y-axis, so the function is $h(x) = \log(2 - x)$.

31. This is the graph of $f(x) = \log x$.

32.

x-intercept: $(3, 0)$
vertical asymptote: $x = 2$

33.

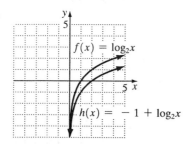

x-intercept: $(2, 0)$
vertical asymptote: $x = 0$

34.

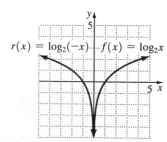

x-intercept: $(-1, 0)$
vertical asymptote: $x = 0$

35. The domain of f consists of all x for which $x + 5 > 0$.
Solving this inequality for x, we obtain $x > -5$.
Thus the domain of f is $(-5, \infty)$

36. The domain of f consists of all x for which $3 - x > 0$.
Solving this inequality for x, we obtain $x < 3$.
Thus, the domain of f is $(-\infty, 3)$.

37. The domain of f consists of all x for which $(x - 1)^2 > 0$.
Solving this inequality for x, we obtain $x < 1$ or $x > 1$. Thus, the domain of f is $(-\infty, 1)$ or $(1, \infty)$.

38. Because $\ln e^x = x$, we conclude $\ln e^{6x} = 6x$.

39. Because $e^{\ln x} = x$, we conclude $e^{\ln \sqrt{x}} = \sqrt{x}$.

40. Because $10^{\log x} = x$, we conclude $10^{\log 4x^2} = 4x^2$.

41. $R = \log \dfrac{1000 I_0}{I_0} = \log 1000 = 3$
The Richter scale magnitude is 3.0.

42. a. $f(0) = 76 - 18\log(0 + 1) = 76$
When first given, the average score was 76.

b. $f(2) = 76 - 18\log(2 + 1) \approx 67$
$f(4) = 76 - 18\log(4 + 1) \approx 63$
$f(6) = 76 - 18\log(6 + 1) \approx 61$
$f(8) = 76 - 18\log(8 + 1) \approx 59$
$f(12) = 76 - 18\log(12 + 1) \approx 56$
After 2, 4, 6, 8, and 12 months, the average scores are about 67, 63, 61, 59, and 56, respectively.

c.

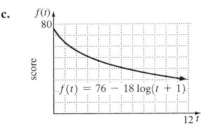

time (months)

Retention decreases as time passes.

43. $t = \dfrac{1}{0.06} \ln\left(\dfrac{12}{12 - 5}\right) \approx 8.98$

It will take about 9 weeks.

44. $\log_6\left(36x^3\right)$

$= \log_6 36 + \log_6 x^3$

$= \log_6 36 + 3\log_6 x$

$= 2 + 3\log_6 x$

45. $\log_4 \dfrac{\sqrt{x}}{64} = \log_4 x^{\frac{1}{2}} - \log_4 64$

$= \dfrac{1}{2}\log_4 x \quad 3$

46. $\log_2 \dfrac{xy^2}{64} = \log_2 xy^2 - \log_2 64$

$= \log_2 x + \log_2 y^2 - \log_2 64$

$= \log_2 x + 2\log_2{}^{y-6}$

47. $\ln \sqrt[3]{\dfrac{x}{e}}$

$= \ln\left(\dfrac{x}{e}\right)^{\frac{1}{3}}$

$= \dfrac{1}{3}\left[\ln x - \ln e\right]$

$= \dfrac{1}{3}\ln x - \dfrac{1}{3}\ln e$

$= \dfrac{1}{3}\ln x - \dfrac{1}{3}$

48. $\log_b 7 + \log_b 3$

$= \log_b(7 \cdot 3)$

$= \log_b 21$

49. $\log 3 - 3\log x$

$= \log 3 - \log x^3$

$= \log \dfrac{3}{x^3}$

50. $3\ln x + 4\ln y$

$= \ln x^3 + \ln y^4$

$= \ln\left(x^3 y^4\right)$

51. $\dfrac{1}{2}\ln x - \ln y$

$= \ln x^{\frac{1}{2}} - \ln y$

$= \ln \dfrac{\sqrt{x}}{y}$

52. $\log_6 72{,}348 = \dfrac{\log 72{,}348}{\log 6} \approx 6.2448$

53. $\log_4 0.863 = \dfrac{\ln 0.863}{\ln 4} \approx -0.1063$

54. $8^x = 12{,}143$

$\ln 8^x = \ln 12{,}143$

$x\ln 8 = \ln 12{,}143$

$x = \dfrac{\ln 12{,}143}{\ln 8} \approx 4.523$

The solution set is $\left\{\dfrac{\ln 12{,}143}{\ln 8}\right\}$,

approximately 4.523.

55. $9e^{5x} = 1269$

$e^{5x} = 141$

$\ln e^{5x} = \ln 141$

$5x = \ln 141$

$x = \dfrac{\ln 141}{5}$

The solution set is $\left\{\dfrac{\ln 141}{5}\right\}$, approximately

0.990.

56. $e^{12-5x} - 7 = 123$

$$e^{12-5x} = 130$$
$$\ln e^{12-5x} = \ln 130$$
$$12 - 5x = \ln 130$$
$$5x = 12 - \ln 130$$
$$x = \frac{12 - \ln 130}{5} \approx 1.426$$

The solution set is
$x = \dfrac{12 - \ln 130}{5}$, approximately 1.426

57. $5^{4x+2} = 37,500$

$$\ln 5^{4x+2} = \ln 37,500$$
$$(4x + 2)\ln 5 = \ln 37,500$$
$$4x \ln 5 + 2 \ln 5 = \ln 37,500$$
$$4x \ln 5 = \ln 37,500 - 2 \ln 5$$
$$x = \frac{\ln 37,500 - 2 \ln 5}{4 \ln 5}$$

The solution set is $\left\{ \dfrac{\ln 37,500 - 2 \ln 5}{4 \ln 5} \right\}$,
approximately 1.136.

58. $e^{2x} - e^x - 6 = 0$

$$\left(e^x - 3\right)\left(e^x + 2\right) = 0$$
$$e^x - 3 = 0 \quad \text{or} \quad e^x + 2 = 0$$
$$e^x = 3 \qquad\quad e^x = -2$$
$$\ln e^x = \ln 3 \quad\;\; \ln e^x = \ln(-2)$$
$$x = \ln 3 \qquad\qquad x = \ln(-2)$$
$$x = \ln 3 \approx 1.099 \quad \ln(-2) \text{ does not exist.}$$

The solution set is $\{\ln 3\}$,
approximately 1.099.

59. $\log_4(3x - 5) = 3$

$$3x - 5 = 4^3$$
$$3x - 5 = 64$$
$$3x = 69$$
$$x = 23$$

The solutions set is $\{23\}$.

60. $\log_2(x + 3) + \log_2(x - 3) = 4$

$$\log_2(x + 3)(x - 3) = 4$$
$$\log_2(x^2 - 9) = 4$$
$$x^2 - 9 = 2^4$$
$$x^2 - 9 = 16$$
$$x^2 = 25$$
$$x = \pm 5$$

$x = -5$ does not check because $\log_2(-5 + 3)$
does not exist.
The solution set is $\{5\}$.

61. $\log_3(x - 1) - \log_3(x + 2) = 2$

$$\log_3 \frac{x - 1}{x + 2} = 2$$
$$\frac{x - 1}{x - 2} = 3^2$$
$$\frac{x - 1}{x + 2} = 9$$
$$x - 1 = 9(x + 2)$$
$$x - 1 = 9x + 18$$
$$8x = -19$$
$$x = -\frac{19}{8}$$

$x = -\dfrac{19}{8}$ does not check because

$\log_3\left(-\dfrac{19}{8} - 1\right)$ does not exist.
The solution set is $\varnothing$.

62. $\ln x = -1$

$$x = e^{-1} = \frac{1}{e} \approx 0.368$$

The solution set is $\left\{ \dfrac{1}{e} \right\}$,
approximately 0.368.

63. $3 + 4 \ln 2x = 15$

$$4 \ln 2x = 12$$
$$\ln 2x = 3$$
$$2^x = e^3$$
$$x = \frac{e^3}{2} \approx 10.043$$

The solution set is $\left\{ \dfrac{e^3}{2} \right\}$,

approximately 10.043

64. $13 = 10.1e^{0.005t}$

$$e^{0.005t} = \frac{13}{10.1}$$

$$\ln e^{0.005t} = \ln \frac{13}{10.1}$$

$$0.005t = \ln \frac{13}{10.1}$$

$$t = \frac{\ln \frac{13}{10.1}}{0.005} \approx 50$$

The population will reach 13 million about 50 years after 1992, in 2042.

65. $280 \cdot 2 = 364(1.005)^t$

$$364(1.005)^t = 560$$

$$1.005^t = \frac{20}{13}$$

$$\ln 1.005^t = \ln \frac{20}{13}$$

$$t \ln 1.005 = \ln \frac{20}{13}$$

$$t = \frac{\ln \frac{20}{13}}{\ln 1.005} \approx 86$$

The carbon dioxide concentration will be double the preindustrial level about 86 years after 2000, in 2086.

66. $30,000 = 15,557 + 5259 \ln x$

$$5259 \ln x = 14,443$$

$$\ln x = \frac{14,443}{5259}$$

$$x = e^{14,443/5259} \approx 16$$

The average cost of a new car will be $30,000 about 16 years after 1989, in 2005.

67. $20,000 = 12,500 \left(1 + \frac{0.065}{4} \right)^{4t}$

$$12,500(1.01625)^{4t} = 20,000$$

$$(1.01625)^{4t} = 1.6$$

$$\ln(1.01625)^{4t} = \ln 1.6$$

$$4t \ln 1.01625 = \ln 1.6$$

$$t = \frac{\ln 1.6}{4 \ln 1.01625} \approx 7.3$$

It will take about 7.3 years.

68. $3 \cdot 50,000 = 50,000e^{0.075t}$

$$50,000e^{0.075t} = 150,000$$

$$e^{0.075} = 3$$

$$\ln e^{0.075t} = \ln 3$$

$$0.075t = \ln 3$$

$$t = \frac{\ln 3}{0.075} \approx 14.6$$

It will take about 14.6 years.

69. When an investment value triples, $A = 3P$.

$$3P = Pe^{5r}$$

$$e^{5r} = 3$$

$$\ln e^{5r} = \ln 3$$

$$5r = \ln 3$$

$$r = \frac{\ln 3}{5} \approx 0.2197$$

The interest rate would need to be about 21.97%

70. **a.** $t = 1997 - 1980 = 17$

$$e^{17k} = \frac{29.3}{14.6}$$

$$\ln e^{17k} = \ln \frac{29.3}{14.6}$$

$$17k = \ln \frac{29.3}{14.6}$$

$$k = \frac{\ln \left(\frac{29.3}{14.6} \right)}{14.6} \approx 0.041$$

b. $t = 2005 - 1980 = 25$

$$A = 14.6e^{0.041(25)} \approx 40.7$$

In 2005, the population will be about 40.7 million.

c. $50 = 14.6e^{0.041t}$

$$e^{0.041t} = \frac{50}{14.6}$$

$$\ln e^{0.041t} = \ln \frac{50}{14.6}$$

$$0.041t = \ln \frac{50}{14.6}$$

$$t = \frac{\ln \left(\frac{50}{14.6} \right)}{0.041} \approx 30$$

The population will reach 50 million about 30 years after 1980, in 2010.

71. If the remaining amount is 15% of the original amount, them $A = 0.15A_0$.

$$0.15A_0 = A_0e^{-0.000121t}$$
$$e^{-0.000121t} = 0.15$$
$$\ln e^{-0.000121t} = \ln 0.15$$
$$-0.000121t = \ln 0.15$$
$$t = \frac{\ln 0.15}{-0.000121} \approx 15,67$$

At the time of discovery, the paintings were about 15,679 years old.

72. a. When the outbreak began, $t = 0$.

$$f(0) = \frac{171}{1 + 18.6e^{-0.0747(0)}} \approx 9$$

When the outbreak began, about 9 people were infected.

b. $f(45) = \dfrac{171}{1 + 18.6e^{-0.0747(45)}} \approx 104$

After 45 days, about 104 people were infected.

c. In the logistics growth model,

$$f(t) = \frac{c}{1 + ae^{-bt}},$$ the constant c

represents the limiting size that $f(t)$ can attain. The limiting size of the population that became infected was 171; Yes, the limiting size according to the model is 171, but $261 - 83 = 178$ people actually died.

73. $y = 73(2.6)^x$ is equivalent to

$y = 73e^{(\ln 2.6)x}$; Using $\ln 2.6 \approx 0.956$;

$y = 73e^{0.956x}$.

74. $y = 6.5(0.43)^x$ is equivalent to

$y = 6.5e^{(\ln 0.43)x}$; Using $\ln 0.43 \approx -0.844$;

$y = 6.5e^{-0.844x}$.

75. The high projection might be best modeled by an exponential function, the medium projection by a linear function, and the low projection by a quadratic function; If the low projection is modeled by a quadratic

function, the leading coefficient would be negative since the parabola opens downward.

76. linear model:
$y = 0.5055x - 8.5905$
$r = 0.9451995388$

quadratic model:
$$y = 0.0042934712x^2 - 0.1041729153x + 5.038408856$$
$$R^2 = 0.9883582557$$

exponential model:
$y = 3.38051786(1.0235357)^x$
$r = 0.9945619484$

logarithmic model:
$y = -20.94062012 + 12.53110237\ln x$
$r = 0.6748503469$

The exponential model best fits the given data. 2050 is 151 years after 1899.
$y = 3.38051786(1.0235357)^{151} \approx 113.4$
In 2050, the U.S. population age 65 and over will be about 113.4 million.

Chapter 4 Test

1.

2.
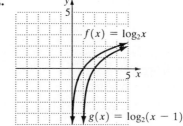

3. $125 = 5^3$

4. $\log_{36} 6 = \dfrac{1}{2}$

5. The domain of f consists of all x for which $3 - x > 0$. Solving this inequality for x, we obtain $x < 3$.
Thus, the domain of f is $(-\infty, 3)$.

6. $\log_4\left(64x^5\right) = \log_4 64 + \log_4 x^5$
$$= 3 + 5\log_4 x$$

7. $\log_3 \dfrac{\sqrt[3]{x}}{81} = \log_3 x^{\frac{1}{3}} - \log_3 81$
$$= \dfrac{1}{3}\log_3 x - 4$$

8. $6\log x + 2\log y = \log x^6 + \log y^2$
$$= \log\left(x^6 y^2\right)$$

9. $\ln 7 - 3\ln x = \ln 7 - \ln x^3$
$$= \ln \dfrac{7}{x^3}$$

10. $\log_{15} 71 = \dfrac{\log 71}{\log 15} \approx 1.5741$

11. $5^x = 1.4$
$\ln 5^x = \ln 1.4$
$x \ln 5 = \ln 1.4$
$$x = \dfrac{\ln 1.4}{\ln 5} \approx 0.2091$$
The solution set is $\left\{\dfrac{\ln 1.4}{\ln 5}\right\}$,
approximately 0.2091.

12. $400e^{0.005x} = 1600$
$e^{0.005x} = 4$
$\ln e^{0.005x} = \ln 4$
$0.005x = \ln 4$
$$x = \dfrac{\ln 4}{0.005} \approx 277.2589$$
The solution set is $\left\{\dfrac{\ln 4}{0.005}\right\}$,
approximately 277.2589.

13. $e^{2x} - 6e^x + 5 = 0$
$\left(e^x - 5\right)\left(e^x - 1\right) = 0$

$e^x - 5 = 0$	or	$e^x - 1 = 0$
$e^x = 5$		$e^x = 1$
$\ln e^x = \ln 5$		$\ln e^x = \ln 1$
$x = \ln 5$		$x = \ln 1$
$x \approx 1.6094$		$x = 0$

The solution set is $\{0, \ln 5\}$; $\ln \approx 1.6094$.

14. $\log_6(4x - 1) = 3$
$4x - 1 = 6^3$
$4x - 1 = 216$
$4x = 217$
$$x = \dfrac{217}{4}$$
The solution set is $\left\{\dfrac{217}{4}\right\}$.

15. $\log x + \log(x + 15) = 2$
$\log\left(x^2 + 15x\right) = 2$
$x^2 + 15x = 10^2$
$x^2 + 15x - 100 = 0$
$(x + 20)(x - 5) = 0$
$x + 20 = 0$ or $x - 5 = 0$
$x = -20 \qquad x = 5$
$x = -20$ does not check because $\log(-20)$ does not exist.
The solution set is $\{5\}$.

16. $2\ln 3x = 8$

    $\ln 3x = 4$

    $3x = e^4$

    $x = \dfrac{e^4}{3} \approx 18.1994$

    The solution set is $\left\{\dfrac{e^4}{3}\right\}$,

    approximately 18.1994.

17. 6.5% compounded semiannualy:

    $A = 3{,}000\left(1 + \dfrac{0.065}{2}\right)^{2(10)} \approx \$5{,}687.51$

    6% compounded continuously:

    $A = 3{,}000e^{0.06(10)} \approx \$5{,}466.36$

    6.5% compounded semiannually yields about $221 more than 6% compounded continuously.

18. $D = 10\log\dfrac{10^{12}I_0}{I_0}$

    $= 10\log 10^{12}$

    $= 10\cdot 12$

    $= 120$

    The loudness of the sound is 120 decibels.

19. **a.** In 1959, $t = 0$.

    $89.18e^{-0.004(0)} = 89.18$

    In 1959, about 89% of married men were employed.

    b. The percentage is decreasing since $k = -0.004 < 1$.

    c. $77 = 89.18e^{-0.004t}$

    $e^{-0.004t} = \dfrac{77}{89.18}$

    $\ln e^{-0.004t} = \ln\dfrac{77}{89.18}$

    $-0.004t = \ln\dfrac{77}{89.18}$

    $t = \dfrac{\ln\frac{77}{89.18}}{-0.004} \approx 37$

    77% of U.S. married men were employed about 37 years after 1959, in 1996.

20. In 1980, $t = 0$ and $A_0 = 484$.

    In 1990, $t = 1990 - 1980 = 10$ and $A = 509$.

    $509 = 484e^{k(10)}$

    $e^{k(10)} = \dfrac{509}{484}$

    $\ln e^{k(10)} = \ln\dfrac{509}{484}$

    $k = \dfrac{\ln\frac{509}{484}}{10} \approx 0.005$

    The exponential growth function is $A = 484e^{0.005t}$.

21. When the amount remaining is 5%, $A = 0.05A_0$.

    $0.05A_0 = A_0e^{-0.000121t}$

    $e^{-0.000121t} = 0.05$

    $\ln e^{-0.000121t} = \ln 0.05$

    $-0.000121t = \ln 0.05$

    $t = \dfrac{\ln 0.05}{-0.000121} \approx 24{,}758$

    The man died about 24,758 years ago.

22. **a.** $f(0) = \dfrac{140}{1 + 9e^{-0.165(0)}} = 14$

    Fourteen elk were initially introduced to the habitat.

    b. $f(10) = \dfrac{140}{1 + 9e^{-0.165(10)}} \approx 51$

    After 10 years, about 51 elk are expected.

    c. In the logistic growth model,

    $f(t) = \dfrac{c}{1 + ae^{-bt}}$,

    the constant c represents the limiting size that $f(t)$ can attain. The limiting size of the elk population is 140 elk.

Cumulative Review Exercises (Chapters 1–4)

1. $|3x - 4| = 2$

$3x - 4 = 2$ or $3x - 4 = -2$

$3x = 6$ $3x = 2$

$x = 2$ $x = \dfrac{2}{3}$

The solution set is $\left\{ \dfrac{2}{3}, 2 \right\}$.

2. $\sqrt{2x - 5} - \sqrt{x - 3} = 1$

$\sqrt{2x - 5} = 1 + \sqrt{x - 3}$

$\left(\sqrt{2x - 5} \right)^2 = \left(1 + \sqrt{x - 3} \right)^2$

$2x - 5 = 1 + 2\sqrt{x - 3} + x - 3$

$2x - 5 = x - 2 + 2\sqrt{x - 3}$

$x - 3 = 2\sqrt{x - 3}$

$(x - 3)^2 = \left(2\sqrt{x - 3} \right)^2$

$(x - 3)^2 = 4(x - 3)$

$x^2 - 6x + 9 = 4x - 12$

$x^2 - 10x + 21 = 0$

$(x - 3)(x - 7) = 0$

$x = 3$ or $x = 7$

Both solutions satisfy the original equation when checked.

The solution set is $\{3, 7\}$.

3. $x^4 + x^3 - 3x^2 - x + 2 = 0$

p: $\pm 1, \pm 2$

q: ± 1

$\dfrac{p}{q}$: $\pm 1, \pm 2$

-2	1	1	-3	-1	2
		-2	2	2	-2
	1	-1	-1	1	0

$(x + 2)(x^3 - x^2 - x + 1) = 0$

$(x + 2)[x^2(x - 1) - (x - 1)] = 0$

$(x + 2)(x^2 - 1)(x - 1) = 0$

$(x + 2)(x + 1)(x - 1)(x - 1) = 0$

$(x + 2)(x + 1)(x - 1)^2 = 0$

$x + 2 = 0$ or $x + 1 = 0$ or $x - 1 = 0$

$x = -2$ $x = -1$ $x = 1$

The solution set is $\{-2, -1, 1\}$.

4. $e^{5x} - 32 = 96$

$e^{5x} = 128$

$\ln e^{5x} = \ln 128$

$5x = \ln 128$

$x = \dfrac{\ln 128}{5} \approx 0.9704$

The solution set is $\left\{ \dfrac{\ln 128}{5} \right\}$,

approximately 0.9704.

5. $\log_2(x + 5) + \log_2(x - 1) = 4$

$\log_2[(x + 5)(x - 1)] = 4$

$(x + 5)(x - 1) = 2^4$

$x^2 + 4x - 5 = 16$

$x^2 + 4x - 21 = 0$

$(x + 7)(x - 3) = 0$

$x + 7 = 0$ or $x - 3 = 0$

$x = -7$ $x = 3$

$x = -7$ does not check because $\log_2(-7 + 5)$

does not exist.

The solution set is $\{3\}$.

6. $14 - 5x \geq -6$

$-5x \geq -20$

$x \leq 4$

The solution set is $(-\infty, 4]$.

7. $|2x - 4| \leq 2$

$2x - 4 \leq 2$ and $2x - 4 \geq -2$

$2x \leq 6$ $2x \geq 2$

$x \leq 3$ and $x \geq 1$

The solution set is $[1, 3]$.

8. $m = \dfrac{3-(-3)}{1-3} = \dfrac{6}{-2} = -3$

Using (1, 3) point-slope form:

$y - 3 = -3(x - 1)$

slope-intercept form:

$y - 3 = -3(x - 1)$

$y - 3 = -3x + 3$

$y = -3x + 6$

9. $(f \circ g)(x) = f(x + 2)$

$\qquad = (x + 2)^2$

$\qquad = x^2 + 4x + 4$

$(g \circ f)(x) = g\left(x^2\right)$

$\qquad = x^2 + 2$

10. $f(x) = 2x - 7$

$y = 2x - 7$

$x = 2y - 7$

$x + 7 = 2y$

$\dfrac{x + 7}{2} = y$

$f^{-1}(x) = \dfrac{x + 7}{2}$

11.

$$\begin{array}{r} x^2 + 3x - 3 \\ x+2\overline{\smash{)}\,x^3\ \_5x^2 + 3x - 10} \\ \underline{x^3 + 2x^2} \\ 3x^2 + 3x \\ \underline{3x^2 + 6x} \\ -3x - 10 \\ \underline{-3x -\ 6} \\ -4 \end{array}$$

Quotient: $x^2 + 3x - 3 - \dfrac{4}{x + 2}$

12. $f(x) = 4x^3 - 7x - 3$

$p = \pm 1, \pm 3$

$q = \pm 1, \pm 2, \pm 4$

$\dfrac{p}{q} = \pm 1, \pm \dfrac{1}{2}, \pm \dfrac{1}{4}, \pm 3, \pm \dfrac{3}{2}, \pm \dfrac{3}{4}$

13. $y = kx^2$

$12 = k \cdot 3^2$

$k = \dfrac{12}{9} = \dfrac{4}{3}$

$y = \dfrac{4}{3}x^2$

$y = \dfrac{4}{3}(15)^2$

$y = 300$

14. If $1 + i$ is a root, $1 - i$ is a root.

$(x - 1 + i)(x - 1 - i)$

$= x^2 - x - xi - x + 1 + i + xi - i - i^2$

$= x^2 - 2x + 2$

$$\begin{array}{r} x - 2 \\ x^2 - 2x + 2\overline{\smash{)}\,x^3 - 4x^2 + 6x - 4} \\ \underline{x^3 - 2x^2 + 2x} \\ -2x^2 + 4x - 4 \\ \underline{-2x^2 + 4x - 4} \\ 0 \end{array}$$

$x - 2 = 0$

$x = 2$

The solution set is $\{1 + i, 1 - i, 2\}$.

15. Circle with center: (3, –2) and radius of 2

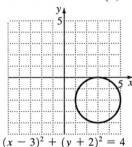

$(x - 3)^2 + (y + 2)^2 = 4$

16. Parabola with vertex: (2, –1)

$f(x) = (x - 2)^2 - 1$

17. *x*-intercepts:

$$x^2 - 1 = 0$$
$$x^2 = 1$$
$$x = \pm 1$$

The *x*-intercepts are $(1, 0)$ and $(-1, 0)$.

vertical asymptotes:

$$x^2 - 4 = 0$$
$$x^2 = 4$$
$$x = \pm 2$$

The vertical asymptotes are $x = 2$ and $x = -2$.

Horizontal asymptote: $y = 1$

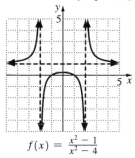

$$f(x) = \frac{x^2 - 1}{x^2 - 4}$$

18. *x*-intercepts:

$$x - 2 = 0 \quad \text{or} \quad x + 1 = 0$$
$$x = 2 \quad\quad \text{or} \quad x = -1$$

The *x*-intercepts are $(2, 0)$ and $(-1, 0)$.

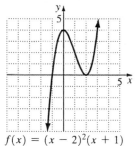

$$f(x) = (x - 2)^2 (x + 1)$$

19.

$$40x + 10(1.5x) = 660$$
$$40x + 15x = 660$$
$$55x = 660$$
$$x = 12$$

Your normal hourly salary is $12 per hour.

20.

$$\frac{1}{2} = 1 - K \ln(3 + 1)$$
$$K \ln 4 = \frac{1}{2}$$
$$K = \frac{\frac{1}{2}}{\ln 4} \approx 0.361$$
$$F = 1 - 0.361 \ln(t + 1)$$
$$= 1 - 0.361 \ln(6 + 1)$$
$$= 1 - 0.361 \ln 7$$
$$\approx 0.3$$

About $\frac{3}{10}$ of the people in the group remember all the words in a list 6 hours after memorizing them.

Chapter 5

Check Point Exercises

1. a. A 30° angle lies in quadrant I and is shown in the following graph.

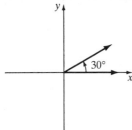

b. A 210° angle is a positive angle. It has a counterclockwise rotation of 180° followed by a counterclockwise rotation of 30°. The angle lies in quadrant III and is shown in the following graph.

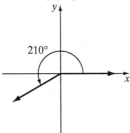

c. A −120° angle is a negative angle. It has a clockwise rotation of 90° followed by a clockwise rotation of 30° The angle lies in quadrant III and is shown in the following graph.

d. A 390° angle is a positive angle. It has a counterclockwise rotation of 360°, one complete rotation, followed by a counterclockwise rotation of 30°. The angle lies in quadrant I and is shown in the following graph.

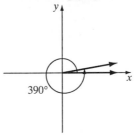

2. a. For a 400° angle, subtract 360° to find a positive coterminal angle.
$$400° - 360° = 40°$$

b. For a −135° angle, add 360° to find a positive coterminal angle.
$$-135° + 360° = 225°$$

3. a. $\theta = 78°$
Complement $= 90° - 78° = 12°$
Supplement $= 180° - 78° = 102°$
For a 78° angle, the complement is a 12° angle and the supplement is a 102° angle.

b. $\alpha = 150°$
For the angle's complement, we consider subtracting 150° from 90°. The difference is negative. Because we use only positive angles for complements, a 150° angle has no complement. It does, however, have a supplement.
Supplement $= 180° - 150° = 30°$
The supplement of a 150° angle is a 30° angle.

4. The radian measure of a central angle is the length of the intercepted arc, *s,* divided by the circle's radius, *r.* The length of the intercepted arc is 42 feet: $s = 42$ feet. The circle's radius is 12 feet: $r = 12$ feet. Now use the formula for radian measure to find the radian measure of θ.

$$\theta = \frac{s}{r} = \frac{42 \text{ feet}}{12 \text{ feet}} = 3.5$$

Thus, the radian measure of θ is 3.5

5. a. $\quad 60° = 60° \cdot \dfrac{\pi \text{ radians}}{180°} = \dfrac{60\pi}{180}$ radians

$\qquad = \dfrac{\pi}{3}$ radians

b. $\quad 270° = 270° \cdot \dfrac{\pi \text{ radians}}{180°} = \dfrac{270\pi}{180}$ radians

$\qquad = \dfrac{3\pi}{2}$ radians

c. $\quad -300° - -300° \cdot \dfrac{\pi \text{ radians}}{180°} = \dfrac{-300\pi}{180}$ radians

$\qquad = -\dfrac{5\pi}{3}$ radians

6. a. $\quad \dfrac{\pi}{4}$ radians $= \dfrac{\cancel{\pi} \text{ radians}}{4} \cdot \dfrac{180°}{\cancel{\pi} \text{ radians}}$

$\qquad = \dfrac{180°}{4} = 45°$

b. $\quad -\dfrac{4\pi}{3}$ radians $= -\dfrac{4\cancel{\pi} \text{ radians}}{3} \cdot \dfrac{180°}{\cancel{\pi} \text{ radians}}$

$\qquad = -\dfrac{4 \cdot 180°}{3} = -240°$

c. $\quad 6$ radians $= 6 \text{ radians} \cdot \dfrac{180°}{\pi \text{ radians}}$

$\qquad = \dfrac{6 \cdot 180°}{\pi} \approx 343.8°$

7. The formula $s = r\theta$ can only be used when θ is expressed in radians. Thus, we begin by converting 45° to radians. Multiply by $\dfrac{\pi \text{ radians}}{180°}$.

$$45° = 45° \cdot \frac{\pi \text{ radians}}{180°} = \frac{45}{180}\pi \text{ radians}$$

$$= \frac{\pi}{4} \text{ radians}$$

Now we can use the formula $s = r\theta$ to find the length of the arc. The circle's radius is 6 inches : $r = 6$ inches. The measure of the central angle in radians is $\dfrac{\pi}{4} : \theta = \dfrac{\pi}{4}$. The length of the arc intercepted by this central angle is

$$s = r\theta = (6 \text{ inches})\left(\frac{\pi}{4}\right) = \frac{6\pi}{4} \text{ inches} \approx 4.71 \text{ inches}$$

8. We are given ω, the angular speed.
$\omega = 45$ revolutions per minute
We use the formula $v = r\omega$ to find v, the linear speed. Before applying the formula, we must express ω in radians per minute.

$$\omega = \frac{45 \text{ \cancel{revolutions}}}{1 \text{ minute}} \cdot \frac{2\pi \text{ radians}}{1 \text{ \cancel{revolutions}}}$$

$$= \frac{90\pi \text{ radians}}{1 \text{ minute}} \text{ or } \frac{90\pi}{1 \text{ minute}}$$

The angular speed of the propeller is 90π radians per minute. The linear speed is

$$v = r\omega = 1.5 \text{ inches} \cdot \frac{90\pi}{1 \text{ minute}} = \frac{135\pi \text{ inches}}{\text{minute}}$$

The linear speed is 135π inches per minute, which is approximately 424 inches per minute.

Exercise Set 5.1

1. $90° < 145° < 180°$
quadrant II

3. $-100° + 360° = 260°$
$180° < 260° < 270°$
quadrant III

5. $362° - 360° = 2°$
$0° < 2° < 90°$
quadrant I

7. obtuse
$(90° < \theta < 180°)$

9. straight
$$\left(\frac{1}{2} \text{ rotation}\right)$$

11. 135° is a positive angle. It has a counter-clockwise rotation of 90° followed by a counterclockwise rotation of 45°. The angle lies in quadrant II and is shown in the following graph.

13. −150° is a negative angle. It has a clockwise rotation of 90° followed by a clockwise rotation of 60°. The angle lies in quadrant III and is shown in the following graph.

15. 420° is a positive angle. It has a counter-clockwise rotation of 360°, one complete rotation, followed by a counterclockwise rotation of 60°. The angle lies in quadrant I and is shown in the following graph.

17. −90° is a negative angle. It has a clockwise rotation of 90°. The angle is a quadrantal angle and is shown in the following graph.

19. $395° − 360° = 35°$

21. $−150° + 360° = 210°$

23. $−45° + 360° = 315°$

25. 52°
Complement $= 90° − 52° = 38°$;
Supplement $= 180° − 52° = 128°$

27. 37.4°
Complement $= 90° − 37.4° = 52.6°$;
Supplement $= 180° − 37.4° = 142.6°$

29. 111°
Since subtracting 111° from 90° is negative, there is no complement.
Supplement $= 180° − 111° = 69°$

31. $\theta = \dfrac{s}{r} = \dfrac{40 \text{ inches}}{10 \text{ inches}} = 4$ radians

33. $\theta = \dfrac{s}{r} = \dfrac{8 \text{ yards}}{6 \text{ yards}} = \dfrac{4}{3}$ radians

35. $\theta = \dfrac{s}{r} = \dfrac{400 \text{ centimeters}}{100 \text{ centimeters}} = 4$ radians

37. $45° = 45° \cdot \dfrac{\pi \text{ radians}}{180°}$
$= \dfrac{45\pi}{180}$ radians
$= \dfrac{\pi}{4}$ radians

39. $135° = 135° \cdot \dfrac{\pi \text{ radians}}{180°}$

$\qquad = \dfrac{135\pi}{180} \text{ radians}$

$\qquad = \dfrac{3\pi}{4} \text{ radians}$

41. $300° = 300° \cdot \dfrac{\pi \text{ radians}}{180°}$

$\qquad = \dfrac{300\pi}{180} \text{ radians}$

$\qquad = \dfrac{5\pi}{3} \text{ radians}$

43. $-225° = -225° \cdot \dfrac{\pi \text{ radians}}{180°}$

$\qquad = -\dfrac{225\pi}{180} \text{ radians}$

$\qquad = -\dfrac{5\pi}{4} \text{ radians}$

45. $\dfrac{\pi}{2} \text{ radians} = \dfrac{\pi \text{ radians}}{2} \cdot \dfrac{180°}{\pi \text{ radians}}$

$\qquad = \dfrac{180°}{2}$

$\qquad = 90°$

47. $\dfrac{2\pi}{3} \text{ radians} = \dfrac{2\pi \text{ radians}}{3} \cdot \dfrac{180°}{\pi \text{ radians}}$

$\qquad = \dfrac{2 \cdot 180°}{3}$

$\qquad = 120°$

49. $\dfrac{7\pi}{6} \text{ radians} = \dfrac{7\pi \text{ radians}}{6} \cdot \dfrac{180°}{\pi \text{ radians}}$

$\qquad = \dfrac{7 \cdot 180°}{6}$

$\qquad = 210°$

51. $-3\pi \text{ radians} = -3\pi \text{ radians} \cdot \dfrac{180°}{\pi \text{ radians}}$

$\qquad = -3 \cdot 180°$

$\qquad = -540°$

53. $18° = 18° \cdot \dfrac{\pi \text{ radians}}{180°}$

$\qquad = \dfrac{18\pi}{180} \text{ radians}$

$\qquad \approx 0.31 \text{ radians}$

55. $-40° = -40° \cdot \dfrac{\pi \text{ radians}}{180°}$

$\qquad = -\dfrac{40\pi}{180} \text{ radians}$

$\qquad \approx -0.70 \text{ radians}$

57. $200° = 200° \cdot \dfrac{\pi \text{ radians}}{180°}$

$\qquad = \dfrac{200\pi}{180} \text{ radians}$

$\qquad \approx 3.49 \text{ radians}$

59. $2 \text{ radians} = 2 \text{ radians} \cdot \dfrac{180°}{\pi \text{ radians}}$

$\qquad = \dfrac{2 \cdot 180°}{\pi}$

$\qquad \approx 114.59°$

61. $\dfrac{\pi}{13} \text{ radians} = \dfrac{\pi \text{ radians}}{13} \cdot \dfrac{180°}{\pi \text{ radians}}$

$\qquad = \dfrac{180°}{13}$

$\qquad \approx 13.85°$

63. $-4.8 \text{ radians} = -4.8 \text{ radians} \cdot \dfrac{180°}{\pi \text{ radians}}$

$\qquad = \dfrac{-4.8 \cdot 180°}{\pi}$

$\qquad \approx -275.02°$

65. $r = 12$ inches, $\theta = 45°$

Begin by converting 45° to radians, in order to use the formula $s = r\theta$.

$45° = 45° \cdot \dfrac{\pi \text{ radians}}{180°} = \dfrac{\pi}{4} \text{ radians}$

Now use the formula $s = r\theta$.

$s = r\theta = 12 \cdot \dfrac{\pi}{4} = 3\pi$ inches ≈ 9.42 inches

67. $r = 8$ feet, $\theta = 225°$

Begin by converting 225° to radians, in order to use the formula $s = r\theta$.

$$225° = 225° \cdot \frac{\pi \text{ radians}}{180°} = \frac{5\pi}{4} \text{ radians}$$

Now use the formula $s = r\theta$.

$$s = r\theta = 8 \cdot \frac{5\pi}{4} = 10\pi \text{ feet} \approx 31.42 \text{ feet}$$

69. 6 revolutions per second

$$= \frac{6 \text{ revolutions}}{1 \text{ second}} \cdot \frac{2\pi \text{ radians}}{1 \text{ revolution}} = \frac{12\pi \text{ radians}}{1 \text{ second}}$$

$$= 12\pi \text{ radians per second}$$

71. First, convert to degrees.

$$\frac{1}{6} \text{ revolution} = \frac{1}{6} \text{ revolution} \cdot \frac{360°}{1 \text{ revolution}}$$

$$= \frac{1}{6} \cdot 360° = 60°$$

Now, convert 60° to radians.

$$60° = 60° \cdot \frac{\pi \text{ radians}}{180°} = \frac{60\pi}{180} \text{ radians}$$

$$= \frac{\pi}{3} \text{ radians}$$

Therefore, $\frac{1}{6}$ revolution is equivalent to 60° or $\frac{\pi}{3}$ radians.

73. The distance that the tip of the minute hand moves is given by its arc length, s. Since $s = r\theta$, we begin by finding r and θ. We are given that $r = 8$ inches. The minute hand moves from 12 to 2 o'clock, or $\frac{1}{6}$ of a complete revolution. The formula $s = r\theta$ can only be used when θ is expressed in radians. We must convert $\frac{1}{6}$ revolution to radians.

$$\frac{1}{6} \text{ revolution} = \frac{1}{6} \text{ revolution} \cdot \frac{2\pi \text{ radians}}{1 \text{ revolution}}$$

$$= \frac{\pi}{3} \text{ radians}$$

The distance the tip of the minute hand moves is

$$s = r\theta = (8 \text{ inches})\left(\frac{\pi}{3}\right) = \frac{8\pi}{3} \text{ inches}$$

$$\approx 8.38 \text{ inches}.$$

75. The length of each arc is given by $s = r\theta$. We are given that $r = 24$ inches and $\theta = 90°$. The formula $s = r\theta$ can only be used when θ is expressed in radians.

$$90° = 90° \cdot \frac{\pi \text{ radians}}{180°} = \frac{90\pi}{180} \text{ radians}$$

$$= \frac{\pi}{2} \text{ radians}$$

The length of each arc is

$$s = r\theta = (24 \text{ inches})\left(\frac{\pi}{2}\right) = 12\pi \text{ inches}$$

$$\approx 37.70 \text{ inches}.$$

77. Recall that $\theta = \frac{s}{r}$. We are given that $s = 8000$ miles and $r = 4000$ miles.

$$\theta = \frac{s}{r} = \frac{8000 \text{ miles}}{4000 \text{ miles}} = 2 \text{ radians}$$

Now, convert 2 radians to degrees.

$$2 \text{ radians} = 2 \text{ radians} \cdot \frac{180°}{\pi \text{ radians}} \approx 114.59°$$

79. Recall that $s = r\theta$. We are given that $r = 4000$ miles and $\theta = 30°$. The formula $s = r\theta$ can only be used when θ is expressed in radians.

$$30° = 30° \cdot \frac{\pi \text{ radians}}{180°} = \frac{30\pi}{180} \text{ radians}$$

$$= \frac{\pi}{6} \text{ radians}$$

$$s = r\theta = (4000 \text{ miles})\left(\frac{\pi}{6}\right) \approx 2094 \text{ miles}$$

To the nearest mile, the distance from A to B is 2094 miles.

81. Linear speed is given by $v = r\omega$. We are given that $\omega = \dfrac{\pi}{12}$ radians per hour and $r = 4000$ miles. Therefore,

$$v = r\omega = (4000 \text{ miles})\left(\frac{\pi}{12}\right)$$

$$= \frac{4000\pi}{12} \text{ miles per hour}$$

$$\approx 1047 \text{ miles per hour}$$

The linear speed is about 1047 miles per hour.

83. Linear speed is given by $v = r\omega$. We are given that $r = 12$ feet and the wheel rotates at 20 revolutions per minute.
20 revolutions per minute

$$= 20 \text{ revolutions per minute} \cdot \frac{2\pi \text{ radians}}{1 \text{ revolution}}$$

$$= 40\pi \text{ radians per minute}$$

$$v = r\omega = (12 \text{ feet})(40\pi)$$

$$\approx 1508 \text{ feet per minute}$$

The linear speed of the wheel is about 1508 feet per minute.

85.–95. Answers may vary.

97.
```
30°15'10"
        30.25277778
■
```

99.
```
30.42°▸DMS
       30°25'12"
■
```

101. A right angle measures 90° and

$$90° = \frac{\pi}{2} \text{ radians} \approx 1.57 \text{ radians.}$$

If $\theta = \dfrac{3}{2}$ radians $= 1.5$ radians, θ is smaller than a right angle.

103. $s = r\theta$
Begin by changing $\theta = 26°$ to radians.

$$26° = 26° \cdot \frac{\pi}{180°} = \frac{13\pi}{90} \text{ radians}$$

$$s = 4000 \cdot \frac{13\pi}{90}$$

$$\approx 1815 \text{ miles}$$

To the nearest mile, Miami, Florida is 1815 miles north of the equator.

Section 5.2

Checkpoint Exercises

1. Use the Pythagorean Theorem,
$c^2 = a^2 + b^2$, to find c.
$a = 3,\ b = 4$
$c^2 = a^2 + b^2 = 3^2 + 4^2 = 9 + 16 = 25$
$c = \sqrt{25} = 5$
Referring to these lengths as opposite, adjacent, and hypotenuse, we have

$$\sin\theta = \frac{\text{opposite}}{\text{hypotenuse}} = \frac{3}{5}$$

$$\cos\theta = \frac{\text{adjacent}}{\text{hypotenuse}} = \frac{4}{5}$$

$$\tan\theta = \frac{\text{opposite}}{\text{adjacent}} = \frac{3}{4}$$

$$\csc\theta = \frac{\text{hypotenuse}}{\text{opposite}} = \frac{5}{3}$$

$$\sec\theta = \frac{\text{hypotenuse}}{\text{adjacent}} = \frac{5}{4}$$

$$\cot\theta = \frac{\text{adjacent}}{\text{opposite}} = \frac{4}{3}$$

2. Apply the definitions of these three trigonometric functions.

$$\csc 45° = \frac{\text{length of hypotenuse}}{\text{length of side opposite } 45°}$$

$$= \frac{\sqrt{2}}{1} = \sqrt{2}$$

$$\sec 45° = \frac{\text{length of hypotenuse}}{\text{length of side adjacent to } 45°}$$

$$= \frac{\sqrt{2}}{1} = \sqrt{2}$$

$$\cot 45° = \frac{\text{length of side adjacent to } 45°}{\text{length of side opposite } 45°}$$

$$= \frac{1}{1} = 1$$

3. $\tan 60° = \dfrac{\text{length of side opposite } 60°}{\text{length of side adjacent to } 60°}$

$$= \frac{\sqrt{3}}{1} = \sqrt{3}$$

$$\tan 30° = \frac{\text{length of side opposite } 30°}{\text{length of side adjacent to } 30°}$$

$$= \frac{1}{\sqrt{3}} = \frac{1}{\sqrt{3}} \cdot \frac{\sqrt{3}}{3} = \frac{\sqrt{3}}{3}$$

4. $\tan \theta = \dfrac{\sin \theta}{\cos \theta} = \dfrac{\frac{2}{3}}{\frac{\sqrt{5}}{3}}$

$$= \frac{2}{3} \cdot \frac{3}{\sqrt{5}} = \frac{2}{\sqrt{5}}$$

$$= \frac{2}{\sqrt{5}} \cdot \frac{\sqrt{5}}{5} = \frac{2\sqrt{5}}{5}$$

$$\csc \theta = \frac{1}{\sin \theta} = \frac{1}{\frac{2}{3}} = \frac{3}{2}$$

$$\sec \theta = \frac{1}{\cos \theta} = \frac{1}{\frac{\sqrt{5}}{3}} = \frac{3}{\sqrt{5}}$$

$$= \frac{3}{\sqrt{5}} \cdot \frac{\sqrt{5}}{\sqrt{5}} = \frac{3\sqrt{5}}{5}$$

$$\cot \theta = \frac{1}{\tan \theta} = \frac{1}{\frac{2}{\sqrt{5}}} = \frac{\sqrt{5}}{2}$$

5. We can find the value of $\cos \theta$ by using the Pythagorean identity

$$\sin^2 \theta + \cos^2 \theta = 1$$

$$\left(\frac{1}{2}\right)^2 + \cos^2 \theta = 1$$

$$\frac{1}{4} + \cos^2 \theta = 1$$

$$\cos^2 \theta = 1 - \frac{1}{4}$$

$$\cos^2 \theta = \frac{3}{4}$$

$$\cos \theta = \sqrt{\frac{3}{4}} = \frac{\sqrt{3}}{2}$$

6. a. $\sin 46° = \cos(90° - 46°) = \cos 44°$

b. $\cot \dfrac{\pi}{12} = \tan\left(\dfrac{\pi}{2} - \dfrac{\pi}{12}\right)$

$$= \tan\left(\frac{6\pi}{12} - \frac{\pi}{12}\right)$$

$$= \tan \frac{5\pi}{12}$$

7.

Scientific Calculator Solution			
Function	Mode	Keystrokes	Display (rounded to four places)
a. sin 72.8°	Degree	72.8 $\boxed{\text{SIN}}$	0.9553
b. csc 1.5	Radian	1.5 $\boxed{\text{SIN}}$ $\boxed{1/x}$	1.0025

Graphing Calculator Solution			
Function	Mode	Keystrokes	Display (rounded to four places)
a. sin 72.8°	Degree	$\boxed{\text{SIN}}$ 72.8 $\boxed{\text{ENTER}}$	0.9553
b. csc 1.5	Radian	$\boxed{(}$ $\boxed{\text{SIN}}$ 1.5 $\boxed{)}$ $\boxed{x^{-1}}$ $\boxed{\text{ENTER}}$	1.0025

8. Because we have a known angle, an unknown opposite side, and a known adjacent side, we select the tangent function.

$$\tan 24° = \frac{a}{750}$$
$$a = 750 \tan 24°$$
$$a \approx 750(0.4452) \approx 334$$

The distance across the lake is approximately 334 yards.

9. $\tan\theta = \dfrac{\text{side opposite } \theta}{\text{side adjacent to } \theta} = \dfrac{14}{10}$

Use a calculator in degree mode to find θ.

Scientific Calculator	Graphing Calculator
14 $\boxed{\div}$ 10 $\boxed{=}$ $\boxed{\text{TAN}^{-1}}$	$\boxed{\text{TAN}^{-1}}$ $\boxed{(}$ 14 $\boxed{\div}$ 10 $\boxed{)}$ $\boxed{\text{ENTER}}$

The display should show approximately 54. Thus, the angle of elevation of the sun is approximately 54°.

Exercise Set 5.2

1. $c^2 = 9^2 + 12^2 = 225$

$c = \sqrt{225} = 15$

$\sin\theta = \dfrac{\text{opposite}}{\text{hypotenuse}} = \dfrac{9}{15} = \dfrac{3}{5}$

$\cos\theta = \dfrac{\text{adjacent}}{\text{hypotenuse}} = \dfrac{12}{15} = \dfrac{4}{5}$

$\tan\theta = \dfrac{\text{opposite}}{\text{adjacent}} = \dfrac{9}{12} = \dfrac{3}{4}$

$\csc\theta = \dfrac{\text{hypotenuse}}{\text{opposite}} = \dfrac{15}{9} = \dfrac{5}{3}$

$\sec\theta = \dfrac{\text{hypotenuse}}{\text{adjacent}} = \dfrac{15}{12} = \dfrac{5}{4}$

$\cot\theta = \dfrac{\text{adjacent}}{\text{opposite}} = \dfrac{12}{9} = \dfrac{4}{3}$

3. $a^2 + 21^2 = 29^2$

$a^2 = 841 - 441 = 400$

$a = \sqrt{400} = 20$

$\sin\theta = \dfrac{\text{opposite}}{\text{hypotenuse}} = \dfrac{20}{29}$

$\cos\theta = \dfrac{\text{adjacent}}{\text{hypotenuse}} = \dfrac{21}{29}$

$\tan\theta = \dfrac{\text{opposite}}{\text{adjacent}} = \dfrac{20}{21}$

$\csc\theta = \dfrac{\text{hypotenuse}}{\text{opposite}} = \dfrac{29}{20}$

$\sec\theta = \dfrac{\text{hypotenuse}}{\text{adjacent}} = \dfrac{29}{21}$

$\cot\theta = \dfrac{\text{adjacent}}{\text{opposite}} = \dfrac{21}{20}$

5. $10^2 + b^2 = 26^2$

$b^2 = 676 - 100 = 576$

$b = \sqrt{576} = 24$

$\sin\theta = \dfrac{\text{opposite}}{\text{hypotenuse}} = \dfrac{10}{26} = \dfrac{5}{13}$

$\cos\theta = \dfrac{\text{adjacent}}{\text{hypotenuse}} = \dfrac{24}{26} = \dfrac{12}{13}$

$\tan\theta = \dfrac{\text{opposite}}{\text{adjacent}} = \dfrac{10}{24} = \dfrac{5}{12}$

$\csc\theta = \dfrac{\text{hypotenuse}}{\text{opposite}} = \dfrac{26}{10} = \dfrac{13}{5}$

$\sec\theta = \dfrac{\text{hypotenuse}}{\text{adjacent}} = \dfrac{26}{24} = \dfrac{13}{12}$

$\cot\theta = \dfrac{\text{adjacent}}{\text{opposite}} = \dfrac{24}{10} = \dfrac{12}{5}$

7. $21^2 + b^2 = 35^2$

$b^2 = 1225 - 441 = 784$

$b = \sqrt{784} = 28$

$\sin\theta = \dfrac{\text{opposite}}{\text{hypotenuse}} = \dfrac{28}{35} = \dfrac{4}{5}$

$\cos\theta = \dfrac{\text{adjacent}}{\text{hypotenuse}} = \dfrac{21}{35} = \dfrac{3}{5}$

$\tan\theta = \dfrac{\text{opposite}}{\text{adjacent}} = \dfrac{28}{21} = \dfrac{4}{3}$

$\csc\theta = \dfrac{\text{hypotenuse}}{\text{opposite}} = \dfrac{35}{28} = \dfrac{5}{4}$

$\sec\theta = \dfrac{\text{hypotenuse}}{\text{adjacent}} = \dfrac{35}{21} = \dfrac{5}{3}$

$\cot\theta = \dfrac{\text{adjacent}}{\text{opposite}} = \dfrac{21}{28} = \dfrac{3}{4}$

9. $\cos 30° = \dfrac{\text{length of side adjacent to } 30°}{\text{length of hypotenuse}}$

$= \dfrac{\sqrt{3}}{2}$

11. $\sec 45° = \dfrac{\text{length of hypotenuse}}{\text{length of side adjacent to } 45°}$

$= \dfrac{\sqrt{2}}{1} = \sqrt{2}$

13. $\tan\dfrac{\pi}{3} = \tan 60°$

$\qquad = \dfrac{\text{length of side opposite } 60°}{\text{length of side adjacent to } 60°}$

$\qquad = \dfrac{\sqrt{3}}{1} = \sqrt{3}$

15. $\sin\dfrac{\pi}{4} - \cos\dfrac{\pi}{4} = \sin 45° - \cos 45°$

$\qquad\qquad = \dfrac{1}{\sqrt{2}} - \dfrac{1}{\sqrt{2}} = 0$

17. $\tan\theta = \dfrac{\sin\theta}{\cos\theta} = \dfrac{\frac{8}{17}}{\frac{15}{17}} = \dfrac{8}{15}$

$\csc\theta = \dfrac{1}{\sin\theta} = \dfrac{1}{\frac{8}{17}} = \dfrac{17}{8}$

$\sec\theta = \dfrac{1}{\cos\theta} = \dfrac{1}{\frac{15}{17}} = \dfrac{17}{15}$

$\cot\theta = \dfrac{\cos\theta}{\sin\theta} = \dfrac{\frac{15}{17}}{\frac{8}{17}} = \dfrac{15}{8}$

19. $\tan\theta = \dfrac{\sin\theta}{\cos\theta} = \dfrac{\frac{1}{3}}{\frac{2\sqrt{2}}{3}} = \dfrac{1}{2\sqrt{2}}$

$\qquad = \dfrac{1}{2\sqrt{2}} \cdot \dfrac{\sqrt{2}}{\sqrt{2}} = \dfrac{\sqrt{2}}{4}$

$\csc\theta = \dfrac{1}{\sin\theta} = \dfrac{1}{\frac{1}{3}} = \dfrac{3}{1} = 3$

$\sec\theta = \dfrac{1}{\cos\theta} = \dfrac{1}{\frac{2\sqrt{2}}{3}} = \dfrac{3}{2\sqrt{2}}$

$\qquad = \dfrac{3}{2\sqrt{2}} \cdot \dfrac{\sqrt{2}}{\sqrt{2}} = \dfrac{3\sqrt{2}}{4}$

$\cot\theta = \dfrac{\cos\theta}{\sin\theta} = \dfrac{\frac{2\sqrt{2}}{3}}{\frac{1}{3}}$

$\qquad = \dfrac{2\sqrt{2}}{1} = 2\sqrt{2}$

21. $\sin^2\theta + \cos^2\theta = 1$

$\left(\dfrac{6}{7}\right)^2 + \cos^2\theta = 1$

$\dfrac{36}{49} + \cos^2\theta = 1$

$\cos^2\theta = 1 - \dfrac{36}{49}$

$\cos^2\theta = \dfrac{13}{49}$

$\cos\theta = \sqrt{\dfrac{13}{49}} = \dfrac{\sqrt{13}}{7}$

23. $\sin^2\theta + \cos^2\theta = 1$

$\left(\dfrac{\sqrt{39}}{8}\right)^2 + \cos^2\theta = 1$

$\dfrac{39}{64} + \cos^2\theta = 1$

$\cos^2\theta = 1 - \dfrac{39}{64}$

$\cos^2\theta = \dfrac{25}{64}$

$\cos\theta = \sqrt{\dfrac{25}{64}} = \dfrac{5}{8}$

25. $\sin 37° \csc 37° = \sin 37° \cdot \dfrac{1}{\sin 37°} = 1$

27. We can find the value of the expression by using the Pythagorean identity

$\sin^2\theta + \cos^2\theta = 1$.

$\sin^2\dfrac{\pi}{9} + \cos^2\dfrac{\pi}{9} = 1$

29. We can find the value of the expression by using the Pythagorean identity

$1 + \tan^2\theta = \sec^2\theta$.

$\sec^2 23° - \tan^2 23° = 1$

31. $\sin 7° = \cos(90° - 7°) = \cos 83°$

33. $\csc 25° = \sec(90° - 25°) = \sec 65°$

35. $\tan\dfrac{\pi}{9} = \cot\left(\dfrac{\pi}{2} - \dfrac{\pi}{9}\right) = \cot\left(\dfrac{9\pi}{18} - \dfrac{2\pi}{18}\right) = \cot\dfrac{7\pi}{18}$

37. $\cos\dfrac{2\pi}{5} = \sin\left(\dfrac{\pi}{2} - \dfrac{2\pi}{5}\right) = \sin\left(\dfrac{5\pi}{10} - \dfrac{4\pi}{10}\right) = \sin\dfrac{\pi}{10}$

39.

Scientific Calculator Solution			
Function	**Mode**	**Keystrokes**	**Display** (rounded to four places)
sin 38°	Degree	38 SIN	.6157

Graphing Calculator Solution			
Function	**Mode**	**Keystrokes**	**Display** (rounded to four places)
sin 38°	Degree	SIN 38 ENTER	.6157

41.

Scientific Calculator Solution			
Function	**Mode**	**Keystrokes**	**Display** (rounded to four places)
tan 32.7°	Degree	32.7 TAN	.6420

Graphing Calculator Solution			
Function	**Mode**	**Keystrokes**	**Display** (rounded to four places)
sin 32.7°	Degree	TAN 32.7 ENTER	.6420

43.

Scientific Calculator Solution			
Function	**Mode**	**Keystrokes**	**Display** (rounded to four places)
csc 17°	Degree	17 SIN 1/x	3.4203

Graphing Calculator Solution			
Function	**Mode**	**Keystrokes**	**Display** (rounded to four places)
csc 17°	Degree	(SIN 17) x^{-1} ENTER	3.4203

45.

Scientific Calculator Solution			
Function	**Mode**	**Keystrokes**	**Display** (rounded to four places)
$\cos \dfrac{\pi}{10}$	Radian	π ÷ 10 = COS	.9511

Graphing Calculator Solution			
Function	**Mode**	**Keystrokes**	**Display** (rounded to four places)
$\cos \dfrac{\pi}{10}$	Radian	COS (π ÷ 10) ENTER	.9511

47.

Scientific Calculator Solution			
Function	**Mode**	**Keystrokes**	**Display** (rounded to four places)
$\cot \dfrac{\pi}{12}$	Radian	π ÷ 12 = TAN 1/x	3.7321

Graphing Calculator Solution			
Function	**Mode**	**Keystrokes**	**Display** (rounded to four places)
$\cot \dfrac{\pi}{12}$	Radian	(TAN (π ÷ 12)) x^{-1} ENTER	3.7321

49. $\tan 37° = \dfrac{a}{250}$
$a = 250 \tan 37°$
$a \approx 250(0.7536) \approx 188$ cm

51. $\cos 34° = \dfrac{b}{220}$
$b = 220 \cos 34°$
$b \approx 220(0.8290) \approx 182$ in.

53. $\sin 23° = \dfrac{16}{c}$
$c = \dfrac{16}{\sin 23°} \approx \dfrac{16}{0.3907} \approx 41$ m

55.

Scientific Calculator	Graphing Calculator	Display (rounded to the nearest degree)
.2974 SIN^{-1}	SIN^{-1} .2974 ENTER	17

If $\sin \theta = 0.2974$, then $\theta \approx 17°$.

57.

Scientific Calculator	Graphing Calculator	Display (rounded to the nearest degree)
4.6252 $\boxed{\text{TAN}^{-1}}$	$\boxed{\text{TAN}^{-1}}$ 4.6252 $\boxed{\text{ENTER}}$	78

If $\tan\theta = 4.6252$, then $\theta \approx 78°$.

59.

Scientific Calculator	Graphing Calculator	Display (rounded to three places)
.4112 $\boxed{\text{COS}^{-1}}$	$\boxed{\text{COS}^{-1}}$ .4112 $\boxed{\text{ENTER}}$	1.147

If $\cos\theta = 0.4112$, then $\theta \approx 1.147$ radians.

61.

Scientific Calculator	Graphing Calculator	Display (rounded to three places)
.4169 $\boxed{\text{TAN}^{-1}}$	$\boxed{\text{TAN}^{-1}}$ .4169 $\boxed{\text{ENTER}}$	.395

If $\tan\theta = 0.4169$, then $\theta \approx 0.395$ radians.

63. $\tan 40° = \dfrac{a}{630}$

$a = 630 \tan 40°$

$a \approx 630(0.8391) \approx 529$

The distance across the lake is approximately 529 yards.

65. $\tan\theta = \dfrac{125}{172}$

Use a calculator in degree mode to find θ.

Scientific Calculator	Graphing Calculator
125 $\boxed{\div}$ 172 $\boxed{=}$ $\boxed{\text{TAN}^{-1}}$	$\boxed{\text{TAN}^{-1}}$ $\boxed{(}$ 125 $\boxed{\div}$ 172 $\boxed{)}$ $\boxed{\text{ENTER}}$

The display should show approximately 36. Thus, the angle of elevation of the sun is approximately 36°.

67. $\sin 10° = \dfrac{500}{c}$

$c = \dfrac{500}{\sin 10°} \approx \dfrac{500}{0.1736} \approx 2880$

The plane has flown approximately 2880 feet.

69. $\cos\theta = \dfrac{60}{75}$

Use a calculator in degree mode to find θ.

Scientific Calculator	Graphing Calculator
$60 \boxed{\div} 75 \boxed{=} \boxed{\text{COS}^{-1}}$	$\boxed{\text{COS}^{-1}} \boxed{(} 60 \boxed{\div} 75 \boxed{)} \boxed{\text{ENTER}}$

The display should show approximately 37. Thus, the angle between the wire and the pole is approximately 37°.

71.–81. Answers may vary.

83.

θ	0.4	0.3	0.2	0.1	0.01	0.001	0.0001	0.00001
$\cos\theta$	0.92106	0.9553	0.98007	0.995004	0.99995	0.9999995	0.999999995	1
$\dfrac{\cos\theta - 1}{\theta}$	−0.19735	−0.149	−0.09965	−0.04996	−0.005	−0.0005	−0.00005	0

$\dfrac{\cos\theta - 1}{\theta}$ approaches 0 as θ approaches 0.

85. Answers may vary.

87. a. Let a = distance of the ship from the lighthouse.

$\tan 35° = \dfrac{250}{a}$

$a = \dfrac{250}{\tan 35°} \approx \dfrac{250}{0.7002} \approx 357$

The ship is approximately 357 feet from the lighthouse.

b. Let b = the plane's height above the lighthouse.

$\tan 22° = \dfrac{b}{357}$

$b = 357 \tan 22° \approx 357(0.4040) \approx 144$

$144 + 250 = 394$

The plane is approximately 394 feet above the water.

Section 5.3

Checkpoint Exercises

1. We need values for x, y, and r. Because $P = (4, -3)$ is a point on the terminal side of θ, $x = 4$ and $y = -3$. Furthermore,

$$r = \sqrt{x^2 + y^2} = \sqrt{4^2 + (-3)^2} = \sqrt{16 + 9}$$
$$= \sqrt{25} = 5$$

Now that we know x, y, and r, we can find the six trigonometric functions of θ.

$$\sin\theta = \frac{y}{r} = \frac{-3}{5} = -\frac{3}{5}$$

$$\cos\theta = \frac{x}{r} = \frac{4}{5}$$

$$\tan\theta = \frac{y}{x} = \frac{-3}{4} = -\frac{3}{4}$$

$$\csc\theta = \frac{r}{y} = \frac{5}{-3} = -\frac{5}{3}$$

$$\sec\theta = \frac{r}{x} = \frac{5}{4}$$

$$\cot\theta = \frac{x}{y} = \frac{4}{-3} = -\frac{4}{3}$$

2. **a.** $\theta = 0° = 0$ radians

   The terminal side of the angle is on the positive x-axis. Select the point $P = (1,0)$: $x = 1, y = 0, r = 1$

   Apply the definitions of the cosine and cosecant functions.

   $$\cos 0° = \cos 0 = \frac{x}{r} = \frac{1}{1} = 1$$

   $$\csc 0° = \csc 0 = \frac{r}{y} = \frac{1}{0}, \text{ undefined}$$

   b. $\theta = 90° = \frac{\pi}{2}$ radians

   The terminal side of the angle is on the positive y-axis. Select the point $P = (0,1)$: $x = 0, y = 1, r = 1$

   Apply the definitions of the cosine and cosecant functions.

   $$\cos 90° = \cos\frac{\pi}{2} = \frac{x}{r} = \frac{0}{1} = 0$$

   $$\csc 90° = \csc\frac{\pi}{2} = \frac{r}{y} = \frac{1}{1} = 1$$

   c. $\theta = 180° = \pi$ radians

   The terminal side of the angle is on the negative x-axis. Select the point $P = (-1,0)$: $x = -1, y = 0, r = 1$

   Apply the definitions of the cosine and cosecant functions.

   $$\cos 180° = \cos\pi = \frac{x}{r} = \frac{-1}{1} = -1$$

   $$\csc 180° = \csc\pi = \frac{r}{y} = \frac{1}{0}, \text{ undefined}$$

   d. $\theta = 270° = \frac{3\pi}{2}$ radians

   The terminal side of the angle is on the negative y-axis. Select the point $P = (0,-1)$: $x = 0, y = -1, r = 1$

   Apply the definitions of the cosine and cosecant functions.

   $$\cos 270° = \cos\frac{3\pi}{2} = \frac{x}{r} = \frac{0}{1} = 0$$

   $$\csc 270° = \csc\frac{3\pi}{2} = \frac{r}{y} = \frac{1}{-1} = -1$$

3. Because $\sin\theta < 0$, θ cannot lie in quadrant I; all the functions are positive in quadrant I. Furthermore, θ cannot lie in quadrant II; $\sin\theta$ is positive in quadrant II. Thus, with $\sin\theta < 0$, θ lies in quadrant III or quadrant IV. We are also given that $\cos\theta < 0$. Because quadrant III is the only quadrant in which cosine is negative and the sine is negative, we conclude that θ lies in quadrant III.

4. Because the tangent is negative and the cosine is negative, θ lies in quadrant II. In quadrant II, x is negative and y is positive.

   Thus, $\tan\theta = -\frac{1}{3} = \frac{y}{x} = \frac{1}{-3}$

   $$x = -3, \ y = 1$$

   Furthermore,

   $$r = \sqrt{x^2 + y^2} = \sqrt{(-3)^2 + 1^2} = \sqrt{9 + 1} = \sqrt{10}$$

   Now that we know x, y, and r, we can find $\sin\theta$ and $\sec\theta$.

   $$\sin\theta = \frac{y}{r} = \frac{1}{\sqrt{10}} = \frac{1}{\sqrt{10}} \cdot \frac{\sqrt{10}}{\sqrt{10}} = \frac{\sqrt{10}}{10}$$

   $$\sec\theta = \frac{r}{x} = \frac{\sqrt{10}}{-3} = -\frac{\sqrt{10}}{3}$$

5. a. Because 210° lies between 180° and 270°, it is in quadrant III. The reference angle is $\theta' = 210° - 180° = 30°$.

b. Because $\dfrac{7\pi}{4}$ lies between $\dfrac{3\pi}{2} = \dfrac{6\pi}{4}$ and $2\pi = \dfrac{8\pi}{4}$, it is in quadrant IV. The reference angle is
$$\theta' = 2\pi - \frac{7\pi}{4} = \frac{8\pi}{4} - \frac{7\pi}{4} = \frac{\pi}{4}.$$

c. Because –240° lies between –180° and –270°, it is in quadrant II. The reference angle is $\theta = 240 - 180 = 60°$.

d. Because 3.6 lies between $\pi \approx 3.14$ and $\dfrac{3\pi}{2} \approx 4.71$, it is in quadrant III. The reference angle is $\theta' = 3.6 - \pi \approx 0.46$.

6. a. 300° lies in quadrant IV. The reference angle is $\theta' = 360° - 300° = 60°$.
$$\sin 60° = \frac{\sqrt{3}}{2}$$
Because the sine is negative in quadrant IV, $\sin 300° = -\sin 60° = -\dfrac{\sqrt{3}}{2}$.

b. $\dfrac{5\pi}{4}$ lies in quadrant III. The reference angle is $\theta' = \dfrac{5\pi}{4} - \pi = \dfrac{5\pi}{4} - \dfrac{4\pi}{4} = \dfrac{\pi}{4}$.
$$\tan \frac{\pi}{4} = 1$$
Because the tangent is positive in quadrant III, $\tan \dfrac{5\pi}{4} = +\tan \dfrac{\pi}{4} = 1$.

c. $-\dfrac{\pi}{6}$ lies in quadrant IV. The reference angle is $\theta' = \dfrac{\pi}{6}$.
$$\sec \frac{\pi}{6} = \frac{2\sqrt{3}}{3}$$
Because the secant is positive in quadrant IV,
$$\sec\left(-\frac{\pi}{6}\right) = +\sec\frac{\pi}{6} = \frac{2\sqrt{3}}{3}.$$

Exercise Set 5.3

1. We need values for x, y, and r. Because $P = (-4, 3)$ is a point on the terminal side of θ, $x = -4$ and $y = 3$. Furthermore,
$$r = \sqrt{x^2 + y^2} = \sqrt{(-4)^2 + 3^2} = \sqrt{16+9} = \sqrt{25} =$$
Now that we know x, y, and r, we can find the six trigonometric functions of θ.
$$\sin\theta = \frac{y}{r} = \frac{3}{5}$$
$$\cos\theta = \frac{x}{r} = \frac{-4}{5} = -\frac{4}{5}$$
$$\tan\theta = \frac{y}{x} = \frac{3}{-4} = -\frac{3}{4}$$
$$\csc\theta = \frac{r}{y} = \frac{5}{3}$$
$$\sec\theta = \frac{r}{x} = \frac{5}{-4} = -\frac{5}{4}$$
$$\cot\theta = \frac{x}{y} = \frac{-4}{3} = -\frac{4}{3}$$

3. We need values for x, y, and r. Because $P = (2, 3)$ is a point on the terminal side of θ, $x = 2$ and $y = 3$. Furthermore,
$$r = \sqrt{x^2 + y^2} = \sqrt{2^2 + 3^2} = \sqrt{4+9} = \sqrt{13}$$
Now that we know x, y, and r, we can find the six trigonometric functions of θ.
$$\sin\theta = \frac{y}{r} = \frac{3}{\sqrt{13}} = \frac{3}{\sqrt{13}}\cdot\frac{\sqrt{13}}{\sqrt{13}} = \frac{3\sqrt{13}}{13}$$
$$\cos\theta = \frac{x}{r} = \frac{2}{\sqrt{13}} = \frac{2}{\sqrt{13}}\cdot\frac{\sqrt{13}}{\sqrt{13}} = \frac{2\sqrt{13}}{13}$$
$$\tan\theta = \frac{y}{x} = \frac{3}{2}$$
$$\csc\theta = \frac{r}{y} = \frac{\sqrt{13}}{3}$$
$$\sec\theta = \frac{r}{x} = \frac{\sqrt{13}}{2}$$
$$\cot\theta = \frac{x}{y} = \frac{2}{3}$$

5. We need values for x, y, and r. Because $P = (3, -3)$ is a point on the terminal side of θ, $x = 3$ and $y = -3$. Furthermore,

$$r = \sqrt{x^2 + y^2} = \sqrt{3^2 + (-3)^2} = \sqrt{9 + 9}$$
$$= \sqrt{18} = 3\sqrt{2}$$

Now that we know x, y, and r, we can find the six trigonometric functions of θ.

$$\sin\theta = \frac{y}{r} = \frac{-3}{3\sqrt{2}} = \frac{-1}{\sqrt{2}} \cdot \frac{\sqrt{2}}{\sqrt{2}} = -\frac{\sqrt{2}}{2}$$

$$\cos\theta = \frac{x}{r} = \frac{3}{3\sqrt{2}} = \frac{1}{\sqrt{2}} \cdot \frac{\sqrt{2}}{\sqrt{2}} = \frac{\sqrt{2}}{2}$$

$$\tan\theta = \frac{y}{x} = \frac{-3}{3} = -1$$

$$\csc\theta = \frac{r}{y} = \frac{3\sqrt{2}}{-3} = -\sqrt{2}$$

$$\sec\theta = \frac{r}{x} = \frac{3\sqrt{2}}{3} = \sqrt{2}$$

$$\cot\theta = \frac{x}{y} = \frac{3}{-3} = -1$$

7. We need values for x, y, and r. Because $P = (-2, -5)$ is a point on the terminal side of θ, $x = -2$ and $y = -5$. Furthermore,

$$r = \sqrt{x^2 + y^2} = \sqrt{(-2)^2 + (-5)^2} = \sqrt{4 + 25} = \sqrt{29}$$

Now that we know x, y, and r, we can find the six trigonometric functions of θ.

$$\sin\theta = \frac{y}{r} = \frac{-5}{\sqrt{29}} = \frac{-5}{\sqrt{29}} \cdot \frac{\sqrt{29}}{\sqrt{29}} = -\frac{5\sqrt{29}}{29}$$

$$\cos\theta = \frac{x}{r} = \frac{-2}{\sqrt{29}} = \frac{-2}{\sqrt{29}} \cdot \frac{\sqrt{29}}{\sqrt{29}} = -\frac{2\sqrt{29}}{29}$$

$$\tan\theta = \frac{y}{x} = \frac{-5}{-2} = \frac{5}{2}$$

$$\csc\theta = \frac{r}{y} = \frac{\sqrt{29}}{-5} = -\frac{\sqrt{29}}{5}$$

$$\sec\theta = \frac{r}{x} = \frac{\sqrt{29}}{-2} = -\frac{\sqrt{29}}{2}$$

$$\cot\theta = \frac{x}{y} = \frac{-2}{-5} = \frac{2}{5}$$

9. $\theta = \pi$ radians
The terminal side of the angle is on the negative x-axis. Select the point $P = (-1, 0)$: $x = -1$, $y = 0$, $r = 1$ Apply the definition of the cosine function.

$$\cos\pi = \frac{x}{r} = \frac{-1}{1} = -1$$

11. $\theta = \pi$ radians
The terminal side of the angle is on the negative x-axis. Select the point $P = (-1, 0)$: $x = -1$, $y = 0$, $r = 1$ Apply the definition of the secant function.

$$\sec\pi = \frac{r}{x} = \frac{1}{-1} = -1$$

13. $\theta = \frac{3\pi}{2}$ radians

The terminal side of the angle is on the negative y-axis. Select the point $P = (0, -1)$: $x = 0$, $y = -1$, $r = 1$ Apply the definition of the tangent function.

$$\tan\frac{3\pi}{2} = \frac{y}{x} = \frac{-1}{0}, \text{ undefined}$$

15. $\theta = \frac{\pi}{2}$ radians

The terminal side of the angle is on the positive y-axis. Select the point $P = (0, 1)$: $x = 0$, $y = 1$, $r = 1$ Apply the definition of the cotangent function. $\cot\frac{\pi}{2} = \frac{x}{y} = \frac{0}{1} = 0$

17. Because $\sin\theta > 0$, θ cannot lie in quadrant III or quadrant IV; the sine function is negative in those quadrants. Thus, with $\sin\theta > 0$, θ lies in quadrant I or quadrant II. We are also given that $\cos\theta > 0$. Because quadrant I is the only quadrant in which the cosine is positive and sine is positive, we conclude that θ lies in quadrant I.

19. Because $\sin\theta < 0$, θ cannot lie in quadrant I or quadrant II; the sine function is positive in those two quadrants. Thus, with $\sin\theta < 0$, θ lies in quadrant III or quadrant IV. We are also given that $\cos\theta < 0$. Because quadrant III is the only quadrant in which the cosine is positive and the sine is negative, we conclude that θ lies in quadrant III.

21. Because $\tan\theta < 0$, θ cannot lie in quadrant I or quadrant III; the tangent function is positive in those quadrants. Thus, with $\tan\theta < 0$, θ lies in quadrant II or quadrant IV. We are also given that $\cos\theta < 0$. Because quadrant II is the only quadrant in which the cosine is negative and the tangent is negative, we conclude that θ lies in quadrant II.

23. In quadrant III x is negative and y is negative. Thus, $\cos\theta = -\dfrac{3}{5} = \dfrac{x}{r} = \dfrac{-3}{5}$, $x = -3$, $r = 5$. Furthermore,

$$r^2 = x^2 + y^2$$
$$5^2 = (-3)^2 + y^2$$
$$y^2 = 25 - 9 = 16$$
$$y = -\sqrt{16} = -4$$

Now that we know x, y, and r, we can find the remaining trigonometric functions of θ.

$$\sin\theta = \frac{y}{r} = \frac{-4}{5} = -\frac{4}{5}$$
$$\tan\theta = \frac{y}{x} = \frac{-4}{-3} = \frac{4}{3}$$
$$\csc\theta = \frac{r}{y} = \frac{5}{-4} = -\frac{5}{4}$$
$$\sec\theta = \frac{r}{x} = \frac{5}{-3} = -\frac{5}{3}$$
$$\cot\theta = \frac{x}{y} = \frac{-3}{-4} = \frac{3}{4}$$

25. In quadrant II x is negative and y is positive. Thus, $\sin\theta = \dfrac{5}{13} = \dfrac{y}{r}$, $y = 5$, $r = 13$.

Furthermore,
$$x^2 + y^2 = r^2$$
$$x^2 + 5^2 = 13^2$$
$$x^2 = 169 - 25 = 144$$
$$x = -\sqrt{144} = -12$$

Now that we know x, y, and r, we can find the remaining trigonometric functions of θ.

$$\cos\theta = \frac{x}{r} = \frac{-12}{13} = -\frac{12}{13}$$
$$\tan\theta = \frac{y}{x} = \frac{5}{-12} = -\frac{5}{12}$$
$$\csc\theta = \frac{r}{y} = \frac{13}{5}$$
$$\sec\theta = \frac{r}{x} = \frac{13}{-12} = -\frac{13}{12}$$
$$\cot\theta = \frac{x}{y} = \frac{-12}{5} = -\frac{12}{5}$$

27. Because $270° < \theta < 360°$, θ is in quadrant IV. In quadrant IV x is positive and y is negative. Thus, $\cos\theta = \dfrac{8}{17} = \dfrac{x}{r}$, $x = 8$, $r = 17$. Furthermore

$$x^2 + y^2 = r^2$$
$$8^2 + y^2 = 17^2$$
$$y^2 = 289 - 64 = 225$$
$$y = -\sqrt{225} = -15$$

Now that we know x, y, and r, we can find the remaining trigonometric functions of θ.

$$\sin\theta = \frac{y}{r} = \frac{-15}{17} = -\frac{15}{17}$$
$$\tan\theta = \frac{y}{x} = \frac{-15}{8} = -\frac{15}{8}$$
$$\csc\theta = \frac{r}{y} = \frac{17}{-15} = -\frac{17}{15}$$
$$\sec\theta = \frac{r}{x} = \frac{17}{8}$$
$$\cot\theta = \frac{x}{y} = \frac{8}{-15} = -\frac{8}{15}$$

29. Because the tangent is negative and the sine is positive, θ lies in quadrant II. In quadrant II, x is negative and y is positive. Thus,
$$\tan\theta = -\frac{2}{3} = \frac{y}{x} = \frac{2}{-3}, \; x = -3, \; y = 2.$$
Furthermore,
$$r = \sqrt{x^2 + y^2} = \sqrt{(-3)^2 + 2^2} = \sqrt{9+4} = \sqrt{13}$$
Now that we know x, y, and r, we can find the remaining trigonometric functions of θ.
$$\sin\theta = \frac{y}{r} = \frac{2}{\sqrt{13}} = \frac{2}{\sqrt{13}} \cdot \frac{\sqrt{13}}{\sqrt{13}} = \frac{2\sqrt{13}}{13}$$
$$\cos\theta = \frac{x}{r} = \frac{-3}{\sqrt{13}} = \frac{-3}{\sqrt{13}} \cdot \frac{\sqrt{13}}{\sqrt{13}} = -\frac{3\sqrt{13}}{13}$$
$$\csc\theta = \frac{r}{y} = \frac{\sqrt{13}}{2}$$
$$\sec\theta = \frac{r}{x} = \frac{\sqrt{13}}{-3} = -\frac{\sqrt{13}}{3}$$
$$\cot\theta = \frac{x}{y} = \frac{-3}{2} = -\frac{3}{2}$$

31. Because the tangent is positive and the cosine is negative, θ lies in quadrant III. In quadrant III, x is negative and y is negative. Thus, $\tan\theta = \frac{4}{3} = \frac{y}{x} = \frac{-4}{-3}, x = -3, y = -4.$
Furthermore,
$$r = \sqrt{x^2 + y^2} = \sqrt{(-3)^2 + (-4)^2} = \sqrt{9+16} = \sqrt{25} = 5$$
Now that we know x, y, and r, we can find the remaining trigonometric functions of θ.
$$\sin\theta = \frac{y}{r} = \frac{-4}{5} = -\frac{4}{5}$$
$$\cos\theta = \frac{x}{r} = \frac{-3}{5} = -\frac{3}{5}$$
$$\csc\theta = \frac{r}{y} = \frac{5}{-4} = -\frac{5}{4}$$
$$\sec\theta = \frac{r}{x} = \frac{5}{-3} = -\frac{5}{3}$$
$$\cot\theta = \frac{x}{y} = \frac{-3}{-4} = \frac{3}{4}$$

33. Because the secant is negative and the tangent is positive, θ lies in quadrant III. In quadrant III, x is negative and y is negative.

Thus, $\sec\theta = -3 = \frac{r}{x} = \frac{3}{-1}, \; x = -1, r = 3.$
Furthermore,
$$x^2 + y^2 = r^2$$
$$(-1)^2 + y^2 = 3^2$$
$$y^2 = 9 - 1 = 8$$
$$y = -\sqrt{8} = -2\sqrt{2}$$
Now that we know x, y, and r, we can find the remaining trigonometric functions of θ.
$$\sin\theta = \frac{y}{r} = \frac{-2\sqrt{2}}{3} = -\frac{2\sqrt{2}}{3}$$
$$\cos\theta = \frac{x}{r} = \frac{-1}{3} = -\frac{1}{3}$$
$$\tan\theta = \frac{y}{x} = \frac{-2\sqrt{2}}{-1} = 2\sqrt{2}$$
$$\csc\theta = \frac{r}{y} = \frac{3}{-2\sqrt{2}} = \frac{3}{-2\sqrt{2}} \cdot \frac{\sqrt{2}}{\sqrt{2}} = -\frac{3\sqrt{2}}{4}$$
$$\cot\theta = \frac{x}{y} = \frac{-1}{-2\sqrt{2}} = \frac{1}{2\sqrt{2}} \cdot \frac{\sqrt{2}}{\sqrt{2}} = \frac{\sqrt{2}}{4}$$

35. Because $160°$ lies between $90°$ and $180°$, it is in quadrant II. The reference angle is $\theta' = 180° - 160° = 20°$.

37. Because $205°$ lies between $180°$ and $270°$, it is in quadrant III. The reference angle is $\theta' = 205° - 180° = 25°$.

39. Because $355°$ lies between $270°$ and $360°$, it is in quadrant IV. The reference angle is $\theta' = 360° - 355° = 5°$.

41. Because $\frac{7\pi}{4}$ lies between $\frac{3\pi}{2} = \frac{6\pi}{4}$ and $2\pi = \frac{8\pi}{4}$, it is in quadrant IV. The reference angle is $\theta' = 2\pi - \frac{7\pi}{4} = \frac{8\pi}{4} - \frac{7\pi}{4} = \frac{\pi}{4}$.

43. Because $\frac{5\pi}{6}$ lies between $\frac{\pi}{2} = \frac{3\pi}{6}$ and $\pi = \frac{6\pi}{6}$, it is in quadrant II. The reference angle is $\theta' = \pi - \frac{5\pi}{6} = \frac{6\pi}{6} - \frac{5\pi}{6} = \frac{\pi}{6}$.

45. Because $-150°$ lies between $-90°$ and $-180°$, it is in quadrant III. The reference angle is $\theta' = 180° - 150° = 30°$.

47. Because $-335°$ lies between $-270°$ and $-360°$, it is in quadrant I. The reference angle is $\theta' = 360° - 335° = 25°$.

49. Because 4.7 lies between $\pi \approx 3.14$ and $\dfrac{3\pi}{2} \approx 4.71$, it is in quadrant III. The reference angle is $\theta' = 4.7 - \pi \approx 1.56$.

51. $225°$ lies in quadrant III. The reference angle is $\theta' = 225° - 180° = 45°$.

$$\cos 45° = \frac{\sqrt{2}}{2}$$

Because the cosine is negative in quadrant III, $\cos 225° = -\cos 45° = -\dfrac{\sqrt{2}}{2}$.

53. $210°$ lies in quadrant III. The reference angle is $\theta' = 210° - 180° = 30°$.

$$\tan 30° = \frac{\sqrt{3}}{3}$$

Because the tangent is positive in quadrant III, $\tan 210° = \tan 30° = \dfrac{\sqrt{3}}{3}$.

55. $420°$ lies in quadrant I. The reference angle is $\theta' = 420° - 360° = 60°$.

$$\tan 60° = \sqrt{3}$$

Because the tangent is positive in quadrant I, $\tan 420° = \tan 60° = \sqrt{3}$.

57. $\dfrac{2\pi}{3}$ lies in quadrant II. The reference angle is $\theta' = \pi - \dfrac{2\pi}{3} = \dfrac{3\pi}{3} - \dfrac{2\pi}{3} = \dfrac{\pi}{3}$.

$$\sin \frac{\pi}{3} = \frac{\sqrt{3}}{2}$$

Because the sine is positive in quadrant II,

$$\sin \frac{2\pi}{3} = \sin \frac{\pi}{3} = \frac{\sqrt{3}}{2}.$$

59. $\dfrac{7\pi}{6}$ lies in quadrant III. The reference angle is $\theta' = \dfrac{7\pi}{6} - \pi = \dfrac{7\pi}{6} - \dfrac{6\pi}{6} = \dfrac{\pi}{6}$.

$$\csc \frac{\pi}{6} = 2$$

Because the cosecant is negative in quadrant III, $\csc \dfrac{7\pi}{6} = -\csc \dfrac{\pi}{6} = -2$.

61. $\dfrac{9\pi}{4}$ lies in quadrant I. The reference angle is

$$\theta' = \frac{9\pi}{4} - 2\pi = \frac{9\pi}{4} - \frac{8\pi}{4} = \frac{\pi}{4}.$$

$$\tan \frac{\pi}{4} = 1$$

Because the tangent is positive in quadrant I,

$$\tan \frac{9\pi}{4} = \tan \frac{\pi}{4} = 1$$

63. $-240°$ lies in quadrant II. The reference angle is $\theta' = 240° - 180° = 60°$.

$$\sin 60° = \frac{\sqrt{3}}{2}$$

Because the sine is positive in quadrant II,

$$\sin(-240°) = \sin 60° = \frac{\sqrt{3}}{2}.$$

65. $-\dfrac{\pi}{4}$ lies in quadrant IV. The reference angle is $\theta' = \dfrac{\pi}{4}$.

$$\tan \frac{\pi}{4} = 1$$

Because the tangent is negative in quadrant IV, $\tan\left(-\dfrac{\pi}{4}\right) = -\tan \dfrac{\pi}{4} = -1$

67.–71. Answers may vary.

Section 5.4

Checkpoint Exercises

1. The point P on the unit circle that corresponds to $t = \pi$ has coordinates $(-1, 0)$. We use $x = -1$ and $y = 0$ to find the values of the trigonometric functions.

$$\sin \pi = y = 0$$
$$\cos \pi = x = -1$$
$$\tan \pi = \frac{y}{x} = \frac{0}{-1} = 0$$
$$\sec \pi = \frac{1}{x} = \frac{1}{-1} = -1$$

By definition, $\csc t = \frac{1}{y}$ and $\cot t = \frac{x}{y}$, because $y = 0$, $\csc \pi$ and $\cot \pi$ are undefined.

2. **a.** $\cos(-60°) = \cos 60° = \dfrac{1}{2}$

   b. $\tan\left(-\dfrac{\pi}{6}\right) = -\tan\dfrac{\pi}{6} = -\dfrac{\sqrt{3}}{3}$

3. **a.** $\cos 405° = \cos(360° + 45°)$
   $$= \cos 45° = \dfrac{\sqrt{2}}{2}$$

   b. $\tan\dfrac{7\pi}{3} = \tan\left(2\pi + \dfrac{\pi}{3}\right) = \tan\dfrac{\pi}{3} = \sqrt{3}$

Exercise Set 5.4

1. The point P on the unit circle has coordinates $\left(-\dfrac{15}{17}, \dfrac{8}{17}\right)$. We use $x = -\dfrac{15}{17}$ and $y = \dfrac{8}{17}$ to find the values of the trigonometric functions.

$$\sin t = y = \frac{8}{17}$$
$$\cos t = x = -\frac{15}{17}$$
$$\tan t = \frac{y}{x} = \frac{\frac{8}{17}}{-\frac{15}{17}} = \frac{8}{17}\left(-\frac{17}{15}\right) = -\frac{8}{15}$$
$$\csc t = \frac{1}{y} = \frac{1}{\frac{8}{17}} = 1 \cdot \frac{17}{8} = \frac{17}{8}$$
$$\sec t = \frac{1}{x} = \frac{1}{-\frac{15}{17}} = 1 \cdot -\frac{17}{15} = -\frac{17}{15}$$
$$\cot t = \frac{x}{y} = \frac{-\frac{15}{17}}{\frac{8}{17}} = -\frac{15}{17} \cdot \frac{17}{8} = -\frac{15}{8}$$

3. The point P on the unit circle that cooresponds to $t = -\dfrac{\pi}{4}$ has coordinates $\left(\dfrac{\sqrt{2}}{2}, -\dfrac{\sqrt{2}}{2}\right)$. We use $x = \dfrac{\sqrt{2}}{2}$ and $y = -\dfrac{\sqrt{2}}{2}$ to find the values of the trigonometric functions.

$$\sin\left(-\frac{\pi}{4}\right) = y = -\frac{\sqrt{2}}{2}$$
$$\cos\left(-\frac{\pi}{4}\right) = x = \frac{\sqrt{2}}{2}$$
$$\tan\left(-\frac{\pi}{4}\right) = \frac{y}{x} = \frac{-\frac{\sqrt{2}}{2}}{\frac{\sqrt{2}}{2}} = -\frac{\sqrt{2}}{2} \cdot \frac{2}{\sqrt{2}} = -1$$
$$\csc\left(-\frac{\pi}{4}\right) = \frac{1}{y} = \frac{1}{-\frac{\sqrt{2}}{2}} = 1 \cdot \left(-\frac{2}{\sqrt{2}}\right) = -\frac{2}{\sqrt{2}}$$
$$= -\frac{2}{\sqrt{2}} \cdot \frac{\sqrt{2}}{\sqrt{2}} = -\frac{2\sqrt{2}}{2} = -\sqrt{2}$$
$$\sec\left(-\frac{\pi}{4}\right) = \frac{1}{x} = \frac{1}{\frac{\sqrt{2}}{2}} = 1 \cdot \frac{2}{\sqrt{2}} = \frac{2}{\sqrt{2}} = \frac{2}{\sqrt{2}} \cdot \frac{\sqrt{2}}{\sqrt{2}}$$
$$= \frac{2\sqrt{2}}{2} = \sqrt{2}$$
$$\cot\left(-\frac{\pi}{4}\right) = \frac{x}{y} = \frac{\frac{\sqrt{2}}{2}}{-\frac{\sqrt{2}}{2}} = \frac{\sqrt{2}}{2}\left(-\frac{2}{\sqrt{2}}\right) = -1$$

5. $\sin(-45°) = -\sin 45° = -\dfrac{\sqrt{2}}{2}$

7. $\sec\left(-\dfrac{\pi}{3}\right) = \sec\left(\dfrac{\pi}{3}\right) = 2$

9. $\cos 585° = \cos(360° + 225°)$
$= \cos 225° = -\cos 45°$
$= -\dfrac{\sqrt{2}}{2}$

11. $\cot\dfrac{7\pi}{3} = \cot\left(2\pi + \dfrac{\pi}{3}\right) = \cot\dfrac{\pi}{3} = \dfrac{\sqrt{3}}{3}$

13. a. $H = 12 + 8.3\sin\left[\dfrac{2\pi}{365}(80-80)\right]$
$= 12 + 8.3\sin 0 = 12 + 8.3(0)$
$= 12$
There are 12 hours of daylight in Fairbanks on March 21.

b. $H = 12 + 8.3\sin\left[\dfrac{2\pi}{365}(172-80)\right]$
$\approx 12 + 8.3\sin(1.5837)$
≈ 20.3
There are about 20.3 hours of daylight in Fairbanks on June 21.

c. $H = 12 + 8.3\sin\left[\dfrac{2\pi}{365}(355-80)\right]$
$\approx 12 + 8.3\sin(4.7339)$
≈ 3.7
There are about 3.7 hours of daylight in Fairbanks on December 21.

15. a. For $t = 7$,
$E = \sin\dfrac{\pi}{14}\cdot 7 = \sin\dfrac{\pi}{2} = 1$;
For $t = 14$,
$E = \sin\dfrac{\pi}{14}\cdot 14 = \sin\pi = 0$;
For $t = 21$,
$E = \sin\dfrac{\pi}{14}\cdot 21 = \sin\dfrac{3\pi}{2} = -1$;

For $t = 28$,
$E = \sin\dfrac{\pi}{14}\cdot 28 = \sin 2\pi = \sin 0 = 0$;
For $t = 35$,
$E = \sin\dfrac{\pi}{14}\cdot 35 = \sin\dfrac{5\pi}{2} = \sin\dfrac{\pi}{2} = 1$;
Observations may vary.

b. Because $E(35) = E(7) = 1$, the period is $35 - 7 = 28$ or 28 days.

17.–21. Answers may vary.

23. 91° lies in quadrant II. The reference angle is $\theta' = 180° - 91° = 89°$.
Becasue the cosine is negative in quadrant II, $\cos 91° = -\cos 89°$.
Likewise, 92°, 93°, . . . , 178°, and 179° all lie in quadrant II. Their reference angles are
$\theta' = 180° - 92° = 88°$
$\theta' = 180° - 93° = 87°$
$\vdots$
$\theta' = 180° - 178° = 2°$
$\theta' = 180° - 179° = 1°$
Because the cosine is negative in quadrant II, $\cos 92° = -\cos 88°$
$\cos 93° = -\cos 87°$
$\vdots$
$\cos 178° = -\cos 2°$
$\cos 179° = -\cos 1°$
Also, $\cos 180° = -1 = -\cos 0°$
Thus,
$\cos 0° + \cos 1° + \cdots + \cos 88° + \cos 89° + \cos 90°$
$+ \cos 91° + \cos 92° + \cdots + \cos 179° + \cos 180°$
$= \cos 0° + \cos 1° + \cdots + \cos 88°$
$+ \cos 89° + \cos 90° - \cos 89° - \cos 88° -$
$\cdots - \cos 1° - \cos 0°$
$= \cos 90°$
$= 0$

25. Because $f(x) = \sin x$, $f(x)$ is an odd function. Thus, $f(-a) = -f(a)$. Therefore,
$f(a) + 2f(-a) = f(a) - 2f(a)$
$= \dfrac{1}{4} - 2\cdot\dfrac{1}{4}$
$= -\dfrac{1}{4}$

Section 5.5

Checkpoint Exercises

1. The equation $y = 3\sin x$ is of the form
    $y = A\sin x$ with $A = 3$. Thus, the amplitude
    is $|A| = |3| = 3$. The period for both
    $y = 3\sin x$ and $y = \sin x$ is 2π. We find the
    three x–intercepts, the maximum point, and
    the minimum point on the interval $[0, 2\pi]$
    by dividing the period, 2π, by 4,
    $\dfrac{\text{period}}{4} = \dfrac{2\pi}{4} = \dfrac{\pi}{2}$, then by adding quarter-
    periods to generate x-values for each of the
    key points. The five x-values are
    $x = 0$
    $x = 0 + \dfrac{\pi}{2} = \dfrac{\pi}{2}$
    $x = \dfrac{\pi}{2} + \dfrac{\pi}{2} = \pi$
    $x = \pi + \dfrac{\pi}{2} = \dfrac{3\pi}{2}$
    $x = \dfrac{3\pi}{2} + \dfrac{\pi}{2} - 2\pi$
    We evaluate the function at each value of x.

x	$y = 3\sin x$	coordinates
0	$y = 3\sin 0 = 3 \cdot 0 = 0$	$(0, 0)$
$\dfrac{\pi}{2}$	$y = 3\sin\dfrac{\pi}{2} = 3 \cdot 1 = 3$	$\left(\dfrac{\pi}{2}, 3\right)$
π	$y = 3\sin \pi = 3 \cdot 0 = 0$	$(\pi, 0)$
$\dfrac{3\pi}{2}$	$y = 3\sin\dfrac{3\pi}{2}$ $= 3 \cdot (-1) = -3$	$\left(\dfrac{3\pi}{2}, -3\right)$
2π	$y = 3\sin 2\pi = 3 \cdot 0 = 0$	$(2\pi, 0)$

Connect the five points with a smooth curve
and graph one complete cycle of the given
function with the graph of $y = \sin x$.

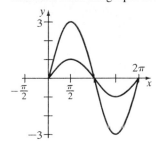

2. The equation $y = -\dfrac{1}{2}\sin x$ is of the form
    $y = A\sin x$ with $A = -\dfrac{1}{2}$. Thus, the
    amplitude is $|A| = \left|-\dfrac{1}{2}\right| = \dfrac{1}{2}$. The period for
    both $y = -\dfrac{1}{2}\sin x$ and $y = \sin x$ is 2π.
    Find the x–values for the five key points by
    dividing the period, 2π, by 4,
    $\dfrac{\text{period}}{4} = \dfrac{2\pi}{4} = \dfrac{\pi}{2}$, then by adding quarter-
    periods. The five x-values are
    $x = 0$
    $x = 0 + \dfrac{\pi}{2} = \dfrac{\pi}{2}$
    $x = \dfrac{\pi}{2} + \dfrac{\pi}{2} = \pi$
    $x = \pi + \dfrac{\pi}{2} = \dfrac{3\pi}{2}$
    $x = \dfrac{3\pi}{2} + \dfrac{\pi}{2} = 2\pi$
    We evaluate the function at each value of x.

x	$y = -\dfrac{1}{2}\sin x$	coordinates
0	$y = -\dfrac{1}{2}\sin 0$ $= -\dfrac{1}{2}\cdot 0 = 0$	$(0,\,0)$
$\dfrac{\pi}{2}$	$y = -\dfrac{1}{2}\sin\dfrac{\pi}{2}$ $= -\dfrac{1}{2}\cdot 1 = -\dfrac{1}{2}$	$\left(\dfrac{\pi}{2},\,-\dfrac{1}{2}\right)$
π	$y = -\dfrac{1}{2}\sin \pi$ $= -\dfrac{1}{2}\cdot 0 = 0$	$(\pi,\,0)$
$\dfrac{3\pi}{2}$	$y = -\dfrac{1}{2}\sin\dfrac{3\pi}{2}$ $= -\dfrac{1}{2}(-1) = \dfrac{1}{2}$	$\left(\dfrac{3\pi}{2},\,\dfrac{1}{2}\right)$
2π	$y = -\dfrac{1}{2}\sin 2\pi$ $= -\dfrac{1}{2}\cdot 0 = 0$	$(2\pi,\,0)$

Connect the five key points with a smooth curve and graph one complete cycle of the given function with the graph of $y = \sin x$.

Extend the pattern of each graph to the left and right as desired.

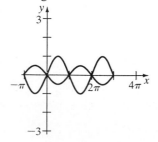

3. The equation $y = 2\sin\dfrac{1}{2}x$ is of the form

$y = A\sin Bx$ with $A = 2$ and $B = \dfrac{1}{2}$.

The amplitude is $|A| = |2| = 2$.

The period is $\dfrac{2\pi}{B} = \dfrac{2\pi}{\frac{1}{2}} = 4\pi$.

Find the x–values for the five key points by dividing the period, 4π, by 4,

$\dfrac{\text{period}}{4} = \dfrac{4\pi}{4} = \pi$, then by adding quarter-periods. The five x-values are

$x = 0$
$x = 0 + \pi = \pi$
$x = \pi + \pi = 2\pi$
$x = 2\pi + \pi = 3\pi$
$x = 3\pi + \pi = 4\pi$

We evaluate the function at each value of x.

x	$y = 2\sin\dfrac{1}{2}x$	coordinates
0	$y = 2\sin\left(\dfrac{1}{2}\cdot 0\right)$ $= 2\sin 0$ $= 2\cdot 0 = 0$	$(0,\,0)$
π	$y = 2\sin\left(\dfrac{1}{2}\cdot \pi\right)$ $= 2\sin\dfrac{\pi}{2} = 2\cdot 1 = 2$	$(\pi,\,2)$
2π	$y = 2\sin\left(\dfrac{1}{2}\cdot 2\pi\right)$ $= 2\sin \pi = 2\cdot 0 = 0$	$(2\pi,\,0)$
3π	$y = 2\sin\left(\dfrac{1}{2}\cdot 3\pi\right)$ $= 2\sin\dfrac{3\pi}{2}$ $= 2\cdot(-1) = -2$	$(3\pi,\,-2)$
4π	$y = 2\sin\left(\dfrac{1}{2}\cdot 4\pi\right)$ $= 2\sin 2\pi = 2\cdot 0 = 0$	$(4\pi,\,0)$

Connect the five key points with a smooth curve and graph one complete cycle of the given function. Extend the pattern of the graph another full period to the right.

4. The equation $y = 3\sin\left(2x - \dfrac{\pi}{3}\right)$ is of the form $y = A\sin(Bx - C)$ with $A = 3$, $B = 2$, and $C = \dfrac{\pi}{3}$. The amplitude is $|A| = |3| = 3$.

The period is $\dfrac{2\pi}{B} = \dfrac{2\pi}{2} = \pi$.

The phase shift is $\dfrac{C}{B} = \dfrac{\frac{\pi}{3}}{2} = \dfrac{\pi}{3} \cdot \dfrac{1}{2} = \dfrac{\pi}{6}$.

Find the x-values for the five key points by dividing the period, π, by 4, $\dfrac{\text{period}}{4} = \dfrac{\pi}{4}$, then by adding quarter-periods to the value of x where the cycle begins, $x = \dfrac{\pi}{6}$. The five x-values are

$x = \dfrac{\pi}{6}$

$x = \dfrac{\pi}{6} + \dfrac{\pi}{4} = \dfrac{2\pi}{12} + \dfrac{3\pi}{12} = \dfrac{5\pi}{12}$

$x = \dfrac{5\pi}{12} + \dfrac{\pi}{4} = \dfrac{5\pi}{12} + \dfrac{3\pi}{12} = \dfrac{8\pi}{12} = \dfrac{2\pi}{3}$

$x = \dfrac{2\pi}{3} + \dfrac{\pi}{4} = \dfrac{8\pi}{12} + \dfrac{3\pi}{12} = \dfrac{11\pi}{12}$

$x = \dfrac{11\pi}{12} + \dfrac{\pi}{4} = \dfrac{11\pi}{12} + \dfrac{3\pi}{12} = \dfrac{14\pi}{12} = \dfrac{7\pi}{6}$

We evaluate the function at each value of x.

x	$y = 3\sin\left(2x - \dfrac{\pi}{3}\right)$	coordinates
$\dfrac{\pi}{6}$	$\begin{aligned} y &= 3\sin\left(2 \cdot \dfrac{\pi}{6} - \dfrac{\pi}{3}\right) \\ &= 3\sin 0 = 3 \cdot 0 = 0 \end{aligned}$	$\left(\dfrac{\pi}{6}, 0\right)$
$\dfrac{5\pi}{12}$	$\begin{aligned} y &= 3\sin\left(2 \cdot \dfrac{5\pi}{12} - \dfrac{\pi}{3}\right) \\ &= 3\sin\left(\dfrac{5\pi}{6} - \dfrac{2\pi}{6}\right) \\ &= 3\sin\dfrac{3\pi}{6} = 3\sin\dfrac{\pi}{2} \\ &= 3 \cdot 1 = 3 \end{aligned}$	$\left(\dfrac{5\pi}{12}, 3\right)$
$\dfrac{2\pi}{3}$	$\begin{aligned} y &= 3\sin\left(2 \cdot \dfrac{2\pi}{3} - \dfrac{\pi}{3}\right) \\ &= 3\sin\left(\dfrac{4\pi}{3} - \dfrac{\pi}{3}\right) \\ &= 3\sin\dfrac{3\pi}{3} = 3\sin\pi \\ &= 3 \cdot 0 = 0 \end{aligned}$	$\left(\dfrac{2\pi}{3}, 0\right)$
$\dfrac{11\pi}{12}$	$\begin{aligned} y &= 3\sin\left(2 \cdot \dfrac{11\pi}{12} - \dfrac{\pi}{3}\right) \\ &= 3\sin\left(\dfrac{11\pi}{6} - \dfrac{2\pi}{6}\right) \\ &= 3\sin\dfrac{9\pi}{6} = 3\sin\dfrac{3\pi}{2} \\ &= 3(-1) = -3 \end{aligned}$	$\left(\dfrac{11\pi}{12}, 3\right)$
$\dfrac{7\pi}{6}$	$\begin{aligned} y &= 3\sin\left(2 \cdot \dfrac{7\pi}{6} - \dfrac{\pi}{3}\right) \\ &= 3\sin\dfrac{6\pi}{3} = 3\sin 2\pi \\ &= 3 \cdot 0 = 0 \end{aligned}$	$\left(\dfrac{7\pi}{6}, 0\right)$

Connect the five key points with a smooth curve and graph one complete cycle of the given graph.

5. The equation $y = -4\cos\pi x$ is of the form
   $y = A\cos Bx$ with $A = -4$, and $B = \pi$.
   Thus, the amplitude is $|A| = |-4| = 4$.

   The period is $\dfrac{2\pi}{B} = \dfrac{2\pi}{\pi} = 2$.

   Find the x-values for the five key points by
   dividing the period, 2, by 4,
   $\dfrac{\text{period}}{4} = \dfrac{2}{4} = \dfrac{1}{2}$, then by adding quarter-
   periods to the value of x where the cycle
   begins. The five x-values are
   $x = 0$

   $x = 0 + \dfrac{1}{2} = \dfrac{1}{2}$

   $x = \dfrac{1}{2} + \dfrac{1}{2} = 1$

   $x = 1 + \dfrac{1}{2} = \dfrac{3}{2}$

   $x = \dfrac{3}{2} + \dfrac{1}{2} = 2$

   We evaluate the function at each value of x.

x	$y = -4\cos\pi x$	coordinates
0	$y = -4\cos(\pi \cdot 0)$ $= -4\cos 0$ $= -4 \cdot 1 = -4$	$(0, -4)$
$\dfrac{1}{2}$	$y = -4\cos\left(\pi \cdot \dfrac{1}{2}\right)$ $= -4\cos\dfrac{\pi}{2}$ $= -4 \cdot 0 = 0$	$\left(\dfrac{1}{2}, 0\right)$
1	$y = -4\cos(\pi \cdot 1)$ $= -4\cos\pi$ $= -4 \cdot (-1) = 4$	$(1, 4)$
$\dfrac{3}{2}$	$y = -4\cos\left(\pi \cdot \dfrac{3}{2}\right)$ $= -4\cos\dfrac{3\pi}{2}$ $= -4 \cdot 0 = 0$	$\left(\dfrac{3}{2}, 0\right)$
2	$y = -4\cos(\pi \cdot 2)$ $= -4\cos 2\pi$ $= -4 \cdot 1 = -4$	$(2, -4)$

Connect the five key points with a smooth
curve and graph one complete cycle of the
given function. Extend the pattern of the
graph another full period to the left.

6. $y = \dfrac{3}{2}\cos(2x + \pi) = \dfrac{3}{2}\cos(2x - (-\pi))$
   The equation is of the form
   $y = A\cos(Bx - C)$ with $A = \dfrac{3}{2}$, $B = 2$, and
   $C = -\pi$.

   Thus, the amplitude is $|A| = \left|\dfrac{3}{2}\right| = \dfrac{3}{2}$.

   The period is $\dfrac{2\pi}{B} = \dfrac{2\pi}{2} = \pi$.

   The phase shift is $\dfrac{C}{B} = \dfrac{-\pi}{2} = -\dfrac{\pi}{2}$.

   Find the x-values for the five key points by

   dividing the period, π, by 4, $\dfrac{\text{period}}{4} = \dfrac{\pi}{4}$,

   then by adding quarter-periods to the value

   of x where the cycle begins, $x = -\dfrac{\pi}{2}$.

   The five x-values are

$$x = -\frac{\pi}{2}$$

$$x = -\frac{\pi}{2} + \frac{\pi}{4} = -\frac{\pi}{4}$$

$$x = -\frac{\pi}{4} + \frac{\pi}{4} = 0$$

$$x = 0 + \frac{\pi}{4} = \frac{\pi}{4}$$

$$x = \frac{\pi}{4} + \frac{\pi}{4} = \frac{\pi}{2}$$

We evaluate the function at each value of x.

x	$y = \dfrac{3}{2}\cos(2x + \pi)$	coordinates
$-\dfrac{\pi}{2}$	$y = \dfrac{3}{2}\cos(-\pi + \pi)$ $= \dfrac{3}{2} \cdot 1 = \dfrac{3}{2}$	$\left(-\dfrac{\pi}{2}, \dfrac{3}{2}\right)$
$-\dfrac{\pi}{4}$	$y = \dfrac{3}{2}\cos\left(-\dfrac{\pi}{2} + \pi\right)$ $= \dfrac{3}{2} \cdot 0 = 0$	$\left(-\dfrac{\pi}{4}, 0\right)$
0	$y = \dfrac{3}{2}\cos(0 + \pi)$ $= \dfrac{3}{2} \cdot -1 = -\dfrac{3}{2}$	$\left(0, -\dfrac{3}{2}\right)$
$\dfrac{\pi}{4}$	$y = \dfrac{3}{2}\cos\left(\dfrac{\pi}{2} + \pi\right)$ $= \dfrac{3}{2} \cdot 0 = 0$	$\left(\dfrac{\pi}{4}, 0\right)$
$\dfrac{\pi}{2}$	$y = \dfrac{3}{2}\cos(\pi + \pi)$ $= \dfrac{3}{2} \cdot 1 = \dfrac{3}{2}$	$\left(\dfrac{\pi}{2}, \dfrac{3}{2}\right)$

Connect the five key points with a smooth curve and graph one complete cycle of the given graph.

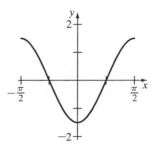

7. The graph of $y = 2\cos x + 1$ is the graph of $y = 2\cos x$ shifted one unit upwards. The period for both functions is 2π. The quarter-period is $\dfrac{2\pi}{4}$ or $\dfrac{\pi}{2}$. The cycle begins at $x = 0$. Add quarter-periods to generate x-values for the key points.

$$x = 0$$

$$x = 0 + \frac{\pi}{2} = \frac{\pi}{2}$$

$$x = \frac{\pi}{2} + \frac{\pi}{2} = \pi$$

$$x = \pi + \frac{\pi}{2} = \frac{3\pi}{2}$$

$$x = \frac{3\pi}{2} + \frac{\pi}{2} = 2\pi$$

We evaluate the function at each value of x.

x	$y = 2\cos x + 1$	coordinates
0	$y = 2\cos 0 + 1$ $= 2 \cdot 1 + 1 = 3$	$(0, 3)$
$\dfrac{\pi}{2}$	$y = 2\cos\dfrac{\pi}{2} + 1$ $= 2 \cdot 0 + 1 = 1$	$\left(\dfrac{\pi}{2}, 1\right)$
π	$y = 2\cos\pi + 1$ $= 2 \cdot (-1) + 1 = -1$	$(\pi, -1)$
$\dfrac{3\pi}{2}$	$y = 2\cos\dfrac{3\pi}{2} + 1$ $= 2 \cdot 0 + 1 = 1$	$\left(\dfrac{3\pi}{2}, 1\right)$
2π	$y = 2\cos 2\pi + 1$ $= 2 \cdot 1 + 1 = 3$	$(2\pi, 3)$
2π	$y = 2\cos 2\pi + 1$ $= 2 \cdot 1 + 1 = 3$	$(2\pi, 3)$

By connecting the points with a smooth curve, we obtain one period of the graph.

8. A, the amplitude, is the maximum value of y. The graph shows that this maximum value is 4, Thus, $A = 4$. The period is $\dfrac{\pi}{2}$, and period $= \dfrac{2\pi}{B}$.

   Thus, $\dfrac{\pi}{2} = \dfrac{2\pi}{B}$
   $$\pi B = 4\pi$$
   $$B = 4$$

   Substitute these values into $y = A \sin Bx$. The graph is modeled by $y = 4 \sin 4x$.

9. Because the hours of daylight ranges from a minimum of 10 hours to a maximum of 14 hours, the curve oscillates about the middle value, 12 hours. Thus, $D = 12$. The maximum number of hours is 2 hours above 12 hours. Thus, $A = 2$. The graph shows that one complete cycle occurs in 12–0, or 12 months. The period is 12. Thus,

   $$12 = \dfrac{2\pi}{B}$$
   $$12B = 2\pi$$
   $$B = \dfrac{2\pi}{12} = \dfrac{\pi}{6}$$

   The graph shows that the starting point of the cycle is shifted from 0 to 3. The phase shift, $\dfrac{C}{B}$, is 3.

$$3 = \dfrac{C}{B}$$
$$3 = \dfrac{C}{\frac{\pi}{6}}$$
$$\dfrac{\pi}{2} = C$$

Substitute these values into $y = A\sin(Bx - C) + D$. The number of hours of daylight is modeled by

$$y = 2\sin\left(\dfrac{\pi}{6}x - \dfrac{\pi}{2}\right) + 12.$$

Exercise Set 5.5

1. The equation $y = 4\sin x$ is of the form $y = A \sin x$ with $A = 4$. Thus, the amplitude is $|A| = |4| = 4$. The period is 2π. The quarter-period is $\dfrac{2\pi}{4}$ or $\dfrac{\pi}{2}$. The cycle begins at $x = 0$. Add quarter-periods to generate x-values for the key points.
   $x = 0$
   $x = 0 + \dfrac{\pi}{2} = \dfrac{\pi}{2}$
   $x = \dfrac{\pi}{2} + \dfrac{\pi}{2} = \pi$
   $x = \pi + \dfrac{\pi}{2} = \dfrac{3\pi}{2}$
   $x = \dfrac{3\pi}{2} + \dfrac{\pi}{2} = 2\pi$

   We evaluate the function at each value of x.

x	$y = 4\sin x$	coordinates
0	$y = 4\sin 0 = 4 \cdot 0 = 0$	$(0, 0)$
$\dfrac{\pi}{2}$	$y = 4\sin\dfrac{\pi}{2} = 4 \cdot 1 = 4$	$\left(\dfrac{\pi}{2}, 4\right)$
π	$y = 4\sin \pi = 4 \cdot 0 = 0$	$(\pi, 0)$
$\dfrac{3\pi}{2}$	$y = 4\sin\dfrac{3\pi}{2}$ $= 4(-1) = -4$	$\left(\dfrac{3\pi}{2}, -4\right)$
2π	$y = 4\sin 2\pi = 4 \cdot 0 = 0$	$(2\pi, 0)$

Connect the five key points with a smooth curve and graph one complete cycle of the given function with the graph of $y = \sin x$.

3. The equation $y = \dfrac{1}{3} \sin x$ is of the form

$y = A \sin x$ with $A = \dfrac{1}{3}$. Thus, the amplitude

is $|A| = \left| \dfrac{1}{3} \right| = \dfrac{1}{3}$. The period is 2π. The

quarter-period is $\dfrac{2\pi}{4}$ or $\dfrac{\pi}{2}$. The cycle

begins at $x = 0$. Add quarter-periods to generate x-values for the key points.
$x = 0$

$x = 0 + \dfrac{\pi}{2} = \dfrac{\pi}{2}$

$x = \dfrac{\pi}{2} + \dfrac{\pi}{2} = \pi$

$x = \pi + \dfrac{\pi}{2} = \dfrac{3\pi}{2}$

$x = \dfrac{3\pi}{2} + \dfrac{\pi}{2} = 2\pi$

We evaluate the function at each value of x.

x	$y = \dfrac{1}{3} \sin x$	coordinates
0	$y = \dfrac{1}{3} \sin 0 = \dfrac{1}{3} \cdot 0 = 0$	$(0, 0)$
$\dfrac{\pi}{2}$	$y = \dfrac{1}{3} \sin \dfrac{\pi}{2} = \dfrac{1}{3} \cdot 1 = \dfrac{1}{3}$	$\left(\dfrac{\pi}{2}, \dfrac{1}{3} \right)$
π	$y = \dfrac{1}{3} \sin \pi = \dfrac{1}{3} \cdot 0 = 0$	$(\pi, 0)$

$\dfrac{3\pi}{2}$	$y = \dfrac{1}{3} \sin \dfrac{3\pi}{2}$ $= \dfrac{1}{3}(-1) = -\dfrac{1}{3}$	$\left(\dfrac{3\pi}{2}, -\dfrac{1}{3} \right)$
2π	$y = \dfrac{1}{3} \sin 2\pi = \dfrac{1}{3} \cdot 0 = 0$	$(2\pi, 0)$

Connect the five key points with a smooth curve and graph one complete cycle of the given function with the graph of $y = \sin x$.

5. The equation $y = -3 \sin x$ is of the form
$y = A \sin x$ with $A = -3$. Thus, the amplitude
is $|A| = |-3| = 3$. The period is 2π. The

quarter-period is $\dfrac{2\pi}{4}$ or $\dfrac{\pi}{2}$. The cycle

begins at $x = 0$. Add quarter-periods to generate x-values for the key points.
$x = 0$

$x = 0 + \dfrac{\pi}{2} = \dfrac{\pi}{2}$

$x = \dfrac{\pi}{2} + \dfrac{\pi}{2} = \pi$

$x = \pi + \dfrac{\pi}{2} = \dfrac{3\pi}{2}$

$x = \dfrac{3\pi}{2} + \dfrac{\pi}{2} = 2\pi$

We evaluate the function at each value of x.

x	$y = -3\sin x$	coordinates
0	$y = -3\sin x$ $= -3 \cdot 0 = 0$	$(0, 0)$
$\dfrac{\pi}{2}$	$y = -3\sin \dfrac{\pi}{2}$ $= -3 \cdot 1 = -3$	$\left(\dfrac{\pi}{2}, -3\right)$
π	$y = -3\sin \pi$ $= -3 \cdot 0 = 0$	$(\pi, 0)$
$\dfrac{3\pi}{2}$	$y = -3\sin \dfrac{3\pi}{2}$ $= -3(-1) = 3$	$\left(\dfrac{3\pi}{2}, 3\right)$
2π	$y = -3\sin 2\pi$ $= -3 \cdot 0 = 0$	$(2\pi, 0)$

Connect the five key points with a smooth curve and graph one complete cycle of the given function with the graph of $y = \sin x$.

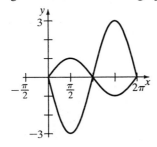

7. The equation $y = \sin 2x$ is of the form $y = A \sin Bx$ with $A = 1$ and $B = 2$. The amplitude is $|A| = |1| = 1$. The period is $\dfrac{2\pi}{B} = \dfrac{2\pi}{2} = \pi$. The quarter-period is $\dfrac{\pi}{4}$. The cycle begins at $x = 0$. Add quarter-periods to generate x-values for the key points.

$x = 0$

$x = 0 + \dfrac{\pi}{4}$

$x = \dfrac{\pi}{4} + \dfrac{\pi}{4} = \dfrac{\pi}{2}$

$x = \dfrac{\pi}{2} + \dfrac{\pi}{4} = \dfrac{3\pi}{4}$

$x = \dfrac{3\pi}{4} + \dfrac{\pi}{4} = \pi$

We evaluate the function at each value of x.

x	$y = \sin 2x$	coordinates
0	$y = \sin 2 \cdot 0 = \sin 0 = 0$	$(0, 0)$
$\dfrac{\pi}{4}$	$y = \sin\left(2 \cdot \dfrac{\pi}{4}\right)$ $= \sin \dfrac{\pi}{2} = 1$	$\left(\dfrac{\pi}{4}, 1\right)$
$\dfrac{\pi}{2}$	$y = \sin\left(2 \cdot \dfrac{\pi}{2}\right)$ $= \sin \pi = 0$	$\left(\dfrac{\pi}{2}, 0\right)$
$\dfrac{3\pi}{4}$	$y = \sin\left(2 \cdot \dfrac{3\pi}{4}\right)$ $= \sin \dfrac{3\pi}{2} = -1$	$\left(\dfrac{3\pi}{4}, -1\right)$
π	$y = \sin(2 \cdot \pi)$ $= \sin 2\pi = 0$	$(\pi, 0)$

Connect the five key points with a smooth curve and graph one complete cycle of the given function.

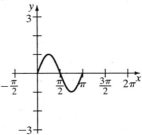

9. The equation $y = 3\sin \dfrac{1}{2}x$ is of the form $y = A \sin Bx$ with $A = 3$ and $B = \dfrac{1}{2}$. The amplitude is $|A| = |3| = 3$. The period is $\dfrac{2\pi}{B} = \dfrac{2\pi}{\frac{1}{2}} = 2\pi \cdot 2 = 4\pi$. The quarter-period is $\dfrac{4\pi}{4} = \pi$. The cycle begins at $x = 0$. Add quarter-periods to generate x-values for the key points.

$x = 0$
$x = 0 + \pi = \pi$
$x = \pi + \pi = 2\pi$
$x = 2\pi + \pi = 3\pi$
$x = 3\pi + \pi = 4\pi$
We evaluate the function at each value of x.

x	$y = 3\sin\dfrac{1}{2}x$	coordinates
0	$y = 3\sin\left(\dfrac{1}{2}\cdot 0\right)$ $= 3\sin 0 = 3\cdot 0 = 0$	$(0, 0)$
π	$y = 3\sin\left(\dfrac{1}{2}\cdot\pi\right)$ $= 3\sin\dfrac{\pi}{2} = 3\cdot 1 = 3$	$(\pi, 3)$
2π	$y = 3\sin\left(\dfrac{1}{2}\cdot 2\pi\right)$ $= 3\sin\pi = 3\cdot 0 = 0$	$(2\pi, 0)$
3π	$y = 3\sin\left(\dfrac{1}{2}\cdot 3\pi\right)$ $= 3\sin\dfrac{3\pi}{2}$ $= 3(-1) = -3$	$(3\pi, -3)$
4π	$y = 3\sin\left(\dfrac{1}{2}\cdot 4\pi\right)$ $= 3\sin 2\pi = 3\cdot 0 = 0$	$(4\pi, 0)$

Connect the five points with a smooth curve and graph one complete cycle of the given function.

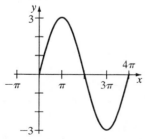

11. The equation $y = 4\sin\pi x$ is of the form $y = A\sin Bx$ with $A = 4$ and $B = \pi$. The amplitude is $|A| = |4| = 4$. The period is $\dfrac{2\pi}{B} = \dfrac{2\pi}{\pi} = 2$. The quarter-period is $\dfrac{2}{4} = \dfrac{1}{2}$. The cycle begins at $x = 0$. Add quarter-periods to generate x-values for the key points.
$x = 0$
$x = 0 + \dfrac{1}{2} = \dfrac{1}{2}$
$x = \dfrac{1}{2} + \dfrac{1}{2} = 1$
$x = 1 + \dfrac{1}{2} = \dfrac{3}{2}$
$x = \dfrac{3}{2} + \dfrac{1}{2} = 2$
We evaluate the function at each value of x.

x	$y = 4\sin\pi x$	coordinates
0	$y = 4\sin(\pi\cdot 0)$ $= 4\sin 0 = 4\cdot 0 = 0$	$(0, 0)$
$\dfrac{1}{2}$	$y = 4\sin\left(\pi\cdot\dfrac{1}{2}\right)$ $= 4\sin\dfrac{\pi}{2} = 4(1) = 4$	$\left(\dfrac{1}{2}, 4\right)$
1	$y = 4\sin(\pi\cdot 1)$ $= 4\sin\pi = 4\cdot 0 = 0$	$(1, 0)$
$\dfrac{3}{2}$	$y = 4\sin\left(\pi\cdot\dfrac{3}{2}\right)$ $= 4\sin\dfrac{3\pi}{2}$ $= 4(-1) = -4$	$\left(\dfrac{3}{2}, -4\right)$
2	$y = 4\sin(\pi\cdot 2)$ $= 4\sin 2\pi = 4\cdot 0 = 0$	$(2, 0)$

Connect the five points with a smooth curve and graph one complete cycle of the given function.

13. The equation $y = -3\sin 2\pi x$ is of the form $y = A\sin Bx$ with $A = -3$ and $B = 2\pi$. The amplitude is $|A| = |-3| = 3$. The period is $\dfrac{2\pi}{B} = \dfrac{2\pi}{2\pi} = 1$. The quarter-period is $\dfrac{1}{4}$. The cycle begins at $x = 0$. Add quarter-periods to generate x-values for the key points.

$x = 0$

$x = 0 + \dfrac{1}{4} = \dfrac{1}{4}$

$x = \dfrac{1}{4} + \dfrac{1}{4} = \dfrac{1}{2}$

$x = \dfrac{1}{2} + \dfrac{1}{4} = \dfrac{3}{4}$

$x = \dfrac{3}{4} + \dfrac{1}{4} = 1$

We evaluate the function at each value of x.

x	$y = -3\sin 2\pi x$	coordinates
0	$y = -3\sin(2\pi \cdot 0)$ $= -3\sin 0$ $= -3 \cdot 0 = 0$	$(0, 0)$
$\dfrac{1}{4}$	$y = -3\sin\left(2\pi \cdot \dfrac{1}{4}\right)$ $= -3\sin\dfrac{\pi}{2}$ $= -3 \cdot 1 = -3$	$\left(\dfrac{1}{4}, -3\right)$
$\dfrac{1}{2}$	$y = -3\sin\left(2\pi \cdot \dfrac{1}{2}\right)$ $= -3\sin\pi$ $= -3 \cdot 0 = 0$	$\left(\dfrac{1}{2}, 0\right)$

$\dfrac{3}{4}$	$y = -3\sin\left(2\pi \cdot \dfrac{3}{4}\right)$ $= -3\sin\dfrac{3\pi}{2}$ $= -3(-1) = 3$	$\left(\dfrac{3}{4}, 3\right)$
1	$y = -3\sin(2\pi \cdot 1)$ $= -3\sin 2\pi$ $= -3 \cdot 0 = 0$	$(1, 0)$

Connect the five points with a smooth curve and graph one complete cycle of the given function.

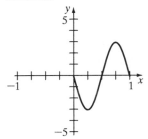

15. The equation $y = -\sin\dfrac{2}{3}x$ is of the form $y = A\sin Bx$ with $A = -1$ and $B = \dfrac{2}{3}$. The amplitude is $|A| = |-1| = 1$. The period is $\dfrac{2\pi}{B} = \dfrac{2\pi}{\frac{2}{3}} = 2\pi \cdot \dfrac{3}{2} = 3\pi$. The quarter-period is $\dfrac{3\pi}{4}$. The cycle begins at $x = 0$. Add quarter-periods to generate x-values for the key points.

$x = 0$

$x = 0 + \dfrac{3\pi}{4} = \dfrac{3\pi}{4}$

$x = \dfrac{3\pi}{4} + \dfrac{3\pi}{4} = \dfrac{3\pi}{2}$

$x = \dfrac{3\pi}{2} + \dfrac{3\pi}{4} = \dfrac{9\pi}{4}$

$x = \dfrac{9\pi}{4} + \dfrac{3\pi}{4} = 3\pi$

We evaluate the function at each value of x.

x	$y = -\sin\dfrac{2}{3}x$	coordinates
0	$y = -\sin\left(\dfrac{2}{3} \cdot 0\right)$ $= -\sin 0 = 0$	$(0, 0)$
$\dfrac{3\pi}{4}$	$y = -\sin\left(\dfrac{2}{3} \cdot \dfrac{3\pi}{4}\right)$ $= -\sin\dfrac{\pi}{2} = -1$	$\left(\dfrac{3\pi}{4}, -1\right)$
$\dfrac{3\pi}{2}$	$y = -\sin\left(\dfrac{2}{3} \cdot \dfrac{3\pi}{2}\right)$ $= -\sin\pi = 0$	$\left(\dfrac{3\pi}{2}, 0\right)$
$\dfrac{9\pi}{4}$	$y = -\sin\left(\dfrac{2}{3} \cdot \dfrac{9\pi}{4}\right)$ $= -\sin\dfrac{3\pi}{2}$ $= -(-1) = 1$	$\left(\dfrac{9\pi}{4}, 1\right)$
3π	$y = -\sin\left(\dfrac{2}{3} \cdot 3\pi\right)$ $= -\sin 2\pi = 0$	$(3\pi, 0)$

Connect the five points with a smooth curve and graph one complete cycle of the given function.

17. The equation $y = \sin(x - \pi)$ is of the form $y = A\sin(Bx - C)$ with $A = 1$, $B = 1$, and $C = \pi$. The amplitude is $|A| = |1| = 1$. The period is $\dfrac{2\pi}{B} = \dfrac{2\pi}{1} = 2\pi$. The phase shift is $\dfrac{C}{B} = \dfrac{\pi}{1} = \pi$. The quarter-period is $\dfrac{2\pi}{4} = \dfrac{\pi}{2}$. The cycle begins at $x = \pi$. Add quarter-periods to generate x-values for the key points.

$$x = \pi$$
$$x = \pi + \frac{\pi}{2} = \frac{3\pi}{2}$$
$$x = \frac{3\pi}{2} + \frac{\pi}{2} = 2\pi$$
$$x = 2\pi + \frac{\pi}{2} = \frac{5\pi}{2}$$
$$x = \frac{5\pi}{2} + \frac{\pi}{2} = 3\pi$$

We evaluate the function at each value of x.

x	$y = \sin(x - \pi)$	coordinates
π	$y = \sin(\pi - \pi)$ $= \sin 0 = 0$	$(\pi, 0)$
$\dfrac{3\pi}{2}$	$y = \sin\left(\dfrac{3\pi}{2} - \pi\right)$ $= \sin\dfrac{\pi}{2} = 1$	$\left(\dfrac{3\pi}{2}, 1\right)$
2π	$y = \sin(2\pi - \pi)$ $= \sin\pi = 0$	$(2\pi, 0)$
$\dfrac{5\pi}{2}$	$y = \sin\left(\dfrac{5\pi}{2} - \pi\right)$ $= \sin\dfrac{3\pi}{2} = -1$	$\left(\dfrac{5\pi}{2}, -1\right)$
3π	$y = \sin(3\pi - \pi)$ $= \sin 2\pi = 0$	$(3\pi, 0)$

Connect the five points with a smooth curve and graph one complete cycle of the given function.

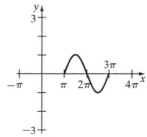

19. The equation $y = \sin(2x - \pi)$ is of the form $y = A\sin(Bx - C)$ with $A = 1$, $B = 2$, and $C = \pi$. The amplitude is $|A| = |1| = 1$. The period is $\dfrac{2\pi}{B} = \dfrac{2\pi}{2} = \pi$. The phase shift is $\dfrac{C}{B} = \dfrac{\pi}{2}$. The quarter-period is $\dfrac{\pi}{4}$. The cycle begins at $x = \dfrac{\pi}{2}$. Add quarter-periods to generate x-values for the key points.

$x = \dfrac{\pi}{2}$

$x = \dfrac{\pi}{2} + \dfrac{\pi}{4} = \dfrac{3\pi}{4}$

$x = \dfrac{3\pi}{4} + \dfrac{\pi}{4} = \pi$

$x = \pi + \dfrac{\pi}{4} = \dfrac{5\pi}{4}$

$x = \dfrac{5\pi}{4} + \dfrac{\pi}{4} = \dfrac{3\pi}{2}$

We evaluate the function at each value of x.

x	$y = \sin(2x - \pi)$	coordinates
$\dfrac{\pi}{2}$	$y = \sin\left(2 \cdot \dfrac{\pi}{2} - \pi\right)$ $= \sin(\pi - \pi)$ $= \sin 0 = 0$	$\left(\dfrac{\pi}{2}, 0\right)$
$\dfrac{3\pi}{4}$	$y = \sin\left(2 \cdot \dfrac{3\pi}{4} - \pi\right)$ $= \sin\left(\dfrac{3\pi}{2} - \pi\right)$ $= \sin\dfrac{\pi}{2} = 1$	$\left(\dfrac{3\pi}{4}, 1\right)$
π	$y = \sin(2 \cdot \pi - \pi)$ $= \sin(2\pi - \pi)$ $= \sin\pi = 0$	$(\pi, 0)$
$\dfrac{5\pi}{4}$	$y = \sin\left(2 \cdot \dfrac{5\pi}{4} - \pi\right)$ $= \sin\left(\dfrac{5\pi}{2} - \pi\right)$ $= \sin\dfrac{3\pi}{2} = -1$	$\left(\dfrac{5\pi}{4}, -1\right)$
$\dfrac{3\pi}{2}$	$y = \sin\left(2 \cdot \dfrac{3\pi}{2} - \pi\right)$ $= \sin(3\pi - \pi)$ $= \sin 2\pi = 0$	$\left(\dfrac{3\pi}{2}, 0\right)$

Connect the five points with a smooth curve and graph one complete cycle of the given function.

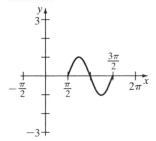

21. The equation $y = 3\sin(2x - \pi)$ is of the form $y = A\sin(Bx - C)$ with $A = 3$, $B = 2$, and $C = \pi$. The amplitude is $|A| = |3| = 3$. The period is $\dfrac{2\pi}{B} = \dfrac{2\pi}{2} = \pi$. The phase shift is $\dfrac{C}{B} = \dfrac{\pi}{2}$. The quarter-period is $\dfrac{\pi}{4}$. The cycle begins at $x = \dfrac{\pi}{2}$. Add quarter-periods to generate x-values for the key points.

$x = \dfrac{\pi}{2}$

$x = \dfrac{\pi}{2} + \dfrac{\pi}{4} = \dfrac{3\pi}{4}$

$x = \dfrac{3\pi}{4} + \dfrac{\pi}{4} = \pi$

$x = \pi + \dfrac{\pi}{4} = \dfrac{5\pi}{4}$

$x = \dfrac{5\pi}{4} + \dfrac{\pi}{4} = \dfrac{3\pi}{2}$

We evaluate the function at each value of x.

x	$y = 3\sin(2x - \pi)$	coordinates
$\dfrac{\pi}{2}$	$y = 3\sin\left(2 \cdot \dfrac{\pi}{2} - \pi\right)$ $= 3\sin(\pi - \pi)$ $= 3\sin 0 = 3 \cdot 0 = 0$	$\left(\dfrac{\pi}{2}, 0\right)$
$\dfrac{3\pi}{4}$	$y = 3\sin\left(2 \cdot \dfrac{3\pi}{4} - \pi\right)$ $= 3\sin\left(\dfrac{3\pi}{2} - \pi\right)$ $= 3\sin\dfrac{\pi}{2} = 3 \cdot 1 = 3$	$\left(\dfrac{3\pi}{4}, 3\right)$
π	$y = 3\sin(2 \cdot \pi - \pi)$ $= 3\sin(2\pi - \pi)$ $= 3\sin \pi = 3 \cdot 0 = 0$	$(\pi, 0)$
$\dfrac{5\pi}{4}$	$y = 3\sin\left(2 \cdot \dfrac{5\pi}{4} - \pi\right)$ $= 3\sin\left(\dfrac{5\pi}{2} - \pi\right)$ $= 3\sin\dfrac{3\pi}{2}$ $= 3(-1) = -3$	$\left(\dfrac{5\pi}{4}, -3\right)$
$\dfrac{3\pi}{2}$	$y = 3\sin\left(2 \cdot \dfrac{3\pi}{2} - \pi\right)$ $= 3\sin(3\pi - \pi)$ $= 3\sin 2\pi = 3 \cdot 0 = 0$	$\left(\dfrac{3\pi}{2}, 0\right)$

Connect the five points with a smooth curve and graph one complete cycle of the given function.

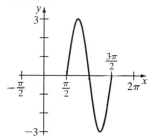

23. $y = \dfrac{1}{2}\sin\left(x + \dfrac{\pi}{2}\right) = \dfrac{1}{2}\sin\left(x - \left(-\dfrac{\pi}{2}\right)\right)$

The equation $y = \dfrac{1}{2}\sin\left(x - \left(-\dfrac{\pi}{2}\right)\right)$ is of the

form $y = A\sin(Bx - C)$ with $A = \dfrac{1}{2}$, $B = 1$,

and $C = -\dfrac{\pi}{2}$. The amplitude is

$|A| = \left|\dfrac{1}{2}\right| = \dfrac{1}{2}$. The period is

$\dfrac{2\pi}{B} = \dfrac{2\pi}{1} = 2\pi$. The phase shift is

$\dfrac{C}{B} = \dfrac{-\frac{\pi}{2}}{1} = -\dfrac{\pi}{2}$. The quarter-period is

$\dfrac{2\pi}{4} = \dfrac{\pi}{2}$. The cycle begins at $x = -\dfrac{\pi}{2}$. Add

quarter-periods to generate x-values for the key points.

$x = -\dfrac{\pi}{2}$

$x = -\dfrac{\pi}{2} + \dfrac{\pi}{2} = 0$

$x = 0 + \dfrac{\pi}{2} = \dfrac{\pi}{2}$

$x = \dfrac{\pi}{2} + \dfrac{\pi}{2} = \pi$

$x = \pi + \dfrac{\pi}{2} = \dfrac{3\pi}{2}$

We evaluate the function at each value of x.

x	$y = \dfrac{1}{2}\sin\left(x + \dfrac{\pi}{2}\right)$	coordinates
$-\dfrac{\pi}{2}$	$y = \dfrac{1}{2}\sin\left(-\dfrac{\pi}{2} + \dfrac{\pi}{2}\right)$ $= \dfrac{1}{2}\sin 0 = \dfrac{1}{2}\cdot 0 = 0$	$\left(-\dfrac{\pi}{2}, 0\right)$
0	$y = \dfrac{1}{2}\sin\left(0 + \dfrac{\pi}{2}\right)$ $= \dfrac{1}{2}\sin\dfrac{\pi}{2} = \dfrac{1}{2}\cdot 1 = \dfrac{1}{2}$	$\left(0, \dfrac{1}{2}\right)$
$\dfrac{\pi}{2}$	$y = \dfrac{1}{2}\sin\left(\dfrac{\pi}{2} + \dfrac{\pi}{2}\right)$ $= \dfrac{1}{2}\sin\pi = \dfrac{1}{2}\cdot 0 = 0$	$\left(\dfrac{\pi}{2}, 0\right)$
π	$y = \dfrac{1}{2}\sin\left(\pi + \dfrac{\pi}{2}\right)$ $= \dfrac{1}{2}\sin\dfrac{3\pi}{2}$ $= \dfrac{1}{2}\cdot(-1) = -\dfrac{1}{2}$	$\left(\pi, -\dfrac{1}{2}\right)$
$\dfrac{3\pi}{2}$	$y = \dfrac{1}{2}\sin\left(\dfrac{3\pi}{2} + \dfrac{\pi}{2}\right)$ $= \dfrac{1}{2}\sin 2\pi$ $= \dfrac{1}{2}\cdot 0 = 0$	$\left(\dfrac{3\pi}{2}, 0\right)$

Connect the five points with a smooth curve and graph one complete cycle of the given function.

25. $y = -2\sin\left(2x + \dfrac{\pi}{2}\right) = -2\sin\left(2x - \left(-\dfrac{\pi}{2}\right)\right)$

The equation $y = -2\sin\left(2x - \left(-\dfrac{\pi}{2}\right)\right)$ is of the form $y = A\sin(Bx - C)$ with $A = -2$, $B = 2$, and $C = -\dfrac{\pi}{2}$. The amplitude is $|A| = |-2| = 2$. The period is $\dfrac{2\pi}{B} = \dfrac{2\pi}{2} = \pi$. The phase shift is $\dfrac{C}{B} = \dfrac{-\frac{\pi}{2}}{2} = -\dfrac{\pi}{2}\cdot\dfrac{1}{2} = -\dfrac{\pi}{4}$. The quarter-period is $\dfrac{\pi}{4}$. The cycle begins at $x = -\dfrac{\pi}{4}$.

Add quarter-periods to generate x-values for the key points.

$x = -\dfrac{\pi}{4}$

$x = -\dfrac{\pi}{4} + \dfrac{\pi}{4} = 0$

$x = 0 + \dfrac{\pi}{4} = \dfrac{\pi}{4}$

$x = \dfrac{\pi}{4} + \dfrac{\pi}{4} = \dfrac{\pi}{2}$

$x = \dfrac{\pi}{2} + \dfrac{\pi}{4} = \dfrac{3\pi}{4}$

We evaluate the function at each value of x.

x	$y = -2\sin\left(2x + \dfrac{\pi}{2}\right)$	coordinates
$-\dfrac{\pi}{4}$	$y = -2\sin\left(2\cdot\left(-\dfrac{\pi}{4}\right) + \dfrac{\pi}{2}\right)$ $= -2\sin\left(-\dfrac{\pi}{2} + \dfrac{\pi}{2}\right)$ $= -2\sin 0 = -2\cdot 0 = 0$	$\left(-\dfrac{\pi}{4}, 0\right)$
0	$y = -2\sin\left(2\cdot 0 + \dfrac{\pi}{2}\right)$ $= -2\sin\left(0 + \dfrac{\pi}{2}\right)$ $= -2\sin\dfrac{\pi}{2}$ $= -2\cdot 1 = -2$	$(0, -2)$
$\dfrac{\pi}{4}$	$y = -2\sin\left(2\cdot\dfrac{\pi}{4} + \dfrac{\pi}{2}\right)$ $= -2\sin\left(\dfrac{\pi}{2} + \dfrac{\pi}{2}\right)$ $= -2\sin\pi$ $= -2\cdot 0 = 0$	$\left(\dfrac{\pi}{4}, 0\right)$
$\dfrac{\pi}{2}$	$y = -2\sin\left(2\cdot\dfrac{\pi}{2} + \dfrac{\pi}{2}\right)$ $= -2\sin\left(\pi + \dfrac{\pi}{2}\right)$ $= -2\sin\dfrac{3\pi}{2}$ $= -2(-1) = 2$	$\left(\dfrac{\pi}{2}, 2\right)$
$\dfrac{3\pi}{4}$	$y = -2\sin\left(2\cdot\dfrac{3\pi}{4} + \dfrac{\pi}{2}\right)$ $= -2\sin\left(\dfrac{3\pi}{2} + \dfrac{\pi}{2}\right)$ $= -2\sin 2\pi$ $= -2\cdot 0 = 0$	$\left(\dfrac{3\pi}{4}, 0\right)$

Connect the five points with a smooth curve and graph one complete cycle of the given function.

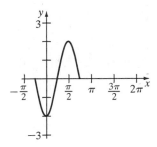

27. $y = 3\sin(\pi x + 2)$

The equation $y = 3\sin(\pi x - (-2))$ is of the form $y = A\sin(Bx - C)$ with $A = 3$, $B = \pi$, and $C = -2$. The amplitude is $|A| = |3| = 3$.

The period is $\dfrac{2\pi}{B} = \dfrac{2\pi}{\pi} = 2$. The phase shift is $\dfrac{C}{B} = \dfrac{-2}{\pi} = -\dfrac{2}{\pi}$. The quarter-period is $\dfrac{2}{4} = \dfrac{1}{2}$. The cycle begins at $x = -\dfrac{2}{\pi}$. Add quarter-periods to generate x-values for the key points.

$x = -\dfrac{2}{\pi}$

$x = -\dfrac{2}{\pi} + \dfrac{1}{2} = \dfrac{\pi - 4}{2\pi}$

$x = \dfrac{\pi - 4}{2\pi} + \dfrac{1}{2} = \dfrac{\pi - 2}{\pi}$

$x = \dfrac{\pi - 2}{\pi} + \dfrac{1}{2} = \dfrac{3\pi - 4}{2\pi}$

$x = \dfrac{3\pi - 4}{2\pi} + \dfrac{1}{2} = \dfrac{2\pi - 2}{\pi}$

We evaluate the function at each value of x.

x	$y = 3\sin(\pi x + 2)$	coordinates
$-\dfrac{2}{\pi}$	$y = 3\sin\left(\pi\left(-\dfrac{2}{\pi}\right)+2\right)$ $= 3\sin(-2+2)$ $= 3\sin 0 = 3 \cdot 0 = 0$	$\left(-\dfrac{2}{\pi}, 0\right)$
$\dfrac{\pi-4}{2\pi}$	$y = 3\sin\left(\pi\left(\dfrac{\pi-4}{2\pi}\right)+2\right)$ $= 3\sin\left(\dfrac{\pi-4}{2}+2\right)$ $= 3\sin\left(\dfrac{\pi}{2}-2+2\right)$ $= 3\sin\dfrac{\pi}{2}$ $= 3 \cdot 1 = 3$	$\left(\dfrac{\pi-4}{2\pi}, 3\right)$
$\dfrac{\pi-2}{\pi}$	$y = 3\sin\left(\pi\left(\dfrac{\pi-2}{\pi}\right)+2\right)$ $= 3\sin(\pi-2+2)$ $= 3\sin\pi = 3\cdot 0 = 0$	$\left(\dfrac{\pi-2}{\pi}, 0\right)$
$\dfrac{3\pi-4}{2\pi}$	$y = 3\sin\left(\pi\left(\dfrac{3\pi-4}{2\pi}\right)+2\right)$ $= 3\sin\left(\dfrac{3\pi-4}{2}+2\right)$ $= 3\sin\left(\dfrac{3\pi}{2}-2+2\right)$ $= 3\sin\dfrac{3\pi}{2}$ $= 3(-1) = -3$	$\left(\dfrac{5\pi}{4}, -3\right)$
$\dfrac{2\pi-2}{\pi}$	$y = 3\sin\left(\pi\left(\dfrac{2\pi-2}{\pi}\right)+2\right)$ $= 3\sin(2\pi-2+2)$ $= 3\sin 2\pi = 3\cdot 0 = 0$	$\left(\dfrac{2\pi-2}{\pi}, 0\right)$

Connect the five points with a smooth curve and graph one complete cycle of the given function.

29. $y = -2\sin(2\pi x + 4\pi) = -2\sin(2\pi x - (-4\pi))$

The equation $y = -2\sin(2\pi x - (-4\pi))$ is of the form $y = A\sin(Bx - C)$ with $A = -2$, $B = 2\pi$, and $C = -4\pi$. The amplitude is $|A| = |-2| = 2$. The period is $\dfrac{2\pi}{B} = \dfrac{2\pi}{2\pi} = 1$.

The phase shift is $\dfrac{C}{B} = \dfrac{-4\pi}{2\pi} = -2$. The

quarter-period is $\dfrac{1}{4}$. The cycle begins at

$x = -2$. Add quarter-periods to generate x-values for the key points.

$x = -2$

$x = -2 + \dfrac{1}{4} = -\dfrac{7}{4}$

$x = -\dfrac{7}{4} + \dfrac{1}{4} = -\dfrac{3}{2}$

$x = -\dfrac{3}{2} + \dfrac{1}{4} = -\dfrac{5}{4}$

$x = -\dfrac{5}{4} + \dfrac{1}{4} = -1$

We evaluate the function at each value of x.

x	$y = -2\sin(2\pi x + 4\pi)$	coordinates
-2	$y = -2\sin(2\pi(-2) + 4\pi)$ $= -2\sin(-4\pi + 4\pi)$ $= -2\sin 0$ $= -2 \cdot 0 = 0$	$(-2, 0)$
$-\dfrac{7}{4}$	$y = -2\sin\left(2\pi\left(-\dfrac{7}{4}\right) + 4\pi\right)$ $= -2\sin\left(-\dfrac{7\pi}{2} + 4\pi\right)$ $= -2\sin\dfrac{\pi}{2} = -2 \cdot 1 = -2$	$\left(-\dfrac{7}{4}, -2\right)$
$-\dfrac{3}{2}$	$y = -2\sin\left(2\pi\left(-\dfrac{3}{2}\right) + 4\pi\right)$ $= -2\sin(-3\pi + 4\pi)$ $= -2\sin \pi = -2 \cdot 0 = 0$	$\left(-\dfrac{3}{2}, 0\right)$
$-\dfrac{5}{4}$	$y = -2\sin\left(2\pi\left(-\dfrac{5}{4}\right) + 4\pi\right)$ $= -2\sin\left(-\dfrac{5\pi}{2} + 4\pi\right)$ $= -2\sin\dfrac{3\pi}{2}$ $= -2(-1) = 2$	$\left(-\dfrac{5}{4}, 2\right)$
-1	$y = -2\sin(2\pi(-1) + 4\pi)$ $= -2\sin(-2\pi + 4\pi)$ $= -2\sin 2\pi$ $= -2 \cdot 0 = 0$	$(-1, 0)$

Connect the five points with a smooth curve and graph one complete cycle of the given function.

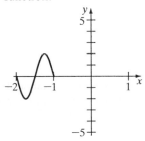

31. The equation $y = 2\cos x$ is of the form $y = A\cos x$ with $A = 2$. Thus, the amplitude is $|A| = |2| = 2$. The period is 2π. The quarter-period is $\dfrac{2\pi}{4}$ or $\dfrac{\pi}{2}$. The cycle begins at $x = 0$. Add quarter-periods to generate x-values for the key points.

$x = 0$

$x = 0 + \dfrac{\pi}{2} = \dfrac{\pi}{2}$

$x = \dfrac{\pi}{2} + \dfrac{\pi}{2} = \pi$

$x = \pi + \dfrac{\pi}{2} = \dfrac{3\pi}{2}$

$x = \dfrac{3\pi}{2} + \dfrac{\pi}{2} = 2\pi$

We evaluate the function at each value of x.

x	$y = 2\cos x$	coordinates
0	$y = 2\cos 0$ $= 2 \cdot 1 = 2$	$(0, 2)$
$\dfrac{\pi}{2}$	$y = 2\cos\dfrac{\pi}{2}$ $= 2 \cdot 0 = 0$	$\left(\dfrac{\pi}{2}, 0\right)$
π	$y = 2\cos \pi$ $= 2 \cdot (-1) = -2$	$(\pi, -2)$
$\dfrac{3\pi}{2}$	$y = 2\cos\dfrac{3\pi}{2}$ $= 2 \cdot 0 = 0$	$\left(\dfrac{3\pi}{2}, 0\right)$
2π	$y = 2\cos 2\pi$ $= 2 \cdot 1 = 2$	$(2\pi, 2)$

Connect the five points with a smooth curve and graph one complete cycle of the given function with the graph of $y = 2\cos x$.

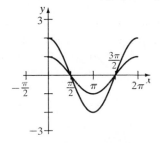

33. The equation $y = -2\cos x$ is of the form $y = A\cos x$ with $A = -2$. Thus, the amplitude is $|A| = |-2| = 2$. The period is 2π. The quarter-period is $\dfrac{2\pi}{4}$ or $\dfrac{\pi}{2}$. The cycle begins at $x = 0$. Add quarter-periods to generate x-values for the key points.

$x = 0$

$x = 0 + \dfrac{\pi}{2} = \dfrac{\pi}{2}$

$x = \dfrac{\pi}{2} + \dfrac{\pi}{2} = \pi$

$x = \pi + \dfrac{\pi}{2} = \dfrac{3\pi}{2}$

$x = \dfrac{3\pi}{2} + \dfrac{\pi}{2} = 2\pi$

We evaluate the function at each value of x.

x	$y = -2\cos x$	coordinates
0	$y = -2\cos 0$ $= -2 \cdot 1 = -2$	$(0, -2)$
$\dfrac{\pi}{2}$	$y = -2\cos\dfrac{\pi}{2}$ $= -2 \cdot 0 = 0$	$\left(\dfrac{\pi}{2}, 0\right)$
π	$y = -2\cos \pi$ $= -2 \cdot (-1) = 2$	$(\pi, 2)$
$\dfrac{3\pi}{2}$	$y = -2\cos\dfrac{3\pi}{2}$ $= -2 \cdot 0 = 0$	$\left(\dfrac{3\pi}{2}, 0\right)$
2π	$y = -2\cos 2\pi$ $= -2 \cdot 1 = -2$	$(2\pi, -2)$

Connect the five points with a smooth curve and graph one complete cycle of the given function with the graph of $y = \cos x$.

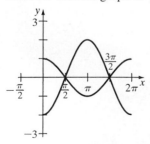

35. The equation $y = \cos 2x$ is of the form $y = A\cos Bx$ with $A = 1$ and $B = 2$. Thus, the amplitude is $|A| = |1| = 1$. The period is $\dfrac{2\pi}{B} = \dfrac{2\pi}{2} = \pi$. The quarter-period is $\dfrac{\pi}{4}$. The cycle begins at $x = 0$. Add quarter-periods to generate x-values for the key points.

$x = 0$

$x = 0 + \dfrac{\pi}{4} = \dfrac{\pi}{4}$

$x = \dfrac{\pi}{4} + \dfrac{\pi}{4} = \dfrac{\pi}{2}$

$x = \dfrac{\pi}{2} + \dfrac{\pi}{4} = \dfrac{3\pi}{4}$

$x = \dfrac{3\pi}{4} + \dfrac{\pi}{4} = \pi$

We evaluate the function at each value of x.

x	$y = \cos 2x$	coordinates
0	$y = \cos(2 \cdot 0)$ $= \cos 0 = 1$	$(0, 1)$
$\dfrac{\pi}{4}$	$y = \cos\left(2 \cdot \dfrac{\pi}{4}\right)$ $= \cos\dfrac{\pi}{2} = 0$	$\left(\dfrac{\pi}{4}, 0\right)$
$\dfrac{\pi}{2}$	$y = \cos\left(2 \cdot \dfrac{\pi}{2}\right)$ $= \cos \pi = -1$	$\left(\dfrac{\pi}{2}, -1\right)$
$\dfrac{3\pi}{4}$	$y = \cos\left(2 \cdot \dfrac{3\pi}{4}\right)$ $= \cos\dfrac{3\pi}{2} = 0$	$\left(\dfrac{3\pi}{4}, 0\right)$
π	$y = \cos(2 \cdot \pi)$ $= \cos 2\pi = 1$	$(\pi, 1)$

Connect the five points with a smooth curve and graph one complete cycle of the given function.

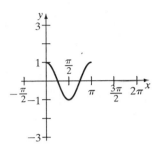

37. The equation $y = 4\cos 2\pi x$ is of the form $y = A\cos Bx$ with $A = 4$ and $B = 2\pi$. Thus, the amplitude is $|A| = |4| = 4$. The period is $\dfrac{2\pi}{B} = \dfrac{2\pi}{2\pi} = 1$. The quarter-period is $\dfrac{1}{4}$. The cycle begins at $x = 0$. Add quarter-periods to generate x-values for the key points.

$x = 0$

$x = 0 + \dfrac{1}{4} = \dfrac{1}{4}$

$x = \dfrac{1}{4} + \dfrac{1}{4} = \dfrac{1}{2}$

$x = \dfrac{1}{2} + \dfrac{1}{4} = \dfrac{3}{4}$

$x = \dfrac{3}{4} + \dfrac{1}{4} = 1$

We evaluate the function at each value of x.

x	$y = 4\cos 2\pi x$	coordinates
0	$y = 4\cos(2\pi \cdot 0)$ $= 4\cos 0$ $= 4 \cdot 1 = 4$	$(0, 4)$
$\dfrac{1}{4}$	$y = 4\cos\left(2\pi \cdot \dfrac{1}{4}\right)$ $= 4\cos\dfrac{\pi}{2}$ $= 4 \cdot 0 = 0$	$\left(\dfrac{1}{4}, 0\right)$
$\dfrac{1}{2}$	$y = 4\cos\left(2\pi \cdot \dfrac{1}{2}\right)$ $= 4\cos\pi$ $= 4 \cdot (-1) = -4$	$\left(\dfrac{1}{2}, -4\right)$

$\dfrac{3}{4}$	$y = 4\cos\left(2\pi \cdot \dfrac{3}{4}\right)$ $= 4\cos\dfrac{3\pi}{2}$ $= 4 \cdot 0 = 0$	$\left(\dfrac{3}{4}, 0\right)$
1	$y = 4\cos(2\pi \cdot 1)$ $= 4\cos 2\pi$ $= 4 \cdot 1 = 4$	$(1, 4)$

Connect the five points with a smooth curve and graph one complete cycle of the given function.

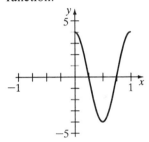

39. The equation $y = -4\cos\dfrac{1}{2}x$ is of the form $y = A\cos Bx$ with $A = -4$ and $B = \dfrac{1}{2}$. Thus, the amplitude is $|A| = |-4| = 4$. The period is $\dfrac{2\pi}{B} = \dfrac{2\pi}{\frac{1}{2}} = 2\pi \cdot 2 = 4\pi$. The quarter-period is $\dfrac{4\pi}{4} = \pi$. The cycle begins at $x = 0$. Add quarter-periods to generate x-values for the key points.

$x = 0$

$x = 0 + \pi = \pi$

$x = \pi + \pi = 2\pi$

$x = 2\pi + \pi = 3\pi$

$x = 3\pi + \pi = 4\pi$

We evaluate the function at each value of x.

x	$y = -4\cos\frac{1}{2}x$	coordinates
0	$y = -4\cos\left(\frac{1}{2}\cdot 0\right)$ $= -4\cos 0$ $= -4\cdot 1 = -4$	$(0, -4)$
π	$y = -4\cos\left(\frac{1}{2}\cdot \pi\right)$ $= -4\cos\frac{\pi}{2}$ $= -4\cdot 0 = 0$	$(\pi, 0)$
2π	$y = -4\cos\left(\frac{1}{2}\cdot 2\pi\right)$ $= -4\cos \pi$ $= -4\cdot(-1) = 4$	$(2\pi, 4)$
3π	$y = -4\cos\left(\frac{1}{2}\cdot 3\pi\right)$ $= -4\cos\frac{3\pi}{2}$ $= -4\cdot 0 = 0$	$(3\pi, 0)$
4π	$y = -4\cos\left(\frac{1}{2}\cdot 4\pi\right)$ $= -4\cos 2\pi$ $= -4\cdot 1 = -4$	$(4\pi, -4)$

Connect the five points with a smooth curve and graph one complete cycle of the given function.

41. The equation $y = -\frac{1}{2}\cos\frac{\pi}{3}x$ is of the form $y = A\cos Bx$ with $A = -\frac{1}{2}$ and $B = \frac{\pi}{3}$.

Thus, the amplitude is $|A| = \left|-\frac{1}{2}\right| = \frac{1}{2}$. The period is $\frac{2\pi}{B} = \frac{2\pi}{\frac{\pi}{3}} = 2\pi\cdot\frac{3}{\pi} = 6$. The quarter-period is $\frac{6}{4} = \frac{3}{2}$. The cycle begins at $x = 0$. Add quarter-periods to generate x-values for the key points.
$x = 0$
$x = 0 + \frac{3}{2} = \frac{3}{2}$
$x = \frac{3}{2} + \frac{3}{2} = 3$
$x = 3 + \frac{3}{2} = \frac{9}{2}$
$x = \frac{9}{2} + \frac{3}{2} = 6$
We evaluate the function at each value of x.

x	$y = -\dfrac{1}{2}\cos\dfrac{\pi}{3}x$	coordinates
0	$y = -\dfrac{1}{2}\cos\left(\dfrac{\pi}{3} \cdot 0\right)$ $= -\dfrac{1}{2}\cos 0$ $= -\dfrac{1}{2} \cdot 1 = -\dfrac{1}{2}$	$\left(0, -\dfrac{1}{2}\right)$
$\dfrac{3}{2}$	$y = -\dfrac{1}{2}\cos\left(\dfrac{\pi}{3} \cdot \dfrac{3}{2}\right)$ $= -\dfrac{1}{2}\cos\dfrac{\pi}{2}$ $= -\dfrac{1}{2} \cdot 0 = 0$	$\left(\dfrac{3}{2}, 0\right)$
3	$y = -\dfrac{1}{2}\cos\left(\dfrac{\pi}{3} \cdot 3\right)$ $= -\dfrac{1}{2}\cos \pi$ $= -\dfrac{1}{2} \cdot (-1) = \dfrac{1}{2}$	$\left(3, \dfrac{1}{2}\right)$
$\dfrac{9}{2}$	$y = -\dfrac{1}{2}\cos\left(\dfrac{\pi}{3} \cdot \dfrac{9}{2}\right)$ $= -\dfrac{1}{2}\cos\dfrac{3\pi}{2}$ $= -\dfrac{1}{2} \cdot 0 = 0$	$\left(\dfrac{9}{2}, 0\right)$
6	$y = -\dfrac{1}{2}\cos\left(\dfrac{\pi}{3} \cdot 6\right)$ $= -\dfrac{1}{2}\cos 2\pi$ $= -\dfrac{1}{2} \cdot 1 = -\dfrac{1}{2}$	$\left(6, -\dfrac{1}{2}\right)$

Connect the five points with a smooth curve and graph one complete cycle of the given function.

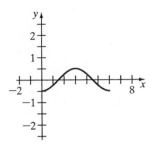

43. The equation $y = 3\cos(2x - \pi)$ is of the form $y = A\cos Bx$ with $A = 3$, and $B = 2$, and $C = \pi$. Thus, the amplitude is $|A| = |3| = 3$. The period is $\dfrac{2\pi}{B} = \dfrac{2\pi}{2} = \pi$.

The phase shift is $\dfrac{C}{B} = \dfrac{\pi}{2}$. The quarter-period is $\dfrac{\pi}{4}$. The cycle begins at $x = \dfrac{\pi}{2}$.

Add quarter-periods to generate x-values for the key points.

$x = \dfrac{\pi}{2}$

$x = \dfrac{\pi}{2} + \dfrac{\pi}{4} = \dfrac{3\pi}{4}$

$x = \dfrac{3\pi}{4} + \dfrac{\pi}{4} = \pi$

$x = \pi + \dfrac{\pi}{4} = \dfrac{5\pi}{4}$

$x = \dfrac{5\pi}{4} + \dfrac{\pi}{4} = \dfrac{3\pi}{2}$

We evaluate the function at each value of x.

x	$y = 3\cos(2x - \pi)$	coordinates
$\dfrac{\pi}{2}$	$y = 3\cos\left(2 \cdot \dfrac{\pi}{2} - \pi\right)$ $= 3\cos(\pi - \pi)$ $= 3\cos 0 = 3 \cdot 1 = 3$	$\left(\dfrac{\pi}{2}, 3\right)$
$\dfrac{3\pi}{4}$	$y = 3\cos\left(2 \cdot \dfrac{3\pi}{4} - \pi\right)$ $= 3\cos\left(\dfrac{3\pi}{2} - \pi\right)$ $= 3\cos\dfrac{\pi}{2} = 3 \cdot 0 = 0$	$\left(\dfrac{3\pi}{4}, 0\right)$
π	$y = 3\cos(2 \cdot \pi - \pi)$ $= 3\cos(2\pi - \pi)$ $= 3\cos \pi$ $= 3 \cdot (-1) = -3$	$(\pi, -3)$
$\dfrac{5\pi}{4}$	$y = 3\cos\left(2 \cdot \dfrac{5\pi}{4} - \pi\right)$ $= 3\cos\left(\dfrac{5\pi}{2} - \pi\right)$ $= 3\cos\dfrac{3\pi}{2} = 3 \cdot 0 = 0$	$\left(\dfrac{5\pi}{4}, 0\right)$
$\dfrac{3\pi}{2}$	$y = 3\cos\left(2 \cdot \dfrac{3\pi}{2} - \pi\right)$ $= 3\cos(3\pi - \pi)$ $= 3\cos 2\pi = 3 \cdot 1 = 3$	$\left(\dfrac{3\pi}{2}, 3\right)$

Connect the five points with a smooth curve and graph one complete cycle of the given function

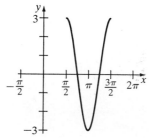

45. $y = \dfrac{1}{2}\cos\left(3x + \dfrac{\pi}{2}\right) = \dfrac{1}{2}\cos\left(3x - \left(-\dfrac{\pi}{2}\right)\right)$

The equation $y = \dfrac{1}{2}\cos\left(3x - \left(-\dfrac{\pi}{2}\right)\right)$ is of

the form $y = A\cos(Bx - C)$ with $A = \dfrac{1}{2}$, and

$B = 3$, and $C = -\dfrac{\pi}{2}$. Thus, the amplitude is

$|A| = \left|\dfrac{1}{2}\right| = \dfrac{1}{2}$. The period is $\dfrac{2\pi}{B} = \dfrac{2\pi}{3}$.

The phase shift is $\dfrac{C}{B} = \dfrac{-\frac{\pi}{2}}{3} = -\dfrac{\pi}{2} \cdot \dfrac{1}{3} = -\dfrac{\pi}{6}$.

The quarter-period is $\dfrac{\frac{2\pi}{3}}{4} = \dfrac{2\pi}{3} \cdot \dfrac{1}{4} = \dfrac{\pi}{6}$. The

cycle begins at $x = -\dfrac{\pi}{6}$. Add quarter-

periods to generate x-values for the key points.

$x = -\dfrac{\pi}{6}$

$x = -\dfrac{\pi}{6} + \dfrac{\pi}{6} = 0$

$x = 0 + \dfrac{\pi}{6} = \dfrac{\pi}{6}$

$x = \dfrac{\pi}{6} + \dfrac{\pi}{6} = \dfrac{\pi}{3}$

$x = \dfrac{\pi}{3} + \dfrac{\pi}{6} = \dfrac{\pi}{2}$

We evaluate the function at each value of x.

x	$y = \dfrac{1}{2}\cos\left(3x + \dfrac{\pi}{2}\right)$	coordinates
$-\dfrac{\pi}{6}$	$y = \dfrac{1}{2}\cos\left(3 \cdot \left(-\dfrac{\pi}{6}\right) + \dfrac{\pi}{2}\right)$ $= \dfrac{1}{2}\cos\left(-\dfrac{\pi}{2} + \dfrac{\pi}{2}\right)$ $= \dfrac{1}{2}\cos 0 = \dfrac{1}{2} \cdot 1 = \dfrac{1}{2}$	$\left(-\dfrac{\pi}{6}, \dfrac{1}{2}\right)$
0	$y = \dfrac{1}{2}\cos\left(3 \cdot 0 + \dfrac{\pi}{2}\right)$ $= \dfrac{1}{2}\cos\left(0 + \dfrac{\pi}{2}\right)$ $= \dfrac{1}{2}\cos\dfrac{\pi}{2} = \dfrac{1}{2} \cdot 0 = 0$	$(0, 0)$
$\dfrac{\pi}{6}$	$y = \dfrac{1}{2}\cos\left(3 \cdot \dfrac{\pi}{6} + \dfrac{\pi}{2}\right)$ $= \dfrac{1}{2}\cos\left(\dfrac{\pi}{2} + \dfrac{\pi}{2}\right)$ $= \dfrac{1}{2}\cos\pi$ $= \dfrac{1}{2} \cdot (-1) = -\dfrac{1}{2}$	$\left(\dfrac{\pi}{6}, -\dfrac{1}{2}\right)$
$\dfrac{\pi}{3}$	$y = \dfrac{1}{2}\cos\left(3 \cdot \dfrac{\pi}{3} + \dfrac{\pi}{2}\right)$ $= \dfrac{1}{2}\cos\left(\pi + \dfrac{\pi}{2}\right)$ $= \dfrac{1}{2}\cos\dfrac{3\pi}{2} = \dfrac{1}{2} \cdot 0 = 0$	$\left(\dfrac{\pi}{3}, 0\right)$
$\dfrac{\pi}{2}$	$y = \dfrac{1}{2}\cos\left(3 \cdot \dfrac{\pi}{2} + \dfrac{\pi}{2}\right)$ $= \dfrac{1}{2}\cos\left(\dfrac{3\pi}{2} + \dfrac{\pi}{2}\right)$ $= \dfrac{1}{2}\cos 2\pi = \dfrac{1}{2} \cdot 1 = \dfrac{1}{2}$	$\left(\dfrac{\pi}{2}, \dfrac{1}{2}\right)$

Connect the five points with a smooth curve and graph one complete cycle of the given function

47. The equation $y = -3\cos\left(2x - \dfrac{\pi}{2}\right)$ is of the form $y = A\cos(Bx - C)$ with $A = -3$, and $B = 2$, and $C = \dfrac{\pi}{2}$. Thus, the amplitude is $|A| = |-3| = 3$. The period is $\dfrac{2\pi}{B} = \dfrac{2\pi}{2} = \pi$. The phase shift is $\dfrac{C}{B} = \dfrac{\frac{\pi}{2}}{2} = \dfrac{\pi}{2} \cdot \dfrac{1}{2} = \dfrac{\pi}{4}$. The quarter-period is $\dfrac{\pi}{4}$. The cycle begins at $x = \dfrac{\pi}{4}$. Add quarter-periods to generate x-values for the key points.

$$x = \dfrac{\pi}{4}$$
$$x = \dfrac{\pi}{4} + \dfrac{\pi}{4} = \dfrac{\pi}{2}$$
$$x = \dfrac{\pi}{2} + \dfrac{\pi}{4} = \dfrac{3\pi}{4}$$
$$x = \dfrac{3\pi}{4} + \dfrac{\pi}{4} = \pi$$
$$x = \pi + \dfrac{\pi}{4} = \dfrac{5\pi}{4}$$

We evaluate the function at each value of x.

x	$y = -3\cos\left(2x - \dfrac{\pi}{2}\right)$	coordinates
$\dfrac{\pi}{4}$	$\begin{aligned} y &= -3\cos\left(2 \cdot \dfrac{\pi}{4} - \dfrac{\pi}{2}\right) \\ &= -3\cos\left(\dfrac{\pi}{2} - \dfrac{\pi}{2}\right) \\ &= -3\cos 0 \\ &= -3 \cdot 1 = -3 \end{aligned}$	$\left(\dfrac{\pi}{4}, -3\right)$
$\dfrac{\pi}{2}$	$\begin{aligned} y &= -3\cos\left(2 \cdot \dfrac{\pi}{2} - \dfrac{\pi}{2}\right) \\ &= -3\cos\left(\pi - \dfrac{\pi}{2}\right) \\ &= -3\cos\dfrac{\pi}{2} \\ &= -3 \cdot 0 = 0 \end{aligned}$	$\left(\dfrac{\pi}{2}, 0\right)$
$\dfrac{3\pi}{4}$	$\begin{aligned} y &= -3\cos\left(2 \cdot \dfrac{3\pi}{4} - \dfrac{\pi}{2}\right) \\ &= -3\cos\left(\dfrac{3\pi}{2} - \dfrac{\pi}{2}\right) \\ &= -3\cos \pi \\ &= -3 \cdot (-1) = 3 \end{aligned}$	$\left(\dfrac{3\pi}{4}, 3\right)$
π	$\begin{aligned} y &= -3\cos\left(2 \cdot \pi - \dfrac{\pi}{2}\right) \\ &= -3\cos\left(2\pi - \dfrac{\pi}{2}\right) \\ &= -3\cos\dfrac{3\pi}{2} \\ &= -3 \cdot 0 = 0 \end{aligned}$	$(\pi, 0)$
$\dfrac{5\pi}{4}$	$\begin{aligned} y &= -3\cos\left(2 \cdot \dfrac{5\pi}{4} - \dfrac{\pi}{2}\right) \\ &= -3\cos\left(\dfrac{5\pi}{2} - \dfrac{\pi}{2}\right) \\ &= -3\cos 2\pi \\ &= -3 \cdot 1 = -3 \end{aligned}$	$\left(\dfrac{5\pi}{4}, -3\right)$

Connect the five points with a smooth curve and graph one complete cycle of the given function

49. $y = 2\cos(2\pi x + 8\pi) = 2\cos(2\pi x - (-8\pi))$
The equation $y = 2\cos(2\pi x - (-8\pi))$ is of the form $y = A\cos(Bx - C)$ with $A = 2$, $B = 2\pi$, and $C = -8\pi$. Thus, the amplitude is $|A| = |2| = 2$. The period is
$\dfrac{2\pi}{B} = \dfrac{2\pi}{2\pi} = 1$. The phase shift is
$\dfrac{C}{B} = \dfrac{-8\pi}{2\pi} = -4$. The quarter-period is $\dfrac{1}{4}$.
The cycle begins at $x = -4$. Add quarter-periods to generate x-values for the key points.
$x = -4$
$x = -4 + \dfrac{1}{4} = -\dfrac{15}{4}$
$x = -\dfrac{15}{4} + \dfrac{1}{4} = -\dfrac{7}{2}$
$x = -\dfrac{7}{2} + \dfrac{1}{4} = -\dfrac{13}{4}$
$x = -\dfrac{13}{4} + \dfrac{1}{4} = -3$
We evaluate the function at each value of x.

x	$y = 2\cos(2\pi x + 8\pi)$	coordinates
-4	$y = 2\cos(2\pi(-4) + 8\pi)$ $= 2\cos(-8\pi + 8\pi)$ $= 2\cos 0 = 2 \cdot 1 = 2$	$(-4, 2)$
$-\dfrac{15}{4}$	$y = 2\cos\left(2\pi\left(-\dfrac{15}{4}\right) + 8\pi\right)$ $= 2\cos\left(-\dfrac{15\pi}{2} + 8\pi\right)$ $= 2\cos\dfrac{\pi}{2} = 2 \cdot 0 = 0$	$\left(-\dfrac{15}{4}, 0\right)$
$-\dfrac{7}{2}$	$y = 2\cos\left(2\pi\left(-\dfrac{7}{2}\right) + 8\pi\right)$ $= 2\cos(-7\pi + 8\pi)$ $= 2\cos\pi$ $= 2 \cdot (-1) = -2$	$\left(-\dfrac{7}{2}, -2\right)$
$-\dfrac{13}{4}$	$y = 2\cos\left(2\pi\left(-\dfrac{13}{4}\right) + 8\pi\right)$ $= 2\cos\left(-\dfrac{13\pi}{2} + 8\pi\right)$ $= 2\cos\dfrac{3\pi}{2} = 2 \cdot 0 = 0$	$\left(-\dfrac{13}{4}, 0\right)$
-3	$y = 2\cos(2\pi(-3) + 8\pi)$ $= 2\cos(-6\pi + 8\pi)$ $= 2\cos 2\pi = 2 \cdot 1 = 2$	$(-3, 2)$

Connect the five points with a smooth curve and graph one complete cycle of the given function

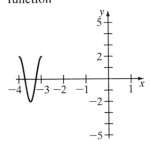

51. The graph of $y = \sin x + 2$ is the graph of $y = \sin x$ shifted up 2 units upward. The period for both functions is 2π. The quarter-period is $\dfrac{2\pi}{4}$ or $\dfrac{\pi}{2}$. The cycle begins at $x = 0$. Add quarter-periods to generate x-values for the key points.

$x = 0$

$x = 0 + \dfrac{\pi}{2} = \dfrac{\pi}{2}$

$x = \dfrac{\pi}{2} + \dfrac{\pi}{2} = \pi$

$x = \pi + \dfrac{\pi}{2} = \dfrac{3\pi}{2}$

$x = \dfrac{3\pi}{2} + \dfrac{\pi}{2} = 2\pi$

We evaluate the function at each value of x.

x	$y = \sin x + 2$	coordinates
0	$y = \sin 0 + 2$ $= 0 + 2 = 2$	$(0, 2)$
$\dfrac{\pi}{2}$	$y = \sin\dfrac{\pi}{2} + 2$ $= 1 + 2 = 3$	$\left(\dfrac{\pi}{2}, 3\right)$
π	$y = \sin\pi + 2$ $= 0 + 2 = 2$	$(\pi, 2)$
$\dfrac{3\pi}{2}$	$y = \sin\dfrac{3\pi}{2} + 2$ $= -1 + 2 = 1$	$\left(\dfrac{3\pi}{2}, 1\right)$
2π	$y = \sin 2\pi + 2$ $= 0 + 2 = 2$	$(2\pi, 2)$

By connecting the points with a smooth curve we obtain one period of the graph.

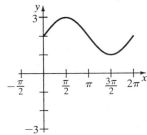

53. The graph of $y = \cos x - 3$ is the graph of $y = \cos x$ shifted 3 units downward. The period for both functions is 2π. The quarter-period is $\dfrac{2\pi}{4}$ or $\dfrac{\pi}{2}$. The cycle begins at $x = 0$. Add quarter-periods to generate x-values for the key points.

$x = 0$

$x = 0 + \dfrac{\pi}{2} = \dfrac{\pi}{2}$

$x = \dfrac{\pi}{2} + \dfrac{\pi}{2} = \pi$

$x = \pi + \dfrac{\pi}{2} = \dfrac{3\pi}{2}$

$x = \dfrac{3\pi}{2} + \dfrac{\pi}{2} = 2\pi$

We evaluate the function at each value of x.

x	$y = \cos x - 3$	coordinates
0	$y = \cos 0 - 3$ $= 1 - 3 = -2$	$(0, -2)$
$\dfrac{\pi}{2}$	$y = \cos \dfrac{\pi}{2} - 3$ $= 0 - 3 = -3$	$\left(\dfrac{\pi}{2}, -3\right)$
π	$y = \cos \pi - 3$ $= -1 - 3 = -4$	$(\pi, -4)$
$\dfrac{3\pi}{2}$	$y = \cos \dfrac{3\pi}{2} - 3$ $= 0 - 3 = -3$	$\left(\dfrac{3\pi}{2}, -3\right)$
2π	$y = \cos 2\pi - 3$ $= 1 - 3 = -2$	$(2\pi, -2)$

By connecting the points with a smooth curve we obtain one period of the graph.

55. The graph of $y = 2\sin \frac{1}{2}x + 1$ is the graph of $y = 2\sin \frac{1}{2}x$ shifted one unit upward. The amplitude for both functions is $|2| = 2$. The period for both functions is $\dfrac{2\pi}{\frac{1}{2}} = 2\pi \cdot 2 = 4\pi$. The quarter-period is $\dfrac{4\pi}{4} = \pi$. The cycle begins at $x = 0$. Add quarter-periods to generate x-values for the key points.

$x = 0$

$x = 0 + \pi = \pi$

$x = \pi + \pi = 2\pi$

$x = 2\pi + \pi = 3\pi$

$x = 3\pi + \pi = 4\pi$

We evaluate the function at each value of x.

x	$y = 2\sin \dfrac{1}{2}x + 1$	coordinates
0	$y = 2\sin\left(\dfrac{1}{2} \cdot 0\right) + 1$ $= 2\sin 0 + 1$ $= 2 \cdot 0 + 1 = 0 + 1 = 1$	$(0, 1)$
π	$y = 2\sin\left(\dfrac{1}{2} \cdot \pi\right) + 1$ $= 2\sin \dfrac{\pi}{2} + 1$ $= 2 \cdot 1 + 1 = 2 + 1 = 3$	$(\pi, 3)$
2π	$y = 2\sin\left(\dfrac{1}{2} \cdot 2\pi\right) + 1$ $= 2\sin \pi + 1$ $= 2 \cdot 0 + 1 = 0 + 1 = 1$	$(2\pi, 1)$
3π	$y = 2\sin\left(\dfrac{1}{2} \cdot 3\pi\right) + 1$ $= 2\sin \dfrac{3\pi}{2} + 1$ $= 2 \cdot (-1) + 1$ $= -2 + 1 = -1$	$(3\pi, -1)$
4π	$y = 2\sin\left(\dfrac{1}{2} \cdot 4\pi\right) + 1$ $= 2\sin 2\pi + 1$ $= 2 \cdot 0 + 1 = 0 + 1 = 1$	$(4\pi, 1)$

By connecting the points with a smooth curve we obtain one period of the graph.

57. The graph of $y = -3\cos 2\pi x + 2$ is the graph of $y = -3\cos 2\pi x$ shifted 2 units upward.

The amplitude for both functions is $|-3| = 3$. The period for both functions is $\dfrac{2\pi}{2\pi} = 1$. The quarter-period is $\dfrac{1}{4}$. The cycle begins at $x = 0$. Add quarter-periods to generate x-values for the key points.

$x = 0$

$x = 0 + \dfrac{1}{4} = \dfrac{1}{4}$

$x = \dfrac{1}{4} + \dfrac{1}{4} = \dfrac{1}{2}$

$x = \dfrac{1}{2} + \dfrac{1}{4} = \dfrac{3}{4}$

$x = \dfrac{3}{4} + \dfrac{1}{4} = 1$

We evaluate the function at each value of x.

x	$y = -3\cos 2\pi x + 2$	coordinates
0	$y = -3\cos(2\pi \cdot 0) + 2$ $= -3\cos 0 + 2$ $= -3 \cdot 1 + 2$ $= -3 + 2 = -1$	$(0, -1)$
$\dfrac{1}{4}$	$y = -3\cos\left(2\pi \cdot \dfrac{1}{4}\right) + 2$ $= -3\cos\dfrac{\pi}{2} + 2$ $= -3 \cdot 0 + 2$ $= 0 + 2 = 2$	$\left(\dfrac{1}{4}, 2\right)$
$\dfrac{1}{2}$	$y = -3\cos\left(2\pi \cdot \dfrac{1}{2}\right) + 2$ $= -3\cos\pi + 2$ $= -3 \cdot (-1) + 2$ $= 3 + 2 = 5$	$\left(\dfrac{1}{2}, 5\right)$
$\dfrac{3}{4}$	$y = -3\cos\left(2\pi \cdot \dfrac{3}{4}\right) + 2$ $= -3\cos\dfrac{3\pi}{2} + 2$ $= -3 \cdot 0 + 2$ $= 0 + 2 = 2$	$\left(\dfrac{3}{4}, 2\right)$
1	$y = -3\cos(2\pi \cdot 1) + 2$ $= -3\cos 2\pi + 2$ $= -3 \cdot 1 + 2$ $= -3 + 2 = -1$	$(1, -1)$

By connecting the points with a smooth curve we obtain one period of the graph.

59. The period is the number of days from 1/24/00 to 2/26/00.

$7 + 26 = 33$

The period of the physical cycle is about 33 days.

61. The period is the number of days from 2/05/00 to 2/28/00.

$28 - 5 = 23$

The period of the intellectual cycle is 23 days.

63. In the month of March, 3/21/00 would be the best day to meet an on-line friend for the first time, because the emotional cycle is at a maximum.

65. Answers may vary.

67. The information gives the five key point of the graph.

(0, 14) corresponds to June,
(3, 12) corresponds to September,
(6, 10) corresponds to December,
(9, 12) corresponds to March,
(12, 14) corresponds to June

By connecting the five key points with a smooth curve we graph the information from June of one year to June of the following year.

69. The function $y = 3\sin\dfrac{2\pi}{365}(x - 79) + 12$ is of

the form $y = A\sin B\left(x - \dfrac{C}{B}\right) + D$ with

$A = 3$ and $B = \dfrac{2\pi}{365}$.

a. The amplitude is $|A| = |3| = 3$.

b. The period is
$$\dfrac{2\pi}{B} = \dfrac{2\pi}{\frac{2\pi}{365}} = 2\pi \cdot \dfrac{365}{2\pi} = 365.$$

c. The longest day of the year will have the most hours of daylight. This occurs when the sine function equals 1.
$$y = 3\sin\dfrac{2\pi}{365}(x - 79) + 12$$
$$y = 3(1) + 12$$
$$y = 15$$
There will be 15 hours of daylight.

d. The shortest day of the year will have the least hours of daylight. This occurs when the sine function equals −1.
$$y = 3\sin\dfrac{2\pi}{365}(x - 79) + 12$$
$$y = 3(-1) + 12$$
$$y = 9$$
There will be 9 hours of daylight.

e. The amplitude is 3. The period is 365.

The phase shift is $\dfrac{C}{B} = 79$. The quarter-

period is $\dfrac{365}{4} = 91.25$. The cycle begins

at $x = 79$. Add quarter-periods to find the x-values of the key points.
$$x = 79$$
$$x = 79 + 91.25 = 170.25$$
$$x = 170.25 + 91.25 = 261.5$$
$$x = 261.5 + 91.25 = 352.75$$
$$x = 352.75 + 91.25 = 444$$
Because we are graphing for $0 \le x \le 365$, we will evaluate the function for the first four x-values along with $x = 0$ and $x = 365$. Using a calculator we have the following points.
(0, 9.07) (79, 12) (170.25, 15)
(261.5, 12) (352.75, 9) (365, 9.07)
By connecting the points with a smooth curve we obtain one period of the graph, starting on January 1.

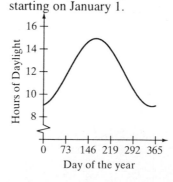

71. Because the depth of the water ranges from a minimum of 6 feet to a maximum of 12 feet, the curve oscillates about the middle value, 9 feet. Thus, $D = 9$. The maximum depth of the water is 3 feet above 9 feet. Thus, $A = 3$. The graph shows that one complete cycle occurs in 12-0, or 12 hours. The period is 12. Thus,

$$12 = \frac{2\pi}{B}$$
$$12B = 2\pi$$
$$B = \frac{2\pi}{12} = \frac{\pi}{6}$$

Substitute these values into $y = A\cos Bx + D$. The depth of the water is modeled by $y = 3\cos\frac{\pi x}{6} + 9$.

73.–81. Answers may vary.

83. Exercise 35

Exercise 37

Exercise 39

Exercise 41

Exercise 43

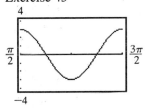

85. The function
$y = 3\sin(2x + \pi) = 3\sin(2x - (-\pi))$ is of the form $y = A\sin(Bx - C)$ with $A = 3$, $B = 2$, and $C = -\pi$. The amplitude is $|A| = |3| = 3$. The period is $\frac{2\pi}{B} = \frac{2\pi}{2} = \pi$. The cycle begins at $x = \frac{C}{B} = \frac{-\pi}{2} = -\frac{\pi}{2}$ We choose $-\frac{\pi}{2} \le x \le \frac{3\pi}{2}$, and $-4 \le y \le 4$ for our graph.

87. The function

$$y = 0.2\sin\left(\frac{\pi}{10}x + \pi\right) = 0.2\sin\left(\frac{\pi}{10}x - (-\pi)\right)$$

is of the form $y = A\sin(Bx - C)$ with

$A = 0.2$, $B = \dfrac{\pi}{10}$, and $C = -\pi$. The

amplitude is $|A| = |0.2| = 0.2$. The period is

$\dfrac{2\pi}{B} = \dfrac{2\pi}{\frac{\pi}{10}} = 2\pi \cdot \dfrac{10}{\pi} = 20$. The cycle begins

at $x = \dfrac{C}{B} = \dfrac{-\pi}{\frac{\pi}{10}} = -\pi \cdot \dfrac{10}{\pi} = -10$. We choose

$-10 \le x \le 30$, and $-1 \le y \le 1$ for our graph.

89.

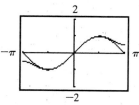

The graphs appear to be the same from

$-\dfrac{\pi}{2}$ to $\dfrac{\pi}{2}$.

91.

The graph is similar to $y = \sin x$, except the amplitude is greater and the curve is less smooth.

93. a.

b. $y = 22.61\sin(0.50x - 2.04) + 57.17$

c.

95. To graph $y = \sin x + \cos x$, we will make a table of values of (x, y) on the graph of $y = \sin x + \cos x$ for $0 \le x \le 2\pi$.

x	0	$\dfrac{\pi}{4}$	$\dfrac{\pi}{2}$	$\dfrac{3\pi}{4}$	π	$\dfrac{5\pi}{4}$	$\dfrac{3\pi}{2}$	$\dfrac{7\pi}{4}$	2π
y	1	1.4	1	0	-1	-1.4	-1	0	1

We connect these points with a smooth curve to obtain the graph shown.

97. Because the y-values range from a maximum of 2 to a minimum of -2, the curve oscillates about 0. Thus, there is no vertical shift, $D = 0$. The maximum y-value is 2. Thus, $A = 2$. The graph shows that one complete cycle occurs in $\dfrac{\pi}{4} - \left(-\dfrac{\pi}{4}\right)$, or $\dfrac{\pi}{2}$ units.

Thus, $\dfrac{\pi}{2} = \dfrac{2\pi}{B}$

$$B\pi = 4\pi$$
$$R = \dfrac{4\pi}{\pi} = 4$$

The graph shows that the starting point of the cycle is shifted from 0 to $-\dfrac{\pi}{4}$.

The phase shift is $-\dfrac{\pi}{4}$.

$$-\dfrac{\pi}{4} = \dfrac{C}{B}$$
$$-\dfrac{\pi}{4} = \dfrac{C}{4}$$
$$-\pi = C$$

Substitute these values into $y = A\cos(Bx - C) + D$.

This graph is the equation $y = 2\cos(4x - (-\pi)) = 2\cos(4x + \pi)$.

Section 5.6

Checkpoint Exercises

1. We solve the equations

$$2x = -\frac{\pi}{2} \quad \text{and} \quad 2x = \frac{\pi}{2}$$
$$x = -\frac{\pi}{4} \qquad\qquad x = \frac{\pi}{4}$$

Thus, two consecutive asymptotes occur at $x = -\dfrac{\pi}{4}$ and $x = \dfrac{\pi}{4}$. Midway between these asymptotes is $x = 0$. An x-intercept is 0 and the graph passes through $(0, 0)$. Because the coefficient of the tangent is 3, the points on the graph midway between an x-intercept and the asymptotes have y-coordinates of -3 and 3. We use the two asymptotes, the x-intercept, and the points midway between to graph one period of $y = 3\tan 2x$ from $-\dfrac{\pi}{4}$ to $\dfrac{\pi}{4}$. In order to graph for $-\dfrac{\pi}{4} < x < \dfrac{3\pi}{4}$, we continue the pattern and extend the graph another full period to the right.

2. We solve the equations

$$x - \frac{\pi}{2} = -\frac{\pi}{2} \quad \text{and} \quad x - \frac{\pi}{2} = \frac{\pi}{2}$$
$$x = \frac{\pi}{2} - \frac{\pi}{2} \qquad\qquad x = \frac{\pi}{2} + \frac{\pi}{2}$$
$$x = 0 \qquad\qquad\qquad x = \pi$$

Thus, two consecutive asymptotes occur at $x = 0$ and $x = \pi$.

$$x\text{-intercept } = \frac{0 + \pi}{2} = \frac{\pi}{2}$$

An x-intercept is $\dfrac{\pi}{2}$ and the graph passes through $\left(\dfrac{\pi}{2}, 0\right)$. Because the coefficient of the tangent is 1, the points on the graph midway between an x-intercept and the asymptotes have y-coordinates of -1 and 1. We use the two consecutive asymptotes, $x = 0$ and $x = \pi$, to graph one full period of $y = \tan\left(x - \dfrac{\pi}{2}\right)$ from 0 to π. We continue the pattern and extend the graph another full period to the right.

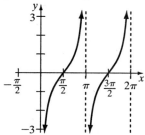

3. We solve the equations

$$\frac{\pi}{2}x = 0 \quad \text{and} \quad \frac{\pi}{2}x = \pi$$

$$x = 0 \qquad\qquad x = \frac{\pi}{\frac{\pi}{2}}$$

$$x = 2$$

Two consecutive asymptotes occur at $x = 0$ and $x = 2$. Midway between $x = 0$ and $x = 2$ is $x = 1$. An x-intercept is 1 and the graph passes through $(1, 0)$. Because the coefficient of the cotangent is $\frac{1}{2}$, the points on the graph midway between an x-intercept and the asymptotes have y-coordinates of $-\frac{1}{2}$ and $\frac{1}{2}$. We use the two consecutive asymptotes, $x = 0$ and $x = 2$, to graph one full period of $y = \frac{1}{2}\cot\frac{\pi}{2}x$. The curve is repeated along the x-axis one full period as shown.

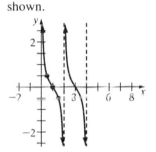

4. The x-intercepts of $y = \sin\left(x + \frac{\pi}{4}\right)$

correspond to vertical asymptotes of

$$y = \csc\left(x + \frac{\pi}{4}\right).$$

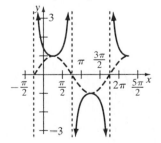

5. Graph the reciprocal cosine function, $y = 2\cos 2x$. The equation is of the form $y = A\cos Bx$ with $A = 2$ and $B = 2$.

amplitude: $|A| = |2| = 2$

$$\text{period: } \frac{2\pi}{B} = \frac{2\pi}{2} = \pi$$

Use quarter-periods, $\frac{\pi}{4}$, to find x-values for the five key points. Starting with $x = 0$, the x-values are $0, \frac{\pi}{4}, \frac{\pi}{2}, \frac{3\pi}{4}$, and π.

Evaluating the function at each value of x, the key points are $(0, 2)$, $\left(\frac{\pi}{4}, 0\right)$, $\left(\frac{\pi}{2}, -2\right)$, $\left(\frac{3\pi}{4}, 0\right)$, $(\pi, 2)$. In order to graph for $-\frac{3\pi}{4} \le x \le \frac{3\pi}{4}$, we use the first four points and extend the graph $-\frac{3\pi}{4}$ units to the left.

Use the graph to obtain the graph of the reciprocal function. Draw vertical asymptotes through the x-intercepts, and use them as guides to graph $y = 2\sec 2x$.

Exercise Set 5.6

For 1 and 3, in the given functions, $B = 1$.

1. The graph has an asymptote at $x = -\dfrac{\pi}{2}$.

    The phase shift, $\dfrac{C}{B}$, from $\dfrac{\pi}{2}$ to $-\dfrac{\pi}{2}$ is $-\pi$

    units. Thus, $\dfrac{C}{B} = -\pi$

    $\dfrac{C}{1} = -\pi$

    $C = -\pi$

    The function with $C = -\pi$ is $y = \tan(x + \pi)$.

3. The graph has an asymptote at $x = \pi$.

    $\pi = \dfrac{\pi}{2} + C$

    $C = \dfrac{\pi}{2}$

    The function is $y = -\tan\left(x - \dfrac{\pi}{2}\right)$.

5. We solve the equations

    $\dfrac{x}{4} = -\dfrac{\pi}{2}$ and $\dfrac{x}{4} = \dfrac{\pi}{2}$

    $x = \left(-\dfrac{\pi}{2}\right)4$ $x = \left(\dfrac{\pi}{2}\right)4$

    $x = -2\pi$ $x = 2\pi$

    Thus, two consecutive asymptotes occur at $x = -2\pi$ and $x = 2\pi$.

    $x\text{-intercept} = \dfrac{-2\pi + 2\pi}{2} = \dfrac{0}{2} = 0$

    An x-intercept is 0 and the graph passes through (0, 0). Because the coefficient of the tangent is 3, the points on the graph midway between an x-intercept and the asymptotes have y-coordinates of –3 and 3. We use the two consecutive asymptotes, $x = -2\pi$ and $x = 2\pi$, to graph one full period of

    $y = 3 \tan \dfrac{x}{4}$ from -2π to 2π. We continue

    the pattern and extend the graph another full period to the right.

7. We solve the equations

    $2x = -\dfrac{\pi}{2}$ and $2x = \dfrac{\pi}{2}$

    $x = \dfrac{-\frac{\pi}{2}}{2}$ $x = \dfrac{\frac{\pi}{2}}{2}$

    $x = -\dfrac{\pi}{4}$ $x = \dfrac{\pi}{4}$

    Thus, two consecutive asymptotes occur at

    $x = -\dfrac{\pi}{4}$ and $x = \dfrac{\pi}{4}$.

    $x\text{-intercept} = \dfrac{-\frac{\pi}{4} + \frac{\pi}{4}}{2} = \dfrac{0}{2} = 0$

    An x-intercept is 0 and the graph passes through (0, 0). Because the coefficient of the

    tangent is $\dfrac{1}{2}$, the points on the graph

    midway between an x-intercept and the

    asymptotes have y-coordinates of $-\dfrac{1}{2}$ and

    $\dfrac{1}{2}$. We use the two consecutive asymptotes,

    $x = -\dfrac{\pi}{4}$ and $x = \dfrac{\pi}{4}$, to graph one full period

    of $y = \dfrac{1}{2} \tan 2x$ from $-\dfrac{\pi}{4}$ to $\dfrac{\pi}{4}$. We

    continue the pattern and extend the graph another full period to the right.

9. We solve the equations

$$\frac{1}{2}x = -\frac{\pi}{2} \quad \text{and} \quad \frac{1}{2}x = \frac{\pi}{2}$$

$$x = \left(-\frac{\pi}{2}\right)2 \qquad x = \left(\frac{\pi}{2}\right)2$$

$$x = -\pi \qquad\qquad x = \pi$$

Thus, two consecutive asymptotes occur at $x = -\pi$ and $x = \pi$.

$$x\text{-intercept} = \frac{-\pi + \pi}{2} = \frac{0}{2} = 0$$

An x-intercept is 0 and the graph passes through $(0, 0)$. Because the coefficient of the tangent is –2, the points on the graph midway between an x-intercept and the asymptotes have y-coordinates of 2 and –2. We use the two consecutive asymptotes, $x = -\pi$ and $x = \pi$, to graph one full period of $y = -2\tan\frac{1}{2}x$ from $-\pi$ to π. We continue the pattern and extend the graph another full period to the right.

11. We solve the equations

$$x - \pi = -\frac{\pi}{2} \qquad \text{and} \quad x - \pi = \frac{\pi}{2}$$

$$x = -\frac{\pi}{2} + \pi \qquad\qquad x = \frac{\pi}{2} + \pi$$

$$x = \frac{\pi}{2} \qquad\qquad\qquad x = \frac{3\pi}{2}$$

Thus, two consecutive asymptotes occur at $x = \frac{\pi}{2}$ and $x = \frac{3\pi}{2}$.

$$x\text{-intercept} = \frac{\frac{\pi}{2} + \frac{3\pi}{2}}{2} = \frac{\frac{4\pi}{2}}{2} = \frac{4\pi}{4} = \pi$$

An x-intercept is π and the graph passes through $(\pi, 0)$. Because the coefficient of the tangent is 1, the points on the graph midway between an x-intercept and the asymptotes have y-coordinates of –1 and 1.

We use the two consecutive asymptotes, $x = \frac{\pi}{2}$ and $x = \frac{3\pi}{2}$, to graph one full period of $y = \tan(x - \pi)$ from $\frac{\pi}{2}$ to $\frac{3\pi}{2}$. We continue the pattern and extend the graph another full period to the right.

For 13 and 15, in the given functions, $B = 1$.

13. There is no phase shift. Thus,

$$\frac{C}{B} = 0$$

$$\frac{C}{1} = 0$$

$$C = 0$$

Because the points on the graph midway between an x-intercept and the asymptotes have y-coordinates of –1 and 1, $A = -1$. The function with $C = 0$ and $A = -1$ is $y = -\cot x$.

15. The graph has an asymptote at $-\frac{\pi}{2}$. The phase shift, $\frac{C}{B}$, from 0 to $-\frac{\pi}{2}$ is $-\frac{\pi}{2}$ units.

Thus, $\frac{C}{B} = -\frac{\pi}{2}$

$$\frac{C}{1} = -\frac{\pi}{2}$$

$$C = -\frac{\pi}{2}$$

The function with $C = -\frac{\pi}{2}$ is

$$y = \cot\left(x + \frac{\pi}{2}\right).$$

313

17. We solve the equations $x = 0$ and $x = \pi$.
Two consecutive asymptotes occur at
$x = 0$ and $x = \pi$.

$$x\text{-intercept} = \frac{0 + \pi}{2} = \frac{\pi}{2}$$

An x-intercept is $\frac{\pi}{2}$ and the graph passes

through $\left(\frac{\pi}{2}, 0\right)$. Because the coefficient of

the cotangent is 2, the points on the graph
midway between an x-intercept and the
asymptotes have y-coordinates of 2 and -2.
We use the two consecutive asymptotes,
$x = 0$ and $x = \pi$, to graph one full period of
$y = 2\cot x$. The curve is repeated along the
x-axis one full period as shown.

19. We solve the equations
$2x = 0$ and $2x = \pi$
$x = 0$ $\qquad x = \frac{\pi}{2}$
Two consecutive asymptotes occur at $x = 0$

and $x = \frac{\pi}{2}$.

$$x\text{-intercept} = \frac{0 + \frac{\pi}{2}}{2} = \frac{\frac{\pi}{2}}{2} = \frac{\pi}{4}$$

An x-intercept is $\frac{\pi}{4}$ and the graph passes

through $\left(\frac{\pi}{4}, 0\right)$. Because the coefficient of

the cotangent is $\frac{1}{2}$, the points on the graph

midway between an x-intercept and the

asymptotes have y-coordinates of $\frac{1}{2}$ and

$-\frac{1}{2}$. We use the two consecutive

asymptotes, $x = 0$ and $x = \frac{\pi}{2}$, to graph one

full period of $y = \frac{1}{2}\cot 2x$. The curve is

repeated along the x-axis one full period as
shown.

21. We solve the equations

$\frac{\pi}{2}x = 0$ and $\frac{\pi}{2}x = \pi$

$x = 0$ $\qquad x = \frac{\pi}{\frac{\pi}{2}}$

$\qquad\qquad\qquad x = 2$

Two consecutive asymptotes occur at $x = 0$
and $x = 2$.

$$x\text{-intercept} = \frac{0 + 2}{2} = \frac{2}{2} = 1$$

An x-intercept is 1 and the graph passes
through $(1, 0)$. Because the coefficient of the
cotangent is -3, the points on the graph
midway between an x-intercept and the
asymptotes have y-coordinates of -3 and 3.
We use the two consecutive asymptotes,
$x = 0$ and $x = 2$, to graph one full period of

$y = -3\cot\frac{\pi}{2}x$. The curve is repeated along

the x-axis one full period as shown.

23. We solve the equations

$$x + \frac{\pi}{2} = 0 \qquad \text{and} \quad x + \frac{\pi}{2} = \pi$$

$$x = 0 - \frac{\pi}{2} \qquad\qquad x = \pi - \frac{\pi}{2}$$

$$x = -\frac{\pi}{2} \qquad\qquad x = \frac{\pi}{2}$$

Two consecutive asymptotes occur at

$$x = -\frac{\pi}{2} \text{ and } x = \frac{\pi}{2}.$$

$$x\text{-intercept} = \frac{-\frac{\pi}{2} + \frac{\pi}{2}}{2} = \frac{0}{2} = 0$$

An x-intercept is 0 and the graph passes through $(0, 0)$. Because the coefficient of the cotangent is 3, the points on the graph midway between an x-intercept and the asymptotes have y-coordinates of 3 and -3. We use the two consecutive asymptotes,

$$x = -\frac{\pi}{2} \text{ and } x = \frac{\pi}{2}, \text{ to graph one full period}$$

of $y = 3\cot\left(x + \dfrac{\pi}{2}\right)$. The curve is repeated

along the x-axis one full period as shown.

25. The x-intercepts of $y = -\dfrac{1}{2}\sin\dfrac{x}{2}$ corresponds to vertical asymptotes of

$y = -\dfrac{1}{2}\csc\dfrac{x}{2}$. Draw the vertical asymptotes, and use them as a guide to sketch the graph

of $y = -\dfrac{1}{2}\csc\dfrac{x}{2}$.

27. The x-intercepts of $y = \dfrac{1}{2}\cos 2\pi x$ corresponds to vertical asymptotes of

$y = \dfrac{1}{2}\sec 2\pi x$. Draw the vertical asymptotes, and use them as a guide to sketch the graph

of $y = \dfrac{1}{2}\sec 2\pi x$.

29. Graph the reciprocal sine function, $y = 3\sin x$. The equation is of the form $y = A\sin Bx$ with $A = 3$ and $B = 1$.

amplitude: $|A| = |3| = 3$

period: $\dfrac{2\pi}{B} = \dfrac{2\pi}{1} = 2\pi$

Use quarter-periods, $\dfrac{\pi}{2}$, to find x-values for the five key points. Starting with $x = 0$, the x-values are 0, $\dfrac{\pi}{2}$, π, $\dfrac{3\pi}{2}$, and 2π.

Evaluating the function at each value of x, the key points are $(0, 0)$, $\left(\dfrac{\pi}{2}, 3\right)$, $(\pi, 0)$, $\left(\dfrac{3\pi}{2}, -3\right)$, and $(2\pi, 0)$. Use these key points to graph $y = 3\sin x$ from 0 to 2π. Extend the graph one cycle to the right. Use the graph to obtain the graph of the reciprocal function. Draw vertical asymptotes through the x-intercepts, and use them as guides to graph $y = 3\csc x$.

31. Graph the reciprocal sine function, $y = \dfrac{1}{2}\sin\dfrac{x}{2}$. The equation is of the form $y = A\sin Bx$ with $A = \dfrac{1}{2}$ and $B = \dfrac{1}{2}$.

amplitude: $|A| = \left|\dfrac{1}{2}\right| = \dfrac{1}{2}$

period: $\dfrac{2\pi}{B} = \dfrac{2\pi}{\frac{1}{2}} = 2\pi \cdot 2 = 4\pi$

Use quarter-periods, π, to find x-values for the five key points. Starting with $x = 0$, the x-values are 0, π, 2π, 3π, and 4π.

Evaluating the function at each value of x, the key points are $(0, 0)$, $\left(\pi, \dfrac{1}{2}\right)$, $(2\pi, 0)$, $\left(3\pi, -\dfrac{1}{2}\right)$, and $(4\pi, 0)$. Use these key points to graph $y = \dfrac{1}{2}\sin\dfrac{x}{2}$ from 0 to 4π. Extend the graph one cycle to the right. Use the graph to obtain the graph of the reciprocal function. Draw vertical asymptotes through the x-intercepts, and use them as guides to graph $y = \dfrac{1}{2}\csc\dfrac{x}{2}$.

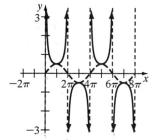

33. Graph the reciprocal cosine function, $y = 2\cos x$. The equation is of the form $y = A\cos Bx$ with $A = 2$ and $B = 1$.

    amplitude: $|A| = |2| = 2$

    period: $\dfrac{2\pi}{B} = \dfrac{2\pi}{1} = 2\pi$

    Use quarter-periods, $\dfrac{\pi}{2}$, to find x-values for the five key points. Starting with $x = 0$, the x-values are 0, $\dfrac{\pi}{2}$, π, $\dfrac{3\pi}{2}$, 2π. Evaluating the function at each value of x, the key points are $(0, 2)$, $\left(\dfrac{\pi}{2}, 0\right)$, $(\pi, -2)$, $\left(\dfrac{3\pi}{2}, 0\right)$, and $(2\pi, 2)$. Use these key points to graph $y = 2\cos x$ from 0 to 2π. Extend the graph one cycle to the right. Use the graph to obtain the graph of the reciprocal function. Draw vertical asymptotes through the x-intercepts, and use them as guides to graph $y = 2\sec x$.

35. Graph the reciprocal cosine function, $y = \cos\dfrac{x}{3}$. The equation is of the form $y = A\cos Bx$ with $A = 1$ and $B = \dfrac{1}{3}$.

    amplitude: $|A| = |1| = 1$

    period: $\dfrac{2\pi}{B} = \dfrac{2\pi}{\frac{1}{3}} = 2\pi \cdot 3 = 6\pi$

    Use quarter-periods, $\dfrac{6\pi}{4} = \dfrac{3\pi}{2}$, to find x-values for the five key points. Starting with $x = 0$, the x-values are 0, $\dfrac{3\pi}{2}$, 3π, $\dfrac{9\pi}{2}$, and 6π. Evaluating the function at each value of x, the key points are $(0, 1)$, $\left(\dfrac{3\pi}{2}, 0\right)$, $(3\pi, -1)$, $\left(\dfrac{9\pi}{2}, 0\right)$, and $(6\pi, 1)$. Use these key points to graph $y = \cos\dfrac{x}{3}$ from 0 to 6π. Extend the graph one cycle to the right. Use the graph to obtain the graph of the reciprocal function. Draw vertical asymptotes through the x-intercepts, and use them as guides to graph $y = \sec\dfrac{x}{3}$.

37. Graph the reciprocal sine function,
$y = -2\sin \pi x$. The equation is of the form
$y = A\sin Bx$ with $A = -2$ and $B = \pi$.

amplitude: $|A| = |-2| = 2$

period: $\dfrac{2\pi}{B} = \dfrac{2\pi}{\pi} = 2$

Use quarter-periods, $\dfrac{2}{4} = \dfrac{1}{2}$, to find
x-values for the five key points. Starting
with $x = 0$, the x-values are 0, $\dfrac{1}{2}$, 1, $\dfrac{3}{2}$, and
2. Evaluating the function at each value of x,
the key points are $(0, 0)$, $\left(\dfrac{1}{2}, -2\right)$, $(1, 0)$,

$\left(\dfrac{3}{2}, 2\right)$, and $(2, 0)$. Use these key points to
graph $y = -2\sin \pi x$ from 0 to 2. Extend the
graph one cycle to the right. Use the graph to
obtain the graph of the reciprocal function.
Draw vertical asymptotes through the
x-intercepts, and use them as guides to graph
$y = -2\csc \pi x$.

39. Graph the reciprocal cosine function,
$y = -\dfrac{1}{2}\cos \pi x$. The equation is of the form

$y = A\cos Bx$ with $A = -\dfrac{1}{2}$ and $B = \pi$.

amplitude: $|A| = \left|-\dfrac{1}{2}\right| = \dfrac{1}{2}$

period: $\dfrac{2\pi}{B} = \dfrac{2\pi}{\pi} = 2$

Use quarter-periods, $\dfrac{2}{4} = \dfrac{1}{2}$, to find x-values
for the five key points. Starting with $x = 0$,
the x-values are 0, $\dfrac{1}{2}$, 1, $\dfrac{3}{2}$, and 2.
Evaluating the function at each value of x,
the key points are $\left(0, -\dfrac{1}{2}\right)$, $\left(\dfrac{1}{2}, 0\right)$, $\left(1, \dfrac{1}{2}\right)$,

$\left(\dfrac{3}{2}, 0\right)$, $\left(2, -\dfrac{1}{2}\right)$. Use these key points to

graph $y = -\dfrac{1}{2}\cos \pi x$ from 0 to 2. Extend the
graph one cycle to the right. Use the graph to
obtain the graph of the reciprocal function.
Draw vertical asymptotes through the
x-intercepts, and use them as guides to graph

$y = -\dfrac{1}{2}\sec \pi x$.

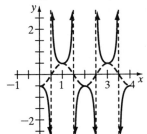

41. Graph the reciprocal sine function, $y = \sin(x - \pi)$. The equation is of the form $y = A\sin(Bx - C)$ with $A = 1$, and $B = 1$, and $C = \pi$.

amplitude: $|A| = |1| = 1$

period: $\dfrac{2\pi}{B} = \dfrac{2\pi}{1} = 2\pi$

phase shift: $\dfrac{C}{B} = \dfrac{\pi}{1} = \pi$

Use quarter-periods, $\dfrac{2\pi}{4} = \dfrac{\pi}{2}$, to find x-values for the five key points. Starting with $x = \pi$, the x-values are π, $\dfrac{3\pi}{2}$, 2π, $\dfrac{5\pi}{2}$, and 3π. Evaluating the function at each value of x, the key points are $(\pi, 0)$, $\left(\dfrac{3\pi}{2}, 1\right)$, $(2\pi, 0)$, $\left(\dfrac{5\pi}{2}, -1\right)$, $(3\pi, 0)$. Use these key points to graph $y = \sin(x - \pi)$ from π to 3π. Extend the graph one cycle to the right. Use the graph to obtain the graph of the reciprocal function. Draw vertical asymptotes through the x-intercepts, and use them as guides to graph $y = \csc(x - \pi)$.

43. Graph the reciprocal cosine function, $y = 2\cos(x + \pi)$. The equation is of the form $y = A\cos(Bx + C)$ with $A = 2$, $B = 1$, and $C = -\pi$.

amplitude: $|A| = |2| = 2$

period: $\dfrac{2\pi}{B} = \dfrac{2\pi}{1} = 2\pi$

phase shift: $\dfrac{C}{B} = \dfrac{-\pi}{1} = -\pi$

Use quarter-periods, $\dfrac{2\pi}{4} = \dfrac{\pi}{2}$, to find x-values for the five key points. Starting with $x = -\pi$, the x-values are $-\pi$, $-\dfrac{\pi}{2}$, 0, $\dfrac{\pi}{2}$, and π. Evaluating the function at each value of x, the key points are $(-\pi, 2)$, $\left(-\dfrac{\pi}{2}, 0\right)$, $(0, -2)$, $\left(\dfrac{\pi}{2}, 0\right)$, and $(\pi, 2)$. Use these key points to graph $y = 2\cos(x + \pi)$ from $-\pi$ to π. Extend the graph one cycle to the right. Use the graph to obtain the graph of the reciprocal function. Draw vertical asymptotes through the x-intercepts, and use them as guides to graph $y = 2\sec(x + \pi)$.

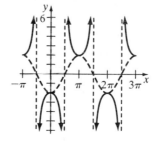

45. $d = 12 \tan 2\pi t$

   a. We solve the equations

$$2\pi t = -\frac{\pi}{2} \quad \text{and} \quad 2\pi t = \frac{\pi}{2}$$

$$t = \frac{-\frac{\pi}{2}}{2\pi} \qquad\qquad t = \frac{\frac{\pi}{2}}{2\pi}$$

$$t = -\frac{1}{4} \qquad\qquad t = \frac{1}{4}$$

Thus, two consecutive asymptotes occur

at $x = -\frac{1}{4}$ and $x = \frac{1}{4}$.

$$x\text{-intercept} = \frac{-\frac{1}{4}+\frac{1}{4}}{2} = \frac{0}{2} = 0$$

An x-intercept is 0 and the graph passes through $(0, 0)$. Because the coefficient of the tangent is 12, the points on the graph midway between an x-intercept and the asymptotes have y-coordinates of -12 and 12. Use the two consecutive

asymptotes, $x = -\frac{1}{4}$ and $x = \frac{1}{4}$, to

graph one full period of $d = 12 \tan 2\pi t$. To graph on $[0, 2]$, continue the pattern and extend the graph to 2. (We do not use the left hand side of the first period of the graph on $[0, 2]$.)

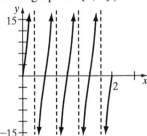

   b. The function is undefined for $t = 0.25$, 0.75, 1.25, and 1.75.
The beacon is shining parallel to the wall at these times.

47. We want a function that relates the acute angle with the hypotenuse and the adjacent leg. Use the secant function.

$$\sec x = \frac{d}{10}$$
$$d = 10 \sec x$$

Graph the reciprocal cosine function, $y = 10 \cos x$. The equation is of the form $y = A \cos Bx$ with $A = 10$ and $B = 1$.

amplitude: $|A| = |10| = 10$

period: $\dfrac{2\pi}{B} = \dfrac{2\pi}{1} = 2\pi$

For $-\dfrac{\pi}{2} < x < \dfrac{\pi}{2}$, use the x-values $-\dfrac{\pi}{2}$, 0,

and $\dfrac{\pi}{2}$ to find the key points $\left(-\dfrac{\pi}{2}, 0\right)$,

$(0, 10)$, and $\left(\dfrac{\pi}{2}, 0\right)$. Connect these points

with a smooth curve, then draw vertical asymptotes through the x-intercepts, and use them as guides to graph $d = 10 \sec x$ on

$$\left[-\frac{\pi}{2}, \frac{\pi}{2}\right].$$

49.

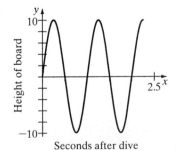

51.–57. Answers may vary.

For 59 and 61, the graphing utility graphs the asymptotes as a solid line when in the connected mode, but doesn't graph the asymptotes when in the dot mode.

59. Exercise 5

Exercise 7

61. Exercise 29

Exercise 31

63. period: $\dfrac{\pi}{B} = \dfrac{\pi}{\frac{1}{4}} = \pi \cdot 4 = 4\pi$

Graph $y = \tan \dfrac{x}{4}$ for $0 \le x \le 8\pi$.

65. period: $\dfrac{\pi}{B} = \dfrac{\pi}{2}$

Graph $y = \cot 2x$ for $0 \le x \le \pi$.

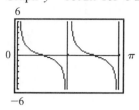

67. period: $\dfrac{\pi}{B} = \dfrac{\pi}{\pi} = 1$

Graph $y = \dfrac{1}{2}\tan \pi x$ for $0 \le x \le 2$.

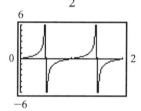

69. period: $\dfrac{2\pi}{B} = \dfrac{2\pi}{\frac{1}{2}} = 2\pi \cdot 2 = 4\pi$

Graph the functions for $0 \le x \le 8\pi$.

71. period: $\dfrac{2\pi}{B} = \dfrac{2\pi}{2} = \pi$

phase shift: $\dfrac{C}{B} = \dfrac{\frac{\pi}{6}}{2} = \dfrac{\pi}{12}$

Thus, we include $\dfrac{\pi}{12} \le x \le \dfrac{25\pi}{12}$ in our

graph, and graph for $0 \le x \le \dfrac{5\pi}{2}$.

73.

The graph shows that carbon dioxide concentration rises and falls each year, but over all the concentration increased from 1990 to 2000.

75. The graph has the shape of a cotangent function with consecutive asymptotes at $x = 0$ and $x = \dfrac{2\pi}{3}$. The period is

$$\frac{2\pi}{3} - 0 = \frac{2\pi}{3}. \text{ Thus,}$$

$$\frac{\pi}{B} = \frac{2\pi}{3}$$

$$2\pi B = 3\pi$$

$$B = \frac{3\pi}{2\pi} = \frac{3}{2}$$

The points on the graph midway between an x-intercept and the asymptotes have y-coordinates of 1 and -1. Thus, $A = 1$. There is no phase shift. Thus, $C = 0$. An equation for this graph is $y = \cot\dfrac{3}{2}x$.

77. $y = 2^{-x}\sin x$

2^{-x} decreases the amplitude as x gets larger. Examples may vary.

Section 5.7

Checkpoint Exercises

1. Let $\theta = \sin^{-1}\dfrac{\sqrt{3}}{2}$, then $\sin\theta = \dfrac{\sqrt{3}}{2}$.

The only angle in the interval $\left[-\dfrac{\pi}{2}, \dfrac{\pi}{2}\right]$ that

satisfies $\sin\theta = \dfrac{\sqrt{3}}{2}$ is $\dfrac{\pi}{3}$. Thus, $\theta = \dfrac{\pi}{3}$, or

$\sin^{-1}\dfrac{\sqrt{3}}{2} = \dfrac{\pi}{3}$.

2. Let $\theta = \sin^{-1}\left(-\dfrac{\sqrt{2}}{2}\right)$, then $\sin\theta = -\dfrac{\sqrt{2}}{2}$.

The only angle in the interval $\left[-\dfrac{\pi}{2}, \dfrac{\pi}{2}\right]$ that

satisfies $\cos\theta = -\dfrac{\sqrt{2}}{2}$ is $-\dfrac{\pi}{4}$. Thus

$\theta = -\dfrac{\pi}{4}$, or $\sin^{-1}\left(-\dfrac{\sqrt{2}}{2}\right) = -\dfrac{\pi}{4}$.

3. Let $\theta = \cos^{-1}\left(-\dfrac{1}{2}\right)$, then $\cos\theta = -\dfrac{1}{2}$. The

only angle in the interval $[0, \pi]$ that satisfies

$\cos\theta = -\dfrac{1}{2}$ is $\dfrac{2\pi}{3}$. Thus, $\theta = \dfrac{2\pi}{3}$, or

$\cos^{-1}\left(-\dfrac{1}{2}\right) = \dfrac{2\pi}{3}$.

4. Let $\theta = \tan^{-1}(-1)$, then $\tan\theta = -1$. The

only angle in the interval $\left(-\dfrac{\pi}{2}, \dfrac{\pi}{2}\right)$ that

satisfies $\tan\theta = -1$ is $-\dfrac{\pi}{4}$. Thus $\theta = -\dfrac{\pi}{4}$ or

$\tan^{-1}\theta = -\dfrac{\pi}{4}$.

5.

Scientific Calculator Solution			
Function	**Mode**	**Keystrokes**	**Display** (rounded to four places)
a. $\cos^{-1}\left(\dfrac{1}{3}\right)$	Radian	1 ÷ 3 = COS⁻¹	1.2310
b. $\tan^{-1}(-35.85)$	Radian	35.85 +/− TAN⁻¹	−1.5429

Graphing Calculator Solution			
Function	**Mode**	**Keystrokes**	**Display** (rounded to four places)
a. $\cos^{-1}\left(\dfrac{1}{3}\right)$	Radian	COS⁻¹ (1 ÷ 3) ENTER	1.2310
b. $\tan^{-1}(-35.85)$	Radian	TAN⁻¹ − 35.85 ENTER	−1.5429

6. a. $\cos\left(\cos^{-1} 0.7\right)$

$x = 0.7$, x is in $[-1, 1]$ so $\cos(\cos^{-1} 0.7) = 0.7$

b. $\sin^{-1}(\sin \pi)$

$x = \pi$, x is not in $\left[-\dfrac{\pi}{2}, \dfrac{\pi}{2}\right]$. x is in the domain of $\sin x$, so $\sin^{-1}(\sin \pi) = \sin^{-1}(0) = 0$

c. $\cos\left(\cos^{-1} \pi\right)$

$x = \pi$, x is not in $[-1, 1]$ so $\cos\left(\cos^{-1} \pi\right)$ is not defined.

7. Let $\theta = \tan^{-1}\left(\dfrac{3}{4}\right)$, then $\tan\theta = \dfrac{3}{4}$. Because $\tan\theta$ is positive, θ is in the first quadrant.

We use the Pythagorean Theorem to find r.

$r^2 = 3^2 + 4^2 = 9 + 16 = 25$

$r = \sqrt{25} = 5$

We use the right triangle to find the exact value.

$$\sin\left(\tan^{-1}\dfrac{3}{4}\right) = \sin\theta = \dfrac{\text{side opposite }\theta}{\text{hypotenuse}} = \dfrac{3}{5}$$

8. Let $\theta = \sin^{-1}\left(-\dfrac{1}{2}\right)$, then $\sin\theta = -\dfrac{1}{2}$.
Because $\sin\theta$ is negative, θ is in quadrant IV.

We use the Pythagorean Theorem to find x.

$x^2 + (-1)^2 = 2^2$

$x^2 + 1 = 4$

$x^2 = 3$

$x = \sqrt{3}$

We use values for x and r to find the exact value.

$$\cos\left[\sin^{-1}\left(-\dfrac{1}{2}\right)\right] = \cos\theta = \dfrac{x}{r} = \dfrac{\sqrt{3}}{2}$$

9. Let $\theta = \tan^{-1}x$, then $\tan\theta = x = \dfrac{x}{1}$.

We use the Pythagorean Theorem to find the third side, a.

$a^2 = x^2 + 1^2$

$a = \sqrt{x^2 + 1}$

We use the right triangle to write the algebraic expression.

$$\sec\left(\tan^{-1}x\right) = \sec\theta = \dfrac{\sqrt{x^2+1}}{1} = \sqrt{x^2+1}$$

Exercise Set 5.7

1. Let $\theta = \sin^{-1}\dfrac{1}{2}$, then $\sin\theta = \dfrac{1}{2}$. The only angle in the interval $\left[-\dfrac{\pi}{2}, \dfrac{\pi}{2}\right]$ that satisfies $\sin\theta = \dfrac{1}{2}$ is $\dfrac{\pi}{6}$. Thus, $\theta = \dfrac{\pi}{6}$, or $\sin^{-1}\dfrac{1}{2} = \dfrac{\pi}{6}$.

3. Let $\theta = \sin^{-1}\dfrac{\sqrt{2}}{2}$, then $\sin\theta = \dfrac{\sqrt{2}}{2}$. The only angle in the interval $\left[-\dfrac{\pi}{2}, \dfrac{\pi}{2}\right]$ that satisfies $\sin\theta = \dfrac{\sqrt{2}}{2}$ is $\dfrac{\pi}{4}$. Thus $\theta = \dfrac{\pi}{4}$, or $\sin^{-1}\dfrac{\sqrt{2}}{2} = \dfrac{\pi}{4}$.

5. Let $\theta = \sin^{-1}\left(-\dfrac{1}{2}\right)$, then $\sin\theta = -\dfrac{1}{2}$. The only angle in the interval $\left[-\dfrac{\pi}{2}, \dfrac{\pi}{2}\right]$ that satisfies $\sin\theta = -\dfrac{1}{2}$ is $-\dfrac{\pi}{6}$. Thus $\theta = -\dfrac{\pi}{6}$, or $\sin^{-1}\left(-\dfrac{1}{2}\right) = -\dfrac{\pi}{6}$.

7. Let $\theta = \cos^{-1} \dfrac{\sqrt{3}}{2}$, then $\cos\theta = \dfrac{\sqrt{3}}{2}$. The only angle in the interval $[0, \pi]$ that satisfies $\cos\theta = \dfrac{\sqrt{3}}{2}$ is $\dfrac{\pi}{6}$. Thus $\theta = \dfrac{\pi}{6}$, or $\cos^{-1} \dfrac{\sqrt{3}}{2} = \dfrac{\pi}{6}$.

9. Let $\theta = \cos^{-1}\left(-\dfrac{\sqrt{2}}{2}\right)$, then $\cos\theta = -\dfrac{\sqrt{2}}{2}$. The only angle in the interval $[0, \pi]$ that satisfies $\cos\theta = -\dfrac{\sqrt{2}}{2}$ is $\dfrac{3\pi}{4}$. Thus $\theta = \dfrac{3\pi}{4}$, or $\cos^{-1}\left(-\dfrac{\sqrt{2}}{2}\right) = \dfrac{3\pi}{4}$.

11. Let $\theta = \cos^{-1} 0$, then $\cos\theta = 0$. The only angle in the interval $[0, \pi]$ that satisfies $\cos\theta = 0$ is $\dfrac{\pi}{2}$. Thus $\theta = \dfrac{\pi}{2}$, or $\cos^{-1} 0 = \dfrac{\pi}{2}$.

13. Let $\theta = \tan^{-1} \dfrac{\sqrt{3}}{3}$, then $\tan\theta = \dfrac{\sqrt{3}}{3}$. The only angle in the interval $\left(-\dfrac{\pi}{2}, \dfrac{\pi}{2}\right)$ that satisfies $\tan\theta = \dfrac{\sqrt{3}}{3}$ is $\dfrac{\pi}{6}$. Thus $\theta = \dfrac{\pi}{6}$, or $\tan^{-1} \dfrac{\sqrt{3}}{3} = \dfrac{\pi}{6}$.

15. Let $\theta = \tan^{-1} 0$, then $\tan\theta = 0$. The only angle in the interval $\left(-\dfrac{\pi}{2}, \dfrac{\pi}{2}\right)$ that satisfies $\tan\theta = 0$ is 0. Thus $\theta = 0$, or $\tan^{-1} 0 = 0$.

17. Let $\theta = \tan^{-1}\left(-\sqrt{3}\right)$, then $\tan\theta = -\sqrt{3}$. The only angle in the interval $\left(-\dfrac{\pi}{2}, \dfrac{\pi}{2}\right)$ that satisfies $\tan\theta = -\sqrt{3}$ is $-\dfrac{\pi}{3}$. Thus $\theta = -\dfrac{\pi}{3}$, or $\tan^{-1}\left(-\sqrt{3}\right) = -\dfrac{\pi}{3}$.

19.

Scientific Calculator Solution			
Function	**Mode**	**Keystrokes**	**Display** (rounded to two places)
$\sin^{-1} 0.3$	Radian	0.3 $\boxed{\text{SIN}^{-1}}$	0.30

Graphing Calculator Solution			
Function	**Mode**	**Keystrokes**	**Display** (rounded to two places)
$\sin^{-1} 0.3$	Radian	$\boxed{\text{SIN}^{-1}}$ 0.3 $\boxed{\text{ENTER}}$	0.30

21.

Scientific Calculator Solution			
Function	**Mode**	**Keystrokes**	**Display** (rounded to two places)
$\sin^{-1}(-0.32)$	Radian	0.32 $\boxed{+/-}$ $\boxed{\text{SIN}^{-1}}$	-0.33

Graphing Calculator Solution			
Function	**Mode**	**Keystrokes**	**Display** (rounded to two places)
$\sin^{-1}(-0.32)$	Radian	$\boxed{\text{SIN}^{-1}}$ $\boxed{-}$ 0.32 $\boxed{\text{ENTER}}$	-0.33

23.

Scientific Calculator Solution			
Function	**Mode**	**Keystrokes**	**Display** (rounded to two places)
$\cos^{-1}\left(\dfrac{3}{8}\right)$	Radian	3 $\boxed{\div}$ 8 $\boxed{=}$ $\boxed{\text{COS}^{-1}}$	1.19

Graphing Calculator Solution			
Function	**Mode**	**Keystrokes**	**Display** (rounded to two places)
$\cos^{-1}\left(\dfrac{3}{8}\right)$	Radian	$\boxed{\text{COS}^{-1}}$ $\boxed{(}$ 3 $\boxed{\div}$ 8 $\boxed{)}$ $\boxed{\text{ENTER}}$	1.19

25.

Scientific Calculator Solution			
Function	**Mode**	**Keystrokes**	**Display** (rounded to two places)
$\cos^{-1}\dfrac{\sqrt{5}}{7}$	Radian	5 $\boxed{\sqrt{\ }}$ $\boxed{\div}$ 7 $\boxed{=}$ $\boxed{\text{COS}^{-1}}$	1.25

Graphing Calculator Solution			
Function	**Mode**	**Keystrokes**	**Display** (rounded to two places)
$\cos^{-1}\dfrac{\sqrt{5}}{7}$	Radian	$\boxed{\text{COS}^{-1}}$ $\boxed{(}$ $\boxed{\sqrt{\ }}$ 5 $\boxed{\div}$ 7 $\boxed{)}$ $\boxed{\text{ENTER}}$	1.25

27.

Scientific Calculator Solution			
Function	**Mode**	**Keystrokes**	**Display** (rounded to two places)
$\tan^{-1}(-20)$	Radian	20 $\boxed{+/-}$ $\boxed{\text{TAN}^{-1}}$	-1.52

Graphing Calculator Solution			
Function	**Mode**	**Keystrokes**	**Display** (rounded to two places)
$\tan^{-1}(-20)$	Radian	$\boxed{\text{TAN}^{-1}}$ $\boxed{-}$ 20 $\boxed{\text{ENTER}}$	-1.52

29.

Scientific Calculator Solution			
Function	**Mode**	**Keystrokes**	**Display** (rounded to two places)
$\tan^{-1}\left(-\sqrt{473}\right)$	Radian	473 $\boxed{\sqrt{}}$ $\boxed{+/-}$ $\boxed{\text{TAN}^{-1}}$	-1.52

Graphing Calculator Solution			
Function	**Mode**	**Keystrokes**	**Display** (rounded to two places)
$\tan^{-1}\left(-\sqrt{473}\right)$	Radian	$\boxed{\text{TAN}^{-1}}$ $\boxed{(}$ $\boxed{-}$ $\boxed{\sqrt{}}$ 473 $\boxed{)}$ $\boxed{\text{ENTER}}$	-1.52

31. $\sin\left(\sin^{-1}0.9\right)$

$x = 0.9$, x is in $[-1, 1]$, so $\sin(\sin^{-1}0.9) = 0.9$

33. $\sin^{-1}\left(\sin\dfrac{\pi}{3}\right)$

$x = \dfrac{\pi}{3}$, x is in $\left[-\dfrac{\pi}{2}, \dfrac{\pi}{2}\right]$, so $\sin^{-1}\left(\sin\dfrac{\pi}{3}\right) = \dfrac{\pi}{3}$

35. $\sin^{-1}\left(\sin\dfrac{5\pi}{6}\right)$

$x = \dfrac{5\pi}{6}$, x is not in $\left[-\dfrac{\pi}{2}, \dfrac{\pi}{2}\right]$, x is in the domain of $\sin x$, so $\sin^{-1}\left(\sin\dfrac{5\pi}{6}\right) = \sin^{-1}\left(\dfrac{1}{2}\right) = \dfrac{\pi}{6}$

37. $\tan\left(\tan^{-1}125\right)$

$x = 125$, x is a real number, so $\tan\left(\tan^{-1}125\right) = 125$

39. $\tan^{-1}\left[\tan\left(-\dfrac{\pi}{6}\right)\right]$

$x = -\dfrac{\pi}{6}$, x is in $\left(-\dfrac{\pi}{2}, \dfrac{\pi}{2}\right)$, so $\tan^{-1}\left[\tan\left(-\dfrac{\pi}{6}\right)\right] = -\dfrac{\pi}{6}$

41. $\tan^{-1}\left(\tan\dfrac{2\pi}{3}\right)$

$x = \dfrac{2\pi}{3}$, x is not in $\left(-\dfrac{\pi}{2}, \dfrac{\pi}{2}\right)$, x is in the domain of $\tan x$, so $\tan^{-1}\left(\tan\dfrac{2\pi}{3}\right) = \tan^{-1}\left(-\sqrt{3}\right) = -\dfrac{\pi}{3}$

43. $\sin^{-1}(\sin \pi)$

$x = \pi$, x is not in $\left[-\dfrac{\pi}{2}, \dfrac{\pi}{2}\right]$,

x is in the domain of $\sin x$, so

$\sin^{-1}(\sin \pi) = \sin^{-1} 0 = 0$

45. $\sin\left(\sin^{-1} \pi\right)$

$x = \pi$, x is not in $[-1, 1]$, so $\sin\left(\sin^{-1} \pi\right)$ is

not defined.

47. Let $\theta = \sin^{-1} \dfrac{4}{5}$, then $\sin \theta = \dfrac{4}{5}$. Because

$\sin \theta$ is positive, θ is in the first quadrant.

We use the Pythagorean Theorem to find x.

$x^2 + 4^2 = 5^2$

$\qquad x^2 = 25 - 16 = 9$

$\qquad\quad x = 3$

We use the right triangle to find the exact value.

$\cos\left(\sin^{-1} \dfrac{4}{5}\right) = \cos \theta = \dfrac{3}{5}$

49. Let $\theta = \cos^{-1} \dfrac{5}{13}$, then $\cos \theta = \dfrac{5}{13}$. Because

$\cos \theta$ is positive, θ is in the first quadrant.

We use the Pythagorean Theorem to find y.

$y^2 + 5^2 = 13^2$

$\qquad y^2 = 169 - 25 = 144$

$\qquad\quad y = 12$

We use the right triangle to find the exact value.

$\tan\left(\cos^{-1} \dfrac{5}{13}\right) = \tan \theta = \dfrac{12}{5}$

51. Let $\theta = \sin^{-1}\left(-\dfrac{3}{5}\right)$, then $\sin \theta = -\dfrac{3}{5}$.

Because $\sin \theta$ is negative, θ is in quadrant IV.

We use the Pythagorean Theorem to find x.

$x^2 + (-3)^2 = 5^2$

$\qquad x^2 = 25 - 9 = 16$

$\qquad\quad x = 4$

We use the right triangle to find the exact value.

$\tan\left[\sin^{-1}\left(-\dfrac{3}{5}\right)\right] = \tan \theta = -\dfrac{3}{4}$

53. Let, $\theta = \cos^{-1} \dfrac{\sqrt{2}}{2}$, then $\cos \theta = \dfrac{\sqrt{2}}{2}$.

Because $\cos \theta$ is positive, θ is in the first quadrant.

We use the Pythagorean Theorem to find y.

$\left(\sqrt{2}\right)^2 + y^2 = 2^2$

$\qquad y^2 = 4 - 2 = 2$

$\qquad\quad y = \sqrt{2}$

We use the right triangle to find the exact value.

$\sin\left(\cos^{-1} \dfrac{\sqrt{2}}{2}\right) = \sin \theta = \dfrac{\sqrt{2}}{2}$

55. Let $\theta = \sin^{-1}\left(-\dfrac{1}{4}\right)$, then $\sin\theta = -\dfrac{1}{4}$.

Because $\sin\theta$ is negative, θ is in quadrant IV.

We use the Pythagorean Theorem to find x.

$$x^2 + (-1)^2 = 4^2$$
$$x^2 = 16 - 1 = 15$$
$$x = \sqrt{15}$$

We use the right triangle to find the exact value.

$$\sec\left[\sin^{-1}\left(-\frac{1}{4}\right)\right] = \sec\theta = \frac{4}{\sqrt{15}} = \frac{4}{\sqrt{15}} \cdot \frac{\sqrt{15}}{\sqrt{15}}$$
$$= \frac{4\sqrt{15}}{15}$$

57. Let $\theta = \cos^{-1}\left(-\dfrac{1}{3}\right)$, then $\cos\theta = -\dfrac{1}{3}$.

Because $\cos\theta$ is negative, θ is in quadrant II.

We use the Pythagorean Theorem to find y.

$$(-1)^2 + y^2 = 3^2$$
$$y^2 = 9 - 1 = 8$$
$$y = \sqrt{8} = 2\sqrt{2}$$

We use the right triangle to find the exact value.

$$\tan\left[\cos^{-1}\left(-\frac{1}{3}\right)\right] = \tan\theta = \frac{2\sqrt{2}}{-1} = -2\sqrt{2}$$

59. Let $\theta = \cos^{-1}\left(-\dfrac{\sqrt{3}}{2}\right)$, then $\cos\theta = -\dfrac{\sqrt{3}}{2}$.

Because $\cos\theta$ is negative, θ is in quadrant II.

We use the Pythagorean Theorem to find y.

$$\left(-\sqrt{3}\right)^2 + y^2 = 2^2$$
$$y^2 = 4 - 3 = 1$$
$$y = 1$$

We use the right triangle to find the exact value.

$$\csc\left[\cos^{-1}\left(-\frac{\sqrt{3}}{2}\right)\right] = \csc\theta = \frac{2}{1} = 2$$

61. Let $\theta = \cos^{-1} x$, then $\cos\theta = x = \dfrac{x}{1}$.

We use the Pythagorean Theorem to find the third side, b.

$$x^2 + b^2 = 1^2$$
$$b^2 = 1 - x^2$$
$$b = \sqrt{1 - x^2}$$

We use the right triangle to write the algebraic expression.

$$\tan\left(\cos^{-1} x\right) = \tan\theta = \frac{\sqrt{1 - x^2}}{x}$$

63. Let $\theta = \sin^{-1}\dfrac{1}{x}$, then $\sin\theta = \dfrac{1}{x}$.

We use the Pythagorean Theorem to find the third side, a.

$$a^2 + 1^2 = x^2$$
$$a^2 = x^2 - 1$$
$$a = \sqrt{x^2 - 1}$$

We use the right triangle to write the algebraic expression.

$$\cos\left(\sin^{-1}\frac{1}{x}\right) = \cos\theta = \frac{\sqrt{x^2 - 1}}{x}$$

65. Let $\theta = \sin^{-1}\dfrac{x}{\sqrt{x^2 + 4}}$, then

$$\sin\theta = \frac{x}{\sqrt{x^2 + 4}}.$$

We use the Pythagorean Theorem to find the third side, a.

$$a^2 + x^2 = \left(\sqrt{x^2 + 4}\right)^2$$
$$a^2 = x^2 + 4 - x^2 = 4$$
$$a = 2$$

We use the right triangle to write the algebraic expression.

$$\sec\left(\sin^{-1}\frac{x}{\sqrt{x^2 + 4}}\right) = \sec\theta = \frac{\sqrt{x^2 + 4}}{2}$$

67. a. $y = \sec x$ is the reciprocal of $y = \cos x$. The x-values for the key points in the interval $[0, \pi]$ are $0, \dfrac{\pi}{4}, \dfrac{\pi}{2}, \dfrac{3\pi}{4}$, and π. The key points are $(0, 1)$, $\left(\dfrac{\pi}{4}, \dfrac{\sqrt{2}}{2}\right)$, $\left(\dfrac{\pi}{2}, 0\right)$, $\left(\dfrac{3\pi}{4}, -\dfrac{\sqrt{2}}{2}\right)$, and $(\pi, -1)$,

We draw a vertical asymptote at $x = \dfrac{\pi}{2}$.

We now draw our graph from $(0, 1)$ through $\left(\dfrac{\pi}{4}, \sqrt{2}\right)$ to ∞ on the left side of the asymptote. From $-\infty$ on the right side of the asymptote through $\left(\dfrac{3\pi}{4}, -\sqrt{2}\right)$ to $(\pi, -1)$.

b. With this restricted domain, no horizontal line intersects the graph of $y = \sec x$ more than once, so the function is one-to-one and has an inverse function.

c. Reflecting the graph of the restricted secant function about the line $y = x$, we get the graph of $y = \sec^{-1} x$.

69. $\theta = \tan^{-1}\dfrac{33}{x} - \tan^{-1}\dfrac{8}{x}$

x	θ
5	$\tan^{-1}\dfrac{33}{5} - \tan^{-1}\dfrac{8}{5} \approx 0.408$ radians
10	$\tan^{-1}\dfrac{33}{10} - \tan^{-1}\dfrac{8}{10} \approx 0.602$ radians
15	$\tan^{-1}\dfrac{33}{15} - \tan^{-1}\dfrac{8}{15} \approx 0.654$ radians
20	$\tan^{-1}\dfrac{33}{20} - \tan^{-1}\dfrac{8}{20} \approx 0.645$ radians
25	$\tan^{-1}\dfrac{33}{25} - \tan^{-1}\dfrac{8}{25} \approx 0.613$ radians

71. $\theta = 2\tan^{-1}\dfrac{21.634}{28} \approx 1.3157$ radians;

$1.3157\left(\dfrac{180}{\pi}\right) \approx 75.4°$

73. $\tan^{-1}b - \tan^{-1}a = \tan^{-1}2 - \tan^{-1}0$
≈ 1.1071 square units

75.–85. Answers may vary.

87. The domain of $y = \cos^{-1}x$ is the interval $[-1, 1]$, and the range is the interval $[0, \pi]$. Because the second equation is the first equation with 1 subtracted from the variable, we will move our x max to π, and graph in a $\left[-\dfrac{\pi}{2}, \pi, \dfrac{\pi}{4}\right]$ by $[0, 4, 1]$ viewing rectangle.

The graph of the second equation is the graph of the first equation shifted right 1 unit.

89. The domain of $y = \sin^{-1}x$ is the interval $[-1, 1]$, and the range is $\left[-\dfrac{\pi}{2}, \dfrac{\pi}{2}\right]$. Because the second equation is the first equation plus 1, and with 2 added to the variable, we will move our y max to 3, and move our x min to $-\pi$, and graph in a $\left[-\pi, \dfrac{\pi}{2}, \dfrac{\pi}{2}\right]$ by $[-2, 3, 1]$ viewing rectangle.

The graph of the second equation is the graph of the first equation shifted left 2 units and up 1 unit.

91.

It seems $\sin^{-1}x + \cos^{-1}x = \dfrac{\pi}{2}$ for $-1 \le x \le 1$.

93. $2\sin^{-1}x = \dfrac{\pi}{4}$

$\sin^{-1}x = \dfrac{\pi}{8}$

$x = \sin\dfrac{\pi}{8}$

95. Let α equal the acute angle in the smaller right triangle.

$\tan\alpha = \dfrac{8}{x}$

so $\tan^{-1}\dfrac{8}{x} = \alpha$

$\tan(\alpha + \theta) = \dfrac{33}{x}$

so $\tan^{-1}\dfrac{33}{x} = \alpha + \theta$

$\theta = \alpha + \theta - \alpha = \tan^{-1}\dfrac{33}{x} - \tan^{-1}\dfrac{8}{x}$

Section 5.8

Checkpoint Exercises

1. We begin by finding the measure of angle B. Because $C = 90°$ and the sum of a triangle's angles is $180°$, we see that $A + B = 90°$. Thus, $B = 90° - A = 90° - 62.7° = 27.3°$. Now we find b. Because we have a known angle, a known opposite side, and an unknown adjacent side, we use the tangent function.

$$\tan 62.7° = \frac{8.4}{b}$$

$$b = \frac{8.4}{\tan 62.7°} \approx 4.34$$

Finally, we need to find c. Because we have a known angle, a known opposite side and an unknown hypotenuse, we use the sine function.

$$\sin 62.7° = \frac{8.4}{c}$$

$$c = \frac{8.4}{\sin 62.7} \approx 9.45$$

In summary, $B = 27.3°$, $b \approx 4.34$, and $c \approx 9.45$.

2. Using a right triangle, we have a known angle, an unknown opposite side, a, and a known adjacent side. Therefore, we use the tangent function.

$$\tan 85.4° = \frac{a}{80}$$

$$a = 80 \tan 85.4° \approx 994$$

The Eiffel tower is approximately 994 feet high.

3. Using a right triangle, we have an unknown angle, A, a known opposite side, and a known hypotenuse. Therefore, we use the sine function.

$$\sin A = \frac{6.7}{13.8}$$

$$A = \sin^{-1} \frac{6.7}{13.8} \approx 29.0°$$

The wire makes an angle of approximately $29.0°$ with the ground.

4. Using two right triangles, a smaller right triangle corresponding to the smaller angle of elevation drawn inside a larger right triangle corresponding to the larger angle of elevation, we have a known angle, an unknown opposite side, a in the smaller triangle, b in the larger triangle, and a known adjacent side in each triangle. Therefore, we use the tangent function.

$$\tan 32° = \frac{a}{800}$$

$$a = 800 \tan 32° \approx 499.9$$

$$\tan 35° = \frac{b}{800}$$

$$b = 800 \tan 35° \approx 560.2$$

The height of the sculpture of Lincoln's face is $560.2 - 499.9$, or approximately 60.3 feet.

5. a. We need the acute angle between ray OD and the north-south line through O. The measurement of this angle is given to be $25°$. The angle is measured from the south side of the north-south line and lies east of the north-south line. Thus, the bearing from O to D is S 25°E.

   b. We need the acute angle between ray OC and the north-south line through O. This angle measures $90° - 75° = 15°$. This angle is measured from the south side of the north-south line and lies west of the north-south line. Thus the bearing from O to C is S 15° W.

6. a. Your distance from the entrance to the trail system is represented by the hypotenuse, c, of a right triangle. Because we know the length of the two sides of the right triangle, we find c using the Pythagorean Theorem. We have

   $$c^2 = a^2 + b^2 = (2.3)^2 + (3.5)^2 = 17.54$$

   $$c = \sqrt{17.54} \approx 4.2$$

   You are approximately 4.2 miles from the entrance to the trail system.

b. To find your bearing from the entrance to the trail system, consider a north-south line passing through the entrance. The acute angle from this line to the ray on which you lie is $31° + \theta$. Because we are measuring the angle from the south side of the line and you are west of the entrance, your bearing from the entrance is $S(31° + \theta)W$. To find θ, we use a right triangle and the tangent function.

$$\tan\theta = \frac{3.5}{2.3}$$

$$\theta = \tan^{-1}\frac{3.5}{2.3} \approx 56.7°$$

Thus, $31° + \theta = 31° + 56.7° = 87.7°$. Your bearing from the entrance to the trail system is S 87.7° W.

7. When the object is released $(t = 0)$, the ball's distance, d, from its rest position is 6 inches down. Because it is down, d is negative: when $t = 0$, $d = -6$. Notice the greatest distance from rest position occurs at $t = 0$. Thus, we will use the equation with the cosine function, $y = a\cos\omega t$, to model the ball's motion. Recall that $|a|$ is the maximum distance. Because the ball initially moves down, $a = -6$. The value of ω can be found using the formula for the period.

$$\text{period} = \frac{2\pi}{\omega} = 4$$
$$2\pi = 4\omega$$
$$\omega = \frac{2\pi}{4} = \frac{\pi}{2}$$

Substitute these values into $d = a\cos wt$. The equation for the ball's simple harmonic motion is $d = -6\cos\frac{\pi}{2}t$.

8. We begin by identifying values for a and ω.

$d = 12\cos\frac{\pi}{4}t$, $a = 12$ and $\omega = \frac{\pi}{4}$.

a. The maximum displacement from the rest position is the amplitude. Because $a = 12$, the maximum displacement is 12 centimeters.

b. The frequency, f, is

$$f = \frac{\omega}{2\pi} = \frac{\frac{\pi}{4}}{2\pi} = \frac{\pi}{4}\cdot\frac{1}{2\pi} = \frac{1}{8}$$

The frequency is $\frac{1}{8}$ cycle per second.

c. The time required for one cycle is the period.

$$\text{period} = \frac{2\pi}{\omega} = \frac{2\pi}{\frac{\pi}{4}} = 2\pi\cdot\frac{4}{\pi} = 8$$

The time required for one cycle is 8 seconds.

Exercise Set 5.8

1. Find the measure of angle B. Because $C = 90°$, $A + B = 90°$. Thus, $B = 90° - A = 90° - 23.5° = 66.5°$. Because we have a known angle, a known adjacent side, and an unknown opposite side, we use the tangent function.

$$\tan 23.5° = \frac{a}{10}$$
$$a = 10\tan 23.5° \approx 4.35$$

Because we have a known angle, a known adjacent side, and an unknown hypotenuse, we use the cosine function.

$$\cos 23.5° = \frac{10}{c}$$
$$c = \frac{10}{\cos 23.5°} \approx 10.90$$

In summary, $B = 66.5°$, $a \approx 4.35$, and $c \approx 10.90$.

3. Find the measure of angle B. Because $C = 90°$, $A + B = 90°$. Thus, $B = 90° - A = 90° - 52.6° = 37.4°$. Because we have a known angle, a known hypotenuse, and an unknown opposite side, we use the sine function.

$$\sin 52.6 = \frac{a}{54}$$
$$a = 54\sin 52.6° \approx 42.90$$

Because we have a known angle, a known hypotenuse, and an unknown adjacent side, we use the cosine function.

$$\cos 52.6° = \frac{b}{54}$$
$$b = 54\cos 52.6° \approx 32.80$$

In summary, $B = 37.4°$, $a \approx 42.90$, and $b \approx 32.80$.

5. Find the measure of angle A. Because $C = 90°$, $A + B = 90°$.
Thus, $A = 90° - B = 90° - 16.8° = 73.2°$.
Because we have a known angle, a known opposite side and an unknown adjacent side, we use the tangent function.

$$\tan 16.8° = \frac{30.5}{a}$$

$$a = \frac{30.5}{\tan 16.8°} \approx 101.02$$

Because we have a known angle, a known opposite side, and an unknown hypotenuse, we use the sine function.

$$\sin 16.8° = \frac{30.5}{c}$$

$$c = \frac{30.5}{\sin 16.8°} \approx 105.52$$

In summary, $A = 73.2°$, $a \approx 101.02$, and $c \approx 105.52$.

7. Find the measure of angle A. Because we have a known hypotenuse, a known opposite side, and an unknown angle, we use the sine function.

$$\sin A = \frac{30.4}{50.2}$$

$$A = \sin^{-1}\left(\frac{30.4}{50.2}\right) \approx 37.3°$$

Find the measure of angle B. Because $C = 90°$, $A + B = 90°$. Thus,
$B = 90° - A \approx 90° - 37.3° = 52.7°$.
Because we have a known hypotenuse, a known opposite side, and an unknown adjacent side, we use the Pythagorean Theorem.

$$a^2 + b^2 = c^2$$

$$(30.4)^2 + b^2 = (50.2)^2$$

$$b^2 = (50.2)^2 - (30.4)^2 = 1595.88$$

$$b = \sqrt{1595.88} \approx 39.95$$

In summary, $A \approx 37.3°$, $B \approx 52.7°$, and $b \approx 39.95$.

9. Find the measure of angle A. Because we have a known opposite side, a known adjacent side, and an unknown angle, we use the tangent function.

$$\tan A = \frac{10.8}{24.7}$$

$$A = \tan^{-1}\left(\frac{10.8}{24.7}\right) \approx 23.6°$$

Find the measure of angle B. Because $C = 90°$, $A + B = 90°$.
Thus, $B = 90° - A \approx 90° - 23.6° = 66.4°$.
Because we have a known opposite side, a known adjacent side, and an unknown hypotenuse, we use the Pythagorean Theorem.

$$c^2 = a^2 + b^2 = (10.8)^2 + (24.7)^2 = 726.73$$

$$c = \sqrt{726.73} \approx 26.96$$

In summary, $A \approx 23.6°$, $B \approx 66.4°$, and $c \approx 26.96$.

11. Find the measure of angle A. Because we have a known hypotenuse, a known adjacent side, and unknown angle, we use the cosine function.

$$\cos A = \frac{2}{7}$$

$$A = \cos^{-1}\left(\frac{2}{7}\right) \approx 73.4°$$

Find the measure of angle B. Because $C = 90°$, $A + B = 90°$.
Thus, $B = 90° - A \approx 90° - 73.4° = 16.6°$.
Because we have a known hypotenuse, a known adjacent side, and an unknown opposite side, we use the Pythagorean Theorem.

$$a^2 + b^2 = c^2$$

$$a^2 + (2)^2 = (7)^2$$

$$a^2 = (7)^2 - (2)^2 = 45$$

$$a = \sqrt{45} \approx 6.71$$

In summary, $A \approx 73.4°$, $B \approx 16.6°$, and $a \approx 6.71$.

13. We need the acute angle between ray OA and the north-south line through O. This angle measure $90° - 75° = 15°$. This angle is measured from the north side of the north-south line and lies east of the north-south line. Thus, the bearing from O and A is N 15° E.

15. The measurement of this angle is given to be 80°. The angle is measured from the south side of the north-south line and lies west of the north-south line. Thus, the bearing from O to C is S 80° W.

17. When the object is released ($t = 0$), the object's distance, d, from its rest position is 6 centimeters down. Because it is down, d is negative: When $t = 0$, $d = -6$. Notice the greatest distance from rest position occurs at $t = 0$. Thus, we will use the equation with the cosine function, $y = a\cos\omega t$ to model the object's motion. Recall that $|a|$ is the maximum distance. Because the object initially moves down, $a = -6$. The value of ω can be found using the formula for the period.

$$\text{period} = \frac{2\pi}{\omega} = 4$$
$$2\pi = 4\omega$$
$$\omega = \frac{2\pi}{4} = \frac{\pi}{2}$$

Substitute these values into $d = a\cos\omega t$. The equation for the object's simple harmonic motion is $d = -6\cos\frac{\pi}{2}t$.

19. When the object is released ($t = 0$), the object's distance, d, from its rest position is 0 inches: When $t = 0$, $d = 0$. Therefore, we will use the equation with the sine function, $y = a\sin\omega t$, to model the object's motion.

Recall that $|a|$ is the maximum distance. Because the object initially moves up, and has an amplitude of 3 inches, $a = 3$. The value of ω can be found using the formula for the period.

$$\text{period} = \frac{2\pi}{\omega} = 1.5$$
$$2\pi = 1.5\omega$$
$$\omega = \frac{2\pi}{1.5} = \frac{4\pi}{3}$$

Substitute these values into $d = a\sin\omega t$. The equation for the object's simple harmonic motion is $d = 3\sin\frac{4\pi}{3}t$.

21. We begin by identifying values for a and ω.

$$d = 5\cos\frac{\pi}{2}t, \ a = 5 \text{ and } \omega = \frac{\pi}{2}$$

a. The maximum displacement from the rest position is the amplitude. Because $a = 5$, the maximum displacement is 5 inches.

b. The frequency, f, is

$$f = \frac{\omega}{2\pi} = \frac{\frac{\pi}{2}}{2\pi} = \frac{\pi}{2} \cdot \frac{1}{2\pi} = \frac{1}{4}.$$

The frequency is $\frac{1}{4}$ cycle per second.

c. The time required for one cycle is the period.

$$\text{period} = \frac{2\pi}{\omega} = \frac{2\pi}{\frac{\pi}{2}} = 2\pi \cdot \frac{2}{\pi} = 4$$

The time required for one cycle is 4 seconds.

23. We begin by identifying values for a and ω.
$$d = -6\cos 2\pi t, \ a = -6 \text{ and } \omega = 2\pi$$

a. The maximum displacement from the rest position is the amplitude. Because $a = -6$, the maximum displacement is 6 inches.

b. The frequency, f, is

$$f = \frac{\omega}{2\pi} = \frac{2\pi}{2\pi} = 1.$$

The frequency is 1 cycle per second.

c. The time required for one cycle is the period.

$$\text{period} = \frac{2\pi}{\omega} = \frac{2\pi}{2\pi} = 1$$

The time required for one cycle is 1 second.

25. We begin by identifying values for a and ω.

$$d = \frac{1}{2}\sin 2t, \ a = \frac{1}{2} \text{ and } \omega = 2$$

a. The maximum displacement from the rest position is the amplitude. Because $a = \frac{1}{2}$, the maximum displacement is $\frac{1}{2}$ inch.

b. The frequency, f, is

$$f = \frac{\omega}{2\pi} = \frac{2}{2\pi} = \frac{1}{\pi} \approx 0.32.$$

The frequency is approximately 0.32 cycle per second.

c. The time required for one cycle is the period.

$$\text{period} = \frac{2\pi}{\omega} = \frac{2\pi}{2} = \pi \approx 3.14$$

The time required for one cycle is approximately 3.14 seconds.

27. We begin by identifying values for a and ω.

$$d = -5\sin\frac{2\pi}{3}t, \ a = -5 \text{ and } \omega = \frac{2\pi}{3}$$

a. The maximum displacement from the rest position is the amplitude. Because $a = -5$, the maximum displacement is 5 inches.

b. The frequency, f, is

$$f = \frac{\omega}{2\pi} = \frac{\frac{2\pi}{3}}{2\pi} = \frac{2\pi}{3} \cdot \frac{1}{2\pi} = \frac{1}{3}.$$

The frequency is $\frac{1}{3}$ cycle per second.

c. The time required for one cycle is the period.

$$\text{period} = \frac{2\pi}{\omega} = \frac{2\pi}{\frac{2\pi}{3}} = 2\pi \cdot \frac{3}{2\pi} = 3$$

The time required for one cycle is 3 seconds.

29. Using a right triangle, we have a known angle, an unknown opposite side, a, and a known adjacent side. Therefore, we use tangent function.

$$\tan 21.3° = \frac{a}{5280}$$
$$a = 5280\tan 21.3° \approx 2059$$

The height of the tower is approximately 2059 feet.

31. Using a right triangle, we have a known angle, a known opposite side, and an unknown adjacent side, a. Therefore, we use the tangent function.

$$\tan 23.7° = \frac{305}{a}$$
$$a = \frac{305}{\tan 23.7°} \approx 695$$

The ship is approximately 695 feet from the statue's base.

33. The angle of depression from the helicopter to point P is equal to the angle of elevation from point P to the helicopter. Using a right triangle, we have a known angle, a known opposite side, and an unknown adjacent side, d. Therefore, we use the tangent function.

$$\tan 36° = \frac{1000}{d}$$
$$d = \frac{1000}{\tan 36°} \approx 1376$$

The island is approximately 1376 feet off the coast.

35. Using a right triangle, we have an unknown angle, A, a known opposite side, and a known hypotenuse. Therefore, we use the sine function.

$$\sin A = \frac{6}{23}$$
$$A = \sin^{-1}\left(\frac{6}{23}\right) \approx 15.1°$$

The ramp makes an angle of approximately 15.1° with the ground.

37. Using the two right triangles, we have a known angle, an unknown opposite side, a in the smaller triangle, b in the larger triangle, and a known adjacent side in each triangle. Therefore, we use the tangent function.

$$\tan 19.2° = \frac{a}{125}$$
$$a = 125\tan 19.2° \approx 43.5$$

$$\tan 31.7° = \frac{b}{125}$$
$$b = 125\tan 31.7° \approx 77.2$$

The balloon rises approximately $77.2 - 43.5$ or 33.7 feet.

39. Using a right triangle, we have a known angle, a known hypotenuse, and unknown sides. To find the opposite side, a, we use the sine function.

$$\sin 53° = \frac{a}{150}$$
$$a = 150 \sin 53° \approx 120$$

To find the adjacent side, b, we use the cosine function.

$$\cos 53° = \frac{b}{150}$$
$$b = 150 \cos 53° \approx 90$$

The boat has traveled approximately 90 miles north and 120 miles east.

41. The bearing from the fire to the second ranger is N 28° E. Using a right triangle, we have a known angle, a known opposite side, and an unknown adjacent side, b. Therefore, we use the tangent function.

$$\tan 28° = \frac{7}{b}$$
$$b = \frac{7}{\tan 28°} \approx 13.2$$

The first ranger is 13.2 miles from the fire, to the nearest tenth of a mile.

43. Using a right triangle, we have a known adjacent side, a known opposite side, and an unknown angle, A. Therefore, we use the tangent function.

$$\tan A = \frac{1.5}{2}$$
$$A = \tan\left(\frac{1.5}{2}\right) \approx 37°$$

We need the acute angle between the ray that runs from your house through your location, and the north-south line through your house. This angle measures approximately $90° - 37° = 53°$. This angle is measured from the north side of the north-south line and lies west of the north-south line. Thus, the bearing from your house to you is N 53° W.

45. To find the jet's bearing from the control tower, consider a north-south line passing through the tower. The acute angle from this line to the ray on which the jet lies is $35° + \theta$. Because we are measuring the angle from the north side of the line and the jet is east of the tower, the jet's bearing from the tower is N $(35° + \theta)$ E. To find θ, we use a right triangle and the tangent function.

$$\tan \theta = \frac{7}{5}$$
$$\theta = \tan^{-1}\left(\frac{7}{5}\right) \approx 54.5°$$

Thus, $35° + \theta = 35° + 54.5° = 89.5°$. The jet's bearing from the control tower is N 89.5° E.

47. The frequency, f, is $f = \frac{\omega}{2\pi}$, so

$$\frac{1}{2} = \frac{\omega}{2\pi}$$
$$\omega = \frac{1}{2} \cdot 2\pi = \pi$$

Because the amplitude is 6 feet, $a = 6$. Thus, the equation for the object's simple harmonic motion is $d = 6 \sin \pi t$.

49. The frequency, f, is $f = \frac{\omega}{2\pi}$, so

$$264 = \frac{\omega}{2\pi}$$
$$\omega = 264 \cdot 2\pi = 528\pi$$

Thus, the equation for the tuning fork's simple harmonic motion is $d = \sin 528\pi t$.

51.–57. Answers may vary.

59. $y = -6e^{-0.09x} \cos 2\pi x$

10 complete oscillations occur.

61. Let d be the adjacent side to the 40° angle. Using the right triangles, we have a known angle and unknown sides in both triangles. We use the tangent function.

$$\tan 20° = \frac{h}{75 + d}$$
$$h = (75 + d)\tan 20°$$

Also, $\tan 40° = \dfrac{h}{d}$

$$h = d\tan 40°$$

Using the transitive property we have

$$(75 + d)\tan 20° = d\tan 40°$$
$$75\tan 20° + d\tan 20° = d\tan 40°$$
$$d\tan 40° - d\tan 20° = 75\tan 20°$$
$$d(\tan 40° - \tan 20°) = 75\tan 20°$$
$$d = \frac{75\tan 20°}{\tan 40° - \tan 20°}$$

Thus, $h = d\tan 40°$

$$= \frac{75\tan 20°}{\tan 40° - \tan 20°}\tan 40° \approx 48$$

The height of the building is approximately 48 feet.

Review Exercises

1. A 190° angle is a positive angle. It has a counterclockwise rotation of 180° followed by a counterclockwise rotation of 10°. The angle lies in quadrant III and is shown in the following graph.

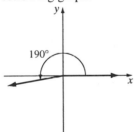

2. A −135° angle is a negative angle. It has a clockwise rotation of 90° followed by a clockwise rotation of 45°. The angle lies in quadrant III and is shown in the following graph.

3. A $\dfrac{5\pi}{6}$ angle is a positive angle. It has a counterclockwise rotation of $\dfrac{\pi}{2}$ followed by a counterclockwise rotation of $\dfrac{\pi}{3}$. The angle lies in quadrant II and is shown in the following graph.

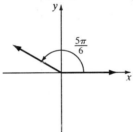

4. A $-\dfrac{2\pi}{3}$ angle is a negative angle. It has a clockwise rotation of $\dfrac{\pi}{2}$ followed by a clockwise rotation of $\dfrac{\pi}{6}$. The angle lies in quadrant III and is shown in the following graph.

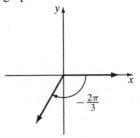

5. For a 400° angle, subtract 360°.
$$400° - 360° = 40°$$

6. For a $-85°$ angle, add $360°$.
$$-85° + 360° = 275°$$

7. complement $= 90° - 73° = 17°$;
supplement $= 180° - 73° = 107°$

8. no complement;
supplement $= \pi - \dfrac{2\pi}{3}$
$$= \dfrac{3\pi}{3} - \dfrac{2\pi}{3} = \dfrac{\pi}{3} \text{ radians}$$

9. The radian measure of a central angle is the length of the intercepted arc divided by the circle's radius.
$$\theta = \dfrac{27}{6} = 4.5 \text{ radians}$$

10. $15° = 15° \cdot \dfrac{\pi \text{ radians}}{180°} = \dfrac{15\pi}{180} \text{ radian}$
$$= \dfrac{\pi}{12} \text{ radian}$$

11. $120° = 120° \cdot \dfrac{\pi \text{ radians}}{180°} = \dfrac{120\pi}{180} \text{ radian}$
$$= \dfrac{2\pi}{3} \text{ radian}$$

12. $315° = 315° \cdot \dfrac{\pi \text{ radians}}{180°} = \dfrac{315\pi}{180} \text{ radian}$
$$= \dfrac{7\pi}{4} \text{ radian}$$

13. $\dfrac{5\pi}{3} \text{ radians} = \dfrac{5\pi}{3} \text{ radians} \cdot \dfrac{180°}{\pi \text{ radians}}$
$$= \dfrac{5 \cdot 180°}{3} = 300°$$

14. $\dfrac{7\pi}{5} \text{ radians} = \dfrac{7\pi}{5} \text{ radians} \cdot \dfrac{180°}{\pi \text{ radians}}$
$$= \dfrac{7 \cdot 180°}{5} = 252°$$

15. $-\dfrac{5\pi}{6} \text{ radians} = -\dfrac{5\pi}{6} \text{ radians} \cdot \dfrac{180°}{\pi \text{ radians}}$
$$= -\dfrac{5 \cdot 180°}{6} = -150°$$

16. $135° = 135° \cdot \dfrac{\pi \text{ radians}}{180°} = \dfrac{135 \cdot \pi}{180} \text{ radians}$
$$= \dfrac{3\pi}{4} \text{ radians}$$
$$s = r\theta$$
$$s = (10 \text{ ft})\left(\dfrac{3\pi}{4}\right) = \dfrac{15\pi}{2} \text{ ft} \approx 23.56 \text{ ft}$$

17. $\dfrac{10.3 \text{ revolutions}}{1 \text{ minute}} \cdot \dfrac{2\pi \text{ radians}}{1 \text{ revolution}}$
$$= \dfrac{20.6\pi \text{ radians}}{1 \text{ minute}} = 20.6\pi \text{ radians per minute}$$

18. Use $v = r\omega$ where v is the linear speed and ω is the angular speed in radians per minute.
$$\omega = \dfrac{2250 \text{ revolutions}}{1 \text{ minute}} \cdot \dfrac{2\pi \text{ radians}}{1 \text{ revolution}}$$
$$= 4500\pi \text{ radians per minute}$$
$$v = 3 \text{ feet} \dfrac{4500\pi}{\text{minute}} = \dfrac{13,500\pi \text{ feet}}{\text{min}}$$
$$\approx 42,412 \text{ ft per min}$$

19. Use the Pythagorean Theorem, $c^2 = a^2 + b^2$, to find c with $a = 9$ and $b = 12$.
$$c^2 = 9^2 + 12^2 = 225$$
$$c = \sqrt{225} = 15$$
$$\sin\theta = \dfrac{\text{opposite}}{\text{hypotenuse}} = \dfrac{9}{15} = \dfrac{3}{5}$$
$$\cos\theta = \dfrac{\text{adjacent}}{\text{hypotenuse}} = \dfrac{12}{15} = \dfrac{4}{5}$$
$$\tan\theta = \dfrac{\text{opposite}}{\text{adjacent}} = \dfrac{9}{12} = \dfrac{3}{4}$$
$$\csc\theta = \dfrac{\text{hypotenuse}}{\text{opposite}} = \dfrac{15}{9} = \dfrac{5}{3}$$
$$\sec\theta = \dfrac{\text{hypotenuse}}{\text{adjacent}} = \dfrac{15}{12} = \dfrac{5}{4}$$
$$\cot\theta = \dfrac{\text{adjacent}}{\text{opposite}} = \dfrac{12}{9} = \dfrac{4}{3}$$

20. Use a right triangle with a 60° angle. The side opposite 60° has length equal to $\sqrt{3}$, and the side adjacent to 60° has length equal to 1.

$$\tan 60° = \frac{\text{length of side opposite } 60°}{\text{length of side adjacent to } 60°}$$

$$= \frac{\sqrt{3}}{1} = \sqrt{3}$$

21. Use a right triangle with an angle of $\frac{\pi}{4}$ radian. Each leg has length equal to 1, and the hypotenuse has length equal to $\sqrt{2}$.

$$\cos \frac{\pi}{4} = \frac{\text{length of side adjacent to } \frac{\pi}{4}}{\text{length of hypotenuse}}$$

$$= \frac{1}{\sqrt{2}} = \frac{1}{\sqrt{2}} \cdot \frac{\sqrt{2}}{\sqrt{2}} = \frac{\sqrt{2}}{2}$$

22. Use a right triangle with an angle of $\frac{\pi}{6}$ radian. The side adjacent to $\frac{\pi}{6}$ has a length equal to $\sqrt{3}$, and the hypotenuse has length equal to 2.

$$\sec \frac{\pi}{6} = \frac{\text{length of hypotenuse}}{\text{length of side adjacent to } \frac{\pi}{6}}$$

$$= \frac{2}{\sqrt{3}} = \frac{2}{\sqrt{3}} \cdot \frac{\sqrt{3}}{\sqrt{3}} = \frac{2\sqrt{3}}{3}$$

23. $\sin^2 \frac{\pi}{5} + \cos^2 \frac{\pi}{5} = 1$
This is a Pythagorean Identity.

24. We can find the value of $\cos \theta$ by using the Pythagorean identity.
$$\sin^2 \theta + \cos^2 \theta = 1$$

$$\left(\frac{2}{\sqrt{7}} \right)^2 + \cos^2 \theta = 1$$

$$\frac{4}{7} + \cos^2 \theta = 1$$

$$\cos^2 \theta = 1 - \frac{4}{7}$$

$$\cos^2 \theta = \frac{3}{7}$$

$$\cos \theta = \frac{\sqrt{3}}{\sqrt{7}} = \frac{\sqrt{3}\sqrt{7}}{\sqrt{7} \cdot \sqrt{7}} = \frac{\sqrt{21}}{7}$$

Thus, $\cos \theta = \frac{\sqrt{21}}{7}$.

25. $\sin 70° = \cos(90° - 70°)$
$= \cos 20°$

26. $\cos \frac{\pi}{2} = \sin \left(\frac{\pi}{2} - \frac{\pi}{2} \right) = \sin 0$

27. $\tan 23° = \frac{a}{100}$
$a = 100 \tan 23°$
$a \approx 100(0.4245) \approx 42 \text{ mm}$

28. $\sin 61° = \frac{20}{c}$
$c = \frac{20}{\sin 61°}$
$c \approx \frac{20}{0.8746} \approx 23 \text{ cm}$

29. $\sin 48° = \frac{a}{50}$
$a = 50 \sin 48°$
$a \approx 50(0.7431) \approx 37 \text{ in.}$

30. $\frac{1}{2} \text{ mi.} = \frac{1}{2} \cdot 5280 \text{ ft} = 2640 \text{ ft}$
$\sin 17° = \frac{a}{2640}$
$a = 2640 \cdot \sin 17°$
$a \approx 2640(0.2924) \approx 772$
The hiker gains 772 feet of altitude.

31. $\tan 32° = \dfrac{d}{50}$

$\qquad d = 50 \tan 32°$

$\qquad d \approx 50(0.6249) \approx 31$

The distance across the lake is about 31 meters.

32. $\tan \theta = \dfrac{6}{4}$

Use a calculator in degree mode to find θ.

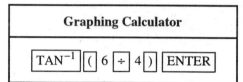

The display should show approximately 56. Thus, the angle of elevation of the sun is approximately 56°.

33. We need values for x, y, and r. Because $P = (-1, -5)$ is a point on the terminal side of θ, $x = -1$ and $y = -5$. Furthermore,

$$r = \sqrt{(-1)^2 + (-5)^2}$$
$$= \sqrt{1 + 25} = \sqrt{26}$$

Now that we know x, y, and r, we can find the six trigonometric functions of θ.

$\sin \theta = \dfrac{y}{r} = \dfrac{-5}{\sqrt{26}} = \dfrac{-5\sqrt{26}}{\sqrt{26} \cdot \sqrt{26}} = -\dfrac{5\sqrt{26}}{26}$

$\cos \theta = \dfrac{x}{r} = \dfrac{-1}{\sqrt{26}} = \dfrac{-1\sqrt{26}}{\sqrt{26} \cdot \sqrt{26}} = -\dfrac{\sqrt{26}}{26}$

$\tan \theta = \dfrac{y}{x} = \dfrac{-5}{-1} = 5$

$\csc \theta = \dfrac{r}{y} = \dfrac{\sqrt{26}}{-5} = -\dfrac{\sqrt{26}}{5}$

$\sec \theta = \dfrac{r}{x} = \dfrac{\sqrt{26}}{-1} = -\sqrt{26}$

$\cot \theta = \dfrac{x}{y} = \dfrac{-1}{-5} = \dfrac{1}{5}$

34. We need values for x, y, and r. Because $P = (0, -1)$ is a point on the terminal side of θ, $x = 0$ and $y = -1$. Furthermore,

$$r = \sqrt{x^2 + y^2} = \sqrt{0^2 + (-1)^2}$$
$$= \sqrt{0 + 1} = \sqrt{1} = 1$$

Now that we know x, y, and r, we can find the six trigonometric functions of θ.

$\sin \theta = \dfrac{y}{r} = \dfrac{-1}{1} = -1$

$\cos \theta = \dfrac{x}{r} = \dfrac{0}{1} = 0$

$\tan \theta = \dfrac{y}{x} = \dfrac{-1}{0}$, undefined

$\csc \theta = \dfrac{r}{y} = \dfrac{1}{-1} = -1$

$\sec \theta = \dfrac{r}{x} = \dfrac{1}{0}$, undefined

$\cot \theta = \dfrac{x}{y} = \dfrac{0}{-1} = 0$

35. Because $\tan \theta > 0$, θ cannot lie in quadrant II and quadrant IV; the tangent function is negative in those two quadrants. Thus, with $\tan \theta > 0$, θ lies in quadrant I or quadrant III. We are also given that $\sec \theta > 0$. Because quadrant I is the only quadrant in which the tangent is positive and the secant is positive, we conclude that θ lies in quadrant I.

36. Because $\tan \theta > 0$, θ cannot lie in quadrant II and quadrant IV; the tangent function is negative in those two quadrants. Thus, with $\tan \theta > 0$, θ lies in quadrant I or quadrant III. We are also given that $\cos \theta < 0$. Because quadrant III is the only quadrant in which the tangent is positive and the cosine is negative, we conclude that θ lies in quadrant III.

37. Because the cosine is positive and the sine is negative, θ lies in quadrant IV. In quadrant IV, x is positive and y is negative. Thus,

$\cos\theta = \dfrac{2}{5} = \dfrac{x}{r}$, $x = 2$, $r = 5$. Furthermore,

$$x^2 + y^2 = r^2$$
$$2^2 + y^2 = 5^2$$
$$y^2 = 25 - 4 = 21$$
$$y = -\sqrt{21}$$

Now that we know x, y, and r, we can find the six trigonometric functions of θ.

$$\sin\theta = \frac{y}{r} = \frac{-\sqrt{21}}{5} = -\frac{\sqrt{21}}{5}$$

$$\tan\theta = \frac{y}{x} = \frac{-\sqrt{21}}{2} = -\frac{\sqrt{21}}{2}$$

$$\csc\theta = \frac{r}{y} = \frac{5}{-\sqrt{21}} = -\frac{5\sqrt{21}}{\sqrt{21}\cdot\sqrt{21}} = -\frac{5\sqrt{21}}{21}$$

$$\sec\theta = \frac{r}{x} = \frac{5}{2}$$

$$\cot\theta = \frac{x}{y} = \frac{2}{-\sqrt{21}} = \frac{2\sqrt{21}}{\sqrt{21}\cdot\sqrt{21}} = \frac{2\sqrt{21}}{21}$$

38. Because the tangent is negative and the sine is positive, θ lies in quadrant II. In quadrant II x is negative and y is positive, Thus,

$\tan\theta = -\dfrac{1}{3} = \dfrac{y}{x} = \dfrac{1}{-3}$, $x = -3$, $y = 1$.

Furthermore,

$$r = \sqrt{x^2 + y^2} = \sqrt{(-3)^2 + 1^2} = \sqrt{9+1} = \sqrt{10}$$

Now that we know x, y, and r, we can find the six trigonometric functions of θ.

$$\sin\theta = \frac{y}{r} = \frac{1}{\sqrt{10}} = \frac{1\cdot\sqrt{10}}{\sqrt{10}\cdot\sqrt{10}} = \frac{\sqrt{10}}{10}$$

$$\cos\theta = \frac{x}{r} = \frac{-3}{\sqrt{10}} = -\frac{3\sqrt{10}}{\sqrt{10}\cdot\sqrt{10}} = -\frac{3\sqrt{10}}{10}$$

$$\csc\theta = \frac{r}{y} = \frac{\sqrt{10}}{1} = \sqrt{10}$$

$$\sec\theta = \frac{r}{x} = \frac{\sqrt{10}}{-3} = -\frac{\sqrt{10}}{3}$$

$$\cot\theta = \frac{x}{y} = \frac{-3}{1} = -3$$

39. Because $265°$ lies between $180°$ and $270°$, it is in quadrant III.
The reference angle is
$\theta' = 265° - 180° = 85°$.

40. Because $\dfrac{5\pi}{8}$ lies between $\dfrac{\pi}{2} = \dfrac{4\pi}{8}$ and $\pi = \dfrac{8\pi}{8}$, it is in quadrant II.
The reference angle is
$\theta' = \pi - \dfrac{5\pi}{8} = \dfrac{8\pi}{8} - \dfrac{5\pi}{8} = \dfrac{3\pi}{8}$.

41. Because $-410°$ lies between $-360°$ and $-450°$, it is in quadrant IV.
The reference angle is
$\theta' = 410° - 360° = 50°$.

42. $240°$ lies in quadrant III.
The reference angle is
$\theta' = 240° - 180° = 60°$.
$\sin 60° = \dfrac{\sqrt{3}}{2}$
In quadrant III, $\sin\theta < 0$, so
$\sin 240° = -\sin 60° = -\dfrac{\sqrt{3}}{2}$.

43. $120°$ lies in quadrant II.
The reference angle is
$\theta' = 180° - 120° = 60°$.
$\tan 60° = \sqrt{3}$
In quadrant II, $\tan\theta < 0$, so
$\tan 120° = -\tan 60° = -\sqrt{3}$.

44. $\dfrac{7\pi}{4}$ lies in quadrant IV.
The reference angle is
$\theta' = 2\pi - \dfrac{7\pi}{4} = \dfrac{8\pi}{4} - \dfrac{7\pi}{4} = \dfrac{\pi}{4}$.
$\sec\dfrac{\pi}{4} = \sqrt{2}$
In quadrant IV, $\sec\theta > 0$, so
$\sec\dfrac{7\pi}{4} = \sec\dfrac{\pi}{4} = \sqrt{2}$.

45. $\dfrac{11\pi}{6}$ lies in quadrant IV.

The reference angle is

$$\theta' = 2\pi - \frac{11\pi}{6} = \frac{12\pi}{6} - \frac{11\pi}{6} = \frac{\pi}{6}.$$

$$\cos\frac{\pi}{6} = \frac{\sqrt{3}}{2}$$

In quadrant IV, $\cos\theta > 0$, so

$$\cos\frac{11\pi}{6} = \cos\frac{\pi}{6} = \frac{\sqrt{3}}{2}.$$

46. $-210°$ lies in quadrant II.
The reference angle is
$\theta' = 210° - 180° = 30°$.
$\cot 30° = \sqrt{3}$
In quadrant II, $\cot\theta < 0$, so
$\cot(-210°) = -\cot 30° = -\sqrt{3}$.

47. $-\dfrac{2\pi}{3}$ lies in quadrant III.

The reference angle is

$$\theta' = \pi + \frac{-2\pi}{3} = \frac{3\pi}{3} - \frac{2\pi}{3} = \frac{\pi}{3}.$$

$$\csc\left(\frac{\pi}{3}\right) = \frac{2\sqrt{3}}{3}$$

In quadrant III, $\csc\theta < 0$, so

$$\csc\left(-\frac{2\pi}{3}\right) = -\csc\left(\frac{\pi}{3}\right) = -\frac{2\sqrt{3}}{3}.$$

48. $-\dfrac{\pi}{3}$ lies in quadrant IV.

The reference angle is

$$\theta' = \frac{\pi}{3}.$$

$$\sin\left(\frac{\pi}{3}\right) = \frac{\sqrt{3}}{2}$$

In quadrant IV, $\sin\theta < 0$, so

$$\sin\left(-\frac{\pi}{3}\right) = -\sin\left(\frac{\pi}{3}\right) = -\frac{\sqrt{3}}{2}.$$

49. $495°$ lies in quadrant II.
$495° - 360° = 135°$
The reference angle is
$\theta' = 180° - 135° = 45°$.

$$\sin 45° = \frac{\sqrt{2}}{2}$$

In quadrant II, $\sin\theta > 0$, so

$$\sin 495° = \sin 45° = \frac{\sqrt{2}}{2}.$$

50. $\dfrac{13\pi}{4}$ lies in quadrant III.

$$\frac{13\pi}{4} - 2\pi = \frac{13\pi}{4} - \frac{8\pi}{4} = \frac{5\pi}{4}$$

The reference angle is

$$\theta' = \frac{5\pi}{4} - \pi = \frac{5\pi}{4} - \frac{4\pi}{4} = \frac{\pi}{4}.$$

$$\tan\frac{\pi}{4} = 1$$

In quadrant III, $\tan\theta > 0$, so

$$\tan\frac{13\pi}{4} = \tan\frac{\pi}{4} = 1.$$

51. The equation $y = 3\sin 4x$ is of the form $y = A\sin Bx$ with $A = 3$ and $B = 4$. The amplitude is $|A| = |3| = 3$. The period is $\dfrac{2\pi}{B} = \dfrac{2\pi}{4} = \dfrac{\pi}{2}$. The quarter-period is $\dfrac{\frac{\pi}{2}}{4} = \dfrac{\pi}{2} \cdot \dfrac{1}{4} = \dfrac{\pi}{8}$. The cycle begins at $x = 0$.
Add quarter-periods to generate x-values for the key points.

$x = 0$

$x = 0 + \dfrac{\pi}{8} = \dfrac{\pi}{8}$

$x = \dfrac{\pi}{8} + \dfrac{\pi}{8} = \dfrac{\pi}{4}$

$x = \dfrac{\pi}{4} + \dfrac{\pi}{8} = \dfrac{3\pi}{8}$

$x = \dfrac{3\pi}{8} + \dfrac{\pi}{8} = \dfrac{\pi}{2}$

We evaluate the function at each value of x.

x	$y = 3\sin 4x$	coordinates
0	$y = 3\sin(4 \cdot 0) = 3\sin 0$ $= 3 \cdot 0 = 0$	$(0, 0)$
$\dfrac{\pi}{8}$	$y = 3\sin\left(4 \cdot \dfrac{\pi}{8}\right)$ $= 3\sin\dfrac{\pi}{2} = 3 \cdot 1 = 3$	$\left(\dfrac{\pi}{8}, 3\right)$
$\dfrac{\pi}{4}$	$y = 3\sin\left(4 \cdot \dfrac{\pi}{4}\right)$ $= 3\sin \pi = 3 \cdot 0 = 0$	$\left(\dfrac{\pi}{4}, 0\right)$
$\dfrac{3\pi}{8}$	$y = 3\sin\left(4 \cdot \dfrac{3\pi}{8}\right)$ $= 3\sin\dfrac{3\pi}{2} = 3 \cdot (-1)$ $= -3$	$\left(\dfrac{3\pi}{8}, -3\right)$
$\dfrac{\pi}{2}$	$y = 3\sin\left(4 \cdot \dfrac{\pi}{2}\right)$ $= 3\sin 2\pi = 3 \cdot 0$ $= 0$	$(2\pi, 0)$

Connect the five key points with a smooth curve and graph one complete cycle of the given function.

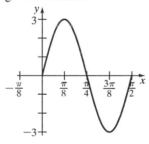

52. The equation $y = -2\cos 2x$ is of the form $y = A\cos Bx$ with $A = -2$ and $B = 2$. The amplitude is $|A| = |-2| = 2$. The period is $\dfrac{2\pi}{B} = \dfrac{2\pi}{2} = \pi$. The quarter-period is $\dfrac{\pi}{4}$. The cycle begins at $x = 0$. Add quarter-periods to generate x-values for the key points.

$x = 0$

$x = 0 + \dfrac{\pi}{4} = \dfrac{\pi}{4}$

$x = \dfrac{\pi}{4} + \dfrac{\pi}{4} = \dfrac{\pi}{2}$

$x = \dfrac{\pi}{2} + \dfrac{\pi}{4} = \dfrac{3\pi}{4}$

$x = \dfrac{3\pi}{4} + \dfrac{\pi}{4} = \pi$

We evaluate the function at each value of x.

x	$y = -2\cos 2x$	coordinates
0	$y = -2\cos(2 \cdot 0)$ $= -2\cos 0 = -2 \cdot 1$ $= -2$	$(0, -2)$
$\dfrac{\pi}{4}$	$y = -2\cos\left(2 \cdot \dfrac{\pi}{4}\right)$ $= -2\cos\dfrac{\pi}{2} = -2 \cdot 0$ $= 0$	$\left(\dfrac{\pi}{4}, 0\right)$
$\dfrac{\pi}{2}$	$y = -2\cos\left(2 \cdot \dfrac{\pi}{2}\right)$ $= -2\cos \pi = -2 \cdot -1$ $= 2$	$\left(\dfrac{\pi}{2}, 2\right)$
$\dfrac{3\pi}{4}$	$y = -2\cos\left(2 \cdot \dfrac{3\pi}{4}\right)$ $= -2\cos\dfrac{3\pi}{2} = -2 \cdot 0$ $= 0$	$\left(\dfrac{3\pi}{4}, 0\right)$
π	$y = -2\cos(2 \cdot \pi)$ $= -2\cos 2\pi = -2 \cdot 1$ $= -2$	$(\pi, -2)$

Connect the five key points with a smooth curve and graph one complete cycle of the given function.

53. The equation $y = 2\cos\dfrac{1}{2}x$ is of the form

$y = A\cos Bx$ with $A = 2$ and $B = \dfrac{1}{2}$. The

amplitude is $|A| = |2| = 2$. The period is

$\dfrac{2\pi}{B} = \dfrac{2\pi}{\frac{1}{2}} = 2\pi \cdot 2 = 4\pi$. The quarter-period

is $\dfrac{4\pi}{4} = \pi$. The cycle begins at $x = 0$. Add

quarter-periods to generate x-values for the
key points.
$x = 0$
$x = 0 + \pi = \pi$
$x = \pi + \pi = 2\pi$
$x = 2\pi + \pi = 3\pi$
$x = 3\pi + \pi = 4\pi$
We evaluate the function at each value of x.

x	$y = 2\cos\dfrac{1}{2}x$	coordinates
0	$y = 2\cos\left(\dfrac{1}{2}\cdot 0\right)$ $= 2\cos 0 = 2\cdot 1 = 2$	$(0, 2)$
π	$y = 2\cos\left(\dfrac{1}{2}\cdot \pi\right)$ $= 2\cos\dfrac{\pi}{2} = 2\cdot 0 = 0$	$(\pi, 0)$
2π	$y = 2\cos\left(\dfrac{1}{2}\cdot 2\pi\right)$ $= 2\cos\pi = 2\cdot(-1)$ $= -2$	$(2\pi, -2)$

3π	$y = 2\cos\left(\dfrac{1}{2}\cdot 3\pi\right)$ $= 2\cos\dfrac{3\pi}{2} = 2\cdot 0 = 0$	$(3\pi, 0)$
4π	$y = 2\cos\left(\dfrac{1}{2}\cdot 4\pi\right)$ $= 2\cos 2\pi = 2\cdot 1 = 2$	$(4\pi, 2)$

Connect the five key points with a smooth
curve and graph one complete cycle of the
given function.

54. The equation $y = \dfrac{1}{2}\sin\dfrac{\pi}{3}x$ is of the form

$y = A\sin Bx$ with $A = \dfrac{1}{2}$ and $B = \dfrac{\pi}{3}$. The

amplitude is $|A| = \left|\dfrac{1}{2}\right| = \dfrac{1}{2}$. The period is

$\dfrac{2\pi}{B} = \dfrac{2\pi}{\frac{\pi}{3}} = 2\pi \cdot \dfrac{3}{\pi} = 6$. The quarter-period is

$\dfrac{6}{4} = \dfrac{3}{2}$. The cycle begins at $x = 0$. Add

quarter-periods to generate x-values for the
key points.
$x = 0$
$x = 0 + \dfrac{3}{2} = \dfrac{3}{2}$
$x = \dfrac{3}{2} + \dfrac{3}{2} = 3$
$x = 3 + \dfrac{3}{2} = \dfrac{9}{2}$
$x = \dfrac{9}{2} + \dfrac{3}{2} = 6$
We evaluate the function at each value of x.

x	$y = \dfrac{1}{2}\sin\dfrac{\pi}{3}x$	coordinates
0	$y = \dfrac{1}{2}\sin\left(\dfrac{\pi}{3}\cdot 0\right)$ $= \dfrac{1}{2}\sin 0 = \dfrac{1}{2}\cdot 0 = 0$	$(0, 0)$
$\dfrac{3}{2}$	$y = \dfrac{1}{2}\sin\left(\dfrac{\pi}{3}\cdot\dfrac{3}{2}\right)$ $= \dfrac{1}{2}\sin\dfrac{\pi}{2} = \dfrac{1}{2}\cdot 1$ $= \dfrac{1}{2}$	$\left(\dfrac{3}{2}, \dfrac{1}{2}\right)$
3	$y = \dfrac{1}{2}\sin\left(\dfrac{\pi}{3}\cdot 3\right)$ $= \dfrac{1}{2}\sin\pi = \dfrac{1}{2}\cdot 0 = 0$	$(3, 0)$
$\dfrac{9}{2}$	$y = \dfrac{1}{2}\sin\left(\dfrac{\pi}{3}\cdot\dfrac{9}{2}\right)$ $= \dfrac{1}{2}\sin\dfrac{3\pi}{2} = \dfrac{1}{2}\cdot(-1)$ $= -\dfrac{1}{2}$	$\left(\dfrac{9}{2}, -\dfrac{1}{2}\right)$
6	$y = \dfrac{1}{2}\sin\left(\dfrac{\pi}{3}\cdot 6\right)$ $= \dfrac{1}{2}\sin 2\pi = \dfrac{1}{2}\cdot 0$ $= 0$	$(6, 0)$

Connect the five key points with a smooth curve and graph one complete cycle of the given function.

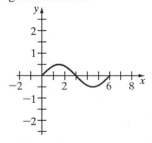

55. The equation $y = -\sin\pi x$ is of the form $y = A\sin Bx$ with $A = -1$ and $B = \pi$. The amplitude is $|A| = |-1| = 1$. The period is $\dfrac{2\pi}{B} = \dfrac{2\pi}{\pi} = 2$. The quarter-period is $\dfrac{2}{4} = \dfrac{1}{2}$. The cycle begins at $x = 0$. Add quarter-periods to generate x-values for the key points.

$x = 0$

$x = 0 + \dfrac{1}{2} = \dfrac{1}{2}$

$x = \dfrac{1}{2} + \dfrac{1}{2} = 1$

$x = 1 + \dfrac{1}{2} = \dfrac{3}{2}$

$x = \dfrac{3}{2} + \dfrac{1}{2} = 2$

We evaluate the function at each value of x.

x	$y = -\sin\pi x$	coordinates
0	$y = -\sin(\pi\cdot 0)$ $= -\sin 0 = -0 = 0$	$(0, 0)$
$\dfrac{1}{2}$	$y = -\sin\left(\pi\cdot\dfrac{1}{2}\right)$ $= -\sin\dfrac{\pi}{2} = -1$	$\left(\dfrac{1}{2}, -1\right)$
1	$y = -\sin(\pi\cdot 1)$ $= -\sin\pi = -0 = 0$	$(1, 0)$
$\dfrac{3}{2}$	$y = -\sin\left(\pi\cdot\dfrac{3}{2}\right)$ $= -\sin\dfrac{3\pi}{2}$ $= -(-1) = 1$	$\left(\dfrac{3}{2}, 1\right)$
2	$y = -\sin(\pi\cdot 2)$ $= -\sin 2\pi = -0 = 0$	$(2, 0)$

Connect the five key points with a smooth curve and graph one complete cycle of the given function.

56. The equation $y = 3\cos\dfrac{x}{3}$ is of the form

$y = A\cos Bx$ with $A = 3$ and $B = \dfrac{1}{3}$. The

amplitude is $|A| = |3| = 3$. The period is

$\dfrac{2\pi}{B} = \dfrac{2\pi}{\frac{1}{3}} = 2\pi \cdot 3 = 6\pi$. The quarter-period

is $\dfrac{6\pi}{4} = \dfrac{3\pi}{2}$. The cycle begins at $x = 0$. Add

quarter-periods to generate x-values for the
key points.

$x = 0$

$x = 0 + \dfrac{3\pi}{2} = \dfrac{3\pi}{2}$

$x = \dfrac{3\pi}{2} + \dfrac{3\pi}{2} = 3\pi$

$x = 3\pi + \dfrac{3\pi}{2} = \dfrac{9\pi}{2}$

$x = \dfrac{9\pi}{2} + \dfrac{3\pi}{2} = 6\pi$

We evaluate the function at each value of x.

x	$y = 3\cos\dfrac{x}{3}$	coordinates
0	$y = 3\cos\left(\dfrac{0}{3}\right)$ $= 3\cos 0 = 3 \cdot 1 = 3$	$(0, 3)$
$\dfrac{3\pi}{2}$	$y = 3\cos\left(\dfrac{\frac{3\pi}{2}}{3}\right)$ $= 3\cos\dfrac{\pi}{2} = 3 \cdot 0 = 0$	$\left(\dfrac{3\pi}{2}, 0\right)$

3π	$y = 3\cos\left(\dfrac{3\pi}{3}\right)$ $= 3\cos\pi = 3 \cdot (-1)$ $= -3$	$(3\pi, -3)$
$\dfrac{9\pi}{2}$	$y = 3\cos\left(\dfrac{\frac{9\pi}{2}}{3}\right)$ $= 3\cos\dfrac{3\pi}{2}$ $= 3 \cdot 0 = 0$	$\left(\dfrac{9\pi}{2}, 0\right)$
6π	$y = 3\cos\left(\dfrac{6\pi}{3}\right)$ $= 3\cos 2\pi$ $= 3 \cdot 1 = 3$	$(6\pi, 3)$

Connect the five key points with a smooth
curve and graph one complete cycle of the
given function.

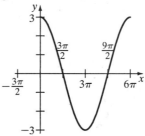

57. The equation $y = 2\sin(x - \pi)$ is of the form
$y = A\sin(Bx - C)$ with $A = 2$, $B = 1$, and
$C = \pi$. The amplitude is $|A| = |2| = 2$.

The period is $\dfrac{2\pi}{B} = \dfrac{2\pi}{1} = 2\pi$. The phase

shift is $\dfrac{C}{B} = \dfrac{\pi}{1} = \pi$. The quarter-period is

$\dfrac{2\pi}{4} = \dfrac{\pi}{2}$. The cycle begins at $x = \pi$. Add

quarter-periods to generate x-values for the
key points.

$x = \pi$

$x = \pi + \dfrac{\pi}{2} = \dfrac{3\pi}{2}$

$x = \dfrac{3\pi}{2} + \dfrac{\pi}{2} = 2\pi$

$x = 2\pi + \dfrac{\pi}{2} = \dfrac{5\pi}{2}$

$x = \dfrac{5\pi}{2} + \dfrac{\pi}{2} = 3\pi$

We evaluate the function at each value of x.

x	$y = 2\sin(x - \pi)$	coordinates
π	$y = 2\sin(\pi - \pi)$ $= 2\sin 0 = 2 \cdot 0 = 0$	$(\pi, 0)$
$\dfrac{3\pi}{2}$	$y = 2\sin\left(\dfrac{3\pi}{2} - \pi\right)$ $= 2\sin\dfrac{\pi}{2} = 2 \cdot 1 = 2$	$\left(\dfrac{3\pi}{2}, 2\right)$
2π	$y = 2\sin(2\pi - \pi)$ $= 2\sin \pi = 2 \cdot 0 = 0$	$(2\pi, 0)$
$\dfrac{5\pi}{2}$	$y = 2\sin\left(\dfrac{5\pi}{2} - \pi\right)$ $= 2\sin\dfrac{3\pi}{2} = 2 \cdot (-1)$ $= -2$	$\left(\dfrac{5\pi}{2}, -2\right)$
3π	$y = 2\sin(3\pi - \pi)$ $= 2\sin 2\pi = 2 \cdot 0 = 0$	$(3\pi, 0)$

Connect the five key points with a smooth curve and graph one complete cycle of the given function.

58. $y = -3\cos(x + \pi) = -3\cos(x - (-\pi))$
The equation $y = -3\cos(x - (-\pi))$ is of the form $y = A\cos(Bx - C)$ with $A = -3$,

$B = 1$, and $C = -\pi$. The amplitude is $|A| = |-3| = 3$.

The period is $\dfrac{2\pi}{B} = \dfrac{2\pi}{1} = 2\pi$. The phase shift is $\dfrac{C}{B} = \dfrac{-\pi}{1} = -\pi$. The quarter-period is $\dfrac{2\pi}{4} = \dfrac{\pi}{2}$. The cycle begins at $x = -\pi$. Add quarter-periods to generate x-values for the key points.

$x = -\pi$

$x = -\pi + \dfrac{\pi}{2} = -\dfrac{\pi}{2}$

$x = -\dfrac{\pi}{2} + \dfrac{\pi}{2} = 0$

$x = 0 + \dfrac{\pi}{2} = \dfrac{\pi}{2}$

$x = \dfrac{\pi}{2} + \dfrac{\pi}{2} = \pi$

We evaluate the function at each value of x.

x	$y = -3\cos(x + \pi)$	coordinates
$-\pi$	$y = -3\cos(-\pi + \pi)$ $= -3\cos 0 = -3 \cdot 1$ $= -3$	$(-\pi, -3)$
$-\dfrac{\pi}{2}$	$y = -3\cos\left(-\dfrac{\pi}{2} + \pi\right)$ $= -3\cos\dfrac{\pi}{2} = -3 \cdot 0$ $= 0$	$\left(-\dfrac{\pi}{2}, 0\right)$
0	$y = -3\cos(0 + \pi)$ $= -3\cos \pi = -3 \cdot (-1)$ $= 3$	$(0, 3)$
$\dfrac{\pi}{2}$	$y = -3\cos\left(\dfrac{\pi}{2} + \pi\right)$ $= -3\cos\dfrac{3\pi}{2} = -3 \cdot 0$ $= 0$	$\left(\dfrac{\pi}{2}, 0\right)$
π	$y = -3\cos(\pi + \pi)$ $= -3\cos 2\pi = -3 \cdot 1$ $= -3$	$(\pi, -3)$

Connect the five key points with a smooth curve and graph one complete cycle of the given function.

59. $y = \dfrac{3}{2}\cos\left(2x + \dfrac{\pi}{4}\right) = \dfrac{3}{2}\cos\left(2x - \left(-\dfrac{\pi}{4}\right)\right)$

The equation $y = \dfrac{3}{2}\cos\left(2x - \left(-\dfrac{\pi}{4}\right)\right)$ is of

the form $y = A\cos(Bx - C)$ with $A = \dfrac{3}{2}$,

$B = 2$, and $C = -\dfrac{\pi}{4}$. The amplitude is

$|A| = \left|\dfrac{3}{2}\right| = \dfrac{3}{2}$.

The period is $\dfrac{2\pi}{B} = \dfrac{2\pi}{2} = \pi$. The phase shift

is $\dfrac{C}{B} = \dfrac{-\frac{\pi}{4}}{2} = -\dfrac{\pi}{4} \cdot \dfrac{1}{2} = -\dfrac{\pi}{8}$. The quarter-

period is $\dfrac{\pi}{4}$. The cycle begins at $x = -\dfrac{\pi}{8}$.

Add quarter-periods to generate x-values for
the key points.

$x = -\dfrac{\pi}{8}$

$x = -\dfrac{\pi}{8} + \dfrac{\pi}{4} = \dfrac{\pi}{8}$

$x = \dfrac{\pi}{8} + \dfrac{\pi}{4} = \dfrac{3\pi}{8}$

$x = \dfrac{3\pi}{8} + \dfrac{\pi}{4} = \dfrac{5\pi}{8}$

$x = \dfrac{5\pi}{8} + \dfrac{\pi}{4} = \dfrac{7\pi}{8}$

We evaluate the function at each value of x.

x	$y = \dfrac{3}{2}\cos\left(2x + \dfrac{\pi}{4}\right)$	coordinates
$-\dfrac{\pi}{8}$	$y = \dfrac{3}{2}\cos\left(2 \cdot \left(-\dfrac{\pi}{8}\right) + \dfrac{\pi}{4}\right)$ $= \dfrac{3}{2}\cos\left(-\dfrac{\pi}{4} + \dfrac{\pi}{4}\right)$ $= \dfrac{3}{2}\cos 0 = \dfrac{3}{2} \cdot 1 = \dfrac{3}{2}$	$\left(-\dfrac{\pi}{8}, \dfrac{3}{2}\right)$
$\dfrac{\pi}{8}$	$y = \dfrac{3}{2}\cos\left(2 \cdot \dfrac{\pi}{8} + \dfrac{\pi}{4}\right)$ $= \dfrac{3}{2}\cos\left(\dfrac{\pi}{4} + \dfrac{\pi}{4}\right)$ $= \dfrac{3}{2}\cos\dfrac{\pi}{2} = \dfrac{3}{2} \cdot 0 = 0$	$\left(\dfrac{\pi}{8}, 0\right)$
$\dfrac{3\pi}{8}$	$y = \dfrac{3}{2}\cos\left(2 \cdot \dfrac{3\pi}{8} + \dfrac{\pi}{4}\right)$ $= \dfrac{3}{2}\cos\left(\dfrac{3\pi}{4} + \dfrac{\pi}{4}\right)$ $= \dfrac{3}{2}\cos\pi = \dfrac{3}{2} \cdot (-1)$ $= -\dfrac{3}{2}$	$\left(\dfrac{3\pi}{8}, -\dfrac{3}{2}\right)$
$\dfrac{5\pi}{8}$	$y = \dfrac{3}{2}\cos\left(2 \cdot \dfrac{5\pi}{8} + \dfrac{\pi}{4}\right)$ $= \dfrac{3}{2}\cos\left(\dfrac{5\pi}{4} + \dfrac{\pi}{4}\right)$ $= \dfrac{3}{2}\cos\dfrac{3\pi}{2}$ $= \dfrac{3}{2} \cdot 0 = 0$	$\left(\dfrac{5\pi}{8}, 0\right)$
$\dfrac{7\pi}{8}$	$y = \dfrac{3}{2}\cos\left(2 \cdot \dfrac{7\pi}{8} + \dfrac{\pi}{4}\right)$ $= \dfrac{3}{2}\cos\left(\dfrac{7\pi}{4} + \dfrac{\pi}{4}\right)$ $= \dfrac{3}{2}\cos 2\pi$ $= \dfrac{3}{2} \cdot 1 = \dfrac{3}{2}$	$\left(\dfrac{7\pi}{8}, \dfrac{3}{2}\right)$

Connect the five key points with a smooth curve and graph one complete cycle of the given function.

60. $y = \dfrac{5}{2}\sin\left(2x + \dfrac{\pi}{2}\right) = \dfrac{5}{2}\sin\left(2x - \left(-\dfrac{\pi}{2}\right)\right)$

The equation $y = \dfrac{5}{2}\sin\left(2x - \left(-\dfrac{\pi}{2}\right)\right)$ is of

the form $y = A\sin(Bx - C)$ with $A = \dfrac{5}{2}$,

$B = 2$, and $C = -\dfrac{\pi}{2}$. The amplitude is

$|A| = \left|\dfrac{5}{2}\right| = \dfrac{5}{2}$.

The period is $\dfrac{2\pi}{B} = \dfrac{2\pi}{2} = \pi$. The phase shift

is $\dfrac{C}{B} = \dfrac{-\frac{\pi}{2}}{2} = -\dfrac{\pi}{2}\cdot\dfrac{1}{2} = -\dfrac{\pi}{4}$. The quarter-

period is $\dfrac{\pi}{4}$. The cycle begins at $x = -\dfrac{\pi}{4}$.

Add quarter-periods to generate x-values for the key points.

$x = -\dfrac{\pi}{4}$

$x = -\dfrac{\pi}{4} + \dfrac{\pi}{4} = 0$

$x = 0 + \dfrac{\pi}{4} = \dfrac{\pi}{4}$

$x = \dfrac{\pi}{4} + \dfrac{\pi}{4} = \dfrac{\pi}{2}$

$x = \dfrac{\pi}{2} + \dfrac{\pi}{4} = \dfrac{3\pi}{4}$

We evaluate the function at each value of x.

x	$y = \dfrac{5}{2}\sin\left(2x + \dfrac{\pi}{2}\right)$	coordinates
$-\dfrac{\pi}{4}$	$y = \dfrac{5}{2}\sin\left(2\cdot\left(-\dfrac{\pi}{4}\right) + \dfrac{\pi}{2}\right)$ $= \dfrac{5}{2}\sin\left(-\dfrac{\pi}{2} + \dfrac{\pi}{2}\right)$ $= \dfrac{5}{2}\sin 0 = \dfrac{5}{2}\cdot 0 = 0$	$\left(-\dfrac{\pi}{4}, 0\right)$
0	$y = \dfrac{5}{2}\sin\left(2\cdot 0 + \dfrac{\pi}{2}\right)$ $= \dfrac{5}{2}\sin\left(0 + \dfrac{\pi}{2}\right)$ $= \dfrac{5}{2}\sin\dfrac{\pi}{2} = \dfrac{5}{2}\cdot 1 = \dfrac{5}{2}$	$\left(0, \dfrac{5}{2}\right)$
$\dfrac{\pi}{4}$	$y = \dfrac{5}{2}\sin\left(2\cdot\dfrac{\pi}{4} + \dfrac{\pi}{2}\right)$ $= \dfrac{5}{2}\sin\left(\dfrac{\pi}{2} + \dfrac{\pi}{2}\right)$ $= \dfrac{5}{2}\sin \pi = \dfrac{5}{2}\cdot 0 = 0$	$\left(\dfrac{\pi}{4}, 0\right)$
$\dfrac{\pi}{2}$	$y = \dfrac{5}{2}\sin\left(2\cdot\dfrac{\pi}{2} + \dfrac{\pi}{2}\right)$ $= \dfrac{5}{2}\sin\left(\pi + \dfrac{\pi}{2}\right)$ $= \dfrac{5}{2}\sin\dfrac{3\pi}{2} = \dfrac{5}{2}\cdot(-1)$ $= -\dfrac{5}{2}$	$\left(\dfrac{\pi}{2}, -\dfrac{5}{2}\right)$
$\dfrac{3\pi}{4}$	$y = \dfrac{5}{2}\sin\left(2\cdot\dfrac{3\pi}{4} + \dfrac{\pi}{2}\right)$ $= \dfrac{5}{2}\sin\left(\dfrac{3\pi}{2} + \dfrac{\pi}{2}\right)$ $= \dfrac{5}{2}\sin 2\pi = \dfrac{5}{2}\cdot 0 = 0$	$\left(\dfrac{3\pi}{4}, 0\right)$

Connect the five key points with a smooth curve and graph one complete cycle of the given function.

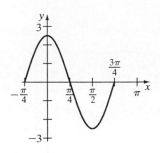

61. The equation $y = -3\sin\left(\dfrac{\pi}{3}x - 3\pi\right)$ is of

the form $y = A\sin(Bx - C)$ with $A = -3$,

$B = \dfrac{\pi}{3}$, and $C = 3\pi$. The amplitude is

$|A| = |-3| = 3$.

The period is $\dfrac{2\pi}{B} = \dfrac{2\pi}{\frac{\pi}{3}} = 2\pi \cdot \dfrac{3}{\pi} = 6$. The

phase shift is $\dfrac{C}{B} = \dfrac{3\pi}{\frac{\pi}{3}} = 3\pi \cdot \dfrac{3}{\pi} = 9$. The

quarter-period is $\dfrac{6}{4} = \dfrac{3}{2}$. The cycle begins

at $x = 9$. Add quarter-periods to generate
x-values for the key points.

$x = 9$

$x = 9 + \dfrac{3}{2} = \dfrac{21}{2}$

$x = \dfrac{21}{2} + \dfrac{3}{2} = 12$

$x = 12 + \dfrac{3}{2} = \dfrac{27}{2}$

$x = \dfrac{27}{2} + \dfrac{3}{2} = 15$

We evaluate the function at each value of x.

x	$y = -3\sin\left(\dfrac{\pi}{3}x - 3\pi\right)$	coordinates
9	$y = -3\sin\left(\dfrac{\pi}{3} \cdot 9 - 3\pi\right)$ $= -3\sin(3\pi - 3\pi)$ $= -3\sin 0 = -3 \cdot 0 = 0$	$(9, 0)$

$\dfrac{21}{2}$	$y = -3\sin\left(\dfrac{\pi}{3} \cdot \dfrac{21}{2} - 3\pi\right)$ $= -3\sin\left(\dfrac{7\pi}{2} - 3\pi\right)$ $= -3\sin\dfrac{\pi}{2} = -3 \cdot 1 = -3$	$\left(\dfrac{21}{2}, -3\right)$
12	$y = -3\sin\left(\dfrac{\pi}{3} \cdot 12 - 3\pi\right)$ $= -3\sin(4\pi - 3\pi)$ $= -3\sin \pi = -3 \cdot 0 = 0$	$(12, 0)$
$\dfrac{27}{2}$	$y = -3\sin\left(\dfrac{\pi}{3} \cdot \dfrac{27}{2} - 3\pi\right)$ $= -3\sin\left(\dfrac{9\pi}{2} - 3\pi\right)$ $= -3\sin\dfrac{3\pi}{2}$ $= -3 \cdot (-1) = 3$	$\left(\dfrac{27}{2}, 3\right)$
15	$y = -3\sin\left(\dfrac{\pi}{3} \cdot 15 - 3\pi\right)$ $= -3\sin(5\pi - 3\pi)$ $= -3\sin 2\pi = -3 \cdot 0 = 0$	$(15, 0)$

Connect the five key points with a smooth
curve and graph one complete cycle of the
given function.

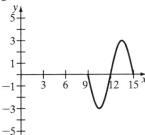

62. The graph of $y = \sin 2x + 1$ is the graph of
$y = \sin 2x$ shifted one unit upward. The

period for both functions is $\dfrac{2\pi}{2} = \pi$. The

quarter-period is $\dfrac{\pi}{4}$. The cycle begins at

$x = 0$. Add quarter-periods to generate
x-values for the key points.

$x = 0$

$x = 0 + \dfrac{\pi}{4} = \dfrac{\pi}{4}$

$x = \dfrac{\pi}{4} + \dfrac{\pi}{4} = \dfrac{\pi}{2}$

$x = \dfrac{\pi}{2} + \dfrac{\pi}{4} = \dfrac{3\pi}{4}$

$x = \dfrac{3\pi}{4} + \dfrac{\pi}{4} = \pi$

We evaluate the function at each value of x.

x	$y = \sin 2x + 1$	coordinates
0	$y = \sin(2 \cdot 0) + 1$ $= \sin 0 + 1 = 0 + 1 = 1$	$(0,\ 1)$
$\dfrac{\pi}{4}$	$y = \sin\!\left(2 \cdot \dfrac{\pi}{4}\right) + 1$ $= \sin\dfrac{\pi}{2} + 1 = 1 + 1 = 2$	$\left(\dfrac{\pi}{4},\ 2\right)$
$\dfrac{\pi}{2}$	$y = \sin\!\left(2 \cdot \dfrac{\pi}{2}\right) + 1$ $= \sin \pi + 1 = 0 + 1 = 1$	$\left(\dfrac{\pi}{2},\ 1\right)$
$\dfrac{3\pi}{4}$	$y = \sin\!\left(2 \cdot \dfrac{3\pi}{4}\right) + 1$ $= \sin\dfrac{3\pi}{2} + 1$ $= -1 + 1 = 0$	$\left(\dfrac{3\pi}{4},\ 0\right)$
π	$y = \sin(2 \cdot \pi) + 1$ $= \sin 2\pi + 1 = 0 + 1 = 1$	$(\pi,\ 1)$

By connecting the points with a smooth curve we obtain one period of the graph.

63. The graph of $y = 2\cos\dfrac{1}{3}x - 2$ is the graph

of $y = 2\cos\dfrac{1}{3}x$ shifted two units downward.
The period for both functions is

$\dfrac{2\pi}{\frac{1}{3}} = 2\pi \cdot 3 = 6\pi.$ The quarter-period is

$\dfrac{6\pi}{4} = \dfrac{3\pi}{2}.$ The cycle begins at $x = 0$. Add
quarter-periods to generate x-values for the
key points.

$x = 0$

$x = 0 + \dfrac{3\pi}{2} = \dfrac{3\pi}{2}$

$x = \dfrac{3\pi}{2} + \dfrac{3\pi}{2} = 3\pi$

$x = 3\pi + \dfrac{3\pi}{2} = \dfrac{9\pi}{2}$

$x = \dfrac{9\pi}{2} + \dfrac{3\pi}{2} = 6\pi$

We evaluate the function at each value of x.

x	$y = 2\cos\dfrac{1}{3}x - 2$	coordinates
0	$y = 2\cos\!\left(\dfrac{1}{3} \cdot 0\right) - 2$ $= 2\cos 0 - 2 = 2 \cdot 1 - 2$ $= 2 - 2 = 0$	$(0,\ 0)$
$\dfrac{3\pi}{2}$	$y = 2\cos\!\left(\dfrac{1}{3} \cdot \dfrac{3\pi}{2}\right) - 2$ $= 2\cos\dfrac{\pi}{2} - 2$ $= 2 \cdot 0 - 2 = 0 - 2$ $= -2$	$\left(\dfrac{3\pi}{2},\ -2\right)$
3π	$y = 2\cos\!\left(\dfrac{1}{3} \cdot 3\pi\right) - 2$ $= 2\cos \pi - 2$ $= 2 \cdot (-1) - 2 = -2 - 2$ $= -4$	$(3\pi,\ -4)$

$\dfrac{9\pi}{2}$	$y = 2\cos\left(\dfrac{1}{3}\cdot\dfrac{9\pi}{2}\right) - 2$	$\left(\dfrac{9\pi}{2},\ -2\right)$
	$= 2\cos\dfrac{3\pi}{2} - 2$	
	$= 2\cdot 0 - 2 = 0 - 2$	
	$= -2$	
6π	$y = 2\cos\left(\dfrac{1}{3}\cdot 6\pi\right) - 2$	$(6\pi,\ 0)$
	$= 2\cos 2\pi - 2$	
	$= 2\cdot 1 - 2 = 2 - 2$	
	$= 0$	

By connecting the points with a smooth curve we obtain one period of the graph.

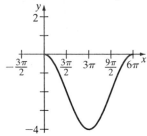

64. a. At midnight $x = 0$. Thus,

$$y = 98.6 + 0.3\sin\left(\dfrac{\pi}{12}\cdot 0 - \dfrac{11\pi}{12}\right)$$

$$= 98.6 + 0.3\sin\left(-\dfrac{11\pi}{12}\right)$$

$$\approx 98.6 + 0.3(-0.2588) \approx 98.52$$

The body temperature is about $98.52°$F.

b. period: $\dfrac{2\pi}{B} = \dfrac{2\pi}{\frac{\pi}{12}} = 2\pi\cdot\dfrac{12}{\pi} = 24$ hours

c. Solve the equation

$$\dfrac{\pi}{12}x - \dfrac{11\pi}{12} = \dfrac{\pi}{2}$$

$$\dfrac{\pi}{12}x = \dfrac{\pi}{2} + \dfrac{11\pi}{12} = \dfrac{6\pi}{12} + \dfrac{11\pi}{12} = \dfrac{17\pi}{12}$$

$$x = \dfrac{17\pi}{12}\cdot\dfrac{12}{\pi} = 17$$

The body temperature is highest for $x = 17$.

$$y = 98.6 + 0.3\sin\left(\dfrac{\pi}{12}\cdot 17 - \dfrac{11\pi}{12}\right)$$

$$= 98.6 + 0.3\sin\dfrac{\pi}{2} = 98.6 + 0.3 = 98.9$$

17 hours after midnight, which is 5 P.M., the body temperature is $98.9°$F.

d. Solve the equation

$$\dfrac{\pi}{12}x - \dfrac{11\pi}{12} = \dfrac{3\pi}{2}$$

$$\dfrac{\pi}{12}x = \dfrac{3\pi}{2} + \dfrac{11\pi}{12} = \dfrac{18\pi}{12} + \dfrac{11\pi}{12} = \dfrac{29\pi}{12}$$

$$x = \dfrac{29\pi}{12}\cdot\dfrac{12}{\pi} = 29$$

The body temperature is lowest for $x = 29$.

$$y = 98.6 + 0.3\sin\left(\dfrac{\pi}{12}\cdot 29 - \dfrac{11\pi}{12}\right)$$

$$= 98.6 + 0.3\sin\left(\dfrac{3\pi}{2}\right)$$

$$= 98.6 + 0.3(-1) = 98.3°$$

29 hours after midnight or 5 hours after midnight, at 5 A.M., the body temperature is $98.3°$F.

e. The graph of

$$y = 98.6 + 0.3\sin\left(\dfrac{\pi}{12}x - \dfrac{11\pi}{12}\right)\text{ is of the}$$

form $y = D + A\sin(Bx - C)$ with

$A = 0.3$, $B = \dfrac{\pi}{12}$, $C = \dfrac{11\pi}{12}$, and $D = 98.6$. The amplitude is $|A| = |0.3| = 0.3$. The period from part (b) is 24. The quarter-period is $\dfrac{24}{4} = 6$. The phase shift is

$$\dfrac{C}{B} = \dfrac{\frac{11\pi}{12}}{\frac{\pi}{12}} = \dfrac{11\pi}{12}\cdot\dfrac{12}{\pi} = 11.\text{ The cycle}$$

begins at $x = 11$. Add quarter-periods to generate x-values for the key points.

$x = 11$
$x = 11 + 6 = 17$
$x = 17 + 6 = 23$
$x = 23 + 6 = 29$
$x = 29 + 6 = 35$

We evaluate the function at each value of x. The key points are $(11, 98.6)$, $(17, 98.9)$, $(23, 98.6)$, $(29, 98.3)$, $(35, 98.6)$. We extend the pattern to the left, and graph the function for $0 \le x \le 24$.

Hours after midnight

65. We solve the equations

$$2x = -\frac{\pi}{2} \quad \text{and} \quad 2x = \frac{\pi}{2}$$

$$x = \frac{-\frac{\pi}{2}}{2} \qquad\qquad x = \frac{\frac{\pi}{2}}{2}$$

$$x = -\frac{\pi}{4} \qquad\qquad x = \frac{\pi}{4}$$

Thus, two consecutive asymptotes occur at

$$x = -\frac{\pi}{4} \text{ and } x = \frac{\pi}{4}.$$

$$x\text{-intercept} = \frac{-\frac{\pi}{4} + \frac{\pi}{4}}{2} = \frac{0}{2} = 0$$

An x-intercept is 0 and the graph passes through (0, 0). Because the coefficient of the tangent is 4, the points on the graph midway between an x-intercept and the asymptotes have y-coordinates of −4 and 4. We use the two consecutive asymptotes. $x = -\frac{\pi}{4}$ and

$x = \frac{\pi}{4}$, to graph one full period of

$y = 4\tan 2x$ from $-\frac{\pi}{4}$ to $\frac{\pi}{4}$. We continue

the pattern and extend the graph another full period to the right.

66. We solve the equations

$$\frac{\pi}{4}x = -\frac{\pi}{2} \quad \text{and} \quad \frac{\pi}{4}x = \frac{\pi}{2}$$

$$x = -\frac{\pi}{2} \cdot \frac{4}{\pi} \qquad\qquad x = \frac{\pi}{2} \cdot \frac{4}{\pi}$$

$$x = -2 \qquad\qquad\qquad x = 2$$

Thus, two consecutive asymptotes occur at $x = -2$ and $x = 2$.

$$x\text{-intercept} = \frac{-2+2}{2} = \frac{0}{2} = 0$$

An x-intercept is 0 and the graph passes through (0, 0). Because the coefficient of the tangent is −2, the points on the graph midway between an x-intercept and the asymptotes have y-coordinates of 2 and −2. We use the two consecutive asymptotes, $x = -2$ and $x = 2$, to graph one full period of

$y = -2\tan\frac{\pi}{4}x$ from −2 to 2. We continue

the pattern and extend the graph another full period to the right.

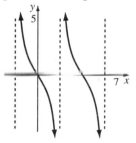

67. We solve the equations

$$x + \pi = -\frac{\pi}{2} \quad \text{and} \quad x + \pi = \frac{\pi}{2}$$

$$x = -\frac{\pi}{2} - \pi \qquad\qquad x = \frac{\pi}{2} - \pi$$

$$x = -\frac{3\pi}{2} \qquad\qquad x = -\frac{\pi}{2}$$

Thus, two consecutive asymptotes occur at

$$x = -\frac{3\pi}{2} \text{ and } x = -\frac{\pi}{2}.$$

$$x\text{-intercept} = \frac{-\frac{3\pi}{2} - \frac{\pi}{2}}{2} = \frac{-2\pi}{2} = -\pi$$

An x-intercept is $-\pi$ and the graph passes through $(-\pi, 0)$. Because the coefficient of the tangent is 1, the points on the graph midway between an x-intercept and the asymptotes have y-coordinates of −1 and 1.

We use the two consecutive asymptotes,

$x = -\dfrac{3\pi}{2}$ and $x = -\dfrac{\pi}{2}$, to graph one full

period of $y = \tan(x + \pi)$ from $-\dfrac{3\pi}{2}$ to $-\dfrac{\pi}{2}$.

We continue the pattern and extend the graph another full period to the right.

68. We solve the equations

$$x - \frac{\pi}{4} = -\frac{\pi}{2} \qquad \text{and} \qquad x - \frac{\pi}{4} = \frac{\pi}{2}$$
$$x = -\frac{\pi}{2} + \frac{\pi}{4} \qquad\qquad x = \frac{\pi}{2} + \frac{\pi}{4}$$
$$x = -\frac{\pi}{4} \qquad\qquad\qquad x = \frac{3\pi}{4}$$

Thus, two consecutive asymptotes occur at

$x = -\dfrac{\pi}{4}$ and $x = -\dfrac{3\pi}{4}$.

$$x\text{-intercept} = \frac{-\frac{\pi}{4} - \frac{3\pi}{4}}{2} = \frac{\frac{\pi}{2}}{2} = \frac{\pi}{4}$$

An x-intercept is $\dfrac{\pi}{4}$ and the graph passes

through $\left(\dfrac{\pi}{4}, 0\right)$. Because the coefficient of

the tangent is –1, the points on the graph midway between an x-intercept and the asymptotes have y-coordinates of 1 and –1. We use the two consecutive asymptotes,

$x = -\dfrac{\pi}{4}$ and $x = \dfrac{3\pi}{4}$, to graph one full

period of $y = -\tan\left(x - \dfrac{\pi}{4}\right)$ from $-\dfrac{\pi}{4}$ to

$\dfrac{3\pi}{4}$. We continue the pattern and extend the graph another full period to the right.

69. We solve the equations

$$3x = 0 \quad \text{and} \quad 3x = \pi$$
$$x = 0 \qquad\qquad x = \frac{\pi}{3}$$

Thus, two consecutive asymptotes occur at

$x = 0$ and $x = \dfrac{\pi}{3}$.

$$x\text{-intercept} = \frac{0 + \frac{\pi}{3}}{2} = \frac{\frac{\pi}{3}}{2} = \frac{\pi}{6}$$

An x-intercept is $\dfrac{\pi}{6}$ and the graph passes

through $\left(\dfrac{\pi}{6}, 0\right)$. Because the coefficient of

the tangent is 2, the points on the graph midway between an x-intercept and the asymptotes have y-coordinates of 2 and –2. We use the two consecutive asymptotes,

$x = 0$ and $x = \dfrac{\pi}{3}$, to graph one full period of

$y = 2\cot 3x$ from 0 to $\dfrac{\pi}{3}$. We continue the

pattern and extend the graph another full period to the right.

70. We solve the equations

$$\frac{\pi}{2}x = 0 \quad \text{and} \quad \frac{\pi}{2}x = \pi$$
$$x = 0 \qquad\qquad x = \pi \cdot \frac{2}{\pi}$$
$$x = 2$$

Thus, two consecutive asymptotes occur at $x = 0$ and $x = 2$.

$$x\text{-intercept} = \frac{0+2}{2} = \frac{2}{2} = 1$$

An x-intercept is 1 and the graph passes through $(1, 0)$. Because the coefficient of the cotangent is $-\frac{1}{2}$, the points on the graph midway between an x-intercept and the asymptotes have y-coordinates of $-\frac{1}{2}$ and $\frac{1}{2}$. We use the two consecutive asymptotes, $x = 0$ and $x = 2$, to graph one full period of $y = -\frac{1}{2}\cot\frac{\pi}{2}x$ from 0 to 2. We continue the pattern and extend the graph another full period to the right.

71. We solve the equations

$$x + \frac{\pi}{2} = 0 \qquad \text{and} \quad x + \frac{\pi}{2} = \pi$$
$$x = 0 - \frac{\pi}{2} \qquad\qquad x = \pi - \frac{\pi}{2}$$
$$x = -\frac{\pi}{2} \qquad\qquad x = \frac{\pi}{2}$$

Thus, two consecutive asymptotes occur at $x = -\frac{\pi}{2}$ and $x = \frac{\pi}{2}$.

$$x\text{-intercept} = \frac{-\frac{\pi}{2} + \frac{\pi}{2}}{2} = \frac{0}{2} = 0$$

An x-intercept is 0 and the graph passes

through $(0, 0)$. Because the coefficient of the cotangent is 2, the points on the graph midway between an x-intercept and the asymptotes have y-coordinates of 2 and -2. We use the two consecutive asymptotes,

$x = -\frac{\pi}{2}$ and $x = \frac{\pi}{2}$, to graph one full period

of $y = 2\cot\left(x + \frac{\pi}{2}\right)$ from $-\frac{\pi}{2}$ to $\frac{\pi}{2}$. We

continue the pattern and extend the graph another full period to the right.

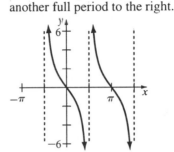

72. Graph the reciprocal cosine function, $y = 3\cos 2\pi x$. The equation is of the form $y = A\cos Bx$ with $A = 3$ and $B = 2\pi$.

amplitude: $|A| = |3| = 3$

period: $\dfrac{2\pi}{B} = \dfrac{2\pi}{2\pi} = 1$

Use quarter-periods, $\frac{1}{4}$, to find x-values for the five key points. Starting with $x = 0$, the x-values are $0, \frac{1}{4}, \frac{1}{2}, \frac{3}{4}, 1$. Evaluating the function at each value of x, the key points are $(0, 3)$, $\left(\frac{1}{4}, 0\right)$, $\left(\frac{1}{2}, -3\right)$, $\left(\frac{3}{4}, 0\right)$, $(1, 3)$.

Use these key points to graph $y = 3\cos 2\pi x$ from 0 to 1. Extend the graph one cycle to the right. Use the graph to obtain the graph of the reciprocal function. Draw vertical asymptotes through the x-intercepts, and use them as guides to graph $y = 3\sec 2\pi x$.

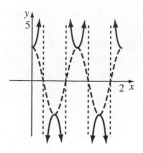

73. Graph the reciprocal sine function, $y = -2\sin \pi x$. The equation is of the form $y = A\sin Bx$ with $A = -2$ and $B = \pi$.

amplitude: $|A| = |-2| = 2$

period: $\dfrac{2\pi}{B} = \dfrac{2\pi}{\pi} = 2$

Use quarter-periods, $\dfrac{2}{4} = \dfrac{1}{2}$, to find x-values for the five key points. Starting with $x = 0$, the x-values are $0, \dfrac{1}{2}, 1, \dfrac{3}{2}, 2$. Evaluating the function at each value of x, the key points are $(0, 0)$, $\left(\dfrac{1}{2}, -2\right)$, $(1, 0)$, $\left(\dfrac{3}{2}, 2\right)$, $(2, 0)$. Use these key points to graph $y = -2\sin \pi x$ from 0 to 2. Extend the graph one cycle to the right. Use the graph to obtain the graph of the reciprocal function. Draw vertical asymptotes through the x-intercepts, and use them as guides to graph $y = -2\csc \pi x$.

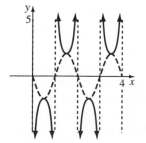

74. Graph the reciprocal cosine function, $y = 3\cos(x + \pi)$. The equation is of the form $y = A\cos(Bx - C)$ with $A = 3$, $B = 1$, and $C = -\pi$.

amplitude: $|A| = |3| = 3$

period: $\dfrac{2\pi}{B} = \dfrac{2\pi}{1} = 2\pi$

phase shift: $\dfrac{C}{B} = \dfrac{-\pi}{1} = -\pi$

Use quarter-periods, $\dfrac{2\pi}{4} = \dfrac{\pi}{2}$, to find x-values for the five key points. Starting with $x = -\pi$, the x-values are $-\pi, -\dfrac{\pi}{2}$, $0, \dfrac{\pi}{2}, \pi$. Evaluating the function at each value of x, the key points are $(-\pi, 3)$, $\left(-\dfrac{\pi}{2}, 0\right)$, $(0, -3)$, $\left(\dfrac{\pi}{2}, 0\right)$, $(\pi, 3)$. Use these key points to graph $y = 3\cos(x + \pi)$ from $-\pi$ to π. Extend the graph one cycle to the right. Use the graph to obtain the graph of the reciprocal function. Draw vertical asymptotes through the x-intercepts, and use them as guides to graph $y = 3\sec(x + \pi)$.

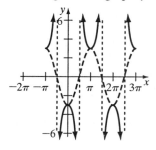

75. Graph the reciprocal sine function, $y = \dfrac{5}{2}\sin(x - \pi)$. The equation is of the form $y = A\sin(Bx - C)$ with $A = \dfrac{5}{2}$, $B = 1$, and $C = \pi$.

amplitude: $|A| = \left|\dfrac{5}{2}\right| = \dfrac{5}{2}$

period: $\dfrac{2\pi}{B} = \dfrac{2\pi}{1} = 2\pi$

phase shift: $\dfrac{C}{B} = \dfrac{\pi}{1} = \pi$

Use quarter-periods, $\dfrac{2\pi}{4} = \dfrac{\pi}{2}$, to find

x-values for the five key points. Starting

with $x = \pi$, the x-values are π, $\dfrac{3\pi}{2}$, 2π,

$\dfrac{5\pi}{2}$, 3π. Evaluating the function at each

value of x, the key points are $(\pi,\, 0)$,

$\left(\dfrac{3\pi}{2}, \dfrac{5}{2}\right)$, $(2\pi,\, 0)$, $\left(\dfrac{5\pi}{2}, -\dfrac{5}{2}\right)$, $(3\pi,\, 0)$.

Use these key points to graph

$y = \dfrac{5}{2}\sin(x - \pi)$ from π to 3π. Extend the

graph one cycle to the right. Use the graph to
obtain the graph of the reciprocal function.
Draw vertical asymptotes through the
x-intercepts, and use them as guides to graph

$y = \dfrac{5}{2}\csc(x - \pi)$.

76. Let $\theta = \sin^{-1} 1$, then $\sin\theta = 1$.

The only angle in the interval $\left[-\dfrac{\pi}{2}, \dfrac{\pi}{2}\right]$ that

satisfies $\sin\theta = 1$ is $\dfrac{\pi}{2}$. Thus $\theta = \dfrac{\pi}{2}$, or

$\sin^{-1} 1 = \dfrac{\pi}{2}$.

77. Let $\theta = \cos^{-1} 1$, then $\cos\theta = 1$.
The only angle in the interval $[0,\, \pi]$ that
satisfies $\cos\theta = 1$ is 0. Thus $\theta = 0$, or
$\cos^{-1} 1 = 0$.

78. Let $\theta = \tan^{-1} 1$, then $\tan\theta = 1$.

The only angle in the interval $\left(-\dfrac{\pi}{2}, \dfrac{\pi}{2}\right)$

that satisfies $\tan\theta = 1$ is $\dfrac{\pi}{4}$. Thus $\theta = \dfrac{\pi}{4}$, or

$\tan^{-1} 1 = \dfrac{\pi}{4}$.

79. Let $\theta = \sin^{-1}\left(-\dfrac{\sqrt{3}}{2}\right)$, then $\sin\theta = -\dfrac{\sqrt{3}}{2}$.

The only angle in the interval $\left[-\dfrac{\pi}{2}, \dfrac{\pi}{2}\right]$ that

satisfies $\sin\theta = -\dfrac{\sqrt{3}}{2}$ is $-\dfrac{\pi}{3}$. Thus

$\theta = -\dfrac{\pi}{3}$, or $\sin^{-1}\left(-\dfrac{\sqrt{3}}{2}\right) = -\dfrac{\pi}{3}$.

80. Let $\theta = \cos^{-1}\left(-\dfrac{1}{2}\right)$, then $\cos\theta = -\dfrac{1}{2}$.

The only angle in the interval $[0,\, \pi]$ that

satisfies $\cos\theta = -\dfrac{1}{2}$ is $\dfrac{2\pi}{3}$. Thus $\theta = \dfrac{2\pi}{3}$,

or $\cos^{-1}\left(-\dfrac{1}{2}\right) = \dfrac{2\pi}{3}$.

81. Let $\theta = \tan^{-1}\left(-\dfrac{\sqrt{3}}{3}\right)$, then $\tan\theta = -\dfrac{\sqrt{3}}{3}$.

The only angle in the interval $\left(-\dfrac{\pi}{2}, \dfrac{\pi}{2}\right)$

that satisfies $\tan\theta = -\dfrac{\sqrt{3}}{3}$ is $-\dfrac{\pi}{6}$.

Thus $\theta = -\dfrac{\pi}{6}$, or $\tan^{-1}\left(-\dfrac{\sqrt{3}}{3}\right) = -\dfrac{\pi}{6}$.

82. Let $\theta = \sin^{-1}\dfrac{\sqrt{2}}{2}$, then $\sin\theta = \dfrac{\sqrt{2}}{2}$. The

only angle in the interval $\left[-\dfrac{\pi}{2}, \dfrac{\pi}{2}\right]$ that

satisfies $\sin\theta = \dfrac{\sqrt{2}}{2}$ is $\dfrac{\pi}{4}$.

Thus, $\cos\left(\sin^{-1}\dfrac{\sqrt{2}}{2}\right) = \cos\dfrac{\pi}{4} = \dfrac{\sqrt{2}}{2}$.

83. Let $\theta = \cos^{-1} 0$, then $\cos\theta = 0$. The only angle in the interval $[0,\ \pi]$ that satisfies

$\cos\theta = 0$ is $\dfrac{\pi}{2}$. Thus,

$\sin\left(\cos^{-1} 0\right) = \sin\dfrac{\pi}{2} = 1$.

84. Let $\theta = \sin^{-1}\left(-\dfrac{1}{2}\right)$, then $\sin\theta = -\dfrac{1}{2}$. The

only angle in the interval $\left[-\dfrac{\pi}{2},\ \dfrac{\pi}{2}\right]$ that

satisfies $\sin\theta = -\dfrac{1}{2}$ is $-\dfrac{\pi}{6}$.

Thus, $\tan\left[\sin^{-1}\left(-\dfrac{1}{2}\right)\right] = \tan\left(-\dfrac{\pi}{6}\right) = -\dfrac{\sqrt{3}}{3}$.

85. Let $\theta = \cos^{-1}\left(-\dfrac{\sqrt{3}}{2}\right)$, then $\cos\theta = -\dfrac{\sqrt{3}}{2}$.

The only angle in the interval $[0,\ \pi]$ that

satisfies $\cos\theta = -\dfrac{\sqrt{3}}{2}$ is $\dfrac{5\pi}{6}$.

Thus, $\tan\left[\cos^{-1}\left(-\dfrac{\sqrt{3}}{2}\right)\right] = \tan\dfrac{5\pi}{6} = -\dfrac{\sqrt{3}}{3}$.

86. Let $\theta = \tan^{-1}\dfrac{\sqrt{3}}{3}$, then $\tan\theta = \dfrac{\sqrt{3}}{3}$.

The only angle in the interval $\left(-\dfrac{\pi}{2},\ \dfrac{\pi}{2}\right)$

that satisfies $\tan\theta = \dfrac{\sqrt{3}}{3}$ is $\dfrac{\pi}{6}$.

Thus $\csc\left(\tan^{-1}\dfrac{\sqrt{3}}{3}\right) = \csc\dfrac{\pi}{6} = 2$.

87. Let $\theta = \tan^{-1}\dfrac{3}{4}$, then $\tan\theta = \dfrac{3}{4}$.

Because $\tan\theta$ is positive, θ is in the first quadrant.

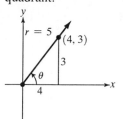

We use the Pythagorean theorem to find r.

$r^2 = 4^2 + 3^2 = 16 + 9 = 25$

$r = \sqrt{25} = 5$

We use the right triangle to find the exact value.

$\cos\left(\tan^{-1}\dfrac{3}{4}\right) = \cos\theta = \dfrac{4}{5}$

88. Let $\theta = \cos^{-1}\dfrac{3}{5}$, then $\cos\theta = \dfrac{3}{5}$.

Because $\cos\theta$ is positive, θ is in the first quadrant.

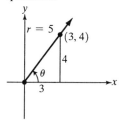

We use the Pythagorean Theorem to find y.

$3^2 + y^2 = 5^2$

$y^2 = 25 - 9 = 16$

$y = \sqrt{16} = 4$

We use the right triangle to find the exact value.

$\sin\left(\cos^{-1}\dfrac{3}{5}\right) = \sin\theta = \dfrac{4}{5}$

89. Let $\theta = \sin^{-1}\left(-\dfrac{3}{5}\right)$, then $\sin\theta = -\dfrac{3}{5}$.

Because $\sin\theta$ is negative, θ is in quadrant IV.

We use the Pythagorean Theorem to find x.

$$x^2 + (-3)^2 = 5^2$$
$$x^2 = 25 - 9 = 16$$
$$x = \sqrt{16} = 4$$

We use the right triangle to find the exact value. $\tan\left[\sin^{-1}\left(-\dfrac{3}{5}\right)\right] = \tan\theta = -\dfrac{3}{4}$

90. Let $\theta = \cos^{-1}\left(-\dfrac{4}{5}\right)$, then $\cos\theta = -\dfrac{4}{5}$.

Because $\cos\theta$ is negative, θ is in quadrant II.

We use the Pythagorean Theorem to find y.

$$(-4)^2 + y^2 = 5^2$$
$$y^2 = 25 - 16 = 9$$
$$y = \sqrt{9} = 3$$

We use the right triangle to find the exact value.

$$\tan\left[\cos^{-1}\left(-\dfrac{4}{5}\right)\right] = \tan\theta = -\dfrac{3}{4}$$

91. $x = \dfrac{\pi}{3}$, x is in $\left[-\dfrac{\pi}{2}, \dfrac{\pi}{2}\right]$, so

$$\sin^{-1}\left(\sin\dfrac{\pi}{3}\right) = \dfrac{\pi}{3}$$

92. $x = \dfrac{2\pi}{3}$, x is not in $\left[-\dfrac{\pi}{2}, \dfrac{\pi}{2}\right]$. x is in the domain of $\sin x$, so

$$\sin^{-1}\left(\sin\dfrac{2\pi}{3}\right) = \sin^{-1}\dfrac{\sqrt{3}}{2} = \dfrac{\pi}{3}$$

93. $\sin^{-1}\left(\cos\dfrac{2\pi}{3}\right) = \sin^{-1}\left(-\dfrac{1}{2}\right)$

Let $\theta = \sin^{-1}\left(-\dfrac{1}{2}\right)$, then $\sin\theta = -\dfrac{1}{2}$. The only angle in the interval $\left[-\dfrac{\pi}{2}, \dfrac{\pi}{2}\right]$ that satisfies $\sin\theta = -\dfrac{1}{2}$ is $-\dfrac{\pi}{6}$. Thus, $\theta = -\dfrac{\pi}{6}$, or $\sin^{-1}\left(\cos\dfrac{2\pi}{3}\right) = \sin^{-1}\left(-\dfrac{1}{2}\right) = -\dfrac{\pi}{6}$.

94. Let $\theta = \tan^{-1}\dfrac{x}{2}$, then $\tan\theta = \dfrac{x}{2}$.

We use the Pythagorean Theorem to find the third side, r.

$$r^2 = x^2 + 2^2$$
$$r = \sqrt{x^2 + 4}$$

We use the right triangle to write the algebraic expression.

$$\cos\left(\tan^{-1}\dfrac{x}{2}\right) = \cos\theta = \dfrac{2}{\sqrt{x^2 + 4}}$$

95. Let $\theta = \sin^{-1}\dfrac{1}{x}$, then $\sin\theta = \dfrac{1}{x}$.

$b = \sqrt{x^2 - 1}$

We use the Pythagorean Theorem to find the third side, b.

$$1^2 + b^2 = x^2$$
$$b^2 = x^2 - 1$$
$$b = \sqrt{x^2 - 1}$$

We use the right triangle to write the algebraic expression.

$$\sec\left(\sin^{-1}\dfrac{1}{x}\right) = \sec\theta = \dfrac{x}{\sqrt{x^2 - 1}}$$

96. Find the measure of angle B. Because $C = 90°$, $A + B = 90°$. Thus,
$B = 90° - A = 90° - 22.3° = 67.7°$
We have a known angle, a known hypotenuse, and an unknown opposite side. We use the sine function.

$$\sin 22.3° = \dfrac{a}{10}$$
$$a = 10\sin 22.3° \approx 3.79$$

We have a known angle, a known hypotenuse, and an unknown adjacent side. We use the cosine function.

$$\cos 22.3° = \dfrac{b}{10}$$
$$b = 10\cos 22.3° \approx 9.25$$

In summary, $B = 67.7°$, $a \approx 3.79$, and $b \approx 9.25$.

97. Find the measure of angle A. Because $C = 90°$, $A + B = 90°$. Thus,
$A = 90° - B = 90° - 37.4° = 52.6°$
We have a known angle, a known opposite side, and an unknown adjacent side. We use the tangent function.

$$\tan 37.4° = \dfrac{6}{a}$$
$$a = \dfrac{6}{\tan 37.4°} \approx 7.85$$

We have a known angle, a known opposite side, and an unknown hypotenuse. We use the sine function.

$$\sin 37.4° = \dfrac{6}{c}$$
$$c = \dfrac{6}{\sin 37.4°} \approx 9.88$$

In summary, $A = 52.6°$, $a \approx 7.85$, and $c \approx 9.88$.

98. Find the measure of angle A. We have a known hypotenuse, a known opposite side, and an unknown angle. We use the sine function.

$$\sin A = \dfrac{2}{7}$$
$$A = \sin^{-1}\left(\dfrac{2}{7}\right) \approx 16.6°$$

Find the measure of angle B. Because $C = 90°$, $A + B = 90°$. Thus,
$B = 90° - A \approx 90° - 16.6° = 73.4°$
We have a known hypotenuse, a known opposite side, and an unknown adjacent side. We use the Pythagorean Theorem.

$$a^2 + b^2 = c^2$$
$$2^2 + b^2 = 7^2$$
$$b^2 = 7^2 - 2^2 = 45$$
$$b = \sqrt{45} \approx 6.71$$

In summary, $A \approx 16.6°$, $B \approx 73.4°$, and $b \approx 6.71$.

99. Find the measure of angle A. We have a known opposite side, a known adjacent side, and an unknown angle. We use the tangent function.

$$\tan A = \frac{1.4}{3.6}$$

$$A = \tan^{-1}\left(\frac{1.4}{3.6}\right) \approx 21.3°$$

Find the measure of angle B. Because $C = 90°$, $A + B = 90°$. Thus,
$B = 90° - A \approx 90° - 21.3° = 68.7°$
We have a known opposite side, a known adjacent side, and an unknown hypotenuse. We use the Pythagorean Theorem.

$$c^2 = a^2 + b^2 = (1.4)^2 + (3.6)^2 = 14.92$$

$$c = \sqrt{14.92} \approx 3.86$$

In summary, $A \approx 21.3°$, $B \approx 68.7°$, and $c \approx 3.86$.

100. Using a right triangle, we have a known angle, an unknown opposite side, h, and a known adjacent side. Therefore, we use the tangent function.

$$\tan 25.6° = \frac{h}{80}$$
$$h = 80 \tan 25.6°$$
$$\approx 38.3$$

The building is about 38 feet high.

101. Using a right triangle, we have a known angle, an unknown opposite side, h, and a known adjacent side. Therefore, we use the tangent function.

$$\tan 40° = \frac{h}{60}$$
$$h = 60 \tan 40° \approx 50 \text{ yd}$$

The second building is 50 yds taller than the first. Total height = $40 + 50 = 90$ yd.

102. Using two right triangles, a smaller right triangle corresponding to the smaller angle of elevation drawn inside a larger right triangle corresponding to the larger angle of elevation, we have a known angle, a known opposite side, and an unknown adjacent side, d, in the smaller triangle. Therefore, we use the tangent function.

$$\tan 68° = \frac{125}{d}$$

$$d = \frac{125}{\tan 68°} \approx 50.5$$

We now have a known angle, a known adjacent side, and an unknown opposite side, h, in the larger triangle. Again, we use the tangent function.

$$\tan 71° = \frac{h}{50.5}$$
$$h = 50.5 \tan 71° \approx 146.7$$

The height of the antenna is $146.7 - 125$, or 21.7 ft, to the nearest tenth of a foot.

103. We need the acute angle between ray OA and the north-south line through O. This angle measures $90° - 55° = 35°$. This angle measured from the north side of the north-south line and lies east of the north-south line. Thus the bearing from O to A is N35°E.

104. We need the acute angle between ray OA and the north-south line through O. This angle measures $90° - 55° = 35°$. This angle measured from the south side of the north-south line and lies west of the north-south line. Thus the bearing from O to A is S35°W.

105. Using a right triangle, we have a known angle, a known adjacent side, and an unknown opposite side, d. Therefore, we use the tangent function.

$$\tan 64° = \frac{d}{12}$$
$$d = 12 \tan 64° \approx 24.6$$

The ship is about 24.6 miles from the lighthouse.

106.

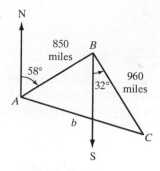

a. Using the figure,
$B = 58° + 32° = 90°$
Thus, we use the Pythagorean Theorem to find the distance from city A to city C.
$850^2 + 960^2 = b^2$
$b^2 = 722,500 + 921,600$
$b^2 = 1,644,100$
$b = \sqrt{1,644,100} \approx 1282.2$
The distance from city A to city B is about 1282.2 miles.

b. Using the figure,
$$\tan A = \frac{\text{opposite}}{\text{adjacent}} = \frac{960}{850} \approx 1.1294$$
$A \approx \tan^{-1}(1.1294) \approx 48°$
$180° - 58° - 48° = 74°$
The bearing from city A to city C is S74°E.

107. $d = 20\cos\frac{\pi}{4}t$

$a = 20$ and $\omega = \frac{\pi}{4}$

a. maximum displacement:
$|a| = |20| = 20\,\text{cm}$

b. $f = \dfrac{\omega}{2\pi} = \dfrac{\frac{\pi}{4}}{2\pi} = \dfrac{\pi}{4}\cdot\dfrac{1}{2\pi} = \dfrac{1}{8}$
frequency: $\dfrac{1}{8}$ cycle per second

c. period: $\dfrac{2\pi}{\omega} = \dfrac{2\pi}{\frac{\pi}{4}} = 2\pi\cdot\dfrac{4}{\pi} = 8$
The time required for one cycle is 8 seconds.

108. $d = \frac{1}{2}\sin 4t$

$a = \frac{1}{2}$ and $\omega = 4$

a. maximum displacement:
$$|a| = \left|\frac{1}{2}\right| = \frac{1}{2}\,\text{cm}$$

b. $f = \dfrac{\omega}{2\pi} = \dfrac{4}{2\pi} = \dfrac{2}{\pi} \approx 0.64$
frequency: 0.64 cycle per second

c. period: $\dfrac{2\pi}{\omega} = \dfrac{2\pi}{4} = \dfrac{\pi}{2} \approx 1.57$
The time required for one cycle is about 1.57 seconds.

109. Because the distance of the object from the rest position at $t = 0$ is a maximum, we use the form $d = a\cos\omega t$. The period is $\dfrac{2\pi}{\omega}$ so,
$$2 = \frac{2\pi}{\omega}$$
$$\omega = \frac{2\pi}{2} = \pi$$
Because the amplitude is 30 inches, $|a| = 30$. because the object starts below its rest position $a = -30$. the equation for the object's simple harmonic motion is
$d = -30\cos\pi t$.

110. Because the distance of the object from the rest position at $t = 0$ is 0, we use the form $d = a\sin\omega t$. The period is $\dfrac{2\pi}{\omega}$ so
$$5 = \frac{2\pi}{\omega}$$
$$\omega = \frac{2\pi}{5}$$
Because the amplitude is $\dfrac{1}{4}$ inch, $|a| = \dfrac{1}{4}$. a is positive since the object begins in an upward direction. The equation for the object's simple harmonic motion is
$$d = \frac{1}{4}\sin\frac{2\pi}{5}t.$$

Chapter 5 Test

1. $135° = 135° \cdot \dfrac{\pi \, \text{radians}}{180°}$

   $= \dfrac{135\pi}{180} \, \text{radians}$

   $= \dfrac{3\pi}{4} \, \text{radians}$

2. supplement: $\pi - \dfrac{9\pi}{13} = \dfrac{13\pi}{13} - \dfrac{9\pi}{13} = \dfrac{4\pi}{13}$

3. $75° = 75° \cdot \dfrac{\pi \, \text{radians}}{180°} = \dfrac{75\pi}{180} \, \text{radians}$

   $= \dfrac{5\pi}{12} \, \text{radians}$

   $s = r\theta$

   $s = 20\left(\dfrac{5\pi}{12}\right) = \dfrac{25\pi}{3} \, \text{ft} \approx 26.18 \, \text{ft}$

4. We need values for x, y, and r. Because $P = (-2, 5)$ is a point on the terminal side of θ, $x = -2$ and $y = 5$. Furthermore,

   $r = \sqrt{x^2 + y^2} = \sqrt{(-2)^2 + (5)^2}$
   $= \sqrt{4 + 25} = \sqrt{29}$

   Now that we know x, y, and r, we can find the six trigonometric functions of θ.

   $\sin\theta = \dfrac{y}{r} = \dfrac{5}{\sqrt{29}} = \dfrac{5\sqrt{29}}{\sqrt{29}\sqrt{29}} = \dfrac{5\sqrt{29}}{29}$

   $\cos\theta = \dfrac{x}{r} = \dfrac{-2}{\sqrt{29}} = -\dfrac{2\sqrt{29}}{\sqrt{29}\sqrt{29}} = -\dfrac{2\sqrt{29}}{29}$

   $\tan\theta = \dfrac{y}{x} = \dfrac{5}{-2} = -\dfrac{5}{2}$

   $\csc\theta = \dfrac{r}{y} = \dfrac{\sqrt{29}}{5}$

   $\sec\theta = \dfrac{r}{x} = \dfrac{\sqrt{29}}{-2} = -\dfrac{\sqrt{29}}{2}$

   $\cot\theta = \dfrac{x}{y} = \dfrac{-2}{5} = -\dfrac{2}{5}$

5. Because $\cos\theta < 0$, θ cannot lie in quadrant I and quadrant IV; the cosine function is positive in those two quadrants. Thus, with $\cos\theta < 0$, θ lies in quadrant II or quadrant III. We are also given that $\cot\theta > 0$. Because quadrant III is the only quadrant in which the cosine is negative and the cotangent is positive, we conclude that θ lies in quadrant III.

6. Because the cosine is positive and the tangent is negative, θ lies in quadrant IV. In quadrant IV x is positive and y is negative.

   Thus, $\cos\theta = \dfrac{1}{3} = \dfrac{x}{r}$, $x = 1$, $r = 3$.

   Furthermore,

   $x^2 + y^2 = r^3$
   $1^2 + y^2 = 3^2$
   $y^2 = 9 - 1 = 8$
   $y = -\sqrt{8} = -2\sqrt{2}$

   Now that we know x, y, and r, we can find the six trigonometric functions of θ.

   $\sin\theta = \dfrac{y}{r} = \dfrac{-2\sqrt{2}}{3} = -\dfrac{2\sqrt{2}}{3}$

   $\tan\theta = \dfrac{y}{x} = \dfrac{-2\sqrt{2}}{1} = -2\sqrt{2}$

   $\csc\theta = \dfrac{r}{y} = \dfrac{3}{-2\sqrt{2}} = -\dfrac{3\sqrt{2}}{2\sqrt{2}\cdot\sqrt{2}} = -\dfrac{3\sqrt{2}}{4}$

   $\sec\theta = \dfrac{r}{x} = \dfrac{3}{1} = 3$

   $\cot\theta = \dfrac{x}{y} = \dfrac{1}{-2\sqrt{2}} = -\dfrac{1\cdot\sqrt{2}}{2\sqrt{2}\sqrt{2}} = -\dfrac{\sqrt{2}}{4}$

7. $\tan\dfrac{\pi}{6}\cos\dfrac{\pi}{3} - \cos\dfrac{\pi}{2} = \dfrac{\sqrt{3}}{3}\cdot\dfrac{1}{2} - 0 = \dfrac{\sqrt{3}}{6}$

8. $300°$ lies in quadrant IV.
   The reference angle is
   $\theta' = 360° - 300° = 60°$
   $\tan 60° = \sqrt{3}$
   In quadrant IV, $\tan\theta < 0$, so
   $\tan 300° = -\tan 60 = -\sqrt{3}$.

9. $\dfrac{7\pi}{4}$ lies in quadrant IV.
   The reference angle is
   $\theta' = 2\pi - \dfrac{7\pi}{4} = \dfrac{8\pi}{4} - \dfrac{7\pi}{4} = \dfrac{\pi}{4}$
   $\sin\dfrac{\pi}{4} = \dfrac{\sqrt{2}}{2}$
   In quadrant IV, $\sin\theta < 0$, so
   $\sin\dfrac{7\pi}{4} = -\sin\dfrac{\pi}{4} = -\dfrac{\sqrt{2}}{2}$.

10. The equation $y = 3\sin 2x$ is of the form $y = A\sin Bx$ with $A = 3$ and $B = 2$. The amplitude is $|A| = |3| = 3$. The period is $\dfrac{2\pi}{B} = \dfrac{2\pi}{2} = \pi$. The quarter-period is $\dfrac{\pi}{4}$. The cycle begins at $x = 0$. Add quarter-periods to generate x-values for the key points.

$x = 0$

$x = 0 + \dfrac{\pi}{4} = \dfrac{\pi}{4}$

$x = \dfrac{\pi}{4} + \dfrac{\pi}{4} = \dfrac{\pi}{2}$

$x = \dfrac{\pi}{2} + \dfrac{\pi}{4} = \dfrac{3\pi}{4}$

$x = \dfrac{3\pi}{4} + \dfrac{\pi}{4} = \pi$

We evaluate the function at each value of x.

x	$y = 3\sin 2x$	coordinates
0	$y = 3\sin(2 \cdot 0) = 3\sin 0$ $= 3 \cdot 0 = 0$	$(0, 0)$
$\dfrac{\pi}{4}$	$y = 3\sin\left(2 \cdot \dfrac{\pi}{4}\right)$ $= 3\sin\dfrac{\pi}{2} = 3 \cdot 1 = 3$	$\left(\dfrac{\pi}{4}, 3\right)$
$\dfrac{\pi}{2}$	$y = 3\sin\left(2 \cdot \dfrac{\pi}{2}\right)$ $= 3\sin\pi = 3 \cdot 0 = 0$	$\left(\dfrac{\pi}{2}, 0\right)$
$\dfrac{3\pi}{4}$	$y = 3\sin\left(2 \cdot \dfrac{3\pi}{4}\right)$ $= 3\sin\dfrac{3\pi}{2} = 3 \cdot (-1)$ $= -3$	$\left(\dfrac{3\pi}{4}, -3\right)$
π	$y = 3\sin(2 \cdot \pi)$ $= 3\sin 2\pi = 3 \cdot 0$ $= 0$	$(\pi, 0)$

Connect the five key points with a smooth curve and graph one complete cycle of the given function.

11. The equation $y = -2\cos\left(x - \dfrac{\pi}{2}\right)$ is of the form $y = A\cos(Bx - C)$ with $A = -2$, $B = 1$, and $C = \dfrac{\pi}{2}$. The amplitude is $|A| = |-2| = 2$. The period is $\dfrac{2\pi}{B} = \dfrac{2\pi}{1} = 2\pi$. The phase shift is $\dfrac{C}{B} = \dfrac{\frac{\pi}{2}}{1} = \dfrac{\pi}{2}$. The quarter-period is $\dfrac{2\pi}{4} = \dfrac{\pi}{2}$. The cycle begins at $x = \dfrac{\pi}{2}$. Add quarter-periods to generate x-values for the key points.

$x = \dfrac{\pi}{2}$

$x = \dfrac{\pi}{2} + \dfrac{\pi}{2} = \pi$

$x = \pi + \dfrac{\pi}{2} = \dfrac{3\pi}{2}$

$x = \dfrac{3\pi}{2} + \dfrac{\pi}{2} = 2\pi$

$x = 2\pi + \dfrac{\pi}{2} = \dfrac{5\pi}{2}$

We evaluate the function at each value of x.

x	$y = -2\cos\left(x - \dfrac{\pi}{2}\right)$	coordinates
$\dfrac{\pi}{2}$	$y = -2\cos\left(\dfrac{\pi}{2} - \dfrac{\pi}{2}\right)$ $= -2\cos 0$ $= -2 \cdot 1 = -2$	$\left(\dfrac{\pi}{2}, -2\right)$
π	$y = -2\cos\left(\pi - \dfrac{\pi}{2}\right)$ $= -2\cos\dfrac{\pi}{2}$ $= -2 \cdot 0 = 0$	$(\pi, 0)$
$\dfrac{3\pi}{2}$	$y = -2\cos\left(\dfrac{3\pi}{2} - \dfrac{\pi}{2}\right)$ $= -2\cos\pi$ $= -2 \cdot (-1) = 2$	$\left(\dfrac{3\pi}{2}, 2\right)$
2π	$y = -2\cos\left(2\pi - \dfrac{\pi}{2}\right)$ $= -2\cos\dfrac{3\pi}{2}$ $= -2 \cdot 0 = 0$	$(2\pi, 0)$
$\dfrac{5\pi}{2}$	$y = -2\cos\left(\dfrac{5\pi}{2} - \dfrac{\pi}{2}\right)$ $= -2\cos 2\pi$ $= -2 \cdot 1 = -2$	$\left(\dfrac{5\pi}{2}, -2\right)$

Connect the five key points with a smooth curve and graph one complete cycle of the given function.

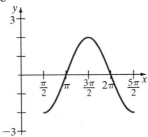

12. We solve the equations
$$\frac{x}{2} = -\frac{\pi}{2} \quad \text{and} \quad \frac{x}{2} = \frac{\pi}{2}$$
$$x = -\frac{\pi}{2} \cdot 2 \qquad x = \frac{\pi}{2} \cdot 2$$
$$x = -\pi \qquad\qquad x = \pi$$

Thus, two consecutive asymptotes occur at $x = -\pi$ and $x = \pi$.

$$x\text{-intercept} = \frac{-\pi + \pi}{2} = \frac{0}{2} = 0$$

An x-intercept is 0 and the graph passes through $(0, 0)$. Because the coefficient of the tangent is 2, the points on the graph midway between an x-intercept and the asymptotes have y-coordinates of -2 and 2. We use the two consecutive asymptotes, $x = -\pi$ and $x = \pi$, to graph one full period of
$$y = 2\tan\frac{x}{2} \text{ from } -\pi \text{ to } \pi.$$

13. Graph the reciprocal sine function, $y = -\dfrac{1}{2}\sin\pi x$. The equation is of the form
$$y = A\sin Bx \text{ with } A = -\frac{1}{2} \text{ and } B = \pi.$$

amplitude: $|A| = \left|-\dfrac{1}{2}\right| = \dfrac{1}{2}$

period: $\dfrac{2\pi}{B} = \dfrac{2\pi}{\pi} = 2$

Use quarter-periods, $\dfrac{2}{4} = \dfrac{1}{2}$, to find x-values for the five key points. Starting with $x = 0$, the x-values are $0, \dfrac{1}{2}, 1, \dfrac{3}{2}, 2$. Evaluating the function at each value of x, the key points are $(0, 3)$,
$$\left(\frac{1}{2}, -\frac{1}{2}\right), (1, 0), \left(\frac{3}{2}, \frac{1}{2}\right), (2, 0).$$

Use these key points to graph
$y = -\frac{1}{2}\sin \pi x$ from 0 to 2. Use the graph to
obtain the graph of the reciprocal function.
Draw vertical asymptotes through the *x*-
intercepts, and use them as guides to graph
$y = -\frac{1}{2}\csc \pi x$.

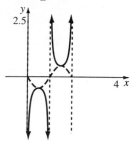

14. Let $\theta = \cos^{-1}\left(-\frac{1}{2}\right)$, then $\cos \theta = -\frac{1}{2}$.
Because $\cos \theta$ is negative, θ is in
quadrant II.

We use the Pythagorean Theorem to find y.
$$(-1)^2 + y^2 = 2^2$$
$$y^2 = 4 - 1 = 3$$
$$y = \sqrt{3}$$
We use the right triangle to find the exact
value.
$$\tan\left[\cos^{-1}\left(-\frac{1}{2}\right)\right] = \tan \theta = \frac{\sqrt{3}}{-1} = -\sqrt{3}$$

15. Find the measure of angle *B*. Because
$C = 90°$, $A + B = 90°$. Thus,
$B = 90° - A = 90° - 21° = 69°$.
We have a known angle, a known
hypotenuse, and an unknown opposite side.
We use the sine function.
$$\sin 21° = \frac{a}{13}$$
$$a = 13\sin 21° \approx 4.7$$
We have a known angle, a known
hypotenuse, and an unknown adjacent side.
We use the cosine function.
$$\cos 21° = \frac{b}{13}$$
$$b = 13\cos 21° \approx 12.1$$
In summary, $B = 69°$, $a \approx 4.7$, and $b \approx 12.1$.

16. Using a right triangle, we have a known
angle, an unknown opposite side, *h*, and a
known adjacent side. Therefore, we use the
tangent function.
$$\tan 37° = \frac{h}{30}$$
$$h = 30\tan 37° \approx 23$$
The building is about 23 yards high.

17. Using a right triangle, we have a known
hypotenuse, a known opposite side, and an
unknown angle. Therefore, we use the sine
function.
$$\sin \theta = \frac{43}{73}$$
$$\theta = \sin^{-1}\left(\frac{43}{73}\right) \approx 36.1°$$
The rope makes an angle of about 36.1° with
the pole.

18. We need the acute angle between ray *OP*
and the north-south line through *O*. This
angle measures $90° - 10°$. This angle is
measured from the north side of the north-
south line and lies west of the north-south
line. Thus the bearing from *O* to *P* is
N80°W.

19. $d = -6\cos \pi t$
$a = -6$ and $\omega = \pi$

a. maximum displacement:
$|a| = |-6| = 6$ in.

b. $f = \dfrac{\omega}{2\pi} = \dfrac{\pi}{2\pi} = \dfrac{1}{2}$

frequency: $\dfrac{1}{2}$ cycle per second

c. period $= \dfrac{2\pi}{\omega} = \dfrac{2\pi}{\pi} = 2$

The time required for one cycle is
2 seconds.

20. Trigonometric functions are periodic.

Cumulative Review Exercises (Chapters 1-5)

1. $x^2 = 18 + 3x$
$x^2 - 3x - 18 = 0$
$(x - 6)(x + 3) = 0$
$x - 6 = 0$ or $x + 3 = 0$
$x = 6$ $x = -3$
The solution set is $\{-3, 6\}$.

2. $x^3 + 5x^2 - 4x - 20 = 0$
$x^2(x + 5) - 4(x + 5) = 0$
$(x^2 - 4)(x + 5) = 0$
$(x - 2)(x + 2)(x + 5) = 0$
$x - 2 = 0$ or $x + 2 = 0$ or $x + 5 = 0$
$x = 2$ $x = -2$ $x = -5$
The solution set is $\{-5, -2, 2\}$.

3. $\log_2 x + \log_2(x - 2) = 3$
$\log_2 x(x - 2) = 3$
$x(x - 2) = 2^3$
$x^2 - 2x = 2^3$
$x^2 - 2x - 8 = 0$
$(x - 4)(x + 2) = 0$
$x - 4 = 0$ or $x + 2 = 0$
$x = 4$ $x = -2$
$x = -2$ is extraneous
The solution set is $\{4\}$

4. $\sqrt{x - 3} + 5 = x$
$\sqrt{x - 3} = x - 5$
$\left(\sqrt{x - 3}\right)^2 = (x - 5)^2$
$x - 3 = x^2 - 10x + 25$
$x^2 - 11x + 28 = 0$
$(x - 4)(x - 7) = 0$
$x - 4 = 0$ or $x - 7 = 0$
$x = 4$ $x = 7$
$\sqrt{4 - 3} + 5 \overset{?}{=} 4$
$1 + 5 \overset{?}{=} 4$ false
$x = 4$ is not a solution
$\sqrt{7 - 3} + 5 \overset{?}{=} 7$
$\sqrt{4} + 5 \overset{?}{=} 7$
$2 + 5 \overset{?}{=} 7$ true
The solution set is $\{7\}$.

5. $x^3 - 4x^2 + x + 6 = 0$
$p: \pm 1, \pm 2, \pm 3, \pm 6$
$q: \pm 1$
$\dfrac{p}{q}: \pm 1, \pm 2, \pm 3, \pm 6$

$$
\begin{array}{r|rrrr}
2 & 1 & -4 & 1 & 6 \\
  &   & 2 & -4 & -6 \\
\hline
  & 1 & -2 & -3 & 0
\end{array}
$$

$x^3 - 4x^2 + x + 6 = (x - 2)\left(x^2 - 2x - 3\right)$
Thus,
$x^3 - 4x^2 + x + 6 = 0$
$(x - 2)\left(x^2 - 2x - 3\right) = 0$
$(x - 2)(x - 3)(x + 1) = 0$
$x - 2 = 0$ or $x - 3 = 0$ or $x + 1 = 0$
$x = 2$ $x = 3$ $x = -1$
The solution set is $\{-1, 2, 3\}$

6. $|2x - 5| \le 11$
$-11 \le 2x - 5 \le 11$
$-6 \le 2x \le 16$
$-3 \le x \le 8$
The solution set is $\{x \mid -3 \le x \le 8\}$

7. $f(x) = \sqrt{x-6}$

$x = \sqrt{y-6}$

$x^2 = y-6$

$y = x^2 + 6$

$f^{-1}(x) = x^2 + 6$

8.

$$
\begin{array}{r}
4x^2 - \dfrac{14}{5}x - \dfrac{17}{25} \\
5x + 2\overline{)20x^3 - 6x^2 - 9x + 10} \\
\underline{20x^3 + 8x^2} \\
-14x^2 - 9x \\
\underline{-14x^2 - \dfrac{28}{5}x} \\
-\dfrac{17}{5}x + 10 \\
\underline{-\dfrac{17}{5}x - \dfrac{34}{25}} \\
\dfrac{284}{25}
\end{array}
$$

The quotient is

$4x^2 - \dfrac{14}{5}x - \dfrac{17}{25} + \dfrac{284}{25(5x+2)}$.

9. $\log 25 + \log 40 = \log(25 \cdot 40)$

$= \log 1000$

$= \log 10^3$

$= 3$

10. $\dfrac{14\pi}{9}$ radians $= \dfrac{14\pi}{9}$ radians $\cdot \dfrac{180°}{\pi \text{ radians}}$

$= \dfrac{14 \cdot 180°}{9} = 280°$

11. $3x^4 - 2x^3 + 5x^2 + x - 9 = 0$

The sign changes 3 times so the equation has at most 3 positive real roots;

$f(-x) = 3x^4 + 2x^3 + 5x^2 - x - 9$

The sign changes 1 time, so the equation has at most 1 negative real root.

12. $f(x) = \dfrac{x}{x^2 - 1}$

vertical asymptotes:

$x^2 - 1 = 0$, $x = 1$ and $x = -1$

horizontal asymptote:

$m = 1$ and $n = 2$ so $m < n$

and the x-axis is a horizontal asymptote.

x-intercept: $(0,0)$

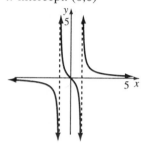

13. $(x-2)^2 + y^2 = 1$

The graph is a circle with center $(2,0)$ and $r = 1$.

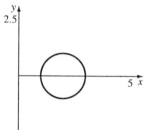

14. $y = (x-1)(x+2)^2$

x-intercepts: $(1,0)$ and $(-2,0)$

y-intercept: $y = (-1)(2)^2 = -4$

$(0,-4)$

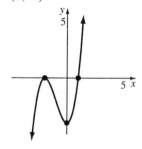

15. $y = \sin\left(2x + \dfrac{\pi}{2}\right) = \sin\left(2x - \left(-\dfrac{\pi}{2}\right)\right)$

The equation $y = \sin\left(2x - \left(-\dfrac{\pi}{2}\right)\right)$ is of the

form $y = A\sin(Bx - C)$ with $A = 1$, $B = 2$,

and $C = -\dfrac{\pi}{2}$. The amplitude is $|A| = |1| = 1$

The period is $\dfrac{2\pi}{B} = \dfrac{2\pi}{2} = \pi$. The phase shift

is $\dfrac{C}{B} = \dfrac{-\frac{\pi}{2}}{2} = -\dfrac{\pi}{2} \cdot \dfrac{1}{2} = -\dfrac{\pi}{4}$. The quarter-

period is $\dfrac{\pi}{4}$. The cycle begins at $x = -\dfrac{\pi}{4}$.

Add quarter-periods to generate x-values for
the key points.

$x = -\dfrac{\pi}{4}$, $x = -\dfrac{\pi}{4} + \dfrac{\pi}{4} = 0$, $x = 0 + \dfrac{\pi}{4} = \dfrac{\pi}{4}$,

$x = \dfrac{\pi}{4} + \dfrac{\pi}{4} = \dfrac{\pi}{2}$, $x = \dfrac{\pi}{2} + \dfrac{\pi}{4} = \dfrac{3\pi}{4}$

To graph from 0 to π, we evaluate the
function at the last four key points and at
$x = \pi$.

x	$y = \sin\left(2x + \dfrac{\pi}{2}\right)$	coordinates
0	$y = \sin\left(2 \cdot 0 + \dfrac{\pi}{2}\right)$ $= \sin\left(0 + \dfrac{\pi}{2}\right) = \sin\dfrac{\pi}{2}$ $= 1$	$(0, 1)$
$\dfrac{\pi}{4}$	$y = \sin\left(2 \cdot \dfrac{\pi}{4} + \dfrac{\pi}{2}\right)$ $= \sin\left(\dfrac{\pi}{2} + \dfrac{\pi}{2}\right)$ $= \sin\pi = 0$	$\left(\dfrac{\pi}{4}, 0\right)$
$\dfrac{\pi}{2}$	$y = \sin\left(2 \cdot \dfrac{\pi}{2} + \dfrac{\pi}{2}\right)$ $= \sin\left(\pi + \dfrac{\pi}{2}\right)$ $= \sin\dfrac{3\pi}{2} = -1$	$\left(\dfrac{\pi}{2}, -1\right)$

| $\dfrac{3\pi}{4}$ | $y = \sin\left(2 \cdot \dfrac{3\pi}{4} + \dfrac{\pi}{2}\right)$ $= \sin\left(\dfrac{3\pi}{2} + \dfrac{\pi}{2}\right)$ $= \sin 2\pi = 0$ | $\left(\dfrac{3\pi}{4}, 0\right)$ |
| π | $y = \sin\left(2 \cdot \pi + \dfrac{\pi}{2}\right)$ $= \sin\left(2\pi + \dfrac{\pi}{2}\right)$ $= \sin\dfrac{5\pi}{2} = 1$ | $(\pi, 1)$ |

Connect the points with a smooth curve and
extend the graph one cycle to the right to
graph from 0 to 2π.

16. We solve the equations

$$3x = -\frac{\pi}{2} \quad \text{and} \quad 3x = \frac{\pi}{2}$$

$$x = \frac{-\frac{\pi}{2}}{3} \qquad\qquad x = \frac{\frac{\pi}{2}}{3}$$

$$x = -\frac{\pi}{6} \qquad\qquad x = \frac{\pi}{6}$$

Thus, two consecutive asymptotes occur at

$$x = -\frac{\pi}{6} \quad \text{and} \quad x = \frac{\pi}{6}.$$

$$x\text{-intercept} = \frac{-\frac{\pi}{6} + \frac{\pi}{6}}{2} = \frac{0}{2} = 0$$

An x-intercept is 0 and the graph passes through (0, 0). Because the coefficient of the tangent is 2, the points on the graph midway between an x-intercept and the asymptotes have y-coordinates of -2 and 2. We use the two consecutive asymptotes, $x = -\frac{\pi}{6}$ and

$x = \frac{\pi}{6}$, to graph one full period of

$y = 2\tan 3x$ from $-\frac{\pi}{6}$ to $\frac{\pi}{6}$. Extend the pattern to the right to graph two complete cycles.

17. $C(p) = 30,000 + 2500p$
$R(p) = 3125p$
$30,000 + 2500p = 3125p$
$\qquad\quad 30,000 = 625p$
$\qquad\qquad\qquad p = 48$

48 performances must be played for you to break even.

18. a. Let t be the number of years after 1991. When $t = 0$, $A = 10.2$. Thus,

$$10.2 = A_0 e^{k(0)}$$
$$10.2 = A_0 \cdot 1$$
$$10.2 = A_0$$

When $t = 7$, $A = 86.7$. Thus,

$$86.7 = 10.2 e^{k(7)}$$
$$\frac{86.7}{80.2} = e^{7k}$$
$$\ln\left(\frac{86.7}{10.2}\right) = 7k$$
$$k = \frac{1}{7}\ln\left(\frac{86.7}{10.2}\right)$$
$$k \approx 0.3057$$

Thus, $A = 10.2 e^{0.3057t}$

b. Find t when $A = 200$.

$$200 = 10.2 e^{0.3057t}$$
$$\frac{200}{10.2} = e^{0.3057t}$$
$$\ln\left(\frac{200}{10.2}\right) = 0.3057t$$
$$t = \frac{\ln\left(\frac{200}{10.2}\right)}{0.3057}$$
$$t \approx 9.7$$

The number of 800 numbers should reach 20 billion by $1991 + 9.7 \approx 2001$.

19. $2200 = \dfrac{k}{3.5}$
$\quad\; k = 7700$
$\quad\; h = \dfrac{7700}{5} = 1540$

The rate of heat loss is 1540 Btu per hour.

20. Using a right triangle, we have a known opposite side, a known adjacent side, and an unknown angle. Therefore, we use the tangent function.

$$\tan\theta = \frac{200}{50} = 4$$
$$\theta = \tan^{-1}(4) \approx 76°$$

The angle of elevation is about $76°$.

Chapter 6

Section 6.1

Check Point Exercises

1. $\csc x \tan x = \dfrac{1}{\cancel{\sin x}} \cdot \dfrac{\cancel{\sin x}}{\cos x}$

$= \dfrac{1}{\cos x}$

$= \sec x$

We worked with the left side and arrived at the right side. Thus, the identity is verified.

2. $\cos x \cot x + \sin x = \cos x \cdot \dfrac{\cos x}{\sin x} + \sin x$

$= \dfrac{\cos^2 x}{\sin x} + \sin x$

$= \dfrac{\cos^2 x}{\sin x} + \sin x \cdot \dfrac{\sin x}{\sin x}$

$= \dfrac{\cos^2 x}{\sin x} + \dfrac{\sin^2 x}{\sin x}$

$= \dfrac{\cos^2 x + \sin^2 x}{\sin x}$

$= \dfrac{1}{\sin x}$

$= \csc x$

We worked with the left side and arrived at the right side. Thus, the identity is verified.

3. $\sin x - \sin x \cos^2 x = \sin x \left(1 - \cos^2 x\right)$

$= \sin x \cdot \sin^2 x$

$= \sin^3 x$

We worked with the left side and arrived at the right side. Thus, the identity is verified.

4. $\dfrac{\sin x}{1 + \cos x} + \dfrac{1 + \cos x}{\sin x}$

$= \dfrac{\sin x (\sin x)}{(1 + \cos x)(\sin x)} + \dfrac{(1 + \cos x)(1 + \cos x)}{(\sin x)(1 + \cos x)}$

$= \dfrac{\sin^2 x}{(1 + \cos x)(\sin x)} + \dfrac{1 + 2\cos x + \cos^2 x}{(1 + \cos x)(\sin x)}$

$= \dfrac{\sin^2 x + 1 + 2\cos x + \cos^2 x}{(1 + \cos x)(\sin x)}$

$= \dfrac{\sin^2 x + \cos^2 x + 1 + 2\cos x}{(1 + \cos x)(\sin x)}$

$= \dfrac{1 + 1 + 2\cos x}{(1 + \cos x)(\sin x)}$

$= \dfrac{2 + 2\cos x}{(1 + \cos x)(\sin x)}$

$= \dfrac{2(\cancel{1 + \cos x})}{(\cancel{1 + \cos x})(\sin x)}$

$= \dfrac{2}{\sin x}$

$= 2\csc x$

We worked with the left side and arrived at the right side. Thus, the identity is verified.

5. $\dfrac{\cos x}{1 + \sin x} = \dfrac{\cos x}{(1 + \sin x)} \cdot \dfrac{1 - \sin x}{1 - \sin x}$

$= \dfrac{\cos x (1 - \sin x)}{1 - \sin^2 x}$

$= \dfrac{\cos x (1 - \sin x)}{\cos^2 x}$

$= \dfrac{1 - \sin x}{\cos x}$

We worked with the left side and arrived at the right side. Thus, the identity is verified.

6. $\dfrac{\sec x + \csc(-x)}{\sec x \csc x} = \dfrac{\sec x + (-\csc x)}{\sec x \csc x}$

$= \dfrac{\sec x - \csc x}{\sec x \csc x}$

$= \dfrac{\frac{1}{\cos x} - \frac{1}{\sin x}}{\frac{1}{\cos x} \cdot \frac{1}{\sin x}}$

$= \dfrac{\frac{\sin x}{\cos x \sin x} - \frac{\cos x}{\cos x \sin x}}{\frac{1}{\cos x \sin x}}$

$= \dfrac{\frac{\sin x - \cos x}{\cos x \sin x}}{\frac{1}{\cos x \sin x}}$

$= \dfrac{\sin x - \cos x}{\cos x \sin x} \div \dfrac{1}{\cos x \sin x}$

$= \dfrac{\sin x - \cos x}{\cos x \sin x} \cdot \dfrac{\cos x \sin x}{1}$

$= \sin x - \cos x$

We worked with the left side and arrived at the right side. Thus, the identity is verified.

7. Left side:

$\dfrac{1}{1+\sin\theta} + \dfrac{1}{1-\sin\theta}$

$= \dfrac{1(1-\sin\theta)}{(1+\sin\theta)(1-\sin\theta)} + \dfrac{1(1+\sin\theta)}{(1-\sin\theta)(1+\sin\theta)}$

$= \dfrac{1-\sin\theta+1+\sin\theta}{(1+\sin\theta)(1-\sin\theta)}$

$= \dfrac{2}{(1+\sin\theta)(1-\sin\theta)}$

$= \dfrac{2}{1-\sin^2\theta}$

Right side:

$2 + 2\tan^2\theta = 2 + 2\left(\dfrac{\sin^2\theta}{\cos^2\theta}\right)$

$= \dfrac{2\cos^2\theta}{\cos^2\theta} + \dfrac{2\sin^2\theta}{\cos^2\theta}$

$= \dfrac{2\cos^2\theta + 2\sin^2\theta}{\cos^2\theta}$

$= \dfrac{2}{\cos^2\theta} = \dfrac{2}{1-\sin^2\theta}$

The identity is verified because both sides are equal to $\dfrac{2}{1-\sin^2\theta}$.

Exercise Set 6.1

1. $\sin x \sec x = \sin x \cdot \dfrac{1}{\cos x}$

$= \dfrac{\sin x}{\cos x}$

$= \tan x$

We worked with the left side and arrived at the right side. Thus, the identity is verified.

3. $\tan(-x)\cos x = -\tan x \cdot \cos x$

$= -\dfrac{\sin x}{\cos x} \cdot \cos x$

$= -\sin x$

We worked with the left side and arrived at the right side. Thus, the identity is verified.

5. $\tan x \csc x \cos x = \dfrac{\sin x}{\cos x} \cdot \dfrac{1}{\sin x} \cdot \cos x$

$= 1$

We worked with the left side and arrived at the right side. Thus, the identity is verified.

7. $\sec x - \sec x \sin^2 x = \sec x(1-\sin^2 x)$

$= \sec x(\cos^2 x)$

$= \dfrac{1}{\cos x}\left(\cos^2 x\right)$

$= \dfrac{\cos x}{\cos x} \cdot \cos x$

$= \cos x$

We worked with the left side and arrived at the right side. Thus, the identity is verified.

9. $\cos^2 x - \sin^2 x = \left(1-\sin^2 x\right) - \sin^2 x$

$= 1 - \sin^2 x - \sin^2 x$

$= 1 - 2\sin^2 x$

We worked with the left side and arrived at the right side. Thus, the identity is verified.

11.
$$\csc\theta - \sin\theta = \frac{1}{\sin\theta} - \sin\theta$$
$$= \frac{1}{\sin\theta} - \frac{\sin^2\theta}{\sin\theta}$$
$$= \frac{1 - \sin^2\theta}{\sin\theta}$$
$$= \frac{\cos^2\theta}{\sin\theta}$$
$$= \frac{\cos\theta}{\sin\theta} \cdot \cos\theta$$
$$= \cot\theta\cos\theta$$

We worked with the left side and arrived at the right side. Thus, the identity is verified.

13.
$$\frac{\tan\theta\cot\theta}{\csc\theta} = \frac{\dfrac{\sin\theta}{\cos\theta} \cdot \dfrac{\cos\theta}{\sin\theta}}{\dfrac{1}{\sin\theta}}$$
$$= \frac{1}{\dfrac{1}{\sin\theta}}$$
$$= 1 \div \frac{1}{\sin\theta}$$
$$= 1 \cdot \frac{\sin\theta}{1}$$
$$= \sin\theta$$

We worked with the left side and arrived at the right side. Thus, the identity is verified.

15.
$$\sin^2\theta\left(1 + \cot^2\theta\right) = \sin^2\theta\left(\csc^2\theta\right)$$
$$= \sin^2\theta \cdot \frac{1}{\sin^2\theta}$$
$$= 1$$

We worked with the left side and arrived at the right side. Thus, the identity is verified.

17.
$$\frac{1 - \cos^2 t}{\cos t} = \frac{\sin^2 t}{\cos t}$$
$$= \sin t \cdot \frac{\sin t}{\cos t}$$
$$= \sin t \tan t$$

We worked with the right side and arrived at the left side. Thus, the identity is verified.

19.
$$\frac{\csc^2 t}{\cot t} = \frac{\dfrac{1}{\sin^2 t}}{\dfrac{\cos t}{\sin t}}$$
$$= \frac{1}{\sin^2 t} \div \frac{\cos t}{\sin t}$$
$$= \frac{1}{\sin^2 t} \cdot \frac{\sin t}{\cos t}$$
$$= \frac{1}{\sin t} \cdot \frac{1}{\sin t} \cdot \frac{\sin t}{\cos t}$$
$$= \frac{1}{\sin t} \cdot \frac{1}{\cos t}$$
$$= \csc t \sec t$$

We worked with the left side and arrived at the right side. Thus, the identity is verified.

21.
$$\frac{\tan^2 t}{\sec t} = \frac{\sec^2 t - 1}{\sec t}$$
$$= \frac{\sec^2 t}{\sec t} - \frac{1}{\sec t}$$
$$= \frac{\sec t}{\sec t} \cdot \sec t - \frac{1}{\sec t}$$
$$= \sec t - \cos t$$

We worked with the left side and arrived at the right side. Thus, the identity is verified.

23.
$$\frac{\sin t}{\csc t} + \frac{\cos t}{\sec t} = \frac{\sin t}{\dfrac{1}{\sin t}} + \frac{\cos t}{\dfrac{1}{\cos t}}$$
$$= \sin t \div \frac{1}{\sin t} + \cos t \div \frac{1}{\cos t}$$
$$= \sin t \cdot \frac{\sin t}{1} + \cos t \cdot \frac{\cos t}{1}$$
$$= \sin^2 t + \cos^2 t$$
$$= 1$$

We worked with the left side and arrived at the right side. Thus, the identity is verified.

25. $\tan t + \dfrac{\cos t}{1+\sin t}$

$= \dfrac{\sin t}{\cos t} + \dfrac{\cos t}{1+\sin t}$

$= \dfrac{\sin t}{\cos t} \cdot \dfrac{1+\sin t}{1+\sin t} + \dfrac{\cos t}{\cos t} \cdot \dfrac{\cos t}{1+\sin t}$

$= \dfrac{\sin t + \sin^2 t}{\cos t(1+\sin t)} + \dfrac{\cos^2 t}{\cos t(1+\sin t)}$

$= \dfrac{\sin t + \sin^2 t + \cos^2 t}{\cos t(1+\sin t)}$

$= \dfrac{\sin t + 1}{\cos t(1+\sin t)}$

$= \dfrac{\cancel{1+\sin t}}{\cos t(\cancel{1+\sin t})}$

$= \dfrac{1}{\cos t}$

$= \sec t$

We worked with the left side and arrived at the right side. Thus, the identity is verified.

27. $1 - \dfrac{\sin^2 x}{1+\cos x} = 1 - \dfrac{\sin^2 x}{1+\cos x} \cdot \dfrac{1-\cos x}{1-\cos x}$

$= 1 - \dfrac{\sin^2 x(1-\cos x)}{1-\cos^2 x}$

$= 1 - \dfrac{\cancel{\sin^2 x}(1-\cos x)}{\cancel{\sin^2 x}}$

$= 1 - (1-\cos x)$

$= 1 - 1 + \cos x$

$= \cos x$

We worked with the left side and arrived at the right side. Thus, the identity is verified.

29. $\dfrac{\cos x}{1-\sin x} + \dfrac{1-\sin x}{\cos x}$

$= \dfrac{\cos x}{1-\sin x} \cdot \dfrac{1+\sin x}{1+\sin x} + \dfrac{1-\sin x}{\cos x}$

$= \dfrac{\cos x(1+\sin x)}{1-\sin^2 x} + \dfrac{1-\sin x}{\cos x}$

$= \dfrac{\cos x(1+\sin x)}{\cos^2 x} + \dfrac{1-\sin x}{\cos x}$

$= \dfrac{\cancel{\cos x}}{\cancel{\cos x}} \cdot \dfrac{1+\sin x}{\cos x} + \dfrac{1-\sin x}{\cos x}$

$= \dfrac{1+\sin x}{\cos x} + \dfrac{1-\sin x}{\cos x}$

$= \dfrac{1+\sin x + 1 - \sin x}{\cos x}$

$= \dfrac{2}{\cos x}$

$= 2 \cdot \dfrac{1}{\cos x}$

$= 2\sec x$

We worked with the left side and arrived at the right side. Thus, the identity is verified.

31. $\sec^2 x \csc^2 x = \left(1+\tan^2 x\right)\csc^2 x$

$= \csc^2 x + \tan^2 x \csc^2 x$

$= \csc^2 x + \dfrac{\cancel{\sin^2 x}}{\cos^2 x} \cdot \dfrac{1}{\cancel{\sin^2 x}}$

$= \csc^2 x + \dfrac{1}{\cos^2 x}$

$= \csc^2 x + \sec^2 x$

$= \sec^2 x + \csc^2 x$

We worked with the left side and arrived at the right side. Thus, the identity is verified.

33. $\dfrac{\sec x - \csc x}{\sec x + \csc x} = \dfrac{\dfrac{1}{\cos x} - \dfrac{1}{\sin x}}{\dfrac{1}{\cos x} + \dfrac{1}{\sin x}} = \dfrac{\dfrac{1}{\cos x} - \dfrac{1}{\sin x}}{\dfrac{1}{\cos x} + \dfrac{1}{\sin x}} \cdot \dfrac{\sin x}{\sin x} = \dfrac{\dfrac{\sin x}{\cos x} - \dfrac{\sin x}{\sin x}}{\dfrac{\sin x}{\cos x} + \dfrac{\sin x}{\sin x}} = \dfrac{\tan x - 1}{\tan x + 1}$

We worked with the left side and arrived at the right side. Thus, the identity is verified.

35. $\dfrac{\sin^2 x - \cos^2 x}{\sin x + \cos x} = \dfrac{\sin^2 x - \cos^2 x}{\sin x + \cos x} \cdot \dfrac{\sin x - \cos x}{\sin x - \cos x} = \dfrac{\left(\sin^2 x - \cos^2 x\right)(\sin x - \cos x)}{\sin^2 x - \cos^2 x}$

$\qquad = \sin x - \cos x$

We worked with the left side and arrived at the right side. Thus, the identity is verified.

37. $\tan^2 2x + \sin^2 2x + \cos^2 2x = \tan^2 2x + 1 = \sec^2 2x$

We worked with the left side and arrived at the right side. Thus, the identity is verified.

39. $\dfrac{\tan 2\theta + \cot 2\theta}{\csc 2\theta} = \dfrac{\dfrac{\sin 2\theta}{\cos 2\theta} + \dfrac{\cos 2\theta}{\sin 2\theta}}{\dfrac{1}{\sin 2\theta}} = \dfrac{\dfrac{\sin 2\theta}{\cos 2\theta} \cdot \dfrac{\sin 2\theta}{\sin 2\theta} + \dfrac{\cos 2\theta}{\cos 2\theta} \cdot \dfrac{\cos 2\theta}{\sin 2\theta}}{\dfrac{1}{\sin 2\theta}}$

$\qquad = \dfrac{\dfrac{\sin^2 2\theta}{\cos 2\theta \sin 2\theta} + \dfrac{\cos^2 2\theta}{\cos 2\theta \sin 2\theta}}{\dfrac{1}{\sin 2\theta}}$

$\qquad = \dfrac{\dfrac{\sin^2 2\theta + \cos^2 2\theta}{\cos 2\theta \sin 2\theta}}{\dfrac{1}{\sin 2\theta}} = \dfrac{\sin^2 2\theta + \cos^2 2\theta}{\cos 2\theta \sin 2\theta} \div \dfrac{1}{\sin 2\theta}$

$\qquad = \dfrac{1}{\cos 2\theta \sin 2\theta} \cdot \sin 2\theta = \dfrac{1}{\cos 2\theta}$

$\qquad = \sec 2\theta$

We worked with the left side and arrived at the right side. Thus, the identity is verified.

41. $\dfrac{\tan x + \tan y}{1 - \tan x \tan y} = \dfrac{\dfrac{\sin x}{\cos x} + \dfrac{\sin y}{\cos y}}{1 - \dfrac{\sin x}{\cos x} \cdot \dfrac{\sin y}{\cos y}} = \dfrac{\dfrac{\sin x}{\cos x} + \dfrac{\sin y}{\cos y}}{1 - \dfrac{\sin x \sin y}{\cos x \cos y}} \cdot \dfrac{\cos x \cos y}{\cos x \cos y}$

$\qquad = \dfrac{\dfrac{\sin x}{\cos x} \cdot \dfrac{\cos x \cos y}{1} + \dfrac{\sin y}{\cos y} \cdot \dfrac{\cos x \cos y}{1}}{\cos x \cos y - \dfrac{\sin x \sin y}{\cos x \cos y} \cdot \dfrac{\cos x \cos y}{1}}$

$\qquad = \dfrac{\sin x \cos y + \cos x \sin y}{\cos x \cos y - \sin x \sin y}$

We worked with the left side and arrived at the right side. Thus, the identity is verified.

43. Left side:

$$(\sec x - \tan x)^2 = \left(\frac{1}{\cos x} - \frac{\sin x}{\cos x} \right)^2$$

$$= \left(\frac{1 - \sin x}{\cos x} \right)^2$$

$$= \frac{(1 - \sin x)^2}{\cos^2 x}$$

Right side:

$$\frac{1 - \sin x}{1 + \sin x} = \frac{1 - \sin x}{1 + \sin x} \cdot \frac{1 - \sin x}{1 - \sin x}$$

$$= \frac{(1 - \sin x)^2}{1 - \sin^2 x}$$

$$= \frac{(1 - \sin x)^2}{\cos^2 x}$$

The identity is verified because both sides are equal to $\dfrac{(1 - \sin x)^2}{\cos^2 x}$.

45.
$$\frac{\tan t}{\sec t - 1} = \frac{\tan t}{\sec t - 1} \cdot \frac{\sec t + 1}{\sec t + 1}$$

$$= \frac{\tan t (\sec t + 1)}{\sec^2 t - 1}$$

$$= \frac{\tan t (\sec t + 1)}{\tan^2 t}$$

$$= \frac{\cancel{\tan t}}{\cancel{\tan t}} \cdot \frac{\sec t + 1}{\tan t}$$

$$= \frac{\sec t + 1}{\tan t}$$

We worked with the right side and arrived at the left side. Thus, the identity is verified.

47. Left side:

$$\frac{1 + \cos t}{1 - \cos t} = \frac{1 + \cos t}{1 - \cos t} \cdot \frac{1 + \cos t}{1 + \cos t}$$

$$= \frac{(1 + \cos t)^2}{1 - \cos^2 t}$$

$$= \frac{(1 + \cos t)^2}{\sin^2 t}$$

Right side:

$$(\csc t + \cot t)^2 = \left(\frac{1}{\sin t} + \frac{\cos t}{\sin t} \right)^2$$

$$= \left(\frac{1 + \cos t}{\sin t} \right)^2$$

$$= \frac{(1 + \cos t)^2}{\sin^2 t}$$

The identity is verified because both sides are equal to $\dfrac{(1 + \cos t)^2}{\sin^2 t}$.

49. $\cos^4 t - \sin^4 t = \left(\cos^2 t - \sin^2 t \right)\left(\cos^2 t + \sin^2 t \right)$

$$= \left(\cos^2 t - \sin^2 t \right) \cdot 1$$

$$= 1 - \sin^2 t - \sin^2 t$$

$$= 1 - 2 \sin^2 t$$

We worked with the left side and arrived at the right side. Thus, the identity is verified.

51.
$$\frac{\sin \theta - \cos \theta}{\sin \theta} + \frac{\cos \theta - \sin \theta}{\cos \theta}$$

$$= \frac{(\sin \theta - \cos \theta) \cos \theta}{\cos \theta \sin \theta} + \frac{(\cos \theta - \sin \theta) \sin \theta}{\cos \theta \sin \theta}$$

$$= \frac{\sin \theta \cos \theta - \cos^2 \theta + \sin \theta \cos \theta - \sin^2 \theta}{\sin \theta \cos \theta}$$

$$= \frac{2 \sin \theta \cos \theta - \left(\cos^2 \theta + \sin^2 \theta \right)}{\sin \theta \cos \theta}$$

$$= \frac{2 \sin \theta \cos \theta - 1}{\sin \theta \cos \theta}$$

$$= \frac{2 \sin \theta \cos \theta}{\sin \theta \cos \theta} - \frac{1}{\sin \theta \cos \theta}$$

$$= 2 - \frac{1}{\sin \theta} \cdot \frac{1}{\cos \theta}$$

$$= 2 - \csc \theta \sec \theta$$

$$= 2 - \sec \theta \csc \theta$$

We worked with the left side and arrived at the right side. Thus, the identity is verified.

53. $\left(\tan^2\theta+1\right)\left(\cos^2\theta+1\right)=\tan^2\theta\cos^2\theta+\tan^2\theta+\cos^2\theta+1$

$$=\frac{\sin^2\theta}{\cos^2\theta}\cdot\cos^2\theta+\tan^2\theta+\cos^2\theta+1$$
$$=\sin^2\theta+\tan^2\theta+\cos^2\theta+1$$
$$=\sin^2\theta+\cos^2\theta+\tan^2\theta+1$$
$$=1+\tan^2\theta+1$$
$$=\tan^2\theta+2$$

We worked with the left side and arrived at the right side. Thus, the identity is verified.

55. $(\cos\theta-\sin\theta)^2+(\cos\theta+\sin\theta)^2=\cos^2\theta-2\cos\theta\sin\theta+\sin^2\theta+\cos^2\theta+2\cos\theta\sin\theta+\sin^2\theta$

$$=\cos^2\theta+\sin^2\theta+\cos^2\theta+\sin^2\theta$$
$$=1+1=2$$

We worked with the left side and arrived at the right side. Thus, the identity is verified.

57. $\dfrac{\cos^2x-\sin^2x}{1-\tan^2x}=\dfrac{\cos^2x-\sin^2x}{1-\dfrac{\sin^2x}{\cos^2x}}=\dfrac{\cos^2x-\sin^2x}{\dfrac{\cos^2x}{\cos^2x}-\dfrac{\sin^2x}{\cos^2x}}=\dfrac{\cos^2x-\sin^2x}{\dfrac{\cos^2x-\sin^2x}{\cos^2x}}$

$$=\left(\cos^2x-\sin^2x\right)\div\frac{\cos^2x-\sin^2x}{\cos^2x}$$
$$=\left(\cos^2x-\sin^2x\right)\left(\frac{\cos^2x}{\cos^2x-\sin^2x}\right)$$
$$=\cos^2x$$

We worked with the left side and arrived at the right side. Thus, the identity is verified.

59. $(\sec x-\tan x)^2=\left(\dfrac{1}{\cos x}-\dfrac{\sin x}{\cos x}\right)^2$

$$=\left(\frac{1-\sin x}{\cos x}\right)^2=\frac{(1-\sin x)^2}{\cos^2x}$$
$$=\frac{(1-\sin x)^2}{1-\sin^2x}=\frac{(1-\sin x)(1-\sin x)}{(1-\sin x)(1+\sin x)}$$
$$=\frac{1-\sin x}{1+\sin x}$$

We worked with the left side and arrived at the right side. Thus, the identity is verified.

61.–63. Answers may vary.

65.

$$\sec x(\sin x - \cos x) + 1 = \frac{1}{\cos x}(\sin x - \cos x) + 1$$
$$= \frac{\sin x}{\cos x} - \frac{\cos x}{\cos x} + 1$$
$$= \tan x - 1 + 1$$
$$= \tan x$$

We worked with the right side and arrived at the left side. Thus, the identity is verified.

67.

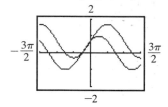

The graphs do not coincide. Values for x may vary.

69.

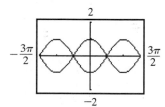

The graphs do not coincide. Values for x may vary.

71.

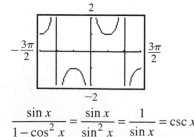

$$\frac{\sin x}{1 - \cos^2 x} = \frac{\sin x}{\sin^2 x} = \frac{1}{\sin x} = \csc x$$

We worked with the left side and arrived at the right side. Thus, the identity is verified.

73.

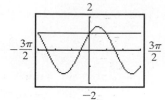

The graphs do not coincide. Values for x may vary.

75. $\dfrac{\sin x - \cos x + 1}{\sin x + \cos x - 1}$

$$= \frac{\sin x - \cos x + 1}{\sin x + \cos x - 1} \cdot \frac{\sin x - \cos x - 1}{\sin x - \cos x - 1}$$
$$= \frac{\sin^2 x - 2\sin x \cos x + \cos^2 x - 1}{\sin^2 x - 2\sin x - \cos^2 x + 1}$$
$$= \frac{\sin^2 x + \cos^2 x - 2\sin x \cos x - 1}{\sin^2 x - 2\sin x - \left(1 - \sin^2 x\right) + 1}$$
$$= \frac{1 - 2\sin x \cos x - 1}{\sin^2 x - 2\sin x - 1 + \sin^2 x + 1}$$
$$= \frac{-2\sin x \cos x}{2\sin^2 x - 2\sin x}$$
$$= \frac{-2\sin x \cos x}{2\sin x(\sin x - 1)}$$
$$= \frac{-\cos x}{\sin x - 1}$$
$$= \frac{-\cos x}{\sin x - 1} \cdot \frac{\sin x + 1}{\sin x + 1}$$
$$= \frac{-\cos x(\sin x + 1)}{\sin^2 x - 1}$$
$$= \frac{-\cos x(\sin x + 1)}{-\cos^2 x}$$
$$= \frac{-\cos x}{-\cos x} \cdot \frac{\sin x + 1}{\cos x}$$
$$= \frac{\sin x + 1}{\cos x}$$

We worked with the left side and arrived at the right side. Thus, the identity is verified.

77. Answers may vary.

Section 6.2

Check Point Exercises

1. $\cos 30° = \cos(90° - 60°)$
$$= \cos 90° \cos 60° + \sin 90° \sin 60°$$
$$= 0 \cdot \frac{1}{2} + 1 \cdot \frac{\sqrt{3}}{2}$$
$$= 0 + \frac{\sqrt{3}}{2}$$
$$= \frac{\sqrt{3}}{2}$$

2. $\cos 70° \cos 40° + \sin 70° \sin 40°$
$$= \cos(70 - 40°)$$
$$= \cos 30°$$
$$= \frac{\sqrt{3}}{2}$$

3. $\dfrac{\cos(\alpha - \beta)}{\cos \alpha \cos \beta} = \dfrac{\cos \alpha \cos \beta + \sin \alpha \sin \beta}{\cos \alpha \cos \beta}$
$$= \frac{\cos \alpha}{\cos \alpha} \cdot \frac{\cos \beta}{\cos \beta} + \frac{\sin \alpha}{\cos \alpha} \cdot \frac{\sin \beta}{\cos \beta}$$
$$= 1 \cdot 1 + \tan \alpha \cdot \tan \beta$$
$$= 1 + \tan \alpha \tan \beta$$

We worked with the left side and arrived at the right side. Thus, the identity is verified.

4. $\sin \dfrac{5\pi}{12} = \sin\left(\dfrac{\pi}{6} + \dfrac{\pi}{4}\right)$
$$= \sin \frac{\pi}{6} \cos \frac{\pi}{4} + \cos \frac{\pi}{6} \sin \frac{\pi}{4}$$
$$= \frac{1}{2} \cdot \frac{\sqrt{2}}{2} + \frac{\sqrt{3}}{2} \cdot \frac{\sqrt{2}}{2}$$
$$= \frac{\sqrt{2}}{4} + \frac{\sqrt{6}}{4}$$
$$= \frac{\sqrt{2} + \sqrt{6}}{4}$$

5. **a.** $\sin \alpha = \dfrac{4}{5} = \dfrac{y}{r}$

We find x using the Pythagorean Theorem.
$$x^2 + y^2 = r^2$$
$$x^2 + 4^2 = 5^2$$
$$x^2 + 16 = 25$$
$$x^2 = 9$$
Because α lies in quadrant II, x is negative.
$$x = -\sqrt{9} = -3$$
Thus, $\cos \alpha = \dfrac{x}{r} = \dfrac{-3}{5} = -\dfrac{3}{5}$.

b. $\sin \beta = \dfrac{1}{2} = \dfrac{y}{r}$

We find x using the Pythagorean Theorem.
$$x^2 + y^2 = r^2$$
$$x^2 + 1^2 = 2^2$$
$$x^2 + 1 = 4$$
$$x^2 = 3$$
Because β lies in quadrant I, x is positive.
$$x = \sqrt{3}$$
Thus, $\cos \beta = \dfrac{x}{r} = \dfrac{\sqrt{3}}{2}$.

c. $\cos(\alpha + \beta) = \cos \alpha \cos \beta - \sin \alpha \sin \beta$
$$= -\frac{3}{5} \cdot \frac{\sqrt{3}}{2} - \frac{4}{5} \cdot \frac{1}{2}$$
$$= -\frac{3\sqrt{3}}{10} - \frac{4}{10}$$
$$= \frac{-3\sqrt{3} - 4}{10}$$

d. $\sin(\alpha + \beta) = \sin \alpha \cos \beta + \cos \alpha \sin \beta$
$$= \frac{4}{5} \cdot \frac{\sqrt{3}}{2} + \left(-\frac{3}{5}\right) \cdot \frac{1}{2}$$
$$= \frac{4\sqrt{3}}{10} - \frac{3}{10}$$
$$= \frac{4\sqrt{3} - 3}{10}$$

6. a. The graph appears to be the sine curve,
$y = \sin x$.
It cycles through intercept, maximum, intercept, minimum and back to intercept. Thus, $y = \sin x$ also describes the graph.

b. $\cos\left(x + \dfrac{3\pi}{2}\right) = \cos x \cos\dfrac{3\pi}{2} - \sin x \sin\dfrac{3\pi}{2}$
$= \cos x \cdot 0 - \sin x \cdot (-1)$
$= \sin x$

This verifies our observation that
$y = \cos\left(x + \dfrac{3\pi}{2}\right)$ and $y = \sin x$ describe the same graph.

7. $\tan(x + \pi) = \dfrac{\tan x + \tan \pi}{1 - \tan x \tan \pi}$
$= \dfrac{\tan x + 0}{1 - \tan x \cdot 0}$
$= \dfrac{\tan x}{1}$
$= \tan x$

Exercise Set 6.2

1. $\cos(45° - 30°) = \cos 45° \cos 30° + \sin 45° \sin 30°$
$= \dfrac{\sqrt{2}}{2} \cdot \dfrac{\sqrt{3}}{2} + \dfrac{\sqrt{2}}{2} \cdot \dfrac{1}{2}$
$= \dfrac{\sqrt{6}}{4} + \dfrac{\sqrt{2}}{4}$
$= \dfrac{\sqrt{6} + \sqrt{2}}{4}$

3. $\cos\left(\dfrac{3\pi}{4} - \dfrac{\pi}{6}\right) = \cos\dfrac{3\pi}{4}\cos\dfrac{\pi}{6} + \sin\dfrac{3\pi}{4}\sin\dfrac{\pi}{6}$
$= -\dfrac{\sqrt{2}}{2} \cdot \dfrac{\sqrt{3}}{2} + \dfrac{\sqrt{2}}{2} \cdot \dfrac{1}{2}$
$= -\dfrac{\sqrt{6}}{4} + \dfrac{\sqrt{2}}{4}$
$= \dfrac{\sqrt{2} - \sqrt{6}}{4}$

5. a. $\cos 50° \cos 20° + \sin 50° \sin 20°$
$= \cos\alpha\cos\beta + \sin\alpha\sin\beta$
Thus, $\alpha = 50°$ and $\beta = 20°$.

b. $\cos 50° \cos 20° + \sin 50° \sin 20°$
$= \cos(50° - 20°)$
$= \cos 30°$

c. $\cos 30° = \dfrac{\sqrt{3}}{2}$

7. a. $\cos\dfrac{5\pi}{12}\cos\dfrac{\pi}{12} + \sin\dfrac{5\pi}{12}\sin\dfrac{\pi}{12}$
$= \cos\alpha\cos\beta + \sin\alpha\sin\beta$
Thus, $\alpha = \dfrac{5\pi}{12}$ and $\beta = \dfrac{\pi}{12}$.

b. $\cos\dfrac{5\pi}{12}\cos\dfrac{\pi}{12} + \sin\dfrac{5\pi}{12}\sin\dfrac{\pi}{12}$
$= \cos\left(\dfrac{5\pi}{12} - \dfrac{\pi}{12}\right)$
$= \cos\dfrac{4\pi}{12}$
$= \cos\dfrac{\pi}{3}$

c. $\cos\dfrac{\pi}{3} = \dfrac{1}{2}$

9. $\dfrac{\cos(\alpha - \beta)}{\cos\alpha\sin\beta} = \dfrac{\cos\alpha\cos\beta - \sin\alpha\sin\beta}{\cos\alpha\sin\beta}$
$= \dfrac{\cos\alpha}{\cos\alpha} \cdot \dfrac{\cos\beta}{\sin\beta} - \dfrac{\sin\alpha}{\cos\alpha} \cdot \dfrac{\sin\beta}{\sin\beta}$
$= 1 \cdot \cot\beta + \tan\alpha \cdot 1$
$= \tan\alpha + \cot\beta$

11. $\cos\left(x - \dfrac{\pi}{4}\right) = \cos x \cos\dfrac{\pi}{4} + \sin x \sin\dfrac{\pi}{4}$
$= \cos x \cdot \dfrac{\sqrt{2}}{2} + \sin x \cdot \dfrac{\sqrt{2}}{2}$
$= \dfrac{\sqrt{2}}{2}(\cos x + \sin x)$

13. $\sin(45° - 30°) = \sin 45° \cos 30° - \cos 45° \sin 30°$

$$= \frac{\sqrt{2}}{2} \cdot \frac{\sqrt{3}}{2} - \frac{\sqrt{2}}{2} \cdot \frac{1}{2}$$

$$= \frac{\sqrt{6}}{4} - \frac{\sqrt{2}}{4}$$

$$= \frac{\sqrt{6} - \sqrt{2}}{4}$$

15. $\sin(105°) = \sin(60° + 45°)$

$$= \sin 60° \cos 45° + \cos 60° \sin 45°$$

$$= \frac{\sqrt{3}}{2} \cdot \frac{\sqrt{2}}{2} + \frac{1}{2} \cdot \frac{\sqrt{2}}{2}$$

$$= \frac{\sqrt{6}}{4} + \frac{\sqrt{2}}{4}$$

$$= \frac{\sqrt{6} + \sqrt{2}}{4}$$

17. $\tan(30° + 45°) = \dfrac{\tan 30° + \tan 45°}{1 - \tan 30° \tan 45°}$

$$= \frac{\frac{\sqrt{3}}{3} + 1}{1 - \frac{\sqrt{3}}{3} \cdot 1}$$

$$= \frac{\left(\frac{\sqrt{3}}{3} + 1\right) \cdot \left(1 + \frac{\sqrt{3}}{3}\right)}{\left(1 - \frac{\sqrt{3}}{3}\right) \cdot \left(1 + \frac{\sqrt{3}}{3}\right)}$$

$$= \frac{\frac{\sqrt{3}}{3} + \frac{1}{3} + 1 + \frac{\sqrt{3}}{3}}{1 - \frac{1}{3}}$$

$$= \frac{\frac{2\sqrt{3}}{3} + \frac{4}{3}}{\frac{2}{3}}$$

$$= \left(\frac{2\sqrt{3} + 4}{3}\right) \cdot \frac{3}{2}$$

$$= \frac{2\left(\sqrt{3} + 2\right)}{2}$$

$$= \sqrt{3} + 2$$

19. $\tan(240° - 45°) = \dfrac{\tan 240° - \tan 45°}{1 + \tan 240° \tan 45°}$

$$= \frac{\sqrt{3} - 1}{1 + \sqrt{3} \cdot 1}$$

$$= \frac{\left(\sqrt{3} - 1\right) \cdot \left(1 - \sqrt{3}\right)}{\left(1 + \sqrt{3}\right) \cdot \left(1 - \sqrt{3}\right)}$$

$$= \frac{\sqrt{3} - 3 - 1 + \sqrt{3}}{1 - 3}$$

$$= \frac{2\sqrt{3} - 4}{-2}$$

$$= \frac{-2\left(2 - \sqrt{3}\right)}{-2}$$

$$= 2 - \sqrt{3}$$

21. $\cos\left(\dfrac{3\pi}{4} + \dfrac{\pi}{6}\right) = \cos\dfrac{3\pi}{4}\cos\dfrac{\pi}{6} - \sin\dfrac{3\pi}{4}\sin\dfrac{\pi}{6}$

$$= -\frac{\sqrt{2}}{2} \cdot \frac{\sqrt{3}}{2} - \frac{\sqrt{2}}{2} \cdot \frac{1}{2}$$

$$= -\frac{\sqrt{6}}{4} - \frac{\sqrt{2}}{4}$$

$$= \frac{-\sqrt{6} - \sqrt{2}}{4}$$

$$= -\frac{\sqrt{6} + \sqrt{2}}{4}$$

23. $\cos\dfrac{5\pi}{12} = \cos\left(\dfrac{8\pi}{12} - \dfrac{3\pi}{12}\right)$

$$= \cos\left(\frac{2\pi}{3} - \frac{\pi}{4}\right)$$

$$= \cos\frac{2\pi}{3}\cos\frac{\pi}{4} + \sin\frac{2\pi}{3}\sin\frac{\pi}{4}$$

$$= -\frac{1}{2} \cdot \frac{\sqrt{2}}{2} + \frac{\sqrt{3}}{2} \cdot \frac{\sqrt{2}}{2}$$

$$= -\frac{\sqrt{2}}{4} + \frac{\sqrt{6}}{4}$$

$$= \frac{\sqrt{6} - \sqrt{2}}{4}$$

25. $\sin 25° \cos 5° + \cos 25° \sin 5° = \sin(25° + 5°)$

$$= \sin 30°$$

$$= \frac{1}{2}$$

27. $\dfrac{\tan 10° + \tan 35°}{1 - \tan 10° \tan 35°} = \tan(10° + 35°)$

$\qquad\qquad\qquad\qquad = \tan 45°$

$\qquad\qquad\qquad\qquad = 1$

29. $\sin \dfrac{5\pi}{12} \cos \dfrac{\pi}{4} - \cos \dfrac{5\pi}{12} \sin \dfrac{\pi}{4} = \sin\left(\dfrac{5\pi}{12} - \dfrac{\pi}{4}\right)$

$\qquad\qquad\qquad\qquad\qquad\qquad = \sin\left(\dfrac{2\pi}{12}\right)$

$\qquad\qquad\qquad\qquad\qquad\qquad = \sin\left(\dfrac{\pi}{6}\right)$

$\qquad\qquad\qquad\qquad\qquad\qquad = \dfrac{1}{2}$

31. $\dfrac{\tan \frac{\pi}{5} - \tan \frac{\pi}{30}}{1 + \tan \frac{\pi}{5} \tan \frac{\pi}{30}} = \tan\left(\dfrac{\pi}{5} - \dfrac{\pi}{30}\right)$

$\qquad\qquad\qquad\qquad = \tan\left(\dfrac{5\pi}{30}\right) = \tan\left(\dfrac{\pi}{6}\right)$

$\qquad\qquad\qquad\qquad = \dfrac{\sqrt{3}}{3}$

33. $\sin\left(x + \dfrac{\pi}{2}\right) = \sin x \cos \dfrac{\pi}{2} + \cos x \sin \dfrac{\pi}{2}$

$\qquad\qquad\qquad = \sin x \cdot 0 + \cos x \cdot 1$

$\qquad\qquad\qquad = \cos x$

35. $\cos\left(x - \dfrac{\pi}{2}\right) = \cos x \cos \dfrac{\pi}{2} + \sin x \sin \dfrac{\pi}{2}$

$\qquad\qquad\qquad = \cos x \cdot 0 + \sin x \cdot 1$

$\qquad\qquad\qquad = \sin x$

37. $\tan(2\pi - x) = \dfrac{\tan 2\pi - \tan x}{1 + \tan 2\pi \tan x}$

$\qquad\qquad\qquad = \dfrac{0 - \tan x}{1 + 0 \cdot \tan x}$

$\qquad\qquad\qquad = -\tan x$

39. $\sin(\alpha + \beta) + \sin(\alpha - \beta)$

$\quad = \sin \alpha \cos \beta + \cos \alpha \sin \beta$

$\quad + \sin \alpha \cos \beta - \cos \alpha \sin \beta$

$\quad = 2 \sin \alpha \cos \beta$

41. $\dfrac{\sin(\alpha - \beta)}{\cos \alpha \cos \beta} = \dfrac{\sin \alpha \cos \beta - \cos \alpha \sin \beta}{\cos \alpha \cos \beta}$

$\qquad\qquad\quad = \dfrac{\sin \alpha \cos \beta}{\cos \alpha \cos \beta} - \dfrac{\cos \alpha \sin \beta}{\cos \alpha \cos \beta}$

$\qquad\qquad\quad = \tan \alpha \cdot 1 - 1 \cdot \tan \beta$

$\qquad\qquad\quad = \tan \alpha - \tan \beta$

43. $\tan\left(\theta + \dfrac{\pi}{4}\right) = \dfrac{\tan \theta + \tan \frac{\pi}{4}}{1 - \tan \theta \tan \frac{\pi}{4}}$

$\qquad\qquad\quad = \dfrac{\tan \theta + 1}{1 - \tan \theta}$

$\qquad\qquad\quad = \dfrac{\frac{\sin \theta}{\cos \theta} + \frac{\cos \theta}{\cos \theta}}{\frac{\cos \theta}{\cos \theta} - \frac{\sin \theta}{\cos \theta}}$

$\qquad\qquad\quad = \dfrac{\frac{\sin \theta + \cos \theta}{\cos \theta}}{\frac{\cos \theta - \sin \theta}{\cos \theta}}$

$\qquad\qquad\quad = \dfrac{\sin \theta + \cos \theta}{\cos \theta} \cdot \dfrac{\cos \theta}{\cos \theta - \sin \theta}$

$\qquad\qquad\quad = \dfrac{\sin \theta + \cos \theta}{\cos \theta - \sin \theta}$

$\qquad\qquad\quad = \dfrac{\cos \theta + \sin \theta}{\cos \theta - \sin \theta}$

45. $\cos(\alpha + \beta) \cos(\alpha - \beta)$

$\quad = (\cos \alpha \cos \beta - \sin \alpha \sin \beta)$

$\quad \cdot (\cos \alpha \cos \beta + \sin \alpha \sin \beta)$

$\quad = \cos^2 \alpha \cos^2 \beta - \sin^2 \alpha \sin^2 \beta$

$\quad = \left(1 - \sin^2 \alpha\right) \cos^2 \beta - \sin^2 \alpha \left(1 - \cos^2 \beta\right)$

$\quad = \cos^2 \beta - \sin^2 \alpha \cos^2 \beta$

$\quad - \sin^2 \alpha + \sin^2 \alpha \cos^2 \beta$

$\quad = \cos^2 \beta - \sin^2 \alpha$

47. $\dfrac{\sin(\alpha+\beta)}{\sin(\alpha-\beta)}$

$=\dfrac{\sin\alpha\cos\beta+\cos\alpha\sin\beta}{\sin\alpha\cos\beta-\cos\alpha\sin\beta}$

$=\dfrac{\sin\alpha\cos\beta+\cos\alpha\sin\beta}{\sin\alpha\cos\beta-\cos\alpha\sin\beta}\cdot\dfrac{\frac{1}{\cos\alpha\cos\beta}}{\frac{1}{\cos\alpha\cos\beta}}$

$=\dfrac{\frac{\sin\alpha\cos\beta+\cos\alpha\sin\beta}{\cos\alpha\cos\beta}}{\frac{\sin\alpha\cos\beta-\cos\alpha\sin\beta}{\cos\alpha\cos\beta}}$

$=\dfrac{\frac{\sin\alpha\cos\beta}{\cos\alpha\cos\beta}+\frac{\cos\alpha\sin\beta}{\cos\alpha\cos\beta}}{\frac{\sin\alpha\cos\beta}{\cos\alpha\cos\beta}-\frac{\cos\alpha\sin\beta}{\cos\alpha\cos\beta}}$

$=\dfrac{\tan\alpha\cdot1+1\cdot\tan\beta}{\tan\alpha\cdot1-1\cdot\tan\beta}$

$=\dfrac{\tan\alpha+\tan\beta}{\tan\alpha-\tan\beta}$

49. $\dfrac{\cos(x+h)-\cos x}{h}$

$=\dfrac{\cos x\cos h-\sin x\sin h-\cos x}{h}$

$=\dfrac{\cos x\cos h-\cos x-\sin x\sin h}{h}$

$=\dfrac{\cos x(\cos h-1)-\sin x\sin h}{h}$

$=\cos x\cdot\dfrac{\cos h-1}{h}-\sin x\cdot\dfrac{\sin h}{h}$

51. $\sin2\alpha=\sin(\alpha+\alpha)$
$=\sin\alpha\cos\alpha+\cos\alpha\sin\alpha$
$=2\sin\alpha\cos\alpha$

53. $\tan2\alpha=\tan(\alpha+\alpha)$
$=\dfrac{\tan\alpha+\tan\alpha}{1-\tan\alpha\tan\alpha}$
$=\dfrac{2\tan\alpha}{1-\tan^2\alpha}$

55. $\tan(\alpha+\beta)=\dfrac{\sin(\alpha+\beta)}{\cos(\alpha+\beta)}$

$=\dfrac{\sin\alpha\cos\beta+\cos\alpha\sin\beta}{\cos\alpha\cos\beta-\sin\alpha\sin\beta}$

$=\dfrac{\sin\alpha\cos\beta+\cos\alpha\sin\beta}{\cos\alpha\cos\beta-\sin\alpha\sin\beta}\cdot\dfrac{\frac{1}{\cos\alpha\cos\beta}}{\frac{1}{\cos\alpha\cos\beta}}$

$=\dfrac{\frac{\sin\alpha\cos\beta+\cos\alpha\sin\beta}{\cos\alpha\cos\beta}}{\frac{\cos\alpha\cos\beta-\sin\alpha\sin\beta}{\cos\alpha\cos\beta}}$

$=\dfrac{\frac{\sin\alpha\cos\beta}{\cos\alpha\cos\beta}+\frac{\cos\alpha\sin\beta}{\cos\alpha\cos\beta}}{\frac{\cos\alpha\cos\beta}{\cos\alpha\cos\beta}-\frac{\sin\alpha\sin\beta}{\cos\alpha\cos\beta}}$

$=\dfrac{\tan\alpha+\tan\beta}{1-\tan\alpha\tan\beta}$

57. $\sin\alpha=\dfrac{3}{5}=\dfrac{y}{r}$
We find x using the Pythagorean Theorem.
$x^2+y^2=r^2$
$x^2+3^2=5^2$
$x^2+9=25$
$x^2=16$
Because α lies in quadrant I, x is positive.
$x=4$

Thus, $\cos\alpha=\dfrac{x}{r}=\dfrac{4}{5}$, and

$\tan\alpha=\dfrac{\sin\alpha}{\cos\alpha}=\dfrac{\frac{3}{5}}{\frac{4}{5}}=\dfrac{3}{4}.$

$\sin\beta=\dfrac{5}{13}=\dfrac{y}{r}$
We find x using the Pythagorean Theorem.
$x^2+y^2=r^2$
$x^2+5^2=13^2$
$x^2+25=169$
$x^2=144$
Because β lies in quadrant II, x is negative.
$x=-12$

Thus, $\cos\beta=\dfrac{x}{r}=\dfrac{-12}{13}=-\dfrac{12}{13}$, and

$\tan\beta=\dfrac{\sin\beta}{\cos\beta}=\dfrac{\frac{5}{13}}{-\frac{12}{13}}=-\dfrac{5}{12}.$

a. $\cos(\alpha + \beta) = \cos\alpha\cos\beta - \sin\alpha\sin\beta$

$$= \frac{4}{5}\cdot\left(-\frac{12}{13}\right) - \frac{3}{5}\cdot\frac{5}{13} = -\frac{63}{65}$$

b. $\sin(\alpha + \beta) = \sin\alpha\cos\beta + \cos\alpha\sin\beta$

$$= \frac{3}{5}\cdot\left(-\frac{12}{13}\right) + \frac{4}{5}\cdot\frac{5}{13} = -\frac{16}{65}$$

c. $\tan(\alpha + \beta) = \dfrac{\tan\alpha + \tan\beta}{1 - \tan\alpha\tan\beta}$

$$= \frac{\frac{3}{4} + \left(-\frac{5}{12}\right)}{1 - \frac{3}{4}\cdot\left(-\frac{5}{12}\right)} = \frac{\frac{4}{12}}{\frac{63}{48}} = \frac{16}{63}$$

59. $\tan\alpha = -\dfrac{3}{4} = \dfrac{3}{-4} = \dfrac{y}{x}$

We find r using the Pythagorean Theorem.

$$x^2 + y^2 = r^2$$
$$(-4)^2 + 3^2 = r^2$$
$$16 + 9 = r^2$$
$$25 = r^2$$

Because r is a distance, it is positive.

$$r = 5$$

Thus, $\cos\alpha = \dfrac{x}{r} = \dfrac{-4}{5} = -\dfrac{4}{5}$, and

$$\sin\alpha = \frac{y}{r} = \frac{3}{5}.$$

$\cos\beta = \dfrac{1}{3} = \dfrac{x}{r}$

We find y using the Pythagorean Theorem.

$$x^2 + y^2 = r^2$$
$$1^2 + y^2 = 3^2$$
$$1 + y^2 = 9$$
$$y^2 = 8$$

Because β lies in quadrant I, y is positive.

$$y = \sqrt{8} = 2\sqrt{2}$$

Thus, $\sin\beta = \dfrac{y}{r} = \dfrac{2\sqrt{2}}{3}$, and

$$\tan\beta = \frac{\sin\beta}{\cos\beta} = \frac{\frac{2\sqrt{2}}{3}}{\frac{1}{3}} = 2\sqrt{2}.$$

a. $\cos(\alpha + \beta) = \cos\alpha\cos\beta - \sin\alpha\sin\beta$

$$= \left(-\frac{4}{5}\right)\cdot\frac{1}{3} - \frac{3}{5}\cdot\frac{2\sqrt{2}}{3}$$
$$= -\frac{4}{15} - \frac{6\sqrt{2}}{15}$$
$$= \frac{-4 - 6\sqrt{2}}{15}$$
$$= -\frac{4 + 6\sqrt{2}}{15}$$

b. $\sin(\alpha + \beta) = \sin\alpha\cos\beta + \cos\alpha\sin\beta$

$$= \frac{3}{5}\cdot\frac{1}{3} + \left(-\frac{4}{5}\right)\cdot\frac{2\sqrt{2}}{3}$$
$$= \frac{3}{15} - \frac{8\sqrt{2}}{15}$$
$$= \frac{3 - 8\sqrt{2}}{15}$$

c. $\tan(\alpha + \beta) = \dfrac{\tan\alpha + \tan\beta}{1 - \tan\alpha\tan\beta}$

$$= \frac{-\frac{3}{4} + 2\sqrt{2}}{1 - \left(-\frac{3}{4}\right)\left(2\sqrt{2}\right)}$$
$$= \frac{\frac{-3 + 8\sqrt{2}}{4}}{\frac{4 + 6\sqrt{2}}{4}}$$
$$= \frac{-3 + 8\sqrt{2}}{4 + 6\sqrt{2}}\cdot\frac{\left(4 - 6\sqrt{2}\right)}{\left(4 - 6\sqrt{2}\right)}$$
$$= \frac{-108 + 50\sqrt{2}}{-56}$$
$$= \frac{54 - 25\sqrt{2}}{28}$$

61. $\cos\alpha = \dfrac{8}{17} = \dfrac{x}{r}$

We find y using the Pythagorean Theorem.

$x^2 + y^2 = r^2$

$8^2 + y^2 = 17^2$

$64 + y^2 = 289$

$\quad y^2 = 225$

Because α lies in quadrant IV, y is negative.

$y = -15$

Thus, $\sin\alpha = \dfrac{y}{r} = \dfrac{-15}{17} = -\dfrac{15}{17}$, and

$\tan\alpha = \dfrac{\sin\alpha}{\cos\alpha} = \dfrac{-\frac{15}{17}}{\frac{8}{17}} = -\dfrac{15}{8}$.

$\sin\beta = -\dfrac{1}{2} = \dfrac{-1}{2} = \dfrac{y}{r}$

We find x using the Pythagorean Theorem.

$x^2 + y^2 = r^2$

$x^2 + (-1)^2 = 2^2$

$x^2 + 1 = 4$

$x^2 = 3$

Because β lies in quadrant III, x is negative.

$x = -\sqrt{3}$

Thus, $\cos\beta = \dfrac{x}{r} = \dfrac{-\sqrt{3}}{2} = -\dfrac{\sqrt{3}}{2}$, and

$\tan\beta = \dfrac{\sin\beta}{\cos\beta} = \dfrac{-\frac{1}{2}}{-\frac{\sqrt{3}}{2}} = \dfrac{1}{\sqrt{3}} = \dfrac{\sqrt{3}}{3}$.

a. $\cos(\alpha+\beta) = \cos\alpha\cos\beta - \sin\alpha\sin\beta$

$= \dfrac{8}{17}\cdot\left(-\dfrac{\sqrt{3}}{2}\right) - \left(-\dfrac{15}{17}\right)\left(-\dfrac{1}{2}\right)$

$= \dfrac{-8\sqrt{3}-15}{34}$

$= -\dfrac{8\sqrt{3}+15}{34}$

b. $\sin(\alpha+\beta) = \sin\alpha\cos\beta + \cos\alpha\sin\beta$

$= \left(-\dfrac{15}{17}\right)\cdot\left(-\dfrac{\sqrt{3}}{2}\right) + \dfrac{8}{17}\cdot\left(-\dfrac{1}{2}\right)$

$= \dfrac{15\sqrt{3}-8}{34}$

c. $\tan(\alpha+\beta) = \dfrac{\tan\alpha+\tan\beta}{1-\tan\alpha\tan\beta}$

$= \dfrac{-\frac{15}{8}+\frac{\sqrt{3}}{3}}{1-\left(-\frac{15}{8}\right)\cdot\frac{\sqrt{3}}{3}}$

$= \dfrac{\frac{-45+8\sqrt{3}}{24}}{\frac{24+15\sqrt{3}}{24}}$

$= \dfrac{-45+8\sqrt{3}}{24+15\sqrt{3}}$

$= \dfrac{-45+8\sqrt{3}}{24+15\sqrt{3}} \cdot \dfrac{24-15\sqrt{3}}{24-15\sqrt{3}}$

$= \dfrac{-1440+867\sqrt{3}}{-99}$

$= \dfrac{480-289\sqrt{3}}{33}$

63. a. The graph appears to be the sine curve, $y = \sin x$. It cycles through intercept, maximum, minimum and back to intercept. Thus, $y = \sin x$ also describes the graph.

b. $\sin(\pi - x) = \sin\pi\cos x - \cos\pi\sin x$

$\qquad\qquad = 0\cdot\cos x - (-1)\cdot\sin x$

$\qquad\qquad = \sin x$

This verifies our observation that $y = \sin(\pi - x)$ and $y = \sin x$ describe the same graph.

65. a. The graph appears to be 2 times the cosine curve, $y = 2\cos x$. It cycles through maximum, intercept, minimum, intercept and back to maximum. Thus $y = 2\cos x$ also describes the graph.

b. $\sin\left(x + \dfrac{\pi}{2}\right) + \sin\left(\dfrac{\pi}{2} - x\right)$

$= \sin x \cos\dfrac{\pi}{2} + \cos x \sin\dfrac{\pi}{2} + \sin\dfrac{\pi}{2}\cos x$

$\quad - \cos\dfrac{\pi}{2}\sin x$

$= \sin x \cdot 0 + \cos x \cdot 1 + 1 \cdot \cos x - 0 \cdot \sin x$

$= \cos x + \cos x$

$= 2\cos x$

This verifies our observation that

$y = \sin\left(x + \dfrac{\pi}{2}\right) + \sin\left(\dfrac{\pi}{2} - x\right)$ and

$y = 2\cos x$ describe the same graph.

67. $\tan\theta = \dfrac{3}{2} = \dfrac{y}{x}$

We find r using the Pythagorean Theorem.

$x^2 + y^2 = r^2$

$2^2 + 3^3 = r^2$

$4 + 9 = r^2$

$13 = r^2$

Because r is a distance, it is positive.

$r = \sqrt{13}$

Thus, $\sin\theta = \dfrac{y}{r} = \dfrac{3}{\sqrt{13}}$

and $\cos\theta = \dfrac{x}{r} = \dfrac{2}{\sqrt{13}}$

$\sqrt{13}\cos(t - \theta) = \sqrt{13}(\cos t \cos\theta + \sin t \sin\theta)$

$= \sqrt{13}\left(\cos t \cdot \dfrac{2}{\sqrt{13}} + \sin t \cdot \dfrac{3}{\sqrt{13}}\right)$

$= \cos t \cdot 2 + \sin t \cdot 3$

$= 2\cos t + 3\sin t$

For the equation $y = \sqrt{13}\cos(t - \theta)$, the

amplitude is $\left|\sqrt{13}\right| = \sqrt{13}$, and the period is

$\dfrac{2\pi}{1} = 2\pi$.

69.–75. Answers may vary.

77.

$\tan(\pi - x) = \dfrac{\tan\pi - \tan x}{1 + \tan\pi\tan x}$

$= \dfrac{0 - \tan x}{1 + 0 \cdot \tan x}$

$= \dfrac{-\tan x}{1}$

$= -\tan x$

79.

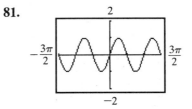

The graphs do not coincide. Values for x may vary.

81.

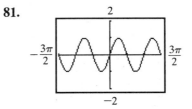

$\sin 1.2x \cos 0.8x + \cos 1.2x \sin 0.8x$

$\sin(1.2x + 0.8x)$

$\sin 2x$

83. $\dfrac{\sin(x-y)}{\cos x \cos y} + \dfrac{\sin(y-z)}{\cos y \cos z} + \dfrac{\sin(z-x)}{\cos z \cos x}$

$= \dfrac{\sin x \cos y - \cos x \sin y}{\cos x \cos y} + \dfrac{\sin y \cos z - \cos y \sin z}{\cos y \cos z} + \dfrac{\sin z \cos x - \cos z \sin x}{\cos z \cos x}$

$= \dfrac{\sin x \cos y}{\cos x \cos y} - \dfrac{\cos x \sin y}{\cos y \cos y} + \dfrac{\sin y \cos z}{\cos y \cos z} - \dfrac{\cos y \sin z}{\cos y \cos z} + \dfrac{\sin z \cos x}{\cos z \cos x} - \dfrac{\cos z \sin x}{\cos z \cos x}$

$= \dfrac{\sin x}{\cos x} - \dfrac{\sin y}{\cos y} + \dfrac{\sin y}{\cos y} - \dfrac{\sin z}{\cos z} + \dfrac{\sin z}{\cos z} - \dfrac{\sin x}{\cos x}$

$= 0$

85. Let $\alpha = \sin^{-1} x$, where $-\dfrac{\pi}{2} \le \alpha \le \dfrac{\pi}{2}$.

$\sin \alpha = x$

Because x is positive, $\sin \alpha$ is positive. Thus α is in quadrant I. Using a right triangle in quadrant I with $\sin \alpha = x = \dfrac{x}{1}$, the third side a can be found using the Pythagorean Theorem.

$a^2 + x^2 = 1^2$

$\qquad a^2 = 1 - x^2$

$\qquad a = \sqrt{1 - x^2}$

Thus $\cos \alpha = \dfrac{\sqrt{1-x^2}}{1} = \sqrt{1-x^2}$. Let $\beta = \cos^{-1} y$, where $0 \le \beta \le \pi$, $\cos \beta = y$

Because y is positive, $\cos \beta$ is positive. Thus β is in quadrant I. Using a right triangle in quadrant I with $\cos \beta = y = \dfrac{y}{1}$, the third side b can be found using the Pythagorean Theorem.

$b^2 + y^2 = 1^2$

$\qquad b^2 = 1 - y^2$

$\qquad b = \sqrt{1 - y^2}$

Thus, $\sin \beta = \dfrac{\sqrt{1-y^2}}{1} = \sqrt{1-y^2}$.

$\cos\left(\sin^{-1} x - \cos^{-1} y\right) = \cos(\alpha - \beta) = \cos \alpha \cos \beta + \sin \alpha \sin \beta$

$\qquad\qquad = \sqrt{1-x^2} \cdot y + x \cdot \sqrt{1-y^2}$

$\qquad\qquad = y\sqrt{1-x^2} + x\sqrt{1-y^2}$

Section 6.3

Check Point Exercises

1. $\sin\theta = \dfrac{4}{5} = \dfrac{y}{r}$

We find x using the Pythagorean Theorem.
Because θ lies in quadrant II, x is negative.

$x^2 + 4^2 = 5^2$

$\qquad x^2 = 5^2 - 4^2 = 9$

$\qquad x = -\sqrt{9} = -3$

Now we use values for x, y, and r to find the required values.

a. $\sin 2\theta = 2\sin\theta\cos\theta$

$\qquad = 2\left(\dfrac{4}{5}\right)\left(-\dfrac{3}{5}\right) = -\dfrac{24}{25}$

b. $\cos 2\theta = \cos^2\theta - \sin^2\theta$

$\qquad = \left(-\dfrac{3}{5}\right)^2 - \left(\dfrac{4}{5}\right)^2 = \dfrac{9}{25} - \dfrac{16}{25}$

$\qquad = -\dfrac{7}{25}$

c. $\tan 2\theta = \dfrac{2\tan\theta}{1-\tan^2\theta}$

$\qquad = \dfrac{2\left(-\frac{4}{3}\right)}{1-\left(-\frac{4}{3}\right)^2} = \dfrac{-\frac{8}{3}}{1-\frac{16}{9}} = \dfrac{-\frac{8}{3}}{-\frac{7}{9}}$

$\qquad = \left(-\dfrac{8}{3}\right)\left(-\dfrac{9}{7}\right) = \dfrac{24}{7}$

2. The given expression is the right side of the formula for $\cos 2\theta$ with $\theta = 15°$.

$\cos^2 15° - \sin^2 15° = \cos(2 \cdot 15°)$

$\qquad\qquad = \cos 30° = \dfrac{\sqrt{3}}{2}$

3. $\sin 3\theta = \sin(2\theta + \theta)$

$\qquad = \sin 2\theta\cos\theta + \cos 2\theta\sin\theta$

$\qquad = 2\sin\theta\cos\theta\cos\theta + (2\cos^2\theta - 1)\sin\theta$

$\qquad = 2\sin\theta\cos^2\theta + 2\sin\theta\cos^2\theta - \sin\theta$

$\qquad = 4\sin\theta\cos^2\theta - \sin\theta$

$\qquad = 4\sin\theta(1-\sin^2\theta) - \sin\theta$

$\qquad = 4\sin\theta - 4\sin^3\theta - \sin\theta$

$\qquad = 3\sin\theta - 4\sin^3\theta$

By working with the left side and expressing it in a form identical to the right side, we have verified the identity.

4. $\sin^4 x = \left(\sin^2 x\right)^2$

$\qquad = \left(\dfrac{1-\cos 2x}{2}\right)^2$

$\qquad = \dfrac{1 - 2\cos 2x + \cos^2 2x}{4}$

$\qquad = \dfrac{1}{4} - \dfrac{1}{2}\cos 2x + \dfrac{1}{4}\cos^2 2x$

$\qquad = \dfrac{1}{4} - \dfrac{1}{2}\cos 2x + \dfrac{1}{4}\left(\dfrac{1+\cos 2(2x)}{2}\right)$

$\qquad = \dfrac{1}{4} - \dfrac{1}{2}\cos 2x + \dfrac{1}{8} + \dfrac{1}{8}\cos 4x$

$\qquad = \dfrac{3}{8} - \dfrac{1}{2}\cos 2x + \dfrac{1}{8}\cos 4x$

5. Because $105°$ lies in quadrant II, $\cos 105° < 0$.

$\cos 105° = \cos\left(\dfrac{210°}{2}\right)$

$\qquad = -\sqrt{\dfrac{1+\cos 210°}{2}}$

$\qquad = -\sqrt{\dfrac{1+\frac{\sqrt{3}}{2}}{2}}$

$\qquad = -\sqrt{\dfrac{2+\sqrt{3}}{4}}$

$\qquad = -\dfrac{\sqrt{2+\sqrt{3}}}{2}$

6. $\dfrac{\sin 2\theta}{1+\cos 2\theta} = \dfrac{2\sin\theta\cos\theta}{1+\left(1-2\sin^2\theta\right)}$

$\qquad = \dfrac{2\sin\theta\cos\theta}{2-2\sin^2\theta}$

$\qquad = \dfrac{2\sin\theta\cos\theta}{2\left(1-\sin^2\theta\right)}$

$\qquad = \dfrac{2\sin\theta\cos\theta}{2\cos^2\theta}$

$\qquad = \dfrac{\sin\theta}{\cos\theta} = \tan\theta$

The right side simplifies to $\tan\theta$, the expression on the left side. Thus, the identity is verified.

7. $\dfrac{\sec\alpha}{\sec\alpha\csc\alpha+\csc\alpha} = \dfrac{\dfrac{1}{\cos\alpha}}{\dfrac{1}{\cos\alpha}\cdot\dfrac{1}{\sin\alpha}+\dfrac{1}{\sin\alpha}}$

$\qquad = \dfrac{\dfrac{1}{\cos\alpha}}{\dfrac{1}{\cos\alpha\sin\alpha}+\dfrac{\cos\alpha}{\cos\alpha\sin\alpha}}$

$\qquad = \dfrac{\dfrac{1}{\cos\alpha}}{\dfrac{1+\cos\alpha}{\cos\alpha\sin\alpha}}$

$\qquad = \dfrac{1}{\cos\alpha}\cdot\dfrac{\cos\alpha\sin\alpha}{1+\cos\alpha}$

$\qquad = \dfrac{\sin\alpha}{1+\cos\alpha}$

$\qquad = \tan\dfrac{\alpha}{2}$

We worked with the right side and arrived at the left side. Thus, the identity is verified.

Exercise Set 6.3

1. $\sin 2\theta = 2\sin\theta\cos\theta = 2\left(\dfrac{3}{5}\right)\left(\dfrac{4}{5}\right) = \dfrac{24}{25}$

3. $\tan 2\theta = \dfrac{2\tan\theta}{1-\tan^2\theta}$

$\qquad = \dfrac{2\left(\frac{3}{4}\right)}{1-\left(\frac{3}{4}\right)^2} = \dfrac{\frac{3}{2}}{1-\frac{9}{16}}$

$\qquad = \dfrac{\frac{3}{2}}{\frac{7}{16}} = \left(\dfrac{3}{2}\right)\left(\dfrac{16}{7}\right) = \dfrac{24}{7}$

Use this information to solve problem 5.

$\tan\alpha = \dfrac{7}{24} = \dfrac{y}{x}$

We find r using the Pythagorean Theorem. Because r is a distance it is positive.

$x^2 + y^2 = r^2$

$24^2 + 7^2 = r^2$

$576 + 49 = r^2$

$625 = r^2$

$r = 25$

$\sin\alpha = \dfrac{y}{r} = \dfrac{7}{25}$

$\cos\alpha = \dfrac{x}{r} = \dfrac{24}{25}$

5. $\cos 2\alpha = \cos^2\alpha - \sin^2\alpha$

$\qquad = \left(\dfrac{24}{25}\right)^2 - \left(\dfrac{7}{25}\right)^2 = \dfrac{576}{625} - \dfrac{49}{625}$

$\qquad = \dfrac{527}{625}$

7. $\sin\theta = \dfrac{15}{17} = \dfrac{y}{r}$

We find x using the Pythagorean Theorem. Because θ lies in quadrant II, x is negative.

$x^2 + 15^2 = 17^2$

$x^2 = 17^2 - 15^2 = 64$

$x = -\sqrt{64} = -8$

Now we use values for x, y, and r to find the required values.

a. $\sin 2\theta = 2\sin\theta\cos\theta$

$\qquad = 2\left(\dfrac{15}{17}\right)\left(-\dfrac{8}{17}\right) = -\dfrac{240}{289}$

b. $\cos 2\theta = \cos^2\theta - \sin^2\theta$

$\qquad = \left(-\dfrac{8}{17}\right)^2 - \left(\dfrac{15}{17}\right)^2 = \dfrac{64}{289} - \dfrac{225}{289}$

$\qquad = -\dfrac{161}{289}$

c. $\tan 2\theta = \dfrac{2\tan\theta}{1-\tan^2\theta}$

$$= \dfrac{2\left(-\frac{15}{8}\right)}{1-\left(-\frac{15}{8}\right)^2} = \dfrac{-\frac{15}{4}}{1-\frac{225}{64}} = \dfrac{-\frac{15}{4}}{-\frac{161}{64}}$$

$$= \left(-\dfrac{15}{4}\right)\left(-\dfrac{64}{161}\right) = \dfrac{240}{161}$$

9. $\cos\theta = \dfrac{24}{25} = \dfrac{x}{r}$

We find y using the Pythagorean Theorem.
Because θ lies in quadrant IV, y is negative.

$24^2 + y^2 = 25^2$

$\quad y^2 = 25^2 - 24^2 = 49$

$\quad\; y = -\sqrt{49} = -7$

Now we use values for x, y, and r to find the required values.

a. $\sin 2\theta = 2\sin\theta\cos\theta$

$$= 2\left(-\dfrac{7}{25}\right)\left(\dfrac{24}{25}\right) = -\dfrac{336}{625}$$

b. $\cos 2\theta = \cos^2\theta - \sin^2\theta$

$$= \left(\dfrac{24}{25}\right)^2 - \left(-\dfrac{7}{25}\right)^2$$

$$= \dfrac{576}{625} - \dfrac{49}{625} = \dfrac{527}{625}$$

c. $\tan 2\theta = \dfrac{2\tan\theta}{1-\tan^2\theta}$

$$= \dfrac{2\left(-\frac{7}{24}\right)}{1-\left(-\frac{7}{24}\right)^2} = \dfrac{-\frac{7}{12}}{1-\frac{49}{576}} = \dfrac{-\frac{7}{12}}{\frac{527}{576}}$$

$$= \left(-\dfrac{7}{12}\right)\left(\dfrac{576}{527}\right) = -\dfrac{336}{527}$$

11. $\cot\theta = 2 = \dfrac{-2}{-1} = \dfrac{x}{y}$

We find r using the Pythagorean Theorem.
Because r is a distance, it is positive.

$r^2 = (-2)^2 + (-1)^2 = 5$

$\quad r = \sqrt{5}$

Now we use values for x, y, and r to find the required values.

a. $\sin 2\theta = 2\sin\theta\cos\theta$

$$= 2\left(-\dfrac{1}{\sqrt{5}}\right)\left(-\dfrac{2}{\sqrt{5}}\right) = \dfrac{4}{5}$$

b. $\cos 2\theta = \cos^2\theta - \sin^2\theta$

$$= \left(-\dfrac{2}{\sqrt{5}}\right)^2 - \left(-\dfrac{1}{\sqrt{5}}\right)^2$$

$$= \dfrac{4}{5} - \dfrac{1}{5} = \dfrac{3}{5}$$

c. $\tan 2\theta = \dfrac{2\tan\theta}{1-\tan^2\theta}$

$$= \dfrac{2\left(\frac{1}{2}\right)}{1-\left(\frac{1}{2}\right)^2} = \dfrac{1}{1-\frac{1}{4}} = \dfrac{1}{\frac{3}{4}}$$

$$= (1)\left(\dfrac{4}{3}\right) = \dfrac{4}{3}$$

13. $\sin\theta = -\dfrac{9}{41} = \dfrac{-9}{41} = \dfrac{y}{r}$

We find x using the Pythagorean Theorem.
Because θ lies in quadrant III, x is negative.

$x^2 + (-9)^2 = 41^2$

$\quad x^2 = 41^2 - (-9)^2 = 1600$

$\quad\; x = -\sqrt{1600} = -40$

Now we use values for x, y, and r to find the required values.

a. $\sin 2\theta = 2\sin\theta\cos\theta$

$$= 2\left(-\dfrac{9}{41}\right)\left(-\dfrac{40}{41}\right) = \dfrac{720}{1681}$$

b. $\cos 2\theta = \cos^2\theta - \sin^2\theta$

$$= \left(-\dfrac{40}{41}\right)^2 - \left(-\dfrac{9}{41}\right)^2$$

$$= \dfrac{1600}{1681} - \dfrac{81}{1681}$$

$$= \dfrac{1519}{1681}$$

c. $\tan 2\theta = \dfrac{2\tan\theta}{1-\tan^2\theta}$

$$= \dfrac{2\left(\frac{9}{40}\right)}{1-\left(\frac{9}{40}\right)^2} = \dfrac{\frac{9}{20}}{1-\frac{81}{1600}} = \dfrac{\frac{9}{20}}{\frac{1519}{1600}}$$

$$= \left(\dfrac{9}{20}\right)\left(\dfrac{1600}{1519}\right) = \dfrac{720}{1519}$$

15. The given expression is the right side of the formula for $\sin 2\theta$ with $\theta = 15°$.

$2\sin 15° \cos 15° = \sin(2\cdot 15°)$

$$= \sin 30° = \dfrac{1}{2}$$

17. The given expression is the right side of the formula for $\cos 2\theta$ with $\theta = 75°$.

$\cos^2 75° - \sin^2 75° = \cos(2\cdot 75°)$

$$= \cos 150° = -\dfrac{\sqrt{3}}{2}$$

19. The given expression is the right side of the formula for $\cos 2\theta$ with $\theta = \dfrac{\pi}{8}$.

$2\cos^2 \dfrac{\pi}{8} - 1 = \cos\left(2\cdot\dfrac{\pi}{8}\right)$

$$= \cos\dfrac{\pi}{4} = \dfrac{\sqrt{2}}{2}$$

21. The given expression is the right side of the formula for $\tan 2\theta$ with $\theta = \dfrac{\pi}{12}$.

$\dfrac{2\tan\frac{\pi}{12}}{1-\tan^2\frac{\pi}{12}} = \tan\left(2\cdot\dfrac{\pi}{12}\right) = \tan\dfrac{\pi}{6} = \dfrac{\sqrt{3}}{3}$

23. $\dfrac{2\tan\theta}{1+\tan^2\theta} = \dfrac{2\cdot\frac{\sin\theta}{\cos\theta}}{\frac{\cos^2\theta}{\cos^2\theta}+\frac{\sin^2\theta}{\cos^2\theta}}$

$$= \dfrac{\frac{2\sin\theta}{\cos\theta}}{\frac{\cos^2\theta+\sin^2\theta}{\cos^2\theta}}$$

$$= \dfrac{\frac{2\sin\theta}{\cos\theta}}{\frac{1}{\cos^2\theta}}$$

$$= \dfrac{2\sin\theta}{\cos\theta}\cdot\dfrac{\cos^2\theta}{1}$$

$$= 2\sin\theta\cos\theta$$

$$= \sin 2\theta$$

We worked with the right side and arrived at the left side. Thus, the identity is verified.

25. $(\sin\theta + \cos\theta)^2 = \sin^2\theta + 2\sin\theta\cos\theta + \cos^2\theta$

$$= \sin^2\theta + \cos^2\theta + 2\sin\theta\cos\theta$$

$$= 1 + 2\sin\theta\cos\theta$$

$$= 1 + \sin 2\theta$$

We worked with the left side and arrived at the right side. Thus, the identity is verified.

27. $\sin^2 x + \cos 2x = \sin^2 x + \cos^2 x - \sin^2 x$

$$= \cos^2 x$$

We worked with the left side and arrived at the right side. Thus, the identity is verified.

29. $\dfrac{\sin 2x}{1-\cos 2x} = \dfrac{2\sin x\cos x}{1-\left(\cos^2 x - \sin^2 x\right)}$

$$= \dfrac{2\sin x\cos x}{1-\cos^2 x + \sin^2 x}$$

$$= \dfrac{2\sin x\cos x}{\sin^2 + \sin^2 x}$$

$$= \dfrac{2\sin x\cos x}{2\sin^2 x}$$

$$= \dfrac{\cos x}{\sin x}$$

$$= \cot x$$

We worked with the right side and arrived at the left side. Thus, the identity is verified.

31. $\tan t \cos 2t = \dfrac{\sin t}{\cos t} \cdot \left(2\cos^2 t - 1\right)$

$$= \dfrac{2\sin t \cos^2 t}{\cos t} - \dfrac{\sin t}{\cos t}$$

$$= 2\sin t \cos t - \tan t$$

$$= \sin 2t - \tan t$$

We worked with the right side and arrived at the left side. Thus, the identity is verified.

33. $\sin 4t = \sin(2t + 2t)$

$$= \sin 2t \cos 2t + \cos 2t \sin 2t$$

$$= \cos 2t(\sin 2t + \sin 2t)$$

$$= \cos 2t \cdot 2 \sin 2t$$

$$= \left(\cos^2 t - \sin^2 t\right) \cdot 2 \cdot 2 \sin t \cos t$$

$$= 4\sin t \cos^3 t - 4\sin^3 t \cos t$$

We worked with the left side and arrived at the right side. Thus, the identity is verified.

35. $6\sin^2 x = 6\left(\dfrac{1 - \cos 2x}{2}\right) = 3 - 3\cos 2x$

37. $\sin^2 x \cos^2 x = \left(\dfrac{1 - \cos 2x}{2}\right)\left(\dfrac{1 + \cos 2x}{2}\right)$

$$= \dfrac{1 - \cos^2 2x}{4}$$

$$= \dfrac{1}{4} - \dfrac{1}{4}\cos^2 2x$$

$$= \dfrac{1}{4} - \dfrac{1}{4}\left(\dfrac{1 + \cos(2 \cdot 2x)}{2}\right)$$

$$= \dfrac{1}{4} - \dfrac{1}{8}(1 + \cos 4x)$$

$$= \dfrac{1}{4} - \dfrac{1}{8} - \dfrac{1}{8}\cos 4x$$

$$= \dfrac{1}{8} - \dfrac{1}{8}\cos 4x$$

39. Because $15°$ lies in quadrant I, $\sin 15° > 0$.

$$\sin 15° = \sin\dfrac{30°}{2}$$

$$= \sqrt{\dfrac{1 - \cos 30°}{2}} = \sqrt{\dfrac{1 - \frac{\sqrt{3}}{2}}{2}}$$

$$= \sqrt{\dfrac{2 - \sqrt{3}}{4}} = \dfrac{\sqrt{2 - \sqrt{3}}}{2}$$

41. Because $157.5°$ lies in quadrant II, $\cos 157.5° < 0$.

$$\cos 157.5° = \cos\dfrac{315°}{2} = -\sqrt{\dfrac{1 + \cos 315°}{2}}$$

$$= -\sqrt{\dfrac{1 + \frac{\sqrt{2}}{2}}{2}} = -\sqrt{\dfrac{2 + \sqrt{2}}{4}}$$

$$= -\dfrac{\sqrt{2 + \sqrt{2}}}{2}$$

43. Because $75°$ lies in quadrant I, $\tan 75° > 0$.

$$\tan 75° = \tan\dfrac{150°}{2} = \dfrac{1 - \cos 150°}{\sin 150°}$$

$$= \dfrac{1 - \left(-\frac{\sqrt{3}}{2}\right)}{\frac{1}{2}} = 2 + \sqrt{3}$$

45. Because $\dfrac{7\pi}{8}$ lies in quadrant II, $\tan\dfrac{7\pi}{8} < 0$.

$$\tan\dfrac{7\pi}{8} = \tan\left(\dfrac{\frac{7\pi}{4}}{2}\right) = \dfrac{1 - \cos\frac{7\pi}{4}}{\sin\frac{7\pi}{4}}$$

$$= \dfrac{1 - \frac{\sqrt{2}}{2}}{-\frac{\sqrt{2}}{2}} = -\dfrac{2}{\sqrt{2}} + 1$$

$$= -\sqrt{2} + 1$$

47. $\sin\dfrac{\theta}{2} = \sqrt{\dfrac{1 - \cos\theta}{2}}$

$$= \sqrt{\dfrac{1 - \frac{4}{5}}{2}} = \sqrt{\dfrac{1}{10}}$$

$$= \dfrac{1}{\sqrt{10}} = \dfrac{\sqrt{10}}{10}$$

49. $\tan\dfrac{\theta}{2} = \dfrac{1 - \cos\theta}{\sin\theta}$

$$= \dfrac{1 - \frac{4}{5}}{\frac{3}{5}}$$

$$= \dfrac{1}{3}$$

Use this information to solve problem 51.

$$\tan \alpha = \frac{7}{24} = \frac{y}{x}$$

We find r using the Pythagorean Theorem. Because r is a distance, it is positive.

$$x^2 + y^2 = r^2$$
$$24^2 + 7^2 = r^2$$
$$576 + 49 = r^2$$
$$625 = r^2$$
$$r = 25$$
$$\sin \alpha = \frac{y}{r} = \frac{7}{25}, \quad \cos \alpha = \frac{x}{r} = \frac{24}{25}$$

51. $\cos \dfrac{\alpha}{2} = \sqrt{\dfrac{1 + \cos \alpha}{2}} = \sqrt{\dfrac{1 + \frac{24}{25}}{2}} = \sqrt{\dfrac{49}{50}}$

$$= \frac{7}{5\sqrt{2}} = \frac{7\sqrt{2}}{10}$$

53. $2 \sin \dfrac{\theta}{2} \cos \dfrac{\theta}{2} = 2 \cdot \sqrt{\dfrac{1 - \cos \theta}{2}} \cdot \sqrt{\dfrac{1 + \cos \theta}{2}}$

$$= 2 \sqrt{\dfrac{1 - \frac{4}{5}}{2}} \cdot \sqrt{\dfrac{1 + \frac{4}{5}}{2}}$$

$$= 2 \cdot \sqrt{\dfrac{1}{10}} \cdot \sqrt{\dfrac{9}{10}}$$

$$= 2 \cdot \frac{1}{\sqrt{10}} \cdot \frac{3}{\sqrt{10}}$$

$$= \frac{6}{10} = \frac{3}{5}$$

55. $\tan \alpha = \dfrac{4}{3} = \dfrac{-4}{-3} = \dfrac{y}{x}$

We find r using the Pythagorean Theorem. Because r is a distance, it is positive.

$$r^2 = (-4)^2 + (-3)^2 = 25$$
$$r = \sqrt{25} = 5$$

Now we use the values for x, y, and r to find the required values. Because α lies in

quadrant III, $\dfrac{\alpha}{2}$ lies in quadrant II. Thus,

$$\sin \frac{\alpha}{2} > 0, \quad \cos \frac{\alpha}{2} < 0, \text{ and } \tan \frac{\alpha}{2} < 0.$$

a. $\sin \dfrac{\alpha}{2} = \sqrt{\dfrac{1 - \cos \alpha}{2}} = \sqrt{\dfrac{1 - \left(-\frac{3}{5}\right)}{2}}$

$$= \sqrt{\dfrac{8}{10}} = \sqrt{\dfrac{4}{5}} = \frac{2}{\sqrt{5}}$$

$$= \frac{2\sqrt{5}}{5}$$

b. $\cos \dfrac{\alpha}{2} = -\sqrt{\dfrac{1 + \cos \alpha}{2}} = -\sqrt{\dfrac{1 + -\frac{3}{5}}{2}}$

$$= -\sqrt{\dfrac{2}{10}} = -\sqrt{\dfrac{1}{5}} = -\frac{1}{\sqrt{5}}$$

$$= -\frac{\sqrt{5}}{5}$$

c. $\tan \dfrac{\alpha}{2} = \dfrac{1 - \cos \alpha}{\sin \alpha} = \dfrac{1 - \left(-\frac{3}{5}\right)}{-\frac{4}{5}}$

$$= \frac{5 + 3}{-4} = \frac{8}{-4} = -2$$

57. $\sec \alpha = -\dfrac{13}{5} = \dfrac{13}{-5} = \dfrac{r}{x}$

We find y using the Pythagorean Theorem. Because α lies in quadrant II, y is positive.

$$(-5)^2 + y^2 = (13)^2$$
$$y^2 = (13)^2 - (-5)^2 = 144$$
$$y = \sqrt{144} = 12$$

Now we use the values for x, y, and r to find the required values. Because α lies in

quadrant II, $\dfrac{\alpha}{2}$ lies in quadrant I. Thus,

$$\sin \frac{\alpha}{2} > 0, \quad \cos \frac{\alpha}{2} > 0, \text{ and } \tan \frac{\alpha}{2} > 0.$$

a. $\sin \dfrac{\alpha}{2} = \sqrt{\dfrac{1 - \cos \alpha}{2}} = \sqrt{\dfrac{1 - \left(-\frac{5}{13}\right)}{2}}$

$$= \sqrt{\dfrac{18}{26}} = \sqrt{\dfrac{9}{13}} = \frac{3}{\sqrt{13}}$$

$$= \frac{3\sqrt{13}}{13}$$

b. $\cos\dfrac{\alpha}{2} = \sqrt{\dfrac{1+\cos\alpha}{2}} = \sqrt{\dfrac{1+\left(-\frac{5}{13}\right)}{2}}$

$= \sqrt{\dfrac{8}{26}} = \sqrt{\dfrac{4}{13}} = \dfrac{2}{\sqrt{13}}$

$= \dfrac{2\sqrt{13}}{13}$

c. $\tan\dfrac{\alpha}{2} = \dfrac{1-\cos\alpha}{\sin\alpha} = \dfrac{1-\left(-\frac{5}{13}\right)}{\frac{12}{13}}$

$= \dfrac{13+5}{12} = \dfrac{18}{12} = \dfrac{3}{2}$

59. $\sin^2\dfrac{\theta}{2} = \dfrac{1-\cos 2\left(\frac{\theta}{2}\right)}{2}$

$= \dfrac{1-\cos\theta}{2} \cdot \dfrac{\frac{1}{\cos\theta}}{\frac{1}{\cos\theta}}$

$= \dfrac{\frac{1-\cos\theta}{\cos\theta}}{\frac{2}{\cos\theta}}$

$= \dfrac{\frac{1}{\cos\theta} - \frac{\cos\theta}{\cos\theta}}{2 \cdot \frac{1}{\cos\theta}}$

$= \dfrac{\sec\theta - 1}{2\sec\theta}$

We worked with the left side and arrived at the right side. Thus, the identity is verified.

61. $\cos^2\dfrac{\theta}{2} = \dfrac{1+\cos 2\left(\frac{\theta}{2}\right)}{2}$

$= \dfrac{1+\cos\theta}{2}$

$= \dfrac{1+\cos\theta}{2} \cdot \dfrac{\frac{\sin\theta}{\cos\theta}}{\frac{\sin\theta}{\cos\theta}}$

$= \dfrac{\frac{\sin\theta}{\cos\theta} + \sin\theta}{2 \cdot \frac{\sin\theta}{\cos\theta}}$

$= \dfrac{\tan\theta + \sin\theta}{2\tan\theta}$

$= \dfrac{\sin\theta + \tan\theta}{2\tan\theta}$

We worked with the left side and arrived at the right side. Thus, the identity is verified.

63. $\tan\dfrac{\alpha}{2} = \dfrac{\sin\alpha}{1+\cos\alpha}$

$= \dfrac{\sin\alpha}{1+\cos\alpha} \cdot \dfrac{\frac{1}{\cos\alpha}}{\frac{1}{\cos\alpha}}$

$= \dfrac{\frac{\sin\alpha}{\cos\alpha}}{\frac{1+\cos\alpha}{\cos\alpha}}$

$= \dfrac{\tan\alpha}{\frac{1}{\cos\alpha} + \frac{\cos\alpha}{\cos\alpha}}$

$= \dfrac{\tan\alpha}{\sec\alpha + 1}$

We worked with the left side and arrived at the right side. Thus, the identity is verified.

65. $\dfrac{\sin x}{1-\cos x} = \dfrac{\sin x}{1-\cos x} \cdot \dfrac{\frac{1}{\sin x}}{\frac{1}{\sin x}}$

$= \dfrac{\frac{\sin x}{\sin x}}{\frac{1-\cos x}{\sin x}}$

$= \dfrac{1}{\tan\frac{x}{2}}$

$= \cot\dfrac{x}{2}$

We worked with the right side and arrived at the left side. Thus, the identity is verified.

67. $\tan\dfrac{x}{2} + \cot\dfrac{x}{2} = \dfrac{1-\cos x}{\sin x} + \dfrac{1}{\tan\frac{x}{2}}$

$= \dfrac{1-\cos x}{\sin x} + \dfrac{1}{\frac{\sin x}{1+\cos x}}$

$= \dfrac{1-\cos x}{\sin x} + \dfrac{1+\cos x}{\sin x}$

$= \dfrac{1-\cos x + 1 + \cos x}{\sin x}$

$= \dfrac{2}{\sin x} = 2\csc x$

We worked with the left side and arrived at the right side. Thus, the identity is verified.

69. a. $\dfrac{v_o^2}{16}\sin\theta\cos\theta = \dfrac{v_o^2}{32} \cdot 2\sin\theta\cos\theta$

$= \dfrac{v_o^2}{32} \cdot \sin 2\theta$

b. $\sin\alpha$ is at a maximum in the interval

$[0,\ 2\pi]$ when $\alpha = \dfrac{\pi}{2}$, so $\sin 2\theta$ is at a

maximum when $2\theta = \dfrac{\pi}{2}$ or $\theta = \dfrac{\pi}{4}$.

71. $\theta = \dfrac{\pi}{4}$

$$\sin\frac{\theta}{2} = \sqrt{\frac{1-\cos\theta}{2}}$$

$$= \sqrt{\frac{1-\cos\frac{\pi}{4}}{2}}$$

$$= \sqrt{\frac{1-\frac{\sqrt{2}}{2}}{2}}$$

$$= \sqrt{\frac{2-\sqrt{2}}{4}}$$

$$= \frac{\sqrt{2-\sqrt{2}}}{2}$$

$$\sin\frac{\theta}{2} = \frac{1}{M}$$

$$\frac{\sqrt{2-\sqrt{2}}}{2} = \frac{1}{M}$$

$$M = \frac{2}{\sqrt{2-\sqrt{2}}}$$

$$= \frac{2\sqrt{2-\sqrt{2}}}{2-\sqrt{2}}$$

$$= \frac{2\sqrt{2-\sqrt{2}}}{2-\sqrt{2}}\cdot\frac{2+\sqrt{2}}{2+\sqrt{2}}$$

$$= \frac{4\sqrt{2-\sqrt{2}} + 2\sqrt{2}\sqrt{2-\sqrt{2}}}{4-2}$$

$$= \frac{2\left(2\sqrt{2-\sqrt{2}} + \sqrt{2}\sqrt{2-\sqrt{2}}\right)}{2}$$

$$= 2\sqrt{2-\sqrt{2}} + \sqrt{2}\sqrt{2-\sqrt{2}}$$

$$= \sqrt{2-\sqrt{2}}\cdot\left(2+\sqrt{2}\right) \approx 2.6$$

73.–83.   Answers may vary.

85.

$$3 - 6\sin^2 x = 3 - 6\left(\frac{1-\cos 2x}{2}\right)$$
$$= 3 - 3(1-\cos 2x)$$
$$= 3 - 3 + 3\cos 2x$$
$$= 3\cos 2x$$

We worked with the left side and arrived at the right side. Thus, the identity is verified.

87.

The graphs do not coincide.
Values for x may vary.

89.
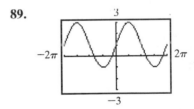

a.   The graph appears to be the sum of 1 and 2 times the sine curve, $y = 1 + 2\sin x$. If you subtract 1 from the graph, it cycles through intercept, maximum, intercept, minimum, and back to intercept. Thus, $y = 1 + 2\sin x$ also describes the graph.

b. $\dfrac{1-2\cos 2x}{2\sin x-1} = \dfrac{1-2\left(1-2\sin^2 x\right)}{2\sin x-1} = \dfrac{1-2+4\sin^2 x}{2\sin x-1}$

$\qquad\qquad = \dfrac{4\sin^2 x-1}{2\sin x-1} = \dfrac{(2\sin x-1)(2\sin x+1)}{2\sin x-1}$

$\qquad\qquad = 2\sin x+1 = 1+2\sin x$

This verifies our observation that $y = \dfrac{1-2\cos 2x}{2\sin x-1}$ and $y = 1+2\sin x$ describe the same graph.

91.
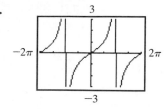

a. The graph appears to be the tangent of half the angle. It cycles from negative infinity through intercept to positive infinity. Thus, $y = \tan\dfrac{x}{2}$ also describes the graph.

b. $\tan\dfrac{x}{2} = \dfrac{1-\cos x}{\sin x} = \dfrac{1}{\sin x} - \dfrac{\cos x}{\sin x} = \csc x - \cot x$

This verifies our observation that $y = \csc x - \cot x$ and $y = \tan\dfrac{x}{2}$ describe the same graph.

93. $\sin^6 x = \left(\sin^2 x\right)^3 = \left(\dfrac{1-\cos 2x}{2}\right)^3$

$\qquad = \dfrac{1-3\cos 2x+3\cos^2 2x-\cos^3 2x}{8}$

$\qquad = \dfrac{1}{8} - \dfrac{3}{8}\cos 2x + \dfrac{3}{8}\cos^2 2x - \dfrac{1}{8}\cos 2x\cos^2 2x$

$\qquad = \dfrac{1}{8} - \dfrac{3}{8}\cos 2x + \dfrac{3}{8}\left[\dfrac{1+\cos(2\cdot 2x)}{2}\right] - \dfrac{1}{8}\cos 2x\left[\dfrac{1+\cos(2\cdot 2x)}{2}\right]$

$\qquad = \dfrac{1}{8} - \dfrac{3}{8}\cos 2x + \dfrac{3}{16}(1+\cos 4x) - \dfrac{1}{16}\cos 2x(1+\cos 4x)$

$\qquad = \dfrac{1}{8} - \dfrac{3}{8}\cos 2x + \dfrac{3}{16} + \dfrac{3}{16}\cos 4x - \dfrac{1}{16}\cos 2x - \dfrac{1}{16}\cos 2x\cos 4x$

$\qquad = \dfrac{5}{16} - \dfrac{7}{16}\cos 2x + \dfrac{3}{16}\cos 4x - \dfrac{1}{16}\cos 2x\cos 4x$

Section 6.4

Check Point Exercises

1. a. $\sin 5x \sin 2x$

$$= \frac{1}{2}[\cos(5x - 2x) - \cos(5x + 2x)]$$

$$= \frac{1}{2}[\cos 3x - \cos 7x]$$

b. $\cos 7x \cos x$

$$= \frac{1}{2}[\cos(7x - x) + \cos(7x + x)]$$

$$= \frac{1}{2}[\cos 6x + \cos 8x]$$

2. a. $\sin 7x + \sin 3x$

$$= 2\sin\left(\frac{7x + 3x}{2}\right)\cos\left(\frac{7x - 3x}{2}\right)$$

$$= 2\sin\left(\frac{10x}{2}\right)\cos\left(\frac{4x}{2}\right)$$

$$= 2\sin 5x \cos 2x$$

b. $\cos 3x + \cos 2x$

$$= 2\cos\left(\frac{3x + 2x}{2}\right)\cos\left(\frac{3x - 2x}{2}\right)$$

$$= 2\cos\left(\frac{5x}{2}\right)\cos\left(\frac{x}{2}\right)$$

3.

$$\frac{\cos 3x - \cos x}{\sin 3x + \sin x} = \frac{-2\sin\left(\frac{3x + x}{2}\right)\sin\left(\frac{3x - x}{2}\right)}{\sin 3x + \sin x}$$

$$= \frac{-2\sin\left(\frac{3x + x}{2}\right)\sin\left(\frac{3x - x}{2}\right)}{2\sin\left(\frac{3x + x}{2}\right)\cos\left(\frac{3x - x}{2}\right)}$$

$$= \frac{-2\sin\left(\frac{4x}{2}\right)\sin\left(\frac{2x}{2}\right)}{2\sin\left(\frac{4x}{2}\right)\cos\left(\frac{2x}{2}\right)}$$

$$= \frac{-\cancel{2}\sin\cancel{2x}\sin x}{\cancel{2}\sin\cancel{2x}\cos x} = \frac{-\sin x}{\cos x}$$

$$= -\tan x$$

We worked with the left side and arrived at the right side. Thus, the identity is verified.

Exercise Set 6.4

1. $\sin 6x \sin 2x = \frac{1}{2}[\cos(6x - 2x) - \cos(6x + 2x)]$

$$= \frac{1}{2}[\cos 4x - \cos 8x]$$

3. $\cos 7x \cos 3x = \frac{1}{2}[\cos(7x - 3x) + \cos(7x + 3x)]$

$$= \frac{1}{2}[\cos 4x + \cos 10x]$$

5. $\sin x \cos 2x = \frac{1}{2}[\sin(x + 2x) + \sin(x - 2x)]$

$$= \frac{1}{2}[\sin 3x + \sin(-x)]$$

$$= \frac{1}{2}[\sin 3x - \sin x]$$

7. $\cos\frac{3x}{2}\sin\frac{x}{2} = \frac{1}{2}\left[\sin\left(\frac{3x}{2} + \frac{x}{2}\right) - \sin\left(\frac{3x}{2} - \frac{x}{2}\right)\right]$

$$= \frac{1}{2}\left[\sin\left(\frac{4x}{2}\right) - \sin\left(\frac{2x}{2}\right)\right]$$

$$= \frac{1}{2}[\sin 2x - \sin x]$$

9. $\sin 6x + \sin 2x = 2\sin\left(\frac{6x + 2x}{2}\right)\cos\left(\frac{6x - 2x}{2}\right)$

$$= 2\sin\left(\frac{8x}{2}\right)\cos\left(\frac{4x}{2}\right)$$

$$= 2\sin 4x \cos 2x$$

11. $\sin 7x - \sin 3x = 2\sin\left(\frac{7x - 3x}{2}\right)\cos\left(\frac{7x + 3x}{2}\right)$

$$= 2\sin\left(\frac{4x}{2}\right)\cos\left(\frac{10x}{2}\right)$$

$$= 2\sin 2x \cos 5x$$

13. $\cos 4x + \cos 2x = 2\cos\left(\frac{4x + 2x}{2}\right)\cos\left(\frac{4x - 2x}{2}\right)$

$$= 2\cos\left(\frac{6x}{2}\right)\cos\left(\frac{2x}{2}\right)$$

$$= 2\cos 3x \cos x$$

15.　$\sin x + \sin 2x = 2\sin\left(\dfrac{x+2x}{2}\right)\cos\left(\dfrac{x-2x}{2}\right)$

$\qquad\qquad\qquad = 2\sin\left(\dfrac{3x}{2}\right)\cos\left(\dfrac{-x}{2}\right)$

$\qquad\qquad\qquad = 2\sin\dfrac{3x}{2}\cos\dfrac{x}{2}$

17.　$\cos\dfrac{3x}{2} + \cos\dfrac{x}{2} = 2\cos\left(\dfrac{\frac{3x}{2}+\frac{x}{2}}{2}\right)\cos\left(\dfrac{\frac{3x}{2}-\frac{x}{2}}{2}\right)$

$\qquad\qquad\qquad\quad = 2\cos\left(\dfrac{4x}{4}\right)\cos\left(\dfrac{2x}{4}\right)$

$\qquad\qquad\qquad\quad = 2\cos x\cos\dfrac{x}{2}$

19.　$\sin 75° + \sin 15°$

$\qquad = 2\sin\left(\dfrac{75°+15°}{2}\right)\cos\left(\dfrac{75°-15°}{2}\right)$

$\qquad = 2\sin(45°)\cos(30°)$

$\qquad = 2\left(\dfrac{\sqrt{2}}{2}\right)\left(\dfrac{\sqrt{3}}{2}\right)$

$\qquad = \dfrac{\sqrt{6}}{2}$

21.　$\sin\dfrac{\pi}{12} - \sin\dfrac{5\pi}{12}$

$\qquad = 2\sin\left(\dfrac{\frac{\pi}{12}-\frac{5\pi}{12}}{2}\right)\cos\left(\dfrac{\frac{\pi}{12}+\frac{5\pi}{12}}{2}\right)$

$\qquad = 2\sin\left(-\dfrac{4\pi}{24}\right)\cos\left(\dfrac{6\pi}{24}\right)$

$\qquad = -2\sin\dfrac{\pi}{6}\cos\dfrac{\pi}{4}$

$\qquad = -2\left(\dfrac{1}{2}\right)\left(\dfrac{\sqrt{2}}{2}\right)$

$\qquad = -\dfrac{\sqrt{2}}{2}$

23.　$\dfrac{\sin 3x - \sin x}{\cos 3x - \cos x} = \dfrac{2\sin\left(\dfrac{3x-x}{2}\right)\cos\left(\dfrac{3x+x}{2}\right)}{-2\sin\left(\dfrac{3x+x}{2}\right)\sin\left(\dfrac{3x-x}{2}\right)}$

$\qquad\qquad\qquad = \dfrac{2\sin\left(\dfrac{2x}{2}\right)\cos\left(\dfrac{4x}{2}\right)}{-2\sin\left(\dfrac{4x}{2}\right)\sin\left(\dfrac{2x}{2}\right)}$

$\qquad\qquad\qquad = \dfrac{2\sin x\cos 2x}{-2\sin 2x\sin x}$

$\qquad\qquad\qquad = -\dfrac{\cos 2x}{\sin 2x} = -\cot 2x$

We worked with the left side and arrived at the right side. Thus, the identity is verified.

25.　$\dfrac{\sin 2x + \sin 4x}{\cos 2x + \cos 4x}$

$\qquad = \dfrac{2\sin\left(\dfrac{2x+4x}{2}\right)\cos\left(\dfrac{2x-4x}{2}\right)}{2\cos\left(\dfrac{2x+4x}{2}\right)\cos\left(\dfrac{2x-4x}{2}\right)}$

$\qquad = \dfrac{2\sin\left(\dfrac{6x}{2}\right)\cos\left(\dfrac{-2x}{2}\right)}{2\cos\left(\dfrac{6x}{2}\right)\cos\left(\dfrac{-2x}{2}\right)}$

$\qquad = \dfrac{2\sin 3x\cos(-x)}{2\cos 3x\cos(-x)}$

$\qquad = \dfrac{\sin 3x}{\cos 3x} = \tan 3x$

We worked with the left side and arrived at the right side. Thus, the identity is verified.

27.　$\dfrac{\sin x - \sin y}{\sin x + \sin y} = \dfrac{2\sin\left(\dfrac{x-y}{2}\right)\cos\left(\dfrac{x+y}{2}\right)}{2\sin\left(\dfrac{x+y}{2}\right)\cos\left(\dfrac{x-y}{2}\right)}$

$\qquad\qquad\qquad = \dfrac{\sin\left(\dfrac{x-y}{2}\right)}{\cos\left(\dfrac{x-y}{2}\right)}\cdot\dfrac{\cos\left(\dfrac{x+y}{2}\right)}{\sin\left(\dfrac{x+y}{2}\right)}$

$\qquad\qquad\qquad = \tan\dfrac{x-y}{2}\cot\dfrac{x+y}{2}$

We worked with the left side and arrived at the right side. Thus, the identity is verified.

29. $\dfrac{\sin x + \sin y}{\cos x + \cos y} = \dfrac{2\sin\left(\dfrac{x+y}{2}\right)\cos\left(\dfrac{x-y}{2}\right)}{2\cos\left(\dfrac{x+y}{2}\right)\cos\left(\dfrac{x-y}{2}\right)} = \dfrac{\sin\left(\dfrac{x+y}{2}\right)}{\cos\left(\dfrac{x+y}{2}\right)} = \tan\dfrac{x+y}{2}$

We worked with the left side and arrived at the right side. Thus, the identity is verified.

31. a. The graph appears to be the cosine curve, $y = \cos x$. It cycles through maximum, intercept, minimum, intercept, and back to maximum. Thus, $y = \cos x$ also describes the graph.

b. $\dfrac{\sin x + \sin 3x}{2\sin 2x} = \dfrac{2\sin\left(\dfrac{x+3x}{2}\right)\cos\left(\dfrac{x-3x}{2}\right)}{2\sin 2x} = \dfrac{2\sin\left(\dfrac{4x}{2}\right)\cos\left(\dfrac{-2x}{2}\right)}{2\sin 2x}$

$\qquad = \dfrac{2\sin 2x\cos(-x)}{2\sin 2x} = \cos(-x) = \cos x$

This verifies our observation that $y = \dfrac{\sin x + \sin 3x}{2\sin 2x}$ and $y = \cos x$ describe the same graph.

33. a. The graph appears to be the tangent of twice the angle. It cycles from intercept to infinity, from negative infinity through the intercept. Thus, $y = \tan 2x$ also describes the graph.

b. $\dfrac{\cos x - \cos 5x}{\sin x + \sin 5x} = \dfrac{-2\sin\left(\dfrac{x+5x}{2}\right)\sin\left(\dfrac{x-5x}{2}\right)}{2\sin\left(\dfrac{x+5x}{2}\right)\cos\left(\dfrac{x-5x}{2}\right)} = \dfrac{-2\sin\left(\dfrac{6x}{2}\right)\sin\left(\dfrac{-4x}{2}\right)}{2\sin\left(\dfrac{6x}{2}\right)\cos\left(\dfrac{4x}{2}\right)}$

$\qquad = \dfrac{-2\sin 3x\sin(-2x)}{2\sin 3x\cos(-2x)} = \dfrac{-\sin(-2x)}{\cos 2x} = \dfrac{\sin 2x}{\cos 2x} = \tan 2x$

This verifies our observation that $y = \dfrac{\cos x - \cos 5x}{\sin x + \sin 5x}$ and $y = \tan 2x$ describe the same graph.

35. a. The low frequency is $l = 852$ cycles per second and the high frequency is $h = 1209$ cycles per second. The sound produced by touching 7 is described by $y = \sin 2\pi(852)t + \sin 2\pi(1209)t$, or $y = \sin 1704\pi t + \sin 2418\pi t$.

b. $y = \sin 1704\pi t + \sin 2418\pi t$

$\quad = 2\sin\left(\dfrac{1704\pi t + 2418\pi t}{2}\right)\cdot\cos\left(\dfrac{1704\pi t - 2418\pi t}{2}\right)$

$\quad = 2\sin 2061\pi t\cdot\cos(-357\pi t)$

$\quad = 2\sin 2061\pi t\cdot\cos 357\pi t$

37.–41. Answers may vary.

43.

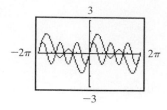

The graphs do not coincide.
Values for *x* may vary.

45.

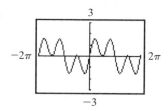

$$\sin x + \sin 3x = 2\sin\left(\frac{x+3x}{2}\right)\cos\left(\frac{x-3x}{2}\right)$$
$$= 2\sin 2x \cos(-x)$$
$$= 2\sin 2x \cos x$$

We worked with the left side and arrived at the right side. Thus, the identity is verified.

47.

49. a.

Answers may vary.

b.

Answers may vary.

c. When $x = \dfrac{\pi}{2}$,

$$\frac{\pi}{2} = 2\left(\frac{\sin\frac{\pi}{2}}{1} - \frac{\sin\left(2\cdot\frac{\pi}{2}\right)}{2} + \frac{\sin\left(3\cdot\frac{\pi}{2}\right)}{3} - \frac{\sin\left(4\cdot\frac{\pi}{2}\right)}{4} + \frac{\sin\left(5\cdot\frac{\pi}{2}\right)}{5} - \frac{\sin\left(6\cdot\frac{\pi}{2}\right)}{6} + \frac{\sin\left(7\cdot\frac{\pi}{2}\right)}{7} - \frac{\sin\left(8\cdot\frac{\pi}{2}\right)}{8} + \cdots\right)$$

$$= 2\left(1 - 0 + \left(-\frac{1}{3}\right) - 0 + \frac{1}{5} - 0 + \left(-\frac{1}{7}\right) - 0 + \cdots\right)$$

$$= 2 - \frac{2}{3} + \frac{2}{5} - \frac{2}{7} + \cdots$$

Multiplying both sides by 2 gives: $\pi = 4 - \dfrac{4}{3} + \dfrac{4}{5} - \dfrac{4}{7} + \cdots$

51.
$$\sin(\alpha + \beta) = \sin \alpha \cos \beta + \cos \alpha \sin \beta$$
$$-[\sin(\alpha - \beta) = \sin \alpha \cos \beta - \cos \alpha \sin \beta]$$
$$\overline{\sin(\alpha + \beta) - \sin(\alpha - \beta) = 2 \cos \alpha \sin \beta}$$

Solve for $\cos \alpha \sin \beta$ by multiplying both sides by $\dfrac{1}{2}$:

$$\frac{1}{2}\left[\sin(\alpha + \beta) - \sin(\alpha - \beta)\right] = \cos \alpha \sin \beta$$

53. $2 \cos \dfrac{\alpha + \beta}{2} \cos \dfrac{\alpha - \beta}{2} = 2 \cdot \dfrac{1}{2}\left[\cos\left(\dfrac{\alpha + \beta}{2} - \dfrac{\alpha - \beta}{2}\right) + \cos\left(\dfrac{\alpha + \beta}{2} + \dfrac{\alpha - \beta}{2}\right)\right]$

$$- \cos\left(\frac{2\beta}{2}\right) + \cos\left(\frac{2\alpha}{2}\right)$$
$$= \cos \beta + \cos \alpha$$
$$= \cos \alpha + \cos \beta$$

Thus, the identity is verified.

55. $\sin 2x + \sin 4x + \sin 6x = \sin 4x + (\sin 2x + \sin 6x)$

$$= \sin 4x + 2\sin\left(\frac{2x + 6x}{2}\right)\cos\left(\frac{2x - 6x}{2}\right)$$
$$= \sin 4x + 2\sin\left(\frac{8x}{2}\right)\cos\left(\frac{-4x}{2}\right)$$
$$= \sin 4x + 2\sin 4x \cos(-2x)$$
$$= \sin 4x + 2\sin 4x \cos 2x$$
$$= \sin(2 \cdot 2x) + 2\sin 4x \cos 2x$$
$$= 2\sin 2x \cos 2x + 2\sin 4x \cos 2x$$
$$= 2\cos 2x(\sin 2x + \sin 4x)$$
$$= 2\cos 2x\left(2\sin\left(\frac{2x + 4x}{2}\right)\cos\left(\frac{2x - 4x}{2}\right)\right)$$
$$= 2\cos 2x \cdot 2\sin\left(\frac{6x}{2}\right)\cos\left(\frac{-2x}{2}\right)$$
$$= 2\cos 2x \cdot 2\sin 3x \cos(-x)$$
$$= 4\cos 2x \sin 3x \cos x$$
$$= 4\cos x \cos 2x \sin 3x$$

We worked with the right side and arrived at the left side. Thus, the identity is verified.

Section 6.5

Check Point Exercises

1.
$$5\sin x = 3\sin x + \sqrt{3}$$
$$5\sin x - 3\sin x = 3\sin x - 3\sin x + \sqrt{3}$$
$$2\sin x = \sqrt{3}$$
$$\sin x = \frac{\sqrt{3}}{2}$$

Because $\sin\frac{\pi}{3} = \frac{\sqrt{3}}{2}$, the solutions for

$\sin x = \frac{\sqrt{3}}{2}$ in $[0, 2\pi)$ are

$$x = \frac{\pi}{3}$$

$$x = \pi - \frac{\pi}{3} = \frac{3\pi}{3} - \frac{\pi}{3} = \frac{2\pi}{3}.$$

Because the period of the sine function is 2π, the solutions are given by

$$x = \frac{\pi}{3} + 2n\pi \quad \text{or}$$

$$x = \frac{2\pi}{3} + 2n\pi$$

where n is any integer.

2. The period of the tangent function is π. In the interval $[0, \pi)$, the only value for which tha tangent function is $\sqrt{3}$ is $\frac{\pi}{3}$. All the

solutions to $\tan 2x = \sqrt{3}$ are given by

$$2x = \frac{\pi}{3} + n\pi$$

$$x = \frac{\pi}{6} + \frac{n\pi}{2}$$

where n is any integer. In the interval $[0, 2\pi)$, we obtain solutions as follows:

Let $n = 0$. $x = \frac{\pi}{6} + \frac{0\pi}{2}$

$$= \frac{\pi}{6}$$

Let $n = 1$. $x = \frac{\pi}{6} + \frac{1\pi}{2}$

$$= \frac{\pi}{6} + \frac{3\pi}{6} = \frac{2\pi}{3}$$

Let $n = 2$. $x = \frac{\pi}{6} + \frac{2\pi}{2}$

$$= \frac{\pi}{6} + \frac{6\pi}{6} = \frac{7\pi}{6}$$

Let $n = 3$. $x = \frac{\pi}{6} + \frac{3\pi}{2}$

$$= \frac{\pi}{6} + \frac{9\pi}{6} = \frac{5\pi}{3}$$

In the interval $[0, 2\pi)$, the solutions are

$\frac{\pi}{6}, \frac{2\pi}{3}, \frac{7\pi}{6},$ and $\frac{5\pi}{3}$.

3. The period of the sine function is 2π. In the interval $[0, 2\pi)$, there are two values

at which the sine function is $\frac{1}{2}$. One is $\frac{\pi}{6}$.

The sine is positive in quadrant II. Thus, the

other value is $\pi - \frac{\pi}{6} = \frac{5\pi}{6}$. All the solutions

to $\sin\frac{x}{3} = \frac{1}{2}$ are given by

$$\frac{x}{3} = \frac{\pi}{6} + 2n\pi$$

$$x = \frac{\pi}{2} + 6n\pi$$

or

$$\frac{x}{3} = \frac{5\pi}{6} + 2n\pi$$

$$x = \frac{5\pi}{2} + 6n\pi$$

where n is any integer. In the interval $[0, 2\pi)$, we obtain solutions as follows:

Let $n = 0$. $x = \frac{\pi}{2}$ or $x = \frac{5\pi}{2}$

If we let $n = 1$, we are adding 6π to each of these expressions. These values of x exceed 2π. Thus in the interval $[0, 2\pi)$, the only

solutions are $\frac{\pi}{2}$ and $\frac{5\pi}{2}$.

4. The given equation is in quadratic form
$2t^2 - 3t + 1 = 0$ with $t = \sin x$.
$$2\sin^2 x - 3\sin x + 1 = 0$$
$$(2\sin x - 1)(\sin x - 1) = 0$$
$2\sin x - 1 = 0$ or $\sin x - 1 = 0$
$\quad 2\sin x = 1 \qquad\qquad\qquad \sin x = 1$
$\quad\quad \sin x = \dfrac{1}{2}$
$\quad\quad\quad x = \dfrac{\pi}{6} \qquad\qquad\qquad x = \dfrac{\pi}{2}$
$\quad x = \pi - \dfrac{\pi}{6} = \dfrac{5\pi}{6}$

The solutions in the interval $[0, 2\pi)$ are
$\dfrac{\pi}{6}, \dfrac{\pi}{2}$, and $\dfrac{5\pi}{6}$.

5. $\qquad\qquad \sin x \tan x = \sin x$
$\quad\quad \sin x \tan x - \sin x = 0$
$\quad\quad\quad \sin x(\tan x - 1) = 0$
$\sin x = 0$ or $\tan x - 1 = 0$
$\quad x = 0 \;\; x = \pi \qquad \tan x = 1$
$\qquad\qquad\qquad\qquad\quad x = \dfrac{\pi}{4}$
$\qquad\qquad\quad x = \pi + \dfrac{\pi}{4} = \dfrac{5\pi}{4}$

The solutions in the interval $[0, 2\pi)$ are
$0, \dfrac{\pi}{4}, \pi$, and $\dfrac{5\pi}{4}$.

6. $\qquad\qquad \cos 2x + \sin x = 0$
$\quad\quad 1 - 2\sin^2 x + \sin x = 0$
$\quad\quad -2\sin^2 x + \sin x + 1 = 0$
$\quad\quad 2\sin^2 x - \sin x - 1 = 0$
$\quad\quad (2\sin x + 1)(\sin x - 1) = 0$
$2\sin x + 1 = 0$ or $\sin x - 1 = 0$
$\quad 2\sin x = -1 \qquad\qquad \sin x = 1$
$\quad\quad \sin x = -\dfrac{1}{2} \qquad\qquad x = \dfrac{\pi}{2}$
$\quad x = \pi + \dfrac{\pi}{6} = \dfrac{7\pi}{6}$ or
$\quad x = 2\pi - \dfrac{\pi}{6} = \dfrac{11\pi}{6}$

The solutions in the interval $[0, 2\pi)$ are
$\dfrac{\pi}{2}, \dfrac{7\pi}{6}$, and $\dfrac{11\pi}{6}$.

7. $\qquad \sin x \cos x = -\dfrac{1}{2}$
$\quad 2\sin x \cos x = -1$
$\qquad\quad \sin 2x = -1$
The period of the sine function is 2π. In the interval $[0, 2\pi)$, the sine function is -1 at $\dfrac{3\pi}{2}$. All the solutions to $\sin 2x$ are given by
$$2x = \dfrac{3\pi}{2} + 2n\pi$$
$$x = \dfrac{3\pi}{4} + n\pi,$$
where n is any integer. The solutions in the interval $[0, 2\pi)$ are obtained by letting $n = 0$ and $n = 1$. The solutions are $\dfrac{3\pi}{4}$ and $\dfrac{7\pi}{4}$.

8. $\qquad\qquad\qquad \cos x - \sin x = -1$
$\qquad\qquad (\cos x - \sin x)^2 = (-1)^2$
$\cos^2 x - 2\cos x \sin x + \sin^2 x = 1$
$\cos^2 x + \sin^2 x - 2\cos x \sin x = 1$
$\qquad\qquad 1 - 2\cos x \sin x = 1$
$\qquad\qquad\quad -2\cos x \sin x = 0$
$\qquad\qquad\qquad \cos x \sin x = 0$
$\cos x = 0$ or $\sin x = 0$
$\quad x = \dfrac{\pi}{2} \qquad\qquad x = 0$
$\quad x = \dfrac{3\pi}{2} \qquad\qquad x = \pi$

We check these proposed solutions to see if any are extraneous.
Check 0: $\cos 0 - \sin 0 \overset{?}{=} -1$
$\qquad\qquad\qquad 1 - 0 \overset{?}{=} -1$ False
Check $\dfrac{\pi}{2}$: $\cos\dfrac{\pi}{2} - \sin\dfrac{\pi}{2} \overset{?}{=} -1$
$\qquad\qquad\qquad 0 - 1 \overset{?}{=} -1$ True
Check π: $\cos \pi - \sin \pi \overset{?}{=} -1$
$\qquad\qquad\qquad -1 - 0 \overset{?}{=} -1$ True
Check $\dfrac{3\pi}{2}$: $\cos\dfrac{3\pi}{2} - \sin\dfrac{3\pi}{2} \overset{?}{=} -1$
$\qquad\qquad\qquad 0 - (-1) \overset{?}{=} -1$ False
The actual solutions in the interval $[0, 2\pi)$ are $\dfrac{\pi}{2}$ and π.

Exercise Set 6.5

1. $\cos\dfrac{\pi}{4} \overset{?}{=} \dfrac{\sqrt{2}}{2}$

   $\dfrac{\sqrt{2}}{2} \overset{?}{=} \dfrac{\sqrt{2}}{2}$

   Thus, $\dfrac{\pi}{4}$ is a solution.

3. $\sin\dfrac{\pi}{6} \overset{?}{=} \dfrac{\sqrt{3}}{2}$

   $\dfrac{1}{2} \overset{?}{=} \dfrac{\sqrt{3}}{2}$

   Thus, $\dfrac{\pi}{6}$ is not a solution.

5. $\cos\dfrac{2\pi}{3} \overset{?}{=} -\dfrac{1}{2}$

   $-\dfrac{1}{2} \overset{?}{=} -\dfrac{1}{2}$

   Thus, $\dfrac{2\pi}{3}$ is a solution.

7. $\tan\left(2 \cdot \dfrac{5\pi}{12}\right) \overset{?}{=} -\dfrac{\sqrt{3}}{3}$

   $\tan\left(\dfrac{5\pi}{6}\right) \overset{?}{=} -\dfrac{\sqrt{3}}{3}$

   $-\dfrac{\sqrt{3}}{3} \overset{?}{=} -\dfrac{\sqrt{3}}{3}$

   Thus, $\dfrac{5\pi}{12}$ is a solution.

9. $\cos\dfrac{\pi}{3} \overset{?}{=} \sin\left(2 \cdot \dfrac{\pi}{3}\right)$

   $\dfrac{1}{2} \overset{?}{=} \dfrac{\sqrt{3}}{2}$

   Thus, $\dfrac{\pi}{3}$ is not a solution.

11. $\sin x = \dfrac{\sqrt{3}}{2}$

    Because $\sin\dfrac{\pi}{3} = \dfrac{\sqrt{3}}{2}$, the solutions

    for $\sin x = \dfrac{\sqrt{3}}{2}$ in $[0, 2\pi)$ are

    $x = \dfrac{\pi}{3}$

    $x = \pi - \dfrac{\pi}{3} = \dfrac{3\pi}{3} - \dfrac{\pi}{3} = \dfrac{2\pi}{3}$.

    Because the period of the sine function is 2π, the solutions are given by

    $x = \dfrac{\pi}{3} + 2n\pi$　or　$x = \dfrac{2\pi}{3} + 2n\pi$

    where n is any integer.

13. $\tan x = 1$

    Because $\tan\dfrac{\pi}{4} = 1$, the solution

    for $\tan x = 1$ in $[0, \pi)$ is

    $x = \dfrac{\pi}{4}$.

    Because the period of the tangent function is π, the solutions are given by

    $x = \dfrac{\pi}{4} + n\pi$

    where n is any integer.

15. $\cos x = -\dfrac{1}{2}$

    Because $\cos\dfrac{\pi}{3} = \dfrac{1}{2}$, the solutions

    for $\cos x = -\dfrac{1}{2}$ in $[0, 2\pi)$ are

    $x = \pi - \dfrac{\pi}{3} = \dfrac{3\pi}{3} - \dfrac{\pi}{3} = \dfrac{2\pi}{3}$

    $x = \pi + \dfrac{\pi}{3} = \dfrac{3\pi}{3} + \dfrac{\pi}{3} = \dfrac{4\pi}{3}$.

    Because the period of the cosine function is 2π, the solutions are given by

    $x = \dfrac{2\pi}{3} + 2n\pi$　or　$x = \dfrac{4\pi}{3} + 2n\pi$

    where n is any integer.

17. $\tan x = 0$
Because $\tan 0 = 0$, the solution
for $\tan x = 0$ in $[0, \pi)$ is
$x = 0.$
Because the period of the tangent function is
π, the solutions are given by
$x = 0 + n\pi = n\pi$
where n is any integer.

19. $2\cos x + \sqrt{3} = 0$
$$2\cos x = -\sqrt{3}$$
$$\cos x = -\frac{\sqrt{3}}{2}$$
Because $\cos\dfrac{\pi}{6} = \dfrac{\sqrt{3}}{2}$, the solutions

for $\cos x = -\dfrac{\sqrt{3}}{2}$ in $[0, 2\pi)$ are

$$x = \pi - \frac{\pi}{6} = \frac{6\pi}{6} - \frac{\pi}{6} = \frac{5\pi}{6}$$
$$x = \pi + \frac{\pi}{6} = \frac{6\pi}{6} + \frac{\pi}{6} = \frac{7\pi}{6}.$$

Because the period of the cosine function is
2π, the solutions are given by

$$x = \frac{5\pi}{6} + 2n\pi \quad \text{or} \quad x = \frac{7\pi}{6} + 2n\pi$$

where n is any integer.

21. $4\sin\theta - 1 = 2\sin\theta$
$$4\sin\theta - 2\sin\theta = 1$$
$$2\sin\theta = 1$$
$$\sin\theta = \frac{1}{2}$$
Because $\sin\dfrac{\pi}{6} = \dfrac{1}{2}$, the solutions

for $\sin\theta = \dfrac{1}{2}$ in $[0, 2\pi)$ are

$$\theta = \frac{\pi}{6}$$
$$\theta = \pi - \frac{\pi}{6} = \frac{6\pi}{6} - \frac{\pi}{6} = \frac{5\pi}{6}.$$
Because the period of the sine function is
2π, the solutions are given by

$$\theta = \frac{\pi}{6} + 2n\pi \quad \text{or} \quad \theta = \frac{5\pi}{6} + 2n\pi$$

where n is any integer.

23. $\quad 3\sin\theta + 5 = -2\sin\theta$
$$3\sin\theta + 2\sin\theta = -5$$
$$5\sin\theta = -5$$
$$\sin\theta = -1$$
Because $\sin\dfrac{\pi}{2} = 1$, the solutions

for $\sin\theta = -1$ in $[0, 2\pi)$ are

$$\theta = \pi + \frac{\pi}{2} = \frac{2\pi}{2} + \frac{\pi}{2} = \frac{3\pi}{2}$$
$$\theta = 2\pi - \frac{\pi}{2} = \frac{4\pi}{2} - \frac{\pi}{2} = \frac{3\pi}{2}.$$
Because the period of the sine function is
2π, the solutions are given by

$$\theta = \frac{3\pi}{2} + 2n\pi$$

where n is any integer.

25. The period of the sine function is 2π. In the
interval $[0, 2\pi)$, there are two values at

which the sine function is $\dfrac{\sqrt{3}}{2}$. One is $\dfrac{\pi}{3}$.

The sine is positive in quadrant II; thus, the

other value is $\pi - \dfrac{\pi}{3} = \dfrac{2\pi}{3}$. All the solutions

to $\sin 2x = \dfrac{\sqrt{3}}{2}$ are given by

$$2x = \frac{\pi}{3} + 2n\pi \quad \text{or} \quad 2x = \frac{2\pi}{3} + 2n\pi$$
$$x = \frac{\pi}{6} + n\pi \qquad\qquad x = \frac{\pi}{3} + n\pi$$
Where n is any integer.
The solutions in the interval $[0, 2\pi)$ are
obtained by letting $n = 0$ and $n = 1$.

The solutions are $\dfrac{\pi}{6}, \dfrac{\pi}{3}, \dfrac{7\pi}{6}$, and $\dfrac{4\pi}{3}.$

27. The period of the cosine function is 2π. In the interval $[0, 2\pi)$, there are two values at which the cosine function is $-\dfrac{\sqrt{3}}{2}$. One is $\dfrac{5\pi}{6}$. The cosine is negative in quadrant III; thus, the other value is $2\pi - \dfrac{5\pi}{6} = \dfrac{7\pi}{6}$. All the solutions to

$\cos 4x = -\dfrac{\sqrt{3}}{2}$ are given by

$4x = \dfrac{5\pi}{6} + 2n\pi \quad$ or $\quad 4x = \dfrac{7\pi}{6} + 2n\pi$

$x = \dfrac{5\pi}{24} + \dfrac{n\pi}{2} \qquad\qquad x = \dfrac{7\pi}{24} + \dfrac{n\pi}{2}$

where n is any integer.
The solutions in the interval $[0, 2\pi)$ are obtained by letting $n = 0$, $n = 1$, $n = 2$, and $n = 3$.

The solutions are $\dfrac{5\pi}{24}, \dfrac{7\pi}{24}, \dfrac{17\pi}{24}, \dfrac{19\pi}{24},$

$\dfrac{29\pi}{24}, \dfrac{31\pi}{24}, \dfrac{41\pi}{24}$ and $\dfrac{43\pi}{24}$.

29. The period of the tangent function is π. In the interval $[0, \pi)$, the only value for which the tangent function is $\dfrac{\sqrt{3}}{3}$ is $\dfrac{\pi}{6}$.

All the solutions to $\tan 3x = \dfrac{\sqrt{3}}{3}$ are given by

$3x = \dfrac{\pi}{6} + n\pi$

$x = \dfrac{\pi}{18} + \dfrac{n\pi}{3}$

where n is any integer.
The solutions in the interval $[0, 2\pi)$ are obtained by letting $n = 0$, $n = 1$, $n = 2$, $n = 3$, $n = 4$, and $n = 5$.
The solutions are

$\dfrac{\pi}{18}, \dfrac{7\pi}{18}, \dfrac{13\pi}{18}, \dfrac{19\pi}{18}, \dfrac{25\pi}{18},$ and $\dfrac{31\pi}{18}$.

31. The period of the tangent function is π. In the interval $[0, \pi)$, the only value for which the tangent function is $\sqrt{3}$ is $\dfrac{\pi}{3}$.

All the solutions to $\tan \dfrac{x}{2} = \sqrt{3}$ are given by

$\dfrac{x}{2} = \dfrac{\pi}{3} + n\pi$

$x = \dfrac{2\pi}{3} + 2n\pi$ where n is any integer. The solution in the interval $[0, 2\pi)$ is obtained by letting $n = 0$. The only solution is $\dfrac{2\pi}{3}$.

33. The period of the sine function is 2π. In the interval $[0, 2\pi)$, the only value for which the sine function is -1 is $\dfrac{3\pi}{2}$.

All the solutions to $\sin \dfrac{2\theta}{3} = -1$ are given by

$\dfrac{2\theta}{3} = \dfrac{3\pi}{2} + 2n\pi$

$\theta = \dfrac{9\pi}{4} + 3n\pi$ where n is any integer. All values of θ exceed 2π or are less than zero. Thus, in the interval $[0, 2\pi)$ there is no solution.

35. The period of the secant function is 2π. In the interval $[0, 2\pi)$, there are two values at which the secant function is -2. One is $\dfrac{2\pi}{3}$. The secant is negative in quadrant III; thus, the other value is $2\pi - \dfrac{2\pi}{3} = \dfrac{4\pi}{3}$. All the solutions to $\sec \dfrac{3\theta}{2} = -2$ are given by

$\dfrac{3\theta}{2} = \dfrac{2\pi}{3} + 2n\pi \quad$ or $\quad \dfrac{3\theta}{2} = \dfrac{4\pi}{3} + 2n\pi$

$\theta = \dfrac{4\pi}{9} + \dfrac{4n\pi}{3} \qquad\qquad \theta = \dfrac{8\pi}{9} + \dfrac{4n\pi}{3}$

where n is any integer. The solutions in the interval $[0, 2\pi)$ are obtained by letting $n = 0$ and $n = 1$.

Since $\dfrac{20\pi}{9}$ is not in $[0, 2\pi)$, the solutions are

$\dfrac{4\pi}{9}, \dfrac{8\pi}{9},$ and $\dfrac{16\pi}{9}$.

37. The period of the sine function is 2π. In the interval $[0, 2\pi)$, there are two values at which the sine function is $\dfrac{1}{2}$. One is $\dfrac{\pi}{6}$. The sine is positive in quadrant II; Thus, the other value is $\pi - \dfrac{\pi}{6} = \dfrac{5\pi}{6}$. All the solutions to $\sin\left(2x + \dfrac{\pi}{6}\right) = \dfrac{1}{2}$ are given by

$$2x + \dfrac{\pi}{6} = \dfrac{\pi}{6} + 2n\pi$$
$$2x = 2n\pi$$
$$x = n\pi \qquad \text{or}$$
$$2x + \dfrac{\pi}{6} = \dfrac{5\pi}{6} + 2n\pi$$
$$2x = \dfrac{4\pi}{6} + 2n\pi$$
$$x = \dfrac{2\pi}{6} + n\pi$$
$$x = \dfrac{\pi}{3} + n\pi$$

where n is any integer. The solutions in the interval $[0, 2\pi)$ are obtained by letting $n = 0$ and $n = 1$.

The solutions are $0, \dfrac{\pi}{3}, \pi,$ and $\dfrac{4\pi}{3}$.

39. The given equation is in quadratic form $2t^2 - t - 1 = 0$ with $t = \sin x$.
$$2\sin^2 x - \sin x - 1 = 0$$
$$(2\sin x + 1)(\sin x - 1) = 0$$
$$2\sin x + 1 = 0 \qquad \text{or} \qquad \sin x - 1 = 0$$
$$2\sin x = -1 \qquad\qquad \sin x = 1$$
$$\sin x = -\dfrac{1}{2}$$
$$x = \dfrac{7\pi}{6} \quad x = \dfrac{11\pi}{6} \qquad x = \dfrac{\pi}{2}$$
The solutions in the interval $[0, 2\pi)$ are $\dfrac{\pi}{2}, \dfrac{7\pi}{6},$ and $\dfrac{11\pi}{6}$.

41. The given equation is in quadratic form $2t^2 + 3t + 1 = 0$ with $t = \cos x$.
$$2\cos^2 x + 3\cos x + 1 = 0$$
$$(2\cos x + 1)(\cos x + 1) = 0$$

$$2\cos x + 1 = 0 \qquad \text{or} \qquad \cos x + 1 = 0$$
$$2\cos x = -1 \qquad\qquad \cos x = -1$$
$$\cos x = -\dfrac{1}{2}$$
$$x = \dfrac{2\pi}{3} \quad x = \dfrac{4\pi}{3} \qquad x = \pi$$
The solutions in the interval $[0, 2\pi)$ are $\dfrac{2\pi}{3}, \pi,$ and $\dfrac{4\pi}{3}$.

43. The given equation is in quadratic form $2t^2 = t + 3$ with $t = \sin x$.
$$2\sin^2 x = \sin x + 3$$
$$2\sin^2 x - \sin x - 3 = 0$$
$$(2\sin x - 3)(\sin x + 1) = 0$$
$$2\sin x - 3 = 0 \quad \text{or} \quad \sin x + 1 = 0$$
$$2\sin x = 3 \qquad\qquad \sin x = -1$$
$$\sin x = \dfrac{3}{2} \qquad\qquad x = \dfrac{3\pi}{2}$$
$\sin x$ cannot be greater than 1.

The solution in the interval $[0, 2\pi)$ is $\dfrac{3\pi}{2}$.

45. The given equation is in quadratic form $t^2 - 1 = 0$ with $t = \sin\theta$.
$$\sin^2\theta - 1 = 0$$
$$(\sin\theta - 1)(\sin\theta + 1) = 0$$
$$\sin\theta - 1 = 0 \quad \text{or} \quad \sin\theta + 1 = 0$$
$$\sin\theta = 1 \qquad\qquad \sin\theta = -1$$
$$\theta = \dfrac{\pi}{2} \qquad\qquad \theta = \dfrac{3\pi}{2}$$
The solutions in the interval $[0, 2\pi)$ are $\dfrac{\pi}{2}$ and $\dfrac{3\pi}{2}$.

47. $(\tan x - 1)(\cos x + 1) = 0$
$$\tan x - 1 = 0 \qquad \text{or} \qquad \cos x + 1 = 0$$
$$\tan x = 1 \qquad\qquad \cos x = -1$$
$$x = \dfrac{\pi}{4} \quad x = \dfrac{5\pi}{4} \qquad x = \pi$$
The solutions in the interval $[0, 2\pi)$ are $\dfrac{\pi}{4}, \pi,$ and $\dfrac{5\pi}{4}$.

49. $\left(2\cos x + \sqrt{3}\right)(2\sin x + 1) = 0$

$\quad 2\cos x + \sqrt{3} = 0 \qquad \text{or} \quad 2\sin x + 1 = 0$

$\qquad 2\cos x = -\sqrt{3} \qquad\qquad 2\sin x = -1$

$\qquad\quad \cos x = -\dfrac{\sqrt{3}}{2} \qquad\qquad \sin x = -\dfrac{1}{2}$

$x = \dfrac{5\pi}{6} \quad x = \dfrac{7\pi}{6} \qquad\qquad x = \dfrac{7\pi}{6} \quad x = \dfrac{11\pi}{6}$

The solutions in the interval $[0, 2\pi)$ are

$\dfrac{5\pi}{6}, \dfrac{7\pi}{6},$ and $\dfrac{11\pi}{6}$.

51. $\cot x(\tan x - 1) = 0$

$\cot x = 0 \quad \text{or} \quad \tan x - 1 = 0$

$\qquad\qquad\qquad\qquad \tan x = 1$

$x = \dfrac{\pi}{2} \quad x = \dfrac{3\pi}{2} \quad x = \dfrac{\pi}{4} \quad x = \dfrac{5\pi}{4}$

The solutions in the interval $[0, 2\pi)$ are

$\dfrac{\pi}{4}, \dfrac{\pi}{2}, \dfrac{5\pi}{4},$ and $\dfrac{3\pi}{2}$.

53. $\sin x + 2\sin x \cos x = 0$

$\quad \sin x(1 + 2\cos x) = 0$

$\quad \sin x = 0 \quad \text{or} \quad 1 + 2\cos x = 0$

$\qquad\qquad\qquad\qquad 2\cos x = -1$

$\qquad\qquad\qquad\qquad \cos x = -\dfrac{1}{2}$

$x = 0 \quad x = \pi \quad x = \dfrac{2\pi}{3} \quad x = \dfrac{4\pi}{3}$

The solutions in the interval $[0, 2\pi)$ are

$0, \dfrac{2\pi}{3}, \pi,$ and $\dfrac{4\pi}{3}$.

55. $\tan^2 x \cos x = \tan^2 x$

$\tan^2 x \cos x - \tan^2 x = 0$

$\quad \tan^2 x(\cos x - 1) = 0$

$\tan^2 x = 0 \qquad \text{or} \qquad \cos x - 1 = 0$

$\tan x = 0 \qquad\qquad\qquad \cos x = 1$

$x = 0 \quad x = \pi \qquad\qquad\qquad x = 0$

The solutions in the interval $[0, 2\pi)$ are 0 and π.

57. $\qquad 2\cos^2 x + \sin x - 1 = 0$

$\qquad 2\left(1 - \sin^2 x\right) + \sin x - 1 = 0$

$\qquad 2 - 2\sin^2 x + \sin x - 1 = 0$

$\qquad -2\sin^2 x + \sin x + 1 = 0$

$\qquad 2\sin^2 x - \sin x - 1 = 0$

$\qquad (2\sin x + 1)(\sin x - 1) = 0$

$\quad 2\sin x + 1 = 0 \qquad \text{or} \qquad \sin x - 1 = 0$

$\qquad 2\sin x = -1 \qquad\qquad\qquad \sin x = 1$

$\qquad\quad \sin x = -\dfrac{1}{2}$

$x = \dfrac{7\pi}{6} \quad x = \dfrac{11\pi}{6} \qquad\qquad x = \dfrac{\pi}{2}$

The solutions in the interval $[0, 2\pi)$ are

$\dfrac{\pi}{2}, \dfrac{7\pi}{6},$ and $\dfrac{11\pi}{6}$.

59. $\qquad \sin^2 x - 2\cos x - 2 = 0$

$\qquad 1 - \cos^2 x - 2\cos x - 2 = 0$

$\qquad\quad -\cos^2 x - 2\cos x - 1 = 0$

$\qquad\quad \cos^2 x + 2\cos x + 1 = 0$

$\qquad\quad (\cos x + 1)(\cos x + 1) = 0$

$\qquad\qquad\qquad \cos x + 1 = 0$

$\qquad\qquad\qquad\quad \cos x = -1$

$\qquad\qquad\qquad\qquad\quad x = \pi$

The solution in the interval $[0, 2\pi)$ is π.

61. $\qquad\qquad 4\cos^2 x = 5 - 4\sin x$

$\qquad\quad 4\cos^2 x + 4\sin x - 5 = 0$

$\quad 4\left(1 - \sin^2 x\right) + 4\sin x - 5 = 0$

$\qquad 4 - 4\sin^2 x + 4\sin x - 5 = 0$

$\qquad\quad -4\sin^2 x + 4\sin x - 1 = 0$

$\qquad\quad 4\sin^2 x - 4\sin x + 1 = 0$

$\qquad (2\sin x - 1)(2\sin x - 1) = 0$

$\qquad\qquad\qquad 2\sin x - 1 = 0$

$\qquad\qquad\qquad\quad 2\sin x = 1$

$\qquad\qquad\qquad\quad \sin x = \dfrac{1}{2}$

$\qquad\qquad\qquad x = \dfrac{\pi}{6} \quad x = \dfrac{5\pi}{6}$

The solutions in the interval $[0, 2\pi)$ are

$\dfrac{\pi}{6}$ and $\dfrac{5\pi}{6}$.

63.
$$\sin 2x = \cos x$$
$$2\sin x \cos x = \cos x$$
$$2\sin x \cos x - \cos x = 0$$
$$\cos x (2\sin x - 1) = 0$$
$$\cos x = 0 \quad \text{or} \quad 2\sin x - 1 = 0$$
$$2\sin x = 1$$
$$\sin x = \frac{1}{2}$$
$$x = \frac{\pi}{2} \quad x = \frac{3\pi}{2} \qquad x = \frac{\pi}{6} \quad x = \frac{5\pi}{6}$$

The solutions in the interval $[0, 2\pi)$ are
$$\frac{\pi}{6}, \frac{\pi}{2}, \frac{5\pi}{6}, \text{and } \frac{3\pi}{2}.$$

65.
$$\cos 2x = \cos x$$
$$2\cos^2 x - 1 = \cos x$$
$$2\cos^2 x - 1 - \cos x = 0$$
$$2\cos^2 x - \cos x - 1 = 0$$
$$(2\cos x + 1)(\cos x - 1) = 0$$
$$2\cos x + 1 = 0 \qquad \text{or} \qquad \cos x - 1 = 0$$
$$2\cos x = -1 \qquad\qquad\qquad \cos x = 1$$
$$\cos x = -\frac{1}{2} \qquad\qquad\qquad \cos x = 1$$
$$x = \frac{2\pi}{3} \quad x = \frac{4\pi}{3} \qquad\qquad x = 0$$

The solutions in the interval $[0, 2\pi)$ are
$$0, \frac{2\pi}{3}, \text{and } \frac{4\pi}{3}.$$

67.
$$\cos 2x + 5\cos x + 3 = 0$$
$$2\cos^2 x - 1 + 5\cos x + 3 = 0$$
$$2\cos^2 x + 5\cos x + 2 = 0$$
$$(2\cos x + 1)(\cos x + 2) = 0$$
$$2\cos x + 1 = 0 \quad \text{or} \quad \cos x + 2 = 0$$
$$2\cos x = -1 \qquad\qquad \cos x = -2$$
$$\cos x = -\frac{1}{2}$$
$$x = \frac{2\pi}{3} \quad x = \frac{4\pi}{3} \qquad \cos x \text{ cannot}$$
$$\text{be less than } -1$$

The solutions in the interval $[0, 2\pi)$ arc
$$\frac{2\pi}{3} \text{ and } \frac{4\pi}{3}.$$

69.
$$\sin x \cos x = \frac{\sqrt{2}}{4}$$
$$2\sin x \cos x = \frac{\sqrt{2}}{2}$$
$$\sin 2x = \frac{\sqrt{2}}{2}$$

The period of the sine function is 2π. In the interval $[0, 2\pi)$, there are two values at which the sine function is $\frac{\sqrt{2}}{2}$. One is $\frac{\pi}{4}$. The sine is positive in quadrant II; thus, the other valuc is $\pi - \frac{\pi}{4} = \frac{3\pi}{4}$. All the solutions to $\sin 2x = \frac{\sqrt{2}}{2}$ are given by

$$2x = \frac{\pi}{4} + 2n\pi \quad \text{or} \quad 2x = \frac{3\pi}{4} + 2n\pi$$
$$x = \frac{\pi}{8} + n\pi \qquad\qquad x = \frac{3\pi}{8} + n\pi$$

where n is any integer.
The solutions in the interval $[0, 2\pi)$ are obtained by letting $n = 0$ and $n = 1$.

The solutions are $\frac{\pi}{8}, \frac{3\pi}{8}, \frac{9\pi}{8}, \text{and } \frac{11\pi}{8}.$

71.

$$\sin x + \cos x = 1$$
$$(\sin x + \cos x)^2 = 1^2$$
$$\sin^2 x + 2\sin x \cos x + \cos^2 x = 1$$
$$\sin^2 x + \cos^2 x + 2\sin x \cos x = 1$$
$$1 + 2\sin x \cos x = 1$$
$$2\sin x \cos x = 0$$
$$\sin x \cos x = 0$$
$$\sin x = 0 \quad \text{or} \quad \cos x = 0$$

$$x = 0 \qquad\qquad x = \frac{\pi}{2}$$
$$x = \pi \qquad\qquad x = \frac{3\pi}{2}$$

We check these proposed solutions to see if any are extraneous.

Check 0: $\sin 0 + \cos 0 \overset{?}{=} 1$

$$0 + 1 \quad \overset{?}{=} 1 \quad \text{True}$$

Check $\dfrac{\pi}{2}$: $\sin \dfrac{\pi}{2} + \cos \dfrac{\pi}{2} \overset{?}{=} 1$

$$1 + 0 \quad \overset{?}{=} 1 \quad \text{True}$$

Check π: $\sin \pi + \cos \pi \overset{?}{=} 1$

$$0 + (-1) \overset{?}{=} 1 \quad \text{False}$$

Check $\dfrac{3\pi}{2}$: $\sin \dfrac{3\pi}{2} + \cos \dfrac{3\pi}{2} \overset{?}{=} 1$

$$-1 + 0 \qquad \overset{?}{=} 1 \quad \text{False}$$

The actual solutions in the interval

$[0, 2\pi)$ are 0 and $\dfrac{\pi}{2}$.

73.

$$\sin\left(x + \frac{\pi}{4}\right) + \sin\left(x - \frac{\pi}{4}\right) = 1$$
$$\frac{1}{2}\left[\sin\left(x + \frac{\pi}{4}\right) + \sin\left(x - \frac{\pi}{4}\right)\right] = 1 \cdot \frac{1}{2}$$
$$\sin x \cos\frac{\pi}{4} = \frac{1}{2}$$
$$\sin x \cdot \frac{\sqrt{2}}{2} = \frac{1}{2}$$
$$\sin x = \frac{1}{\sqrt{2}}$$
$$\sin x = \frac{\sqrt{2}}{2}$$

$$x = \frac{\pi}{4} \quad \text{or} \quad x = \frac{3\pi}{4}$$

The solutions in the interval $[0, 2\pi)$ are

$\dfrac{\pi}{4}$ and $\dfrac{3\pi}{4}$.

75.

$$\sin 2x \cos x + \cos 2x \sin x = \frac{\sqrt{2}}{2}$$
$$\sin(2x + x) = \frac{\sqrt{2}}{2}$$
$$\sin 3x = \frac{\sqrt{2}}{2}$$

The period of the sine function is 2π. In the interval $[0, 2\pi)$, there are two values at

which the sine function is $\dfrac{\sqrt{2}}{2}$. One is $\dfrac{\pi}{4}$.

The sine function is positive in quadrant II;

thus, the other value is $\pi - \dfrac{\pi}{4} = \dfrac{3\pi}{4}$. All the

solutions to $\sin 3x = \dfrac{\sqrt{2}}{2}$ are given by

$$3x = \frac{\pi}{4} + 2n\pi \quad \text{or} \quad 3x = \frac{3\pi}{4} + 2n\pi$$
$$x = \frac{\pi}{12} + \frac{2n\pi}{3} \qquad\qquad x = \frac{\pi}{4} + \frac{2n\pi}{3}$$

where n is any integer. The solutions in the interval $[0, 2\pi)$ are obtained by letting $n = 0$, $n = 1$, and $n = 2$. The solutions are

$$\frac{\pi}{12}, \frac{\pi}{4}, \frac{3\pi}{4}, \frac{11\pi}{12}, \frac{17\pi}{12}, \text{ and } \frac{19\pi}{12}.$$

77.

$$\tan x + \sec x = 1$$
$$\tan x - 1 = -\sec x$$
$$(\tan x - 1)^2 = (-\sec x)^2$$
$$\tan^2 x - 2\tan x + 1 = \sec^2 x$$
$$\tan^2 x - 2\tan x + 1 = 1 + \tan^2 x$$
$$-2\tan x = 0$$
$$\tan x = 0$$

$$x = 0 \quad x = \pi$$

We check these proposed solutions to see if any are extraneous.

Check 0: $\tan 0 + \sec 0 \overset{?}{=} 1$

$$0 + 1 \quad \overset{?}{=} 1 \quad \text{True}$$

Check π: $\tan \pi + \sec \pi \overset{?}{=} 1$

$$0 + (-1) \overset{?}{=} 1 \quad \text{False}$$

The actual solution in the interval $[0, 2\pi)$ is 0.

79. Substitute $y = 0.3$ into the equation and solve for x:

$$0.3 = 0.6 \sin \frac{2\pi}{5} x$$

$$\frac{0.3}{0.6} = \frac{0.6 \sin \frac{2\pi}{5} x}{0.6}$$

$$\frac{1}{2} = \sin \frac{2\pi}{5} x$$

$$\sin \frac{2\pi}{5} x = \frac{1}{2}$$

The period of the sine function is 2π. In the interval $[0, 2\pi)$, there are two values at which the sine function is $\frac{1}{2}$. One is $\frac{\pi}{6}$. The sine is positive in quadrant II; thus, the other value is $\pi - \frac{\pi}{6} = \frac{5\pi}{6}$. All of the solutions to $\sin \frac{2\pi}{5} x = \frac{1}{2}$ are given by

$$\frac{2\pi}{5} x = \frac{\pi}{6} + 2n\pi$$

$$x = \frac{5}{12} + 5n$$

or

$$\frac{2\pi}{5} x = \frac{5\pi}{6} + 2n\pi$$

$$x = \frac{25}{12} + 5n$$

where n is any integer. In the interval $[0, 5]$ we obtain solutions when $n = 0$. The solutions are $\frac{5}{12}$ and $\frac{25}{12}$.

Therefore, we are inhaling at 0.3 liter per second at $x = \frac{5}{12} \approx 0.4$ second and at

$$x = \frac{25}{12} \approx 2.1 \text{ seconds.}$$

81. Substitute $y = 10.5$ into the equation and solve for x:

$$10.5 = 3\sin\left[\frac{2\pi}{365}(x - 79)\right] + 12$$

$$-1.5 = 3\sin\left[\frac{2\pi}{365}(x - 79)\right]$$

$$\frac{-1.5}{3} = \frac{3\sin\left[\frac{2\pi}{365}(x - 79)\right]}{3}$$

$$-\frac{1}{2} = \sin\left[\frac{2\pi}{365}(x - 79)\right]$$

$$\sin\left[\frac{2\pi}{365}(x - 79)\right] = -\frac{1}{2}$$

The period of the sine function is 2π. In the interval $[0, 2\pi)$, there are two values at which the sine function is $-\frac{1}{2}$. One is $\pi + \frac{\pi}{6} = \frac{7\pi}{6}$. The other is $2\pi - \frac{\pi}{6} = \frac{11\pi}{6}$.

All the solutions to $\sin\left[\frac{2\pi}{365}(x - 79)\right] = -\frac{1}{2}$ are given by

$$\frac{2\pi}{365}(x - 79) = \frac{7\pi}{6} + 2n\pi$$

$$x - 79 = \frac{2555}{12} + 365n$$

$$x = \frac{3503}{12} + 365n$$

or

$$\frac{2\pi}{365}(x - 79) = \frac{11\pi}{6} + 2n\pi$$

$$x - 79 = \frac{4015}{12} + 365n$$

$$x = \frac{4963}{12} + 365n$$

where n is any integer.
In the interval $[0, 365]$ we obtain the smallest solution when $n = -1$. That solution is $\frac{583}{12}$. Therefore, 49 days after January 1, Boston has 10.5 hours of daylight.

83. Substitute $d = 2$ into the equation and solve for t:

$$2 = -4\cos\frac{\pi}{3}t$$

$$\frac{2}{-4} = \frac{-4\cos\frac{\pi}{3}t}{-4}$$

$$-\frac{1}{2} = \cos\frac{\pi}{3}t$$

$$\cos\frac{\pi}{3}t = -\frac{1}{2}$$

The period of the cosine function is 2π. In the interval $[0, 2\pi)$, there are two values at which the cosine function is $-\frac{1}{2}$. One is $\frac{2\pi}{3}$. The cosine function is negative in quadrant III; thus, the other value is $2\pi - \frac{2\pi}{3} = \frac{4\pi}{3}$. All solutions to $\cos\frac{\pi}{3}t = -\frac{1}{2}$ are given by

$$\frac{\pi}{3}t = \frac{2\pi}{3} + 2n\pi$$
$$t = 2 + 6n$$

or

$$\frac{\pi}{3}t = \frac{4\pi}{3} + 2n\pi$$
$$t = 4 + 6n$$

where n is any nonnegative integer.

85. Substitute $v_0 = 90$ and $d = 170$, and solve for θ:

$$170 = \frac{90^2}{16}\sin\theta\cos\theta$$

$$\frac{136}{405} = \sin\theta\cos\theta$$

$$2 \cdot \frac{136}{405} = 2\sin\theta\cos\theta$$

$$\frac{272}{405} = \sin 2\theta$$

$$\sin 2\theta = \frac{272}{405}$$

The period of the sine function is $360°$. In the interval $[0, 360°]$, there are two values at which the sine function is $\frac{272}{405}$.

One is $\sin^{-1}\left(\frac{272}{405}\right) \approx 42.19°$. The sine function is positive in quadrant II; Thus, the other value is $180° - 42.19° = 137.81°$. All solutions to $\sin 2\theta = \frac{272}{405}$ are given by

$$2\theta = 42.19° + 360°n$$
$$\theta = 21.095° + 180°n$$

or

$$2\theta = 137.81° + 360°n$$
$$\theta = 68.905° + 180°n$$

where n is any integer.
In the interval $[0, 90°)$ we obtain the solutions by letting $n = 0$. The solutions are approximately $21°$ and $69°$. Therefore, the angle of elevation should be $21°$ or $69°$.

87.–95. Answers may vary.

97.

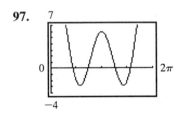

$x = 1.37,$ $x = 2.30$
$x = 3.98,$ or $x = 4.91$

99.

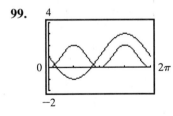

$x = 0.37$ or $x = 2.77$

101.

$x = 0,$ $x = 1.57,$ $x = 2.09,$
$x = 3.14,$ $x = 4.19,$ or $x = 4.71$

103. $2\cos x - 1 + 3\sec x = 0$

$$2\cos x - 1 = -3\sec x$$

$$2\cos x - 1 = \frac{-3}{\cos x}$$

$$\cos x \cdot (2\cos x - 1) = \frac{-3}{\cos x}$$

$$2\cos^2 x - \cos x = -3$$

$$2\cos^2 x - \cos x + 3 = 0$$

The equation is now in quadratic form $2t^2 - t + 3 = 0$. Use the quadratic formula to solve.

$$\cos x = \frac{-(-1) \pm \sqrt{(-1)^2 - 4(2)(3)}}{2(2)}$$

$$\cos x = \frac{1 \pm \sqrt{1 - 24}}{4}$$

$$\cos x = \frac{1 \pm \sqrt{-23}}{4}$$

Since $\dfrac{1 \pm \sqrt{-23}}{4}$ are not real numbers, the equation has no solution.

105.

$$\sin x + 2\sin\frac{x}{2} = \cos\frac{x}{2} + 1$$

$$\sin\left(2 \cdot \frac{x}{2}\right) + 2\sin\frac{x}{2} = \cos\frac{x}{2} + 1$$

$$2\sin\frac{x}{2}\cos\frac{x}{2} + 2\sin\frac{x}{2} = \cos\frac{x}{2} + 1$$

$$2\sin\frac{x}{2}\cos\frac{x}{2} + 2\sin\frac{x}{2} - \cos\frac{x}{2} - 1 = 0$$

$$2\sin\frac{x}{2}\left(\cos\frac{x}{2} + 1\right) - \left(\cos\frac{x}{2} + 1\right) = 0$$

$$\left(\cos\frac{x}{2} + 1\right)\left(2\sin\frac{x}{2} - 1\right) = 0$$

$$\cos\frac{x}{2} + 1 = 0 \quad \text{or} \quad 2\sin\frac{x}{2} - 1 = 0$$

$$\cos\frac{x}{2} = -1 \qquad 2\sin\frac{x}{2} = 1$$

$$\sin\frac{x}{2} = \frac{1}{2}$$

The period of the sine function and cosine function is 2π. In the interval $[0, 2\pi)$, there are two values at which the sine function is $\dfrac{1}{2}$. One is $\dfrac{\pi}{6}$. The other is $\pi - \dfrac{\pi}{6} = \dfrac{5\pi}{6}$.

In the interval $[0, 2\pi)$, the only value at which the cosine function is -1 is π. All of the solutions to $\cos\dfrac{x}{2} = -1$ are given by

$$\frac{x}{2} = \pi + 2n\pi$$

$$x = 2\pi + 4n\pi$$

where n is any integer. All of the solutions to $\sin\dfrac{x}{2} = \dfrac{1}{2}$ are given by

$$\frac{x}{2} = \frac{\pi}{6} + 2n\pi$$

$$x = \frac{\pi}{3} + 4n\pi$$

or

$$\frac{x}{2} = \frac{5\pi}{6} + 2n\pi$$

$$x = \frac{5\pi}{3} + 4n\pi$$

where n is any integer.
The solutions in the interval $[0, 2\pi)$, are obtained by letting $n = 0$. The solutions are $\dfrac{\pi}{3}$ and $\dfrac{5\pi}{3}$.

Review Exercises

1. $\sec x - \cos x = \dfrac{1}{\cos x} - \cos x$

$$= \frac{1}{\cos x} - \frac{\cos x}{1} \cdot \frac{\cos x}{\cos x}$$

$$= \frac{1}{\cos x} - \frac{\cos^2 x}{\cos x}$$

$$= \frac{1 - \cos^2 x}{\cos x}$$

$$= \frac{\sin^2 x}{\cos x}$$

$$= \frac{\sin x}{\cos x} \cdot \sin x$$

$$= \tan x \sin x$$

We worked with the left side and arrived at the right side. Thus, the identity is verified.

2. $\cos x + \sin x \tan x$

$= \dfrac{\cos x}{\cos x} \cdot \cos x + \sin x \cdot \dfrac{\sin x}{\cos x}$

$= \dfrac{\cos^2 x}{\cos x} + \dfrac{\sin^2 x}{\cos x}$

$= \dfrac{\cos^2 x + \sin^2 x}{\cos x}$

$= \dfrac{1}{\cos x} = \sec x$

We worked with the left side and arrived at the right side. Thus, the identity is verified.

3. $\sin^2 \theta (1 + \cot^2 \theta) = \sin^2 \theta + \sin^2 \theta \cot^2 \theta$

$\qquad = \sin^2 \theta + \sin^2 \theta \cdot \dfrac{\cos^2 \theta}{\sin^2 \theta}$

$\qquad = \sin^2 \theta + \cos^2 \theta$

$\qquad = 1$

We worked with the left side and arrived at the right side. Thus, the identity is verified.

4. $(\sec \theta - 1)(\sec \theta + 1) = \sec^2 \theta - 1$

$\qquad\qquad\qquad\quad = 1 + \tan^2 \theta - 1$

$\qquad\qquad\qquad\quad = \tan^2 \theta$

We worked with the left side and arrived at the right side. Thus, the identity is verified.

5. $\dfrac{1}{\sin t - 1} + \dfrac{1}{\sin t + 1}$

$= \dfrac{1}{\sin t - 1} \cdot \dfrac{\sin t + 1}{\sin t + 1} + \dfrac{1}{\sin t + 1} \cdot \dfrac{\sin t - 1}{\sin t - 1}$

$= \dfrac{\sin t + 1}{\sin^2 t - 1} + \dfrac{\sin t - 1}{\sin^2 t - 1}$

$= \dfrac{\sin t + 1 + \sin t - 1}{\sin^2 t - 1}$

$= \dfrac{2 \sin t}{\sin^2 t - 1}$

$= \dfrac{2 \sin t}{-\cos^2 t}$

$= -2 \cdot \dfrac{\sin t}{\cos t} \cdot \dfrac{1}{\cos t}$

$= -2 \tan t \sec t$

We worked with the left side and arrived at the right side. Thus, the identity is verified.

6. $\dfrac{1 + \sin t}{\cos^2 t} = \dfrac{1}{\cos^2 t} + \dfrac{\sin t}{\cos^2 t}$

$\qquad\quad = \sec^2 t + \dfrac{\sin t}{\cos t} \cdot \dfrac{1}{\cos t}$

$\qquad\quad = \tan^2 t + 1 + \tan t \sec t$

We worked with the left side and arrived at the right side. Thus, the identity is verified.

7. $\dfrac{\cos x}{1 - \sin x} = \dfrac{\cos x}{1 - \sin x} \cdot \dfrac{1 + \sin x}{1 + \sin x}$

$\qquad\qquad = \dfrac{\cos x (1 + \sin x)}{1 - \sin^2 x}$

$\qquad\qquad = \dfrac{\cos x (1 + \sin x)}{\cos^2 x}$

$\qquad\qquad = \dfrac{1 + \sin x}{\cos x}$

We worked with the left side and arrived at the right side. Thus, the identity is verified.

8. $1 - \dfrac{\cos^2 x}{1 + \sin x} = \dfrac{1 + \sin x}{1 + \sin x} - \dfrac{\cos^2 x}{1 + \sin x}$

$\qquad\qquad\quad = \dfrac{1 + \sin x - \cos^2 x}{1 + \sin x}$

$\qquad\qquad\quad = \dfrac{1 + \sin x - (1 - \sin^2 x)}{1 + \sin x}$

$\qquad\qquad\quad = \dfrac{\sin x + \sin^2 x}{1 + \sin x}$

$\qquad\qquad\quad = \dfrac{\sin x (1 + \sin x)}{1 + \sin x}$

$\qquad\qquad\quad = \sin x$

We worked with the left side and arrived at the right side. Thus, the identity is verified.

9. $(\tan \theta + \cot \theta)^2$

$= \tan^2 \theta + 2 \tan \theta \cot \theta + \cot^2 \theta$

$= \sec^2 \theta - 1 + 2 \dfrac{\sin \theta}{\cos \theta} \cdot \dfrac{\cos \theta}{\sin \theta} + \csc^2 \theta - 1$

$= \sec^2 \theta - 1 + 2 + \csc^2 \theta - 1$

$= \sec^2 \theta + \csc^2 \theta$

We worked with the left side and arrived at the right side. Thus, the identity is verified.

10. $\dfrac{1}{\sin\theta+\cos\theta}+\dfrac{1}{\sin\theta-\cos\theta}$

$=\dfrac{\sin\theta-\cos\theta}{\sin\theta-\cos\theta}\cdot\dfrac{1}{\sin\theta+\cos\theta}$

$\quad+\dfrac{\sin\theta+\cos\theta}{\sin\theta+\cos\theta}\cdot\dfrac{1}{\sin\theta-\cos\theta}$

$=\dfrac{\sin\theta-\cos\theta}{\sin^2\theta-\cos^2\theta}+\dfrac{\sin\theta+\cos\theta}{\sin^2\theta-\cos^2\theta}$

$=\dfrac{2\sin\theta}{\sin^2\theta-\cos^2\theta}$

$=\dfrac{2\sin\theta}{\sin^2\theta-\cos^2\theta}\cdot\dfrac{\sin^2\theta+\cos^2\theta}{\sin^2\theta+\cos^2\theta}$

$=\dfrac{2\sin\theta\cdot1}{\sin^4\theta-\cos^4\theta}$

$=\dfrac{2\sin\theta}{\sin^4\theta-\cos^4\theta}$

We worked with the left side and arrived at the right side. Thus, the identity is verified.

11. $\dfrac{\cos t}{\cot t-5\cos t}=\dfrac{\cos t}{\cot t-5\cos t}\cdot\dfrac{\frac{1}{\cos t}}{\frac{1}{\cos t}}$

$=\dfrac{\frac{\cos t}{\cos t}}{\frac{\cot t-5\cos t}{\cos t}}$

$=\dfrac{1}{\frac{\cot t}{\cos t}-5}$

$=\dfrac{1}{\frac{\frac{\cos t}{\sin t}}{\cos t}-5}$

$=\dfrac{1}{\frac{\cos t}{\sin t}\cdot\frac{1}{\cos t}-5}$

$=\dfrac{1}{\frac{1}{\sin t}-5}$

$=\dfrac{1}{\csc t-5}$

We worked with the left side and arrived at the right side. Thus, the identity is verified.

12. $\dfrac{1-\cos t}{1+\cos t}=\dfrac{1-\cos t}{1+\cos t}\cdot\dfrac{1-\cos t}{1-\cos t}$

$=\dfrac{(1-\cos t)^2}{1-\cos^2 t}$

$=\dfrac{(1-\cos t)^2}{\sin^2 t}$

$=\left(\dfrac{1-\cos t}{\sin t}\right)^2$

$=\left(\dfrac{1}{\sin t}-\dfrac{\cos t}{\sin t}\right)^2$

$=(\csc t-\cot t)^2$

We worked with the left side and arrived at the right side. Thus, the identity is verified.

13. $\cos(45°+30°)$

$=\cos45°\cos30°-\sin45°\sin30°$

$=\dfrac{\sqrt{2}}{2}\cdot\dfrac{\sqrt{3}}{2}-\dfrac{\sqrt{2}}{2}\cdot\dfrac{1}{2}$

$=\dfrac{\sqrt{6}}{4}-\dfrac{\sqrt{2}}{4}$

$=\dfrac{\sqrt{6}-\sqrt{2}}{4}$

14. $\sin195°=\sin(135°+60°)$

$=\sin135°\cos60°+\cos135°\sin60°$

$=\dfrac{\sqrt{2}}{2}\cdot\dfrac{1}{2}+\left(-\dfrac{\sqrt{2}}{2}\right)\cdot\dfrac{\sqrt{3}}{2}$

$=\dfrac{\sqrt{2}}{4}-\dfrac{\sqrt{6}}{4}$

$=\dfrac{\sqrt{2}-\sqrt{6}}{4}$

15. $\tan\left(\dfrac{4\pi}{3}-\dfrac{\pi}{4}\right)=\dfrac{\tan\frac{4\pi}{3}-\tan\frac{\pi}{4}}{1+\tan\frac{4\pi}{3}\cdot\tan\frac{\pi}{4}}=\dfrac{\sqrt{3}-1}{1+\sqrt{3}\cdot(1)}$

$=\dfrac{\left(\sqrt{3}-1\right)\left(1-\sqrt{3}\right)}{\left(1+\sqrt{3}\right)\left(1-\sqrt{3}\right)}=\dfrac{-\left(1-\sqrt{3}\right)^2}{1-3}$

$=\dfrac{-\left(1-2\sqrt{3}+3\right)}{-2}=\dfrac{1-2\sqrt{3}+3}{2}$

$=\dfrac{4-2\sqrt{3}}{2}=\dfrac{2\left(2-\sqrt{3}\right)}{2}=2-\sqrt{3}$

16. $\tan \dfrac{5\pi}{12} = \tan\left(\dfrac{2\pi}{12} + \dfrac{3\pi}{12}\right)$

$= \tan\left(\dfrac{\pi}{6} + \dfrac{\pi}{4}\right)$

$= \dfrac{\tan \frac{\pi}{6} + \tan \frac{\pi}{4}}{1 - \tan \frac{\pi}{6} \tan \frac{\pi}{4}}$

$= \dfrac{\frac{\sqrt{3}}{3} + 1}{1 - \frac{\sqrt{3}}{3} \cdot 1} = \dfrac{\frac{\sqrt{3}}{3} + 1}{1 - \frac{\sqrt{3}}{3}} \cdot \dfrac{\left(1 + \frac{\sqrt{3}}{3}\right)}{\left(1 + \frac{\sqrt{3}}{3}\right)}$

$= \dfrac{\frac{2\sqrt{3}}{3} + 1 + \frac{1}{3}}{1 - \frac{1}{3}} = \dfrac{\frac{2\sqrt{3}}{3} + \frac{4}{3}}{\frac{2}{3}}$

$= \left(\dfrac{2\sqrt{3}}{3} + \dfrac{4}{3}\right) \cdot \dfrac{3}{2} = \sqrt{3} + 2$

17. $\cos 65° \cos 5° + \sin 65° \sin 5°$
$= \cos(65° - 5°)$
$= \cos 60°$
$= \dfrac{1}{2}$

18. $\sin 80° \cos 50° - \cos 80° \sin 50°$
$= \sin(80° - 50°)$
$= \sin 30°$
$= \dfrac{1}{2}$

19. $\sin\left(x + \dfrac{\pi}{6}\right) - \cos\left(x + \dfrac{\pi}{3}\right)$

$= \sin x \cos \dfrac{\pi}{6} + \cos x \sin \dfrac{\pi}{6}$

$\quad - \left(\cos x \cos \dfrac{\pi}{3} - \sin x \sin \dfrac{\pi}{3}\right)$

$= \sin x \cdot \dfrac{\sqrt{3}}{2} + \cos x \cdot \dfrac{1}{2}$

$\quad - \left(\cos x \cdot \dfrac{1}{2} - \sin x \cdot \dfrac{\sqrt{3}}{2}\right)$

$= 2 \cdot \dfrac{\sqrt{3}}{2} \cdot \sin x$

$= \sqrt{3} \sin x$

We worked with the left side and arrived at the right side. Thus, the identity is verified.

20. $\tan\left(x + \dfrac{3\pi}{4}\right) = \dfrac{\tan x + \tan \frac{3\pi}{4}}{1 - \tan x \tan \frac{3\pi}{4}}$

$= \dfrac{\tan x + (-1)}{1 - \tan x(-1)}$

$= \dfrac{\tan x - 1}{1 + \tan x}$

We worked with the left side and arrived at the right side. Thus, the identity is verified.

21. $\sec(\alpha + \beta)$

$= \dfrac{1}{\cos(\alpha + \beta)}$

$= \dfrac{1}{\cos\alpha \cos\beta - \sin\alpha \sin\beta}$

$= \dfrac{1}{\cos\alpha \cos\beta - \sin\alpha \sin\beta} \cdot \dfrac{\frac{1}{\cos\alpha \cos\beta}}{\frac{1}{\cos\alpha \cos\beta}}$

$= \dfrac{\frac{1}{\cos\alpha \cos\beta}}{\frac{\cos\alpha \cos\beta - \sin\alpha \sin\beta}{\cos\alpha \cos\beta}}$

$= \dfrac{\frac{1}{\cos\alpha} \cdot \frac{1}{\cos\beta}}{\frac{\cos\alpha \cos\beta}{\cos\alpha \cos\beta} - \frac{\sin\alpha \sin\beta}{\cos\alpha \cos\beta}}$

$= \dfrac{\sec\alpha \sec\beta}{1 - \frac{\sin\alpha \sin\beta}{\cos\alpha \cos\beta}}$

$= \dfrac{\sec\alpha \sec\beta}{1 - \tan\alpha \tan\beta}$

We worked with the left side and arrived at the right side. Thus, the identity is verified.

22. $\dfrac{\cos(\alpha - \beta)}{\cos\alpha \cos\beta} = \dfrac{\cos\alpha \cos\beta + \sin\alpha \sin\beta}{\cos\alpha \cos\beta}$

$= \dfrac{\cos\alpha \cos\beta}{\cos\alpha \cos\beta} + \dfrac{\sin\alpha \sin\beta}{\cos\alpha \cos\beta}$

$= 1 + \tan\alpha \tan\beta$

We worked with the left side and arrived at the right side. Thus, the identity is verified.

23. $\cos^4 t - \sin^4 t$
$= \left(\cos^2 t - \sin^2 t\right)\left(\cos^2 t + \sin^2 t\right)$
$= (\cos 2t) \cdot (1)$
$= \cos 2t$
We worked with the left side and arrived at the right side. Thus, the identity is verified.

24. $\sin t - \cos 2t = \sin t - \left(1 - 2\sin^2 t\right)$

$$= \sin t - 1 + 2\sin^2 t$$
$$= 2\sin^2 t + \sin t - 1$$
$$= (2\sin t - 1)(\sin t + 1)$$

We worked with the left side and arrived at the right side. Thus, the identity is verified.

25. $\dfrac{\sin 2\theta - \sin \theta}{\cos 2\theta + \cos \theta} = \dfrac{2\sin\theta\cos\theta - \sin\theta}{2\cos^2\theta - 1 + \cos\theta}$

$$= \dfrac{\sin\theta(2\cos\theta - 1)}{2\cos^2\theta + \cos\theta - 1}$$
$$= \dfrac{\sin\theta(2\cos\theta - 1)}{(2\cos\theta - 1)(\cos\theta + 1)}$$
$$= \dfrac{\sin\theta}{\cos\theta + 1}$$
$$= \dfrac{\sin\theta}{\cos\theta + 1} \cdot \dfrac{\cos\theta - 1}{\cos\theta - 1}$$
$$= \dfrac{\sin\theta(\cos\theta - 1)}{\cos^2\theta - 1}$$
$$= \dfrac{\sin\theta(\cos\theta - 1)}{-\sin^2\theta}$$
$$= \dfrac{-(\cos\theta - 1)}{\sin\theta}$$
$$= \dfrac{1 - \cos\theta}{\sin\theta}$$

We worked with the left side and arrived at the right side. Thus, the identity is verified.

26. $\dfrac{\sin 2\theta}{1 - \sin^2\theta} = \dfrac{2\sin\theta\cos\theta}{\cos^2\theta}$

$$= \dfrac{2\sin\theta}{\cos\theta} \cdot \dfrac{\cos\theta}{\cos\theta}$$
$$= 2\tan\theta$$

We worked with the left side and arrived at the right side. Thus, the identity is verified.

27. $2\sin t\cos t\sec 2t = \sin 2t \cdot \sec 2t$

$$= \sin 2t \cdot \dfrac{1}{\cos 2t}$$
$$= \dfrac{\sin 2t}{\cos 2t}$$
$$= \tan 2t$$

We worked with the right side and arrived at the left side. Thus, the identity is verified.

28. $\cos 4t = \cos(2 \cdot 2t)$

$$= 1 - 2\sin^2 2t$$
$$= 1 - 2(\sin 2t)^2$$
$$= 1 - 2 \cdot (2\sin t\cos t)^2$$
$$= 1 - 2 \cdot 4\sin^2 t\cos^2 t$$
$$= 1 - 8\sin^2 t\cos^2 t$$

We worked with the left side and arrived at the right side. Thus, the identity is verified.

29. $\tan\dfrac{x}{2}(1 + \cos x) = \dfrac{\sin x}{1 + \cos x} \cdot (1 + \cos x)$

$$= \sin x$$

We worked with the left side and arrived at the right side. Thus, the identity is verified.

30. $\tan\dfrac{x}{2} = \dfrac{1 - \cos x}{\sin x}$

$$= \dfrac{1 - \cos x}{\sin x} \cdot \dfrac{\frac{1}{\cos x}}{\frac{1}{\cos x}}$$
$$= \dfrac{\frac{1 - \cos x}{\cos x}}{\frac{\sin x}{\cos x}}$$
$$= \dfrac{\frac{1}{\cos x} - \frac{\cos x}{\cos x}}{\tan x}$$
$$= \dfrac{\sec x - 1}{\tan x}$$

We worked with the left side and arrived at the right side. Thus, the identity is verified.

31. a. The graph appears to be the cosine curve, $y = \cos x$. It cycles through maximum, intercept, minimum, intercept and back to maximum. Thus, $y = \cos x$ also describes the graph.

b. $\sin\left(x - \dfrac{3\pi}{2}\right) = \sin x\cos\dfrac{3\pi}{2} - \cos x\sin\dfrac{3\pi}{2}$

$$= \sin x \cdot 0 - \cos x \cdot (-1)$$
$$= \cos x$$

This verifies our observation that

$y = \sin\left(x - \dfrac{3\pi}{2}\right)$ and $y = \cos x$ describe the same graph.

32. a. The graph appears to be the negative of the sine curve, $y = -\sin x$. It cycles through intercept, minimum, intercept, maximum and back to intercept. Thus, $y = -\sin x$ also describes the graph.

b.
$$\cos\left(x + \frac{\pi}{2}\right) = \cos x \cos\frac{\pi}{2} - \sin x \sin\frac{\pi}{2}$$
$$= \cos x \cdot 0 - \sin x \cdot 1$$
$$= -\sin x$$

This verifies our observation that

$y = \cos\left(x + \dfrac{\pi}{2}\right)$ and $y = -\sin x$ describe

the same graph.

33. a. The graph appears to be the tangent curve, $y = \tan x$. It cycles through intercept to positive infinity, then from negative infinity through the intercept. Thus, $y = \tan x$ also describes the graph.

b.
$$\frac{\tan x - 1}{1 - \cot x} = \frac{\frac{\sin x}{\cos x} - 1}{1 - \frac{\cos x}{\sin x}}$$
$$= \frac{\frac{\sin x}{\cos x} - \frac{\cos x}{\cos x}}{\frac{\sin x}{\sin x} - \frac{\cos x}{\sin x}}$$
$$= \frac{\frac{\sin x - \cos x}{\cos x}}{\frac{\sin x - \cos x}{\sin x}}$$
$$= \frac{\sin x - \cos x}{\cos x} \cdot \frac{\sin x}{\sin x - \cos x}$$
$$= \frac{\sin x}{\cos x}$$
$$= \tan x$$

This verifies our observation that

$y = \dfrac{\tan x - 1}{1 - \cot x}$ and $y = \tan x$ describe

the same graph.

34. $\sin\alpha = \dfrac{3}{5} = \dfrac{y}{r}$

We find x using the Pythagorean Theorem. Because α lies in quadrant I, x is positive.
$$x^2 + 3^2 = 5^2$$
$$x^2 = 5^2 - 3^2 = 16$$
$$x = \sqrt{16} = 4$$

Thus, $\cos\alpha = \dfrac{x}{r} = \dfrac{4}{5}$, and $\tan\alpha = \dfrac{y}{x} = \dfrac{3}{4}$.

$\sin\beta = \dfrac{12}{13} = \dfrac{y}{r}$

We find x using the Pythagorean Theorem. Because β lies in quadrant II, x is negative.
$$x^2 + 12^2 = 13^2$$
$$x^2 = 13^2 - 12^2 = 25$$
$$x = -\sqrt{25} = -5$$

Thus, $\cos\beta = \dfrac{x}{r} = \dfrac{-5}{13} = -\dfrac{5}{13}$, and

$\tan\beta = \dfrac{y}{x} = \dfrac{12}{-5} = -\dfrac{12}{5}$.

a. $\sin(\alpha + \beta) = \sin\alpha\cos\beta + \cos\alpha\sin\beta$
$$= \frac{3}{5}\cdot\left(-\frac{5}{13}\right) + \frac{4}{5}\cdot\frac{12}{13}$$
$$= \frac{33}{65}$$

b. $\cos(\alpha - \beta) = \cos\alpha\cos\beta + \sin\alpha\sin\beta$
$$= \frac{4}{5}\cdot\left(-\frac{5}{13}\right) + \frac{3}{5}\cdot\frac{12}{13}$$
$$= \frac{16}{65}$$

c. $\tan(\alpha + \beta) = \dfrac{\tan\alpha + \tan\beta}{1 - \tan\alpha\tan\beta}$
$$= \frac{\frac{3}{4} + \left(-\frac{12}{5}\right)}{1 - \frac{3}{4}\left(-\frac{12}{5}\right)}$$
$$= \frac{-\frac{33}{20}}{1 + \frac{36}{20}} = \frac{-\frac{33}{20}}{\frac{56}{20}}$$
$$= -\frac{33}{56}$$

d. $\sin 2\alpha = 2\sin\alpha\cos\alpha = 2\cdot\dfrac{3}{5}\cdot\dfrac{4}{5} = \dfrac{24}{25}$

e. $\cos\dfrac{\beta}{2} = \sqrt{\dfrac{1 + \cos\beta}{2}} = \sqrt{\dfrac{1 - \frac{5}{13}}{2}}$
$$= \sqrt{\frac{8}{26}} = \sqrt{\frac{4}{13}} = \frac{2}{\sqrt{13}} = \frac{2\sqrt{13}}{13}$$

35. $\tan \alpha = \dfrac{4}{3} = \dfrac{-4}{-3} = \dfrac{y}{x}$

We find r using the Pythagorean Theorem.
Because r is a distance, it is positive.

$r^2 = (-4)^2 + (-3)^2 = 25$

$r = \sqrt{25} = 5$

Thus, $\sin \alpha = \dfrac{y}{r} = \dfrac{-4}{5} = -\dfrac{4}{5}$, and

$\cos \alpha = \dfrac{x}{r} = \dfrac{-3}{5} = -\dfrac{3}{5}$.

$\tan \beta = \dfrac{5}{12} = \dfrac{y}{x}$

We find r using the Pythagorean Theorem.
Because r is a distance, it is positive.

$r^2 = 5^2 + 12^2 = 169$

$r = \sqrt{169} = 13$

Thus, $\sin \beta = \dfrac{y}{r} = \dfrac{5}{13}$, and $\cos \beta = \dfrac{x}{r} = \dfrac{12}{13}$.

a. $\sin(\alpha + \beta) = \sin \alpha \cos \beta + \cos \alpha \sin \beta$

$= -\dfrac{4}{5} \cdot \dfrac{12}{13} + \left(-\dfrac{3}{5}\right) \cdot \dfrac{5}{13}$

$= -\dfrac{63}{65}$

b. $\cos(\alpha - \beta) = \cos \alpha \cos \beta + \sin \alpha \sin \beta$

$= -\dfrac{3}{5} \cdot \dfrac{12}{13} + \left(-\dfrac{4}{5}\right) \cdot \dfrac{5}{13}$

$= -\dfrac{56}{65}$

c. $\tan(\alpha + \beta) = \dfrac{\tan \alpha + \tan \beta}{1 - \tan \alpha \tan \beta}$

$= \dfrac{\frac{4}{3} + \frac{5}{12}}{1 - \frac{4}{3} \cdot \frac{5}{12}} = \dfrac{\frac{21}{12}}{1 - \frac{20}{36}}$

$= \dfrac{\frac{7}{4}}{\frac{16}{36}} = \dfrac{7}{4} \cdot \dfrac{36}{16} = \dfrac{63}{16}$

d. $\sin 2\alpha = 2 \sin \alpha \cos \alpha$

$= 2 \cdot \left(-\dfrac{4}{5}\right) \cdot \left(-\dfrac{3}{5}\right) = \dfrac{24}{25}$

e. $\cos \dfrac{\beta}{2} = \sqrt{\dfrac{1 + \cos \beta}{2}} = \sqrt{\dfrac{1 + \frac{12}{13}}{2}}$

$= \sqrt{\dfrac{25}{26}} = \dfrac{5}{\sqrt{26}} = \dfrac{5\sqrt{26}}{26}$

36. $\tan \alpha = -3 = \dfrac{3}{-1} = \dfrac{y}{x}$

We find r using the Pythagorean Theorem.
Because r is a distance, it is positive.

$r^2 = 3^2 + (-1)^2 = 10$

$r = \sqrt{10}$

Thus, $\sin \alpha = \dfrac{y}{r} = \dfrac{3}{\sqrt{10}} = \dfrac{3\sqrt{10}}{10}$, and

$\cos \alpha = \dfrac{x}{r} = \dfrac{-1}{\sqrt{10}} = -\dfrac{\sqrt{10}}{10}$.

$\cot \beta = -3 = \dfrac{3}{-1} = \dfrac{x}{y}$

We find r using the Pythagorean Theorem.
Because r is a distance, it is positive.

$r^2 = (-1)^2 + 3^2 = 10$

$r = \sqrt{10}$

Thus, $\sin \beta = \dfrac{y}{r} = \dfrac{-1}{\sqrt{10}} = -\dfrac{\sqrt{10}}{10}$,

$\cos \beta = \dfrac{x}{r} = \dfrac{3}{\sqrt{10}} = \dfrac{3\sqrt{10}}{10}$, and

$\tan \beta = \dfrac{y}{x} = \dfrac{-1}{3} = -\dfrac{1}{3}$.

a. $\sin(\alpha + \beta) = \sin \alpha \cos \beta + \cos \alpha \sin \beta$

$= \dfrac{3\sqrt{10}}{10} \cdot \dfrac{3\sqrt{10}}{10} + \left(-\dfrac{\sqrt{10}}{10}\right) \cdot \left(\dfrac{-\sqrt{10}}{10}\right)$

$= \dfrac{100}{100}$

$= 1$

b. $\cos(\alpha - \beta) = \cos\alpha\cos\beta + \sin\alpha\sin\beta$

$= \left(-\dfrac{\sqrt{10}}{10}\right) \cdot \dfrac{3\sqrt{10}}{10} + \dfrac{3\sqrt{10}}{10} \cdot \left(-\dfrac{\sqrt{10}}{10}\right)$

$= -\dfrac{60}{100}$

$= -\dfrac{3}{5}$

c. $\tan(\alpha + \beta) = \dfrac{\tan\alpha + \tan\beta}{1 - \tan\alpha\tan\beta}$

$= \dfrac{(-3) + \left(-\frac{1}{3}\right)}{1 - (-3)\left(-\frac{1}{3}\right)}$

$= \dfrac{\frac{-10}{3}}{0}$

Since this value is undefined, the tangent function is undefined at $\alpha + \beta$.

d. $\sin 2\alpha = 2\sin\alpha\cos\alpha$

$= 2\left(\dfrac{3\sqrt{10}}{10}\right)\left(-\dfrac{\sqrt{10}}{10}\right)$

$= -\dfrac{3}{5}$

e. $\cos\dfrac{\beta}{2} = \sqrt{\dfrac{1 + \cos\beta}{2}}$

$= \sqrt{\dfrac{1 + \frac{3\sqrt{10}}{10}}{2}}$

$= \sqrt{\dfrac{10 + 3\sqrt{10}}{20}}$

$= \dfrac{\sqrt{10 + 3\sqrt{10}}}{2\sqrt{5}}$

37. $\sin\alpha = -\dfrac{1}{3} = \dfrac{-1}{3} = \dfrac{y}{r}$

We find x using the Pythagorean Theorem. Because α lies in quadrant III, x is negative.

$x^2 + (-1)^2 = 3^2$

$x^2 = 3^2 - (-1)^2 = 8$

$x = -\sqrt{8} = -2\sqrt{2}$

Thus, $\cos\alpha = \dfrac{x}{r} = \dfrac{-2\sqrt{2}}{3} = -\dfrac{2\sqrt{2}}{3}$, and

$\tan\alpha = \dfrac{y}{x} = \dfrac{-1}{-2\sqrt{2}} = \dfrac{\sqrt{2}}{4}$.

$\cos\beta = -\dfrac{1}{3} = \dfrac{-1}{3} = \dfrac{x}{r}$

We find y using the Pythagorean Theorem. Because β lies in quadrant III, y is negative.

$(-1)^2 + y^2 = 3^2$

$y^2 = 3^2 - (-1)^2 = 8$

$y = -\sqrt{8} = -2\sqrt{2}$

Thus, $\sin\beta = \dfrac{y}{r} = \dfrac{-2\sqrt{2}}{3} = -\dfrac{2\sqrt{2}}{3}$, and

$\tan\beta = \dfrac{y}{x} = \dfrac{-2\sqrt{2}}{-1} = 2\sqrt{2}$

a. $\sin(\alpha + \beta)$

$= \sin\alpha\cos\beta + \cos\alpha\sin\beta$

$= -\dfrac{1}{3} \cdot -\dfrac{1}{3} + \left(-\dfrac{2\sqrt{2}}{3}\right)\cdot\left(-\dfrac{2\sqrt{2}}{3}\right)$

$= \dfrac{9}{9} = 1$

b. $\cos(\alpha - \beta)$

$= \cos\alpha\cos\beta + \sin\alpha\sin\beta$

$= -\dfrac{2\sqrt{2}}{3} \cdot \left(-\dfrac{1}{3}\right) + \left(-\dfrac{1}{3}\right)\cdot\left(-\dfrac{2\sqrt{2}}{3}\right)$

$= \dfrac{4\sqrt{2}}{9}$

c. $\tan(\alpha + \beta) = \dfrac{\tan\alpha + \tan\beta}{1 - \tan\alpha\tan B}$

$= \dfrac{\frac{\sqrt{2}}{4} + 2\sqrt{2}}{1 - \left(\frac{\sqrt{2}}{4}\right)(2\sqrt{2})}$

$= \dfrac{\frac{9\sqrt{2}}{4}}{0}$

Since this value is undefined, the tangent function is undefined at $\alpha + \beta$.

d. $\sin 2\alpha = 2\sin\alpha\cos\alpha$

$$= 2\left(-\frac{1}{3}\right)\left(-\frac{2\sqrt{2}}{3}\right) = \frac{4\sqrt{2}}{9}$$

e. $\cos\dfrac{\beta}{2} = -\sqrt{\dfrac{1+\cos\beta}{2}}$

$$= -\sqrt{\frac{1+\left(-\frac{1}{3}\right)}{2}}$$

$$= -\sqrt{\frac{\frac{2}{3}}{2}} = -\sqrt{\frac{1}{3}}$$

$$= -\frac{1}{\sqrt{3}}$$

$$= -\frac{\sqrt{3}}{3}$$

38. The given expression is the right side of the formula for $\cos 2\theta$ with $\theta = 15°$.

$$\cos^2 15° - \sin^2 15° = \cos(2\cdot 15°)$$

$$= \cos 30°$$

$$= \frac{\sqrt{3}}{2}$$

39. The given expression is the right side of the formula for $\tan 2\theta$ with $\theta = \dfrac{5\pi}{12}$.

$$\frac{2\tan\frac{5\pi}{12}}{1-\tan^2\frac{5\pi}{12}} = \tan\left(2\cdot\frac{5\pi}{12}\right)$$

$$= \tan\frac{5\pi}{6}$$

$$= -\frac{\sqrt{3}}{3}$$

40. Because $22.5°$ lies in quadrant I, $\sin 22.5° > 0$.

$$\sin 22.5° = \sin\frac{45°}{2}$$

$$= \sqrt{\frac{1-\cos 45°}{2}} = \sqrt{\frac{1-\frac{\sqrt{2}}{2}}{2}}$$

$$= \sqrt{\frac{2-\sqrt{2}}{4}} = \frac{\sqrt{2-\sqrt{2}}}{2}$$

41. Because $\dfrac{\pi}{12}$ lies in quadrant I, $\tan\dfrac{\pi}{12} > 0$.

$$\tan\frac{\pi}{12} = \tan\frac{\frac{\pi}{6}}{2}$$

$$= \frac{1-\cos\frac{\pi}{6}}{\sin\frac{\pi}{6}} = \frac{1-\frac{\sqrt{3}}{2}}{\frac{1}{2}}$$

$$= 2-\sqrt{3}$$

42. $\sin 6x \sin 4x$

$$= \frac{1}{2}\left[\cos(6x-4x) - \cos(6x+4x)\right]$$

$$= \frac{1}{2}\left[\cos 2x - \cos 10x\right]$$

43. $\sin 7x \cos 3x$

$$= \frac{1}{2}\left[\sin(7x+3x) + \sin(7x-3x)\right]$$

$$= \frac{1}{2}\left[\sin 10x + \sin 4x\right]$$

44. $\sin 2x - \sin 4x$

$$= 2\sin\left(\frac{2x-4x}{2}\right)\cos\left(\frac{2x+4x}{2}\right)$$

$$= 2\sin(-x)\cos 3x$$

$$= -2\sin x\cos 3x$$

45. $\cos 75° + \cos 15°$

$$= 2\cos\left(\frac{75°+15°}{2}\right)\cos\left(\frac{75°-15°}{2}\right)$$

$$= 2\cos 45°\cos 30°$$

$$= 2\left(\frac{\sqrt{2}}{2}\right)\left(\frac{\sqrt{3}}{2}\right) = \frac{\sqrt{6}}{2}$$

46. $\dfrac{\cos 3x + \cos 5x}{\cos 3x - \cos 5x} = \dfrac{2\cos\left(\frac{3x+5x}{2}\right)\cos\left(\frac{3x-5x}{2}\right)}{-2\sin\left(\frac{3x+5x}{2}\right)\sin\left(\frac{3x-5x}{2}\right)}$

$= \dfrac{2\cos\left(\frac{8x}{2}\right)\cos\left(\frac{-2x}{2}\right)}{-2\sin\left(\frac{8x}{2}\right)\sin\left(\frac{-2x}{2}\right)}$

$= \dfrac{2\cos 4x\cos(-x)}{-2\sin 4x\sin(-x)}$

$= \dfrac{2\cos 4x\cos x}{2\sin 4x\sin x}$

$= \dfrac{\cos 4x}{\sin 4x}\cdot\dfrac{\cos x}{\sin x}$

$= \cot 4x\cot x$

$= \cot x\cot 4x$

We worked with the left side and arrived at the right side. Thus, the identity is verified.

47. $\dfrac{\sin 2x + \sin 6x}{\sin 2x - \sin 6x} = \dfrac{2\sin\left(\frac{2x+6x}{2}\right)\cos\left(\frac{2x-6x}{2}\right)}{2\sin\left(\frac{2x-6x}{2}\right)\cos\left(\frac{2x+6x}{2}\right)}$

$= \dfrac{2\sin\left(\frac{8x}{2}\right)\cos\left(\frac{-4x}{2}\right)}{2\sin\left(\frac{-4x}{2}\right)\cos\left(\frac{8x}{2}\right)}$

$= \dfrac{\sin 4x\cos(-2x)}{\sin(-2x)\cos 4x}$

$= -\dfrac{\sin 4x\cos 2x}{\sin 2x\cos 4x}$

$= -\dfrac{\sin 4x}{\cos 4x}\cdot\dfrac{\cos 2x}{\sin 2x}$

$= -\tan 4x\cot 2x$

We worked with the left side and arrived at the right side. Thus, the identity is verified.

48. a. The graph appears to be the cotangent curve, $y = \cot x$. It cycles from positive infinity through the intercept to negative infinity. Thus, $y = \cot x$ also describes the graph.

b. $\dfrac{\cos 3x + \cos x}{\sin 3x - \sin x} = \dfrac{2\cos\left(\frac{3x+x}{2}\right)\cos\left(\frac{3x-x}{2}\right)}{2\sin\left(\frac{3x-x}{2}\right)\cos\left(\frac{3x+x}{2}\right)}$

$= \dfrac{2\cos\left(\frac{4x}{2}\right)\cos\left(\frac{2x}{2}\right)}{2\sin\left(\frac{2x}{2}\right)\cos\left(\frac{4x}{2}\right)}$

$= \dfrac{2\cos 2x\cos x}{2\sin x\cos 2x}$

$= \dfrac{\cos x}{\sin x}$

$= \cot x$

This verifies our observation that

$y = \dfrac{\cos 3x + \cos x}{\sin 3x - \sin x}$ and $y = \cot x$

describe the same graph.

49. $\cos x = -\dfrac{1}{2}$

Because $\cos\dfrac{\pi}{3} = \dfrac{1}{2}$, the solutions for

$\cos x = -\dfrac{1}{2}$ in $[0, 2\pi)$ are $x = \pi - \dfrac{\pi}{3} = \dfrac{2\pi}{3}$

$x = \pi + \dfrac{\pi}{3} = \dfrac{4\pi}{3}$. Because the period of the cosine function is 2π, the solutions are given by $x = \dfrac{2\pi}{3} + 2n\pi$ or $x = \dfrac{4\pi}{3} + 2n\pi$ where n is any integer.

50. $\sin x = \dfrac{\sqrt{2}}{2}$

Because $\sin\dfrac{\pi}{4} = \dfrac{\sqrt{2}}{2}$, the solutions for

$\sin x = \dfrac{\sqrt{2}}{2}$ in $[0, 2\pi)$ are

$x = \dfrac{\pi}{4}$

$x = \pi - \dfrac{\pi}{4} = \dfrac{3\pi}{4}$.

Because the period of the cosine function is 2π, the solutions are given by

$x = \dfrac{\pi}{4} + 2n\pi$ or $x = \dfrac{3\pi}{4} + 2n\pi$

where n is any integer.

51.

$$2\sin x + 1 = 0$$
$$2\sin x = -1$$
$$\sin x = -\frac{1}{2}$$

Because $\sin\dfrac{\pi}{6} = \dfrac{1}{2}$, the solutions for

$\sin x = -\dfrac{1}{2}$ in $[0,\,2\pi)$ are

$$x = \pi + \frac{\pi}{6} = \frac{7\pi}{6}$$
$$x = 2\pi - \frac{\pi}{6} = \frac{11\pi}{6}.$$

Because the period of the sine function is 2π, the solutions are given by

$$x = \frac{7\pi}{6} + 2n\pi \text{ or } x = \frac{11\pi}{6} + 2n\pi$$

where n is any integer.

52.

$$\sqrt{3}\tan x - 1 = 0$$
$$\sqrt{3}\tan x = 1$$
$$\tan x = \frac{1}{\sqrt{3}}$$

Because $\tan\dfrac{\pi}{6} = \dfrac{1}{\sqrt{3}}$, the solution for

$\tan x = \dfrac{1}{\sqrt{3}}$ in $[0,\,\pi)$ is $x = \dfrac{\pi}{6}$.

Because the period of the tangent function is π, the solutions are given by

$$x = \frac{\pi}{6} + n\pi \text{ where } n \text{ is any integer.}$$

53. The period of the cosine function is 2π. In the interval $[0,\,2\pi)$, the only value at which the cosine function is -1 is π. All the solutions to $\cos 2x = -1$ are given by

$$2x = \pi + 2n\pi$$
$$x = \frac{\pi}{2} + n\pi$$

where n is any interger.
The solutions in the interval $[0,\,2\pi)$ are obtained by letting $n = 0$ and $n = 1$.

The solutions are $\dfrac{\pi}{2}$ and $\dfrac{3\pi}{2}$.

54. The period of the sine function is 2π. In the interval $[0,\,2\pi)$, the only value at which the sine function is 1 is $\dfrac{\pi}{2}$. All the solutions to $\sin 3x = 1$ are given by

$$3x = \frac{\pi}{2} + 2n\pi$$
$$x = \frac{\pi}{6} + \frac{2n\pi}{3}$$

where n is any integer. The solutions in the interval $[0,\,2\pi)$ are obtained by letting $n = 0$, $n = 1$, and $n = 2$.

The solutions are $\dfrac{\pi}{6}, \dfrac{5\pi}{6}$, and $\dfrac{9\pi}{6}$.

55. The period of the tangent function is π. In the interval $[0,\,\pi)$, the only value for which the tangent function is -1 is $\dfrac{3\pi}{4}$. All the

solutions to $\tan\dfrac{x}{2} = -1$ are given by

$$\frac{x}{2} = \frac{3\pi}{4} + n\pi$$
$$x = \frac{3\pi}{2} + 2n\pi$$

where n is any integer. The solution in the interval $[0,\,2\pi)$ is obtained by letting $n = 0$.

The solution is $\dfrac{3\pi}{2}$.

56.

$$\tan x = 2\cos x \tan x$$
$$\tan x - 2\cos x \tan x = 0$$
$$\tan x(1 - 2\cos x) = 0$$
$$\tan x = 0 \quad \text{or} \quad 1 - 2\cos x = 0$$
$$x = 0 \ \ x = \pi \qquad\qquad -2\cos x = -1$$
$$\cos x = \frac{1}{2}$$
$$x = \frac{\pi}{3} \qquad x = \frac{5\pi}{3}$$

The solutions in the interval $[0,\,2\pi)$ are 0, $\dfrac{\pi}{3}$, π, and $\dfrac{5\pi}{3}$.

57. The given equation is in quadratic form $t^2 - 2t = 3$ with $t = \cos x$.

$\cos^2 x - 2\cos x = 3$

$\cos^2 x - 2\cos x - 3 = 0$

$(\cos x + 1)(\cos x - 3) = 0$

$\cos x + 1 = 0 \quad$ or $\quad \cos x - 3 = 0$

$\cos x = -1 \qquad\qquad \cos x = 3$

$\quad x = \pi \qquad\qquad\quad \cos x$ cannot be greater than 1.

The solution in the interval $[0, 2\pi)$ is π.

58. $3\cos^2 x + \sin x = 1$

$3\left(1 - \sin^2 x\right) + \sin x = 1$

$3 - 3\sin^2 x + \sin x - 1 = 0$

$-3\sin^2 x + \sin x + 2 = 0$

$3\sin^2 x - \sin x - 2 = 0$

$(3\sin x + 2)(\sin x - 1) = 0$

$3\sin x + 2 = 0 \quad$ or $\quad \sin x - 1 = 0$

$3\sin x = -2 \qquad\qquad \sin x = 1$

$\sin x = -\dfrac{2}{3} \qquad\qquad x = \dfrac{\pi}{2}$

$x = \sin^{-1}\left(-\dfrac{2}{3}\right)$

$x \approx -0.73$

In the interval $[0, 2\pi)$, there are two values at which the sine function is $-\dfrac{2}{3}$.

One is $\pi + 0.73 \approx 3.87$. The other is $2\pi - 0.73 \approx 5.55$.

The solutions in the interval $[0, 2\pi)$ are $\dfrac{\pi}{2}$, 3.87, and 5.55.

59. The given equation is in quadratic form $4t^2 = 1$ with $t = \sin x$.

$4\sin^2 x = 1$

$4\sin^2 x - 1 = 0$

$(2\sin x - 1)(2\sin x + 1) = 0$

$2\sin x - 1 = 0 \quad$ or $\quad 2\sin x + 1 = 0$

$2\sin x = 1 \qquad\qquad 2\sin x = -1$

$\sin x = \dfrac{1}{2} \qquad\qquad \sin x = -\dfrac{1}{2}$

$x = \dfrac{\pi}{6} \quad x = \dfrac{5\pi}{6} \qquad x = \dfrac{7\pi}{6} \quad x = \dfrac{11\pi}{6}$

The solutions in the interval $[0, 2\pi)$ are $\dfrac{\pi}{6}, \dfrac{5\pi}{6}, \dfrac{7\pi}{6}$, and $\dfrac{11\pi}{6}$.

60. $\cos 2x + 2\cos x = 0$

$2\cos^2 x - 1 + 2\cos x = 0$

$2\cos^2 x + 2\cos x - 1 = 0$

The equation is now in quadratic form $2t^2 + 2t - 1 = 0$. Use the quadratic formula to solve.

$\cos x = \dfrac{-2 \pm \sqrt{2^2 - 4(2)(-1)}}{2(2)}$

$= \dfrac{-2 \pm \sqrt{4 + 8}}{4}$

$= \dfrac{-2 \pm \sqrt{12}}{4}$

$= \dfrac{-2 \pm 2\sqrt{3}}{4}$

$= \dfrac{-1 \pm \sqrt{3}}{2}$

$\cos x = \dfrac{-1 + \sqrt{3}}{2} \quad$ or $\quad \cos x = \dfrac{-1 - \sqrt{3}}{2}$

$x = \cos^{-1}\left(\dfrac{-1 + \sqrt{3}}{2}\right) \qquad \cos x \approx -1.37$

$x \approx 1.2 \qquad\qquad \cos x$ cannot be less than -1.

In the interval $[0, 2\pi)$, there are two values at which the cosine function is $\dfrac{-1 + \sqrt{3}}{2}$. One is 1.2. The other is $2\pi - 1.2 \approx 5.08$. The solutions in the interval $[0, 2\pi)$ are 1.2 and 5.08.

61. $\sin 2x = \sqrt{3} \sin x$

$2 \sin x \cos x = \sqrt{3} \sin x$

$2 \sin x \cos x - \sqrt{3} \sin x = 0$

$\sin x \left(2 \cos x - \sqrt{3} \right) = 0$

$\sin x = 0$ or $2 \cos x - \sqrt{3} = 0$

$x = 0 \quad x = \pi \qquad\quad 2 \cos x = \sqrt{3}$

$\qquad\qquad\qquad\qquad \cos x = \dfrac{\sqrt{3}}{2}$

$\qquad\qquad\qquad x = \dfrac{\pi}{6} \quad x = \dfrac{11\pi}{6}$

The solutions in the interval $[0, 2\pi)$ are 0, $\dfrac{\pi}{6}$, π, and $\dfrac{11\pi}{6}$.

62. $\sin x = \tan x$

$\sin x = \dfrac{\sin x}{\cos x}$

$\sin x \cdot \cos x = \sin x$

$\sin x \cos x - \sin x = 0$

$\sin x (\cos x - 1) = 0$

$\sin x = 0$ or $\cos x - 1 = 0$

$x - 0 \quad x - \pi \qquad \cos x - 1$

$\qquad\qquad\qquad\qquad x = 0$

The solutions in the interval $[0, 2\pi)$ are 0 and π.

63. Substitute $d = -3$ into the equation and solve for t:

$-3 = -6 \cos \dfrac{\pi}{2} t$

$\dfrac{-3}{-6} = \dfrac{-6 \cos \frac{\pi}{2} t}{-6}$

$\dfrac{1}{2} = \cos \dfrac{\pi}{2} t$

$\cos \dfrac{\pi}{2} t = \dfrac{1}{2}$

The period of the cosine function is 2π. In the interval $[0, 2\pi)$, there are two values at which the cosine function is $\dfrac{1}{2}$. One is $\dfrac{\pi}{3}$. The cosine function is positive in quadrant IV. Thus, the other value is $2\pi - \dfrac{\pi}{3} = \dfrac{5\pi}{3}$.

All solutions to $\cos \dfrac{\pi}{2} t = \dfrac{1}{2}$ are given by

$\dfrac{\pi}{2} t = \dfrac{\pi}{3} + 2n\pi$

$\dfrac{\pi}{2} t = \dfrac{5\pi}{3} + 2n\pi$

$t = \dfrac{2}{3} + 4n$ or

$t = \dfrac{10}{3} + 4n$

where n is any integer.

64. Substitute $v_0 = 90$ and $d = 100$, and solve for θ:

$100 = \dfrac{90^2}{16} \sin \theta \cos \theta$

$\dfrac{16}{81} = \sin \theta \cos \theta$

$2 \cdot \dfrac{16}{81} = 2 \sin \theta \cos \theta$

$\dfrac{32}{81} = \sin 2\theta$

$\sin 2\theta = \dfrac{32}{81}$

The period of the sine function is $360°$. In the interval $[0, 360°)$, there are two values at which the sine function is $\dfrac{32}{81}$. One is $\sin^{-1} \left(\dfrac{32}{81} \right) \approx 23.27°$. The sine function is positive in quadrant II. Thus, the other value is $180° - 23.27° = 156.73°$. All solutions to $\sin 2\theta = \dfrac{32}{81}$ are given by

$2\theta = 23.27° + 360°n$

$\theta = 11.635° + 180°n$

or

$2\theta = 156.73° + 360°n$

$\theta = 78.365° + 180°n$

where n is any integer.

In the interval $[0, 90°)$ we obtain the solutions by letting $n = 0$. The solutions are approximately $12°$ and $78°$. Therefore, the angle of elevation should be $12°$ or $78°$.

Chapter 6 Test

For problems 1–4: $\sin\alpha = \dfrac{4}{5} = \dfrac{y}{r}$

We find x using the Pythagorean Theorem.
Because α lies in quadrant II, x is negative.

$x^2 + 4^2 = 5^2$

$\qquad x^2 = 5^2 - 4^2 = 9$

$\qquad x = -\sqrt{9} = -3$

Thus, $\cos\alpha = \dfrac{x}{r} = \dfrac{-3}{5} = -\dfrac{3}{5}$, and

$\tan\alpha = \dfrac{y}{x} = \dfrac{4}{-3} = -\dfrac{4}{3}$.

$\cos\beta = \dfrac{5}{13} = \dfrac{x}{r}$

We find y using the Pythagorean Theorem.
Because β lies in quadrant I, y is positive.

$5^2 + y^2 = 13^2$

$\qquad y^2 = 13^2 - 5^2 = 144$

$\qquad y = \sqrt{144} = 12$

Thus, $\sin\beta = \dfrac{y}{r} = \dfrac{12}{13}$, and $\tan\beta = \dfrac{y}{x} = \dfrac{12}{5}$.

1. $\cos(\alpha + \beta) = \cos\alpha\cos\beta - \sin\alpha\sin\beta$

$\quad = -\dfrac{3}{5}\cdot\dfrac{5}{13} - \dfrac{4}{5}\cdot\dfrac{12}{13} = -\dfrac{63}{65}$

2. $\tan(\alpha - \beta) = \dfrac{\tan\alpha - \tan\beta}{1 + \tan\alpha\tan\beta}$

$\quad = \dfrac{-\frac{4}{3} - \frac{12}{5}}{1 + \left(-\frac{4}{3}\right)\cdot\frac{12}{5}} = \dfrac{-\frac{56}{15}}{-\frac{33}{15}} = \dfrac{56}{33}$

3. $\sin 2\alpha = 2\sin\alpha\cos\alpha = 2\left(\dfrac{4}{5}\right)\left(-\dfrac{3}{5}\right) = -\dfrac{24}{25}$

4. $\cos\dfrac{\beta}{2} = \sqrt{\dfrac{1 + \cos\beta}{2}} = \sqrt{\dfrac{1 + \frac{5}{13}}{2}} = \sqrt{\dfrac{18}{26}}$

$\quad = \dfrac{3\sqrt{2}}{\sqrt{26}} = \dfrac{3\sqrt{52}}{26} = \dfrac{3\cdot 2\sqrt{13}}{26}$

$\quad = \dfrac{3\sqrt{13}}{13}$

5. $\sin 105° = \sin(135° - 30°)$

$\quad = \sin 135°\cos 30° - \cos 135°\sin 30°$

$\quad = \dfrac{\sqrt{2}}{2}\cdot\dfrac{\sqrt{3}}{2} - \left(-\dfrac{\sqrt{2}}{2}\right)\dfrac{1}{2}$

$\quad = \dfrac{\sqrt{6}}{4} + \dfrac{\sqrt{2}}{4}$

$\quad = \dfrac{\sqrt{6} + \sqrt{2}}{4}$

6. $\cos x\csc x = \cos x\cdot\dfrac{1}{\sin x}$

$\quad = \dfrac{\cos x}{\sin x}$

$\quad = \cot x$

We worked with the left side and arrived at the right side. Thus, the identity is verified.

7. $\dfrac{\sec x}{\cot x + \tan x} = \dfrac{\frac{1}{\cos x}}{\frac{\cos x}{\sin x} + \frac{\sin x}{\cos x}}$

$\quad = \dfrac{\frac{1}{\cos x}}{\frac{\cos x}{\sin x}\cdot\frac{\cos x}{\cos x} + \frac{\sin x}{\cos x}\cdot\frac{\sin x}{\sin x}}$

$\quad = \dfrac{\frac{1}{\cos x}}{\frac{\cos^2 x + \sin^2 x}{\sin x\cos x}} = \dfrac{\frac{1}{\cos x}}{\frac{1}{\sin x\cos x}}$

$\quad = \dfrac{1}{\cos x}\cdot\dfrac{\sin x\cos x}{1}$

$\quad = \sin x$

We worked with the left side and arrived at the right side. Thus, the identity is verified.

8. $1 - \dfrac{\cos^2 x}{1 + \sin x} = 1 - \dfrac{\left(1 - \sin^2 x\right)}{1 + \sin x}$

$\quad = 1 - \dfrac{(1 + \sin x)(1 - \sin x)}{1 + \sin x}$

$\quad = 1 - (1 - \sin x)$

$\quad = \sin x$

We worked with the left side and arrived at the right side. Thus, the identity is verified.

9. $\cos\left(\theta + \dfrac{\pi}{2}\right) = \cos\theta\cos\dfrac{\pi}{2} - \sin\theta\sin\dfrac{\pi}{2}$

$\quad = \cos\theta\cdot 0 - \sin\theta\cdot 1$

$\quad = -\sin\theta$

We worked with the left side and arrived at the right side. Thus, the identity is verified.

10. $\dfrac{\sin(\alpha-\beta)}{\sin\alpha\cos\beta}=\dfrac{\sin\alpha\cos\beta-\cos\alpha\sin\beta}{\sin\alpha\cos\beta}$

$\qquad\qquad\quad=\dfrac{\sin\alpha\cos\beta}{\sin\alpha\cos\beta}-\dfrac{\cos\alpha\sin\beta}{\sin\alpha\cos\beta}$

$\qquad\qquad\quad=1-\cot\alpha\tan\beta$

We worked with the left side and arrived at the right side. Thus, the identity is verified.

11. $\sin t\cos t(\tan t+\cot t)$

$\quad=\sin t\cos t\left(\dfrac{\sin t}{\cos t}+\dfrac{\cos t}{\sin t}\right)$

$\quad=\dfrac{\sin^2 t\cos t}{\cos t}+\dfrac{\sin t\cos^2 t}{\sin t}$

$\quad=\sin^2 t+\cos^2 t$

$\quad=1$

We worked with the left side and arrived at the right side. Thus, the identity is verified.

12. The period of the sine function is 2π. In the interval $[0,\,2\pi)$, there are two values at which the sine function is $-\dfrac{1}{2}$. One is $\pi+\dfrac{\pi}{6}=\dfrac{7\pi}{6}$. The other is $2\pi-\dfrac{\pi}{6}=\dfrac{11\pi}{6}$.

All the solutions to $\sin 3x=-\dfrac{1}{2}$ are given by $3x=\dfrac{7\pi}{6}+2n\pi$

$\qquad x=\dfrac{7\pi}{18}+\dfrac{2n\pi}{3}$

or

$3x=\dfrac{11\pi}{6}+2n\pi$

$\quad x=\dfrac{11\pi}{18}+\dfrac{2n\pi}{3}$

where n is any integer. The solutions in the interval $[0,\,2\pi)$ are obtained by letting $n=0$, $n=1$, and $n=2$.

The solutions are $\dfrac{7\pi}{18}$, $\dfrac{11\pi}{18}$, $\dfrac{19\pi}{18}$, $\dfrac{23\pi}{18}$, $\dfrac{31\pi}{18}$, and $\dfrac{35\pi}{18}$.

13. $\sin 2x+\cos x=0$

$2\sin x\cos x+\cos x=0$

$\cos x(2\sin x+1)=0$

$\cos x=0$ or $2\sin x+1=0$

$x=\dfrac{\pi}{2}\;\;x=\dfrac{3\pi}{2}\qquad 2\sin x=-1$

$\qquad\qquad\qquad\qquad\sin x=-\dfrac{1}{2}$

$\qquad\qquad\qquad x=\dfrac{7\pi}{6}\;\;x=\dfrac{11\pi}{6}$

The solutions in the interval $[0,\,2\pi)$ are $\dfrac{\pi}{2}$, $\dfrac{7\pi}{6}$, $\dfrac{3\pi}{2}$, and $\dfrac{11\pi}{6}$.

14. The given equation is in quadratic form $2t^2-3t+1=0$ with $t=\cos x$.

$2\cos^2 x-3\cos x+1=0$

$(2\cos x-1)(\cos x-1)=0$

$2\cos x-1=0$ or $\cos x-1=0$

$2\cos x=1\qquad\qquad\cos x=1$

$\cos x=\dfrac{1}{2}\qquad\qquad\;\; x=0$

$x=\dfrac{\pi}{3}\;\;x=\dfrac{5\pi}{3}$

The solutions in the interval $[0,\,2\pi)$ are $0,\dfrac{\pi}{3}$, and $\dfrac{5\pi}{3}$.

15. $2\sin^2 x+\cos x=1$

$2\left(1-\cos^2 x\right)+\cos x-1=0$

$2-2\cos^2 x+\cos x-1=0$

$-2\cos^2 x+\cos x+1=0$

$2\cos^2 x-\cos x-1=0$

$(2\cos x+1)(\cos x-1)=0$

$2\cos x+1=0$ or $\cos x-1=0$

$2\cos x=-1\qquad\qquad\cos x=1$

$\cos x=-\dfrac{1}{2}\qquad\qquad\;\; x=0$

$x=\dfrac{2\pi}{3}\;\;x=\dfrac{4\pi}{3}$

The solutions in the interval $[0,\,2\pi)$ are $0,\dfrac{2\pi}{3}$, and $\dfrac{4\pi}{3}$.

Cumulative Review Exercises (Chapters 1–6)

1. $x^3 + x^2 - x + 15 = 0$
   The possible rational zeros are: $\pm 1, \pm 3, \pm 5, \pm 15$.
   Synthetic division shows that -3 is a zero:

$$
\begin{array}{r|rrrr}
-3 & 1 & 1 & -1 & 15 \\
   &   & -3 & 6 & -15 \\
\hline
   & 1 & -2 & 5 & 0
\end{array}
$$

   The quotient is $x^2 - 2x + 5$. The remaining zeros are found using the quadratic formula:

$$x = \frac{-(-2) \pm \sqrt{(-2)^2 - 4(1)(5)}}{2(1)}$$

$$= \frac{2 \pm \sqrt{4 - 20}}{2} = \frac{2 \pm \sqrt{-16}}{2} = \frac{2 \pm 4i}{2}$$

$$= 1 \pm 2i$$

   All solutions are: -3, $1 + 2i$ and $1 - 2i$.

2.
$$11^{x-1} = 125$$
$$\log 11^{x-1} = \log 125$$
$$(x-1)\log 11 = \log 125$$
$$x - 1 = \frac{\log 125}{\log 11}$$
$$x = \frac{\log 125}{\log 11} + 1$$

   or $x \approx 3.01$

3. $x^2 + 2x - 8 > 0$
   $(x - 2)(x + 4) > 0$
   zero points are $x = 2$ and $x = -4$.

Test Interval	Representative Number	Substitute into $x^2 + 2x - 8 > 0$	Conclusion
$(-\infty, -4)$	-5	$(-5)^2 + 2(-5) - 8 = 25 - 10 - 8 = 7 > 0$	$(-\infty, -4)$ belongs to the solution set.
$(-4, 2)$	0	$0^2 + 2(0) - 8 = -8 > 0$	$(-4, 2)$ does not belong to the solution set.
$(2, \infty)$	3	$3^2 + 2(3) - 8 = 9 + 6 - 8 = 7 > 0$	$(2, \infty)$ belongs to the solution set.

The solution intervals are $(-\infty, -4) \cup (2, \infty)$.

4. $\cos 2x + 3 = 5\cos x$

$2\cos^2 x - 1 + 3 = 5\cos x$

$2\cos^2 x - 5\cos x + 2 = 0$

$(2\cos x - 1)(\cos x - 2) = 0$

$2\cos x - 1 = 0$ or $\cos x - 2 = 0$

$2\cos x = 1$ $\cos x = 2$

$\cos x = \dfrac{1}{2}$ $\cos x$ cannot be greater than 1.

$x = \dfrac{\pi}{3}$ $x = \dfrac{5\pi}{3}$

The solutions in the interval $[0, 2\pi)$ are $\dfrac{\pi}{3}$ and $\dfrac{5\pi}{3}$.

5.

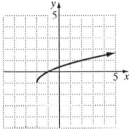

Shift the graph of $y - \sqrt{x}$ left 2 units and down 1 unit.

6.

7.

8.

9.

10.

11. $f(x) = x^2 + 3x - 1$

$\dfrac{f(a+h) - f(a)}{h}$

$= \dfrac{(a+h)^2 + 3(a+h) - 1 - \left(a^2 + 3a - 1\right)}{h}$

$= \dfrac{a^2 + 2ah + h^2 + 3a + 3h - 1 - a^2 - 3a + 1}{h}$

$= \dfrac{2ah + h^2 + 3h}{h}$

$= 2a + h + 3$

12. $\sin 225° = \sin(180° + 45°)$

$= \sin 180° \cos 45° + \cos 180° \sin 45°$

$= 0 \cdot \dfrac{\sqrt{2}}{2} + (-1) \cdot \dfrac{\sqrt{2}}{2}$

$= -\dfrac{\sqrt{2}}{2}$

13. $\sec^4 x - \sec^2 x$

$= \sec^2 x \cdot \sec^2 x - \sec^2 x$

$= \left(1 + \tan^2 x\right)\left(1 + \tan^2 x\right) - \left(1 + \tan^2 x\right)$

$= 1 + 2\tan^2 x + \tan^4 x - 1 - \tan^2 x$

$= \tan^4 x + \tan^2 x$

We worked with the left side and arrived at the right side. Thus, the identity is verified.

14. $320° \times \dfrac{\pi}{180°} = \dfrac{16}{9}\pi$ or 5.59 radians

15.
$$A = Pe^{rt}$$
$$3P = Pe^{0.0575t}$$
$$3 = e^{0.0575t}$$
$$\ln 3 = \ln e^{0.0575t}$$
$$\ln 3 = 0.0575t$$
$$\dfrac{\ln 3}{0.0575} = t$$
$$t \approx 19.1 \text{ years}$$

16.
$$f(x) = \dfrac{2x+1}{x-3}$$
$$y = \dfrac{2x+1}{x-3}$$
$$x = \dfrac{2y+1}{y-3}$$
$$x(y-3) = 2y+1$$
$$xy - 3x = 2y+1$$
$$xy - 2y = 3x+1$$
$$y(x-2) = 3x+1$$
$$y = \dfrac{3x+1}{x-2}$$
$$f^{-1}(x) = \dfrac{3x+1}{x-2}$$

17. The third angle is:
$$B = 180° - 90° - 23° = 67°.$$
Since $\sin\theta = \dfrac{\text{opposite}}{\text{hypotenuse}}$,
$$\sin A = \sin 23° = \dfrac{12}{c}$$
$$c = \dfrac{12}{\sin 23°} \approx 30.71 \text{ and}$$
$$\sin B = \sin 67° = \dfrac{b}{30.71}$$
$$b = 30.71 \cdot \sin 67° \approx 28.27$$
The angles are 90°, 23°, and 67°.
The sides are 12, 30.71, and 28.27.

18. Solve $8.5 = \dfrac{12}{150} \cdot a$

where a is the adult dose.
$$a = \dfrac{(8.5) \cdot 150}{12}$$
$$= 106.25 \text{ mg}$$
$$a \approx 106 \text{ mg}$$

19. Let h be the height of the flagpole. Then
$$\tan 53° = \dfrac{h}{12}$$
$$h = 12 \cdot \tan 53°$$
$$h \approx 15.9 \text{ feet}$$

20. Answers may vary.

Chapter 7

Section 7.1

Check Point Exercises

1. Begin by finding B, the third angle of the triangle.

$$A + B + C = 180°$$
$$64° + B + 82° = 180°$$
$$146° + B = 180°$$
$$B = 34°$$

In this problem, we are given c and C:
$c = 14$ and $C = 82°$. Thus, we use the ratio
$\dfrac{c}{\sin C}$, or $\dfrac{14}{\sin 82°}$, to find the other two
sides. Use the Law of Sines to find a.

$$\frac{a}{\sin A} = \frac{c}{\sin C}$$
$$\frac{a}{\sin 64°} = \frac{14}{\sin 82°}$$
$$a = \frac{14 \sin 64°}{\sin 82°}$$
$$a \approx 13 \text{ centimeters}$$

Use the Law of Sines again, this time to find b.

$$\frac{b}{\sin B} = \frac{c}{\sin C}$$
$$\frac{b}{\sin 34°} = \frac{14}{\sin 82°}$$
$$b = \frac{14 \sin 34°}{\sin 82°}$$
$$b \approx 8 \text{ centimeters}$$

The solution is $B = 34°$, $a \approx 13$ centimeters, and $b \approx 8$ centimeters.

2. Begin by finding B.

$$A + B + C = 180°$$
$$40° + B + 22.5° = 180°$$
$$62.5° + B = 180°$$
$$B = 117.5°$$

In this problem, we are given that $b = 12$ and we find that $B = 117.5°$. Thus, we use the
ratio $\dfrac{b}{\sin B}$, or $\dfrac{12}{\sin 117.5°}$, to find the other
two sides. Use the Law of Sines to find a.

$$\frac{a}{\sin A} = \frac{b}{\sin B}$$
$$\frac{a}{\sin 40°} = \frac{12}{\sin 117.5°}$$
$$a = \frac{12 \sin 40°}{\sin 117.5°} \approx 9$$

Use the Law of Sines again, this time to find c.

$$\frac{c}{\sin C} = \frac{b}{\sin B}$$
$$\frac{c}{\sin 22.5°} = \frac{12}{\sin 117.5°}$$
$$c = \frac{12 \sin 22.5°}{\sin 117.5°} \approx 5$$

The solution is $B = 117.5°$, $a \approx 9$, and $c \approx 5$.

3. The known ratio is $\dfrac{a}{\sin A}$, or $\dfrac{47}{\sin 123°}$.
Because side c is given, we use the Law of Sines to find angle C,

$$\frac{a}{\sin A} = \frac{c}{\sin C}$$
$$\frac{47}{\sin 123°} = \frac{23}{\sin C}$$
$$47 \sin C = 23 \sin 123°$$
$$\sin C = \frac{23 \sin 123°}{47}$$
$$\sin C \approx 0.4104$$

There are two angles possible:
$C_1 \approx 24°$, $C_2 \approx 180° - 24° = 156°$
C_2 is impossible, since $123° + 156° = 279°$.
We find B using C, and the given
information $A = 123°$.
$B = 180° - C_1 - A \approx 180° - 24° - 123° = 33°$
Use the Law of Sines to find side b.

$$\frac{b}{\sin B} = \frac{a}{\sin A}$$
$$\frac{b}{\sin 33°} = \frac{47}{\sin 123°}$$
$$b = \frac{47 \sin 33°}{\sin 123°} \approx 31$$

There is one triangle and the solution is
C_1 (or C) $\approx 24°$, $B \approx 33°$, and $b \approx 31$.

4. The known ratio is $\dfrac{a}{\sin A}$, or $\dfrac{10}{\sin 50°}$.

Because side b is given, we use the Law of Sines to find angle B.

$$\frac{a}{\sin A} = \frac{b}{\sin B}$$

$$\frac{10}{\sin 50} = \frac{20}{\sin B}$$

$$10\sin B = 20\sin 50$$

$$\sin B = \frac{20\sin 50}{10} \approx 1.53$$

Because the sine can never exceed 1, there is no angle B for which $\sin B \approx 1.53$. There is no triangle with the given measurements.

5. The known ratio is $\dfrac{a}{\sin A}$, or $\dfrac{12}{\sin 35°}$.

Because side b is given, we use the Law of Sines to find angle B.

$$\frac{a}{\sin A} = \frac{b}{\sin B}$$

$$\frac{12}{\sin 35°} = \frac{16}{\sin B}$$

$$12\sin B = 16\sin 35°$$

$$\sin B = \frac{16\sin 35°}{12} \approx 0.7648$$

There are two angles possible:

$B_1 \approx 50°$, $B_2 \approx 180° - 50° = 130°$

There are two triangles:

$C_1 = 180° - A - B_1 \approx 180° - 35° - 50° = 95°$

$C_2 = 180° - A - B_2 \approx 180° - 35° - 130° = 15°$

We use the Law of Sines to find c_1 and c_2.

$$\frac{c_1}{\sin C_1} = \frac{a}{\sin A}$$

$$\frac{c_1}{\sin 95°} = \frac{12}{\sin 35°}$$

$$c_1 = \frac{12\sin 95°}{\sin 35°} \approx 21$$

$$\frac{c_2}{\sin C_2} = \frac{a}{\sin A}$$

$$\frac{c_2}{\sin 15°} = \frac{12}{\sin 35°}$$

$$c_2 = \frac{12\sin 15°}{\sin 35°} \approx 5$$

In one triangle, the solution is $B_1 \approx 50°$, $C_1 \approx 95°$, and $c_1 \approx 21$. In the other triangle, $B_2 \approx 130°$, $C_2 \approx 15°$, and $c_2 \approx 5$.

6. The area of the triangle is half the product of the lengths of the two sides times the sine of the included angle.

$$\text{Area} = \frac{1}{2}(8)(12)(\sin 135°) \approx 34$$

The area of the triangle is approximately 34 square meters.

7.

Using a north-south line, the interior angles are found as follows:

$A = 90° - 35° = 55°$

$B = 90° - 49° = 41°$

Find angle C using a 180° angle sum in the triangle.

$C = 180° - A - B = 180° - 55° - 41° = 84°$

The ratio $\dfrac{c}{\sin C}$, or $\dfrac{13}{\sin 84°}$ is now known.

We use this ratio and the Law of Sines to find a.

$$\frac{a}{\sin A} = \frac{c}{\sin C}$$

$$\frac{a}{\sin 55°} = \frac{13}{\sin 84°}$$

$$a = \frac{13\sin 55°}{\sin 84°} \approx 11$$

The fire is approximately 11 miles from station B.

Exercise Set 7.1

1. Begin by finding B.
$$A + B + C = 180°$$
$$42° + B + 96° = 180°$$
$$138° + B = 180°$$
$$B = 42°$$
Use the ratio $\dfrac{c}{\sin C}$, or $\dfrac{12}{\sin 96°}$, to find the other two sides. Use the Law of Sines to find a.
$$\frac{a}{\sin A} = \frac{c}{\sin C}$$
$$\frac{a}{\sin 42°} = \frac{12}{\sin 96°}$$
$$a = \frac{12\sin 42°}{\sin 96°}$$
$$a \approx 8.1$$
Use the Law of Sines again, this time to find b.
$$\frac{b}{\sin B} = \frac{c}{\sin C}$$
$$\frac{b}{\sin 42°} = \frac{12}{\sin 96°}$$
$$b = \frac{12\sin 42°}{\sin 96°}$$
$$b \approx 8.1$$
The solution is $B = 42°$, $a \approx 8.1$, and $b \approx 8.1$.

3. Begin by finding A.
$$A + B + C = 180°$$
$$A + 54° + 82° = 180°$$
$$A + 136° = 180°$$
$$A = 44°$$
Use the ratio $\dfrac{a}{\sin A}$, or $\dfrac{16}{\sin 44°}$, to find the other two sides. Use the Law of Sines to find b.
$$\frac{b}{\sin B} = \frac{a}{\sin A}$$
$$\frac{b}{\sin 54°} = \frac{16}{\sin 44°}$$
$$b = \frac{16\sin 54°}{\sin 44°}$$
$$b \approx 18.6$$

Use the Law of Sines again, this time to find c.
$$\frac{c}{\sin C} = \frac{a}{\sin A}$$
$$\frac{c}{\sin 82°} = \frac{16}{\sin 44°}$$
$$c = \frac{16\sin 82°}{\sin 44°}$$
$$c \approx 22.8$$
The solution is $A = 44°$, $b \approx 18.6$, and $c \approx 22.8$.

5. Begin by finding C.
$$A + B + C = 180°$$
$$48° + 37° + C = 180°$$
$$85° + C = 180°$$
$$C = 95°$$
Use the ratio $\dfrac{a}{\sin A}$, or $\dfrac{100}{\sin 48°}$, to find the other two sides. Use the Law of Sines to find b.
$$\frac{b}{\sin B} = \frac{a}{\sin A}$$
$$\frac{b}{\sin 37°} = \frac{100}{\sin 48°}$$
$$b = \frac{100\sin 37°}{\sin 48°}$$
$$b \approx 81.0$$
Use the Law of Sines again, this time to find c.
$$\frac{c}{\sin C} = \frac{a}{\sin A}$$
$$\frac{c}{\sin 95°} = \frac{100}{\sin 48°}$$
$$c = \frac{100\sin 95°}{\sin 48°}$$
$$c \approx 134.1$$
The solution is $C = 95°$, $b \approx 81.0$, and $c \approx 134.1$.

7. Begin by finding B.

$$A + B + C = 180°$$
$$38° + B + 102° = 180°$$
$$B + 140° = 180°$$
$$B = 40°$$

Use the ratio $\dfrac{a}{\sin A}$, or $\dfrac{20}{\sin 38°}$, to find the other two sides. Use the Law of Sines to find b.

$$\frac{b}{\sin B} = \frac{a}{\sin A}$$
$$\frac{b}{\sin 40°} = \frac{20}{\sin 38°}$$
$$b = \frac{20 \sin 40°}{\sin 38°}$$
$$b \approx 20.9$$

Use the Law of Sines again, this time to find c.

$$\frac{c}{\sin C} = \frac{a}{\sin A}$$
$$\frac{c}{\sin 102°} = \frac{20}{\sin 38°}$$
$$c = \frac{20 \sin 102°}{\sin 38°}$$
$$c \approx 31.8$$

The solution is $B = 40°$, $b \approx 20.9$, and $c \approx 31.8$.

9. Begin by finding C.

$$A + B + C = 180°$$
$$44° + 25° + C = 180°$$
$$69° + C = 180°$$
$$C = 111°$$

Use the ratio $\dfrac{a}{\sin A}$, or $\dfrac{12}{\sin 44°}$, to find the other two sides. Use the Law of Sines to find b.

$$\frac{b}{\sin B} = \frac{a}{\sin A}$$
$$\frac{b}{\sin 25°} = \frac{12}{\sin 44°}$$
$$b = \frac{12 \sin 25°}{\sin 44°}$$
$$b \approx 7.3$$

Use the Law of Sines again, this time to find c.

$$\frac{c}{\sin C} = \frac{a}{\sin A}$$
$$\frac{c}{\sin 111°} = \frac{12}{\sin 44°}$$
$$c = \frac{12 \sin 111°}{\sin 44°}$$
$$c \approx 16.1$$

The solution is $C = 111°$, $b \approx 7.3$, and $c \approx 16.1$.

11. Begin by finding A.

$$A + B + C = 180°$$
$$A + 85° + 15° = 180°$$
$$A + 100° = 180°$$
$$A = 80°$$

Use the ratio $\dfrac{b}{\sin B}$, or $\dfrac{40}{\sin 85°}$, to find the other two sides. Use the Law of Sines to find a.

$$\frac{a}{\sin A} = \frac{b}{\sin B}$$
$$\frac{a}{\sin 80°} = \frac{40}{\sin 85°}$$
$$a = \frac{40 \sin 80°}{\sin 85°}$$
$$a \approx 39.5$$

Use the Law of Sines again, this time to find c.

$$\frac{c}{\sin C} = \frac{b}{\sin B}$$
$$\frac{c}{\sin 15°} = \frac{40}{\sin 85°}$$
$$c = \frac{40 \sin 15°}{\sin 85°}$$
$$c \approx 10.4$$

The solution is $A = 80°$, $a \approx 39.5$, and $c \approx 10.4$.

13. Begin by finding B.
$$A + B + C = 180°$$
$$115° + B + 35° = 180°$$
$$B + 150° = 180°$$
$$B = 30°$$

Use the ratio $\dfrac{c}{\sin C}$, or $\dfrac{200}{\sin 35°}$, to find the other two sides. Use the Law of Sines to find a.
$$\frac{a}{\sin A} = \frac{c}{\sin C}$$
$$\frac{a}{\sin 115°} = \frac{200}{\sin 35°}$$
$$a = \frac{200 \sin 115°}{\sin 35°}$$
$$a \approx 316.0$$

Use the Law of Sines again, this time to find b.
$$\frac{b}{\sin B} = \frac{c}{\sin C}$$
$$\frac{b}{\sin 30°} = \frac{200}{\sin 35°}$$
$$b = \frac{200 \sin 30°}{\sin 35°}$$
$$b \approx 174.3$$

The solution is $B = 30°$, $a \approx 316.0$, and $b \approx 174.3$.

15. Begin by finding C.
$$A + B + C = 180°$$
$$65° + 65° + C = 180°$$
$$130° + C = 180°$$
$$C = 50°$$

Use the ratio $\dfrac{c}{\sin C}$, or $\dfrac{6}{\sin 50°}$, to find the other two sides. Use the Law of Sines to find a.
$$\frac{a}{\sin A} = \frac{c}{\sin C}$$
$$\frac{a}{\sin 65°} = \frac{6}{\sin 50°}$$
$$a = \frac{6 \sin 65°}{\sin 50°}$$
$$a \approx 7.1$$

Use the Law of Sines to find angle B.
$$\frac{b}{\sin B} = \frac{c}{\sin C}$$
$$\frac{b}{\sin 65°} = \frac{6}{\sin 50°}$$
$$b = \frac{6 \sin 65°}{\sin 50°}$$
$$b \approx 7.1$$

The solution is $C = 50°$, $a \approx 7.1$, and $b \approx 7.1$.

17. The known ratio is $\dfrac{a}{\sin A}$, or $\dfrac{20}{\sin 40°}$.

We use the Law of Sines to find angle B.
$$\frac{a}{\sin A} = \frac{b}{\sin B}$$
$$\frac{20}{\sin 40°} = \frac{15}{\sin B}$$
$$20 \sin B = 15 \sin 40°$$
$$\sin B = \frac{15 \sin 40°}{20}$$
$$\sin B \approx 0.4821$$

There are two angles possible:
$$B_1 \approx 29°, \ B_2 \approx 180° - 29° = 151°$$

B_2 is impossible, since $40° + 151° = 191°$.

We find C using B_1 and the given information $A = 40°$.
$$C = 180° - B_1 - A \approx 180° - 29° - 40° = 111°$$

Use the Law of Sines to find side c.
$$\frac{c}{\sin C} = \frac{a}{\sin A}$$
$$\frac{c}{\sin 111°} = \frac{20}{\sin 40°}$$
$$c = \frac{20 \sin 111°}{\sin 40°} \approx 29.0$$

There is one triangle and the solution is B_1 (or B) $\approx 29°$, $C \approx 111°$, and $c \approx 29.0$.

19. The known ratio is $\dfrac{a}{\sin A}$, or $\dfrac{10}{\sin 63°}$.

We use the Law of Sines to find angle C.

$$\frac{a}{\sin A} = \frac{c}{\sin C}$$

$$\frac{10}{\sin 63°} = \frac{8.9}{\sin C}$$

$$10\sin C = 8.9\sin 63°$$

$$\sin C = \frac{8.9\sin 63°}{10}$$

$$\sin C \approx 0.7930$$

There are two angles possible:

$C_1 \approx 52°$, $C_2 \approx 180° - 52° = 128°$

C_2 is impossible, since $63° + 128° = 191°$.
We find B using C_1 and the given
information $A = 63°$.

$B = 180° - C_1 - A \approx 180° - 52° - 63° = 65°$

Use the Law of Sines to find side b.

$$\frac{b}{\sin B} = \frac{a}{\sin A}$$

$$\frac{b}{\sin 65°} = \frac{10}{\sin 63°}$$

$$b = \frac{10\sin 65°}{\sin 63°} \approx 10.2$$

There is one triangle and the solution is
C_1 (or C) $\approx 52°$, $B \approx 65°$, and $b \approx 10.2$.

21. The known ratio is $\dfrac{a}{\sin A}$, or $\dfrac{42.1}{\sin 112°}$.

We use the Law of Sines to find angle C.

$$\frac{a}{\sin A} = \frac{c}{\sin C}$$

$$\frac{42.1}{\sin 112°} = \frac{37}{\sin C}$$

$$42.1\sin C = 37\sin 112°$$

$$\sin C = \frac{37\sin 112°}{42.1}$$

$$\sin C \approx 0.8149$$

There are two angles possible:

$C_1 \approx 55°$, $C_2 \approx 180° - 55° = 125°$

C_2 is impossible, since $112° + 125° = 237°$.
We find B using C_1 and the given
information $A = 112°$.

$B = 180° - C_1 - A \approx 180° - 55° - 112° = 13°$

Use the Law of Sines to find b.

$$\frac{b}{\sin B} = \frac{a}{\sin A}$$

$$\frac{b}{\sin 13°} = \frac{42.1}{\sin 112°}$$

$$b = \frac{42.1\sin 13°}{\sin 112°} \approx 10.2$$

There is one triangle and the solution is
C_1 (or C) $\approx 55°$, $B \approx 13°$, and $b \approx 10.2$.

23. The known ratio is $\dfrac{a}{\sin A}$, or $\dfrac{10}{\sin 30°}$.

We use the Law of Sines to find angle B.

$$\frac{a}{\sin A} = \frac{b}{\sin B}$$

$$\frac{10}{\sin 30°} = \frac{40}{\sin B}$$

$$10\sin B = 40\sin 30°$$

$$\sin B = \frac{40\sin 30°}{10} = 2$$

Because the sine can never exceed 1, there is
no angle B for which $\sin B = 2$. There is no
triangle with the given measurements.

25. The known ratio is $\dfrac{a}{\sin A}$, or $\dfrac{16}{\sin 60°}$.

We use the Law of Sines to find angle B.

$$\frac{a}{\sin A} = \frac{b}{\sin B}$$

$$\frac{16}{\sin 60°} = \frac{18}{\sin B}$$

$$16\sin B = 18\sin 60°$$

$$\sin B = \frac{18\sin 60°}{16}$$

$$\sin B \approx 0.9743$$

There are two angles possible:

$B_1 \approx 77°$, $B_2 \approx 180° - 77° = 103°$

There are two triangles:

$C_1 = 180° - B_1 - A \approx 180° - 77° - 60° = 43°$

$C_2 = 180° - B_2 - A \approx 180° - 103° - 60° = 17°$

Use the Law of Sines to find c_1 and c_2.

$$\frac{c_1}{\sin C_1} = \frac{a}{\sin A}$$

$$\frac{c_1}{\sin 43°} = \frac{16}{\sin 60°}$$

$$c_1 = \frac{16\sin 43°}{\sin 60°} \approx 12.6$$

$$\frac{c_2}{\sin C_2} = \frac{a}{\sin A}$$

$$\frac{c_2}{\sin 17°} = \frac{16}{\sin 60°}$$

$$c_2 = \frac{16\sin 17°}{\sin 60°} \approx 5.4$$

In one triangle, the solution is
$B_1 \approx 77°$, $C_1 \approx 43°$, and $c_1 \approx 12.6$. In the
other triangle, $B_2 \approx 103°$, $C_2 \approx 17°$, and
$c_2 \approx 5.4$.

27. The known ratio is $\dfrac{a}{\sin A}$, or $\dfrac{12}{\sin 37°}$.
We use the Law of Sines to find angle B.

$$\frac{a}{\sin A} = \frac{b}{\sin B}$$

$$\frac{12}{\sin 37°} = \frac{16.1}{\sin B}$$

$$12\sin B = 16.1\sin 37°$$

$$\sin B = \frac{16.1\sin 37°}{12}$$

$$\sin B \approx 0.8074$$

There are two angles possible:
$B_1 \approx 54°$, $B_2 \approx 180° - 54° = 126°$
There are two triangles:
$C_1 = 180° - B_1 - A \approx 180° - 54° - 37° = 89°$
$C_2 = 180° - B_2 - A \approx 180° - 126° - 37° = 17°$
Use the Law of Sines to find c_1 and c_2.

$$\frac{c_1}{\sin C_1} = \frac{a}{\sin A}$$

$$\frac{c_1}{\sin 89°} = \frac{12}{\sin 37°}$$

$$c_1 = \frac{12\sin 89°}{\sin 37°} \approx 19.9$$

$$\frac{c_2}{\sin C_2} = \frac{a}{\sin A}$$

$$\frac{c_2}{\sin 17°} = \frac{12}{\sin 37°}$$

$$c_2 = \frac{12\sin 17°}{\sin 37°} \approx 5.8$$

In one triangle, the solution is
$B_1 \approx 54°$, $C_1 \approx 89°$, and $c_1 \approx 19.9$. In the
other triangle, $B_2 \approx 126°$, $C_2 \approx 17°$, and
$c_2 \approx 5.8$.

29. The known ratio is $\dfrac{a}{\sin A}$, or $\dfrac{22}{\sin 58°}$.
We use the Law of Sines to find angle C.

$$\frac{a}{\sin A} = \frac{c}{\sin C}$$

$$\frac{22}{\sin 58°} = \frac{24.1}{\sin C}$$

$$22\sin C = 24.1\sin 58°$$

$$\sin C = \frac{24.1\sin 58°}{22}$$

$$\sin C \approx 0.9290$$

There are two angles possible:
$C_1 \approx 68°$, $C_2 \approx 180° - 68° = 112°$
There are two triangles:
$B_1 = 180° - C_1 - A \approx 180° - 68° - 58° = 54°$
$B_2 = 180° - C_2 - A \approx 180° - 112° - 58° = 10°$
We use the Law of Sines to find b_1 and b_2.

$$\frac{b_1}{\sin B_1} = \frac{a}{\sin A}$$

$$\frac{b_1}{\sin 54°} = \frac{22}{\sin 58°}$$

$$b_1 = \frac{22\sin 54°}{\sin 58°} \approx 21.0$$

$$\frac{b_2}{\sin B_2} = \frac{a}{\sin A}$$

$$\frac{b_2}{\sin 10°} = \frac{22}{\sin 58°}$$

$$b_2 = \frac{22\sin 10°}{\sin 58°} \approx 4.5$$

In one triangle, the solution is
$C_1 \approx 68°$, $B_1 \approx 54°$, and $b_1 \approx 21.0$. In the
other triangle, $C_2 \approx 112°$, $B_2 \approx 10°$, and
$b_2 \approx 4.5$.

31. The known ratio is $\dfrac{a}{\sin A}$, or $\dfrac{9.3}{\sin 18°}$.

We use the Law of Sines to find angle B.

$$\frac{a}{\sin A} = \frac{b}{\sin B}$$

$$\frac{9.3}{\sin 18°} = \frac{41}{\sin B}$$

$$9.3 \sin B = 41 \sin 18°$$

$$\sin B = \frac{41 \sin 18°}{9.3} \approx 1.36$$

Because the sine can never exceed 1, there is no angle B for which $\sin B = 1.36$. There is no triangle with the given measurements.

33. Area $= \dfrac{1}{2} bc \sin A = \dfrac{1}{2}(20)(40)(\sin 48°) \approx 297$

The area of the triangle is approximately 297 square feet.

35. Area $= \dfrac{1}{2} ac \sin B = \dfrac{1}{2}(3)(6)(\sin 36°) \approx 5$

The area of the triangle is approximately 5 square yards.

37. Area $= \dfrac{1}{2} ab \sin C = \dfrac{1}{2}(4)(6)(\sin 124°) \approx 10$

The area of the triangle is approximately 10 square meters.

39.

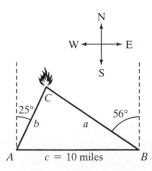

Using a north-south line, the interior angles are found as follows:

$A = 90° - 25° = 65°$

$B = 90° - 56° = 34°$

Find angle C using a 180° angle sum in the triangle.

$C = 180° - A - B = 180° - 65° - 34° = 81°$

The ratio $\dfrac{c}{\sin C}$, or $\dfrac{10}{\sin 81°}$, is now known.

We use this ratio and the Law of Sines to find b and a.

$$\frac{b}{\sin B} = \frac{c}{\sin C}$$

$$\frac{b}{\sin 34°} = \frac{10}{\sin 81°}$$

$$b = \frac{10 \sin 34°}{\sin 81°} \approx 6$$

Station A is about 6 miles from the fire.

$$\frac{a}{\sin A} = \frac{c}{\sin C}$$

$$\frac{a}{\sin 65°} = \frac{10}{\sin 81°}$$

$$a = \frac{10 \sin 65°}{\sin 81°} \approx 9$$

Station B is about 9 miles from the fire.

41.

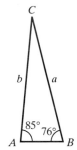

$c = 1200$ yards

Using the figure,

$C = 180° - A - B = 180° - 85° - 76° = 19°$

The ratio $\dfrac{c}{\sin C}$, or $\dfrac{1200}{\sin 19°}$, is now known.

We use this ratio and the Law of Sines to find a and b.

$$\frac{a}{\sin A} = \frac{c}{\sin C}$$

$$\frac{a}{\sin 85°} = \frac{1200}{\sin 19°}$$

$$a = \frac{1200 \sin 85°}{\sin 19°} \approx 3672$$

$$\frac{b}{\sin B} = \frac{c}{\sin C}$$

$$\frac{b}{\sin 76°} = \frac{1200}{\sin 19°}$$

$$b = \frac{1200 \sin 76°}{\sin 19°} \approx 3576$$

The platform is about 3672 yards from one end of the beach and 3576 yards from the other.

43. According to the figure,
$$C = 180° - A - B = 180° - 84.7° - 50° = 45.3°$$
The ratio $\dfrac{c}{\sin C}$, or $\dfrac{171}{\sin 45.3°}$, is now known. We use this ratio and the Law of Sines to find b.
$$\frac{b}{\sin B} = \frac{c}{\sin C}$$
$$\frac{b}{\sin 50°} = \frac{171}{\sin 45.3°}$$
$$b = \frac{171 \sin 50°}{\sin 45.3°} \approx 184$$
The distance is about 184 feet.

45. The ratio $\dfrac{b}{\sin B}$, or $\dfrac{562}{\sin 85.3°}$, is known. We use this ratio, the figure, and the Law of Sines to find c.
$$\frac{c}{\sin C} = \frac{b}{\sin B}$$
$$\frac{c}{\sin 5.7°} = \frac{562}{\sin 85.3°}$$
$$c = \frac{562 \sin 5.7°}{\sin 85.3°} \approx 56$$
The toss was about 56 feet.

47.

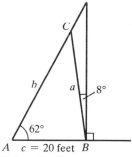

$A \quad c = 20 \text{ feet} \quad B$

Using the figure,
$$B = 90° - 8° = 82°$$
$$C = 180° - A - B = 180° - 62° - 82° = 36°$$
The ratio $\dfrac{c}{\sin C}$, or $\dfrac{20}{\sin 36°}$, is now known. We use this ratio and the Law of Sines to find a.

$$\frac{a}{\sin A} = \frac{c}{\sin C}$$
$$\frac{a}{\sin 62°} = \frac{20}{\sin 36°}$$
$$a = \frac{20 \sin 62°}{\sin 36°} \approx 30$$
The length of the pole is about 30 feet.

49. a. Using the figure and the measurements shown,
$$B = 180° - 44° = 136°$$
$$C = 180° - B - A = 180° - 136° - 37° = 7°$$
The ratio $\dfrac{c}{\sin C}$, or $\dfrac{100}{\sin 7°}$, is now known. We use this ratio and the Law of Sines to find a.
$$\frac{a}{\sin A} = \frac{c}{\sin C}$$
$$\frac{a}{\sin 37°} = \frac{100}{\sin 7°}$$
$$a = \frac{100 \sin 37°}{\sin 7°} \approx 494$$
To the nearest foot, $a = 494$ feet.

b. Let $a = 494$ be the hypotenuse of the right triangle. Then if h represents the height of the tree,
$$\frac{h}{\sin 44°} = \frac{494}{\sin 90°}$$
$$h = \frac{494 \sin 44°}{\sin 90°} \approx 343$$
A typical redwood tree is about 343 feet.

51.

Using the figure,
$B = 90° - 62° = 28°$

The known ratio is $\dfrac{b}{\sin B}$, or $\dfrac{5}{\sin 28°}$.

We use the Law of Sines to find angle C.

$$\frac{b}{\sin B} = \frac{c}{\sin C}$$

$$\frac{5}{\sin 28°} = \frac{7}{\sin C}$$

$$5\sin C = 7\sin 28°$$

$$\sin C = \frac{7\sin 28°}{5} \approx 0.6573$$

There are two angles possible:
$C_1 \approx 41°,\ C_2 \approx 180° - 41° = 139°$

There are two triangles:
$A_1 = 180° - C_1 - B \approx 180° - 41° - 28° = 111°$
$A_2 = 180° - C_2 - B \approx 180° - 139° - 28° = 13°$

We use the Law of Sines to find a_1 and a_2.

$$\frac{a_1}{\sin A_1} = \frac{b}{\sin B}$$

$$\frac{a_1}{\sin 111°} = \frac{5}{\sin 28°}$$

$$a_1 = \frac{5\sin 111°}{\sin 28°} \approx 9.9$$

$$\frac{a_2}{\sin A_2} = \frac{b}{\sin B}$$

$$\frac{a_2}{\sin 13°} = \frac{5}{\sin 28°}$$

$$a_2 = \frac{5\sin 13°}{\sin 28°} \approx 2.4$$

The boat is either 9.9 miles or 2.4 miles from lighthouse B, to the nearest tenth of a mile.

53.–61. Answers may vary.

63. Yes. Explanations may vary.

65.

Using the figure,
$A = 180° - 150° = 30°$
Using the Law of Sines we have,

$$\frac{d}{\sin A} = \frac{36}{\sin 90°}$$

$$\frac{d}{\sin 30°} = \frac{36}{\sin 90°}$$

$$d = \frac{36\sin 30°}{\sin 90°} = 18$$

$$CC' = 18 + 5 + 18 = 41$$

The wingspan CC' is 41 feet.

Section 7.2

Checkpoint Exercises

1. Apply the three-step procedure for solving a SAS triangle. Use the Law of Cosines to find the side opposite the given angle. Thus, we will find a.

$$a^2 = b^2 + c^2 - 2bc\cos A$$

$$a^2 = 7^2 + 8^2 - 2(7)(8)\cos 120°$$

$$= 49 + 64 - 112(-0.5)$$

$$= 169$$

$$a = \sqrt{169} = 13$$

Use the Law of Sines to find the angle opposite the shorter of the two sides. Thus, we will find acute angle B.

$$\frac{b}{\sin B} = \frac{a}{\sin A}$$

$$\frac{7}{\sin B} = \frac{13}{\sin 120°}$$

$$13\sin B = 7\sin 120°$$

$$\sin B = \frac{7\sin 120°}{13} \approx 0.4663$$

$$B \approx 28°$$

Find the third angle.
$C = 180° - A - B \approx 180° - 120° - 28° = 32°$
The solution is $a = 13, B \approx 28°,$ and $C \approx 32°$.

2. Apply the three-step procedure for solving a SSS triangle. Use the Law of Cosines to find the angle opposite the longest side. Thus, we will find angle B.

    $$b^2 = a^2 + c^2 - 2ac \cos B$$
    $$2ac \cos B = a^2 + c^2 - b^2$$
    $$\cos B = \frac{a^2 + c^2 - b^2}{2ac}$$
    $$\cos B = \frac{8^2 + 5^2 - 10^2}{2 \cdot 8 \cdot 5} = -\frac{11}{80}$$
    $$\cos^{-1}\left(\frac{11}{80}\right) \approx 82.1°$$

    B is obtuse, since $\cos B$ is negative.
    $B \approx 180° - 82.1° = 97.9°$
    Use the Law of Sines to find either of the two remaining acute angles. We will find angle A.

    $$\frac{a}{\sin A} = \frac{b}{\sin B}$$
    $$\frac{8}{\sin A} = \frac{10}{\sin 97.9°}$$
    $$10 \sin A = 8 \sin 97.9°$$
    $$\sin A = \frac{8 \sin 97.9°}{10} \approx 0.7924$$
    $$A \approx 52.4°$$

    Find the third angle.
    $C = 180° - A - B \approx 180° - 52.4° - 97.9°$
    $= 29.7°$
    The solution is $B \approx 97.9°$, $A \approx 52.4°$, and $C \approx 29.7°$.

3. The plane flying 400 miles per hour travels $400 \cdot 2 = 800$ miles in 2 hours. Similarly, the other plane travels 700 miles.

    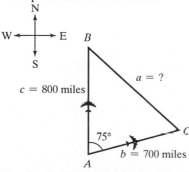

    Use the figure and the Law of Cosines to find a in this SAS situation.

    $$a^2 = b^2 + c^2 - 2bc \cos A$$
    $$a^2 = 700^2 + 800^2 - 2(700)(800) \cos 75°$$
    $$\approx 840,123$$
    $$a \approx \sqrt{840,123} \approx 917$$

    After 2 hours, the planes are approximately 917 miles apart.

4. Begin by calculating one-half the perimeter:

    $$s = \frac{1}{2}(a + b + c) = \frac{1}{2}(6 + 16 + 18) = 20$$

    Use Heron's formula to find the area

    $$\text{Area} = \sqrt{s(s-a)(s-b)(s-c)}$$
    $$= \sqrt{20(20-6)(20-16)(20-18)}$$
    $$= \sqrt{2240} \approx 47$$

    The area of the triangle is approximately 47 square meters.

Exercise Set 7.2

1. Apply the three-step procedure for solving a SAS triangle. Use the Law of Cosines to find the side opposite the given angle. Thus, we will find a.

    $$a^2 = b^2 + c^2 - 2bc \cos A$$
    $$a^2 = 4^2 + 8^2 - 2(4)(8) \cos 46°$$
    $$a^2 = 16 + 64 - 64(\cos 46°)$$
    $$a^2 \approx 35.54$$
    $$a \approx \sqrt{35.54} \approx 6.0$$

    Use the Law of Sines to find the angle opposite the shorter of the two given sides. Thus, we will find acute angle B.

    $$\frac{b}{\sin B} = \frac{a}{\sin A}$$
    $$\frac{4}{\sin B} = \frac{\sqrt{35.54}}{\sin 46°}$$
    $$\sqrt{35.54} \sin B = 4 \sin 46°$$
    $$\sin B = \frac{4 \sin 46°}{\sqrt{35.54}} \approx 0.4827$$
    $$B \approx 29°$$

    Find the third angle.
    $C = 180° - A - B \approx 180° - 46° - 29° = 105°$
    The solution is $a \approx 6.0$, $B \approx 29°$, and $C \approx 105°$.

3. Apply the three-step procedure for solving a SAS triangle. Use the Law of Cosines to find the side opposite the given angle. Thus, we will find c.

$c^2 = a^2 + b^2 - 2ab\cos C$

$c^2 = 6^2 + 4^2 - 2(6)(4)\cos 96°$

$c^2 = 36 + 16 - 48(\cos 96°)$

$c^2 \approx 57.02$

$c \approx \sqrt{57.02} \approx 7.6$

Use the Law of Sines to find the angle opposite the shorter of the two given sides. Thus, we will find acute angle B.

$$\frac{b}{\sin B} = \frac{c}{\sin C}$$

$$\frac{4}{\sin B} = \frac{\sqrt{57.02}}{\sin 96°}$$

$\sqrt{57.02}\sin B = 4\sin 96°$

$$\sin B = \frac{4\sin 96°}{\sqrt{57.02}} \approx 0.5268$$

$$B \approx 32°$$

Find the third angle.

$A = 180° - B - C \approx 180° - 32° - 96° = 52°$

The solution is $c \approx 7.6, A \approx 52°,$ and $B \approx 32°$.

5. Apply the three-step procedure for solving a SSS triangle. Use the Law of Cosines to find the angle opposite the longest side. Since two sides have length 8, we can begin by finding angle B or C.

$b^2 = a^2 + c^2 - 2ac\cos B$

$\cos B = \dfrac{a^2 + c^2 - b^2}{2ac}$

$\cos B = \dfrac{6^2 + 8^2 - 8^2}{2 \cdot 6 \cdot 8} = \dfrac{36}{96} = \dfrac{3}{8}$

$B \approx 68°$

Use the Law of Sines to find either of the two remaining acute angles. We will find angle A.

$$\frac{a}{\sin A} = \frac{b}{\sin B}$$

$$\frac{6}{\sin A} = \frac{8}{\sin 68°}$$

$8\sin A = 6\sin 68°$

$$\sin A = \frac{6\sin 68°}{8} \approx 0.6954$$

$$A \approx 44°$$

Find the third angle.

$C = 180° - B - A \approx 180° - 68° - 44° = 68°$

The solution is $A \approx 44°, B \approx 68°,$ and $C \approx 68°$.

7. Apply the three-step procedure for solving a SSS triangle. Use the Law of Cosines to find the angle opposite the longest side. Thus, we will find angle A

$a^2 = b^2 + c^2 - 2bc\cos A$

$\cos A = \dfrac{b^2 + c^2 - a^2}{2bc}$

$\cos A = \dfrac{4^2 + 3^2 - 6^2}{2 \cdot 4 \cdot 3} = -\dfrac{11}{24}$

A is obtuse, since $\cos A$ is negative.

$\cos^{-1}\left(\dfrac{11}{24}\right) \approx 63°$

$A \approx 180° - 63° = 117°$

Use the Law of Sines to find either of the two remaining acute angles. We will find angle B.

$$\frac{b}{\sin B} = \frac{a}{\sin A}$$

$$\frac{4}{\sin B} = \frac{6}{\sin 117°}$$

$6\sin B = 4\sin 117°$

$$\sin B = \frac{4\sin 117°}{6} \approx 0.5940$$

$$B \approx 36°$$

Find the third angle.

$C = 180° - B - A \approx 180° - 36° - 117° = 27°$

The solution is $A \approx 117°, B \approx 36°,$ and $C \approx 27°$.

9. Apply the three-step procedure for solving a SAS triangle. Use the Law of Cosines to find the side opposite the given angle. Thus, we will find c.

$$c^2 = a^2 + b^2 - 2ab\cos C$$

$$c^2 = 5^2 + 7^2 - 2(5)(7)\cos 42°$$

$$c^2 = 25 + 49 - 70(\cos 42°)$$

$$c^2 \approx 21.98$$

$$c \approx \sqrt{21.98} \approx 4.7$$

Use the Law of Sines to find the angle opposite the shorter of the two given sides. Thus, we will find acute angle A.

$$\frac{a}{\sin A} = \frac{c}{\sin C}$$

$$\frac{5}{\sin A} = \frac{\sqrt{21.98}}{\sin 42°}$$

$$\sqrt{21.98}\sin A = 5\sin 42°$$

$$\sin A = \frac{5\sin 42°}{\sqrt{21.98}} \approx 0.7136$$

$$A \approx 46°$$

Find the third angle.
$$B = 180° - C - A \approx 180° - 42° - 46° = 92°$$
The solution is $c \approx 4.7, A \approx 46°$, and $B \approx 92°$.

11. Apply the three-step procedure for solving a SAS triangle. Use the Law of Cosines to find the side opposite the given angle. Thus, we will find a.

$$a^2 = b^2 + c^2 - 2bc\cos A$$

$$a^2 = 5^2 + 3^2 - 2(5)(3)\cos 102°$$

$$a^2 = 25 + 9 - 30(\cos 102°)$$

$$a^2 \approx 40.24$$

$$a \approx \sqrt{40.24} \approx 6.3$$

Use the Law of Sines to find the angle opposite the shorter of the two given sides. Thus, we will find acute angle C.

$$\frac{c}{\sin C} = \frac{a}{\sin A}$$

$$\frac{3}{\sin C} = \frac{\sqrt{40.24}}{\sin 102°}$$

$$\sqrt{40.24}\sin C = 3\sin 102°$$

$$\sin C = \frac{3\sin 102°}{\sqrt{40.24}} \approx 0.4626$$

$$C \approx 28°$$

Find the third angle.
$$B = 180° - C - A \approx 180° - 28° - 102° = 50°$$
The solution is $a \approx 6.3, C \approx 28°$, and $B \approx 50°$.

13. Apply the three-step procedure for solving a SAS triangle. Use the Law of Cosines to find the side opposite the given angle. Thus, we will find b.

$$b^2 = a^2 + c^2 - 2ac\cos B$$

$$b^2 = 6^2 + 5^2 - 2(6)(5)\cos 50°$$

$$b^2 = 36 + 25 - 60(\cos 50°)$$

$$b^2 \approx 22.43$$

$$b \approx \sqrt{22.43} \approx 4.7$$

Use the Law of Sines to find the angle opposite the shorter of the two given sides. Thus, we will find acute angle C.

$$\frac{c}{\sin C} = \frac{b}{\sin B}$$

$$\frac{5}{\sin C} = \frac{\sqrt{22.43}}{\sin 50°}$$

$$\sqrt{22.43}\sin C = 5\sin 50°$$

$$\sin C = \frac{5\sin 50°}{\sqrt{22.43}} \approx 0.8087$$

$$C \approx 54°$$

Find the third angle.
$$A = 180° - C - B \approx 180° - 54° - 50° = 76°$$
The solution is $b \approx 4.7, C \approx 54°$, and $A \approx 76°$.

15. Apply the three-step procedure for solving a SAS triangle. Use the Law of Cosines to find the side opposite the given angle. Thus, we will find b.

$b^2 = a^2 + c^2 - 2ac\cos 90°$

$b^2 = 5^2 + 2^2 - 2(5)(2)\cos 90°$

$b^2 = 25 + 4 - 20\cos 90°$

$b^2 = 29$

$\quad b = \sqrt{29} \approx 5.4$

(use exact value of b from previous step) Use the Law of Sines to find the angle opposite the shorter of the two given sides. Thus, we will find acute angle C.

$\dfrac{c}{\sin C} = \dfrac{b}{\sin B}$

$\dfrac{2}{\sin C} = \dfrac{\sqrt{29}}{\sin 90°}$

$\sqrt{29}\sin C = 2\sin 90°$

$\quad \sin C = \dfrac{2\sin 90°}{\sqrt{29}} \approx 0.3714$

$\quad\quad C \approx 22°$

Find the third angle.

$A = 180° - C - B \approx 180° - 22° - 90° = 68°$

The solution is $b \approx 5.4, C \approx 22°,$ and $A \approx 68°$.

17. Apply the three-step procedure for solving a SSS triangle. Use the Law of Cosines to find the angle opposite the longest side. Thus, we will find C.

$c^2 = a^2 + b^2 - 2ab\cos C$

$\cos C = \dfrac{a^2 + b^2 - c^2}{2ab}$

$\cos C = \dfrac{5^2 + 7^2 - 10^2}{2 \cdot 5 \cdot 7} = -\dfrac{13}{35}$

C is obtuse, since $\cos C$ is negative.

$\cos^{-1}\left(\dfrac{13}{35}\right) \approx 68°$

$C \approx 180° - 68° = 112°$

Use the Law of Sines to find either of the two remaining angles. We will find angle A.

$\dfrac{a}{\sin A} = \dfrac{c}{\sin C}$

$\dfrac{5}{\sin A} = \dfrac{10}{\sin 112°}$

$10\sin A = 5\sin 112°$

$\quad \sin A = \dfrac{5\sin 112°}{10} \approx 0.4636$

$\quad\quad A \approx 28°$

Find the third angle.

$B = 180° - C - A \approx 180° - 112° - 28° = 40°$

The solution is $C \approx 112°, A \approx 28°,$ and $B \approx 40°$.

19. Apply the three-step procedure for solving a SSS triangle. Use the Law of Cosines to find the angle opposite the longest side. Thus, we will find B.

$\quad b^2 = a^2 + c^2 - 2ac\cos B$

$\cos B = \dfrac{a^2 + c^2 - b^2}{2ac}$

$\cos B = \dfrac{3^2 + 8^2 - 9^2}{2 \cdot 3 \cdot 8} = -\dfrac{1}{6}$

B is obtuse, since $\cos B$ is negative.

$\cos^{-1}\left(\dfrac{1}{6}\right) \approx 80°$

$B \approx 180° - 80° = 100°$

Use the Law of Sines to find either of the two remaining angles. We will find angle A.

$\dfrac{a}{\sin A} = \dfrac{b}{\sin B}$

$\dfrac{3}{\sin A} = \dfrac{9}{\sin 100°}$

$9\sin A = 3\sin 100°$

$\quad \sin A = \dfrac{3\sin 100°}{9} \approx 0.3283$

$\quad\quad A \approx 19°$

Find the third angle.

$C = 180° - B - A \approx 180° - 100° - 19° = 61°$

The solution is $B \approx 100°, A \approx 19°,$ and $C \approx 61°$.

21. Apply the three-step procedure for solving a SSS triangle. Use the Law of Cosines to find any of the three angles, since each side has the same measure.

$$a^2 = b^2 + c^2 - 2bc \cos A$$

$$\cos A = \frac{b^2 + c^2 - a^2}{2bc}$$

$$\cos A = \frac{3^2 + 3^2 - 3^2}{2 \cdot 3 \cdot 3} = \frac{1}{2}$$

$$A = 60°$$

Use the Law of Sines to find either of the two remaining angles. We will find angle B.

$$\frac{b}{\sin B} = \frac{a}{\sin A}$$

$$\frac{3}{\sin B} = \frac{3}{\sin 60°}$$

$$3 \sin B = 3 \sin 60°$$

$$\sin B = \sin 60°$$

$$B = 60°$$

Find the third angle.

$$C = 180° - A - B = 180° - 60° - 60° - 60°$$

The solution is $A = 60°, B = 60°$, and $C = 60°$.

23. Apply the three-step procedure for solving a SSS triangle. Use the Law of Cosines to find the angle opposite the longest side. Thus, we will find A.

$$a^2 = b^2 + c^2 - 2bc \cos A$$

$$\cos A = \frac{b^2 + c^2 - a^2}{2bc}$$

$$\cos A = \frac{22^2 + 50^2 - 73^2}{2 \cdot 22 \cdot 50} = -\frac{469}{440}$$

Since $\cos A$ must be between -1 and 1, no such triangle exists.

25. $s = \frac{1}{2}(a+b+c) = \frac{1}{2}(4+4+2) = 5$

$$\begin{aligned} \text{Area} &= \sqrt{s(s-a)(s-b)(s-c)} \\ &= \sqrt{5(5-4)(5-4)(5-2)} \\ &= \sqrt{15} \approx 4 \end{aligned}$$

The area of the triangle is approximately 4 square feet.

27. $s = \frac{1}{2}(a+b+c) = \frac{1}{2}(14+12+4) = 15$

$$\begin{aligned} \text{Area} &= \sqrt{s(s-a)(s-b)(s-c)} \\ &= \sqrt{15(15-14)(15-12)(15-4)} \\ &= \sqrt{495} \approx 22 \end{aligned}$$

The area of the triangle is approximately 22 square meters.

29. $s = \frac{1}{2}(a+b+c) = \frac{1}{2}(11+9+7) = 13.5$

$$\begin{aligned} \text{Area} &= \sqrt{s(s-a)(s-b)(s-c)} \\ &= \sqrt{13.5(13.5-11)(13.5-9)(13.5-7)} \\ &= \sqrt{987.1875} \approx 31 \end{aligned}$$

The area of the triangle is approximately 31 square yards.

31. Let b = the distance between the ships after three hours.

After three hours, the ship traveling 14 miles per hour has gone $3 \cdot 14$ or 42 miles. Similarly, the ship traveling 10 miles per hour has gone 30 miles.

Using the figure,

$$B = 180° - 75° + 12° = 117°$$

$$b^2 = a^2 + c^2 - 2ac \cos B$$

$$b^2 = 30^2 + 42^2 - 2(30)(42)\cos 117° \approx 3808$$

$$b \approx 61.7$$

After three hours, the ships will be about 61.7 miles apart.

33. Let b = the distance across the lake.
$$b^2 = a^2 + c^2 - 2ac \cos B$$
$$b^2 = 160^2 + 140^2 - 2(160)(140)\cos 80°$$
$$\approx 37,421$$
$$b \approx \sqrt{37,421} \approx 193$$
The distance across the lake is about 193 yards.

35. Assume that Island B is due east of Island A. Let A = angle at Island A.
$$a^2 = b^2 + c^2 - 2bc \cos A$$
$$\cos A = \frac{b^2 + c^2 - a^2}{2bc}$$
$$\cos A = \frac{5^2 + 6^2 - 7^2}{2 \cdot 5 \cdot 6} = \frac{1}{5}$$
$$A \approx 78°$$
Since $90° - 78° = 12°$, you should navigate on a bearing of N12°E.

37. a. Using the figure,
$$B = 90° - 40° = 50°$$
$$b^2 = a^2 + c^2 - 2ac \cos B$$
$$b^2 = 13.5^2 + 25^2 - 2(13.5)(25)\cos 50°$$
$$\approx 373$$
$$b \approx \sqrt{373} \approx 19.3$$
You are about 19.3 miles from the pier.

b.
$$\frac{a}{\sin A} = \frac{b}{\sin B}$$
$$\frac{13.5}{\sin A} = \frac{\sqrt{373}}{\sin 50°}$$
$$\sqrt{373} \sin A = 13.5 \sin 50°$$
$$\sin A = \frac{13.5 \sin 50°}{\sqrt{373}} \approx 0.5355$$
$$A \approx 32°$$
Since $90° - 32° = 58°$, the original bearing could have been S58°E.

39.

In the figure, b = the guy wire anchored downhill, e = the guy wire anchored uphill.
$$B = 90° + 7° = 97°$$
$$E = 90° - 7° = 83°$$
$$b^2 = a^2 + c^2 - 2ac \cos B$$
$$b^2 = 400^2 + 80^2 - 2(400)(80)\cos 97°$$
$$\approx 174,200$$
$$b \approx \sqrt{174,200} \approx 417.4$$
$$e^2 = d^2 + f^2 - 2df \cos E$$
$$e^2 = 400^2 + 80^2 - 2(400)(80)\cos 83°$$
$$\approx 158,600$$
$$e \approx \sqrt{158.600} \approx 398.2$$
The guy wire anchored downhill is about 417.4 feet long. The one anchored uphill is about 398.2 feet long.

41.

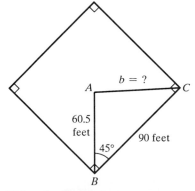

Using the figure,
$$B = 90° \div 2 = 45° \text{ (using symmetry)}$$
$$b^2 = a^2 + c^2 - 2ac \cos B$$
$$b^2 = 90^2 + 60.5^2 - 2(90)(60.5)\cos 45°$$
$$\approx 4060$$
$$b \approx \sqrt{4060} \approx 63.7$$
It is about 63.7 feet from the pitcher's mound to first base.

43. First, find the area using Heron's formula.

$$s = \frac{1}{2}(a+b+c) = \frac{1}{2}(240+300+420) = 480$$

Area

$$= \sqrt{s(s-a)(s-b)(s-c)}$$

$$= \sqrt{480(480-240)(480-300)(480-420)}$$

$$= \sqrt{1,244,160,000} \approx 35,272.65$$

Now multiply by the price per square foot.

$(35,272.65)(3.50) \approx 123,454$

The cost is $123,454, to the nearest dollar.

45.–51. Answers may vary.

53. Let c = distance from A to B,
a = distance from B to C,
b = distance from C to A.
Using the distance formula,

$$c = \sqrt{(4-2)^2 + (-3-1)^2} = \sqrt{20} \approx 4.5$$

$$a = \sqrt{(2-(-2))^2 + (1-4)^2} = \sqrt{25} = 5$$

$$b = \sqrt{(-2-4)^2 + (4-(-3))^2} = \sqrt{85} \approx 9.2$$

Since b is the longest side, B is the largest angle.

$$b^2 = a^2 + c^2 - 2ac\cos B$$

$$\cos B = \frac{a^2 + c^2 - b^2}{2ac}$$

$$\cos B = \frac{5^2 + \left(\sqrt{20}\right)^2 - \left(\sqrt{85}\right)^2}{2 \cdot 5 \cdot \sqrt{20}} = -\frac{4}{\sqrt{20}}$$

B is obtuse, since $\cos B$ is negative.

$$\cos^{-1}\left(\frac{4}{\sqrt{20}}\right) \approx 26.6°$$

$$B \approx 180° - 26.6° = 153.4°$$

The largest angle is about $153.4°$.

Section 7.3

Check Point Exercises

1. a. $(r, \theta) = (3, 315°)$

Because $315°$ is a positive angle, draw $\theta = 315°$ counterclockwise from the polar axis. Because $r > 0$, plot the point by going out 3 units on the terminal side of θ.

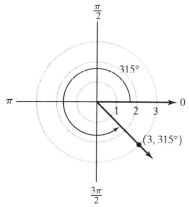

b. $(r, \theta) = (-2, \pi)$

Because π is a positive angle, draw $\theta = \pi$ counterclockwise from the polar axis. Because $r < 0$, plot the point by going out 2 units along the ray opposite the terminal side of θ.

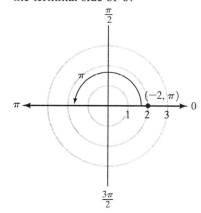

c. $(r,\,\theta) = \left(-1,\,-\dfrac{\pi}{2}\right)$

Because $-\dfrac{\pi}{2}$ is a negative angle, draw

$\theta = -\dfrac{\pi}{2}$ clockwise from the polar axis.

Because $r < 0$, plot the point by going out one unit along the ray opposite the terminal side of θ.

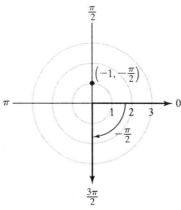

2. a.   Add 2π to the angle and do not change r.

$$\left(5,\,\frac{\pi}{4}\right) = \left(5,\,\frac{\pi}{4} + 2\pi\right) = \left(5,\,\frac{\pi}{4} + \frac{8\pi}{4}\right)$$

$$= \left(5,\,\frac{9\pi}{4}\right)$$

b.   Add π to the angle and replace r by $-r$.

$$\left(5,\,\frac{\pi}{4}\right) = \left(-5,\,\frac{\pi}{4} + \pi\right) = \left(-5,\,\frac{\pi}{4} + \frac{4\pi}{4}\right)$$

$$= \left(-5,\,\frac{5\pi}{4}\right)$$

c.   Subtract 2π from the angle and do not change r.

$$\left(5,\,\frac{\pi}{4}\right) = \left(5,\,\frac{\pi}{4} - 2\pi\right) = \left(5,\,\frac{\pi}{4} - \frac{8\pi}{4}\right)$$

$$= \left(5,\,-\frac{7\pi}{4}\right)$$

3. a. $(r,\,\theta) = (3,\,\pi)$

$x = r\cos\theta = 3\cos\pi = 3(-1) = -3$

$y = r\sin\theta = 3\sin\pi = 3(0) = 0$

The rectangular coordinates of $(3,\pi)$ are $(-3,\,0)$.

b. $(r,\,\theta) = \left(-10,\,\dfrac{\pi}{6}\right)$

$$x = r\cos\theta = -10\cos\frac{\pi}{6} = -10\left(\frac{\sqrt{3}}{2}\right)$$

$$= -5\sqrt{3}$$

$$y = r\sin\theta = -10\sin\frac{\pi}{6} = -10\left(\frac{1}{2}\right) = -5$$

The rectangular coordinates of

$\left(-10,\,\dfrac{\pi}{6}\right)$ are $\left(-5\sqrt{3},\,-5\right)$.

4.

$$r = \sqrt{x^2 + y^2} = \sqrt{1^2 + \left(-\sqrt{3}\right)^2}$$

$$= \sqrt{1 + 3} = \sqrt{4} = 2$$

$$\tan\theta = \frac{y}{x} = \frac{-\sqrt{3}}{1} = -\sqrt{3}$$

Because $\tan\dfrac{\pi}{3} = \sqrt{3}$ and θ lies in quadrant

IV, $\theta = 2\pi - \dfrac{\pi}{3} = \dfrac{6\pi}{3} - \dfrac{\pi}{3} = \dfrac{5\pi}{3}$

The polar coordinates of $\left(1,\,-\sqrt{3}\right)$ are

$$(r,\theta) = \left(2,\,\frac{5\pi}{3}\right)$$

5.

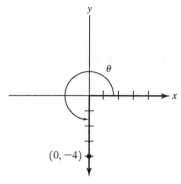

$r = \sqrt{x^2 + y^2} = \sqrt{(0)^2 + (-4)^2} = \sqrt{16} = 4$

The point $(0, -4)$ is on the negative y-axis.

Thus, $\theta = \dfrac{3\pi}{2}$. Polar coordinates of $(0, -4)$

are $\left(4, \dfrac{3\pi}{2}\right)$.

6.
$$3x - y = 6$$
$$3r\cos\theta - r\sin\theta = 6$$
$$r(3\cos\theta - \sin\theta) = 6$$
$$r = \frac{6}{3\cos\theta - \sin\theta}$$

7. a. Use $r^2 = x^2 + y^2$ to convert to a rectangular equation.
$$r = 4$$
$$r^2 = 16$$
$$x^2 + y^2 = 16$$
The rectangular equation for $r = 4$ is $x^2 + y^2 = 16$.

b. Use $\tan\theta = \dfrac{y}{x}$ to convert to a rectangular equation in x and y.
$$\theta = \frac{3\pi}{4}$$
$$\tan\theta = \tan\frac{3\pi}{4}$$
$$\tan\theta = -1$$
$$\frac{y}{x} = -1$$
$$y = -x$$

The rectangular equation for $\theta = \dfrac{3\pi}{4}$ is $y = -x$.

c. Use $r\cos\theta = x$ to convert to a rectangular equation. Express the secant in terms of cosine.
$$r = \sec\theta$$
$$r = \frac{1}{\cos\theta}$$
$$r\cos\theta = 1$$
$$x = 1$$
The rectangular equation for $r = \sec\theta$ is $x = 1$.

Exercise Set 7.3

1. $225°$ is in the third quadrant.
C

3. $\dfrac{5\pi}{4} = 225°$ is in the third quadrant. Since r is negative, the point lies along the ray opposite the terminal side of θ, in the first quadrant.
A

5. $\pi = 180°$ lies on the negative x-axis.
B

7. $-135°$ is measured clockwise $135°$ from the positive x-axis. The point lies in the third quadrant.
C

9. $-\dfrac{3\pi}{4} = -135°$ is measured clockwise $135°$ from the positive x-axis. Since r is negative, the point lies along the ray opposite the terminal side of θ, in the first quadrant.
A

11. Draw $\theta = 45°$ counterclockwise, since θ is positive, from the polar axis. Go out 2 units on the terminal side of θ, since $r > 0$.

13. Draw $\theta = 90°$ counterclockwise, since θ is positive, from the polar axis. Go out 3 units on the terminal side of θ, since $r > 0$.

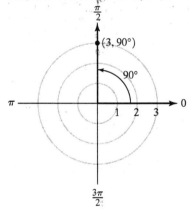

15. Draw $\theta = \dfrac{4\pi}{3} = 240°$ counterclockwise, since θ is positive, from polar axis. Go out 3 units on the terminal side of θ, since $r > 0$.

17. Draw $\theta = \pi = 180°$ counterclockwise, since θ is positive, from the polar axis. Go one unit out on the ray opposite the terminal side of θ, since $r < 0$.

19. Draw $\theta = -\dfrac{\pi}{2} = -90°$ clockwise, since θ is positive, from the polar axis. Go 2 units out on the ray opposite the terminal side of θ, since $r < 0$.

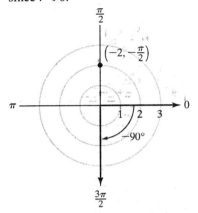

21. Draw $\theta = \dfrac{\pi}{6} = 30°$ counterclockwise, since θ is positive, from the polar axis. Go 5 units out on the terminal side of θ, since $r > 0$.

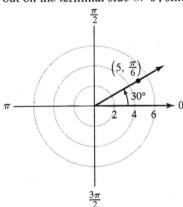

a. Add 2π to the angle and do not change r.

$$\left(5, \dfrac{\pi}{6}\right) = \left(5, \dfrac{\pi}{6} + 2\pi\right) = \left(5, \dfrac{13\pi}{6}\right)$$

b. Add π to the angle and replace r by $-r$.

$$\left(5, \dfrac{\pi}{6}\right) = \left(-5, \dfrac{\pi}{6} + \pi\right) = \left(-5, \dfrac{7\pi}{6}\right)$$

c. Subtract 2π from the angle and do not change r.

$$\left(5, \dfrac{\pi}{6}\right) = \left(5, \dfrac{\pi}{6} - 2\pi\right) = \left(5, -\dfrac{11\pi}{6}\right)$$

23. Draw $\theta = \dfrac{3\pi}{4} = 135°$ counterclockwise, since θ is positive, from the polar axis. Go out 10 units on the terminal side of θ, since $r > 0$.

a. Add 2π to the angle and do not change r.

$$\left(10, \dfrac{3\pi}{4}\right) = \left(10, \dfrac{3\pi}{4} + 2\pi\right) = \left(10, \dfrac{11\pi}{4}\right)$$

b. Add π to the angle and replace r by $-r$.

$$\left(10, \dfrac{3\pi}{4}\right) = \left(-10, \dfrac{3\pi}{4} + \pi\right) = \left(-10, \dfrac{7\pi}{4}\right)$$

c. Subtract 2π from the angle and do not change r.

$$\left(10, \dfrac{3\pi}{4}\right) = \left(10, \dfrac{3\pi}{4} - 2\pi\right) = \left(10, \dfrac{-5\pi}{4}\right)$$

25. Draw $\theta = \dfrac{\pi}{2} = 90°$ counterclockwise, since

θ is positive, from the polar axis. Go 4 units out on the terminal side of θ, since $r > 0$.

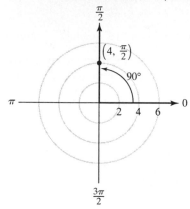

a. Add 2π to the angle and do not change r.

$$\left(4, \frac{\pi}{2}\right) = \left(4, \frac{\pi}{2} + 2\pi\right) = \left(4, \frac{5\pi}{2}\right)$$

b. Add π to the angle and replace r by $-r$.

$$\left(4, \frac{\pi}{2}\right) = \left(-4, \frac{\pi}{2} + \pi\right) = \left(-4, \frac{3\pi}{2}\right)$$

c. Subtract 2π from the angle and do not change r.

$$\left(4, \frac{\pi}{2}\right) = \left(4, \frac{\pi}{2} - 2\pi\right) = \left(4, -\frac{3\pi}{2}\right)$$

27. $x = r\cos\theta = 4\cos 90° = 4 \cdot 0 = 0$
$y = r\sin\theta = 4\sin 90° = 4(1) = 4$
The rectangular coordinates of $(4, 90°)$ are $(0, 4)$.

29. $x = r\cos\theta = 2\cos\dfrac{\pi}{3} = 2\left(\dfrac{1}{2}\right) = 1$

$y = r\sin\theta = 2\sin\dfrac{\pi}{3} = 2\left(\dfrac{\sqrt{3}}{2}\right) = \sqrt{3}$

The rectangular coordinates of $\left(2, \dfrac{\pi}{3}\right)$

are $\left(1, \sqrt{3}\right)$.

31. $x = r\cos\theta = -4\cos\dfrac{\pi}{2} = -4 \cdot 0 = 0$

$y = r\sin\theta = -4\sin\dfrac{\pi}{2} = -4(1) = -4$

The rectangular coordinates of $\left(-4, \dfrac{\pi}{2}\right)$

are $(0, -4)$.

33. $x = r\cos\theta = 7.4\cos 2.5 \approx 7.4(-0.80) \approx -5.9$
$y = r\sin\theta = 7.4\sin 2.5 \approx 7.4(0.60) \approx 4.4$
The rectangular coordinates of $(7.4, 2.5)$ are approximately $(-5.9, 4.4)$.

35.

$$r = \sqrt{x^2 + y^2} = \sqrt{(-2)^2 + (2)^2}$$
$$= \sqrt{4 + 4} = \sqrt{8} = 2\sqrt{2}$$
$$\tan\theta = \frac{y}{x} = \frac{2}{-2} = -1$$

Because $\tan\dfrac{\pi}{4} = 1$ and θ lies in quadrant II,

$$\theta = \pi - \frac{\pi}{4} = \frac{3\pi}{4}.$$

The polar coordinates of $(-2, 2)$ are

$$(r, \theta) = \left(\sqrt{8}, \frac{3\pi}{4}\right) \text{ or } \left(2\sqrt{2}, \frac{3\pi}{4}\right).$$

37.

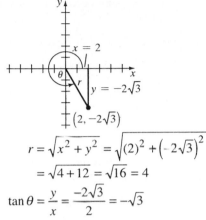

$$r = \sqrt{x^2 + y^2} = \sqrt{(2)^2 + \left(-2\sqrt{3}\right)^2}$$
$$= \sqrt{4 + 12} = \sqrt{16} = 4$$
$$\tan \theta = \frac{y}{x} = \frac{-2\sqrt{3}}{2} = -\sqrt{3}$$

Because $\tan \dfrac{\pi}{3} = \sqrt{3}$ and θ lies in quadrant

IV, $\theta = 2\pi - \dfrac{\pi}{3} = \dfrac{5\pi}{3}$.

The polar coordinates of $\left(2, -2\sqrt{3}\right)$ are

$(r, \theta) = \left(4, \dfrac{5\pi}{3}\right)$.

39.

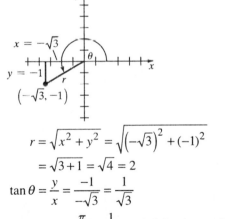

$$r = \sqrt{x^2 + y^2} = \sqrt{\left(-\sqrt{3}\right)^2 + (-1)^2}$$
$$= \sqrt{3 + 1} = \sqrt{4} = 2$$
$$\tan \theta = \frac{y}{x} = \frac{-1}{-\sqrt{3}} = \frac{1}{\sqrt{3}}$$

Because $\tan \dfrac{\pi}{6} = \dfrac{1}{\sqrt{3}}$ and θ lies in quadrant

III, $\theta = \pi + \dfrac{\pi}{6} = \dfrac{7\pi}{6}$.

The polar coordinates of $\left(-\sqrt{3}, -1\right)$ are

$(r, \theta) = \left(2, \dfrac{7\pi}{6}\right)$.

41.

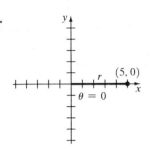

$$r = \sqrt{x^2 + y^2} = \sqrt{(5)^2 + (0)^2} = \sqrt{25} = 5$$
$$\tan \theta = \frac{y}{x} = \frac{0}{5} = 0$$

Because $\tan 0 = 0$ and θ lies on the polar
axis, $\theta = 0$.
The polar coordinates of $(5, 0)$ are
$(r, \theta) = (5, 0)$.

43. $\qquad 3x + y = 7$
$$3r\cos\theta + r\sin\theta = 7$$
$$r(3\cos\theta + \sin\theta) = 7$$
$$r = \frac{7}{3\cos\theta + \sin\theta}$$

45. $\qquad x = 7$
$$r\cos\theta = 7$$
$$r = \frac{7}{\cos\theta}$$

47. $x^2 + y^2 = 9$
$$r^2 = 9$$
$$r = 3$$

49. $x^2 + y^2 = 4x$
$$r^2 = 4r\cos\theta$$
$$r = 4\cos\theta$$

51. $\qquad y^2 = 6x$
$$(r\sin\theta)^2 = 6r\cos\theta$$
$$r^2 \sin^2\theta = 6r\cos\theta$$
$$r\sin^2\theta = 6\cos\theta$$
$$r = \frac{6\cos\theta}{\sin^2\theta}$$

53.
$$r = 8$$
$$r^2 = 64$$
$$x^2 + y^2 = 64$$

55.
$$\theta = \frac{\pi}{2}$$
$$\tan \theta = \tan \frac{\pi}{2}$$
$$\tan \theta \text{ is undefined}$$
$$\frac{y}{x} \text{ is undefined}$$
$$x = 0$$

57. $r \sin \theta = 3$
$$y = 3$$

59.
$$r = 4 \csc \theta$$
$$r = \frac{4}{\sin \theta}$$
$$r \sin \theta = 4$$
$$y = 4$$

61.
$$r = \sin \theta$$
$$r \cdot r = r \cdot \sin \theta$$
$$r^2 = r \sin \theta$$
$$x^2 + y^2 = y$$

63.
$$r = 6 \cos \theta + 4 \sin \theta$$
$$r \cdot r = r(6 \cos \theta + 4 \sin \theta)$$
$$r^2 = 6r \cos \theta + 4r \sin \theta$$
$$x^2 + y^2 = 6x + 4y$$

65.
$$r^2 \sin 2\theta = 2$$
$$r^2 (2 \sin \theta \cos \theta) = 2$$
$$2r \sin \theta \, r \cos \theta = 2$$
$$2yx = 2$$
$$xy = 1$$
$$y = \frac{1}{x}$$

67. The angle is measured counterclockwise from the polar axis.
$$\theta = \frac{2}{3}(360°) = 240° \text{ or } \frac{4\pi}{3}.$$
The distance from the inner circle's center to the outer circle is
$$r = 6 + 3(3) = 6 + 9 = 15$$
The polar coordinates are $(r, \theta) = \left(15, \frac{4\pi}{3} \right)$.

69. (6.3, 50°) represents a sailing speed of 6.3 knots at an angle of 50° to the wind.

71. Out of the four points in this 10-knot-wind situation, you would recommend a sailing angle of 105°. A sailing speed of 7.5 knots is achieved at this angle.

73.–79. Answers may vary.

81.

To three decimal places, the rectangular coordinates are (–2, 3.464).

83.

To three decimal places, the rectangular coordinates are (–1.857, –3.543).

85.

R▸Pr(√(5),2)
3
R▸Pθ(√(5),2)
.7297276562

To three decimal places, the polar coordinates are $(r, \theta) = (3, 0.730)$.

87. Use the distance formula for rectangular coordinates, $d = \sqrt{(x_2 - x_1)^2 + (y_2 - y_1)^2}$.

Let $x_1 = r_1 \cos\theta_1, y_1 = r_1 \sin\theta_1,$
$\quad x_2 = r_2 \cos\theta_2, y_2 = r_2 \sin\theta_2$

$$d = \sqrt{(r_2 \cos\theta_2 - r_1 \cos\theta_1)^2 + (r_2 \sin\theta_2 - r_1 \sin\theta_1)^2}$$

$$= \sqrt{r_2^2 \cos^2\theta_2 - 2r_1 r_2 \cos\theta_1 \cos\theta_2 + r_1^2 \cos^2\theta_1 + r_2^2 \sin^2\theta_2 - 2r_1 r_2 \sin\theta_1 \sin\theta_2 + r_1^2 \sin^2\theta_1}$$

$$= \sqrt{r_2^2(\cos^2\theta_2 + \sin^2\theta_2) + r_1^2(\cos^2\theta_1 + \sin^2\theta_1) - 2r_1 r_2(\cos\theta_1 \cos\theta_2 + \sin\theta_1 \sin\theta_2)}$$

$$= \sqrt{r_2^2(1) + r_1^2(1) - 2r_1 r_2(\cos(\theta_2 - \theta_1))}$$

$$= \sqrt{r_1^2 + r_2^2 - 2r_1 r_2 \cos(\theta_2 - \theta_1)}$$

89.
$$r = 4\cos\theta$$
$$r \cdot r = 4r\cos\theta$$
$$r^2 = 4r\cos\theta$$
$$x^2 + y^2 = 4x$$
$$x^2 - 4x + y^2 = 0$$
$$x^2 - 4x + 4 + y^2 = 0 + 4$$
$$(x - 2)^2 + y^2 = 4$$

The center is $(2, 0)$, the radius is 2.

Section 7.4

Check Point Exercises

1. Construct a partial table of coordinates using multiples of $\dfrac{\pi}{6}$. Then plot the points and join them with a smooth curve.

$r = 4\sin\theta$

θ	r	(r, θ)
0	$4\sin 0 = 4 \cdot 0 = 0$	$(0, 0)$
$\dfrac{\pi}{6}$	$4\sin\dfrac{\pi}{6} = 4 \cdot \dfrac{1}{2} = 2$	$\left(2, \dfrac{\pi}{6}\right)$
$\dfrac{\pi}{3}$	$4\sin\dfrac{\pi}{3} = 4 \cdot \dfrac{\sqrt{3}}{2} = 2\sqrt{3}$	$\left(2\sqrt{3}, \dfrac{\pi}{3}\right)$
$\dfrac{\pi}{2}$	$4\sin\dfrac{\pi}{2} = 4 \cdot 1 = 4$	$\left(4, \dfrac{\pi}{2}\right)$
$\dfrac{2\pi}{3}$	$4\sin\dfrac{2\pi}{3} = 4 \cdot \dfrac{\sqrt{3}}{2} = 2\sqrt{3}$	$\left(2\sqrt{3}, \dfrac{2\pi}{3}\right)$
$\dfrac{5\pi}{6}$	$4\sin\dfrac{5\pi}{6} = 4 \cdot \dfrac{1}{2} = 2$	$\left(2, \dfrac{5\pi}{6}\right)$
π	$4\sin\pi = 4 \cdot 0 = 0$	$(0, \pi)$

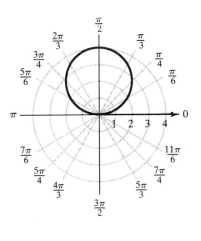

2. **Polar Axis:** Replace θ by $-\theta$ in $r = 1 + \cos\theta$.

$$r = 1 + \cos(-\theta)$$
$$r = 1 + \cos\theta$$

Because the polar equation does not change when θ is replaced by $-\theta$, the graph is symmetric with respect to the polar axis.

The Line $\theta = \dfrac{\pi}{2}$: Replace $(r,\ \theta)$ by $(-r,\ -\theta)$ in $r = 1 + \cos\theta$.

$$-r = 1 + \cos(-\theta)$$
$$-r = 1 + \cos\theta$$
$$r = -1 - \cos\theta$$

Because the polar equation changes when $(r,\ \theta)$ is replaced by $(-r,\ -\theta)$, the equation fails the symmetry

test. The graph may or may not be symmetric with respect to the line $\theta = \dfrac{\pi}{2}$.

The Pole: Replace r by $-r$ in $r = 1 + \cos\theta$.

$$-r = 1 + \cos\theta$$
$$r = -1 - \cos\theta$$

Because the polar equation changes when r is replaced by $-r$, the equation fails the symmetry test. The graph may or may not be symmetric with respect to the pole.

Because the period of the cosine function is 2π, and the graph is symmetric with respect to the polar axis, begin by finding vales of r for values of θ from 0 to π. then graph $r = 1 + \cos\theta$ for these values and reflect the graph about the polar axis.

θ	0	$\dfrac{\pi}{6}$	$\dfrac{\pi}{3}$	$\dfrac{\pi}{2}$	$\dfrac{2\pi}{3}$	$\dfrac{5\pi}{6}$	π
r	2	1.87	1.5	1	0.5	0.13	0

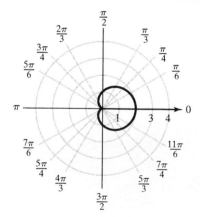

3. $r = 1 - 2\sin\theta$
Check for symmetry:

Polar Axis	The Line $\theta = \dfrac{\pi}{2}$	The Pole
$r = 1 - 2\sin(-\theta)$	$-r = 1 - 2\sin(-\theta)$	$-r = 1 - 2\sin\theta$
$r = 1 - 2(-\sin\theta)$	$-r = 1 + 2\sin\theta$	
$r = 1 + 2\sin\theta$	$r = -1 - 2\sin\theta$	$r = -1 + 2\sin\theta$

There may be no symmetry, since each equation is not equivalent to $r = 1 - 2\sin\theta$. Because the period of the sine function is 2π, we need not consider values of θ beyond 2π.

θ	0	$\dfrac{\pi}{6}$	$\dfrac{\pi}{3}$	$\dfrac{\pi}{2}$	$\dfrac{2\pi}{3}$	$\dfrac{5\pi}{6}$	π
r	1	0	−0.73	−1	−0.73	0	1

θ	$\dfrac{7\pi}{6}$	$\dfrac{4\pi}{3}$	$\dfrac{3\pi}{2}$	$\dfrac{5\pi}{3}$	$\dfrac{11\pi}{6}$	2π
r	2	2.73	3	2.73	2	1

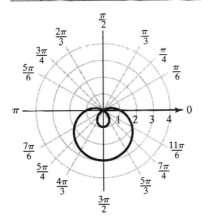

4. $r = 3\cos 2\theta$
    Check for symmetry:

Polar Axis	The Line $\theta = \dfrac{\pi}{2}$	The Pole
$r = 3\cos 2(-\theta)$	$-r = 3\cos 2(-\theta)$	$-r = 3\cos 2\theta$
	$-r = 3\cos 2\theta$	
$r = 3\cos 2\theta$	$r = -3\cos 2\theta$	$r = -3\cos 2\theta$

The graph has symmetry with respect to the polar axis. The graph may or may not be symmetric with respect to the line $\theta = \dfrac{\pi}{2}$ or the pole.

Since the graph is symmetric with respect to the polar axis, calculate values of r for θ from 0 to π. Then, graph $r = 3\cos 2\theta$ for these values and reflect the graph about the polar axis.

θ	0	$\dfrac{\pi}{6}$	$\dfrac{\pi}{3}$	$\dfrac{\pi}{2}$	$\dfrac{2\pi}{3}$	$\dfrac{5\pi}{6}$	π
r	3	1.5	-1.5	-3	-1.5	1.5	3

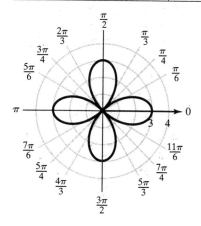

5. $r^2 = 4\cos 2\theta$
Check for symmetry:

Polar Axis	The Line $\theta = \dfrac{\pi}{2}$	The Pole
$r^2 = 4\cos 2(-\theta)$	$(-r)^2 = 4\cos 2(-\theta)$	$(-r)^2 = 4\cos 2\theta$
$r^2 = 4\cos(-2\theta)$	$r^2 = 4\cos(-2\theta)$	
$r^2 = 4\cos 2\theta$	$r^2 = 4\cos 2\theta$	$r^2 = 4\cos 2\theta$

The graph has symmetry with respect to the polar axis, the line $\theta = \dfrac{\pi}{2}$, and the pole.

Calculate values of r for θ from 0 to $\dfrac{\pi}{2}$, and use symmetry to obtain the graph.

θ	0	$\dfrac{\pi}{6}$	$\dfrac{\pi}{4}$	$\dfrac{\pi}{3}$	$\dfrac{\pi}{2}$
r	± 2	± 1.41	0	undef.	undef.

Use symmetry to obtain the graph.

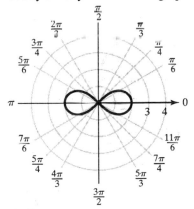

Exercise Set 7.4

1. heart-shaped limaçon or cardiod
$\dfrac{a}{b} = 1$
$r = 0$ when $\theta = \dfrac{\pi}{2}$
The polar equation is $r = 1 - \sin\theta$.

3. circle
$r = 2$ when $\theta = 0$
The polar equation is $r = 2\cos\theta$.

5. rose curve

3 petals $\Rightarrow n = 3$

The polar equation is $r = 3\sin 3\theta$.

7. a. $r = \sin\theta$

Replace θ with $-\theta$.

$r = \sin(-\theta)$

$r = -\sin\theta$

The graph may or may not have symmetry with respect to the polar axis.

b. $r = \sin\theta$

Replace (r, θ) with $(-r, -\theta)$.

$-r = \sin(-\theta)$

$-r = -\sin\theta$

$r = \sin\theta$

The graph has symmetry with respect to the line $\theta = \dfrac{\pi}{2}$.

c. $r = \sin\theta$

Replace r with $-r$.

$-r = \sin\theta$

$r = -\sin\theta$

The graph may or may not have symmetry about the pole.

9. a. $r = 4 + 3\cos\theta$

Replace θ with $-\theta$.

$r = 4 + 3\cos(-\theta)$

$r = 4 + 3\cos\theta$

The graph has symmetry with respect to the polar axis.

b. $r = 4 + 3\cos\theta$

Replace (r, θ) with $(-r, -\theta)$.

$-r = 4 + 3\cos(-\theta)$

$-r = 4 + 3\cos\theta$

$r = -4 - 3\cos\theta$

The graph may or may not have symmetry with respect to the line $\theta = \dfrac{\pi}{2}$.

c. $r = 4 + 3\cos\theta$

Replace r with $-r$.

$-r = 4 + 3\cos\theta$

$r = -4 - 3\cos\theta$

The graph may or may not have symmetry about the pole.

11. a. $r^2 = 16\cos 2\theta$

Replace θ with $-\theta$.

$r^2 = 16\cos 2(-\theta)$

$r^2 = 16\cos(-2\theta)$

$r^2 = 16\cos 2\theta$

The graph has symmetry with respect to the polar axis.

b. $r^2 = 16\cos 2\theta$

Replace (r, θ) with $(-r, -\theta)$.

$(-r)^2 = 16\cos 2(-\theta)$

$r^2 = 16\cos 2\theta$

The graph has symmetry with respect to the line $\theta = \dfrac{\pi}{2}$.

c. $r^2 = 16\cos 2\theta$

Replace r with $-r$.

$(-r)^2 = 16\cos 2\theta$

$r^2 = 16\cos 2\theta$

The graph has symmetry about the pole.

13. $r = 2\cos\theta$
Check for symmetry:

Polar Axis	**The Line** $\theta = \dfrac{\pi}{2}$	**The Pole**
$r = 2\cos(-\theta)$	$-r = 2\cos(-\theta)$	$-r = 2\cos\theta$
	$-r = 2\cos\theta$	
$r = 2\cos\theta$	$r = -2\cos\theta$	$r = -2\cos\theta$

The graph is symmetric with respect to the polar axis. The graph may or may not be symmetric with respect to the line $\theta = \dfrac{\pi}{2}$ or the pole.

Calculate values of r for θ from 0 to π and use symmetry to obtain the graph.

θ	0	$\dfrac{\pi}{6}$	$\dfrac{\pi}{3}$	$\dfrac{\pi}{2}$
r	2	1.73	1	0

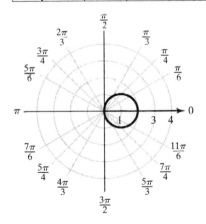

Notice that there are no points in quadrants II or III. Because the cosine is negative in quadrants II and III, r is negative here. This places the points in quadrants IV and I respectively.

15. $r = 1 - \sin\theta$
Check for symmetry:

Polar Axis	The Line $\theta = \dfrac{\pi}{2}$	The Pole
$r = 1 - \sin(-\theta)$	$-r = 1 - \sin(-\theta)$	$-r = 1 - \sin\theta$
	$-r = 1 + \sin\theta$	
$r = 1 + \sin\theta$	$r = -1 - \sin\theta$	$r = -1 + \sin\theta$

There may be no symmetry since each equation is not equivalent to $r = 1 - \sin\theta$. Because the period of the sine function is 2π, we need not consider values of θ beyond 2π.

θ	0	$\dfrac{\pi}{6}$	$\dfrac{\pi}{3}$	$\dfrac{\pi}{2}$	$\dfrac{2\pi}{3}$	$\dfrac{5\pi}{6}$	π
r	1	0.5	0.13	0	0.13	0.5	1

θ	$\dfrac{7\pi}{6}$	$\dfrac{4\pi}{3}$	$\dfrac{3\pi}{2}$	$\dfrac{5\pi}{3}$	$\dfrac{11\pi}{6}$	2π
r	1.5	1.87	2	1.87	1.5	1

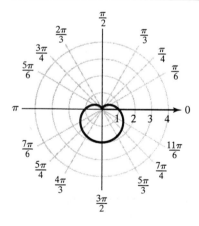

17. $r = 2 + 2\cos\theta$
Check for symmetry:

Polar Axis	The Line $\theta = \dfrac{\pi}{2}$	The Pole
$r = 2 + 2\cos(-\theta)$	$-r = 2 + 2\cos(-\theta)$	$-r = 2 + 2\cos\theta$
	$-r = 2 + 2\cos\theta$	
$r = 2 + 2\cos\theta$	$r = -2 - 2\cos\theta$	$r = -2 - 2\cos\theta$

The graph is symmetric with respect to the polar axis. The graph may or may not be symmetric with respect to the line $\theta = \dfrac{\pi}{2}$ or the pole.

Calculate values of r for θ from 0 to π and use symmetry to obtain the graph.

θ	0	$\dfrac{\pi}{6}$	$\dfrac{\pi}{3}$	$\dfrac{\pi}{2}$	$\dfrac{2\pi}{3}$	$\dfrac{5\pi}{6}$	π
r	4	3.73	3	2	1	0.27	0

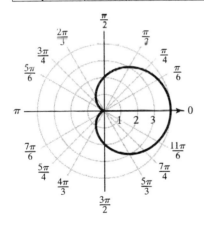

19. $r = 2 + \cos\theta$
Check for symmetry:

Polar Axis	The Line $\theta = \dfrac{\pi}{2}$	The Pole
$r = 2 + \cos(-\theta)$	$-r = 2 + \cos(-\theta)$	$-r = 2 + \cos\theta$
	$-r = 2 + \cos\theta$	
$r = 2 + \cos\theta$	$r = -2 - \cos\theta$	$r = -2 - \cos\theta$

The graph is symmetric with respect to the polar axis. The graph may or may not be symmetric with respect to the line $\theta = \dfrac{\pi}{2}$ or the pole.

Calculate values of r for θ from 0 to π and use symmetry to obtain the graph.

θ	0	$\dfrac{\pi}{6}$	$\dfrac{\pi}{3}$	$\dfrac{\pi}{2}$	$\dfrac{2\pi}{3}$	$\dfrac{5\pi}{6}$	π
r	3	2.87	2.5	2	1.5	1.13	1

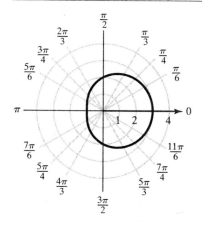

21. $r = 1 + 2\cos\theta$

Check for symmetry:

Polar Axis	The Line $\theta = \dfrac{\pi}{2}$	The Pole
$r = 1 + 2\cos(-\theta)$	$-r = 1 + 2\cos(-\theta)$	$-r = 1 + 2\cos\theta$
	$-r = 1 + 2\cos\theta$	
$r = 1 + 2\cos\theta$	$r = -1 - 2\cos\theta$	$r = -1 - 2\cos\theta$

The graph is symmetric with respect to the polar axis. The graph may or may not be symmetric with respect to the line $\theta = \dfrac{\pi}{2}$ or the pole.

Calculate values of r for θ from 0 to π and use symmetry to obtain the graph.

θ	0	$\dfrac{\pi}{6}$	$\dfrac{\pi}{3}$	$\dfrac{\pi}{2}$	$\dfrac{2\pi}{3}$	$\dfrac{5\pi}{6}$	π
r	3	2.73	2	1	0	−0.73	−1

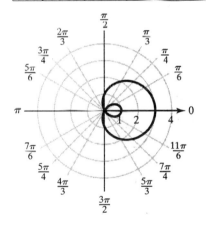

23. $r = 2 - 3\sin\theta$
Check for symmetry:

Polar Axis	**The Line** $\theta = \dfrac{\pi}{2}$	**The Pole**
$r = 2 - 3\sin(-\theta)$	$-r = 2 - 3\sin(-\theta)$	$-r = 2 - 3\sin\theta$
	$-r = 2 + 3\sin\theta$	
$r = 2 + 3\sin\theta$	$r = -2 - 3\sin\theta$	$r = -2 + 3\sin\theta$

There may be no symmetry since each equation is not equivalent to $r = 2 - 3\sin\theta$. Because the period of the sine function is 2π, we need not consider values of θ beyond 2π.

θ	0	$\dfrac{\pi}{6}$	$\dfrac{\pi}{3}$	$\dfrac{\pi}{2}$	$\dfrac{2\pi}{3}$	$\dfrac{5\pi}{6}$	π
r	2	0.5	−0.60	−1	−0.60	0.5	2

θ	$\dfrac{7\pi}{6}$	$\dfrac{4\pi}{3}$	$\dfrac{3\pi}{2}$	$\dfrac{5\pi}{3}$	$\dfrac{11\pi}{6}$	2π
r	3.5	4.60	5	4.60	3.5	2

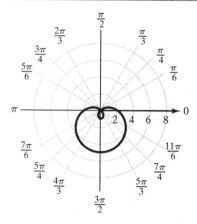

25. $r = 2\cos 2\theta$
Check for symmetry:

Polar Axis	The Line $\theta = \dfrac{\pi}{2}$	The Pole
$r = 2\cos 2(-\theta)$	$-r = 2\cos 2(-\theta)$	$-r = 2\cos 2\theta$
$r = 2\cos(-2\theta)$	$-r = 2\cos(-2\theta)$	
	$-r = 2\cos 2\theta$	
$r = 2\cos 2\theta$	$r = -2\cos 2\theta$	$r = -2\cos 2\theta$

The graph is symmetric with respect to the polar axis. The graph may or may not be symmetric with respect to the line $\theta = \dfrac{\pi}{2}$ or the pole.

Calculate values of r for θ from 0 to π and use symmetry to obtain the graph.

θ	0	$\dfrac{\pi}{6}$	$\dfrac{\pi}{3}$	$\dfrac{\pi}{2}$	$\dfrac{2\pi}{3}$	$\dfrac{5\pi}{6}$	π
r	2	1	-1	-2	-1	1	2

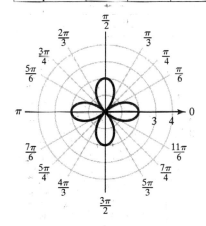

27. $r = 4\sin 3\theta$
Check for symmetry:

Polar Axis	The Line $\theta = \dfrac{\pi}{2}$	The Pole
$r = 4\sin 3(-\theta)$	$-r = 4\sin 3(-\theta)$	$-r = 4\sin 3\theta$
$r = 4\sin(-3\theta)$	$-r = 4\sin(-3\theta)$	
	$-r = -4\sin 3\theta$	
$r = -4\sin 3\theta$	$r = 4\sin 3\theta$	$r = -4\sin 3\theta$

The graph is symmetric with respect to the line $\theta = \dfrac{\pi}{2}$. The graph may or may not be symmetric with respect to the polar axis or the poles.

Calculate values of r for θ from 0 to $\dfrac{\pi}{2}$ and for θ from π to $\dfrac{3\pi}{2}$. Then, use symmetry to obtain the graph.

θ	0	$\dfrac{\pi}{6}$	$\dfrac{\pi}{4}$	$\dfrac{\pi}{3}$	$\dfrac{\pi}{2}$
r	0	4	2.83	0	−4

θ	π	$\dfrac{7\pi}{6}$	$\dfrac{5\pi}{4}$	$\dfrac{4\pi}{3}$	$\dfrac{3\pi}{2}$
r	0	−4	−2.83	0	4

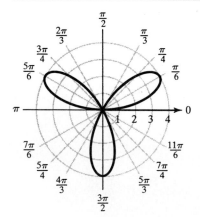

29. $r^2 = 9\cos 2\theta$

Check for symmetry:

Polar Axis	The Line $\theta = \dfrac{\pi}{2}$	The Pole
$r^2 = 9\cos 2(-\theta)$	$(-r)^2 = 9\cos 2(-\theta)$	$(-r)^2 = 9\cos 2\theta$
$r^2 = 9\cos(-2\theta)$	$r^2 = 9\cos(-2\theta)$	
$r^2 = 9\cos 2\theta$	$r^2 = 9\cos 2\theta$	$r^2 = 9\cos 2\theta$

The graph is symmetric with respect to the polar axis, the line $\theta = \dfrac{\pi}{2}$, and the pole.

Note that since $\cos 2\theta$ is negative for $\dfrac{\pi}{4} < \theta < \dfrac{3\pi}{4}$, there is no graph there.

Calculate values of r for θ from 0 to $\dfrac{\pi}{4}$ and use symmetry to obtain the graph.

θ	0	$\dfrac{\pi}{6}$	$\dfrac{\pi}{4}$
r	± 3	± 2.12	0

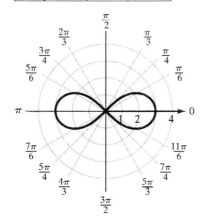

31. $r = 1 - 3\sin\theta$
Check for symmetry:

Polar Axis	The Line $\theta = \dfrac{\pi}{2}$	The Pole
$r = 1 - 3\sin(-\theta)$	$-r = 1 - 3\sin(-\theta)$	$-r = 1 - 3\sin\theta$
	$-r = 1 + 3\sin\theta$	
$r = 1 + 3\sin\theta$	$r = -1 - 3\sin\theta$	$r = -1 + 3\sin\theta$

There may be no symmetry. Since each equation is not equivalent to $r = 1 - 3\sin\theta$. Because the period of the sine function is 2π, we need not consider values of θ beyond 2π.

θ	0	$\dfrac{\pi}{6}$	$\dfrac{\pi}{3}$	$\dfrac{\pi}{2}$	$\dfrac{2\pi}{3}$	$\dfrac{5\pi}{6}$	π
r	1	-0.5	-1.60	-2	-1.60	-0.5	1

θ	$\dfrac{7\pi}{6}$	$\dfrac{4\pi}{3}$	$\dfrac{3\pi}{2}$	$\dfrac{5\pi}{3}$	$\dfrac{11\pi}{6}$	2π
r	2.5	3.60	4	3.60	2.5	1

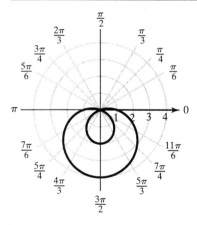

33. $r\cos\theta = -3$

$$r = \frac{-3}{\cos\theta} = -3\sec\theta$$

Check for symmetry:

Polar Axis	The Line $\theta = \dfrac{\pi}{2}$	The Pole
$r = -3\sec(-\theta)$	$-r = -3\sec(-\theta)$	$-r = -3\sec\theta$
	$-r = -3\sec\theta$	
$r = -3\sec\theta$	$r = 3\sec\theta$	$r = 3\sec\theta$

The graph is symmetric with respect to the polar axis. The graph may or may not be symmetric with respect to the line $\theta = \dfrac{\pi}{2}$ or the pole.

Calculate values of r for θ from 0 to π. Then, use symmetry to obtain the graph.

θ	0	$\dfrac{\pi}{6}$	$\dfrac{\pi}{3}$	$\dfrac{\pi}{2}$	$\dfrac{2\pi}{3}$	$\dfrac{5\pi}{6}$	π
r	-3	-3.46	-6	undef.	6	3.46	3

Note that since $\sec\theta$ is undefined when $\theta = \dfrac{\pi}{2}$ and $\theta = \dfrac{3\pi}{2}$, r increases without bound as θ approaches these angles. $r\cos\theta = -3$ is equivalent to $x = -3$.

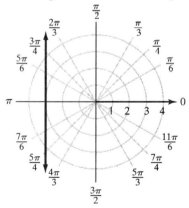

35. Using the graph, sailing at a 60° angle to the wind gives a speed of about 6 knots (to the nearest knot).

37. Using the graph, sailing at a 90° angle to the wind gives a speed of about 8 knots (to the nearest knot).

39. It appears that an angle of 90° gives a maximum speed of about $7\dfrac{1}{2}$ knots.

41.–45. Answers may vary.

47. Exercise 13

Exercise 15

Exercise 17

Exercise 19

Exercise 21

Exercise 23

49.

51.

53.

55.

57.

59.

61.

63.

65.

67. If $\theta\max = 2\pi$, the graph is drawn once.

69. $\theta\,\text{step} = 0.1$

71. $\theta\,\text{step} = 0.1$

73. $r = \sin\theta$

$r = \sin 2\theta$

$r = \sin 3\theta$

$r = \sin 4\theta$

$r = \sin 5\theta$

$r = \sin 6\theta$

As n increases, $\sin n\theta$ increases its number of loops. If n is odd, there are n loops and $\theta\max = \pi$ traces the graph once, while if n is even, there are $2n$ loops and $\theta\max = 2\pi$ traces the graph once.

75. $r = 1 + 2\sin\theta$

$r = 1 + 2\sin 2\theta$

$r = 1 + 2\sin 3\theta$

$r = 1 + 2\sin 4\theta$

$r = 1 + 2\sin 5\theta$

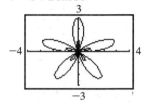

$r = 1 + 2\sin 6\theta$

There are n small petals and n large petals for each value of n. For odd values of n, the small petals are inside the large petals. For even n, they are between the large petals.

77. $\theta\min = 0,\ \theta\max = 2\pi$ $\theta\min = 0,\ \theta\max = 4\pi$ $\theta\min = 0,\ \theta\max = 8\pi$

79. Answers may vary.

81. $r = \dfrac{4}{1 + \sin\theta}$

Check for symmetry:

Polar Axis	**The Line** $\theta = \dfrac{\pi}{2}$	**The Pole**
$r = \dfrac{4}{1 + \sin(-\theta)}$	$-r = \dfrac{4}{1 + \sin(-\theta)}$	$-r = \dfrac{4}{1 + \sin\theta}$
	$-r = \dfrac{4}{1 - \sin\theta}$	
$r = \dfrac{4}{1 - \sin\theta}$	$r = -\dfrac{4}{1 - \sin\theta}$	$r = -\dfrac{4}{1 + \sin\theta}$

There may be no symmetry since each equation is not equivalent to $r = \dfrac{4}{1 + \sin\theta}$.

Calculate values of r for θ from 0 to 2π.

θ	0	$\dfrac{\pi}{6}$	$\dfrac{\pi}{3}$	$\dfrac{\pi}{2}$	$\dfrac{2\pi}{3}$	$\dfrac{5\pi}{6}$	π
r	4	2.67	2.14	2	2.14	2.67	4

θ	$\dfrac{7\pi}{6}$	$\dfrac{4\pi}{3}$	$\dfrac{3\pi}{2}$	$\dfrac{5\pi}{3}$	$\dfrac{11\pi}{6}$	2π
r	8	29.86	undef.	29.86	8	4

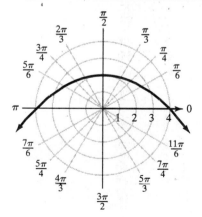

Section 7.5

Check Point Exercises

1. a. $z = 2 + 3i$ corresponds to the point (2, 3). Plot the complex number by moving two units to the right on the real axis and 3 units up parallel to the imaginary axis.

b. $z = -3 - 5i$ corresponds to the point (−3, −5). Plot the complex number by moving three units to the left on the real axis and five units down parallel to the imaginary axis.

c. Because $z = -4 = -4 + 0i$, this complex number corresponds to the point (−4, 0). Plot the complex number by moving four units to the left on the real axis.

d. Because $z = -i = 0 - i$, this complex number corresponds to the point (0, −1). Plot the complex number by moving one unit down on the imaginary axis.

2. a. $z = 5 + 12i$
$a = 5, b = 12$
$$|z| = \sqrt{5^2 + 12^2} = \sqrt{25 + 144} = \sqrt{169} = 13$$

b. $z = 2 - 3i$
$a = 2, b = -3$
$$|z| = \sqrt{2^2 + (-3)^2} = \sqrt{4 + 9} = \sqrt{13}$$

3. $z = -1 - \sqrt{3}i$ corresponds to the point $\left(-1, -\sqrt{3}\right)$.

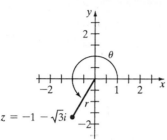

Use $r = \sqrt{a^2 + b^2}$ with $a = -1$ and $b = -\sqrt{3}$ to find r.

$$r = \sqrt{a^2 + b^2} = \sqrt{(-1)^2 + \left(-\sqrt{3}\right)^2}$$
$$= \sqrt{1 + 3} = \sqrt{4} = 2$$

Use $\tan\theta = \dfrac{b}{a}$ with $a = -1$ and $b = -\sqrt{3}$ to find θ.

$$\tan\theta = \frac{b}{a} = \frac{-\sqrt{3}}{-1} = \sqrt{3}$$

Because $\tan\dfrac{\pi}{3} = \sqrt{3}$ and θ lies in

quadrant III, $\theta = \pi + \dfrac{\pi}{3} = \dfrac{3\pi}{3} + \dfrac{\pi}{3} = \dfrac{4\pi}{3}$.

The polar form of $z = -1 - \sqrt{3}i$ is

$$z = r(\cos\theta + i\sin\theta) = 2\left(\cos\frac{4\pi}{3} + i\sin\frac{4\pi}{3}\right).$$

4. The complex number $z = 4(\cos 30° + i\sin 30°)$ is in polar form, with $r = 4$ and $\theta = 30°$. We use exact values for $\cos 30°$ and $\sin 30°$ to write the number in rectangular form.

$$4(\cos 30° + i\sin 30°) = 4\left(\frac{\sqrt{3}}{2} + i\frac{1}{2}\right) = 2\sqrt{3} + 2i$$

The rectangular form of $z = 4(\cos 30° + i\sin 30°)$ is $z = 2\sqrt{3} + 2i$.

5. $z_1 z_2 = [6(\cos 40° + i\sin 40°)][5(\cos 20° + i\sin 20°)] = (6 \cdot 5)[(\cos(40° + 20°) + i\sin(40° + 20°)]$
$\qquad = 30(\cos 60° + i\sin 60°)$

6. $\dfrac{z_1}{z_2} = \dfrac{50\left(\cos\dfrac{4\pi}{3} + i\sin\dfrac{4\pi}{3}\right)}{5\left(\cos\dfrac{\pi}{3} + i\sin\dfrac{\pi}{3}\right)} = \dfrac{50}{5}\left[\cos\left(\dfrac{4\pi}{3} - \dfrac{\pi}{3}\right) + i\sin\left(\dfrac{4\pi}{3} - \dfrac{\pi}{3}\right)\right] = 10(\cos\pi + i\sin\pi)$

7. $[2(\cos 30° + i \sin 30°)]^5 = 2^5[\cos(5 \cdot 30°) + i \sin(5 \cdot 30°)] = 32(\cos 150° + i \sin 150°) = 32\left(-\frac{\sqrt{3}}{2} + i\frac{1}{2}\right)$

$$= -16\sqrt{3} + 16i$$

8. Write $1 + i$ in $r(\cos\theta + i\sin\theta)$ form.

$$r = \sqrt{a^2 + b^2} = \sqrt{1^2 + 1^2} = \sqrt{2}$$

$$\tan\theta = \frac{b}{a} = \frac{1}{1} = 1 \text{ and } \theta = \frac{\pi}{4}$$

$$1 + i = r(\cos\theta + i\sin\theta) = \sqrt{2}\left(\cos\frac{\pi}{4} + i\sin\frac{\pi}{4}\right)$$

Use DeMoivre's Theorem to raise $1 + i$ to the fourth power.

$$(1+i)^4 = \left[\sqrt{2}\left(\cos\frac{\pi}{4} + i\sin\frac{\pi}{4}\right)\right]^4 = \left(\sqrt{2}\right)^4\left[\cos\left(4 \cdot \frac{\pi}{4}\right) + i\sin\left(4 \cdot \frac{\pi}{4}\right)\right] = 4(\cos\pi + i\sin\pi) = 4(-1 + 0i) = -4$$

9. From DeMoivre's Theorem for finding complex roots, the fourth roots of $16(\cos 60° + i\sin 60°)$ are

$$z_k = \sqrt[4]{16}\left[\cos\left(\frac{60° + 360°k}{4}\right) + i\sin\left(\frac{60° + 360°k}{4}\right)\right], \ k = 0, 1, 2, 3.$$

Substitute 0, 1, 2, and 3 for k in the above expression for z_k.

$$z_0 = \sqrt[4]{16}\left[\cos\left(\frac{60° + 360° \cdot 0}{4}\right) + i\sin\left(\frac{60° + 360° \cdot 0}{4}\right)\right] = \sqrt[4]{16}\left[\cos\frac{60°}{4} + i\sin\frac{60°}{4}\right] = 2(\cos 15° + i\sin 15°)$$

$$z_1 = \sqrt[4]{16}\left[\cos\left(\frac{60° + 360° \cdot 1}{4}\right) + i\sin\left(\frac{60° + 360° \cdot 1}{4}\right)\right] = \sqrt[4]{16}\left[\cos\frac{420°}{4} + i\sin\frac{420°}{4}\right]$$

$$= 2(\cos 105° + i\sin 105°)$$

$$z_2 = \sqrt[4]{16}\left[\cos\left(\frac{60° + 360° \cdot 2}{4}\right) + i\sin\left(\frac{60° + 360° \cdot 2}{4}\right)\right] = \sqrt[4]{16}\left[\cos\frac{780°}{4} + i\sin\frac{780°}{4}\right]$$

$$= 2(\cos 195° + i\sin 195°)$$

$$z_3 = \sqrt[4]{16}\left[\cos\left(\frac{60° + 360° \cdot 3}{4}\right) + i\sin\left(\frac{60° + 360° \cdot 3}{4}\right)\right] = \sqrt[4]{16}\left[\cos\frac{1140°}{4} + i\sin\frac{1140°}{4}\right]$$

$$= 2(\cos 285° + i\sin 285°)$$

10. First, write 27 in polar form. $27 = r(\cos\theta + i\sin\theta) = 27(\cos 0 + \sin 0)$. From DeMoivre's theorem for finding complex roots, the cube roots of 27 are

$$z_k = \sqrt[3]{27}\left[\cos\left(\frac{0 + 2\pi k}{3}\right) + i\sin\left(\frac{0 + 2\pi k}{3}\right)\right], \ k = 0, 1, 2.$$

$$z_0 = \sqrt[3]{27}\left[\cos\left(\frac{0 + 2\pi \cdot 0}{3}\right) + i\sin\left(\frac{0 + 2\pi \cdot 0}{3}\right)\right] = 3(\cos 0 + i\sin 0) = 3(1 + i\cdot 0) = 3$$

$$z_1 = \sqrt[3]{27}\left[\cos\left(\frac{0 + 2\pi \cdot 1}{3}\right) + i\sin\left(\frac{0 + 2\pi \cdot 1}{3}\right)\right] = 3\left(\cos\frac{2\pi}{3} + i\sin\frac{2\pi}{3}\right) = 3\left(-\frac{1}{2} + i\cdot\frac{\sqrt{3}}{2}\right) = -\frac{3}{2} + \frac{3\sqrt{3}}{2}i$$

$$z_2 = \sqrt[3]{27}\left[\cos\left(\frac{0 + 2\pi \cdot 2}{3}\right) + i\sin\left(\frac{0 + 2\pi \cdot 2}{3}\right)\right] = 3\left(\cos\frac{4\pi}{3} + i\sin\frac{4\pi}{3}\right) = 3\left(-\frac{1}{2} + i\cdot\left(-\frac{\sqrt{3}}{2}\right)\right) = -\frac{3}{2} - \frac{3\sqrt{3}}{2}i$$

Exercise Set 7.5

1. Because $z = 4i = 0 + 4i$, this complex number corresponds to the point $(0, 4)$.

With $a = 0$ and $b = 4$, $|z| = \sqrt{0^2 + 4^2} = \sqrt{16} = 4$.

3. Because $z = 3 = 3 + 0i$, this complex number corresponds to the point $(3, 0)$.

With $a = 3$ and $b = 0$, $|z| = \sqrt{3^2 + 0^2} = \sqrt{9} = 3$.

5. $z = 3 + 2i$ corresponds to the point $(3, 2)$.

With $a = 3$ and $b = 2$,
$$|z| = \sqrt{3^2 + 2^2} = \sqrt{9 + 4} = \sqrt{13}.$$

7. $z = 3 - i$ corresponds to the point $(3, -1)$.

With $a = 3$ and $b = -1$,
$$|z| = \sqrt{3^2 + (-1)^2} = \sqrt{9 + 1} = \sqrt{10}.$$

9. $z = -3 + 4i$ corresponds to the point $(-3, 4)$.

With $a = -3$ and $b = 4$,
$$|z| = \sqrt{(-3)^2 + 4^2} = \sqrt{9 + 16} = \sqrt{25} = 5.$$

11. $z = 2 + 2i$ corresponds to the point $(2, 2)$.

Use $r = \sqrt{a^2 + b^2}$ and $\tan \theta = \dfrac{b}{a}$, with $a = 2$ and $b = 2$, to find r and θ.

$$r = \sqrt{2^2 + 2^2} = \sqrt{4 + 4} = \sqrt{8} = 2\sqrt{2}$$

$$\tan \theta = \frac{2}{2} = 1$$

Because $\tan \dfrac{\pi}{4} = 1$ and θ lies in quadrant I,

$$\theta = \frac{\pi}{4}.$$

$$z = 2 + 2i = r(\cos \theta + i \sin \theta)$$
$$= 2\sqrt{2}\left(\cos \frac{\pi}{4} + i \sin \frac{\pi}{4}\right)$$
$$\text{or } 2\sqrt{2}(\cos 45° + i \sin 45°)$$

13. $z = -1 - i$ corresponds to the point $(-1, -1)$.

Use $r = \sqrt{a^2 + b^2}$ and $\tan\theta = \dfrac{b}{a}$, with

$a = -1$ and $b = -1$, to find r and θ.

$r = \sqrt{(-1)^2 + (-1)^2} = \sqrt{1+1} = \sqrt{2}$

$\tan\theta = \dfrac{-1}{-1} = 1$

Because $\tan\dfrac{\pi}{4} = 1$ and θ lies in

quadrant III, $\theta = \pi + \dfrac{\pi}{4} = \dfrac{5\pi}{4}$.

$z = -1 - i = r(\cos\theta + i\sin\theta)$

$\quad = \sqrt{2}\left(\cos\dfrac{5\pi}{4} + i\sin\dfrac{5\pi}{4}\right)$

or $\sqrt{2}(\cos 225° + i\sin 225°)$

15. $z = -4i$ corresponds to the point $(0, -4)$.

Use $r = \sqrt{a^2 + b^2}$ and $\tan\theta = \dfrac{b}{a}$, with

$a = 0$ and $b = -4$, to find r and θ.

$r = \sqrt{0^2 + (-4)^2} = \sqrt{16} = 4$

$\tan\theta = \dfrac{-4}{0}$ is undefined.

Because $\tan\dfrac{\pi}{2}$ is undefined and θ lies on

the negative y-axis, $\theta = \dfrac{\pi}{2} + \pi = \dfrac{3\pi}{2}$.

$z = -4i = r(\cos\theta + i\sin\theta)$

$\quad = 4\left(\cos\dfrac{3\pi}{2} + i\sin\dfrac{3\pi}{2}\right)$

or $4(\cos 270° + i\sin 270°)$

17. $z = 2\sqrt{3} - 2i$ corresponds to the point $\left(2\sqrt{3}, -2\right)$.

Use $r = \sqrt{a^2 + b^2}$ and $\tan\theta = \dfrac{b}{a}$, with

$a = 2\sqrt{3}$ and $b = -2$, to find r and θ.

$r = \sqrt{\left(2\sqrt{3}\right)^2 + (-2)^2} = \sqrt{12+4} = \sqrt{16} = 4$

$\tan\theta = \dfrac{-2}{2\sqrt{3}} = -\dfrac{1}{\sqrt{3}}$

Because $\tan\dfrac{\pi}{6} = \dfrac{1}{\sqrt{3}}$ and θ lies in

quadrant IV, $\theta = 2\pi - \dfrac{\pi}{6} = \dfrac{11\pi}{6}$.

$z = 2\sqrt{3} - 2i = r(\cos\theta + i\sin\theta)$

$\quad = 4\left(\cos\dfrac{11\pi}{6} + i\sin\dfrac{11\pi}{6}\right)$

or $4(\cos 330° + i\sin 330°)$

19. $z = -3$ corresponds to the point $(-3, 0)$.

Use $r = \sqrt{a^2 + b^2}$ and $\tan\theta = \dfrac{b}{a}$, with
$a = -3$ and $b = 0$, to find r and θ.

$r = \sqrt{(-3)^2 + 0^2} = \sqrt{9} = 3$

$\tan\theta = \dfrac{0}{-3} = 0$

Because $\tan 0 = 0$ and θ lies on the
negative x-axis, $\theta = 0 + \pi = \pi$.

$z = -3 = r(\cos\theta + i\sin\theta)$
$\quad = 3(\cos\pi + i\sin\pi)$
$\quad$ or $3(\cos 180° + i\sin 180°)$

21. $z = -3\sqrt{2} - 3\sqrt{3}i$ corresponds to the point
$\left(-3\sqrt{2}, -3\sqrt{3}\right)$.

Use $r = \sqrt{a^2 + b^2}$ and $\tan\theta = \dfrac{b}{a}$, with
$a = -3\sqrt{2}$ and $b = -3\sqrt{3}$, to find r and θ.

$r = \sqrt{\left(-3\sqrt{2}\right)^2 + \left(-3\sqrt{3}\right)^2} = \sqrt{18 + 27}$

$\quad = \sqrt{45} = 3\sqrt{5}$

$\tan\theta = \dfrac{-3\sqrt{3}}{-3\sqrt{2}} = \dfrac{\sqrt{3}}{\sqrt{2}} = \dfrac{\sqrt{6}}{2}$

Because θ lies in quadrant III,

$\theta = 180° + \tan^{-1}\left(\dfrac{\sqrt{6}}{2}\right) \approx 180° + 50.8°$

$\quad = 230.8°$

$z = -3\sqrt{2} - 3\sqrt{3}i = r(\cos\theta + i\sin\theta)$
$\quad \approx 3\sqrt{5}(\cos 230.8° + i\sin 230.8°)$

23. $z = -3 + 4i$ corresponds to the point $(-3, 4)$.

Use $r = \sqrt{a^2 + b^2}$ and $\tan\theta = \dfrac{b}{a}$, with
$a = -3$ and $b = 4$, to find r and θ.

$r = \sqrt{(-3)^2 + (4)^2} = \sqrt{9 + 16} = \sqrt{25} = 5$

$\tan\theta = \dfrac{4}{-3} = -\dfrac{4}{3}$

Because θ lies in quadrant II,

$\theta = 180° - \tan^{-1}\left(\dfrac{4}{3}\right) \approx 180° - 53.1° = 126.9°$.

$z = -3 + 4i = r(\cos\theta + i\sin\theta)$
$\quad \approx 5(\cos 126.9° + i\sin 126.9°)$

25. $z = 2 - \sqrt{3}i$ corresponds to the point $\left(2, -\sqrt{3}\right)$.

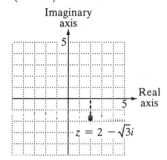

Use $r = \sqrt{a^2 + b^2}$ and $\tan\theta = \dfrac{b}{a}$, with

$a = 2$ and $b = -\sqrt{3}$, to find r and θ.

$$r = \sqrt{2^2 + \left(-\sqrt{3}\right)^2} = \sqrt{4+3} = \sqrt{7}$$

$$\tan\theta = \frac{-\sqrt{3}}{2} = -\frac{\sqrt{3}}{2}$$

Because θ lies in quadrant IV,

$$\theta = 360° - \tan^{-1}\left(\frac{\sqrt{3}}{2}\right) \approx 360° - 40.9° = 319.1°$$

$$z = 2 - \sqrt{3}i = r(\cos\theta + i\sin\theta)$$
$$\approx \sqrt{7}(\cos 319.1° + i\sin 319.1°)$$

27. $6(\cos 30° + i\sin 30°) = 6\left(\dfrac{\sqrt{3}}{2} + i\dfrac{1}{2}\right)$
$$= 3\sqrt{3} + 3i$$

The rectangular form of
$z = 6(\cos 30° + i\sin 30°)$ is $z = 3\sqrt{3} + 3i$.

29. $4(\cos 240° + i\sin 240°) = 4\left(-\dfrac{1}{2} + i\left(-\dfrac{\sqrt{3}}{2}\right)\right)$
$$= -2 - 2\sqrt{3}i$$

The rectangular form of
$z = 4(\cos 240° + i\sin 240°)$ is $z = -2 - 2\sqrt{3}i$.

31. $8\left(\cos\dfrac{7\pi}{4} + i\sin\dfrac{7\pi}{4}\right) = 8\left(\dfrac{\sqrt{2}}{2} + i\left(-\dfrac{\sqrt{2}}{2}\right)\right)$
$$= 4\sqrt{2} - 4\sqrt{2}i$$

The rectangular form of
$8\left(\cos\dfrac{7\pi}{4} + i\sin\dfrac{7\pi}{4}\right)$ is $z = 4\sqrt{2} - 4\sqrt{2}i$.

33. $5\left(\cos\dfrac{\pi}{2} + i\sin\dfrac{\pi}{2}\right) = 5(0 + i(1))$
$$= 5i$$

The rectangular form of
$z = 5\left(\cos\dfrac{\pi}{2} + i\sin\dfrac{\pi}{2}\right)$ is $z = 5i$.

35. $20(\cos 205° + i\sin 205°)$
$$\approx 20(-0.91 + i(-0.42)) = -18.2 - 8.4i$$

The rectangular form of
$z = 20(\cos 205° + i\sin 205°)$ is
$z \approx -18.2 - 8.4i$.

37. $z_1 z_2$
$$= [6(\cos 20° + i\sin 20°)][5(\cos 50° + i\sin 50°)]$$
$$= (6 \cdot 5)[\cos(20° + 50°) + i\sin(20° + 50°)]$$
$$= 30(\cos 70° + i\sin 70°)$$

39. $z_1 z_2$
$$= \left[3\left(\cos\frac{\pi}{5} + i\sin\frac{\pi}{5}\right)\right]\left[4\left(\cos\frac{\pi}{10} + i\sin\frac{\pi}{10}\right)\right]$$
$$= (3 \cdot 4)\left[\cos\left(\frac{\pi}{5} + \frac{\pi}{10}\right) + i\sin\left(\frac{\pi}{5} + \frac{\pi}{10}\right)\right]$$
$$= 12\left(\cos\frac{3\pi}{10} + i\sin\frac{3\pi}{10}\right)$$

41. $z_1 z_2 = \left[\cos\dfrac{\pi}{4} + i\sin\dfrac{\pi}{4}\right]\left[\cos\dfrac{\pi}{3} + i\sin\dfrac{\pi}{3}\right]$
$$= \cos\left(\frac{\pi}{4} + \frac{\pi}{3}\right) + i\sin\left(\frac{\pi}{4} + \frac{\pi}{3}\right)$$
$$= \cos\left(\frac{3\pi}{12} + \frac{4\pi}{12}\right) + i\sin\left(\frac{3\pi}{12} + \frac{4\pi}{12}\right)$$
$$= \cos\frac{7\pi}{12} + i\sin\frac{7\pi}{12}$$

43. Begin by converting $z_1 = 1 + i$ and $z_2 = -1 + i$ to polar form.
For z_1: $a = 1$ and $b = 1$

$$r = \sqrt{a^2 + b^2} = \sqrt{1^2 + 1^2} = \sqrt{2}$$

$$\tan \theta = \frac{b}{a} = \frac{1}{1} = 1 \text{ and } \theta = \frac{\pi}{4}.$$

$$z_1 = r(\cos \theta + i \sin \theta) = \sqrt{2}\left(\cos \frac{\pi}{4} + i \sin \frac{\pi}{4}\right)$$

For z_2: $a = -1$ and $b = 1$

$$r = \sqrt{a^2 + b^2} = \sqrt{(-1)^2 + 1^2} = \sqrt{2}$$

$$\tan \theta = \frac{b}{a} = \frac{1}{-1} = -1$$

Because $\tan \frac{\pi}{4} = 1$ and θ lies in quadrant II, $\theta = \pi - \frac{\pi}{4} = \frac{3\pi}{4}.$

$$z_2 = r(\cos \theta + i \sin \theta) = \sqrt{2}\left(\cos \frac{3\pi}{4} + i \sin \frac{3\pi}{4}\right)$$

Now, find the product.
$z_1 z_2 = (1 + i)(-1 + i)$

$$= \left[\sqrt{2}\left(\cos \frac{\pi}{4} + i \sin \frac{\pi}{4}\right)\right]\left[\sqrt{2}\left(\cos \frac{3\pi}{4} + i \sin \frac{3\pi}{4}\right)\right] = \left(\sqrt{2} \cdot \sqrt{2}\right)\left[\cos\left(\frac{\pi}{4} + \frac{3\pi}{4}\right) + i \sin\left(\frac{\pi}{4} + \frac{3\pi}{4}\right)\right]$$

$$= 2(\cos \pi + i \sin \pi)$$

45. $\dfrac{z_1}{z_2} = \dfrac{20(\cos 75° + i \sin 75°)}{4(\cos 25° + i \sin 25°)} = \dfrac{20}{4}\left[\cos(75° - 25°) + i \sin(75° - 25°)\right]$

$$= 5(\cos 50° + i \sin 50°)$$

47. $\dfrac{z_1}{z_2} = \dfrac{3\left(\cos \dfrac{\pi}{5} + i \sin \dfrac{\pi}{5}\right)}{4\left(\cos \dfrac{\pi}{10} + i \sin \dfrac{\pi}{10}\right)} = \dfrac{3}{4}\left[\cos\left(\dfrac{\pi}{5} - \dfrac{\pi}{10}\right) + i \sin\left(\dfrac{\pi}{5} - \dfrac{\pi}{10}\right)\right] = \dfrac{3}{4}\left(\cos \dfrac{\pi}{10} + i \sin \dfrac{\pi}{10}\right)$

49. $\dfrac{z_1}{z_2} = \dfrac{\cos 80° + i \sin 80°}{\cos 200° + i \sin 200°} = \cos(80° - 200°) + i \sin(80° - 200°) = \cos(-120°) + i \sin(-120°)$

$$= \cos 240° + i \sin 240°$$

51. Begin by converting $z_1 = 2 + 2i$ and $z_2 = 1 + i$ to polar form.

For z_1: $a = 2$ and $b = 2$

$$r = \sqrt{a^2 + b^2} = \sqrt{2^2 + 2^2} = \sqrt{8} = 2\sqrt{2}$$

$$\tan\theta = \frac{b}{a} = \frac{2}{2} = 1 \text{ and } \theta = \frac{\pi}{4}$$

$$z_1 = r(\cos\theta + i\sin\theta) = 2\sqrt{2}\left(\cos\frac{\pi}{4} + i\sin\frac{\pi}{4}\right)$$

For z_2: $a = 1$ and $b = 1$

$$r = \sqrt{a^2 + b^2} = \sqrt{1^2 + 1^2} = \sqrt{2}$$

$$\tan\theta = \frac{b}{a} = \frac{1}{1} = 1 \text{ and } \theta = \frac{\pi}{4}$$

$$z_2 = r(\cos\theta + i\sin\theta) = \sqrt{2}\left(\cos\frac{\pi}{4} + i\sin\frac{\pi}{4}\right).$$

Now, find the quotient.

$$\frac{z_1}{z_2} = \frac{2+2i}{1+i} = \frac{2\sqrt{2}\left(\cos\frac{\pi}{4} + i\sin\frac{\pi}{4}\right)}{\sqrt{2}\left(\cos\frac{\pi}{4} + i\sin\frac{\pi}{4}\right)} = 2\left[\cos\left(\frac{\pi}{4} - \frac{\pi}{4}\right) + i\sin\left(\frac{\pi}{4} - \frac{\pi}{4}\right)\right] = 2(\cos 0 + i\sin 0)$$

53. $[4(\cos 15° + i\sin 15°)]^3 = (4)^3[\cos(3 \cdot 15°) + i\sin(3 \cdot 15°)] = 64(\cos 45° + i\sin 45°) = 64\left(\frac{\sqrt{2}}{2} + i\frac{\sqrt{2}}{2}\right)$

$$= 32\sqrt{2} + 32\sqrt{2}i$$

55. $[2(\cos 80° + i\sin 80°)]^3 = (2)^3[\cos(3 \cdot 80°) + i\sin(3 \cdot 80°)] = 8(\cos 240° + i\sin 240°)$

$$= 8\left(-\frac{1}{2} + i\left(-\frac{\sqrt{3}}{2}\right)\right) = -4 - 4\sqrt{3}i$$

57. $\left[\frac{1}{2}\left(\cos\frac{\pi}{12} + i\sin\frac{\pi}{12}\right)\right]^6 = \left(\frac{1}{2}\right)^6\left[\cos\left(6 \cdot \frac{\pi}{12}\right) + i\sin\left(6 \cdot \frac{\pi}{12}\right)\right] = \frac{1}{64}\left(\cos\frac{\pi}{2} + i\sin\frac{\pi}{2}\right) = \frac{1}{64}(0 + i) = \frac{1}{64}i$

59. $\left[\sqrt{2}\left(\cos\frac{5\pi}{6} + i\sin\frac{5\pi}{6}\right)\right]^4 = \left(\sqrt{2}\right)^4\left[\cos\left(4 \cdot \frac{5\pi}{6}\right) + i\sin\left(4 \cdot \frac{5\pi}{6}\right)\right]$

$$= 4\left(\cos\frac{20\pi}{6} + i\sin\frac{20\pi}{6}\right) = 4\left(\cos\frac{4\pi}{3} + i\sin\frac{4\pi}{3}\right)$$

$$= 4\left(-\frac{1}{2} + i\left(-\frac{\sqrt{3}}{2}\right)\right) = -2 - 2\sqrt{3}i$$

61. Write $1 + i$ in $r(\cos\theta + i\sin\theta)$ form.

$$r = \sqrt{a^2 + b^2} = \sqrt{1^2 + 1^2} = \sqrt{2}$$

$$\tan\theta = \frac{b}{a} = \frac{1}{1} = 1 \text{ and } \theta = \frac{\pi}{4}$$

$$1 + i = r(\cos\theta + i\sin\theta) = \sqrt{2}\left(\cos\frac{\pi}{4} + i\sin\frac{\pi}{4}\right)$$

Use DeMoivre's Theorem to raise $1 + i$ to the fifth power.

$$(1+i)^5 = \left[\sqrt{2}\left(\cos\frac{\pi}{4} + i\sin\frac{\pi}{4}\right)\right]^5 = \left(\sqrt{2}\right)^5\left[\cos\left(5\cdot\frac{\pi}{4}\right) + i\sin\left(5\cdot\frac{\pi}{4}\right)\right]$$

$$= 4\sqrt{2}\left(\cos\frac{5\pi}{4} + i\sin\frac{5\pi}{4}\right) = 4\sqrt{2}\left(-\frac{\sqrt{2}}{2} + i\left(-\frac{\sqrt{2}}{2}\right)\right) = -4 - 4i$$

63. Write $\sqrt{3} - i$ in $r(\cos\theta + i\sin\theta)$ form.

$$r = \sqrt{a^2 + b^2} = \sqrt{\left(\sqrt{3}\right)^2 + (-1)^2} = \sqrt{4} = 2$$

$$\tan\theta = \frac{b}{a} = \frac{-1}{\sqrt{3}} = -\frac{1}{\sqrt{3}}$$

Because $\tan 30° = \dfrac{1}{\sqrt{3}}$ and θ lies in quadrant IV, $\theta = 360° - 30° = 330°$.

$$\sqrt{3} - i = r(\cos\theta + i\sin\theta) = 2(\cos 330° + i\sin 330°)$$

Use DeMoivre's Theorem to raise $\sqrt{3} - i$ to the sixth power.

$$(\sqrt{3} - i)^6 = [2(\cos 330° + i\sin 330°)]^6 = (2)^6[\cos(6\cdot 330°) + i\sin(6\cdot 330°)]$$

$$= 64(\cos 1980° + i\sin 1980°) = 64(\cos 180° + i\sin 180°)$$

$$= 64(-1 + 0i) = -64$$

65. $9(\cos 30° + i\sin 30°)$

$$z_k = \sqrt[2]{9}\left[\cos\left(\frac{30° + 360°k}{2}\right) + i\sin\left(\frac{30° + 360°k}{2}\right)\right], \; k = 0, 1$$

$$z_0 = \sqrt{9}\left[\cos\left(\frac{30° + 360°\cdot 0}{2}\right) + i\sin\left(\frac{30° + 360°\cdot 0}{2}\right)\right] = \sqrt{9}\left[\cos\left(\frac{30°}{2}\right) + i\sin\left(\frac{30°}{2}\right)\right] = 3(\cos 15° + i\sin 15°)$$

$$z_1 = \sqrt{9}\left[\cos\left(\frac{30° + 360°\cdot 1}{2}\right) + i\sin\left(\frac{30° + 360°\cdot 1}{2}\right)\right] = \sqrt{9}\left[\cos\left(\frac{390°}{2}\right) + i\sin\left(\frac{390°}{2}\right)\right] = 3(\cos 195° + i\sin 195°)$$

67. $8(\cos 210° + i \sin 210°)$

$$z_k = \sqrt[3]{8}\left[\cos\left(\frac{210° + 360°k}{3}\right) + i\sin\left(\frac{210° + 360°k}{3}\right)\right], \ k = 0, 1, 2$$

$$z_0 = \sqrt[3]{8}\left[\cos\left(\frac{210° + 360° \cdot 0}{3}\right) + i\sin\left(\frac{210° + 360° \cdot 0}{3}\right)\right] = \sqrt[3]{8}\left[\cos\left(\frac{210°}{3}\right) + i\sin\left(\frac{210°}{3}\right)\right]$$

$$= 2(\cos 70° + i \sin 70°)$$

$$z_1 = \sqrt[3]{8}\left[\cos\left(\frac{210° + 360° \cdot 1}{3}\right) + i\sin\left(\frac{210° + 360° \cdot 1}{3}\right)\right] = \sqrt[3]{8}\left[\cos\left(\frac{570°}{3}\right) + i\sin\left(\frac{570°}{3}\right)\right]$$

$$= 2(\cos 190° + i \sin 190°)$$

$$z_2 = \sqrt[3]{8}\left[\cos\left(\frac{210° + 360° \cdot 2}{3}\right) + i\sin\left(\frac{210° + 360° \cdot 2}{3}\right)\right] = \sqrt[3]{8}\left[\cos\left(\frac{930°}{3}\right) + i\sin\left(\frac{930°}{3}\right)\right]$$

$$= 2(\cos 310° + i \sin 310°)$$

69. $81\left(\cos\dfrac{4\pi}{3} + i\sin\dfrac{4\pi}{3}\right)$

$$z_k = \sqrt[4]{81}\left[\cos\left(\frac{\frac{4\pi}{3} + 2\pi k}{4}\right) + i\sin\left(\frac{\frac{4\pi}{3} + 2\pi k}{4}\right)\right], \ k = 0, 1, 2, 3$$

$$z_0 = \sqrt[4]{81}\left[\cos\left(\frac{\frac{4\pi}{3} + 2\pi \cdot 0}{4}\right) + i\sin\left(\frac{\frac{4\pi}{3} + 2\pi \cdot 0}{4}\right)\right] = \sqrt[4]{81}\left(\cos\frac{\pi}{3} + i\sin\frac{\pi}{3}\right) = 3\left(\frac{1}{2} + i\frac{\sqrt{3}}{2}\right) = \frac{3}{2} + \frac{3\sqrt{3}}{2}i$$

$$z_1 = \sqrt[4]{81}\left[\cos\left(\frac{\frac{4\pi}{3} + 2\pi \cdot 1}{4}\right) + i\sin\left(\frac{\frac{4\pi}{3} + 2\pi \cdot 1}{4}\right)\right] = \sqrt[4]{81}\left(\cos\frac{5\pi}{6} + i\sin\frac{5\pi}{6}\right) = 3\left(-\frac{\sqrt{3}}{2} + i\frac{1}{2}\right) = -\frac{3\sqrt{3}}{2} + \frac{3}{2}i$$

$$z_2 = \sqrt[4]{81}\left[\cos\left(\frac{\frac{4\pi}{3} + 2\pi \cdot 2}{4}\right) + i\sin\left(\frac{\frac{4\pi}{3} + 2\pi \cdot 2}{4}\right)\right] = \sqrt[4]{81}\left(\cos\frac{4\pi}{3} + i\sin\frac{4\pi}{3}\right)$$

$$= 3\left(-\frac{1}{2} + i\left(-\frac{\sqrt{3}}{2}\right)\right) = -\frac{3}{2} - \frac{3\sqrt{3}}{2}i$$

$$z_3 = \sqrt[4]{81}\left[\cos\left(\frac{\frac{4\pi}{3} + 2\pi \cdot 3}{4}\right) + i\sin\left(\frac{\frac{4\pi}{3} + 2\pi \cdot 3}{4}\right)\right] = \sqrt[4]{81}\left(\cos\frac{11\pi}{6} + i\sin\frac{11\pi}{6}\right)$$

$$= 3\left(\frac{\sqrt{3}}{2} + i\left(-\frac{1}{2}\right)\right) = \frac{3\sqrt{3}}{2} - \frac{3}{2}i$$

71. $32 = 32(\cos 0° + i \sin 0°)$

$$z_k = \sqrt[5]{32}\left[\cos\left(\frac{0° + 360°k}{5}\right) + i\sin\left(\frac{0° + 360°k}{5}\right)\right], \; k = 0, 1, 2, 3, 4$$

$$z_0 = \sqrt[5]{32}\left[\cos\left(\frac{0° + 360° \cdot 0}{5}\right) + i\sin\left(\frac{0° + 360° \cdot 0}{5}\right)\right] = \sqrt[5]{32}(\cos 0° + i\sin 0°) = 2(1 + 0i) = 2$$

$$z_1 = \sqrt[5]{32}\left[\cos\left(\frac{0° + 360° \cdot 1}{5}\right) + i\sin\left(\frac{0° + 360° \cdot 1}{5}\right)\right] = \sqrt[5]{32}(\cos 72° + i\sin 72°) \approx 2(0.31 + i(0.95))$$
$$\approx 0.6 + 1.9i$$

$$z_2 = \sqrt[5]{32}\left[\cos\left(\frac{0° + 360° \cdot 2}{5}\right) + i\sin\left(\frac{0° + 360° \cdot 2}{5}\right)\right] = \sqrt[5]{32}(\cos 144° + i\sin 144°) \approx 2(-0.81 + i(0.59))$$
$$\approx -1.6 + 1.2i$$

$$z_3 = \sqrt[5]{32}\left[\cos\left(\frac{0° + 360° \cdot 3}{5}\right) + i\sin\left(\frac{0° + 360° \cdot 3}{5}\right)\right] = \sqrt[5]{32}(\cos 216° + i\sin 216°) \approx 2(-0.81 + i(-0.59))$$
$$\approx -1.6 - 1.2i$$

$$z_4 = \sqrt[5]{32}\left[\cos\left(\frac{0° + 360° \cdot 4}{5}\right) + i\sin\left(\frac{0° + 360° \cdot 4}{5}\right)\right] = \sqrt[5]{32}(\cos 288° + i\sin 288°) \approx 2(0.31 + i(-0.95))$$
$$\approx 0.6 - 1.9i$$

73. $1 = 1(\cos 0° + i \sin 0°)$

$$z_k = \sqrt[3]{1}\left[\cos\left(\frac{0° + 360°k}{3}\right) + i\sin\left(\frac{0° + 360°k}{3}\right)\right], \; k = 0, 1, 2$$

$$z_0 = \sqrt[3]{1}\left[\cos\left(\frac{0° + 360° \cdot 0}{3}\right) + i\sin\left(\frac{0° + 360° \cdot 0}{3}\right)\right] = \sqrt[3]{1}(\cos 0° + i\sin 0°) = 1(1 + 0i) = 1$$

$$z_1 = \sqrt[3]{1}\left[\cos\left(\frac{0° + 360° \cdot 1}{3}\right) + i\sin\left(\frac{0° + 360° \cdot 1}{3}\right)\right] = \sqrt[3]{1}(\cos 120° + i\sin 120°) = 1\left(-\frac{1}{2} + i\frac{\sqrt{3}}{2}\right) = -\frac{1}{2} + \frac{\sqrt{3}}{2}i$$

$$z_2 = \sqrt[3]{1}\left[\cos\left(\frac{0° + 360° \cdot 2}{3}\right) + i\sin\left(\frac{0° + 360° \cdot 2}{3}\right)\right] = \sqrt[3]{1}(\cos 240° + i\sin 240°) = 1\left(-\frac{1}{2} + i\left(-\frac{\sqrt{3}}{2}\right)\right)$$

$$= -\frac{1}{2} - \frac{\sqrt{3}}{2}i$$

75. $1 + i = \sqrt{2}\left(\cos 45^\circ + i \sin 45^\circ\right)$

$$z_k = \sqrt[4]{\sqrt{2}}\left[\cos\left(\frac{45^\circ + 360^\circ k}{4}\right) + i\sin\left(\frac{45^\circ + 360^\circ k}{4}\right)\right], \; k = 0,1,2,3$$

$$z_0 = \sqrt[4]{\sqrt{2}}\left[\cos\left(\frac{45^\circ + 360^\circ \cdot 0}{4}\right) + i\sin\left(\frac{45^\circ + 360^\circ \cdot 0}{4}\right)\right] = \sqrt[4]{\sqrt{2}}\left(\cos 11.25^\circ + i\sin 11.25^\circ\right) \approx 1.1 + 0.2i$$

$$z_1 = \sqrt[4]{\sqrt{2}}\left[\cos\left(\frac{45^\circ + 360^\circ \cdot 1}{4}\right) + i\sin\left(\frac{45^\circ + 360^\circ \cdot 1}{4}\right)\right] = \sqrt[4]{\sqrt{2}}\left(\cos 101.25^\circ + i\sin 101.25^\circ\right) \approx -0.2 + 1.1i$$

$$z_2 = \sqrt[4]{\sqrt{2}}\left[\cos\left(\frac{45^\circ + 360^\circ \cdot 2}{4}\right) + i\sin\left(\frac{45^\circ + 360^\circ \cdot 2}{4}\right)\right] = \sqrt[4]{\sqrt{2}}\left(\cos 191.25^\circ + i\sin 191.25^\circ\right) \approx -1.1 - 0.2i$$

$$z_3 = \sqrt[4]{\sqrt{2}}\left[\cos\left(\frac{45^\circ + 360^\circ \cdot 3}{4}\right) + i\sin\left(\frac{45^\circ + 360^\circ \cdot 3}{4}\right)\right] = \sqrt[4]{\sqrt{2}}\left(\cos 281.25^\circ + i\sin 281.25^\circ\right) \approx 0.2 - 1.1i$$

77. $z = i$

    a. $z_1 = z = i$

$$z_2 = z^2 + z = (i)^2 + i = -1 + i$$

$$z_3 = \left(z^2 + z\right)^2 + z = z_2^2 + z = (-1 + i)^2 + i = -i$$

$$z_4 = \left[\left(z^2 + z\right)^2 + z\right]^2 + z = z_3^2 + z = (-i)^2 + i = -1 + i$$

$$z_5 = z_4^2 + z = (-1 + i)^2 + i = -i$$

$$z_6 = z_5^2 + z = (-i)^2 + i = -1 + i$$

    b. $\left|-1 + i\right| = \sqrt{(-1)^2 + 1^2} = \sqrt{2}$

$$\left|i\right| = \sqrt{0^2 + 1^2} = 1$$

The absolute values of the terms in the sequence are 1 and $\sqrt{2}$.
Choose a complex number with absolute value less than 1, and another with absolute value greater than $\sqrt{2}$. Complex numbers may vary.

79.–89. Answers may vary.

91. Exercise 27

       Exercise 29

       Exercise 31

       Exercise 33

93. $1 = 1(\cos 0° + i \sin 0°)$

$$z_k = \sqrt[4]{1}\left[\cos\left(\frac{0° + 360°k}{4}\right) + i\sin\left(\frac{0° + 360°k}{4}\right)\right], \; k = 0, 1, 2, 3$$

$$z_0 = \sqrt[4]{1}\left[\cos\left(\frac{0° + 360° \cdot 0}{4}\right) + i\sin\left(\frac{0° + 360° \cdot 0}{4}\right)\right] = \sqrt[4]{1}(\cos 0° + i\sin 0) = 1(1 + 0i) = 1$$

$$z_1 = \sqrt[4]{1}\left[\cos\left(\frac{0° + 360° \cdot 1}{4}\right) + i\sin\left(\frac{0° + 360° \cdot 1}{4}\right)\right] = \sqrt[4]{1}(\cos 90° + i\sin 90°) = 1(0 + i(1)) = i$$

$$z_2 = \sqrt[4]{1}\left[\cos\left(\frac{0° + 360° \cdot 2}{4}\right) + i\sin\left(\frac{0° + 360° \cdot 2}{4}\right)\right] = \sqrt[4]{1}(\cos 180° + i\sin 180°) = 1(-1 + 0i) = -1$$

$$z_3 = \sqrt[4]{1}\left[\cos\left(\frac{0° + 360° \cdot 3}{4}\right) + i\sin\left(\frac{0° + 360° \cdot 3}{4}\right)\right] = \sqrt[4]{1}(\cos 270° + i\sin 270°) = 1(0 + i(-1)) = -i$$

95. $x^3 - 8i = 0$

$\qquad x^3 = 8i$

We need to find the complex cube roots of $8i$.

$$8i = 8\left(\cos\frac{\pi}{2} + i\sin\frac{\pi}{2}\right)$$

$$z_k = \sqrt[3]{8}\left[\cos\left(\frac{\frac{\pi}{2} + 2\pi k}{3}\right) + i\sin\left(\frac{\frac{\pi}{2} + 2\pi k}{3}\right)\right], \; k = 0, 1, 2$$

$$z_0 = \sqrt[3]{8}\left[\cos\left(\frac{\frac{\pi}{2} + 2\pi \cdot 0}{3}\right) + i\sin\left(\frac{\frac{\pi}{2} + 2\pi \cdot 0}{3}\right)\right] = \sqrt[3]{8}\left(\cos\frac{\pi}{6} + i\sin\frac{\pi}{6}\right) = 2\left(\frac{\sqrt{3}}{2} + i\left(\frac{1}{2}\right)\right) = \sqrt{3} + i$$

$$z_1 = \sqrt[3]{8}\left[\cos\left(\frac{\frac{\pi}{2} + 2\pi \cdot 1}{3}\right) + i\sin\left(\frac{\frac{\pi}{2} + 2\pi \cdot 1}{3}\right)\right] = \sqrt[3]{8}\left(\cos\frac{5\pi}{6} + i\sin\frac{5\pi}{6}\right) = 2\left(-\frac{\sqrt{3}}{2} + i\left(\frac{1}{2}\right)\right) = -\sqrt{3} + i$$

$$z_2 = \sqrt[3]{8}\left[\cos\left(\frac{\frac{\pi}{2} + 2\pi \cdot 2}{3}\right) + i\sin\left(\frac{\frac{\pi}{2} + 2\pi \cdot 2}{3}\right)\right] = \sqrt[3]{8}\left(\cos\frac{3\pi}{2} + i\sin\frac{3\pi}{2}\right) = 2(0 + i(-1)) = -2i$$

Section 7.6

Check Point Exercises

1. First, we show that **u** and **v** have the same magnitude.

$$\|\mathbf{u}\| = \sqrt{(x_2 - x_1)^2 + (y_2 - y_1)^2}$$
$$= \sqrt{(-2 - (-5))^2 + (6 - 2)^2}$$
$$= \sqrt{3^2 + 4^2}$$
$$= \sqrt{9 + 16}$$
$$= \sqrt{25}$$
$$= 5$$
$$\|\mathbf{v}\| = \sqrt{(x_2 - x_1)^2 + (y_2 - y_1)^2}$$
$$= \sqrt{(5 - 2)^2 + (6 - 2)^2}$$
$$= \sqrt{3^2 + 4^2}$$
$$= \sqrt{9 + 16}$$
$$= \sqrt{25}$$
$$= 5$$

Thus, **u** and **v** have the same magnitude: $\|\mathbf{u}\| = \|\mathbf{v}\|$.

Next, we show that **u** and **v** have the same direction. the line on which **u** lies has slope

$$m = \frac{y_2 - y_1}{x_2 - x_1} = \frac{6 - 2}{-2 - (-5)} = \frac{4}{3}.$$

The line on which **v** lies has slope

$$m = \frac{y_2 - y_1}{x_2 - x_1} = \frac{6 - 2}{5 - 2} = \frac{4}{3}.$$

Because **u** and **v** are both directed toward the upper right on lines having the same slope $\frac{4}{3}$, they have the same direction.

Thus, **u** and **v** have the same magnitude and direction, and **u** = **v**.

2. For the given vector $\mathbf{v} = 3\mathbf{i} - 3\mathbf{j}$, $a = 3$ and $b = -3$. The vector's initial point is the origin, $(0, 0)$. The vector's terminal point is $(a, b) = (3, -3)$. We sketch the vector by drawing an arrow from $(0, 0)$ to $(3, -3)$.

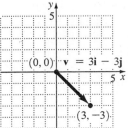

We determine the magnitude of the vector by using the distance formula. Thus, the magnitude is

$$\|\mathbf{v}\| = \sqrt{a^2 + b^2}$$
$$= \sqrt{3^2 + (-3)^2}$$
$$= \sqrt{9 + 9}$$
$$= \sqrt{18}$$
$$= 3\sqrt{2}.$$

3. We identify the values for the variables in the formula.

$$P_1 = (-1, 3) \quad P_2 = (2, 7)$$

       $\uparrow\ \uparrow$ $\uparrow\ \uparrow$
       $x_1\ y_1$ $x_2\ y_2$

Using these values, we write **v** in terms of **i** and **j** as follows:

$$\mathbf{v} = (x_2 - x_1)\mathbf{i} + (y_2 - y_1)\mathbf{j}$$
$$= (2 - (-1))\mathbf{i} + (7 - 3)\mathbf{j}$$
$$= 3\mathbf{i} + 4\mathbf{j}$$

4. a. $\mathbf{v} + \mathbf{w} = (7\mathbf{i} + 3\mathbf{j}) + (4\mathbf{i} - 5\mathbf{j})$
$$= (7 + 4)\mathbf{i} + (3 - 5)\mathbf{j}$$
$$= 11\mathbf{i} - 2\mathbf{j}$$

   b. $\mathbf{v} - \mathbf{w} = (7\mathbf{i} + 3\mathbf{j}) - (4\mathbf{i} - 5\mathbf{j})$
$$= (7 - 4)\mathbf{i} + (3 - (-5))\mathbf{j}$$
$$= 3\mathbf{i} + 8\mathbf{j}$$

5. a. $8\mathbf{v} = 8(7\mathbf{i} + 10\mathbf{j})$
$$= (8 \cdot 7)\mathbf{i} + (8 \cdot 10)\mathbf{j}$$
$$= 56\mathbf{i} + 80\mathbf{j}$$

   b. $-5\mathbf{v} = -5(7\mathbf{i} + 10\mathbf{j})$
$$= (-5 \cdot 7)\mathbf{l} + (-5 \cdot 10)\mathbf{j}$$
$$= -35\mathbf{i} - 50\mathbf{j}$$

6. $6\mathbf{v} - 3\mathbf{w} = 6(7\mathbf{i} + 3\mathbf{j}) - 3(4\mathbf{i} - 5\mathbf{j})$
$$= 42\mathbf{i} + 18\mathbf{j} - 12\mathbf{i} + 15\mathbf{j}$$
$$= (42 - 12)\mathbf{i} + (18 + 15)\mathbf{j}$$
$$= 30\mathbf{i} + 33\mathbf{j}$$

7. First, find the magnitude of **v**.
$$\|\mathbf{v}\| = \sqrt{a^2 + b^2}$$
$$= \sqrt{4^2 + (-3)^2}$$
$$= \sqrt{16 + 9}$$
$$= \sqrt{25}$$
$$= 5$$
A unit vector in the same direction as **v** is
$$\frac{\mathbf{v}}{\|\mathbf{v}\|} = \frac{4\mathbf{i} - 3\mathbf{j}}{5} = \frac{4}{5}\mathbf{i} - \frac{3}{5}\mathbf{j}$$
Now, we must verify that the magnitude of
the vector is 1. The magnitude of $\frac{4}{5}\mathbf{i} - \frac{3}{5}\mathbf{j}$ is
$$\sqrt{\left(\frac{4}{5}\right)^2 + \left(-\frac{3}{5}\right)^2} = \sqrt{\frac{16}{25} + \frac{9}{25}} = \sqrt{\frac{25}{25}} = 1.$$

8. We need to find $\|\mathbf{F}\|$ and θ.

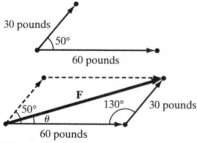

Use the Law of Cosines to find the
magnitude of **F**.
$$\|\mathbf{F}\|^2 = 60^2 + 30^2 - 2(60)(30)\cos 130° \approx 6814$$
$$\|\mathbf{F}\| \approx \sqrt{6814} \approx 82.5$$
The magnitude of the resultant force is about
82.5 pounds.

To find θ, the direction of the resultant
force, we use the Law of Sines.

$$\frac{82.5}{\sin 130°} = \frac{30}{\sin \theta}$$
$$82.5 \sin \theta = 30 \sin 130°$$
$$\sin \theta = \frac{30 \sin 130°}{82.5}$$
$$\theta = \sin^{-1}\left(\frac{30 \sin 130°}{82.5}\right) \approx 16.2°$$

The two given forces are equivalent to a
single force of about 82.5 pounds in the
direction of approximately 16.2° relative to
the 60-pound force.

Exercise Set 7.6

1. a. $\|\mathbf{u}\| = \sqrt{(x_2 - x_1)^2 + (y_2 - y_1)^2}$
$$= \sqrt{(4 - (-1))^2 + (6 - 2)^2}$$
$$= \sqrt{5^2 + 4^2}$$
$$= \sqrt{25 + 16}$$
$$= \sqrt{41}$$

   b. $\|\mathbf{v}\| = \sqrt{(x_2 - x_1)^2 + (y_2 - y_1)^2}$
$$= \sqrt{(5 - 0)^2 + (4 - 0)^2}$$
$$= \sqrt{5^2 + 4^2}$$
$$= \sqrt{25 + 16}$$
$$= \sqrt{41}$$

   c. Since $\|\mathbf{u}\| = \|\mathbf{v}\|$, and **u** and **v** have the
same direction, we can conclude that
u = **v**.

3. a. $\|\mathbf{u}\| = \sqrt{(x_2 - x_1)^2 + (y_2 - y_1)^2}$
$$= \sqrt{(5 - (-1))^2 + (1 - 1)^2}$$
$$= \sqrt{6^2 + 0^2}$$
$$= \sqrt{36 + 0}$$
$$= \sqrt{36}$$
$$= 6$$

b.
$$\| \mathbf{v} \| = \sqrt{(x_2 - x_1)^2 + (y_2 - y_1)^2}$$
$$= \sqrt{(4 - (-2))^2 + (-1 - (-1))^2}$$
$$= \sqrt{6^2 + 0^2}$$
$$= \sqrt{36 + 0}$$
$$= \sqrt{36}$$
$$= 6$$

c. Since $\| \mathbf{u} \| = \| \mathbf{v} \|$, and $\mathbf{u}$ and $\mathbf{v}$ have the same direction, we can conclude that $\mathbf{u} = \mathbf{v}$.

5.

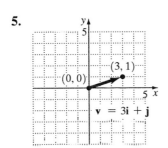

$$\| \mathbf{v} \| = \sqrt{3^2 + 1^2} = \sqrt{9 + 1} = \sqrt{10}$$

7.

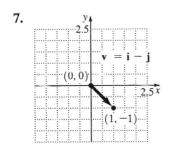

$$\| \mathbf{v} \| = \sqrt{1^2 + (-1)^2} = \sqrt{1 + 1} = \sqrt{2}$$

9.

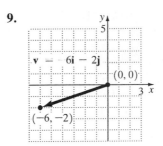

$$\| \mathbf{v} \| = \sqrt{(-6)^2 + (-2)^2}$$
$$= \sqrt{36 + 4}$$
$$= \sqrt{40}$$
$$= 2\sqrt{10}$$

11.

$$\| \mathbf{v} \| = \sqrt{(-4)^2 + 0^2} = \sqrt{16 + 0} = \sqrt{16} = 4$$

13. $\mathbf{v} = (x_2 - x_1)\mathbf{i} + (y_2 - y_1)\mathbf{j}$
$\mathbf{v} = (6 - (-4))\mathbf{i} + (2 - (-4))\mathbf{j} = 10\mathbf{i} + 6\mathbf{j}$

15. $\mathbf{v} = (x_2 - x_1)\mathbf{i} + (y_2 - y_1)\mathbf{j}$
$\mathbf{v} = (-2 - (-8))\mathbf{i} + (3 - 6)\mathbf{j} = 6\mathbf{i} - 3\mathbf{j}$

17. $\mathbf{v} = (x_2 - x_1)\mathbf{i} + (y_2 - y_1)\mathbf{j}$
$\mathbf{v} = (-7 - (-1))\mathbf{i} + (-7 - 7)\mathbf{j} = -6\mathbf{i} - 14\mathbf{j}$

19. $\mathbf{v} = (x_2 - x_1)\mathbf{i} + (y_2 - y_1)\mathbf{j}$
$\mathbf{v} = (6 - (-3))\mathbf{i} + (4 - 4)\mathbf{j} = 9\mathbf{i} + 0\mathbf{j} = 9\mathbf{i}$

21. $\mathbf{u} + \mathbf{v} = (2\mathbf{i} - 5\mathbf{j}) + (-3\mathbf{i} + 7\mathbf{j})$
$= (2 - 3)\mathbf{i} + (-5 + 7)\mathbf{j}$
$= -\mathbf{i} + 2\mathbf{j}$

23.
$$\begin{aligned}
\mathbf{u} - \mathbf{v} &= (2\mathbf{i} - 5\mathbf{j}) - (-3\mathbf{i} + 7\mathbf{j}) \\
&= 2\mathbf{i} - 5\mathbf{j} + 3\mathbf{i} - 7\mathbf{j} \\
&= (2 + 3)\mathbf{i} + (-5 - 7)\mathbf{j} \\
&= 5\mathbf{i} - 12\mathbf{j}
\end{aligned}$$

25.
$$\begin{aligned}
\mathbf{v} - \mathbf{u} &= (-3\mathbf{i} + 7\mathbf{j}) - (2\mathbf{i} - 5\mathbf{j}) \\
&= -3\mathbf{i} + 7\mathbf{j} - 2\mathbf{i} + 5\mathbf{j} \\
&= (-3 - 2)\mathbf{i} + (7 + 5)\mathbf{j} \\
&= -5\mathbf{i} + 12\mathbf{j}
\end{aligned}$$

27. $5\mathbf{v} = 5(-3\mathbf{i} + 7\mathbf{j}) = -15\mathbf{i} + 35\mathbf{j}$

29. $-4\mathbf{w} = -4(-\mathbf{i} - 6\mathbf{j}) = 4\mathbf{i} + 24\mathbf{j}$

31.
$$\begin{aligned}
3\mathbf{w} + 2\mathbf{v} &= 3(-\mathbf{i} - 6\mathbf{j}) + 2(-3\mathbf{i} + 7\mathbf{j}) \\
&= -3\mathbf{i} - 18\mathbf{j} - 6\mathbf{i} + 14\mathbf{j} \\
&= (-3 - 6)\mathbf{i} + (-18 + 14)\mathbf{j} \\
&= -9\mathbf{i} - 4\mathbf{j}
\end{aligned}$$

33.
$$\begin{aligned}
3\mathbf{v} - 4\mathbf{w} &= 3(-3\mathbf{i} + 7\mathbf{j}) - 4(-\mathbf{i} - 6\mathbf{j}) \\
&= -9\mathbf{i} + 21\mathbf{j} + 4\mathbf{i} + 24\mathbf{j} \\
&= (-9 + 4)\mathbf{i} + (21 + 24)\mathbf{j} \\
&= -5\mathbf{i} + 45\mathbf{j}
\end{aligned}$$

35.
$$\begin{aligned}
\| 2\mathbf{u} \| &= \| 2(2\mathbf{i} - 5\mathbf{j}) \| \\
&= \| 4\mathbf{i} - 10\mathbf{j} \| \\
&= \sqrt{4^2 + (-10)^2} \\
&= \sqrt{16 + 100} \\
&= \sqrt{116} \\
&= 2\sqrt{29}
\end{aligned}$$

37.
$$\begin{aligned}
\| \mathbf{w} - \mathbf{u} \| &= \| (-\mathbf{i} - 6\mathbf{j}) - (2\mathbf{i} - 5\mathbf{j}) \| \\
&= \| -\mathbf{i} - 6\mathbf{j} - 2\mathbf{i} + 5\mathbf{j} \| \\
&= \| (-1 - 2)\mathbf{i} + (-6 + 5)\mathbf{j} \| \\
&= \| -3\mathbf{i} - \mathbf{j} \| \\
&= \sqrt{(-3)^2 + (-1)^2} \\
&= \sqrt{9 + 1} \\
&= \sqrt{10}
\end{aligned}$$

39. $\dfrac{\mathbf{v}}{\| \mathbf{v} \|} = \dfrac{6\mathbf{i}}{\sqrt{6^2 + 0^2}} = \dfrac{6\mathbf{i}}{\sqrt{36}} = \dfrac{6\mathbf{i}}{6} = \mathbf{i}$

41.
$$\begin{aligned}
\frac{\mathbf{v}}{\| \mathbf{v} \|} &= \frac{3\mathbf{i} - 4\mathbf{j}}{\sqrt{3^2 + (-4)^2}} \\
&= \frac{3\mathbf{i} - 4\mathbf{j}}{\sqrt{9 + 16}} \\
&= \frac{3\mathbf{i} - 4\mathbf{j}}{\sqrt{25}} \\
&= \frac{3\mathbf{i} - 4\mathbf{j}}{5} \\
&= \frac{3}{5}\mathbf{i} - \frac{4}{5}\mathbf{j}
\end{aligned}$$

43.
$$\begin{aligned}
\frac{\mathbf{v}}{\| \mathbf{v} \|} &= \frac{3\mathbf{i} - 2\mathbf{j}}{\sqrt{3^2 + (-2)^2}} \\
&= \frac{3\mathbf{i} - 2\mathbf{j}}{\sqrt{9 + 4}} \\
&= \frac{3\mathbf{i} - 2\mathbf{j}}{\sqrt{13}} \\
&= \frac{3}{\sqrt{13}}\mathbf{i} - \frac{2}{\sqrt{13}}\mathbf{j}
\end{aligned}$$

45.
$$\begin{aligned}
\frac{\mathbf{v}}{\| \mathbf{v} \|} &= \frac{\mathbf{i} + \mathbf{j}}{\sqrt{1^2 + 1^2}} \\
&= \frac{\mathbf{i} + \mathbf{j}}{\sqrt{2}} \\
&= \frac{\mathbf{i}}{\sqrt{2}} + \frac{\mathbf{j}}{\sqrt{2}} \\
&= \frac{\sqrt{2}}{2}\mathbf{i} + \frac{\sqrt{2}}{2}\mathbf{j}
\end{aligned}$$

47. a.

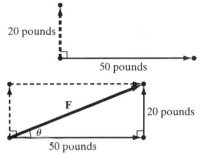

We use the Law of Cosines to find the magnitude of **F**.

$$\|\mathbf{F}\|^2 = 50^2 + 20^2 - 2(50)(20)\cos 90°$$
$$= 2900$$
$$\|\mathbf{F}\| = \sqrt{2900} \approx 53.9$$

The magnitude of the resultant force is about 53.9 pounds.

b. To find θ, the direction of the resultant force, we use the Law of Sines.

$$\frac{53.9}{\sin 90°} = \frac{20}{\sin \theta}$$
$$53.9 \sin \theta = 20 \sin 90°$$
$$\sin \theta = \frac{20 \sin 90°}{53.9}$$
$$\theta = \sin^{-1}\left(\frac{20 \sin 90°}{53.9}\right) \approx 21.8°$$

The resultant force is in the direction of approximately 21.8° relative to the 50-pound force.

49. a.

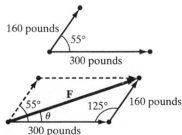

We use the Law of Cosines to find the magnitude of **F**.

$$\|\mathbf{F}\|^2 = 300^2 + 160^2 - 2(300)(160)\cos 125°$$
$$\approx 170,663.3$$
$$\|\mathbf{F}\| \approx \sqrt{170,663.3} \approx 413.1$$

The magnitude of the resultant force is approximately 413.1 pounds.

b. To find θ, the direction of the resultant force we use the Law of Sines.

$$\frac{413.1}{\sin 125°} = \frac{160}{\sin \theta}$$
$$413.1 \sin \theta = 160 \sin 125°$$
$$\sin \theta = \frac{160 \sin 125°}{413.1}$$
$$\theta = \sin^{-1}\left(\frac{160 \sin 125°}{413.1}\right) \approx 18.5°$$

The resultant force is in the direction of approximately 18.5° relative to the 300-pound force.

51. a.

v is the plane's actual speed and direction.

b. $\|\mathbf{v}\|^2 = 260^2 + 45^2 - 2(260)(45)\cos 90°$
$$= 69,625$$
$$\|\mathbf{v}\| = \sqrt{69,625} \approx 263.9$$

The plane's actual speed, to the nearest mile per hour, is 264 miles per hour.

53. $\|\mathbf{v}\|^2 = 160^2 + 75^2 - 2(160)(75)\cos 80°$
$$\approx 27,057.4$$
$$\|\mathbf{v}\| \approx \sqrt{27,057.4} \approx 164.5 \text{ mph is the}$$
resultant speed of the plane.

55.–69. Answers may vary.

71. a. False, $\mathbf{A} + \mathbf{B} = -\mathbf{E} \neq \mathbf{E}$

b. True, $\mathbf{D} + \mathbf{A} + \mathbf{B} + \mathbf{C} = 0$

c. False, $\mathbf{B} - \mathbf{E} \neq \mathbf{G} - \mathbf{F}$

d. False, $\|\mathbf{A}\| = \|\mathbf{C}\|$ so $\|\mathbf{A}\| \neq \|\mathbf{C}\|$ is an incorrect statement

(b) is true.

73.

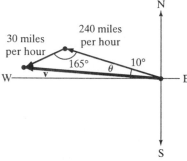

To find the magnitude of **v**, we use the Law of Cosines.

$$\|\mathbf{v}\|^2 = 30^2 + 240^2 - 2(30)(240)\cos 165°$$
$$\approx 72,409.3$$
$$\|\mathbf{v}\| \approx \sqrt{72,409.3} \approx 269.1$$

The plane's true speed relative to the ground is about 269.1 miles per hour. To find the compass heading, relative to the ground, use the Law of Sines.

$$\frac{269.1}{\sin 165°} = \frac{30}{\sin \theta}$$
$$269.1 \sin \theta = 30 \sin 165°$$
$$\sin \theta = \frac{30 \sin 165°}{269.1}$$
$$\theta = \sin^{-1}\left(\frac{30 \sin 165°}{269.1}\right)$$
$$\theta \approx 1.7$$

The compass heading relative to the ground, is approximately $270° + (10° - 1.7°)$
$= 278.3°$

Section 7.7

Check Point Exercises

1. a. $\mathbf{v} \cdot \mathbf{w} = 7(2) + (-4)(-1) = 14 + 4 = 18$

b. $\mathbf{w} \cdot \mathbf{v} = 2(7) + (-1)(-4) = 14 + 4 = 18$

c. $\mathbf{w} \cdot \mathbf{w} = 2(2) + (-1)(-1) = 4 + 1 = 5$

2. $\cos \theta = \dfrac{\mathbf{v} \cdot \mathbf{w}}{\|\mathbf{v}\| \|\mathbf{w}\|}$

$$= \frac{(4\mathbf{i} - 3\mathbf{j}) \cdot (\mathbf{i} + 2\mathbf{j})}{\sqrt{4^2 + (-3)^2}\sqrt{1^2 + 2^2}}$$

$$= \frac{4(1) + (-3)(2)}{\sqrt{25}\sqrt{5}}$$

$$= -\frac{2}{\sqrt{125}}$$

The angle θ between the vector is

$$\theta = \cos^{-1}\left(-\frac{2}{\sqrt{125}}\right) \approx 100.3°.$$

3. $\mathbf{v} \cdot \mathbf{w} = (6\mathbf{i} - 3\mathbf{j}) \cdot (\mathbf{i} + 2\mathbf{j})$
$= 6(1) + (-3)(2)$
$= 6 - 6 = 0$

The dot product is zero. Thus, the given vectors are orthogonal.

4.

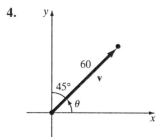

The vector's direction angle, from the positive x-axis to **v**, is $\theta = 90° - 45° = 45°$. Because the jet stream is blowing at 60 miles per hour, $\|\mathbf{v}\| = 60$. Thus,

$$\mathbf{v} = \|\mathbf{v}\|\cos \theta \mathbf{i} + \|\mathbf{v}\|\sin \theta \mathbf{j}$$
$$= 60 \cos 45° \mathbf{i} + 60 \sin 45° \mathbf{j}$$
$$= 60\left(\frac{\sqrt{2}}{2}\right)\mathbf{i} + 60\left(\frac{\sqrt{2}}{2}\right)\mathbf{j}$$
$$= 30\sqrt{2}\mathbf{i} + 30\sqrt{2}\mathbf{j}.$$

5. $\text{proj}_\mathbf{w} \mathbf{v} = \dfrac{\mathbf{v} \cdot \mathbf{w}}{\|\mathbf{w}\|^2} \mathbf{w}$

$= \dfrac{(2\mathbf{i} - 5\mathbf{j}) \cdot (\mathbf{i} - \mathbf{j})}{\left(\sqrt{1^2 + (-1)^2}\right)^2} \mathbf{w}$

$= \dfrac{2(1) + (-5)(-1)}{\left(\sqrt{2}\right)^2} \mathbf{w}$

$= \dfrac{7}{2} \mathbf{w}$

$= \dfrac{7}{2} (\mathbf{i} - \mathbf{j})$

$= \dfrac{7}{2}\mathbf{i} - \dfrac{7}{2}\mathbf{j}$

6. $\text{proj}_\mathbf{w} \mathbf{v} = \dfrac{\mathbf{v} \cdot \mathbf{w}}{\|\mathbf{w}\|^2} \mathbf{w}$

$= \dfrac{(2\mathbf{i} - 5\mathbf{j}) \cdot (\mathbf{i} - \mathbf{j})}{\left(\sqrt{1^2 + (-1)^2}\right)^2} \mathbf{w}$

$= \dfrac{2(1) + (-5)(-1)}{\left(\sqrt{2}\right)^2} \mathbf{w}$

$= \dfrac{7}{2} \mathbf{w}$

$= \dfrac{7}{2} (\mathbf{i} - \mathbf{j})$

$= \dfrac{7}{2}\mathbf{i} - \dfrac{7}{2}\mathbf{j}$

$\mathbf{v}_1 = \text{proj}_\mathbf{w} \mathbf{v} = \dfrac{7}{2}\mathbf{i} - \dfrac{7}{2}\mathbf{j}$

$\mathbf{v}_2 = \mathbf{v} - \mathbf{v}_1$

$= (2\mathbf{i} - 5\mathbf{j}) - \left(\dfrac{7}{2}\mathbf{i} - \dfrac{7}{2}\mathbf{j}\right)$

$= -\dfrac{3}{2}\mathbf{i} - \dfrac{3}{2}\mathbf{j}$

7. $W = \|\mathbf{F}\| \left\| \overrightarrow{AB} \right\| \cos\theta = (20)(150)\cos 30°$

≈ 2598

The work done is approximately 2598 foot-pounds.

Exercise Set 7.7

1. a. $\mathbf{v} \cdot \mathbf{w} = 3(1) + 1(3) = 3 + 3 = 6$

   b. $\mathbf{v} \cdot \mathbf{v} = 3(3) + 1(1) = 9 + 1 = 10$

3. a. $\mathbf{v} \cdot \mathbf{w} = 5(-2) + (-4)(-1) = -10 + 4 = -6$

   b. $\mathbf{v} \cdot \mathbf{v} = 5(5) + (-4)(-4) = 25 + 16 = 41$

5. a. $\mathbf{v} \cdot \mathbf{w} = -6(-10) + (-5)(-8)$
   $= 60 + 40$
   $= 100$

   b. $\mathbf{v} \cdot \mathbf{v} = -6(-6) + (-5)(-5) = 36 + 25 = 61$

7. $\mathbf{v} = 5\mathbf{i} + 0\mathbf{j}$ and $\mathbf{w} = 0\mathbf{i} + \mathbf{j}$

   a. $\mathbf{v} \cdot \mathbf{w} = 5(0) + 0(1) = 0 + 0 = 0$

   b. $\mathbf{v} \cdot \mathbf{v} = 5(5) + 0(0) = 25 + 0 = 25$

9. $\mathbf{u} \cdot (\mathbf{v} + \mathbf{w}) = (2\mathbf{i} - \mathbf{j}) \cdot [(3\mathbf{i} + \mathbf{j}) + (\mathbf{i} + 4\mathbf{j})]$
   $= (2\mathbf{i} - \mathbf{j}) \cdot [(3+1)\mathbf{i} + (1+4)\mathbf{j}]$
   $= (2\mathbf{i} - \mathbf{j}) \cdot (4\mathbf{i} + 5\mathbf{j})$
   $= 2(4) + (-1)(5)$
   $= 8 - 5$
   $= 3$

11. $\mathbf{u} \cdot \mathbf{v} + \mathbf{u} \cdot \mathbf{w}$
   $= (2\mathbf{i} - \mathbf{j}) \cdot (3\mathbf{i} + \mathbf{j}) + (2\mathbf{i} - \mathbf{j}) \cdot (\mathbf{i} + 4\mathbf{j})$
   $= [2(3) + (-1)(1)] + [2(1) + (-1)(4)]$
   $= [6 - 1] + [2 - 4]$
   $= 5 - 2$
   $= 3$

13. $(4\mathbf{u}) \cdot \mathbf{v}$
   $= [4(2\mathbf{i} - \mathbf{j})] \cdot (3\mathbf{i} + \mathbf{j})$
   $= (8\mathbf{i} - 4\mathbf{j}) \cdot (3\mathbf{i} + \mathbf{j})$
   $= 8(3) + (-4)(1)$
   $= 24 - 4$
   $= 20$

15. $4(\mathbf{u} \cdot \mathbf{v})$

$= 4\big[(2\mathbf{i} - \mathbf{j}) \cdot (3\mathbf{i} + \mathbf{j})\big]$

$= 4\big[2(3) + (-1)(1)\big]$

$= 4(6 - 1)$

$= 4(5)$

$= 20$

17. $\cos\theta = \dfrac{\mathbf{v} \cdot \mathbf{w}}{\|\mathbf{v}\|\,\|\mathbf{w}\|}$

$= \dfrac{(2\mathbf{i} - \mathbf{j}) \cdot (3\mathbf{i} + 4\mathbf{j})}{\sqrt{2^2 + (-1)^2}\,\sqrt{3^2 + 4^2}}$

$= \dfrac{2(3) + (-1)(4)}{\sqrt{5}\,\sqrt{25}}$

$= \dfrac{2}{\sqrt{125}}$

The angle θ between the vectors is

$\theta = \cos^{-1}\!\left(\dfrac{2}{\sqrt{125}}\right) \approx 79.7°.$

19. $\cos\theta = \dfrac{\mathbf{v} \cdot \mathbf{w}}{\|\mathbf{v}\|\,\|\mathbf{w}\|}$

$= \dfrac{(-3\mathbf{i} + 2\mathbf{j}) \cdot (4\mathbf{i} - \mathbf{j})}{\sqrt{(-3)^2 + 2^2}\,\sqrt{4^2 + (-1)^2}}$

$= \dfrac{-3(4) + 2(-1)}{\sqrt{13}\,\sqrt{17}}$

$= -\dfrac{14}{\sqrt{221}}$

The angle θ between the vectors is

$\theta = \cos^{-1}\!\left(-\dfrac{14}{\sqrt{221}}\right) \approx 160.3°.$

21. $\cos\theta = \dfrac{\mathbf{v} \cdot \mathbf{w}}{\|\mathbf{v}\|\,\|\mathbf{w}\|}$

$= \dfrac{(6\mathbf{i} + 0\mathbf{j}) \cdot (5\mathbf{i} + 4\mathbf{j})}{\sqrt{6^2 + 0^2}\,\sqrt{5^2 + 4^2}}$

$= \dfrac{6(5) + (0)(4)}{\sqrt{36}\,\sqrt{41}}$

$= \dfrac{30}{\sqrt{1476}}$

The angle θ between the vectors is

$\theta = \cos^{-1}\!\left(\dfrac{30}{\sqrt{1476}}\right) \approx 38.7°.$

23. $\mathbf{v} \cdot \mathbf{w} = (\mathbf{i} + \mathbf{j}) \cdot (\mathbf{i} - \mathbf{j}) = 1(1) + 1(-1) = 1 - 1 = 0$

The dot product is zero. Thus, the given vectors are orthogonal.

25. $\mathbf{v} \cdot \mathbf{w} = (2\mathbf{i} + 8\mathbf{j}) \cdot (4\mathbf{i} - \mathbf{j})$

$= 2(4) + 8(-1)$

$= 8 - 8$

$= 0$

The dot product is zero. Thus, the given vectors are orthogonal.

27. $\mathbf{v} \cdot \mathbf{w} = (2\mathbf{i} - 2\mathbf{j}) \cdot (-\mathbf{i} + \mathbf{j})$

$= 2(-1) + (-2)(1)$

$= -2 - 2$

$= -4$

The dot product is not zero. Thus, the given vectors are not orthogonal.

29. $\mathbf{v} \cdot \mathbf{w} = (3\mathbf{i} + 0\mathbf{j}) \cdot (-4\mathbf{i} + 0\mathbf{j})$

$= 3(-4) + 0(0)$

$= -12 + 0$

$= -12$

The dot product is not zero. Thus, the given vectors are not orthogonal.

31. $\mathbf{v} \cdot \mathbf{w} = (3\mathbf{i} + 0\mathbf{j}) \cdot (0\mathbf{i} - 4\mathbf{j})$

$= 3(0) + 0(-4)$

$= 0 + 0$

$= 0$

The dot product is zero. Thus, the given vectors are orthogonal.

33. $\mathbf{v} = \|\mathbf{v}\|\cos\theta\,\mathbf{i} + \|v\|\sin\theta\,\mathbf{j}$

$= 6\cos 30°\,\mathbf{i} + 6\sin 30°\,\mathbf{j}$

$= 6\left(\dfrac{\sqrt{3}}{2}\right)\mathbf{i} + 6\left(\dfrac{1}{2}\right)\mathbf{j}$

$= 3\sqrt{3}\,\mathbf{i} + 3\mathbf{j}$

35. $\mathbf{v} = \|\mathbf{v}\| \cos \theta \mathbf{i} + \|\mathbf{v}\| \sin \theta \mathbf{j}$

$= 12 \cos 225° \mathbf{i} + 12 \sin 225° \mathbf{j}$

$= 12\left(-\dfrac{\sqrt{2}}{2}\right)\mathbf{i} + 12\left(-\dfrac{\sqrt{2}}{2}\right)\mathbf{j}$

$= -6\sqrt{2}\mathbf{i} - 6\sqrt{2}\mathbf{j}$

37. $\mathbf{v} = \|\mathbf{v}\| \cos \theta \mathbf{i} + \|\mathbf{v}\| \sin \theta \mathbf{j}$

$= \dfrac{1}{2} \cos 113° \mathbf{i} + \dfrac{1}{2} \sin 113° \mathbf{j}$

$\approx \dfrac{1}{2}(-0.39)\mathbf{i} + \dfrac{1}{2}(0.92)\mathbf{j}$

$\approx -0.20\mathbf{i} + 0.46\mathbf{j}$

39. $\text{proj}_{\mathbf{w}} \mathbf{v} = \dfrac{\mathbf{v} \cdot \mathbf{w}}{\|\mathbf{w}\|^2} \mathbf{w}$

$= \dfrac{(3\mathbf{i} - 2\mathbf{j}) \cdot (\mathbf{i} - \mathbf{j})}{\left(\sqrt{1^2 + (-1)^2}\right)^2} \mathbf{w}$

$= \dfrac{3(1) + (-2)(-1)}{\left(\sqrt{2}\right)^2} \mathbf{w}$

$= \dfrac{5}{2} \mathbf{w}$

$= \dfrac{5}{2}(\mathbf{i} - \mathbf{j})$

$= \dfrac{5}{2}\mathbf{i} - \dfrac{5}{2}\mathbf{j}$

$\mathbf{v}_1 = \text{proj}_{\mathbf{w}} \mathbf{v} = \dfrac{5}{2}\mathbf{i} - \dfrac{5}{2}\mathbf{j}$

$\mathbf{v}_2 = \mathbf{v} - \mathbf{v}_1 = (3\mathbf{i} - 2\mathbf{j}) - \left(\dfrac{5}{2}\mathbf{i} - \dfrac{5}{2}\mathbf{j}\right)$

$= \dfrac{1}{2}\mathbf{i} + \dfrac{1}{2}\mathbf{j}$

41. $\text{proj}_{\mathbf{w}} \mathbf{v} = \dfrac{\mathbf{v} \cdot \mathbf{w}}{\|\mathbf{w}\|^2} \mathbf{w}$

$= \dfrac{(\mathbf{i} + 3\mathbf{j}) \cdot (-2\mathbf{i} + 5\mathbf{j})}{\left(\sqrt{(-2)^2 + 5^2}\right)^2} \mathbf{w}$

$= \dfrac{1(-2) + 3(5)}{\left(\sqrt{29}\right)^2} \mathbf{w}$

$= \dfrac{13}{29} \mathbf{w}$

$= \dfrac{13}{29}(-2\mathbf{i} + 5\mathbf{j})$

$= -\dfrac{26}{29}\mathbf{i} + \dfrac{65}{29}\mathbf{j}$

$\mathbf{v}_1 = \text{proj}_{\mathbf{w}} \mathbf{v} = -\dfrac{26}{29}\mathbf{i} + \dfrac{65}{29}\mathbf{j}$

$\mathbf{v}_2 = \mathbf{v} - \mathbf{v}_1$

$= (\mathbf{i} + 3\mathbf{j}) - \left(-\dfrac{26}{29}\mathbf{i} + \dfrac{65}{29}\mathbf{j}\right)$

$= \dfrac{55}{29}\mathbf{i} + \dfrac{22}{29}\mathbf{j}$

43. $\text{proj}_{\mathbf{w}} \mathbf{v} = \dfrac{\mathbf{v} \cdot \mathbf{w}}{\|\mathbf{w}\|^2} \mathbf{w}$

$= \dfrac{(\mathbf{i} + 2\mathbf{j}) \cdot (3\mathbf{i} + 6\mathbf{j})}{\left(\sqrt{3^2 + 6^2}\right)^2} \mathbf{w}$

$= \dfrac{1(3) + 2(6)}{\left(\sqrt{45}\right)^2} \mathbf{w}$

$= \dfrac{15}{45} \mathbf{w}$

$= \dfrac{1}{3} \mathbf{w}$

$= \dfrac{1}{3}(3\mathbf{i} + 6\mathbf{j})$

$= \mathbf{i} + 2\mathbf{j}$

$\mathbf{v}_1 = \text{proj}_{\mathbf{w}} \mathbf{v} = \mathbf{i} + 2\mathbf{j}$

$\mathbf{v}_2 = \mathbf{v} - \mathbf{v}_1$

$= (\mathbf{i} + 2\mathbf{j}) - (\mathbf{i} + 2\mathbf{j})$

$= 0\mathbf{i} + 0\mathbf{j}$

$= \mathbf{0}$

45. $\mathbf{v} = \|\mathbf{v}\|\cos\theta\,\mathbf{i} + \|\mathbf{v}\|\sin\theta\,\mathbf{j}$
$= 44\cos 30°\mathbf{i} + 44\sin 30°\mathbf{j}$
$= 44\left(\dfrac{\sqrt{3}}{2}\right)\mathbf{i} + 44\left(\dfrac{1}{2}\right)\mathbf{j}$
$= 22\sqrt{3}\mathbf{i} + 22\mathbf{j}$

47. $\mathbf{v} = \|\mathbf{v}\|\cos\theta\,\mathbf{i} + \|\mathbf{v}\|\sin\theta\,\mathbf{j}$
$= 150\cos 8°\mathbf{i} + 150\sin 8°\mathbf{j}$
$\approx 148.5\mathbf{i} + 20.9\mathbf{j}$

49. $\mathbf{v}\cdot\mathbf{w} = (240\mathbf{i} + 300\mathbf{j})\cdot(1.90\mathbf{i} + 2.07\mathbf{j})$
$= 240(1.90) + 300(2.07)$
$= 456 + 621$
$= 1077$

$\mathbf{v}\cdot\mathbf{w} = 1007$ means \$1077 in revenue was generated on Monday by the sale of 240 gallons of regular gas at \$1.90 per gallon and 300 gallons of premium gas at \$2.07 per gallon.

51. Since the car is pushed along a level road, the angle between the force and the direction of motion is $\theta = 0$. The work done is
$\mathrm{W} = \|\mathbf{F}\|\,\|\overrightarrow{AB}\|\cos\theta$
$= (95)(80)\cos 0°$
$= 7600.$
The work done is 7600 foot-pounds.

53. $\mathrm{W} = \|\mathbf{F}\|\,\|\overrightarrow{AB}\|\cos\theta$
$= (40)(100)\cos 32°$
≈ 3392
The work done is approximately 3392 foot-pounds.

55. $\mathbf{v} = \|\mathbf{v}\|\cos\theta\,\mathbf{i} + \|\mathbf{v}\|\sin\theta\,\mathbf{j}$
$= 1.5\cos 25°\mathbf{i} + 1.5\sin 25°\mathbf{j}$
$\approx 1.4\mathbf{i} + 0.6\mathbf{j}$
The length of the shadow is $|1.4| = 1.4$ inches

57.

40,000 pounds

12°

a. The number of pounds of force required to prevent the truck from rolling down the hill is given by the magnitude, $\|\mathbf{v}\|$, of the vector $\mathbf{v}$. From the figure, we see that $\sin 12° = \dfrac{\|\mathbf{v}\|}{40,000}$. Thus,
$40,000\sin 12° = \|\mathbf{v}\|$
and $\|\mathbf{v}\| = 40,000\sin 12° \approx 8316$.
So about 8316 pounds of force are required to prevent the truck from rolling down the hill.

b. $\mathbf{v} = \|\mathbf{v}\|\cos\theta\,\mathbf{i} + \|\mathbf{v}\|\sin\theta\,\mathbf{j}$
$\approx 8316\cos 12°\mathbf{i} + 8316\sin 12°\mathbf{j}$
$\approx 8134\mathbf{i} + 1729\mathbf{j}$

59.–69. Answers may vary.

71.
$$(c\mathbf{u}) \cdot \mathbf{v} \overset{?}{=} c(\mathbf{u} \cdot \mathbf{v})$$
$$\left[c(a_1\mathbf{i} + b_1\mathbf{j})\right] \cdot (a_2\mathbf{i} + b_2\mathbf{j}) \overset{?}{=} c\left[(a_1\mathbf{i} + b_1\mathbf{j}) \cdot (a_2\mathbf{i} + b_2\mathbf{j})\right]$$
$$(ca_1)(a_2) + (cb_1)(b_2) \overset{?}{=} c(a_1a_2) + c(b_1b_2)$$

Since a_1, a_2, b_1, b_2 and c are real numbers and multiplication of real numbers is associative,
$(ca_1)(a_2) = c(a_1a_2)$ and $(cb_1)(b_2) = c(b_1b_2)$.
Thus, $(ca_1)(a_2) + (cb_1)(b_2) = c(a_1a_2) + c(b_1b_2)$, so
$$(c\,\mathbf{u}) \cdot \mathbf{v} = c(\mathbf{u} \cdot \mathbf{v}).$$

73.

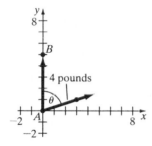

$$W = \|\mathbf{F}\| \left\| \overrightarrow{AB} \right\| \cos\theta$$

We are given that the magnitude of the force is 4 pounds, so $\|\mathbf{F}\| = 4$. We are given that the distance over which the constant force is applied is 5 feet, so $\left\| \overrightarrow{AB} \right\| = 5$. We need θ, the angle between the force and the direction of motion. Let $\mathbf{v} = 0\mathbf{i} + 5\mathbf{j}$ be the vector representing the direction of motion and $\mathbf{w} = 3\mathbf{i} + \mathbf{j}$ be the vector representing the force. Then
$$\cos\theta = \frac{\mathbf{v} \cdot \mathbf{w}}{\|\mathbf{v}\| \|\mathbf{w}\|} = \frac{(0\mathbf{i} + 5\mathbf{j}) \cdot (3\mathbf{i} + \mathbf{j})}{\sqrt{0^2 + 5^2}\sqrt{3^2 + 1^2}} = \frac{0(3) + 5(1)}{\sqrt{25}\sqrt{10}} = \frac{5}{\sqrt{250}}$$

The angle θ between the vectors is $\theta = \cos^{-1}\left(\frac{5}{\sqrt{250}}\right) \approx 71.6°$. Substituting, we have
$$W = \|\mathbf{F}\| \left\| \overrightarrow{AB} \right\| \cos\theta \approx 4(5)\cos 71.6° \approx 6.3$$

Thus, the work done is approximately 6.3 foot-pounds.

75. Let $\mathbf{v} = 15\mathbf{i} - 3\mathbf{j}$ and $\mathbf{w} = -4\mathbf{i} + b\mathbf{j}$. The vectors $\mathbf{v}$ and $\mathbf{w}$ are orthogonal if $\mathbf{v} \cdot \mathbf{w} = 0$.
$\mathbf{v} \cdot \mathbf{w} = (15\mathbf{i} - 3\mathbf{j}) \cdot (-4\mathbf{i} + b\mathbf{j}) = 15(-4) - 3(b) = -60 - 3b$
$\mathbf{v} \cdot \mathbf{w} = 0$ if $-60 - 3b = 0$. Solving the equation for b, we find $b = -20$.

77. We know that $\text{proj}_{\mathbf{w}}\mathbf{v} = \dfrac{\mathbf{v} \cdot \mathbf{w}}{\|\mathbf{w}\|^2}\mathbf{w}$. If the projection of $\mathbf{v}$ onto $\mathbf{w}$ is $\mathbf{v}$, then $\mathbf{v} = \dfrac{\mathbf{v} \cdot \mathbf{w}}{\|\mathbf{w}\|^2}\mathbf{w}$.

Since $\dfrac{\mathbf{v} \cdot \mathbf{w}}{\|\mathbf{w}\|^2}$ is a scalar for all $\mathbf{v}$ and $\mathbf{w}$, let $k = \dfrac{\mathbf{v} \cdot \mathbf{w}}{\|\mathbf{w}\|^2}$. Substituting, we have $\mathbf{v} = k\mathbf{w}$.

When one vector can be expressed as a scalar multiple of another, the vectors have the same direction. Thus, the projection of $\mathbf{v}$ onto $\mathbf{w}$ is $\mathbf{v}$ only if $\mathbf{v}$ and $\mathbf{w}$ have the same direction. Thus, any two vectors, $\mathbf{v}$ and $\mathbf{w}$, having the same direction will satisfy the condition that the projection of $\mathbf{v}$ onto $\mathbf{w}$ is $\mathbf{v}$.

Review Exercises

1. Begin by finding C.

$$A + B + C = 180°$$
$$70° + 55° + C = 180°$$
$$125° + C = 180°$$
$$C = 55°$$

Use the ratio $\dfrac{a}{\sin A}$, or $\dfrac{12}{\sin 70°}$, to find the other two sides. Use the Law of Sines to find b.

$$\frac{b}{\sin B} = \frac{a}{\sin A}$$
$$\frac{b}{\sin 55°} = \frac{12}{\sin 70°}$$
$$b = \frac{12 \sin 55°}{\sin 70°} \approx 10.5$$

Use the Law of Sines again, this time to find c.

$$\frac{c}{\sin C} = \frac{a}{\sin A}$$
$$\frac{c}{\sin 55°} = \frac{12}{\sin 70°}$$
$$c = \frac{12 \sin 55°}{\sin 70°} \approx 10.5$$

The solution is $C = 55°$, $b \approx 10.5$, $c \approx 10.5$.

2. Begin by finding A.

$$A + B + C = 180°$$
$$A + 107° + 30° = 180°$$
$$A + 137° = 180°$$
$$A = 43°$$

Use the ratio $\dfrac{c}{\sin C}$, or $\dfrac{126}{\sin 30°}$, to find the other two sides. Use the Law of Sines to find a.

$$\frac{a}{\sin A} = \frac{c}{\sin C}$$
$$\frac{a}{\sin 43°} = \frac{126}{\sin 30°}$$
$$a = \frac{126 \sin 43°}{\sin 30°} \approx 171.9$$

Use the Law of Sines again, this time to find b.

$$\frac{b}{\sin B} = \frac{c}{\sin C}$$
$$\frac{b}{\sin 107°} = \frac{126}{\sin 30°}$$
$$b = \frac{126 \sin 107°}{\sin 30°} \approx 241.0$$

The solution is
$A = 43°$, $a \approx 171.9$, and $b \approx 241.0$.

3. Apply the three-step procedure for solving a SAS triangle. Use the Law of Cosines to find the side opposite the given angle. Thus, we will find b.

$$b^2 = a^2 + c^2 - 2ac \cos B$$
$$b^2 = 17^2 + 12^2 - 2(17)(12) \cos 66°$$
$$b^2 = 289 + 144 - 408(\cos 66°)$$
$$b^2 \approx 267.05$$
$$b \approx \sqrt{267.05} \approx 16.3$$

Use the Law of Sines to find the angle opposite the shorter of the two given sides. Thus, we will find acute angle C.

$$\frac{c}{\sin C} = \frac{b}{\sin B}$$
$$\frac{12}{\sin C} = \frac{\sqrt{267.05}}{\sin 66°}$$
$$\sqrt{267.05} \sin C = 12 \sin 66°$$
$$\sin C = \frac{12 \sin 66°}{\sqrt{267.05}} \approx 0.6708$$
$$C \approx 42°$$
$$A = 180° - B - C = 180° - 66° - 42° = 72°$$

The solution is
$b \approx 16.3$, $A \approx 72°$, and $C \approx 42°$.

4. Apply the three-step procedure for solving a SSS triangle. Use the Law of Cosines to find the angle opposite the longest side. Thus, we will find angle C.

$$c^2 = a^2 + b^2 - 2ab\cos C$$
$$\cos C = \frac{a^2 + b^2 - c^2}{2ab}$$
$$= \frac{117^2 + 66^2 - 142^2}{2 \cdot 117 \cdot 66} \approx -0.1372$$

C is obtuse because $\cos C$ is negative.
$$\cos^{-1}(0.1372) \approx 82°$$
$$C \approx 180° - 82° = 98°$$

Use the Law of Sines to find either of the two remaining acute angles. We will find angle A.

$$\frac{a}{\sin A} = \frac{c}{\sin C}$$
$$\frac{117}{\sin A} = \frac{142}{\sin 98°}$$
$$142\sin A = 117\sin 98°$$
$$\sin A = \frac{117\sin 98°}{142} \approx 0.8159$$
$$A \approx 55°$$
$$B = 180° - A - C \approx 180° - 55° - 98° = 27°$$

The solution is
$C \approx 98°$, $A \approx 55°$, and $B \approx 27°$.

5. Begin by finding C.
$$A + B + C = 180°$$
$$35° + 25° + C = 180°$$
$$60° + C = 180°$$
$$C = 120°$$

Use the ratio $\dfrac{c}{\sin C}$, or $\dfrac{68}{\sin 120°}$, to find the other two sides. Use the Law of Sines to find a.

$$\frac{a}{\sin A} = \frac{c}{\sin C}$$
$$\frac{a}{\sin 35°} = \frac{68}{\sin 120°}$$
$$a = \frac{68\sin 35°}{\sin 120°} \approx 45.0$$

Use the Law of Sines again, this time to find b.

$$\frac{b}{\sin B} = \frac{c}{\sin C}$$
$$\frac{b}{\sin 25°} = \frac{68}{\sin 120°}$$
$$b = \frac{68\sin 25°}{\sin 120°} \approx 33.2$$

The solution is
$C = 120°$, $a \approx 45.0$, and $b \approx 33.2$.

6. The known ratio is $\dfrac{a}{\sin A}$, or $\dfrac{20}{\sin 39°}$.

Because side b is given, we used the Law of Sines to find angle B.

$$\frac{b}{\sin B} = \frac{a}{\sin A}$$
$$\frac{26}{\sin B} = \frac{20}{\sin 39°}$$
$$\sin B = \frac{26\sin 39°}{20} \approx 0.8181$$
$$B_1 \approx 55°, \ B_2 \approx 180° - 55° = 125°$$
$$C_1 = 180° - A - B_1 \approx 180° - 39° - 55° = 86°$$
$$C_2 = 180° - A - B_2 \approx 180° - 39° - 125° = 16°$$

Use the Law of Sines to find c_1 and c_2.

$$\frac{c_1}{\sin C_1} = \frac{a}{\sin A}$$
$$\frac{c_1}{\sin 86°} = \frac{20}{\sin 39°}$$
$$c_1 = \frac{20\sin 86°}{\sin 39°} \approx 31.7$$
$$\frac{c_2}{\sin C_2} = \frac{a}{\sin A}$$
$$\frac{c_2}{\sin 16°} = \frac{20}{\sin 39°}$$
$$c_2 = \frac{20\sin 16°}{\sin 39°} \approx 8.8$$

There are two triangles. In one triangle, the solution is $B_1 \approx 55°$, $C_1 \approx 86°$, and $c_1 \approx 31.7$. In the other triangle, $B_2 \approx 125°$, $C_2 \approx 16°$, and $c_2 \approx 8.8$.

7. The known ration is $\dfrac{c}{\sin C}$, or $\dfrac{1}{\sin 50°}$.
Because side a is given, we used the Law of Sines to find angle A.

$$\frac{a}{\sin A} = \frac{c}{\sin C}$$

$$\frac{3}{\sin A} = \frac{1}{\sin 50°}$$

$$\sin A = \frac{3\sin 50°}{1} \approx 2.30$$

Because the sine can never exceed 1, there is no triangle with the given measurements.

8. Apply the three-step procedure for solving a SAS triangle. Use the Law of Cosines to find the side opposite the given angle. Thus, we will find a.

$$a^2 = b^2 + c^2 - 2bc\cos A$$

$$a^2 = (11.2)^2 + (48.2)^2 - 2(11.2)(48.2)\cos 162°$$

$$\approx 3475.5$$

$$a \approx \sqrt{3475.5} \approx 59.0$$

Use the Law of Sines to find the angle opposite the shorter of the two given sides. Thus, we will find acute angle B.

$$\frac{b}{\sin B} = \frac{a}{\sin A}$$

$$\frac{11.2}{\sin B} = \frac{\sqrt{3475.5}}{\sin 162°}$$

$$\sin B = \frac{11.2\sin 162°}{\sqrt{3475.5}} \approx 0.0587$$

$$B \approx 3°$$

$$C = 180° - A - B \approx 180° - 162° - 3° = 15°$$

The solution is $a \approx 59.0$, $B \approx 3°$, and $C \approx 15°$.

9. Apply the three-step procedure for solving a SSS triangle. Use the Law of Cosines to find the angle opposite the longest side. Thus, we will find angle B.

$$\cos B = \frac{a^2 + c^2 - b^2}{2ac}$$

$$\cos B = \frac{(26.1)^2 + (36.5)^2 - (40.2)^2}{2 \cdot 26.1 \cdot 36.5}$$

$$\approx 0.2086$$

$$B \approx 78°$$

Use the Law of Sines to find either of the two remaining acute angles. We will find angle A.

$$\frac{a}{\sin A} = \frac{b}{\sin B}$$

$$\frac{26.1}{\sin A} = \frac{40.2}{\sin 78°}$$

$$\sin A = \frac{26.1\sin 78°}{40.2} \approx 0.6351$$

$$A \approx 39°$$

$$C = 180° - A - B \approx 180° - 39° - 78° = 63°$$

The solution is $B \approx 78°$, $A \approx 39°$, and $C \approx 63°$.

10. The known ratio is $\dfrac{a}{\sin A}$, or $\dfrac{6}{\sin 40°}$.
Because side b is given, we used the Law of Sines to find angle B.

$$\frac{b}{\sin B} = \frac{a}{\sin A}$$

$$\frac{4}{\sin B} = \frac{6}{\sin 40°}$$

$$\sin B = \frac{4\sin 40°}{6} \approx 0.4285$$

$$B_1 \approx 25°, \; B_2 \approx 180° - 25° = 155°$$

B_2 is impossible, since $40° + 155° = 195°$.

$$C = 180° - A - B_1 \approx 180° - 40° - 25° = 115°$$

Use the Law of Sines to find c.

$$\frac{c}{\sin C} = \frac{a}{\sin A}$$

$$\frac{c}{\sin 115°} = \frac{6}{\sin 40°}$$

$$c = \frac{6\sin 115°}{\sin 40°} \approx 8.5$$

The solution is B_1 (or B) $\approx 25°$, $C \approx 115°$, and $c \approx 8.5$.

11. The known ratio is $\dfrac{b}{\sin B}$, or $\dfrac{8.7}{\sin 37°}$.
Because side a is given, we use the Law of Sines to find angle A.

$$\frac{a}{\sin A}=\frac{b}{\sin B}$$
$$\frac{12.4}{\sin A}=\frac{8.7}{\sin 37°}$$
$$\sin A=\frac{12.4\sin 37°}{8.7}\approx 0.8578$$

$A_1\approx 59°,\ A_2\approx 180°-59°=121°$
$C_1=180°-A_1-B$
$\quad\approx 180°-59°-37°-84°$
$C_2=180°-A_2-B$
$\quad\approx 180°-121°-37°=22°$
Use the Law of Sines to find c_1 and c_2.

$$\frac{c_1}{\sin C_1}=\frac{b}{\sin B}$$
$$\frac{c_1}{\sin 84°}=\frac{8.7}{\sin 37°}$$
$$c_1=\frac{8.7\sin 84°}{\sin 37°}\approx 14.4$$
$$\frac{c_2}{\sin C_2}=\frac{b}{\sin B}$$
$$\frac{c_2}{\sin 22°}=\frac{8.7}{\sin 37°}$$
$$c_2=\frac{8.7\sin 22°}{\sin 37°}\approx 5.4$$

There are two triangles. In one triangle, the solution is $A_1\approx 59°$, $C_1\approx 84°$, and $c_1\approx 14.4$. In the other triangle, $A_2\approx 121°$, $C_2\approx 22°$, and $c_2\approx 5.4$.

12. The known ratio is $\dfrac{a}{\sin A}$, or $\dfrac{54.3}{\sin 23°}$.
Because side b is given, we used the Law of Sines to find angle B.

$$\frac{b}{\sin B}=\frac{a}{\sin A}$$
$$\frac{22.1}{\sin B}=\frac{54.3}{\sin 23°}$$
$$\sin B=\frac{22.1\sin 23°}{54.3}\approx 0.1590$$

$B_1\approx 9°,\ B_2\approx 180°-9°=171°$
B_2 is impossible, since $23°+171°=194°$.

$C=180°-A-B_1\approx 180°-23°-9°=148°$
Use the Law of Sines to find c.

$$\frac{c}{\sin C}=\frac{a}{\sin A}$$
$$\frac{c}{\sin 148°}=\frac{54.3}{\sin 23°}$$
$$c=\frac{54.3\sin 148°}{\sin 23°}\approx 73.6$$

The solution is B_1 (or B) $\approx 9°$, $C\approx 148°$, and $c\approx 73.6$.

13. Area $=\dfrac{1}{2}ab\sin C$
$\quad =\dfrac{1}{2}(4)(6)\sin 42°$
$\quad \approx 8$
The area of the triangle is approximately 8 square feet.

14. Area $=\dfrac{1}{2}bc\sin A$
$\quad =\dfrac{1}{2}(4)(5)\sin 22°$
$\quad \approx 4$
The area of the triangle is approximately 4 square feet.

15. $s=\dfrac{1}{2}(a+b+c)=\dfrac{1}{2}(2+4+5)=\dfrac{11}{2}$
Area $=\sqrt{s(s-a)(s-b)(s-c)}$
$\quad =\sqrt{\dfrac{11}{2}\left(\dfrac{11}{2}-2\right)\left(\dfrac{11}{2}-4\right)\left(\dfrac{11}{2}-5\right)}$
$\quad =\sqrt{\dfrac{231}{16}}\approx 4$
The area of the triangle is approximately 4 square meters.

16. $s=\dfrac{1}{2}(a+b+c)=\dfrac{1}{2}(2+2+2)=3$
Area $=\sqrt{s(s-a)(s-b)(s-c)}$
$\quad =\sqrt{3(3-2)(3-2)(3-2)}$
$\quad =\sqrt{3}\approx 2$
The area of the triangle is approximately 2 square meters.

17.

Using the figure,
$C = 180° - 60° - 60° = 60°$
Use the Law of Sines to find a.

$$\frac{a}{\sin 60°} = \frac{35}{\sin 60°}$$
$$a = 35$$

The length of the roof is 35 feet.

18. One car travels 60 miles per hour for 30 minutes (half an hour), or $60\left(\frac{1}{2}\right) = 30$ miles. Similarly, the other car travels 25 miles.

Using the figure,
$$b^2 = a^2 + c^2 - 2ac\cos B$$
$$= 25^2 + 30^2 - 2(25)(30)\cos 80° \approx 1264.53$$
$$b \approx \sqrt{1264.53} \approx 35.6$$

The cars will be about 35.6 miles apart.

19. The first plane travels 325 miles per hour for 2 hours, or $325 \cdot 2 = 650$ miles. Similarly, the other plane travels $300 \cdot 2 = 600$ miles.

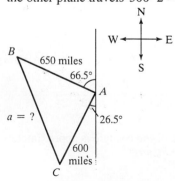

Using the figure,
$A = 180° - 66.5° - 26.5° = 87°$
Use the Law of Cosines to find a.

$$a^2 = b^2 + c^2 - 2bc\cos A$$
$$= 600^2 + 650^2 - 2(600)(650)\cos 87°$$
$$\approx 741,678$$
$$a \approx \sqrt{741,678} \approx 861$$

The planes are about 861 miles apart.

20.

Using the figure,
$C = 180° - A - B = 180° - 55° - 46° = 79°$
Use the Law of Sines to find b.

$$\frac{b}{\sin B} = \frac{a}{\sin A}$$
$$\frac{b}{\sin 46°} = \frac{460}{\sin 55°}$$
$$b = \frac{460\sin 46°}{\sin 55°} \approx 404$$

Use the Law of Sines again, this time to find c.

$$\frac{c}{\sin C} = \frac{a}{\sin A}$$
$$\frac{c}{\sin 79°} = \frac{460}{\sin 55°}$$
$$c = \frac{460\sin 79°}{\sin 55°} \approx 551$$

The lengths are about 404 feet and 551 feet.

21. $s = \dfrac{1}{2}(a + b + c) = \dfrac{1}{2}(260 + 320 + 450) = 515$

$$\text{Area} = \sqrt{s(s-a)(s-b)(s-c)}$$
$$= \sqrt{515(515 - 260)(515 - 320)(515 - 450)}$$
$$= \sqrt{1,664,544,375} \approx 40,798.83$$
$$\text{cost} \approx (5.25)(40,798.83) \approx 214,194$$

The cost is approximately $214,194.

22. Draw $\theta = 60°$ counterclockwise, since, θ is positive, from the polar axis. Go 4 units out on the terminal side of θ, since $r > 0$.

$$x = r\cos\theta = 4\cos 60° = 4\left(\frac{1}{2}\right) = 2$$

$$y = r\sin\theta = 4\sin 60° = 4\left(\frac{\sqrt{3}}{2}\right) = 2\sqrt{3}$$

The rectangular coordinates of $(4, 60°)$ are $\left(2, 2\sqrt{3}\right)$.

23. Draw $\theta = 150°$ counterclockwise, since θ is positive, from the polar axis. Go 3 units out on the terminal side of θ, since $r > 0$.

$$x = r\cos\theta = 3\cos 150° = 3\left(-\frac{\sqrt{3}}{2}\right) = -\frac{3\sqrt{3}}{2}$$

$$y = r\sin\theta = 3\sin 150° = 3\left(\frac{1}{2}\right) = \frac{3}{2}$$

The rectangular coordinates of $(3, 150°)$ are $\left(-\frac{3\sqrt{3}}{2}, \frac{3}{2}\right)$.

24. Draw $\theta = \frac{4\pi}{3} = 240°$ counterclockwise, since θ is positive, from the polar axis. Go 4 units out opposite the terminal side of θ, since $r < 0$.

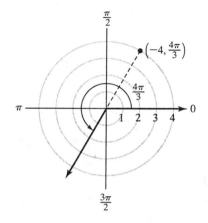

$$x = r\cos\theta = -4\cos\frac{4\pi}{3} = -4\left(-\frac{1}{2}\right) = 2$$

$$y = r\sin\theta = -4\sin\frac{4\pi}{3} = -4\left(-\frac{\sqrt{3}}{2}\right) = 2\sqrt{3}$$

The rectangular coordinates of $\left(-4, \frac{4\pi}{3}\right)$ are $\left(2, 2\sqrt{3}\right)$.

25. Draw $\theta = \dfrac{5\pi}{4} = 225°$ counterclockwise, since θ is positive from the polar axis. Go 2 units out opposite the terminal side of θ, since $r < 0$.

$$x = r\cos\theta = -2\cos\frac{5\pi}{4} = -2\left(-\frac{\sqrt{2}}{2}\right) = \sqrt{2}$$

$$y = r\sin\theta = -2\sin\frac{5\pi}{4} = -2\left(-\frac{\sqrt{2}}{2}\right) = \sqrt{2}$$

The rectangular coordinates of $\left(-2, \dfrac{5\pi}{4}\right)$ are $\left(\sqrt{2}, \sqrt{2}\right)$.

26. Draw $\theta = -\dfrac{\pi}{2} = -90°$ clockwise, since θ is negative, from the polar axis. Go 4 units out opposite the terminal side of θ, since $r < 0$.

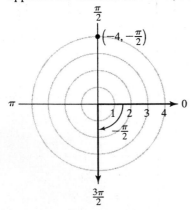

$$x = r\cos\theta = -4\cos\left(-\frac{\pi}{2}\right) = -4(0) = 0$$

$$y = r\sin\theta = -4\sin\left(-\frac{\pi}{2}\right) = -4(-1) = 4$$

The rectangular coordinates of $\left(-4, -\dfrac{\pi}{2}\right)$ are $(0, 4)$.

27. Draw $\theta = -\dfrac{\pi}{4} = -45°$ clockwise, since θ is negative, from the polar axis. Plot the point out 2 units opposite the terminal side of θ, since $r < 0$.

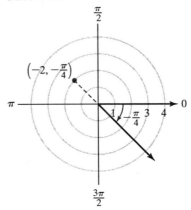

$$x = r\cos\theta = -2\cos\left(-\frac{\pi}{4}\right) = -2\left(\frac{\sqrt{2}}{2}\right) = -\sqrt{2}$$

$$y = r\sin\theta = -2\sin\left(-\frac{\pi}{4}\right) = -2\left(-\frac{\sqrt{2}}{2}\right) = \sqrt{2}$$

The rectangular coordinates of $\left(-2, -\dfrac{\pi}{4}\right)$ are $\left(-\sqrt{2}, \sqrt{2}\right)$.

28. Draw $\theta = \dfrac{\pi}{6} = 30°$ counterclockwise, since θ is positive, from the polar axis. Go out 3 units on the terminal side of θ, since $r > 0$.

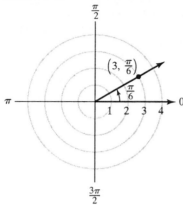

a. $\left(3, \dfrac{\pi}{6}\right) = \left(3, \dfrac{\pi}{6} + 2\pi\right) = \left(3, \dfrac{13\pi}{6}\right)$

b. $\left(3, \dfrac{\pi}{6}\right) = \left(-3, \dfrac{\pi}{6} + \pi\right) = \left(-3, \dfrac{7\pi}{6}\right)$

c. $\left(3, \dfrac{\pi}{6}\right) = \left(3, \dfrac{\pi}{6} - 2\pi\right) = \left(3, -\dfrac{11\pi}{6}\right)$

29. Draw $\theta = \dfrac{2\pi}{3} = 120°$ counterclockwise, since θ is positive, from the polar axis. Go out 3 units on the terminal side of θ, since $r > 0$.

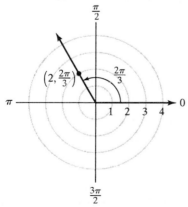

a. $\left(2, \dfrac{2\pi}{3}\right) = \left(2, \dfrac{2\pi}{3} + 2\pi\right) = \left(2, \dfrac{8\pi}{3}\right)$

b. $\left(2, \dfrac{2\pi}{3}\right) = \left(-2, \dfrac{2\pi}{3} + \pi\right) = \left(-2, \dfrac{5\pi}{3}\right)$

c. $\left(2, \dfrac{2\pi}{3}\right) = \left(2, \dfrac{2\pi}{3} - 2\pi\right) = \left(2, -\dfrac{4\pi}{3}\right)$

30. Draw $\theta = \pi = 180°$ counterclockwise, since θ is positive, from the polar axis. Go out 3 units on the terminal side of θ, since $r > 0$.

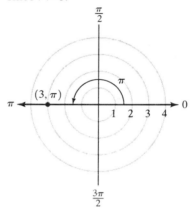

a. $(3, \pi) = (3, \pi + 2\pi) = (3, 3\pi)$

b. $(3, \pi) = (-3, \pi + \pi) = (-3, 2\pi)$

c. $(3, \pi) = (3, \pi - 2\pi) = (3, -\pi)$

31. $(-4, 4)$

$$r = \sqrt{(-4)^2 + (-4)^2} = \sqrt{16 + 16} = \sqrt{32} = 4\sqrt{2}$$

$$\tan\theta = \dfrac{4}{-4} = -1$$

Because $\tan\dfrac{\pi}{4} = 1$ and θ lies in quadrant II,

$$\theta = \pi - \dfrac{\pi}{4} = \dfrac{3\pi}{4}.$$

The polar coordinates of $(-4,4)$ are

$$\left(4\sqrt{2}, \dfrac{3\pi}{4}\right).$$

32. $(3,-3)$

$r = \sqrt{3^2 + (-3)^2} = \sqrt{9+9} = \sqrt{18} = 3\sqrt{2}$

$\tan\theta = \dfrac{-3}{3} = -1$

Because $\tan\dfrac{\pi}{4} = 1$, and θ lies in

quadrant IV, $\theta = 2\pi - \dfrac{\pi}{4} = \dfrac{7\pi}{4}$.

The polar coordinates of $(3, -3)$ are

$\left(3\sqrt{2}, \dfrac{7\pi}{4}\right)$.

33. $(5,12)$

$r = \sqrt{5^2 + 12^2} = \sqrt{25 + 144} = \sqrt{169} = 13$

$\tan\theta = \dfrac{12}{5}$

Because $\tan^{-1}\left(\dfrac{12}{5}\right) \approx 67°$ and θ lies in

quadrant I, $\theta \approx 67°$.
The polar coordinates of $(5,12)$ are
approximately $(13, 67°)$.

34. $(-3,4)$

$r = \sqrt{(-3)^2 + 4^2} = \sqrt{9+16} = \sqrt{25} = 5$

$\tan\theta = \dfrac{4}{-3} = -\dfrac{4}{3}$

Because $\tan^{-1}\left(\dfrac{4}{3}\right) \approx 53°$ and θ lies in

quadrant II, $\theta \approx 180° - 53° = 127°$. The
polar coordinates of $(-3, 4)$ are $(5, 127°)$.

35. $(0,-5)$

$r = \sqrt{0^2 + (-5)^2} = \sqrt{25} = 5$

$\tan\theta = \dfrac{-5}{0}$ is undefined

Because $\tan\dfrac{\pi}{2}$ is undefined and θ lies on

the negative y-axis, $\theta = \dfrac{\pi}{2} + \pi = \dfrac{3\pi}{2}$. The

polar coordinates of $(0,-5)$ are $\left(5, \dfrac{3\pi}{2}\right)$.

36. $(1,0)$

$r = \sqrt{1^2 + 0^2} = \sqrt{1} = 1$

$\tan\theta = \dfrac{0}{1} = 0$

Because $\tan 0 = 0$ and θ lies on the positive
x-axis, $\theta = 0$.
The polar coordinates of $(1,0)$ are $(1,0)$.

37.
$$2x + 3y = 8$$
$$2r\cos\theta + 3r\sin\theta = 8$$
$$r(2\cos\theta + 3\sin\theta) = 8$$
$$r = \dfrac{8}{2\cos\theta + 3\sin\theta}$$

38. $x^2 + y^2 = 100$
$$r^2 = 100$$
$$r = 10$$

39. $5x^2 + 5y^2 = 3y$
$$5(x^2 + y^2) = 3y$$
$$5r^2 = 3r\sin\theta$$
$$5r = 3\sin\theta$$
$$r = \dfrac{3\sin\theta}{5}$$

40.
$$r = 3$$
$$r^2 = 9$$
$$x^2 + y^2 = 9$$

41. $\theta = \dfrac{3\pi}{4}$

$\tan\theta = \tan\dfrac{3\pi}{4} = -1$

$\dfrac{y}{x} = -1$

$y = -x$

42. $r\cos\theta = -1$
$$x = -1$$

43. $r = 5\sec\theta$
$$r = \dfrac{5}{\cos\theta}$$
$$r\cos\theta = 5$$
$$x = 5$$

44.
$$r = 3\cos\theta$$
$$r \cdot r = 3r\cos\theta$$
$$r^2 = 3r\cos\theta$$
$$x^2 + y^2 = 3x$$

45.
$$5r\cos\theta + r\sin\theta = 8$$
$$5x + y = 8$$

46.
$$r^2 \sin 2\theta = 4$$
$$r^2(2\sin\theta\cos\theta) = 4$$
$$2r\sin\theta r\cos\theta = 4$$
$$2yx = 4$$
$$yx = 2$$
$$y = \frac{2}{x}$$

47. $r = 5 + 3\cos\theta$

    a. $r = 5 + 3\cos(-\theta)$
$$r = 5 + 3\cos\theta$$
       The graph has symmetry about the polar axis.

    b. $-r = 5 + 3\cos(-\theta)$
$$-r = 5 + 3\cos\theta$$
$$r = -5 - 3\cos\theta$$
       The graph may or may not have symmetry with respect to the line $\theta = \frac{\pi}{2}$.

    c. $-r = 5 + 3\cos\theta$
$$r = -5 - 3\cos\theta$$
       The graph may or may not have symmetry with respect to the pole.

48. $r = 3\sin\theta$

    a. $r = 3\sin(-\theta)$
$$r = -3\sin\theta$$
       The graph may or may not have symmetry with respect to the polar axis.

    b. $-r = 3\sin(-\theta)$
$$-r = -3\sin\theta$$
$$r = 3\sin\theta$$
       The graph has symmetry with respect to line $\theta = \frac{\pi}{2}$.

    c. $-r = 3\sin\theta$
$$r = -3\sin\theta$$
       The graph may or may not have symmetry with respect to the pole.

49. $r^2 = 9\cos 2\theta$

    a. $r^2 = 9\cos 2(-\theta)$
$$r^2 = 9\cos(-2\theta)$$
$$r^2 = 9\cos 2\theta$$
       The graph has symmetry with respect to the polar axis.

    b. $(-r)^2 = 9\cos 2(-\theta)$
$$r^2 = 9\cos(-2\theta)$$
$$r^2 = 9\cos 2\theta$$
       The graph has symmetry with respect to the line $\theta = \frac{\pi}{2}$.

    c. $(-r)^2 = 9\cos 2\theta$
$$r^2 = 9\cos 2\theta$$
       The graph has symmetry with respect to the pole.

50. $r = 3\cos\theta$
Check for symmetry:

Polar Axis	The Line $\theta = \dfrac{\pi}{2}$	The Pole
$r = 3\cos(-\theta)$	$-r = 3\cos(-\theta)$	$-r = 3\cos\theta$
	$-r = 3\cos\theta$	
$r = 3\cos\theta$	$r = -3\cos\theta$	$r = -3\cos\theta$

The graph has symmetry with respect to the polar axis. The graph may or may not be symmetric with respect to the line $\theta = \dfrac{\pi}{2}$ or the pole. Calculate values of r for θ from 0 to π and use symmetry to obtain the graph.

θ	0	$\dfrac{\pi}{6}$	$\dfrac{\pi}{3}$	$\dfrac{\pi}{2}$	$\dfrac{2\pi}{3}$	$\dfrac{5\pi}{6}$	π
r	3	2.60	1.5	0	−1.5	−2.60	−3

Use symmetry to obtain the graph.

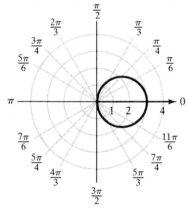

Notice that there are no points in quadrants II or III. Because the cosine is negative in quadrants II and III, r is negative here. This places the points in quadrants IV and I respectively.

51. $r = 2 + 2\sin\theta$
Check for symmetry:

Polar Axis	The Line $\theta = \dfrac{\pi}{2}$	The Pole
$r = 2 + 2\sin(-\theta)$	$-r = 2 + 2\sin(-\theta)$	$-r = 2 + 2\sin\theta$
	$-r = 2 - 2\sin\theta$	
$r = 2 - 2\sin\theta$	$r = -2 + 2\sin\theta$	$r = -2 - 2\sin\theta$

There may be no symmetry, since each equation is not equivalent to $r = 2 + 2\sin\theta$. Calculate values of r for θ from 0 to 2π.

θ	0	$\dfrac{\pi}{6}$	$\dfrac{\pi}{3}$	$\dfrac{\pi}{2}$	$\dfrac{2\pi}{3}$	$\dfrac{5\pi}{6}$	π
r	2	3	3.73	4	3.73	3	2

θ	$\dfrac{7\pi}{6}$	$\dfrac{4\pi}{3}$	$\dfrac{3\pi}{2}$	$\dfrac{5\pi}{3}$	$\dfrac{11\pi}{6}$	2π
r	1	0.27	0	0.27	1	2

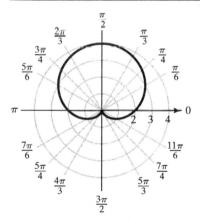

52. $r = \sin 2\theta$
Check for symmetry:

Polar Axis	The Line $\theta = \dfrac{\pi}{2}$	The Pole
$r = \sin 2(-\theta)$	$-r = \sin 2(-\theta)$	$-r = \sin 2\theta$
$r = \sin(-2\theta)$	$-r = \sin(-2\theta)$	
	$-r = -\sin 2\theta$	
$r = -\sin 2\theta$	$r = \sin 2\theta$	$r = -\sin 2\theta$

The graph has symmetry with respect to the line $\theta = \dfrac{\pi}{2}$. The graph may or may not be symmetric with respect to the polar axis or the pole. Calculate values of r for θ from 0 to $\dfrac{\pi}{2}$ and for θ from π to $\dfrac{3\pi}{2}$. Then, use symmetry to obtain the graph.

θ	0	$\dfrac{\pi}{6}$	$\dfrac{\pi}{4}$	$\dfrac{\pi}{3}$	$\dfrac{\pi}{2}$
r	0	0.87	1	0.87	0

θ	π	$\dfrac{7\pi}{6}$	$\dfrac{5\pi}{4}$	$\dfrac{4\pi}{3}$	$\dfrac{3\pi}{2}$
r	0	0.87	1	0.87	0

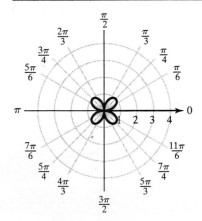

53. $r = 2 + \cos\theta$
Check for symmetry:

Polar Axis	The Line $\theta = \dfrac{\pi}{2}$	The Pole
$r = 2 + \cos(-\theta)$	$-r = 2 + \cos(-\theta)$	$-r = 2 + \cos\theta$
	$-r = 2 + \cos\theta$	
$r = 2 + \cos\theta$	$r = -2 - \cos\theta$	$r = -2 - \cos\theta$

The graph is symmetric with respect to the polar axis. The graph may or may not be symmetric with respect to the line $\theta = \dfrac{\pi}{2}$ or the pole. Calculate values of r for θ from 0 to π and use symmetry to obtain the graph.

θ	0	$\dfrac{\pi}{6}$	$\dfrac{\pi}{3}$	$\dfrac{\pi}{2}$	$\dfrac{2\pi}{3}$	$\dfrac{5\pi}{6}$	π
r	3	2.87	2.5	2	1.5	1.13	1

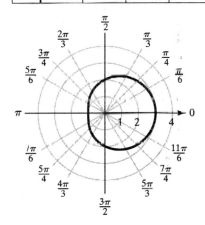

54. $r = 1 + 3\sin\theta$
Check for symmetry:

Polar Axis	The Line $\theta = \dfrac{\pi}{2}$	The Pole
$r = 1 + 3\sin(-\theta)$	$-r = 1 + 3\sin(-\theta)$	$-r = 1 + 3\sin\theta$
	$-r = 1 - 3\sin\theta$	
$r = 1 - 3\sin\theta$	$r = -1 + 3\sin\theta$	$r = -1 - 3\sin\theta$

There may be no symmetry, since each equation is not equivalent to $r = 1 + 3\sin\theta$. Calculate values of r for θ from 0 to 2π.

θ	0	$\dfrac{\pi}{6}$	$\dfrac{\pi}{3}$	$\dfrac{\pi}{2}$	$\dfrac{2\pi}{3}$	$\dfrac{5\pi}{6}$	π
r	1	2.5	3.60	4	3.60	2.5	1

θ	$\dfrac{7\pi}{6}$	$\dfrac{4\pi}{3}$	$\dfrac{3\pi}{2}$	$\dfrac{5\pi}{3}$	$\dfrac{11\pi}{6}$	2π
r	−0.5	−1.60	−2	−1.60	−0.5	1

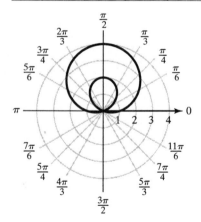

55. $r = 1 - 2\cos\theta$
Check for symmetry:

Polar Axis	The Line $\theta = \dfrac{\pi}{2}$	The Pole
$r = 1 - 2\cos(-\theta)$	$-r = 1 - 2\cos(-\theta)$	$-r = 1 - 2\cos\theta$
	$-r = 1 - 2\cos\theta$	
$r = 1 - 2\cos\theta$	$r = -1 + 2\cos\theta$	$r = -1 + 2\cos\theta$

The graph is symmetric with respect to the polar axis. The graph may or may not be symmetric with respect to the line $\theta = \dfrac{\pi}{2}$ or the pole. Calculate values of r for θ from 0 to π and use symmetry to obtain the graph.

θ	0	$\dfrac{\pi}{6}$	$\dfrac{\pi}{3}$	$\dfrac{\pi}{2}$	$\dfrac{2\pi}{3}$	$\dfrac{5\pi}{6}$	π
r	-1	-0.73	0	1	2	2.73	3

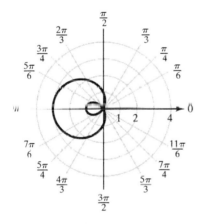

56. $r^2 = \cos 2\theta$

Check for symmetry:

Polar Axis	The Line $\theta = \dfrac{\pi}{2}$	The Pole
$r^2 = \cos 2(-\theta)$	$(-r)^2 = \cos 2(-\theta)$	$(-r)^2 = \cos 2\theta$
$r^2 = \cos(-2\theta)$	$r^2 = \cos(-2\theta)$	
$r^2 = \cos 2\theta$	$r^2 = \cos 2\theta$	$r^2 = \cos 2\theta$

The graph has symmetry with respect to the polar axis, the line $\theta = \dfrac{\pi}{2}$, and the pole.

Calculate values of r for θ from 0 to $\dfrac{\pi}{2}$ and use symmetry to obtain the graph.

θ	0	$\dfrac{\pi}{6}$	$\dfrac{\pi}{4}$	$\dfrac{\pi}{3}$	$\dfrac{\pi}{2}$
r	± 1	± 0.71	0	undef.	undef.

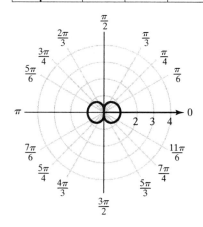

57. $z = 1 - i$ corresponds to the point $(1, -1)$.

Use $r = \sqrt{a^2 + b^2}$ and $\tan\theta = \dfrac{b}{a}$, with $a = 1$ and $b = -1$, to find r and θ.

$r = \sqrt{1^2 + (-1)^2} = \sqrt{1+1} = \sqrt{2}$

$\tan\theta = \dfrac{-1}{1} = -1$

Because $\tan\dfrac{\pi}{4} = 1$ and θ lies in quadrant IV, $\theta = 2\pi - \dfrac{\pi}{4} = \dfrac{7\pi}{4}$.

$z = 1 - i = r(\cos\theta + i\sin\theta)$

$\quad = \sqrt{2}\left(\cos\dfrac{7\pi}{4} + i\sin\dfrac{7\pi}{4}\right)$

or $\sqrt{2}(\cos 315° + i\sin 315°)$

58. $z = -2\sqrt{3} + 2i$ corresponds to the point $(-2\sqrt{3},\ 2)$.

Use $r = \sqrt{a^2 + b^2}$ and $\tan\theta = \dfrac{b}{a}$, with $a = -2\sqrt{3}$ and $b = 2$, to find r and θ.

$r = \sqrt{\left(-2\sqrt{3}\right)^2 + 2^2} = \sqrt{12+4} = \sqrt{16} = 4$

$\tan\theta = \dfrac{2}{-2\sqrt{3}} = -\dfrac{1}{\sqrt{3}}$

Because $\tan 30° = \dfrac{1}{\sqrt{3}}$ and θ lies in quadrant II, $\theta = 180° - 30° = 150°$.

$z = -2\sqrt{3} + 2i$

$\quad = r(\cos\theta + i\sin\theta)$

$\quad = 4(\cos 150° + i\sin 150°)$

or $4\left(\cos\dfrac{5\pi}{6} + i\sin\dfrac{5\pi}{6}\right)$

59. $z = -3 - 4i$ corresponds to the point $(-3, -4)$.

Use $r = \sqrt{a^2 + b^2}$ and $\tan\theta = \dfrac{b}{a}$, with $a = -3$ and $b = -4$, to find r and θ.

$r = \sqrt{(-3)^2 + (-4)^2} = \sqrt{9+16} = \sqrt{25} = 5$

$\tan\theta = \dfrac{-4}{-3} = \dfrac{4}{3}$

Because $\tan^{-1}\left(\dfrac{4}{3}\right) \approx 53°$ and θ lies in quadrant III, $\theta \approx 180° + 53° = 233°$.

$z = -3 - 4i = r(\cos\theta + i\sin\theta)$

$\quad \approx 5(\cos 233° + i\sin 233°)$

60. $z = -5i = 0 - 5i$ corresponds to the point $(0, -5)$.

Use $r = \sqrt{a^2 + b^2}$ and $\tan \theta = \dfrac{b}{a}$, with $a = 0$ and $b = -5$, to find r and θ.

$r = \sqrt{0^2 + (-5)^2} = \sqrt{25} = 5$

$\tan \theta = \dfrac{-5}{0}$ is undefined

Because $\tan \dfrac{\pi}{2}$ is undefined and θ lies on the negative y-axis, $\theta = \dfrac{\pi}{2} + \pi = \dfrac{3\pi}{2}$.

$z = -5i = r(\cos \theta + i \sin \theta) = 5\left(\cos \dfrac{3\pi}{2} + i \sin \dfrac{3\pi}{2}\right)$ or $5(\cos 270° + i \sin 270°)$

61. $8(\cos 60° + i \sin 60°) = 8\left(\dfrac{1}{2} + i\dfrac{\sqrt{3}}{2}\right) = 4 + 4\sqrt{3}i$

The rectangular form of $z = 8(\cos 60° + i \sin 60°)$ is $z = 4 + 4\sqrt{3}i$.

62. $4(\cos 210° + i \sin 210°) = 4\left(-\dfrac{\sqrt{3}}{2} + i\left(-\dfrac{1}{2}\right)\right) = -2\sqrt{3} - 2i$

The rectangular form of $z = 4(\cos 210° + i \sin 210°)$ is $z = -2\sqrt{3} - 2i$.

63. $6\left(\cos \dfrac{2\pi}{3} + i \sin \dfrac{2\pi}{3}\right) = 6\left(-\dfrac{1}{2} + i\dfrac{\sqrt{3}}{2}\right) = -3 + 3\sqrt{3}i$

The rectangular form of $z = 6\left(\cos \dfrac{2\pi}{3} + i \sin \dfrac{2\pi}{3}\right)$ is $z = -3 + 3\sqrt{3}i$.

64. $0.6(\cos 100° + i \sin 100°) \approx 0.6(-0.17 + i(0.98)) \approx -0.1 + 0.6i$

The rectangular form of $z = 0.6(\cos 100° + i \sin 100°)$ is $z \approx -0.1 + 0.6i$.

65. $z_1 z_2 = [3(\cos 40° + i \sin 40°)][5(\cos 70° + i \sin 70°)]$
$= (3 \cdot 5)[\cos(40° + 70°) + i \sin(40° + 70°)]$
$= 15(\cos 110° + i \sin 110°)$

66. $z_1 z_2 = [\cos 210° + i \sin 210°][\cos 55° + i \sin 55°]$
$= \cos(210° + 55°) + i \sin(210° + 55°)$
$= \cos 265° + i \sin 265°$

67. $z_1 z_2 = \left[4\left(\cos\frac{3\pi}{7} + i \sin\frac{3\pi}{7}\right)\right]\left[10\left(\cos\frac{4\pi}{7} + i \frac{4\pi}{7}\right)\right]$
$= (4 \cdot 10)\left[\cos\left(\frac{3\pi}{7} + \frac{4\pi}{7}\right) + i \sin\left(\frac{3\pi}{7} + \frac{4\pi}{7}\right)\right]$
$= 40(\cos \pi + i \sin \pi)$

68. $\dfrac{z_1}{z_2} = \dfrac{10(\cos 10° + i \sin 10°)}{5(\cos 5° + i \sin 5°)} = \dfrac{10}{5}[\cos(10° - 5°) + i \sin(10° - 5°)] = 2(\cos 5° + i \sin 5°)$

69. $\dfrac{z_1}{z_2} = \dfrac{5\left(\cos\frac{4\pi}{3} + i \sin\frac{4\pi}{3}\right)}{10\left(\cos\frac{\pi}{3} + i \sin\frac{\pi}{3}\right)} = \dfrac{5}{10}\left[\cos\left(\frac{4\pi}{3} - \frac{\pi}{3}\right) + i \sin\left(\frac{4\pi}{3} - \frac{\pi}{3}\right)\right] = \dfrac{1}{2}(\cos \pi + i \sin \pi)$

70. $\dfrac{z_1}{z_2} = \dfrac{2\left(\cos\frac{5\pi}{3} + i \sin\frac{5\pi}{3}\right)}{\cos\frac{\pi}{2} + i \sin\frac{\pi}{2}} = 2\left[\cos\left(\frac{5\pi}{3} - \frac{\pi}{2}\right) + i \sin\left(\frac{5\pi}{3} - \frac{\pi}{2}\right)\right]$
$= 2\left[\cos\left(\frac{10\pi}{6} - \frac{3\pi}{6}\right) + i \sin\left(\frac{10\pi}{6} - \frac{3\pi}{6}\right)\right] = 2\left(\cos\frac{7\pi}{6} + i \sin\frac{7\pi}{6}\right)$

71. $[2(\cos 20° + i \sin 20°)]^3 = (2)^3[\cos(3 \cdot 20°) + i \sin(3 \cdot 20°)] = 8(\cos 60° + i \sin 60°)$
$= 8\left(\frac{1}{2} + i \frac{\sqrt{3}}{2}\right) = 4 + 4\sqrt{3}i$

72. $[4(\cos 50° + i \sin 50°)]^3 = (4)^3[\cos(3 \cdot 50°) + i \sin(3 \cdot 50°)] = 64(\cos 150° + i \sin 150°) = 64\left(-\frac{\sqrt{3}}{2} + i \frac{1}{2}\right)$
$= -32\sqrt{3} + 32i$

73. $\left[\frac{1}{2}\left(\cos\frac{\pi}{14} + i \sin\frac{\pi}{14}\right)\right]^7 = \left(\frac{1}{2}\right)^7\left[\cos\left(7 \cdot \frac{\pi}{14}\right) + i \sin\left(7 \cdot \frac{\pi}{14}\right)\right] = \frac{1}{128}\left(\cos\frac{\pi}{2} + i \sin\frac{\pi}{2}\right)$
$= \frac{1}{128}(0 + i1) = \frac{1}{128}i$

74. Write $1 - \sqrt{3}i$ in $r(\cos\theta + i\sin\theta)$ form.

$r = \sqrt{a^2 + b^2} = \sqrt{1^2 + \left(-\sqrt{3}\right)^2} = \sqrt{1+3} = 2$

$\tan\theta = \dfrac{b}{a} = \dfrac{-\sqrt{3}}{1} = -\sqrt{3}$

Because $\tan 60° = \sqrt{3}$ and θ lies in quadrant IV, $\theta = 360° - 60° = 300°$.

$1 - \sqrt{3}i = r(\cos\theta + i\sin\theta) = 2(\cos 300° + i\sin 300°)$

Use DeMoivre's Theorem to raise $1 - \sqrt{3}i$ to the seventh power.

$\left(1 - \sqrt{3}i\right)^7 = [2(\cos 300° + i\sin 300°)]^7$

$\qquad = (2)^7[\cos(7 \cdot 300°) + i\sin(7 \cdot 300°)]$

$\qquad = 128(\cos 2100° + i\sin 2100°)$

$\qquad = 128(\cos 300° + i\sin 300°)$

$\qquad = 128\left(\dfrac{1}{2} + i\left(-\dfrac{\sqrt{3}}{2}\right)\right)$

$\qquad = 64 - 64\sqrt{3}i$

75. Write $-2 - 2i$ in $r(\cos\theta + i\sin\theta)$ form.

$r = \sqrt{a^2 + b^2} = \sqrt{(-2)^2 + (-2)^2} = \sqrt{4+4} = 2\sqrt{2}$

$\tan\theta = \dfrac{b}{a} = \dfrac{-2}{-2} = 1$

Because $\tan\dfrac{\pi}{4} = 1$ and θ lies in quadrant III, $\theta = \pi + \dfrac{\pi}{4} = \dfrac{5\pi}{4}$.

$-2 - 2i = r(\cos\theta + i\sin\theta) = 2\sqrt{2}\left(\cos\dfrac{5\pi}{4} + i\sin\dfrac{5\pi}{4}\right)$

Use DeMoivre's Theorem to raise $-2 - 2i$ to the fifth power.

$(-2 - 2i)^5 = \left[2\sqrt{2}\left(\cos\dfrac{5\pi}{4} + i\sin\dfrac{5\pi}{4}\right)\right]^5$

$\qquad = \left(2\sqrt{2}\right)^5\left[\cos\left(5 \cdot \dfrac{5\pi}{4}\right) + i\sin\left(5 \cdot \dfrac{5\pi}{4}\right)\right]$

$\qquad = 128\sqrt{2}\left(\cos\dfrac{25\pi}{4} + i\sin\dfrac{25\pi}{4}\right)$

$\qquad = 128\sqrt{2}\left(\cos\dfrac{\pi}{4} + i\sin\dfrac{\pi}{4}\right)$

$\qquad = 128\sqrt{2}\left(\dfrac{\sqrt{2}}{2} + i\dfrac{\sqrt{2}}{2}\right)$

$\qquad = 128 + 128i$

76. $49(\cos 50° + i \sin 50°)$

$$z_k = \sqrt[2]{49}\left[\cos\left(\frac{50° + 360°k}{2}\right) + i \sin\left(\frac{50° + 360°k}{2}\right)\right], \ k = 0,1$$

$$z_0 = \sqrt{49}\left[\cos\left(\frac{50° + 360° \cdot 0}{2}\right) + i \sin\left(\frac{50° + 360° \cdot 0}{2}\right)\right] = \sqrt{49}\left[\cos\left(\frac{50°}{2}\right) + i \sin\left(\frac{50°}{2}\right)\right]$$

$$= 7(\cos 25° + i \sin 25°)$$

$$z_1 = \sqrt{49}\left[\cos\left(\frac{50° + 360° \cdot 1}{2}\right) + i \sin\left(\frac{50° + 360° \cdot 1}{2}\right)\right] = \sqrt{49}\left[\cos\left(\frac{410°}{2}\right) + i \sin\left(\frac{410°}{2}\right)\right]$$

$$= 7(\cos 205° + i \sin 205°)$$

77. $125(\cos 165° + i \sin 165°)$

$$z_k = \sqrt[3]{125}\left[\cos\left(\frac{165° + 360°k}{3}\right) + i \sin\left(\frac{165° + 360°k}{3}\right)\right], \ k = 0,1,2$$

$$z_0 = \sqrt[3]{125}\left[\cos\left(\frac{165° + 360° \cdot 0}{3}\right) + i \sin\left(\frac{165° + 360° \cdot 0}{3}\right)\right] = \sqrt[3]{125}\left[\cos\left(\frac{165°}{3}\right) + i \sin\left(\frac{165°}{3}\right)\right]$$

$$= 5(\cos 55° + i \sin 55°)$$

$$z_1 = \sqrt[3]{125}\left[\cos\left(\frac{165° + 360° \cdot 1}{3}\right) + i \sin\left(\frac{165° + 360° \cdot 1}{3}\right)\right] = \sqrt[3]{125}\left[\cos\left(\frac{525°}{3}\right) + i \sin\left(\frac{525°}{3}\right)\right]$$

$$= 5(\cos 175° + i \sin 175°)$$

$$z_2 = \sqrt[3]{125}\left[\cos\left(\frac{165° + 360° \cdot 2}{3}\right) + i \sin\left(\frac{165° + 360° \cdot 2}{3}\right)\right] = \sqrt[3]{125}\left[\cos\left(\frac{885°}{3}\right) + i \sin\left(\frac{885°}{3}\right)\right]$$

$$= 5(\cos 295° + i \sin 295°)$$

78. $16\left(\cos\frac{2\pi}{3} + i \sin\frac{2\pi}{3}\right)$

$$z_k = \sqrt[4]{16}\left[\cos\left(\frac{\frac{2\pi}{3} + 2\pi k}{4}\right) + i \sin\left(\frac{\frac{2\pi}{3} + 2\pi k}{4}\right)\right], \ k = 0,1,2,3$$

$$z_0 = \sqrt[4]{16}\left[\cos\left(\frac{\frac{2\pi}{3} + 2\pi \cdot 0}{4}\right) + i \sin\left(\frac{\frac{2\pi}{3} + 2\pi \cdot 0}{4}\right)\right] = \sqrt[4]{16}\left[\cos\left(\frac{\pi}{6}\right) + i \sin\left(\frac{\pi}{6}\right)\right] = 2\left(\frac{\sqrt{3}}{2} + i\frac{1}{2}\right) = \sqrt{3} + i$$

$$z_1 = \sqrt[4]{16}\left[\cos\left(\frac{\frac{2\pi}{3} + 2\pi \cdot 1}{4}\right) + i \sin\left(\frac{\frac{2\pi}{3} + 2\pi \cdot 1}{4}\right)\right] = \sqrt[4]{16}\left(\cos\frac{2\pi}{3} + i \sin\frac{2\pi}{3}\right) = 2\left(-\frac{1}{2} + i\frac{\sqrt{3}}{2}\right) = -1 + \sqrt{3}i$$

$$z_2 = \sqrt[4]{16}\left[\cos\left(\frac{\frac{2\pi}{3} + 2\pi \cdot 2}{4}\right) + i \sin\left(\frac{\frac{2\pi}{3} + 2\pi \cdot 2}{4}\right)\right] = \sqrt[4]{16}\left(\cos\frac{7\pi}{6} + i \sin\frac{7\pi}{6}\right) = 2\left(-\frac{\sqrt{3}}{2} + i\left(-\frac{1}{2}\right)\right) = -\sqrt{3} - i$$

$$z_3 = \sqrt[4]{16}\left[\cos\left(\frac{\frac{2\pi}{3} + 2\pi \cdot 3}{4}\right) + i \sin\left(\frac{\frac{2\pi}{3} + 2\pi \cdot 3}{4}\right)\right] = \sqrt[4]{16}\left(\cos\frac{5\pi}{3} + i \sin\frac{5\pi}{3}\right) = 2\left(\frac{1}{2} + i\left(-\frac{\sqrt{3}}{2}\right)\right) = 1 - \sqrt{3}i$$

79. $8i = 8(\cos 90° + i \sin 90°)$

$$z_k = \sqrt[3]{8}\left[\cos\left(\frac{90° + 360°k}{3}\right) + i\sin\left(\frac{90° + 360°k}{3}\right)\right], \ k = 0, 1, 2$$

$$z_0 = \sqrt[3]{8}\left[\cos\left(\frac{90° + 360° \cdot 0}{3}\right) + i\sin\left(\frac{90° + 360° \cdot 0}{3}\right)\right] = \sqrt[3]{8}(\cos 30° + i\sin 30°) = 2\left(\frac{\sqrt{3}}{2} + i\frac{1}{2}\right) = \sqrt{3} + i$$

$$z_1 = \sqrt[3]{8}\left[\cos\left(\frac{90° + 360° \cdot 1}{3}\right) + i\sin\left(\frac{90° + 360° \cdot 1}{3}\right)\right] = \sqrt[3]{8}(\cos 150° + i\sin 150°) = 2\left(-\frac{\sqrt{3}}{2} + i\frac{1}{2}\right) = -\sqrt{3} + i$$

$$z_2 = \sqrt[3]{8}\left[\cos\left(\frac{90° + 360° \cdot 2}{3}\right) + i\sin\left(\frac{90° + 360° \cdot 2}{3}\right)\right] = \sqrt[3]{8}(\cos 270° + i\sin 270°) = 2(0 + i(-1)) = -2i$$

80. $-1 = \cos 180° + i \sin 180°$

$$z_k = \sqrt[3]{1}\left[\cos\left(\frac{180° + 360°k}{3}\right) + i\sin\left(\frac{180° + 360°k}{3}\right)\right], \ k = 0, 1, 2$$

$$z_0 = \sqrt[3]{1}\left[\cos\left(\frac{180° + 360° \cdot 0}{3}\right) + i\sin\left(\frac{180° + 360° \cdot 0}{3}\right)\right] = \sqrt[3]{1}(\cos 60° + i\sin 60°) = 1\left(\frac{1}{2} + i\frac{\sqrt{3}}{2}\right) = \frac{1}{2} + \frac{\sqrt{3}}{2}i$$

$$z_1 = \sqrt[3]{1}\left[\cos\left(\frac{180° + 360° \cdot 1}{3}\right) + i\sin\left(\frac{180° + 360° \cdot 1}{3}\right)\right] = \sqrt[3]{1}(\cos 180° + i\sin 180°) = 1(-1 + i0) = -1$$

$$z_2 = \sqrt[3]{1}\left[\cos\left(\frac{180° + 360° \cdot 2}{3}\right) + i\left(\frac{180° + 360° \cdot 2}{3}\right)\right] = \sqrt[3]{1}(\cos 300° + i\sin 300°) = 1\left(\frac{1}{2} + i\left(-\frac{\sqrt{3}}{2}\right)\right) = \frac{1}{2} - \frac{\sqrt{3}}{2}i$$

81. $-1 - i = \sqrt{2}(\cos 225° + i \sin 225°)$

$$z_k = \sqrt[5]{\sqrt{2}}\left[\cos\left(\frac{225° + 360°k}{5}\right) + i\sin\left(\frac{225° + 360°k}{5}\right)\right], \ k = 0, 1, 2, 3, 4$$

$$z_0 = \sqrt[5]{\sqrt{2}}\left[\cos\left(\frac{225° + 360° \cdot 0}{5}\right) + i\sin\left(\frac{225° + 360° \cdot 0}{5}\right)\right] = \sqrt[5]{\sqrt{2}}(\cos 45° + i\sin 45°) = \sqrt[5]{\sqrt{2}}\left(\frac{\sqrt{2}}{2} + i\frac{\sqrt{2}}{2}\right)$$

$$= \frac{\sqrt[5]{8}}{2} + \frac{\sqrt[5]{8}}{2}i$$

$$z_1 = \sqrt[5]{\sqrt{2}}\left[\cos\left(\frac{225° + 360° \cdot 1}{5}\right) + i\sin\left(\frac{225° + 360° \cdot 1}{5}\right)\right] = \sqrt[5]{\sqrt{2}}(\cos 117° + i\sin 117°) \approx -0.49 + 0.95i$$

$$z_2 = \sqrt[5]{\sqrt{2}}\left[\cos\left(\frac{225° + 360° \cdot 2}{5}\right) + i\sin\left(\frac{225° + 360° \cdot 2}{5}\right)\right] = \sqrt[5]{\sqrt{2}}(\cos 189° + i\sin 189°) \approx -1.06 - 0.17i$$

$$z_3 = \sqrt[5]{\sqrt{2}}\left[\cos\left(\frac{225° + 360° \cdot 3}{5}\right) + i\sin\left(\frac{225° + 360° \cdot 3}{5}\right)\right] = \sqrt[5]{\sqrt{2}}(\cos 261° + i\sin 261°) \approx -0.17 - 1.06i$$

$$z_4 = \sqrt[5]{\sqrt{2}}\left[\cos\left(\frac{225° + 360° \cdot 4}{5}\right) + i\sin\left(\frac{225° + 360° \cdot 4}{5}\right)\right] = \sqrt[5]{\sqrt{2}}(\cos 333° + i\sin 333°) \approx 0.95 - 0.49i$$

82.

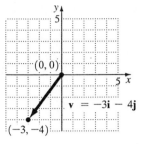

$$\|\mathbf{v}\| = \sqrt{a^2 + b^2}$$
$$= \sqrt{(-3)^2 + (-4)^2}$$
$$= \sqrt{9 + 16}$$
$$= \sqrt{25}$$
$$= 5$$

83.

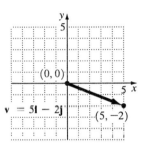

$$\|\mathbf{v}\| = \sqrt{a^2 + b^2}$$
$$= \sqrt{5^2 + (-2)^2}$$
$$= \sqrt{25 + 4}$$
$$= \sqrt{29}$$

84.

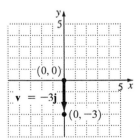

$$\|\mathbf{v}\| = \sqrt{a^2 + b^2}$$
$$= \sqrt{0^2 + (-3)^2}$$
$$= \sqrt{0 + 9}$$
$$= \sqrt{9}$$
$$= 3$$

85. $\mathbf{v} = (x_2 - x_1)\mathbf{i} + (y_2 - y_1)\mathbf{j}$
$$= (5 - 2)\mathbf{i} + [-3 - (-1)]\mathbf{j}$$
$$= 3\mathbf{i} - 2\mathbf{j}$$

86. $\mathbf{v} = (x_2 - x_1)\mathbf{i} + (y_2 - y_1)\mathbf{j}$
$$= [-2 - (-3)\mathbf{i}] + (-2 - 0)\mathbf{j}$$
$$= \mathbf{i} - 2\mathbf{j}$$

87. $\mathbf{v} + \mathbf{w} = (\mathbf{i} - 5\mathbf{j}) + (-2\mathbf{i} + 7\mathbf{j})$
$$= [1 + (-2)]\mathbf{i} + [-5 + 7]\mathbf{j}$$
$$= -\mathbf{i} + 2\mathbf{j}$$

88. $\mathbf{w} - \mathbf{v} = (-2\mathbf{i} + 7\mathbf{j}) - (\mathbf{i} - 5\mathbf{j})$
$$= (-2 - 1)\mathbf{i} + [7 - (-5)]\mathbf{j}$$
$$= -3\mathbf{i} + 12\mathbf{j}$$

89. $6\mathbf{v} - 3\mathbf{w} = 6(\mathbf{i} - 5\mathbf{j}) - 3(-2\mathbf{i} + 7\mathbf{j})$
$$= 6\mathbf{i} - 30\mathbf{j} + 6\mathbf{i} - 21\mathbf{j}$$
$$= 12\mathbf{i} - 51\mathbf{j}$$

90. $\|-2\mathbf{v}\| = |-2|\,\|\mathbf{v}\|$
$$= 2\|\mathbf{v}\|$$
$$= 2\sqrt{a^2 + b^2}$$
$$= 2\sqrt{1^2 + (-5)^2}$$
$$= 2\sqrt{1 + 25}$$
$$= 2\sqrt{26}$$

91. First, find the magnitude of **v**.
$$\|\mathbf{v}\| = \sqrt{a^2 + b^2}$$
$$= \sqrt{8^2 + (-6)^2}$$
$$= \sqrt{64 + 36}$$
$$= \sqrt{100}$$
$$= 10$$
A unit vector in the same direction as **v** is
$$\frac{\mathbf{v}}{\|\mathbf{v}\|} = \frac{8\mathbf{i} - 6\mathbf{j}}{10} = \frac{4}{5}\mathbf{i} - \frac{3}{5}\mathbf{j}.$$

92. First, find the magnitude of **v**.
$$\|\mathbf{v}\| = \sqrt{a^2 + b^2} = \sqrt{(-1)^2 + (2)^2} = \sqrt{1 + 4} = \sqrt{5}$$
A unit vector in the same direction as **v** is
$$\frac{\mathbf{v}}{\|\mathbf{v}\|} = \frac{-\mathbf{i} + 2\mathbf{j}}{\sqrt{5}} = -\frac{1}{\sqrt{5}}\mathbf{i} + \frac{2}{\sqrt{5}}\mathbf{j}.$$

93.

a. Use the Law of Cosines to find the magnitude of **F**.

$$\|\mathbf{F}\|^2 = 200^2 + 100^2 - 2(200)(100)\cos 120°$$
$$= 70,000$$
$$\|\mathbf{F}\| = \sqrt{70,000} \approx 264.6$$

The magnitude of the resultant force, to the nearest pound, is 265 pounds.

b. To find θ, apply the Law of Sines.

$$\frac{265}{\sin 120°} = \frac{100}{\sin \theta}$$
$$265 \sin \theta = 100 \sin 120°$$
$$\sin \theta = \frac{100 \sin 120°}{265}$$
$$\theta = \sin^{-1}\left(\frac{100 \sin 120°}{265}\right)$$
$$\approx 19°$$

The two given forces are equivalent to a single force of about 265 pounds in the direction of approximately 19° relative to the 200-pound force.

94. $\mathbf{u} \cdot (\mathbf{v} + \mathbf{w}) = (5\mathbf{i} + 2\mathbf{j}) \cdot [(\mathbf{i} - \mathbf{j}) + (3\mathbf{i} - 7\mathbf{j})]$
$$= (5\mathbf{i} + 2\mathbf{j}) \cdot [(1+3)\mathbf{i} + (-1 + (-7))\mathbf{j}]$$
$$= (5\mathbf{i} + 2\mathbf{j}) \cdot (4\mathbf{i} - 8\mathbf{j})$$
$$= 5(4) + 2(-8)$$
$$= 20 - 16$$
$$= 4$$

95. $\mathbf{v} \cdot \mathbf{w} = (2\mathbf{i} + 3\mathbf{j}) \cdot (7\mathbf{i} - 4\mathbf{j}) = 2(7) + (3)(-4)$
$$= 14 - 12 = 2$$

$$\cos \theta = \frac{\mathbf{v} \cdot \mathbf{w}}{\|\mathbf{v}\| \|\mathbf{w}\|}$$
$$= \frac{2}{\sqrt{2^2 + 3^2}\sqrt{7^2 + (-4)^2}}$$
$$= \frac{2}{\sqrt{13}\sqrt{65}}$$
$$= \frac{2}{\sqrt{845}}$$

The angle θ between the vectors is
$$\theta = \cos^{-1}\left(\frac{2}{\sqrt{845}}\right) \approx 86.1°.$$

96. $\mathbf{v} \cdot \mathbf{w} = (2\mathbf{i} + 4\mathbf{j}) \cdot (6\mathbf{i} - 11\mathbf{j}) = 2(6) + 4(-11)$
$$= 12 - 44 = -32$$

$$\cos \theta = \frac{\mathbf{v} \cdot \mathbf{w}}{\|\mathbf{v}\| \|\mathbf{w}\|}$$
$$= \frac{-32}{\sqrt{2^2 + 4^2}\sqrt{6^2 + (-11)^2}}$$
$$= \frac{-32}{\sqrt{20}\sqrt{157}}$$
$$= -\frac{32}{\sqrt{3140}}$$

The angle θ between the vectors is
$$\theta = \cos^{-1}\left(-\frac{32}{\sqrt{3140}}\right) \approx 124.8°.$$

97. $\mathbf{v} \cdot \mathbf{w} = (2\mathbf{i} + \mathbf{j}) \cdot (\mathbf{i} - \mathbf{j}) = 2(1) + (1)(-1)$
$$= 2 - 1 = 1$$

$$\cos \theta = \frac{\mathbf{v} \cdot \mathbf{w}}{\|\mathbf{v}\| \|\mathbf{w}\|}$$
$$= \frac{1}{\sqrt{2^2 + 1^2}\sqrt{1^2 + (-1)^2}}$$
$$= \frac{1}{\sqrt{5}\sqrt{2}}$$
$$= \frac{1}{\sqrt{10}}$$

The angle θ between the vectors is
$$\theta = \cos^{-1}\left(\frac{1}{\sqrt{10}}\right) \approx 71.6°.$$

98. $\mathbf{v}\cdot\mathbf{w} = (12\mathbf{i}-8\mathbf{j})\cdot(2\mathbf{i}+3\mathbf{j})$
$= 12(2)+(-8)(3)$
$= 24-24$
$= \mathbf{0}$
The dot product is zero. Thus, the given vectors are orthogonal.

99. $\mathbf{v}\cdot\mathbf{w} = (\mathbf{i}+3\mathbf{j})\cdot(-3\mathbf{i}-\mathbf{j})$
$= 1(-3)+3(-1) = -3-3$
$= -6$
The dot product is not zero. Thus, the given vectors are not orthogonal.

100. $\mathbf{v} = \|\mathbf{v}\|\cos\theta\,\mathbf{i}+\|\mathbf{v}\|\sin\theta\,\mathbf{j}$
$= 12\cos 60°\mathbf{i} + 12\sin 60°\mathbf{j}$
$= 12\left(\frac{1}{2}\right)\mathbf{i}+12\left(\frac{\sqrt{3}}{2}\right)\mathbf{j}$
$= 6\mathbf{i}+6\sqrt{3}\mathbf{j}$

101. $\text{proj}_\mathbf{w}\mathbf{v} = \frac{\mathbf{v}\cdot\mathbf{w}}{\|\mathbf{w}\|^2}\mathbf{w}$
$= \frac{(-2\mathbf{i}+5\mathbf{j})\cdot(5\mathbf{i}+4\mathbf{j})}{\left(\sqrt{5^2+4^2}\right)^2}\mathbf{w}$
$= \frac{-2(5)+5(4)}{\left(\sqrt{41}\right)^2}\mathbf{w}$
$= \frac{10}{41}\mathbf{w}$
$= \frac{10}{41}(5\mathbf{i}+4\mathbf{j})$
$= \frac{50}{41}\mathbf{i}+\frac{40}{41}\mathbf{j}$
$\mathbf{v}_1 = \text{proj}_\mathbf{w}\mathbf{v} = \frac{50}{41}\mathbf{i}+\frac{40}{41}\mathbf{j}$
$\mathbf{v}_2 = \mathbf{v}-\mathbf{v}_1$
$= (-2\mathbf{i}+5\mathbf{j})-\left(\frac{50}{41}\mathbf{i}+\frac{40}{41}\mathbf{j}\right)$
$= -\frac{132}{41}\mathbf{i}+\frac{165}{41}\mathbf{j}$

102. $\text{proj}_\mathbf{w}\mathbf{v} = \frac{\mathbf{v}\cdot\mathbf{w}}{\|\mathbf{w}\|^2}\mathbf{w}$
$= \frac{(-\mathbf{i}+2\mathbf{j})\cdot(3\mathbf{i}-\mathbf{j})}{\left(\sqrt{3^2+(-1)^2}\right)^2}\mathbf{w}$
$= \frac{-1(3)+2(-1)}{\left(\sqrt{10}\right)^2}\mathbf{w}$
$= \frac{-5}{10}\mathbf{w}$
$= -\frac{1}{2}\mathbf{w}$
$= -\frac{1}{2}(3\mathbf{i}-\mathbf{j})$
$= -\frac{3}{2}\mathbf{i}+\frac{1}{2}\mathbf{j}$
$\mathbf{v}_1 = \text{proj}_\mathbf{w}\mathbf{v} = -\frac{3}{2}\mathbf{i}+\frac{1}{2}\mathbf{j}$
$\mathbf{v}_2 = \mathbf{v}-\mathbf{v}_1$
$= (-\mathbf{i}+2\mathbf{j})-\left(-\frac{3}{2}\mathbf{i}+\frac{1}{2}\mathbf{j}\right)$
$= \frac{1}{2}\mathbf{i}+\frac{3}{2}\mathbf{j}$

103. $\text{W} = \|\mathbf{F}\|\|\overrightarrow{AB}\|\cos\theta$
$= (30)(50)\cos 42°$
≈ 1115
The work done is approximately 1115 foot-pounds.

Chapter 7 Test

1. The known ratio is $\frac{a}{\sin A}$, or $\frac{4.8}{\sin 34°}$.
Because angel B is given, we use the Law of Sines to find side b
$\frac{b}{\sin B} = \frac{a}{\sin A}$
$\frac{b}{\sin 68°} = \frac{4.8}{\sin 34°}$
$b = \frac{4.8\sin 68°}{\sin 34°} \approx 8.0$

2. Use the Law of Cosines to find c.
$$c^2 = a^2 + b^2 - 2ab\cos C$$
$$c^2 = 5^2 + 6^2 - 2(5)(6)\cos 68°$$
$$= 61 - 60\cos 68°$$
$$\approx 38.52$$
$$c \approx \sqrt{38.52} \approx 6.2$$

3. $s = \dfrac{1}{2}(a + b + c) = \dfrac{1}{2}(17 + 45 + 32) = 47$
$$\text{Area} = \sqrt{s(s-a)(s-b)(s-c)}$$
$$= \sqrt{47(47-17)(47-45)(47-32)}$$
$$= \sqrt{42,300} \approx 206$$
The area of the triangle is approximately 206 square inches.

4. Draw $\theta = \dfrac{5\pi}{4} = 225°$ counterclockwise, since θ is positive, from the polar axis. Go 4 units out on the terminal side of θ, since $r > 0$.

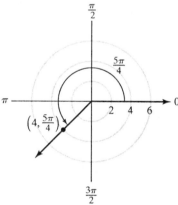

Ordered pairs may vary.

5. $(1, -1)$
$$r = \sqrt{1^2 + (-1)^2} = \sqrt{1+1} = \sqrt{2}$$
$$\tan\theta = \dfrac{-1}{1} = -1$$
Because $\tan\dfrac{\pi}{4} = 1$ and θ lies in quadrant IV, $\theta = 2\pi - \dfrac{\pi}{4} = \dfrac{7\pi}{4}$.
The polar coordinated of $(1, -1)$ are $(r, \theta) = \left(\sqrt{2}, \dfrac{7\pi}{4}\right)$.

6. $x^2 + y^2 = 6x$
$$r^2 = 6r\cos\theta$$
$$r = 6\cos\theta$$

7. $r = 4\csc\theta = \dfrac{4}{\sin\theta}$
$$r\sin\theta = 4$$
$$y = 4$$

8. $r = 1 + \sin\theta$
Check for symmetry:

Polar Axis	The Line $\theta = \dfrac{\pi}{2}$	The Pole
$r = 1 + \sin(-\theta)$	$-r = 1 + \sin(-\theta)$	$-r = 1 + \sin\theta$
	$-r = 1 - \sin\theta$	
$r = 1 - \sin\theta$	$r = -1 + \sin\theta$	$r = -1 - \sin\theta$

There may be no symmetry, since each equation is not equivalent to $r = 1 + \sin\theta$.
Calculate values of r for θ from 0 to 2π.

θ	0	$\dfrac{\pi}{6}$	$\dfrac{\pi}{3}$	$\dfrac{\pi}{2}$	$\dfrac{2\pi}{3}$	$\dfrac{5\pi}{6}$	π
r	1	1.5	1.87	2	1.87	1.5	1

θ	$\dfrac{7\pi}{6}$	$\dfrac{4\pi}{3}$	$\dfrac{3\pi}{2}$	$\dfrac{5\pi}{3}$	$\dfrac{11\pi}{6}$	2π
r	0.5	0.13	0	0.13	0.5	1

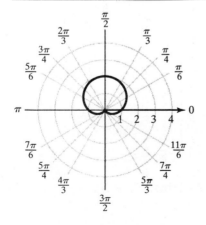

9. $r = 1 + 3\cos\theta$
   Check for symmetry:

Polar Axis	The Line $\theta = \dfrac{\pi}{2}$	The Pole
$r = 1 + 3\cos(-\theta)$	$-r = 1 + 3\cos(-\theta)$	$-r = 1 + 3\cos\theta$
	$-r = 1 + 3\cos\theta$	
$r = 1 + 3\cos\theta$	$r = -1 - 3\cos\theta$	$r = -1 - 3\cos\theta$

The graph has symmetry with respect to the polar axis. The graph may or may not be symmetric with respect to the line $\theta = \dfrac{\pi}{2}$ or the pole. Calculate values of r for θ from 0 to π and use symmetry to complete the graph.

θ	0	$\dfrac{\pi}{6}$	$\dfrac{\pi}{3}$	$\dfrac{\pi}{2}$	$\dfrac{2\pi}{3}$	$\dfrac{5\pi}{6}$	π
r	4	3.60	2.5	1	−0.5	−1.60	−2

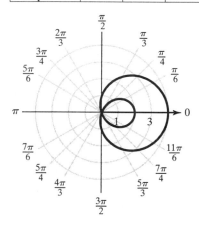

10. Use $r = \sqrt{a^2 + b^2}$ and $\tan\theta = \dfrac{b}{a}$, with $a = -\sqrt{3}$ and $b = 1$, to find r and θ.

$$r = \sqrt{\left(-\sqrt{3}\right)^2 + (1)^2} = \sqrt{3 + 1} = \sqrt{4} = 2$$

$$\tan\theta = \frac{1}{-\sqrt{3}} = -\frac{1}{\sqrt{3}}$$

Because $\tan 30° = \dfrac{1}{\sqrt{3}}$ and θ lies in quadrant II, $\theta = 180° - 30° = 150°$.

The polar form of $z = -\sqrt{3} + i$ is $z = r(\cos\theta + i\sin\theta) = 2(\cos 150° + i\sin 150°)$ or $2\left(\cos\dfrac{5\pi}{6} + i\sin\dfrac{5\pi}{6}\right)$.

11. $5(\cos 15° + i \sin 15°) \cdot 10(\cos 5° + i \sin 5°) = (5 \cdot 10)[\cos(15° + 5°) + i \sin(15° + 5°)]$
$$= 50(\cos 20° + i \sin 20°)$$

12. $\dfrac{2\left(\cos\dfrac{\pi}{2} + i \sin\dfrac{\pi}{2}\right)}{4\left(\cos\dfrac{\pi}{3} + i \sin\dfrac{\pi}{3}\right)} = \dfrac{2}{4}\left[\cos\left(\dfrac{\pi}{2} - \dfrac{\pi}{3}\right) + i \sin\left(\dfrac{\pi}{2} - \dfrac{\pi}{3}\right)\right] = \dfrac{2}{4}\left[\cos\left(\dfrac{3\pi}{6} - \dfrac{2\pi}{6}\right) + i \sin\left(\dfrac{3\pi}{6} - \dfrac{2\pi}{6}\right)\right]$

$$= \dfrac{1}{2}\left(\cos\dfrac{\pi}{6} + i \sin\dfrac{\pi}{6}\right)$$

13. $[2(\cos 10° + i \sin 10°)]^5 = (2)^5[\cos(5 \cdot 10°) + i \sin(5 \cdot 10°)] = 32(\cos 50° + i \sin 50°)$

14. $27 = 27(\cos 0° + i \sin 0°)$

$z_k = \sqrt[3]{27}\left[\cos\left(\dfrac{0° + 360°k}{3}\right) + i \sin\left(\dfrac{0° + 360°k}{3}\right)\right]$, $k = 0, 1, 2$

$z_0 = \sqrt[3]{27}\left[\cos\left(\dfrac{0° + 360° \cdot 0}{3}\right) + i \sin\left(\dfrac{0° + 360° \cdot 0}{3}\right)\right] = \sqrt[3]{27}(\cos 0° + i \sin 0°) = 3(1 + 0i) = 3$

$z_1 = \sqrt[3]{27}\left[\cos\left(\dfrac{0° + 360° \cdot 1}{3}\right) + i \sin\left(\dfrac{0° + 360° \cdot 1}{3}\right)\right] = \sqrt[3]{27}(\cos 120° + i \sin 120°) = 3\left(-\dfrac{1}{2} + i\dfrac{\sqrt{3}}{2}\right)$

$= -\dfrac{3}{2} + \dfrac{3\sqrt{3}}{2}i$

$z_2 = \sqrt[3]{27}\left[\cos\left(\dfrac{0° + 360° \cdot 2}{3}\right) + i \sin\left(\dfrac{0° + 360° \cdot 2}{3}\right)\right] = \sqrt[3]{27}(\cos 240° + i \sin 240°) = 3\left(-\dfrac{1}{2} + i\left(-\dfrac{\sqrt{3}}{2}\right)\right)$

$= -\dfrac{3}{2} - \dfrac{3\sqrt{3}}{2}i$

15. a. $\mathbf{v} = (x_2 - x_1)\mathbf{i} + (y_2 - y_1)\mathbf{j}$
      $\mathbf{v} = [-1 - (-2)]\mathbf{i} + (5 - 3)\mathbf{j} = \mathbf{i} + 2\mathbf{j}$

  b. $\|\mathbf{v}\| = \sqrt{a^2 + b^2} = \sqrt{1^2 + 2^2} = \sqrt{1 + 4} = \sqrt{5}$

16. $3\mathbf{v} - 4\mathbf{w} = 3(-5\mathbf{i} + 2\mathbf{j}) - 4(2\mathbf{i} - 4\mathbf{j}) = -15\mathbf{i} + 6\mathbf{j} - 8\mathbf{i} + 16\mathbf{j}$
      $= (-15 - 8)\mathbf{i} + (6 + 16)\mathbf{j} = -23\mathbf{i} + 22\mathbf{j}$

17. $\mathbf{v} \cdot \mathbf{w} = (-5\mathbf{i} + 2\mathbf{j}) \cdot (2\mathbf{i} - 4\mathbf{j}) = -5(2) + 2(-4) = -10 - 8 = -18$

18.
$$\cos\theta = \frac{\mathbf{v}\cdot\mathbf{w}}{\|\mathbf{v}\|\|\mathbf{w}\|} = \frac{(-5\mathbf{i}+2\mathbf{j})\cdot(2\mathbf{i}-4\mathbf{j})}{\sqrt{(-5)^2+2^2}\sqrt{2^2+(-4)^2}}$$

$$= \frac{(-5)(2)+2(-4)}{\sqrt{29}\sqrt{20}}$$

$$= -\frac{18}{\sqrt{580}}$$

The angle θ between the vectors is
$$\theta = \cos^{-1}\left(-\frac{18}{\sqrt{580}}\right) \approx 138°.$$

19.
$$\text{proj}_{\mathbf{w}}\mathbf{v} = \frac{\mathbf{v}\cdot\mathbf{w}}{\|\mathbf{w}\|^2}\mathbf{w} = \frac{(-5\mathbf{i}+2\mathbf{j})\cdot(2\mathbf{i}-4\mathbf{j})}{\left(\sqrt{2^2+(-4)^2}\right)^2}\mathbf{w}$$

$$= \frac{(-5)(2)+2(-4)}{\left(\sqrt{20}\right)^2}\mathbf{w} = -\frac{18}{20}\mathbf{w}$$

$$= -\frac{9}{10}(2\mathbf{i}-4\mathbf{j}) = -\frac{9}{5}\mathbf{i}+\frac{18}{5}\mathbf{j}$$

20.

Using the figure,
$B = 90° - 50° = 40°$
$A = 90° - 40° = 50°$
$C = 180° - B - A = 180° - 40° - 50° = 90°$
Use the Law of Sines to find b.
$$\frac{b}{\sin B} = \frac{c}{\sin C}$$
$$\frac{b}{\sin 40°} = \frac{1.6}{\sin 90°}$$
$$b = \frac{1.6\sin 40°}{\sin 90°} \approx 1.0$$
The fire is about 1.0 mile from the station.

21. $W = \|\mathbf{F}\|\|\overrightarrow{AB}\|\cos\theta$
$ = (40)(60)\cos 35° \approx 1966$
The work done is approximately 1966 foot-pounds.

Cumulative Review Exercises (Chapters 1–7)

1. $x^4 - x^3 - x^2 - x - 2 = 0$
$\dfrac{p}{q}: \ \pm\dfrac{2}{1}, \pm\dfrac{1}{1}$

-1	1	-1	-1	-1	-2
		-1	2	-1	2
	1	-2	1	-2	0

$$x^4 - x^3 - x^2 - x - 2 = 0$$
$$(x+1)(x^3 - 2x^2 + x - 2) = 0$$
$$(x+1)[x^2(x-2)+1(x-2)] = 0$$
$$(x+1)(x-2)(x^2+1) = 0$$
$$x+1=0 \quad x-2=0 \quad x^2+1=0$$
$$x=-1 \qquad x=2 \qquad x^2=-1$$
$$x=\pm i$$
The solution set is $\{-1, 2\, i, -i\}$.

2. $2\sin^2\theta - 3\sin\theta + 1 = 0, \ 0 \le \theta < 2\pi$
$(2\sin\theta - 1)(\sin\theta - 1) = 0$
$2\sin\theta - 1 = 0 \quad$ or $\quad \sin\theta - 1 = 0$
$\quad 2\sin\theta = 1 \qquad\qquad \sin\theta = 1$
$\quad \sin\theta = \dfrac{1}{2}$

The solutions in the interval $[0, 2\pi)$ are
$\dfrac{\pi}{6}, \dfrac{5\pi}{6},$ and $\dfrac{\pi}{2}.$

3. Begin by solving the related quadratic equation. Thus, we will solve $x^2 + 2x + 3 = 11$.

$$x^2 + 2x + 3 = 11$$
$$x^2 + 2x - 8 = 0$$
$$(x+4)(x-2) = 0$$
$$x + 4 = 0 \quad \text{or} \quad x - 2 = 0$$
$$x = -4 \quad \text{or} \quad x = 2$$

The boundary points are –4 and 2. The boundary points divide the number line into three test intervals, namely $(-\infty, -4)$, $(-4, 2)$, and $(2, \infty)$. Take one representative number within each test interval and substitute that number into the original inequality.

Test Interval	Representative Number	Substitute into $x^2 + 2x + 3 > 11$	Conclusion
$(-\infty, -4)$	–5	$(-5)^2 + 2(-5) + 3 > 11$ $18 > 11$ True	$(-\infty, -4)$ belongs to the solution set.
$(-4, -2)$	0	$0^2 + 2(0) + 3 > 11$ $3 > 11$ False	$(-4, -2)$ does not belong to the solution set.
$(2, \infty)$	3	$3^2 + 2(3) + 3 > 11$ $18 > 11$ True	$(2, \infty)$ belongs to the solution set.

The solution set is $\{x \mid x < -4 \text{ or } x > 2\}$.

4. $\sin\theta\cos\theta = -\dfrac{1}{2}$

$$\frac{\sin 2\theta}{2} = -\frac{1}{2}$$
$$\sin 2\theta = -1$$

The period of the sine function is 2π. In the interval $[0, 2\pi)$, the only value for which the sine function is –1 is $\dfrac{3\pi}{2}$. This means that $2\theta = \dfrac{3\pi}{2}$. Since the period is 2π, all the solutions to $\sin 2\theta = -1$ are given by $2\theta = \dfrac{3\pi}{2} + 2n\pi$

$$\theta = \frac{3\pi}{4} + n\pi$$

where n is any integer.

The solution in the interval $[0, 2\pi)$ is obtained by letting $n = 0$ and $n = 1$. The solutions are $\dfrac{3\pi}{4}$ and $\dfrac{7\pi}{4}$.

5. The equation $y = 3\sin(2x - \pi)$ is of the form $y = A\sin(Bx - C)$ with $A = 3$, $B = 2$, and $C = \pi$. The amplitude is $|A| = |3| = 3$.

   The period is $\dfrac{2\pi}{B} = \dfrac{2\pi}{2} = \pi$. The phase shift

   is $\dfrac{C}{B} = \dfrac{\pi}{2}$. The quarter-period is $\dfrac{\pi}{4}$. The

   cycle begins at $x = \dfrac{\pi}{2}$. Add quarter-periods

   to generate x-values for the key points.

   $x = \dfrac{\pi}{2}$

   $x = \dfrac{\pi}{2} + \dfrac{\pi}{4} = \dfrac{3\pi}{4}$

   $x = \dfrac{3\pi}{4} + \dfrac{\pi}{4} = \pi$

   $x = \pi + \dfrac{\pi}{4} = \dfrac{5\pi}{4}$

   $x = \dfrac{5\pi}{4} + \dfrac{\pi}{4} = \dfrac{3\pi}{2}$

   We evaluate the function at each value of x.

x	$y = 3\sin(2x - \pi)$	coordinates
$\dfrac{\pi}{2}$	$y = 3\sin\left(2 \cdot \dfrac{\pi}{2} - \pi\right)$ $= 3\sin(\pi - \pi)$ $= 3\sin 0 = 3 \cdot 0 = 0$	$\left(\dfrac{\pi}{2}, 0\right)$
$\dfrac{3\pi}{4}$	$y = 3\sin\left(2 \cdot \dfrac{3\pi}{4} - \pi\right)$ $= 3\sin\left(\dfrac{3\pi}{2} - \pi\right)$ $= 3\sin\dfrac{\pi}{2} = 3 \cdot 1 = 3$	$\left(\dfrac{3\pi}{4}, 3\right)$
π	$y = 3\sin(2 \cdot \pi - \pi)$ $= 3\sin(2\pi - \pi)$ $= 3\sin \pi = 3 \cdot 0 = 0$	$(\pi, 0)$

$\dfrac{5\pi}{4}$	$y = 3\sin\left(2 \cdot \dfrac{5\pi}{4} - \pi\right)$ $= 3\sin\left(\dfrac{5\pi}{2} - \pi\right)$ $= 3\sin\dfrac{3\pi}{2}$ $= 3(-1) = -3$	$\left(\dfrac{5\pi}{4}, -3\right)$
$\dfrac{3\pi}{2}$	$y = 3\sin\left(2 \cdot \dfrac{3\pi}{2} - \pi\right)$ $= 3\sin(3\pi - \pi)$ $= 3\sin 2\pi = 3 \cdot 0 = 0$	$\left(\dfrac{3\pi}{2}, 0\right)$

Connect the five points with a smooth curve and graph one complete cycle of the given function.

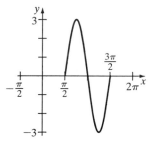

6. The equation $y = -4\cos \pi x$ is of the form $y = A\cos Bx$ with $A = -4$, and $B = \pi$. Thus, the amplitude is $|A| = |-4| = 4$.

   The period is $\dfrac{2\pi}{B} = \dfrac{2\pi}{\pi} = 2$.

   Find the x-values for the five key points by dividing the period, 2, by 4,

   $\dfrac{\text{period}}{4} = \dfrac{2}{4} = \dfrac{1}{2}$, then by adding quarter-

   periods to the value of x where the cycle begins, $x = 0$. The five x-values are

   $x = 0$

   $x = 0 + \dfrac{1}{2} = \dfrac{1}{2}$

   $x = \dfrac{1}{2} + \dfrac{1}{2} = 1$

   $x = 1 + \dfrac{1}{2} = \dfrac{3}{2}$

   $x = \dfrac{3}{2} + \dfrac{1}{2} = 2$

   We evaluate the function at each value of x.

x	$y = -4 \cos \pi x$	coordinates
0	$y = -4\cos(\pi \cdot 0)$ $= -4\cos 0$ $= -4 \cdot 1 = -4$	$(0, -4)$
$\dfrac{1}{2}$	$y = -4\cos\left(\pi \cdot \dfrac{1}{2}\right)$ $= -4\cos\dfrac{\pi}{2}$ $= -4 \cdot 0 = 0$	$\left(\dfrac{1}{2}, 0\right)$
1	$y = -4\cos(\pi \cdot 1)$ $= -4\cos \pi$ $= -4 \cdot (-1) = 4$	$(1, 4)$
$\dfrac{3}{2}$	$y = -4\cos\left(\pi \cdot \dfrac{3}{2}\right)$ $= -4\cos\dfrac{3\pi}{2}$ $= -4 \cdot 0 = 0$	$\left(\dfrac{3}{2}, 0\right)$
2	$y = -4\cos(\pi \cdot 2)$ $= -4\cos 2\pi$ $= -4 \cdot 1 = -4$	$(2, -4)$

Connect the five key points with a smooth curve and graph one complete cycle of the given function.

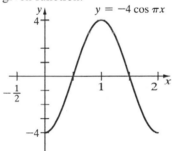

$y = -4 \cos \pi x$

7. $\sin\theta \csc\theta - \cos^2\theta = \sin\theta\left(\dfrac{1}{\sin\theta}\right) - \cos^2\theta$
$$= 1 - \cos^2\theta$$
$$= \sin^2\theta$$

8. $\cos\left(\theta + \dfrac{3\pi}{2}\right) = \cos\theta\cos\dfrac{3\pi}{2} - \sin\theta\sin\dfrac{3\pi}{2}$
$$= \cos\theta(0) - \sin\theta(-1)$$
$$= \sin\theta$$

9. $2x + 4y - 8 = 0$
$$4y = -2x + 8$$
$$\dfrac{4y}{4} = \dfrac{-2x + 8}{4}$$
$$y = -\dfrac{1}{2}x + 2$$

The slope is $-\dfrac{1}{2}$, and the y-intercept is 2.

10. $2\sin\dfrac{\pi}{3} - 3\tan\dfrac{\pi}{6} = 2\left(\dfrac{\sqrt{3}}{2}\right) - 3\left(\dfrac{1}{\sqrt{3}}\right)$
$$= \sqrt{3} - \dfrac{3}{\sqrt{3}}$$
$$= \sqrt{3} - \sqrt{3}$$
$$= 0$$

11. Let $\theta = \tan^{-1}\left(\dfrac{1}{2}\right)$, then $\tan\theta = \dfrac{1}{2}$. Because $\tan\theta$ is positive, θ is in the first quadrant.

Use the Pythagorean Theorem to find r.
$$r = \sqrt{1^2 + 2^2} = \sqrt{1 + 4} = \sqrt{5}$$
Use the right triangle to find the exact value.
$$\sin\left(\tan^{-1}\dfrac{1}{2}\right) = \sin\theta = \dfrac{1}{\sqrt{5}} = \dfrac{\sqrt{5}}{5}$$

12. $f(x) = \sqrt{5 - x}$
$$5 - x \geq 0$$
$$-x \geq -5$$
$$x \leq 5$$
The domain of the function is $\{x \mid x \leq 5\}$.

13.
$$g(x) = \frac{x-3}{x^2-9}$$
$$x^2 - 9 = 0$$
$$(x-3)(x+3) = 0$$
$$x - 3 = 0 \quad \text{or} \quad x + 3 = 0$$
$$x = 3 \qquad\qquad x = -3$$
The domain of the function is
$\{x \mid x \neq 3 \text{ and } x \neq -3\}$.

14. $s(t) = -16t^2 + 48t + 8$
$$= -16\left(t^2 - 3t - \frac{1}{2}\right)$$
$$= -16\left(t^2 - 3t + \frac{9}{4} - \frac{1}{2} - \frac{9}{4}\right)$$
$$= -16\left[\left(t - \frac{3}{2}\right)^2 - \frac{1}{2} - \frac{9}{4}\right]$$
$$= -16\left(t - \frac{3}{2}\right)^2 + 44$$

The ball reaches its maximum height after the first 1.5 seconds. The maximum height is 44 feet.

15. $d = 4\sin 5t$ is of the form $d = a\sin \omega t$ with $a = 4$ and $\omega = 5$.

a. $|a| = |4| = 4$
The maximum displacement is 4 meters.

b. $f = \frac{\omega}{2\pi} = \frac{5}{2\pi}$
The frequency is $\frac{5}{2\pi}$ cycle per second.

c. $\text{period} = \frac{2\pi}{\omega} = \frac{2\pi}{5}$
$\frac{2\pi}{5}$ seconds are required for one cycle.

16. Because 22.5° lies in quadrant I, $\cos 22.5° > 0$.
$$\cos 22.5° = \cos \frac{45°}{2}$$
$$= \sqrt{\frac{1 + \cos 45°}{2}}$$
$$= \sqrt{\frac{1 + \frac{\sqrt{2}}{2}}{2}}$$
$$= \sqrt{\frac{2 + \sqrt{2}}{4}}$$
$$= \frac{\sqrt{2 + \sqrt{2}}}{2}$$

17. a. $3\mathbf{v} - \mathbf{w} = 3(2\mathbf{i} + 7\mathbf{j}) - (\mathbf{i} - 2\mathbf{j})$
$$= 6\mathbf{i} + 21\mathbf{j} - \mathbf{i} + 2\mathbf{j}$$
$$= 5\mathbf{i} + 23\mathbf{j}$$

b. $\mathbf{v} \cdot \mathbf{w} = (2\mathbf{i} + 7\mathbf{j}) \cdot (\mathbf{i} - 2\mathbf{j})$
$$= 2(1) + 7(-2)$$
$$= -12$$

18. $\frac{1}{2}\log_b x - \log_b(x^2 + 1)$
$$= \log_b x^{1/2} - \log_b(x^2 + 1)$$
$$= \log_b \sqrt{x} - \log_b(x^2 + 1)$$
$$= \log_b \frac{\sqrt{x}}{x^2 + 1}$$

19. $(4, -1)$ and $(-8, 5)$
$$m = \frac{5 - (-1)}{-8 - 4} = \frac{6}{-12} = -\frac{1}{2}$$
$$y - (-1) = -\frac{1}{2}(x - 4)$$
$$y + 1 = -\frac{1}{2}x + 2$$
$$y = -\frac{1}{2}x + 1$$

20. $L = A\left(1 - e^{-kt}\right)$

   a. $20 = 300\left(1 - e^{-k(5)}\right)$

                $20 = 300 - 300e^{-5k}$

         $300e^{-5k} = 280$

             $e^{-5k} = \dfrac{14}{15}$

      $\ln\left(e^{-5k}\right) = \ln\left(\dfrac{14}{15}\right)$

           $5k = \ln\left(\dfrac{14}{15}\right)$

             $k = -\dfrac{\ln\left(\frac{14}{15}\right)}{5} \approx 0.014$

   b. $L = 300\left(1 - e^{-0.014(20)}\right) \approx 73$

      After 20 minutes, the student will have learned approximately 73 words.

   c. $260 = 300\left(1 - e^{-0.014t}\right)$

          $\dfrac{13}{15} = 1 - e^{-0.014t}$

         $-\dfrac{2}{15} = -e^{-0.014t}$

          $\dfrac{2}{15} = e^{-0.014t}$

      $\ln\left(\dfrac{2}{15}\right) = \ln\left(e^{-0.014t}\right)$

      $\ln\left(\dfrac{2}{15}\right) = -0.014t$

           $t = -\dfrac{\ln\left(\frac{2}{15}\right)}{0.014} \approx 144$

      It will take about 144 minutes.

Chapter 8

Check Point Exercises

1. $2x - 3y = -4$
   $2(1) - 3(2) \stackrel{?}{=} -4$
   $2 - 6 \stackrel{?}{=} -4$
   $-4 = -4$ true
   $2x + y = 4$
   $2(1) + 2 \stackrel{?}{=} 4$
   $2 + 2 \stackrel{?}{=} 4$
   $4 = 4$ true
   $(1, 2)$ is a solution of the system.

2. $y = 5x - 13$
   $2x + 3y = 12$
   Substitute the expression $5x - 13$ for y in the second equation and solve for x.
   $2x + 3(5x - 13) = 12$
   $2x + 15x - 39 = 12$
   $17x = 51$
   $x = 3$
   Substitute 3 for x in the first equation.
   $y = 5(3) - 13 = 15 - 13 = 2$
   The solution set is $\{(3, 2)\}$.

3. $3x + 2y = -1$
   $x - y = 3$
   Solve the second equation for x.
   $x = y + 3$
   Substitute the expression $y + 3$ for x in the first equation and solve for x.
   $3(y + 3) + 2y = -1$
   $3y + 9 + 2y = -1$
   $5y = -10$
   $y = -2$
   Substitute -2 for y in the equation $x = y + 3$.
   $x = -2 + 3 = 1$
   The solution set is $\{(1, -2)\}$.

4. $4x + 5y = 3$
   $2x - 3y = 7$
   Eliminate x by multiplying the second equation by -2·and adding the resulting equations.

$\begin{aligned} 4x + 5y &= 3 \\ -4x + 6y &= -14 \\ \hline 11y &= -11 \\ y &= -1 \end{aligned}$

Substitute -1 for y in the first equation.
$4x + 5(-1) = 3$
$4x - 5 = 3$
$4x = 8$
$x = 2$
The solution set is $\{(2, -1)\}$.

5. $4x = 5 + 2y$
   $3y = 4 - 2x$
   Arrange the system so that variable terms appear on the left and constants appear on the right.
   $4x - 2y = 5$
   $2x + 3y = 4$
   Eliminate x by multiplying the second equation by -2 and adding the resulting equations.

$\begin{aligned} 4x - 2y &= 5 \\ -4x - 6y &= -8 \\ \hline -8y &= -3 \\ y &= \frac{3}{8} \end{aligned}$

Substitute $\frac{3}{8}$ for y in the first equation.

$4x = 5 + 2\left(\frac{3}{8}\right)$

$4x = 5 + \frac{6}{8} = \frac{46}{8} = \frac{23}{4}$

$x = \frac{23}{16}$

The solution set is $\left\{\left(\frac{23}{16}, \frac{3}{8}\right)\right\}$.

6. The elimination method is used here to solve the system.
$$x + 2y = 4$$
$$3x + 6y = 13$$
Eliminate x by multiplying the first equation by -3 and adding the resulting equations.
$$-3x - 6y = -12$$
$$\underline{3x + 6y = 13}$$
$$0 = 1$$
The false statement $0 = 1$ indicates that the system has no solution. The solution set is the empty set, $\varnothing$.

7. The substitution method is used here to solve the system.
$$y = 4x - 4$$
$$8x - 2y = 8.$$
Substitute the expression $4x - 4$ for y in the second equation and solve for y.
$$8x - 2(4x - 4) = 8$$
$$8x - 8x + 8 = 8$$
$$8 = 8$$
This true statement indicates that the system has infinitely many solutions. The solution set is
$$\{(x, y) \mid y = 4x - 4\} \text{ or } \{(x, y) \mid 8x - 2y = 8\}.$$

8. $N = -20p + 1000$
$N = 5p + 250$
Substitute $-20p + 1000$ for N in the second equation.
$$-20p + 1000 = 5p + 250$$
$$750 = 25p$$
$$p = 30$$
Supply and demand are equal at $30. To find the number of units supplied and sold each week at this price, substitute 30 for p in either the demand or the supply model.
$$N = -20(30) + 1000$$
$$= -600 + 1000$$
$$= 400$$
At a price of $30, 400 units of the product can be supplied and sold.

Exercise Set 8.1

1. $x + 3y = 11$
$2 + 3(3) \overset{?}{=} 11$
$2 + 9 \overset{?}{=} 11$

$11 = 11$ true
$x - 5y = -13$
$2 - 5(3) \overset{?}{=} -13$
$2 - 15 \overset{?}{=} -13$
$-13 = -13$ true
$(2, 3)$ is a solution.

3. $2x + 3y = 17$
$2(2) + 3(5) \overset{?}{=} 17$
$4 + 15 \overset{?}{=} 17$
$19 = 17$ false
$(2, 5)$ is not a solution.

5. $x + y = 4$
$y = 3x$
Substitute the expression $3x$ for y in the first equation and solve for x.
$$x + 3x = 4$$
$$4x = 4$$
$$x = 1$$
Substitute 1 for x in the second equation.
$$y = 3(1) = 3$$
The solution set is $\{(1, 3)\}$.

7. $x + 3y = 8$
$y = 2x - 9$
Substitute the expression $2x - 9$ for y in the first equation and solve for x.
$$x + 3(2x - 9) = 8$$
$$x + 6x - 27 = 8$$
$$7x = 35$$
$$x = 5$$
Substitute 5 for x in the second equation.
$$y = 2(5) - 9 = 10 - 9 = 1$$
The solution set is $\{(5, 1)\}$.

9. $x + 3y = 5$
$4x + 5y = 13$
Solve the first equation for x.
$$x = 5 - 3y$$
Substitute the expression $5 - 3y$ for x in the second equation and solve for y.
$$4(5 - 3y) + 5y = 13$$
$$20 - 12y + 5y = 13$$
$$-7y = -7$$
$$y = 1$$
Substitute 1 for y in the equation $x = 5 - 3y$.
$$x = 5 - 3(1) = 2$$
The solution set is $\{(2, 1)\}$.

11. $2x - y = -5$
$x + 5y = 14$
Solve the first equation for y.
$2x + 5 = y$
Substitute the expression $2x + 5$ for y in the
second equation and solve for x.
$x + 5(2x + 5) = 14$
$x + 10x + 25 = 14$
$11x = -11$
$x = -1$
Substitute -1 for x in the equation $y = 2x + 5$
$y = 2(-1) + 5 = -2 + 5 = 3$
The solution set is $\{(-1, 3)\}$.

13. $2x - y = 3$
$5x - 2y = 10$
Solve the first equation for y.
$2x - 3 = y$
Substitute the expression $2x - 3$ for y in the
second equation and solve for x.
$5x - 2(2x - 3) = 10$
$5x - 4x + 6 = 10$
$x = 4$
Substitute 4 for x in the equation $y = 2x - 3$.
$y = 2(4) - 3 = 8 - 3 = 5$
The solution set is $\{(4, 5)\}$.

15. $x + 8y = 6$
$2x + 4y = -3$
Solve the first equation for x.
$x = 6 - 8y$
Substitute the expression $6 - 8y$ for x in the
second equation and solve for y.
$2(6 - 8y) + 4y = -3$
$12 - 16y + 4y = -3$
$-12y = -15$
$y = \dfrac{15}{12} = \dfrac{5}{4}$

Substitute $\dfrac{5}{4}$ for y in the equation $x = 6 - 8y$.

$x = 6 - 8\left(\dfrac{5}{4}\right) = 6 - 10 = -4$

The solution set is $\left\{\left(-4, \dfrac{5}{4}\right)\right\}$.

17. Eliminate y by adding the equations.
$x + y = 1$
$\underline{x - y = 3}$
$2x = 4$
$x = 2$
Substitute 2 for x in the first equation.
$2 + y = 1$
$y = -1$
The solution set is $\{(2, -1)\}$.

19. Eliminate y by adding the equations.
$2x + 3y = 6$
$\underline{2x - 3y = 6}$
$4x = 12$
$x = 3$
Substitute 3 for x in the first equation.
$2(3) + 3y = 6$
$6 + 3y = 6$
$3y = 0$
$y = 0$
The solution set is $\{(3, 0)\}$.

21. $x + 2y = 2$
$-4x + 3y = 25$
Eliminate x by multiplying the first equation
by 4 and adding the resulting equations.
$4x + 8y = 8$
$\underline{-4x + 3y = 25}$
$11y = 33$
$y = 3$
Substitute 3 for y in the first equation.
$x + 2(3) = 2$
$x + 6 = 2$
$x = -4$
The solution set is $\{(-4, 3)\}$.

23. $4x + 3y = 15$
$2x - 5y = 1$
Eliminate x by multiplying the second
equation by -2 and adding the resulting
equations.
$4x + 3y = 15$
$\underline{-4x + 10y = -2}$
$13y = 13$
$y = 1$
Substitute 1 for y in the second equation.
$2x - 5(1) = 1$
$2x = 6$
$x = 3$
The solution set is $\{(3, 1)\}$.

25. $3x - 4y = 11$
$2x + 3y = -4$
Eliminate x by multiplying the first equation by 2 and the second equation by -3. Add the resulting equations.
$$6x - 8y = 22$$
$$\underline{-6x - 9y = 12}$$
$$-17y = 34$$
$$y = -2$$
Substitute -2 for y in the second equation.
$$2x + 3(-2) = -4$$
$$2x - 6 = -4$$
$$2x = 2$$
$$x = 1$$
The solution set is $\{(1, -2)\}$.

27. $3x = 4y + 1$
$3y = 1 - 4x$
Arrange the system so that variable terms appear on the left and constants appear on the right.
$3x - 4y = 1$
$4x + 3y = 1$
Eliminate y by multiplying the first equation by 3 and the second equation by 4. Add the resulting equations.
$$9x - 12y = 3$$
$$\underline{16x + 12y = 4}$$
$$25x = 7$$
$$x = \frac{7}{25}$$
Substitute $\frac{7}{25}$ for x in the second equation.
$$3y = 1 - 4\left(\frac{7}{25}\right)$$
$$3y = \frac{-3}{25}$$
$$y = \frac{-1}{25}$$
The solution set is $\left\{\left(\frac{7}{25}, -\frac{1}{25}\right)\right\}$.

29. The substitution method is used here to solve the system.
$$x = 9 - 2y$$
$$x + 2y = 13$$
Substitute the expression $9 - 2y$ for x in the second equation and solve for y.
$$9 - 2y + 2y = 13$$
$$9 = 13$$
The false statement $9 = 13$ indicates that the sytem has no solution.
The solution set is the empty set, $\varnothing$.

31. The substitution method is used here to solve the system.
$$y = 3x - 5$$
$$21x - 35 = 7y$$
Substitute the expression $3x - 5$ for y in the second equation and solve for x.
$$21x - 35 = 7(3x - 5)$$
$$21x - 35 = 21x - 35$$
$$-35 = -35$$
This true statement indicates that the system has infinitely many solutions.
The solution set is $\{(x, y) \mid y = 3x - 5\}$ or
$\{(x, y) \mid 21x - 35 = 7y\}$.

33. The elimination method is used here to solve the system.
$$3x - 2y = -5$$
$$4x + y = 8$$
Eliminate y by multiplying the second equation by 2 and adding the resulting equations.
$$3x - 2y = -5$$
$$\underline{8x + 2y = 16}$$
$$11x = 11$$
$$x = 1$$
Substitute 1 for x in the second equation.
$$4(1) + y = 8$$
$$y = 4$$
The solution set is $\{(1, 4)\}$.

35. The elimination method is used here to solve the system.
$$x + 3y = 2$$
$$3x + 9y = 6$$
Eliminate x by multiplying the first equation by -3 and adding the resulting equations.
$$-3x - 9y = -6$$
$$\underline{3x + 9y = 6}$$
$$0 = 0$$
This true statement indicates that the system has infinitely many solutions.
The solution set is $\{(x, y) \mid x + 3y = 2\}$ or $\{(x, y) \mid 3x + 9y = 6\}$.

37. Add the equations to eliminate y.
$$x + y = 7$$
$$\underline{x - y = -1}$$
$$2x = 6$$
$$x = 3$$
Substitute 3 for x in the first equation.
$$3 + y = 7$$
$$y = 4$$
The numbers are 3 and 4.

39. $3x - y = 1$
$x + 2y = 12$
Eliminate y by multiplying the first equation by 2 and adding the resulting equations.
$$6x - 2y = 2$$
$$\underline{x + 2y = 12}$$
$$7x = 14$$
$$x = 2$$
Substitute 2 for x in the first equation.
$$3(2) - y = 1$$
$$6 - y = 1$$
$$-y = -5$$
$$y = 5$$
The numbers are 2 and 5.

41. $N = -25p + 7500$
$N = 5p + 6000$

a. Substitute 40 for p in the demand model.
$$N = -25(40) + 7500$$
$$= -1000 + 7500$$
$$= 6500$$
At $40 a ticket, 6500 tickets can be sold.

Substitute 40 for p in the supply model.
$$N = 5(40) + 6000$$
$$= 200 + 6000$$
$$= 6200$$
At $40 a ticket, 6200 tickets can be supplied.

b. Substitute $-25p + 7500$ for N in the second equation.
$$-25p + 7500 = 5p + 6000$$
$$1500 = 30p$$
$$50 = p$$
Supply and demand are equal at $50 a ticket.
To find the number of tickets supplied and sold at this price, substitute 50 for p into either the demand or supply model.
$$N = -25(50) + 7500$$
$$= -1250 + 7500$$
$$= 6250$$
At a price of $50, 6250 tickets can be supplied and sold.

43. $C(x) = 1.2x + 1080$
$R(x) = 1.6x$
Substitute $1.6x$ for $C(x)$ in the first equation.
$$1.6x = 1.2x + 1080$$
$$0.4x = 1080$$
$$x = 2700$$
2700 gallons must be sold weekly for the station to break even.

45. $x =$ mg of cholesterol in a Quarter Pounder
$y =$ mg of cholesterol in a Whopper with cheese
$$2x + 3y = 520$$
$$3x + y = 353$$
Eliminate y by multiplying the first equation by -3 and adding the resulting equations.
$$2x + 3y = 520$$
$$\underline{-9x - 3y = -1059}$$
$$-7x = -539$$
$$x = 77$$
Substitute 77 for x in the second equation.
$$3(77) + y = 353$$
$$231 + y = 353$$
$$y = 122$$
A Quarter Pounder contains 77 mg of cholesterol. A Whopper contains 122 mg of cholesterol.

47. $10(x - y) = 12.0$

$\quad\quad x + y = 10.4$

Expand the first equation and multiply the second equation by 10. Add the resulting two equations to eliminate y.

$10x - 10y = 12.0$

$\underline{10x + 10y = 104}$

$\quad\quad 20x = 116$

$\quad\quad\quad x = 5.8$

Substitute 5.8 for x in the second equation.

$5.8 + y = 10.4$

$\quad\quad y = 4.6$

On Super Bowl Sunday, 5.8 million pounds of potato chips are consumed.
On Super Bowl Sunday, 4.6 million pounds of tortilla chips are consumed.

49. $M = -0.41x + 22$

$\quad M = -0.18x + 10$

Substitute $-0.41x + 22$ for M in the second equation.

$-0.41x + 22 = -0.18x + 10$

$\quad\quad\quad\quad 12 = 0.23x$

$\quad\quad\quad\quad\quad x \approx 52$

Infant mortality for blacks and whites will be the same about 52 years after 1980 or in the year 2032.
To find the infant mortality of both groups, substitute 52 for x in either mortality model.

$M = -0.18(52) + 10$

$\quad = 9.36 + 10$

$\quad = 0.64$

The rate will be less than 1 death in 1000 live births.

51.–59. Answers may vary.

63. $a_1 x + b_1 y = c_1$

$\quad a_2 x + b_2 y = c_2$

Solve the first equation for x.

$x = \dfrac{c_1 - b_1 y}{a_1}$

Substitute the expression $\dfrac{c_1 - b_1 y}{a_1}$ for x in the second equation and solve for y.

$a_2 \left(\dfrac{c_1 - b_1 y}{a_1} \right) + b_2 y = c_2$

$a_2 \left(\dfrac{c_1 - b_1 y}{a_1} \right) + \dfrac{a_1 b_2 y}{a_1} = c_2$

$\dfrac{a_2 c_1 - a_2 b_1 y + a_1 b_2 y}{a_1} = c_2$

$a_2 c_1 - a_2 b_1 y + a_1 b_2 y = a_1 c_2$

$y(a_1 b_2 - a_2 b_1) = a_1 c_2 - a_2 c_1$

$y = \dfrac{a_1 c_2 - a_2 c_1}{a_1 b_2 - a_2 b_1}$

Substitute the expression $\dfrac{a_1 c_2 - a_2 c_1}{a_1 b_2 - a_2 b_1}$ for y in the first equation and solve for x.

$a_1 x + b_1 \left(\dfrac{a_1 c_2 - a_2 c_1}{a_1 b_2 - a_2 b_1} \right) = c_1$

$a_1 x + \dfrac{a_1 b_1 c_2 - a_2 b_1 c_1}{a_1 b_2 - a_2 b_1} = c_1$

$a_1 x = c_1 - \dfrac{a_1 b_1 c_2 - a_2 b_1 c_1}{a_1 b_2 - a_2 b_1}$

$\quad\quad = \dfrac{c_1(a_1 b_2 - a_2 b_1)}{a_1 b_2 - a_2 b_1} - \dfrac{a_1 b_1 c_2 - a_2 b_1 c_1}{a_1 b_2 - a_2 b_1}$

$\quad\quad = \dfrac{a_1 b_2 c_1 - a_1 b_1 c_2}{a_1 b_2 - a_2 b_1}$

$x = \dfrac{a_1 b_2 c_1 - a_1 b_1 c_2}{a_1 b_2 - a_2 b_1} \div a_1$

$\quad = \dfrac{a_1 b_2 c_1 - a_1 b_1 c_2}{a_1(a_1 b_2 - a_2 b_1)} = \dfrac{a_1(b_2 c_1 - b_1 c_2)}{a_1(a_1 b_2 - a_2 b_1)}$

$x = \dfrac{b_2 c_1 - b_1 c_2}{a_1 b_2 - a_2 b_1}$

65. x = number of hexagons formed
y = number of squares formed
$6x + y = 52$
$x + 4y = 24$
Eliminate x by multiplying the second equation by –6 and adding the resulting equations.
$$6x + y = 52$$
$$\underline{-6x - 24y = -144}$$
$$-23y = -92$$
$$y = 4$$
Substitute 4 for y in the second equation.
$$x + 4(4) = 24$$
$$x + 16 = 24$$
$$x = 8$$
Yes, they should make 8 hexagons and 4 squares.

Section 8.2

Check Point Exercises

1.
$$x - 2y + 3z = 22$$
$$-1 - 2(-4) + 3(5) \stackrel{?}{=} 22$$
$$-1 + 8 + 15 \stackrel{?}{=} 22$$
$$22 = 22 \text{ true}$$
$$2x - 3y - z = 5$$
$$2(-1) - 3(-4) - 5 \stackrel{?}{=} 5$$
$$-2 + 12 - 5 \stackrel{?}{=} 5$$
$$5 = 5 \text{ true}$$
$$3x + y - 5z = -32$$
$$3(-1) - 4 - 5(5) \stackrel{?}{=} -32$$
$$-3 - 4 - 25 \stackrel{?}{=} -32$$
$$-32 = -32 \text{ true}$$
$(-1, -4, 5)$ is a solution of the system.

2.
$$x + 4y - z = 20$$
$$3x + 2y + z = 8$$
$$2x - 3y + 2z = -16$$
Eliminate z from Equations 1 and 2 by adding Equation 1 and Equation 2.
$$x + 4y - z = 20$$
$$\underline{3x + 2y + z = 8}$$
$$4x + 6y = 28 \text{ Equation 4}$$
Eliminate z from Equations 2 and 3 by multiplying Equation 2 by –2 and adding the resulting equation to Equation 3.

$$-6x - 4y - 2z = -16$$
$$\underline{2x - 3y + 2z = -16}$$
$$-4x - 7y = -32 \text{ Equation 5}$$
Solve Equations 4 and 5 for x and y by adding Equation 4 and Equation 5.
$$4x + 6y = 28$$
$$\underline{-4x - 7y = -32}$$
$$-y = -4$$
$$y = 4$$
Substitute 4 for y in Equation 4 and solve for x.
$$4x + 6(4) = 28$$
$$4x + 24 = 28$$
$$4x = 4$$
$$x = 1$$
Substitute 1 for x and 4 for y in Equation 2 and solve for z.
$$3(1) + 2(4) + z = 8$$
$$3 + 8 + z = 8$$
$$11 + z = 8$$
$$z = -3$$
The solution set is $\{(1, 4, -3)\}$.

3.
$$2y - z = 7$$
$$x + 2y + z = 17$$
$$2x - 3y + 2z = -1$$
Eliminate x and z from Equations 2 and 3 by multiplying Equation 2 by –2 and adding the resulting equation to Equation 3.
$$-2x - 4y - 2z = -34$$
$$\underline{2x - 3y + 2z = -1}$$
$$-7y = -35$$
$$y = 5$$
Substitute 5 for y in Equation 1 and solve for z.
$$2(5) - z = 7$$
$$10 - z = 7$$
$$-z = -3$$
$$z = 3$$
Substitute 5 for y and 3 for z in Equation 2 and solve for x.
$$x + 2(5) + 3 = 17$$
$$x + 10 + 3 = 17$$
$$x + 13 = 17$$
$$x = 4$$
The solution set is $\{(4, 5, 3)\}$.

4. $(1, 4), (2, 1), (3, 4)$

$y = ax^2 + bx + c$

Substitute 1 for x and 4 for y in

$y = ax^2 + bx + c$.

$4 = a(1)^2 + b(1) + c$

$4 = a + b + c$ Equation 1

Substitute 2 for x and 1 for y in

$y = ax^2 + bx + c$.

$1 = a(2)^2 + b(2) + c$

$1 = 4a + 2b + c$ Equation 2

Substitute 3 for x and 4 for y in

$y = ax^2 + bx + c$.

$4 = a(3)^2 + b(3) + c$

$4 = 9a + 3b + c$ Equation 3

Eliminate c from Equations 1 and 2 by multiplying Equation 2 by -1 and adding the resulting equation to Equation 1.

$\quad 4 = a + b + c$

$\underline{-1 = -4a - 2b - c}$

$\quad 3 = -3a - b \qquad$ Equation 4

Eliminate c from Equation 2 and 3 by multiplying Equation 3 by -1 and adding the resulting equation to Equation 2.

$\quad 1 = 4a + 2b + c$

$\underline{-4 = -9a - 3b - c}$

$-3 = -5a - b \qquad$ Equation 5

Solve Equations 4 and 5 for a and b by multiplying Equation 5 by -1 and adding the resulting equation to Equation 4.

$3 = -3a - b$

$\underline{3 = 5a + b}$

$6 = 2a$

$a = 3$

Substitute 3 for a in Equation 4 and solve for b.

$\quad 3 = -3(3) - b$

$\quad 3 = -9 - b$

$12 = -b$

$\quad b = -12$

Substitute 3 for a and -12 for b in Equation 1 and solve for c.

$4 = 3 - 12 + c$

$4 = -9 + c$

$c = 13$

Substituting 3 for a, -12 for b, and 13 for c in the quadratic equation $y = ax^2 + bx + c$ gives

$y = 3x^2 - 12x + 13$.

Exercise Set 8.2

1. $x + y + z = 4$

$2 - 1 + 3 \stackrel{?}{=} 4$

$\quad\quad 4 = 4$ true

$x - 2y - z = 1$

$2 - 2(-1) - 3 \stackrel{?}{=} 1$

$\quad 2 + 2 - 3 \stackrel{?}{=} 1$

$\quad\quad\quad\quad 1 = 1$ true

$2x - y - 2 = -1$

$2(2) - (-1) - 2 \stackrel{?}{=} -1$

$\quad 4 + 1 - 2 \stackrel{?}{=} -1$

$\quad\quad\quad\quad 3 = -1$ false

$(2, -1, 3)$ is not a solution.

3. $x - 2y - 2$

$4 - 2(1) \stackrel{?}{=} 2$

$\quad 4 - 2 \stackrel{?}{=} 2$

$\quad\quad 2 = 2$ true

$2x + 3y = 11$

$2(4) + 3(1) \stackrel{?}{=} 11$

$\quad 8 + 3 \stackrel{?}{=} 11$

$\quad\quad\quad 11 = 11$ true

$y - 4z = -7$

$1 - 4(2) \stackrel{?}{=} -7$

$\quad 1 - 8 \stackrel{?}{=} -7$

$\quad\quad -7 = -7$ true

$(4, 1, 2)$ is a solution.

5. $x + y + 2z = 11$
$x + y + 3z = 14$
$x + 2y - z = 5$
Eliminate x and y from Equations 1 and 2 by multiplying Equation 2 by -1 and adding the resulting equation to Equation 1.
$-x - y - 3z = -14$

$\underline{x + y + 2z = 11}$
$-z = -3$
$z = 3$

Substitute 3 for z in Equations 1 and 3.
$x + y + 2(3) = 11$
$x + 2y - (3) = 5$
Simplify:
$x + y = 5$ Equation 4
$x + 2y = 8$ Equation 5
Solve Equations 4 and 5 for x and y by multiplying Equation 5 by -1 and adding the resulting equation to Equation 4.
$x + y = 5$
$\underline{-x - 2y = -8}$
$-y = -3$
$y = 3$

Substitute 3 for z and 3 for y in Equation 2 and solve for x.
$x + 3 + 3(3) = 14$
$x + 12 = 14$
$x = 2$
The solution set is $\{(2, 3, 3)\}$.

7. $4x - y + 2z = 11$
$x + 2y - z = -1$
$2x + 2y - 3z = -1$
Eliminate y from Equation 1 and 2 by multiplying Equation 1 by 2 and adding the resulting equation to Equation 2 and 3.
$8x - 2y + 4z = 22$
$\underline{x + 2y - z = -1}$
$9x + 3z = 21$ Equation 4
Eliminate y from Equations 1 and 3 by multiplying Equation 1 by 2 and adding the resulting equation to Equation 3.
$8x - 2y + 4z = 22$
$\underline{2x + 2y - 3z = -1}$
$10x + z = 21$ Equation 5

Solve Equations 4 and 5 for x and z by multiplying Equation 5 by -3 and adding the resulting equation to Equation 4.
$9x + 3z = 21$
$\underline{-30x - 3z = -63}$
$-21x = -42$
$x = 2$
Substitute 2 for x in Equation 5 and solve for z. $10(2) + z = 21$
$20 + z = 21$
$z = 1$
Substitute 2 for x and 1 for z in Equation 2 and solve for y.
$2 + 2y - 1 = -1$
$2y + 1 = -1$
$2y = -2$
$y = -1$
The solution set is $\{(2, -1, 1)\}$.

9. $3x + 5y + 2z = 0$
$12x - 15y + 4z = 12$
$6x - 25y - 8z = 8$
Eliminate z from Equations 1 and 3 by multiplying Equation 1 by -2 and adding the resulting equation to Equation 2.
$-6x - 10y - 4z = 0$

$\underline{12x - 15y + 4z = 12}$
$6x - 25y = 12$ Equation 4
Eliminate z from Equations 1 and 3 by multiplying Equation 1 by 4 and adding the resulting equation to Equation 3.
$12x + 20y + 8z = 0$

$\underline{6x - 25y - 8z = 8}$
$18x - 5y = 8$ Equation 5
Solve Equations 4 and 5 for x and y by multiplying Equation 4 by -3 and adding the resulting equation to Equation 5.
$-18x + 75y = -36$
$\underline{18x - 5y = 8}$
$70y = -28$
$y = -\dfrac{2}{5}$

Substitute $-\dfrac{2}{5}$ for y in Equation 4 and solve for x.

$$6x - 25\left(-\frac{2}{5}\right) = 12$$
$$6x + 10 = 12$$
$$6x = 2$$
$$x = \frac{2}{6} = \frac{1}{3}$$

Substitute $\frac{1}{3}$ for x and $-\frac{2}{5}$ for y in Equation 1 and solve for z.

$$3\left(\frac{1}{3}\right) + 5\left(-\frac{2}{5}\right) + 2z = 0$$
$$1 - 2 + 2z = 0$$
$$2z - 1 = 0$$
$$2z = 1$$
$$z = \frac{1}{2}$$

The solution set is $\left\{\left(\frac{1}{3}, -\frac{2}{5}, \frac{1}{2}\right)\right\}$.

11. $2x - 4y + 3z = 17$
$x + 2y - z = 0$
$4x - y - z = 6$
Eliminate z from Equations 1 and 2 by multiplying Equation 2 by 3 and adding the resulting equation to Equation 1.
$$2x - 4y + 3z = 17$$
$$\underline{3x + 6y - 3z = 0}$$
$$5x + 2y = 17 \quad \text{Equation 4}$$
Eliminate z from Equations 2 and 3 by multiplying Equation 2 by -1 and adding the resulting equation to Equation 3.
$$-x - 2y + z = 0$$
$$\underline{3x - y - z = 6}$$
$$3x - 3y = 6 \quad \text{Equation 5}$$
Solve Equations 4 and 5 for x and y by multiplying Equation 5 by $\frac{2}{3}$ and adding the resulting equation to Equation 4.
$$5x + 2y = 17$$
$$\underline{2x - 2y = 4}$$
$$7x = 21$$
$$x = 3$$
Substitute 3 for x in Equation 4 and solve for y.

$$5(3) + 2y = 17$$
$$15 + 2y = 17$$
$$2y = 2$$
$$y = 1$$
Substitute 3 for x and 1 for y in Equation 2 and solve for z.
$$3 + 2(1) - z = 0$$
$$3 + 2 - z = 0$$
$$5 - z = 0$$
$$5 = z$$
The solution set is $\{(3, 1, 5)\}$.

13. $2x + y = 2$
$x + y - z = 4$
$3x + 2y + z = 0$
Eliminate z from Equations 2 and 3 by adding Equation 2 and Equation 3.
$$x + y - z = 4$$
$$\underline{3x + 2y + z = 0}$$
$$4x + 3y = 4 \quad \text{Equation 4}$$
Solve Equations 1 and 4 for x and y by multiplying Equation 1 by -3 and adding the resulting equation to Equation 4.
$$-6x - 3y = -6$$
$$\underline{4x + 3y = 4}$$
$$-2x = -2$$
$$x = 1$$
Substitute 1 for x in Equation 1 and solve for y.
$$2(1) + y = 2$$
$$2 + y = 2$$
$$y = 0$$
Substitute 1 for x and 0 for y in Equation 2 and solve for z.
$$1 + 0 - z = 4$$
$$1 - z = 4$$
$$-z = 3$$
$$z = -3$$
The solution set is $\{(1, 0, -3)\}$.

15.
$$x + y = -4$$
$$y - z = 1$$
$$2x + y + 3z = -21$$
Eliminate y from Equations 1 and 2 by multiplying Equation 1 by -1 and adding the resulting equation to Equation 2.
$$-x - y = 4$$
$$\underline{y - z = 1}$$
$$-x - z = 5 \qquad \text{Equation 4}$$
Eliminate y from Equations 2 and 3 by multiplying Equation 2 by -1 and adding the resulting equation to Equation 3.
$$-y + z = -1$$
$$\underline{2x + y + 3z = -21}$$
$$2x + 4z = -22 \qquad \text{Equation 5}$$
Solve Equations 4 and 5 for x and z by multiplying Equation 4 by 2 and adding the resulting equation to Equation 5.
$$-2x - 2z = 10$$
$$\underline{2x + 4z = -22}$$
$$2z = -12$$
$$z = -6$$
Substitute -6 fo z in Equation 2 and solve for y.
$$y - (-6) = 1$$
$$y + 6 = 1$$
$$y = -5$$
Substitute -5 for y in Equation 1 and solve for x
$$x + (-5) = -4$$
$$x = 1$$
The solution set is $\{(1, -5, -6)\}$.

17. $3(2x + y) + 5z = -1$
$2(x - 3y + 4z) = -9$
$4(1 + x) = -3(z - 3y)$
Simplify each equation.
$6x + 3y + 5z = -1$ Equation 4
$2x - 6y + 8z = -9$ Equation 5
$4 + 4x = -3z + 9y$
$4x - 9y + 3z = -4$ Equation 6
Eliminate x from Equations 4 and 5 by multiplying Equation 5 by -3 and adding the resulting equation to Equation 4.

$$-6x + 3y + 5z = -1$$
$$\underline{-6x + 18y - 24z = 27}$$
$$21y - 19z = 26 \qquad \text{Equation 7}$$
Eliminate x from Equations 5 and 6 by multiplying Equation 5 by -2 and adding the resulting equation to Equation 6.
$$-4x + 12y - 16z = 18$$
$$\underline{4x - 9y + 3z = -4}$$
$$3y - 13z = 14 \qquad \text{Equation 8}$$
Solve Equations 7 and 8 for y and z by multiplying Equation 8 by -7 and adding the resulting equation to Equation 7.
$$21y - 19z = 26$$
$$\underline{-21y + 91z = -98}$$
$$72z = -72$$
$$z = -1$$
Substitute -1 for z in Equation 8 and solve for y.
$$3y - 13(-1) = 14$$
$$3y + 13 = 14$$
$$3y = 1$$
$$y = \frac{1}{3}$$
Substitute $\frac{1}{3}$ for y and -1 for z in Equation 5 and solve for x.
$$2x - 6\left(\frac{1}{3}\right) + 8(-1) = -9$$
$$2x - 2 - 8 = -9$$
$$2x - 10 = -9$$
$$2x = 1$$
$$x = \frac{1}{2}$$
The solution set is $\left\{\left(\frac{1}{2}, \frac{1}{3}, -1\right)\right\}$.

19. $x + y + z = 16$
$2x + 3y + 4z = 46$
$5x - y = 31$
Eliminate z from Equations 1 and 2 by multiplying Equation 1 by -4 and adding the resulting equation to Equation 2.
$-4x - 4y - 4z = -64$

$\underline{2x + 3y + 4z = 46}$
$\quad\quad -2x - y = -18 \quad$ Equation 4
Solve Equations 3 and 4 for x and y by multiplying Equation 4 by -1 and adding the resulting equation to Equation 3.
$5x - y = 31$

$\underline{2x + y = 18}$
$\quad\quad 7x = 49$
$\quad\quad\quad x = 7$
Substitute 7 for x in Equation 3 and solve for y.
$5(7) - y = 31$
$35 - y = 31$
$\quad -y = -4$
$\quad\quad y = 4$
Substitute 7 for x and 4 for y in Equation 1 and solve for z.
$7 + 4 + z = 16$
$z + 11 = 16$
$\quad\quad z = 5$
The numbers are 7, 4 and 5.

21. $(-1, 6), (1, 4), (2, 9)$
$y = ax^2 + bx + c$
Substitute -1 for x and 6 for y in
$y = ax^2 + bx + c$.
$6 = a(-1)^2 + b(-1) + c$
$6 = a - b + c \quad\quad$ Equation 1
Substitute 1 for x and 4 for y in
$y = ax^2 + bx + c$.
$4 = a(1)^2 + b(1) + c$
$4 = a + b + c \quad\quad$ Equation 2

Substitute 2 for x and 9 for y in
$y = ax^2 + bx + c$.
$9 = a(2)^2 + b(2) + c$
$9 = 4a + 2b + c \quad\quad$ Equation 3
Eliminate b from Equations 1 and 2 by adding Equation 1 and Equation 2.
$6 = a - b + c$

$\underline{4 = a + b + c}$
$10 = 2a + 2c \quad\quad$ Equation 4
Eliminate b from Equations 1 and 3 by multiplying Equation 1 by 2 and adding the resulting equation to Equation 3.
$12 = 2a - 2b + 2c$

$\underline{9 = 4a + 2b + c}$
$21 = 6a + 3c \quad\quad$ Equation 5
Solve Equations 4 and 5 for a and c by multiplying Equation 4 by -3 and adding the resulting equation to Equation 5.
$-30 = -6a - 6c$

$\underline{21 = 6a + 3c}$
$-9 = -3c$
$\quad c = 3$
Substitute 3 for c in Equation 4 and solve for a.
$10 = 2a + 2(3)$
$10 = 2a + 6$
$4 = 2a$
$a = 2$
Substitute 2 for a and 3 for c in Equation 2 and solve for b.
$4 = 2 + b + 3$
$4 = b + 5$
$b = -1$

Substituting 2 for a, -1 for b, and 3 for c in the quadratic equation $y = ax^2 + bx + c$ gives $y = 2x^2 - x + 3$.

23. $(-1, -4), (1, -2), (2, 5)$

Substitute -1 for x and -4 for y in

$y = ax^2 + bx + c$.

$-4 = a(-1)^2 + b(-1) + c$

$-4 = a - b + c$ Equation 1

Substitute 1 for x and -2 for y in

$y = ax^2 + bx + c$.

$-2 = a(1)^2 + b(1) + c$

$-2 = a + b + c$ Equation 2

Substitute 2 for x and 5 for y in

$y = ax^2 + bx + c$.

$5 = a(2)^2 + b(2) + c$

$5 = 4a + 2b + c$ Equation 3

Eliminate a and b from Equations 1 and 2 by multiplying Equation 1 by -1 and adding the resulting equation to Equation 2.

$4 = -a + b - c$

$\underline{-2 = a + b + c}$

$2 = 2b$

$b = 1$

Eliminate c from Equations 1 and 3 by multiplying Equation 1 by -1 and adding the resulting equation to Equation 3.

$4 = -a + b - c$

$\underline{5 = 4a + 2b + c}$

$9 = 3a + 3b$ Equation 4

Substitute 1 for b in Equation 4 and solve for a.

$9 = 3a + 3(1)$

$9 = 3a + 3$

$6 = 3a$

$a = 2$

Substitute 2 for a and 1 for b in Equation 2 and solve for c.

$-2 = 2 + 1 + c$

$-2 = c + 3$

$c = -5$

Substituting 2 for a, 1 for b, and -5 for c in quadratic equation $y = ax^2 + bx + c$ gives

$y = 2x^2 + x - 5$.

25. $x + y + z = 121,421$

$x - y = 2906$

$y - z = 1041$

Eliminate z from Equations 1 and 3 by adding Equation 1 and Equation 3.

$x + y + z = 121,421$

$\underline{y - z = 1041}$

$x + 2y = 122,462$ Equation 4

Solve Equations 2 and 4 for x and y by multiplying Equation 2 by 2 and adding the resulting equation to Equation 4.

$2x - 2y = 5812$

$\underline{x + 2y = 122,462}$

$3x = 128,274$

$x = 42,758$

Substitute 42,758 for x in Equation 2 and solve for y.

$42,758 - y = 2906$

$y = 39,852$

Substitute 39,852 for y in Equation 3 and solve for z.

$39,852 - z = 1041$

$z = 38,811$

The average starting salary for a chemical engineer is \$42,758.

The average starting salary for a mechanical engineer is \$39,852.

The average starting salary for a electrical engineer is \$38,811.

27. Substitute 1 for x and 46 for y in

$$y = \frac{1}{2}Ax^2 + Bx + C.$$

$$46 = \frac{1}{2}A(1)^2 + B(1) + C$$

$$46 = \frac{1}{2}A + B + C \qquad \text{Equation 1}$$

Substitute 2 for x and 84 for y in

$$y = \frac{1}{2}Ax^2 + Bx + C.$$

$$84 = \frac{1}{2}A(2)^2 + B(2) + C$$

$$84 = 2A + 2B + C \qquad \text{Equation 2}$$

Substitute 3 for x and 114 for y in

$$y = \frac{1}{2}Ax^2 + Bx + C.$$

$$114 = \frac{1}{2}A(3)^2 + B(3) + C$$

$$114 = \frac{9}{2}A + 3B + C = 114 \qquad \text{Equation 3}$$

Eliminate C from Equation 1 and 2 by multiplying Equation 1 by -1 and adding the resulting equation to Equation 2.

$$-46 = -\frac{1}{2}A - B - C$$

$$\underline{84 = 2A + 2B + C}$$

$$38 = \frac{3}{2}A + B$$

$$76 = 3A + 2B \qquad \text{Equation 4}$$

Eliminate C from Equation 2 and 3 by multiplying Equation 2 by -1 and adding the resulting equation to Equation 3.

$$-84 = -2A - 2B - C$$

$$114 = \frac{9}{2}A + 3B + C$$

$$\rule{4cm}{0.4pt}$$

$$30 = \frac{5}{2}A + B$$

$$60 = 5A + 2B \qquad \text{Equation 5}$$

Solve Equations 4 and 5 for A and B by multiplying Equation 5 by -1 and adding the resulting equation to Equation 4.

$$76 = 3A + 2B$$

$$\underline{-60 = -5A - 2B}$$

$$16 = -2A$$

$$-8 = A$$

Substitute -8 for A in Equation 4 and solve for B.

$$76 = 3(-8) + 2B$$

$$76 = -24 + 2B$$

$$100 = 2B$$

$$B = 50$$

Substitute -8 for A and 50 for B in Equation 2 and solve for C.

$$2(-8) + 2(50) + C = 84$$

$$-16 + 100 + C = 84$$

$$84 + C = 84$$

$$C = 0$$

$A = -8; B = 50; C = 0$

Substitute -8 for A, 50 for B, 0 for C and 6 for x in $y = \dfrac{1}{2}Ax^2 + Bx + C.$

$$y = \frac{1}{2}(-8)(6)^2 + (6)(50) + 0$$

$y = 156$ when $x = 6$

When a car is in motion for 6 seconds after the brakes are applied, it travels 156 feet.

29. x = number of $8 tickets sold
y = number of $10 tickets sold
z = number of $12 tickets sold
From the given conditions we have the following system of equations.
$$x + y + z = 400$$
$$8x + 10y + 12z = 3700$$
$$x + y = 7z \text{ or } x + y - 7z = 0$$
Eliminate z from Equations 1 and 2 multiplying Equation 1 by -12 and adding the resulting equation to Equation 2.
$$-12x - 12y - 12z = -4800$$
$$\underline{8x + 10y + 12z = 3700}$$
$$-4x - 2y = -1100 \qquad \text{Equation 4}$$
Eliminate z from Equations 1 and 3 by multiplying Equation 1 by 7 and adding the resulting equation to Equation 3.
$$7x + 7y + 7z = 2800$$
$$\underline{x + y - 7z = 0}$$
$$8x + 8y = 2800 \qquad \text{Equation 5}$$
Solve Equations 4 and 5 for x and y by multiplying Equation 4 by 2 and adding the resulting equation to Equation 5.
$$-8x - 4y = -2200$$
$$\underline{8x + 8y = 2800}$$
$$4y = 600$$
$$y = 150$$
Substitute 150 for y in Equation 5 and solve for x.
$$8x + 8(150) = 2800$$
$$8x = 2800 - 1200$$
$$8x = 1600$$
$$x = 200$$
Substitute 200 for x and 150 for y in Equation 1 and solve for z.
$$200 + 150 + z = 400$$
$$350 + z = 400$$
$$z = 50$$
The number of $8 tickets sold was 200.
The number of $10 tickets sold was 150.
The number of $12 tickets sold was 50.

31. x = amount of money invested at 10%
y = amount of money invested at 12%
z = amount of money invested at 15%
$$x + y + z = 6700$$
$$0.08x + 0.10y + 0.12z = 716$$
$$z = x + y + 300$$
Arrange Equation 3 so that variable terms appear on the left and constants appear on the right.
$$-x - y + z = 300 \quad \text{Equation 4}$$
Eliminate x and y from Equations 1 and 4 by adding Equations 1 and 4.
$$x + y + z = 6700$$
$$\underline{-x - y + z = 300}$$
$$2z = 7000$$
$$z = 3500$$
Substitute 3500 for z in Equation 1 and Equation 2 and simplify.
$$x + y + 3500 = 6700$$
$$x + y = 3200 \quad \text{Equation 5}$$
$$0.08x + 0.10y + 0.12(3500) = 716$$
$$0.08x + 0.10y + 420 = 716$$
$$0.08x + 10y = 296 \quad \text{Equation 6}$$
Solve Equations 5 and 6 for x and y by multiplying Equation 5 by -0.10 and adding the resulting equation to Equation 6.
$$-0.10x - 0.10y = -320$$
$$\underline{0.08x + 0.10y = 296}$$
$$-0.02x = 24$$
$$x = 1200$$
Substitute 1200 for x and 3,500 for z in Equation 1 and solve for y.
$$1200 + y + 3500 = 6700$$
$$y + 4700 = 6700$$
$$y = 2000$$
The person invested $1200 at 8%, $2000 at 10%, and $3500 at 12%.

33.–35. Answers may vary.

41. x = number of triangles
y = number of rectangles
z = number of pentagons
$x + y + z = 40$
$3x + 4y + 5z = 153$
$2y + 5z = 72$
Eliminate x from Equations 1 and 2 by multiplying Equation 1 by –3 and adding the resulting equation to Equation 2.
$-3x - 3y - 3z = -120$

$$\underline{3x + 4y + 5z = 153}$$
$$y + 2z = 33 \qquad \text{Equation 4}$$

Solve for z by multiplying Equation 4 by –2 and adding the resulting equation to Equation 3.
$2y + 5z = 72$

$$\underline{-2y - 4z = -66}$$
$$z = 6$$

Substitute 6 for z in Equation 4 and solve for y.
$y + 2(6) = 33$
$y + 12 = 33$
$y = 21$
Substitute 21 for y and 6 for z in Equation 1 and solve for x.
$x + 21 + 6 = 40$
$x + 27 = 40$
$x = 13$
The painting has 13 triangles, 21 rectangles, and 6 pentagons.

Section 8.3

Check Point Exercises

1. $\dfrac{5x - 1}{(x-3)(x+4)} = \dfrac{A}{x-3} + \dfrac{B}{x+4}$

Multiply both sides of the equation by the least common denominator $(x - 3)(x + 4)$ and divide out common factors.
$5x - 1 = A(x + 4) + B(x - 3)$
$5x - 1 = Ax + 4A + Bx - 3B$
$5x - 1 = (A + B)x + 4A - 3B$

Equate coefficients of like powers of x and equate constant terms.
$A + B = 5$
$4A - 3B = -1$
Solving the above system for A and B we find
$A = 2$ and $B = 3$.
$$\dfrac{5x - 1}{(x-3)(x+4)} = \dfrac{2}{x-3} + \dfrac{3}{x+4}$$

2. $\dfrac{x+2}{x(x-1)^2} = \dfrac{A}{x} + \dfrac{B}{x-1} + \dfrac{C}{(x-1)^2}$

Multiply both sides of the equation by the least common denominator $x(x-1)^2$ and divide out common factors.
$x + 2 = A(x-1)^2 + Bx(x-1) + Cx$
$x + 2 = A\left(x^2 - 2x + 1\right) + Bx^2 - Bx + Cx$
$x + 2 = Ax^2 - 2Ax + A + Bx^2 - Bx + Cx$
$x + 2 = Ax^2 + Bx^2 - 2Ax - Bx + Cx + A$
$x + 2 = (A + B)x^2 + (-2A - B + C)x + A$

Equate coefficients of like powers of x and equate constant terms.
$A + B = 0$
$-2A - B + C = 1$
$A = 2$
Since $A = 2$, we find that $B = -2$ and $C = 3$ by substitution.
$$\dfrac{x+2}{x(x-1)^2} = \dfrac{2}{x} - \dfrac{2}{x-1} + \dfrac{3}{(x-1)^2}$$

3. $\dfrac{8x^2 + 12x - 20}{(x+3)\left(x^2 + x + 2\right)} = \dfrac{A}{x+3} + \dfrac{Bx + C}{x^2 + x + 2}$

Multiply both sides of the equation by the least common denominator $(x+3)\left(x^2 + x + 2\right)$ and divide out common factors.

$8x^2 + 12x - 20 = A\left(x^2 + x + 2\right) + (Bx + C)(x+3)$

$8x^2 + 12x - 20 = Ax^2 + Ax + 2A + Bx^2 + 3Bx + Cx + 3C$

$8x^2 + 12x - 20 = Ax^2 + Bx^2 + Ax + 3Bx + Cx + 2A + 3C$

$8x^2 + 12x - 20 = (A+B)x^2 + (A+3B+C)x + 2A + 3C$

Equate coefficients of like powers of x and equate constant terms.

$A + B = 8$

$A + 3B + C = 12$

$2A + 3C = -20$

Solving the above system for A, B, and C we find $A = 2$, $B = 6$, and $C = -8$.

$\dfrac{8x^2 + 12x - 20}{(x+3)\left(x^2 + x + 2\right)} = \dfrac{2}{x+3} + \dfrac{6x - 8}{x^2 + x + 2}$

4. $\dfrac{2x^3 + x + 3}{\left(x^2 + 1\right)^2} = \dfrac{Ax + B}{x^2 + 1} + \dfrac{Cx + D}{\left(x^2 + 1\right)^2}$

Multiply both sides of the equation by the common denominator $\left(x^2 + 1\right)^2$ and divide out common factors.

$2x^3 + x + 3 = (Ax + B)(x^2 + 1) + Cx + D$

$2x^3 + x + 3 = Ax^3 + Bx^2 + Ax + B + Cx + D$

$2x^3 + x + 3 = Ax^3 + Bx^2 + Ax + Cx + B + D$

$2x^3 + x + 3 = Ax^3 + Bx^2 + (A+C)x + B + D$

Equate coefficients of like powers of x and equate constant terms.

$A = 2$

$B = 0$

$A + C = 1$

$B + D = 3$

Since $A = 2$ and $B = 0$ we find that $C = -1$ and $D = 3$ by substitution.

$\dfrac{2x^3 + x + 3}{\left(x^2 + 1\right)^2} = \dfrac{2x}{x^2 + 1} + \dfrac{-x + 3}{\left(x^2 + 1\right)^2} = \dfrac{2x}{x^2 + 1} - \dfrac{x - 3}{\left(x^2 + 1\right)^2}$

Exercise Set 8.3

1. $\dfrac{11x - 10}{(x-2)(x+1)} = \dfrac{A}{x-2} + \dfrac{B}{x+1}$

3. $\dfrac{6x^2 - 14x - 27}{(x+2)(x-3)^2} = \dfrac{A}{x+2} + \dfrac{B}{x-3} + \dfrac{C}{(x-3)^2}$

5. $\dfrac{5x^2 - 6x + 7}{(x-1)(x^2+1)} = \dfrac{A}{x-1} + \dfrac{Bx+C}{x^2+1}$

7. $\dfrac{x^3 + x^2}{(x^2+4)^2} = \dfrac{Ax+B}{x^2+4} + \dfrac{Cx+D}{(x^2+4)^2}$

9. $\dfrac{x}{(x-3)(x-2)} = \dfrac{A}{x-3} + \dfrac{B}{x-2}$

Multiply both sides of the equation by the least common denominator $(x-3)(x-2)$ and divide out common factors.

$x = A(x-2) + B(x-3)$

$x = Ax - 2A + Bx - 3B$

$x = Ax + Bx - 2A - 3B$

$x = (A+B)x - (2A+3B)$

Equate coefficients of like powers of x, and equate constant terms.

$\quad A + B = 1$

$2A + 3B = 0$

Solving the above system for A and B, we find $A = 3$ and $B = -2$.

$\dfrac{x}{(x-3)(x-2)} = \dfrac{3}{x-3} - \dfrac{2}{x-2}$

11. $\dfrac{3x+50}{(x-9)(x+2)} = \dfrac{A}{x-9} + \dfrac{B}{x+2}$

Multiply both sides of the equation by the least common denominator $(x-9)(x+2)$ and divide out common factors.

$3x + 50 = A(x+2) + B(x-9)$

$3x + 50 = Ax + 2A + Bx - 9B$

$3x + 50 = Ax + Bx + 2A - 9B$

$3x + 50 = (A+B)x + (2A - 9B)$

Equate coefficients of like powers of x, and equate constant terms.

$\quad A + B = 3$

$2A - 9B = 50$

Solving the above system for A and B, we find $A = 7$ and $B = -4$.

$\dfrac{3x+50}{(x-9)(x+2)} = \dfrac{7}{x-9} - \dfrac{4}{x+2}$

13. $\dfrac{7x-4}{x^2 - x - 12} = \dfrac{7x-4}{(x-4)(x+3)} = \dfrac{A}{x-4} + \dfrac{B}{x+3}$

Multiply both sides of the last equation by the least common denominator $(x-4)(x-3)$ and divide out common factors.

$7x - 4 = A(x+3) + B(x-4)$

$7x - 4 = Ax + 3A + Bx - 4B$

$7x - 4 = Ax + Bx + 3A - 4B$

$7x - 4 = (A+B)x + (3A - 4B)$

Equate coefficients of like powers of x, and equate constant terms.

$\quad A + B = 7$

$3A - 4B = -4$

Solving the above system for A and B, we find $A = \dfrac{24}{7}$ and $B = \dfrac{25}{7}$.

$\dfrac{7x-4}{x^2 - x - 12} = \dfrac{24}{7(x-4)} + \dfrac{25}{7(x+3)}$

15. $\dfrac{4x^2 + 13x - 9}{x(x-1)(x+3)} = \dfrac{A}{x} + \dfrac{B}{x-3} + \dfrac{C}{x+3}$

Multiply both sides of the equation by the least common denominator $x(x-1)(x+3)$ and divide out common factors.

$4x^2 + 13x - 9 = A(x-1)(x+3) + Bx(x+3) + Cx(x-1)$

$4x^2 + 13x - 9 = A\left(x^2 + 2x - 3\right) + Bx^2 + 3Bx + Cx^2 - Cx$

$4x^2 + 13x - 9 = Ax^2 + 2Ax - 3A + Bx^2 + 3Bx + Cx^2 - Cx$

$4x^2 + 13x - 9 = Ax^2 + Bx^2 + Cx^2 + 2Ax + 3Bx - Cx - 3A$

$4x^2 + 13x - 9 = (A + B + C)x^2 + (2A + 3B - C)x - 3A$

Equate coefficients of like powers of x, and equate constant terms.

$A + B + C = 4$
$2A + 3B - C = 13$
$\quad\quad -3A = -9$

Solving the above system for A, B, and C, we find $A = 3$ and $B = 2$, and $C = -1$.

$\dfrac{4x^2 + 13x - 9}{x(x-1)(x+3)} = \dfrac{3}{x} + \dfrac{2}{x-1} - \dfrac{1}{x+3}$

17. $\dfrac{4x^2 - 7x - 3}{x^3 - x} = \dfrac{4x^2 - 7x - 3}{x(x+1)(x-1)} = \dfrac{A}{x} + \dfrac{B}{x+1} + \dfrac{C}{x-1}$

Multiply both sides of the last equation by the least common denominator $x(x+1)(x-1)$ and divide out common factors.

$4x^2 - 7x - 3 = A(x+1)(x-1) + Bx(x-1) + Cx(x+1)$

$4x^2 - 7x - 3 = A(x^2 - 1) + Bx^2 - Bx + Cx^2 + Cx$

$4x^2 - 7x - 3 = Ax^2 - A + Bx^2 - Bx + Cx^2 + Cx$

$4x^2 - 7x - 3 = Ax^2 + Bx^2 + Cx^2 - Bx + Cx - A$

$4x^2 - 7x - 3 = (A + B + C)x^2 + (-B + C)x - A$

Equate coefficients of like powers of x, and equate constant terms.

$A + B + C = 4$
$\quad -B + C = -7$
$\quad\quad\; -A = -3$

Solving the above system for A, B, and C, we find $A = 3$ and $B = 4$, and $C = -3$.

$\dfrac{4x^2 - 7x - 3}{x^3 - x} = \dfrac{3}{x} + \dfrac{4}{x+1} - \dfrac{3}{x-1}$

19. $\dfrac{6x-11}{(x-1)^2} = \dfrac{A}{x-1} + \dfrac{B}{(x-1)^2}$

Multiply both sides of the equation by the least common denominator $(x-1)^2$ and divide out common factors.

$6x - 11 = A(x-1) + B$
$6x - 11 = Ax - A + B$

Equate coefficients of like powers of x, and equate constant terms.

$A = 6$
$-A + B = -11$

Since $A = 6$, we find that $B = -5$ by substitution. $\dfrac{6x-11}{(x-1)^2} = \dfrac{6}{x-1} - \dfrac{5}{(x-1)^2}$

21. $\dfrac{x^2-6x+3}{(x-2)^3} = \dfrac{A}{x-2} + \dfrac{B}{(x-2)^2} + \dfrac{C}{(x-2)^3}$

Multiply both sides of the equation by the least common denominator $(x-2)^3$ and divide out common factors.

$x^2 - 6x + 3 = A(x-2)^2 + B(x-2) + C$
$x^2 - 6x + 3 = A(x^2 - 4x + 4) + Bx - 2B + C$
$x^2 - 6x + 3 = Ax^2 - 4Ax + 4A + Bx - 2B + C$
$x^2 - 6x + 3 = Ax^2 - 4Ax + Bx + 4A - 2B + C$
$x^2 - 6x + 3 = Ax^2 + (-4A + B)x + 4A - 2B + C$

Equate coefficients of like powers of x, and equate constant terms.

$A = 1$
$-4A + B = -6$
$4A - 2B + C = 3$

Since $A = 1$, we find that $B = -2$ and $C = -5$ by substitution. $\dfrac{x^2-6x+3}{(x-2)^3} = \dfrac{1}{x-2} - \dfrac{2}{(x-2)^2} - \dfrac{5}{(x-2)^3}$

23. $\dfrac{x^2+2x+7}{x(x-1)^2} = \dfrac{A}{x} + \dfrac{B}{x-1} + \dfrac{C}{(x-1)^2}$

Multiply both sides of the equation by the least common denominator $x(x-1)^2$ and divide out common factors.

$x^2 + 2x + 7 = A(x-1)^2 + Bx(x-1) + Cx$
$x^2 + 2x + 7 = A(x^2 - 2x + 1) + Bx^2 - Bx + Cx$
$x^2 + 2x + 7 = Ax^2 - 2Ax + A + Bx^2 - Bx + Cx$
$x^2 + 2x + 7 = Ax^2 + Bx^2 - 2Ax - Bx + Cx + A$
$x^2 + 2x + 7 = (A+B)x^2 + (-2A - B + C)x + A$

$A + B = 1$
$-2A - B + C = 2$
$A = 7$

Since $A = 7$, we find that $B = -6$ and $C = 10$ by substitution. $\dfrac{x^2+2x+7}{x(x-1)^2} = \dfrac{7}{x} - \dfrac{6}{x-1} + \dfrac{10}{(x-1)^2}$

25. $\dfrac{5x^2 + 21x + 4}{(x+1)^2(x-3)} = \dfrac{A}{x+1} + \dfrac{B}{(x+1)^2} + \dfrac{C}{x-3}$

Multiply both sides of the equation by the least common denominator $(x+1)^2(x-3)$ and divide out common factors.

$5x^2 + 21x + 4 = A(x+1)(x-3) + B(x-3) + C(x+1)^2$

$5x^2 + 21x + 4 = A(x^2 - 2x - 3) + Bx - 3B + C(x^2 + 2x + 1)$

$5x^2 + 21x + 4 = Ax^2 - 2Ax - 3A + Bx - 3B + Cx^2 + 2Cx + C$

$5x^2 + 21x + 4 = Ax^2 + Cx^2 - 2Ax + Bx + 2Cx - 3A - 3B + C$

$5x^2 + 21x + 4 = (A+C)x^2 + (-2A + B + 2C)x - 3A - 3B + C$

Equate coefficients of like powers of x, and equate constant terms.

$A + C = 5$

$-2A + B + 2C = 21$

$-3A - 3B + C = 4$

Solving the above system for A, B, and C, we find $A = -2$, $B = 3$, and $C = 7$.

$\dfrac{5x^2 + 21x + 4}{(x+1)^2(x-3)} = -\dfrac{2}{x+1} + \dfrac{3}{(x+1)^2} + \dfrac{7}{x-3}$

27. $\dfrac{5x^2 - 6x + 7}{(x-1)(x^2+1)} = \dfrac{A}{x-1} + \dfrac{Bx+C}{x^2+1}$

Multiply both sides of the equation by the least common denominator $(x-1)(x^2+1)$ and divide out common factors.

$5x^2 - 6x + 7 = A(x^2 + 1) + (Bx + C)(x-1)$

$5x^2 - 6x + 7 = Ax^2 + A + Bx^2 - Bx + Cx - C$

$5x^2 - 6x + 7 = Ax^2 + Bx^2 - Bx + Cx + A - C$

$5x^2 - 6x + 7 = (A+B)x^2 + (-B+C)x + A - C$

Equate coefficients of like powers of x, and equate constant terms.

$A + B = 5$

$-B + C = -6$

$A - C = 7$

Solving the above system for A, B, and C, we find $A = 3$, $B = 2$, and $C = -4$.

$\dfrac{5x^2 - 6x + 7}{(x-1)(x^2+1)} = \dfrac{3}{x-1} + \dfrac{2x-4}{x^2+1}$

29. $\dfrac{5x^2 + 6x + 3}{(x+1)(x^2 + 2x + 2)} = \dfrac{A}{x+1} + \dfrac{Bx + C}{x^2 + 2x + 2}$

Multiply both sides of the equation by the least common denominator $(x+1)(x^2 + 2x + 2)$ and divide out common factors.

$5x^2 + 6x + 3 = A(x^2 + 2x + 2) + (Bx + C)(x + 1)$

$5x^2 + 6x + 3 = Ax^2 + 2Ax + 2A + Bx^2 + Bx + Cx + C$

$5x^2 + 6x + 3 = Ax^2 + Bx^2 + 2Ax + Bx + Cx + 2A + C$

$5x^2 + 6x + 3 = (A + B)x^2 + (2A + B + C)x + 2A + C$

Equate coefficients of like powers of x, and equate constant terms.

$A + B = 5$

$2A + B + C = 6$

$2A + C = 3$

Solving the above system for A, B, and C, we find $A = 2$, $B = 3$, and $C = -1$.

$\dfrac{5x^2 + 6x + 3}{(x+1)(x^2 + 2x + 2)} = \dfrac{2}{x+1} + \dfrac{3x - 1}{x^2 + 2x + 2}$

31. $\dfrac{6x^2 - x + 1}{x^3 + x^2 + x + 1} = \dfrac{6x^2 - x + 1}{(x+1)(x^2 + 1)} = \dfrac{A}{x+1} + \dfrac{Bx + C}{x^2 + 1}$

Multiply both sides of the last equation by the least common denominator $(x+1)(x^2 + 1)$ and divide out common factors.

$6x^2 - x + 1 = A(x^2 + 1) + (Bx + C)(x + 1)$

$6x^2 - x + 1 = Ax^2 + A + Bx^2 + Bx + Cx + C$

$6x^2 - x + 1 = Ax^2 + Bx^2 + Bx + Cx + A + C$

$6x^2 - x + 1 = (A + B)x^2 + (B + C)x + A + C$

Equate coefficients of like powers of x, and equate constant terms.

$A + B = 6$

$B + C = -1$

$A + C = 1$

Solving the above system for A, B, and C, we find $A = 4$, $B = 2$, and $C = -3$.

$\dfrac{6x^2 - x + 1}{x^3 + x^2 + x + 1} = \dfrac{4}{x+1} + \dfrac{2x - 3}{x^2 + 1}$

33. $\dfrac{x^3 + x^2 + 2}{\left(x^2 + 2\right)^2} = \dfrac{Ax + B}{x^2 + 2} + \dfrac{Cx + D}{\left(x^2 + 2\right)^2}$

Multiply both sides of the last equation by the least common denominator $(x^2 + 2)^2$ and divide out common factors.

$x^3 + x^2 + 2 = (Ax + B)\left(x^2 + 2\right) + Cx + D$

$x^3 + x^2 + 2 = Ax^3 + Bx^2 + 2Ax + 2B + Cx + D$

$x^3 + x^2 + 2 = Ax^3 + Bx^2 + 2Ax + Cx + 2B + D$

$x^3 + x^2 + 2 = Ax^3 + Bx^2 + (2A + C)x + (2B + D)$

Equate coefficients of like powers of x, and equate constant terms.

$A = 1$

$B = 1$

$2A + C = 0$

$2B + D = 2$

Since $A = 1$ and $B = 1$, we find that $C = -2$ and $D = 0$ by substitution.

$\dfrac{x^3 + x^2 + 2}{\left(x^2 + 2\right)^2} = \dfrac{x + 1}{x^2 + 2} - \dfrac{2x}{\left(x^2 + 2\right)^2}$

35. $\dfrac{x^3 - 4x^2 + 9x - 5}{(x^2 - 2x + 3)^2} = \dfrac{Ax + B}{x^2 - 2x + 3} + \dfrac{Cx + D}{(x^2 - 2x + 3)^2}$

Multiply both sides of the equation by the least common denominator $(x^2 - 2x + 3)^2$ and divide out common factors.

$x^3 - 4x^2 + 9x - 5 = (Ax + B)(x^2 - 2x + 3) + Cx + D$

$x^3 - 4x^2 + 9x - 5 = Ax^3 - 2Ax^2 + 3Ax + Bx^2 - 2Bx + 3B + Cx + D$

$x^3 - 4x^2 + 9x - 5 = Ax^3 - 2Ax^2 + Bx^2 + 3Ax - 2Bx + Cx + 3B + D$

$x^3 - 4x^2 + 9x - 5 = Ax^3 + (-2A + B)x^2 + (3A - 2B + C)x + 3B + D$

Equate coefficients of like powers of x, and equate constant terms.

$A = 1$

$-2A + B = -4$

$3A - 2B + C = 9$

$3B + D = -5$

Since $A = 1$, we find that $B = -2$, $C = 2$, and $D = 1$ by substitution.

$\dfrac{x^3 - 4x^2 + 9x - 5}{(x^2 - 2x + 3)^2} = \dfrac{x - 2}{x^2 - 2x + 3} + \dfrac{2x + 1}{(x^2 - 2x + 3)^2}$

37. $\dfrac{4x^2 + 3x + 14}{x^3 - 8} = \dfrac{4x^2 + 3x + 14}{(x-2)\left(x^2 + 2x + 4\right)} = \dfrac{A}{x-2} + \dfrac{Bx + C}{x^2 + 2x + 4}$

Multiply both sides of the last equation by the least common denominator $(x-2)(x^2 + 2x + 4)$ and divide out common factors.

$4x^2 + 3x + 14 = A\left(x^2 + 2x + 4\right) + (Bx + C)(x - 2)$

$4x^2 + 3x + 14 = A^2 + 2Ax + 4A + Bx^2 - 2Bx + Cx - 2C$

$4x^2 + 3x + 14 = Ax^2 + Bx^2 + 2Ax - 2Bx + Cx + 4A - 2C$

$4x^2 + 3x + 14 = (A + B)x^2 + (2A - 2B + C)x + (4A - 2C)$

Equate coefficients of like powers of x, and equate constant terms.

$A + B = 4$

$2A - 2B + C = 3$

$4A - 2C = 14$

Solving the above system for A, B, and C, we find $A = 3$, $B = 1$, and $C = -1$.

$\dfrac{4x^2 + 3x + 4}{x^3 - 8} = \dfrac{3}{x - 2} + \dfrac{x - 1}{x^2 + 2x + 4}$

39. $\dfrac{1}{x(x+1)} = \dfrac{A}{x} + \dfrac{B}{x+1}$

Multiply both sides of the equation by the least common denominator $x(x+1)$ and divide out common factors.

$1 = A(x + 1) + Bx$

$1 = Ax + A + Bx$

$1 = Ax + Bx + A$

$1 = (A + B)x + A$

Equate coefficients of like powers of x, and equate constant terms.

$A + B = 0$

$A = 1$

Since $A = 1$ we find that $B = -1$ by substitution.

$\dfrac{1}{x(x+1)} = \dfrac{1}{x} - \dfrac{1}{x+1}$

$\dfrac{1}{1 \cdot 2} + \dfrac{1}{2 \cdot 3} + \dfrac{1}{3 \cdot 4} + \cdots + \dfrac{1}{99 \cdot 100} = \left(\dfrac{1}{1} - \dfrac{1}{2}\right) + \left(\dfrac{1}{2} - \dfrac{1}{3}\right) + \left(\dfrac{1}{3} - \dfrac{1}{4}\right) + \cdots + \left(\dfrac{1}{99} - \dfrac{1}{100}\right)$

$= \dfrac{1}{1} - \dfrac{1}{100}$

$= \dfrac{99}{100}$

41.–45. Answers may vary.

47. Exercise 9

Exercise 11

Exercise 13

Exercise 15

Exercise 17

49. $\dfrac{ax+b}{(x-c)^2} = \dfrac{A}{x-c} + \dfrac{B}{(x-c)^2}$

Multiply both sides of the equation by the least common denominator $(x-c)^2$ and divide out common factors.

$ax + b = A(x - c) + B$

$ax + b = Ax - Ac + B$

Equate coefficients of like powers of x, and equate constants terms.

$A = a$

$-Ac + B = b$

Since $A = a$, we find that $B = b + Ac = b + ac$ by substitution.

$\dfrac{ax+b}{(x-c)^2} = \dfrac{a}{x-c} + \dfrac{b+ac}{(x-c)^2}$

Section 8.4

Check Point Exercises

1. $x^2 = y - 1$

$4x - y = -1$

Solve the first equation for y.

$y = x^2 + 1$

Substitute the expression $x^2 + 1$ for y in the second equation and solve for x.

$4x - (x^2 + 1) = -1$

$4x - x^2 - 1 = -1$

$x^2 - 4x = 0$

$x(x - 4) = 0$

$x = 0$ or $x - 4 = 0$

$x = 4$

If $x = 0$, $y = (0)^2 + 1 = 1$.

If $x = 4$, $y = (4)^2 + 1 = 17$.

The solution set is $\{(0, 1), (4, 17)\}$.

2. $x + 2y = 0$

$(x - 1)^2 + (y - 1)^2 = 5$

Solve the first equation for x.

$x = -2y$

Substitute the expression $-2y$ for x in the second equation and solve for y.

$(-2y - 1)^2 + (y - 1)^2 = 5$

$4y^2 + 4y + 1 + y^2 - 2y + 1 = 5$

$5y^2 + 2y - 3 = 0$

$(5y - 3)(y + 1) = 0$

$5y - 3 = 0$ or $y + 1 = 0$

$y = \dfrac{3}{5}$ or $y = -1$

If $y = \dfrac{3}{5}$, $x = -2\left(\dfrac{3}{5}\right) = -\dfrac{6}{5}$.

If $y = -1$, $x = -2(-1) = 2$.

The solution set is $\left\{\left(-\dfrac{6}{5}, \dfrac{3}{5}\right), (2, -1)\right\}$.

3. $3x^2 + 2y^2 = 35$
$4x^2 + 3y^2 = 48$

Eliminate the y^2-term by multiplying the first equation by –3 and the second equation by 2. Add the resulting equations.

$-9x^2 - 6y = -105$
$\underline{8x^2 + 6y^2 - 96}$
$-x^2 = -9$
$x^2 = 9$
$x = \pm 3$

If $x = 3$,
$3(3)^2 + 2y^2 = 35$
$y^2 = 4$
$y = \pm 2$

If $x = -3$,
$3(-3)^2 + 2y^2 = 35$
$y^2 = 4$
$y = \pm 2$

The solution set is $\{(3,2),(3,-2),(-3,2),(-3,-2)\}$.

4. $y = x^2 + 5$
$x^2 + y^2 = 25$

Arrange the first equation so that variable terms appear on the left, and constants appear on the right. Add the resulting equations to eliminate the x^2-terms and solve for y.

$-x^2 + y = 5$
$\underline{x^2 + y^2 = 25}$
$y^2 + y = 30$

$y^2 + y - 30 = 0$
$(y + 6)(y - 5) = 0$
$y + 6 = 0 \quad \text{or} \quad y - 5 = 0$
$y = -6 \quad \text{or} \quad y = 5$

If $y = -6$,
$x^2 + (-6)^2 = 25$
$x^2 = -11$

no real solution
If $y = 5$,
$x^2 + (5)^2 = 25$
$x^2 = 0$
$x = 0$
The solution set is $\{(0, 5)\}$.

5. $2x + 2y = 20$
$xy = 21$

Solve the second equation for x.

$x = \dfrac{21}{7}$

Substitute the expression $\dfrac{21}{y}$ for x in the first equation and solve for y.

$2\left(\dfrac{21}{y}\right) + 2y = 20$

$\dfrac{42}{y} + 2y = 20$

$y^2 - 10y + 21 = 0$
$(y - 7)(y - 3) = 0$
$y - 7 = 0 \quad \text{or} \quad y - 3 = 0$
$y = 7 \quad \text{or} \quad y = 3$

If $y = 7$, $x = \dfrac{21}{7} = 3$.

If $y = 3$, $x = \dfrac{21}{3} = 7$.

The dimensions are 7 feet by 3 feet.

Exercise Set 8.4

1. $x + y = 2$
$y = x^2 - 4$

Solve the first equation for y. $y = 2 - x$.
Substitute the expression $2 - x$ for y in the second equation and solve for x.

$2 - x = x^2 - 4$
$x^2 + x - 6 = 0$
$(x + 3)(x - 2) = 0$
$x + 3 = 0 \quad \text{or} \quad x - 2 = 0$
$x = -3 \quad \text{or} \quad x = 2$

If $x = -3$, $y = 2 - (-3) = 5$.
If $x = 2$, $y = 2 - 2 = 0$.
The solution set is $\{(-3, 5), (2, 0)\}$.

3. $x - y = -1$
  $y = x^2 + 2x - 3$

Substitute the expression $x^2 + 2x - 3$ for y in the first equation and solve for x.

$$x - \left(x^2 + 2x - 3\right) = -1$$
$$x - x^2 - 2x + 3 = -1$$
$$x^2 + x - 4 = 0$$
$$x = \frac{-1 \pm \sqrt{1+16}}{2} = \frac{-1 \pm \sqrt{17}}{2}$$

Solve the first equation for y.
$x - y = -1$
  $y = x + 1$

Substitute $\dfrac{-1 \pm \sqrt{17}}{2}$ for x in the equation

$y = x + 1$.

$$y = \frac{-1 \pm \sqrt{17}}{2} + 1 = \frac{-1 \pm \sqrt{17} + 2}{2} = \frac{1 \pm \sqrt{17}}{2}$$

The solution set is

$$\left\{\left(\frac{-1+\sqrt{17}}{2}, \frac{1+\sqrt{17}}{2}\right), \left(\frac{-1-\sqrt{17}}{2}, \frac{1-\sqrt{17}}{2}\right)\right\}.$$

5. $y = x^2 - 4x - 10$
  $y = -x^2 - 2x + 14$

Substitute the expression $x^2 - 4x - 10$ for y in the second equation and solve for x.

$$x^2 - 4x - 10 = -x^2 - 2x + 14$$
$$2x^2 - 2x - 24 = 0$$
$$x^2 - x - 12 = 0$$
$$(x - 4)(x + 3) = 0$$
$$x - 4 = 0 \quad \text{or} \quad x + 3 = 0$$
$$x = 4 \quad \text{or} \quad x = -3$$

If $x = 4$, $y = (4)^2 - 4(4) - 10 = -10$.
If $x = -3$, $y = (-3)^2 - 4(-3) - 10 = 11$.
The solution set is $\{(4, -10),\ (-3, 11)\}$.

7. $x^2 + y^2 = 25$
  $x - y = 1$

Solve the second equation for y. $y = x - 1$
Substitute the expression $x - 1$ for y in the first equation and solve for x.

$$x^2 + (x - 1)^2 = 25$$
$$x^2 + x^2 - 2x + 1 = 25$$
$$2x^2 - 2x - 24 = 0$$
$$x^2 - x - 12 = 0$$
$$(x - 4)(x + 3) = 0$$
$$x - 4 = 0 \quad \text{or} \quad x + 3 = 0$$
$$x = 4 \quad \text{or} \quad x = -3$$

If $x = 4, y = 4 - 1 = 3$.
If $x = -3, y = -3 - 1 = -4$.
The solution set is $\{(4, 3), (-3, -4)\}$.

9. $xy = 6$
  $2x - y = 1$

Solve the first equation for y.

$$y = \frac{6}{x}$$

Substitute the expression $\dfrac{6}{x}$ for y in the second equation and solve for x.

$$2x - \frac{6}{x} = 1$$
$$2x^2 - 6 = x$$
$$2x^2 - x - 6 = 0$$
$$(2x + 3)(x - 2) = 0$$
$$2x + 3 = 0 \quad \text{or} \quad x - 2 = 0$$
$$x = -\frac{3}{2} \quad \text{or} \quad x = 2$$

If $x = -\dfrac{3}{2}, y = \dfrac{6}{-\frac{3}{2}} = -4$.

If $x = 2, y = \dfrac{6}{2} = 3$.

The solution set is $\left\{\left(-\dfrac{3}{2}, -4\right), (2, 3)\right\}$.

11. $y^2 = x^2 - 9$
$2y = x - 3$
Solve the second equation for y.

$$y = \frac{x - 3}{2}$$

Substitute the expression $\frac{x - 3}{2}$ for y in the first equation and solve for x.

$$\left(\frac{x - 3}{2}\right)^2 = x^2 - 9$$

$$\frac{x^2 - 6x + 9}{4} - x^2 - 9$$

$$x^2 - 6x + 9 = 4x^2 - 36$$

$$3x^2 + 6x - 45 = 0$$

$$x^2 + 2x - 15 = 0$$

$$(x + 5)(x - 3) = 0$$

$$x + 5 = 0 \quad \text{or} \quad x - 3 = 0$$

$$x = -5 \quad \text{or} \quad x = 3$$

If $x = -5$, $y = \dfrac{-5 - 3}{2} = -4$.

If $x = 3$, $y = \dfrac{3 - 3}{2} = 0$.

The solution set is $\{(-5, -4), (3, 0)\}$.

13. $xy = 3$
$x^2 + y^2 = 10$
Solve the second equation for y.

$$y = \frac{3}{x}$$

Substitute the expression $\dfrac{3}{x}$ for y in the second equation and solve for x.

$$x^2 + \left(\frac{3}{x}\right)^2 = 10$$

$$x^2 + \frac{9}{x^2} - 10 = 0$$

$$x^4 - 10x^2 + 9 = 0$$

$$\left(x^2 - 9\right)\left(x^2 - 1\right) = 0$$

$$(x - 3)(x + 3)(x - 1)(x + 1) = 0$$

$$x - 3 = 0 \text{ or } x + 3 = 0 \quad \text{or } x - 1 = 0 \text{ or } x + 1 = 0$$

$$x = 3 \text{ or } \quad x = -3 \text{ or } \quad x = 1 \text{ or } \quad x = -1$$

If $x = 3$, $y = \dfrac{3}{3} = 1$.

If $x = -3$, $y = \dfrac{3}{-3} = -1$.

If $x = 1$, $y = \dfrac{3}{1} = 3$.

If $x = -1$, $y = \dfrac{3}{-1} = -3$.

The solution set is
$\{(3, 1), (-3, -1), (1, 3), (-1, -3)\}$.

15 $x + y - 1$
$x^2 + xy - y^2 = -5$
Solve the first equation for y. $y = 1 - x$
Substitute the expression $1 - x$ for y in the second equation and solve for x.

$$x^2 + x(1 - x) - (1 - x)^2 = -5$$

$$x^2 + x - x^2 - \left(1 - 2x + x^2\right) = -5$$

$$x - 1 + 2x - x^2 = -5$$

$$x^2 - 3x - 4 = 0$$

$$(x - 4)(x + 1) = 0$$

$$x - 4 = 0 \quad \text{or} \quad x + 1 - 0$$

$$x = 4 \quad \text{or} \quad x = -1$$

If $x = 4$, $y = 1 - 4 = -3$.
If $x = -1$, $y = 1 - (-1) = 2$.
The solution set is $\{(4, -3), (-1, 2)\}$.

17. $x + y = 1$

$(x-1)^2 + (y+2)^2 = 10$

Solve the first equation for y.

$y = 1 - x$

Substitute the expression $1 - x$ for y in the second equation and solve for x.

$(x-1)^2 + (1-x+2)^2 = 10$

$(x-1)^2 + (3-x)^2 = 10$

$x^2 - 2x + 1 + 9 - 6x + x^2 - 10 = 0$

$2x^2 - 8x = 0$

$x^2 - 4x = 0$

$x(x-4) = 0$

$x = 0 \quad \text{or} \quad x - 4 = 0$

$x = 4$

If $x = 0, y = 1 - 0 = 1$.

If $x = 4, y = 1 - 4 = -3$.

The solution set is $\{(0,1),(4,-3)\}$.

19. Eliminate the y^2–terms by adding the equations.

$x^2 + y^2 = 13$

$\underline{x^2 - y^2 = 5}$

$2x^2 = 18$

$x^2 = 9$

$x = \pm 3$

If $x = 3$,

$(3)^2 + y^2 = 13$

$y^2 = 4$

$y = \pm 2$

If $x = -3$,

$(-3)^2 + y^2 = 13$

$y^2 = 4$

$y = \pm 2$

The solution set is $\{(3, 2), (3, -2), (-3, 2), (-3, -2)\}$.

21. $x^2 - 4y^2 = -7$

$3x^2 + y^2 = 31$

Eliminate the x^2–terms by multiplying the first equation by -3 and adding the resulting equations.

$-3x^2 + 12y^2 = 21$

$\underline{3x^2 + y^2 = 31}$

$13y^2 = 52$

$y^2 = 4$

$y = \pm 2$

If $y = 2$,

$x^2 - 4(2)^2 = -7$

$x^2 = 9$

$x = \pm 3$

If $y = -2$,

$x^2 - 4(-2)^2 = -7$

$x^2 = 9$

$x = \pm 3$

The solution set is

$\{(3,2),(3,-2),(-3,2),(-3,-2)\}$.

23. Arrange the equations so that variable terms appear on the left and constants appear on the right.

$3x^2 + 4y^2 = 16$

$2x^2 - 3y^2 = 5$

Eliminate the y^2–terms by multiplying the first equation by 3 and the second equation by 4. Add the resulting equations.

$9x^2 + 12y^2 = 48$

$\underline{8x^2 - 12y^2 = 20}$

$17x^2 = 68$

$x^2 = 4$

$x = \pm 2$

If $x = 2$,

$3(2)^2 + 4y^2 = 16$

$y^2 = 1$

$y = \pm 1$

If $x = -2$,

$3(-2)^2 + 4y^2 = 16$

$y = \pm 1$

The solution set is

$\{(2, 1), (2, -1), (-2, 1), (-2, -1)\}$.

25.
$$x^2 + y^2 = 25$$
$$(x-8)^2 + y^2 = 41$$

Expand the second equation and eliminate x^2 and y^2–terms by multiplying the first equation by -1 and adding the resulting equations.

$$x^2 - 16x + 64 + y^2 = 41$$
$$\underline{-x^2 - y^2 = -25}$$
$$-16x + 64 = 16$$
$$-16x = -48$$
$$x = 3$$

If $x = 3$,
$$(3)^2 + y^2 = 25$$
$$y^2 = 16$$
$$y = \pm 4$$

The solution set is $\{(3,4),\ (3,-4)\}$.

27.
$$y^2 - x = 4$$
$$x^2 + y^2 = 4$$

Eliminate the y^2–terms by multiplying the first equation by -1 and adding the resulting equations.

$$x - y^2 = -4$$
$$\underline{x^2 + y^2 = 4}$$
$$x^2 + x = 0$$

$$x(x+1) = 0$$
$$x = 0 \quad \text{or} \quad x + 1 = 0$$
$$x = -1$$

If $x = 0$,
$$y^2 = 4$$
$$y = \pm 2$$
If $x = -1$,
$$y^2 - (-1) = 4$$
$$y^2 = 3$$
$$y = \pm\sqrt{3}$$

The solution set is
$$\left\{(0,2),(0,-2),\left(-1,\sqrt{3}\right),\left(-1,-\sqrt{3}\right)\right\}.$$

29. The addition method is used here to solve the system.
$$3x^2 + 4y^2 = 16$$
$$2x^2 - 3y^2 = 5$$

Eliminate the y^2–terms by multiplying the first equation by 3 and the second equation by 4. Add the resulting equations.

$$9x^2 + 12y^2 = 48$$
$$\underline{8x^2 - 12y^2 = 20}$$
$$17x^2 = 68$$
$$x^2 = 4$$
$$x = \pm 2$$

If $x = 2$,
$$3(2)^2 + 4y^2 = 16$$
$$y^2 = 1$$
$$y = \pm 1$$
If $x = -2$,
$$3(-2)^2 + 4y^2 = 16$$
$$y = \pm 1$$

The solution set is
$$\{(2, 1), (2, -1), (-2, 1), (-2, -1)\}.$$

31. The substitution method is used here to solve the system.

$$2x^2 + y^2 = 18$$
$$xy = 4$$

Solve the second equation for y.

$$y = \frac{4}{x}$$

Substitute the expression $\frac{4}{x}$ for y in the first equation and solve for x.

$$2x^2 + \left(\frac{4}{x}\right)^2 = 18$$
$$2x^2 + \frac{16}{x^2} = 18$$
$$2x^4 + 16 = 18x^2$$
$$x^4 - 9x^2 + 8 = 0$$
$$\left(x^2 - 8\right)\left(x^2 - 1\right) = 0$$
$$x^2 - 8 = 0 \quad \text{or} \quad x^2 - 1 = 0$$
$$x^2 = 8 \quad \text{or} \quad x^2 = 1$$
$$x = \pm 2\sqrt{2} \quad \text{or} \quad x = \pm 1$$

If $x = 2\sqrt{2}$, $y = \frac{4}{2\sqrt{2}} = \sqrt{2}$.

If $x = -2\sqrt{2}$, $y = \frac{4}{-2\sqrt{2}} = -\sqrt{2}$.

If $x = 1$, $y = \frac{4}{1} = 4$.

If $x = -1$, $y = \frac{4}{-1} = -4$.

The solution set is

$$\left\{\left(2\sqrt{2}, \sqrt{2}\right), \left(-2\sqrt{2}, -\sqrt{2}\right), (1, 4), (-1, -4)\right\}.$$

33. The substitution method is used here to solve the system.

$$x^2 + 4y^2 = 20$$
$$x + 2y = 6$$

Solve the second equation for x.

$$x = 6 - 2y$$

Substitute the expression $6 - 2y$ for x in the first equation and solve for y.

$$(6 - 2y)^2 + 4y^2 = 20$$
$$36 - 24y + 4y^2 + 4y^2 - 20 = 0$$
$$8y^2 - 24y + 16 = 0$$
$$y^2 - 3y + 2 = 0$$
$$(y - 2)(y - 1) = 0$$
$$y - 2 = 0 \quad \text{or} \quad y - 1 = 0$$
$$y = 2 \quad \text{or} \quad y = 1$$

If $y = 2$, $x = 6 - 2(2) = 2$.

If $y = 1$, $x = 6 - 2(1) = 4$.

The solution set is $\left\{(2, 2), (4, 1)\right\}$.

35. Eliminate y by adding the equations.

$$\begin{aligned} x^3 + y &= 0 \\ \underline{x^2 - y = 0} \\ x^3 + x^2 &= 0 \end{aligned}$$
$$x^2(x + 1) = 0$$
$$x^2 = 0 \quad \text{or} \quad x + 1 = 0$$
$$x = 0 \quad \text{or} \quad x = -1$$

If $x = 0$,

$$(0)^3 + y = 0$$
$$y = 0$$

If $x = -1$,

$$(-1)^3 + y = 0$$
$$y = 1$$

The solution set is $\left\{(0, 0), (-1, 1)\right\}$.

37. The substitution method is used here to solve the system.

$$x^2 + (y-2)^2 = 4$$
$$x^2 - 2y = 0$$

Solve the second equation for x^2.

$$x^2 = 2y$$

Substitute the expression $2y$ for x^2 in the first equation and solve for y.

$$2y + (y-2)^2 = 4$$
$$2y + y^2 - 4y + 4 = 4$$
$$y^2 - 2y = 0$$
$$y(y-2) = 0$$
$$y = 0 \quad \text{or} \quad y - 2 = 0$$
$$y = 2$$

If $y = 0$,
$$x^2 = 2(0)$$
$$x^2 = 0$$
$$x = 0$$
If $y = 2$,
$$x^2 = 2(2)$$
$$x^2 = 4$$
$$x = \pm 2$$

The solution set is $\{(0, 0), (-2, 2), (2, 2)\}$.

39. The substitution method is used here to solve the system.

$$y = (x+3)^2$$
$$x + 2y = -2$$

Solve the first equation for x.

$$x = -2y - 2$$

Substitute the expression $-2y-2$ for x in the first equation and solve for y.

$$y = (-2y - 2 + 3)^2 = (-2y + 1)^2$$
$$y = 4y^2 - 4y + 1$$
$$4y^2 - 5y + 1 = 0$$
$$(4y - 1)(y - 1) = 0$$
$$4y - 1 = 0 \quad \text{or} \quad y - 1 = 0$$
$$y = \frac{1}{4} \quad \text{or} \quad y = 1$$

If $y = \frac{1}{4}$, $x = -2\left(\frac{1}{4}\right) - 2 = -\frac{5}{2}$.

If $y = 1$, $x = -2(1) - 2 = -4$.

The solution set is $\left\{(-4, 1), \left(-\frac{5}{2}, \frac{1}{4}\right)\right\}$.

41. The substitution method is used here to solve the system.

$$x^2 + y^2 + 3y = 22$$
$$2x + y = -1$$

Solve the second equation for y.

$$y = -2x - 1$$

Substitute the expression $-2x-1$ for y in the first equation and solve for x.

$$x^2 + (-2x - 1)^2 + 3(-2x - 1) - 22 = 0$$
$$x^2 + 4x^2 + 4x + 1 - 6x - 3 - 22 = 0$$
$$5x^2 - 2x - 24 = 0$$
$$(5x - 12)(x + 2) = 0$$
$$5x - 12 = 0 \quad \text{or} \quad x + 2 = 0$$
$$x = \frac{12}{5} \quad \text{or} \quad x = -2$$

If $x = \frac{12}{5}$, $y = -2\left(\frac{12}{5}\right) - 1 = -\frac{29}{5}$.

If $x = -2$, $y = -2(-2) - 1 = 3$.

The solution set is $\left\{\left(\frac{12}{5}, -\frac{29}{5}\right), (-2, 3)\right\}$.

43. The substitution method is used here to solve the system.

$$x + y = 10$$
$$xy = 24$$

Solve the first equation for y.

$$y = 10 - x$$

Substitute the expression $10 - x$ for y in the second equation and solve for x.

$$x(10 - x) = 24$$
$$10x - x^2 = 24$$
$$x^2 - 10x + 24 = 0$$
$$(x - 4)(x - 6) = 0$$
$$x - 4 = 0 \quad \text{or} \quad x - 6 = 0$$
$$x = 4 \quad \text{or} \quad x = 6$$

If $x = 4$, $y = 10 - 4 = 6$.
If $x = 6$, $y = 10 - 6 = 4$.
The numbers are 4 and 6.

45. Eliminate the y^2–terms by adding the equations.

$$x^2 - y^2 = 3$$
$$\underline{2x^2 + y^2 = 9}$$
$$3x^2 = 12$$
$$x^2 = 4$$
$$x = \pm 2$$

If $x = 2$,
$$2(2)^2 + y^2 = 9$$
$$y^2 = 1$$
$$y = \pm 1$$

If $x = -2$,
$$2(-2)^2 + y^2 = 9$$
$$y^2 = 1$$
$$y = \pm 1$$

The numbers are 2 and 1, 2 and –1, –2 and 1, or –2 and –1.

47. $16x^2 + 4y^2 = 64$
$$y = x^2 - 4$$

Substitute the expression $x^2 - 4$ for y in the first equation and solve for x.

$$16x^2 + 4\left(x^2 - 4\right)^2 = 64$$
$$16x^2 + 4\left(x^4 - 8x^2 + 16\right) = 64$$
$$16x^2 + 4x^4 - 32x^2 + 64 = 64$$
$$4x^4 - 16x^2 = 0$$
$$x^4 - 4x^2 = 0$$
$$x^2\left(x^2 - 4\right) = 0$$
$$x^2 = 0 \quad \text{or} \quad x^2 - 4 = 0$$
$$x = 0 \quad \text{or} \quad x^2 = 4$$
$$x = \pm 2$$

If $x = 0$, $y = (0)^2 - 4 = -4$.
If $x = 2$, $y = (2)^2 - 4 = 0$.
If $x = -2$, $y = (-2)^2 - 4 = 0$.

It is possible for the comet to intersect the orbiting body at (0, –4), (–2, 0), (2, 0).

49. $2L + 2W = 36$
$$LW = 77$$

Divide each term in the first equation by 2 and solve L.
$$L + W = 18$$
$$L = 18 - W$$

Substitute the expression $18 - W$ for L in the second equation and solve for W.
$$(18 - W)W = 77$$
$$18W - W^2 = 77$$
$$W^2 - 18W + 77 = 0$$
$$(W - 11)(W - 7) = 0$$
$$W - 11 = 0 \quad \text{or} \quad W - 7 = 0$$
$$W = 11 \quad \text{or} \quad W = 7$$

If $W = 11$, $L = 18 - 11 = 7$.
If $W = 7$, $L = 18 - 7 = 11$.
The dimensions are 11 feet by 7 feet.

51. $L^2 + W^2 = 10^2 = 100$
$$LW = 48$$

Solve the second equation for L. $L = \dfrac{48}{W}$

Substitute the expression $\dfrac{48}{W}$ for L in the first equation and solve for W.

$$\left(\frac{48}{W}\right)^2 + W^2 = 100$$
$$\frac{2304}{W^2} + W^2 - 100 = 0$$
$$2304 + W^4 - 100W^2 = 0$$
$$W^4 - 100W^2 + 2304 = 0$$
$$\left(W^2 - 36\right)\left(W^2 - 64\right) = 0$$
$$W^2 - 36 = 0 \quad \text{or} \quad W^2 - 64 = 0$$
$$W^2 = 36 \quad \text{or} \quad W^2 = 64$$
$$W = \pm 6 \quad \text{or} \quad W = \pm 8$$

The width cannot be –6 or –8 inches.
If $W = 6$,
$$L = \frac{48}{6} = 8$$
If $W = 8$,
$$L = \frac{48}{8} = 6$$
The dimensions are 8 inches by 6 inches.

53. $x^2 - y^2 = 21$
$4x + 2y = 24$
Divide each term in the second equation by 2 and solve for y.
$2x + y = 12$
$y = 12 - 2x$
Substitute the expression $12 - 2x$ for y in the first equation and solve for x.

$x^2 - (12 - 2x)^2 = 21$

$x^2 - \left(144 - 48x + 4x^2\right) = 21$

$3x^2 - 48x + 165 = 0$
$x^2 - 16x + 55 = 0$
$(x - 5)(x - 11) = 0$
$x - 5 = 0 \quad \text{or} \quad x - 11 = 0$
$\quad x = 5 \quad \text{or} \quad x = 11$
If $x = 11$, $y = 12 - 2(11) = -10$.
If $x = 5$, $y = 12 - 2(5) = 2$.

The dimensions of the floor are 5 meters by 5 meters and the dimensions of the square that will accomodate the pool are 2 meters by 2 meters.

55.–57. Answers may vary.

59. Exercise 1

Exercise 3

Exercise 5

Exercise 7

Exercise 9

61. **a.** False; a circle and a line will have at most 2 intersection points.

    b. True; a parabola can intersect a circle in 4 points.

    c. False; It is possible for two circles to not intersect.

    d. False; A circle can intersect a parabola at one point. See Check Point 4 for an example.

    (b) is true.

63. By the Pythagorean Theorem:
$$a^2 + b^2 = 10^2 = 100$$
$$a^2 + (b+9)^2 = 17^2$$
Expand the second equation.
$$a^2 + b^2 + 18b + 81 = 289$$
Eliminate the a^2 and b^2–terms by multiplying the first equation by –1 and adding the resulting equations.
$$a^2 + b^2 + 18b = 208$$
$$\underline{-a^2 - b^2 = -100}$$
$$18b = 108$$
$$b = 6$$
$$a^2 + (6)^2 = 100$$
$$a^2 = 64$$
$$a = 8$$

65. $\log x^2 = y + 3$
    $\log x = y - 1$
    $10^{y+3} = x^2$
    $10^{y-1} = x$
Substitute the expression 10^{y-1} for x in the equation $10^{y+3} = x^2$ and solve for y.
$$10^{y+3} = \left(10^{y-1}\right)^2$$
$$10^{y+3} = 10^{2y-2}$$
$$y + 3 = 2y - 2$$
$$y = 5$$
$$x = 10^{5-1} = 10,000$$
The solution set is $\left\{(10,000, 5)\right\}$.

Section 8.5

Check Point Exercises

1. $2x - 4y < 8$
Graph $2x - 4y = 8$ as a dashed line using its x-intercept $(4, 0)$, and its y-intercept $(0, -2)$.
Test $(0, 0)$:
$$2(0) - 4(0) < 8 \,?$$
$$0 < 8 \, \text{true}$$
Shade the half-plane containing $(0, 0)$.

2. $y \geq \dfrac{1}{2}x$

Graph $y = \dfrac{1}{2}x$ as a solid line by using its

slope, $\dfrac{1}{2}$, and its y-intercept $(0, 0)$.

Test $(1, 1)$:

$1 \geq \dfrac{1}{2}(1)?$

$1 \geq \dfrac{1}{2}$ true

Shade the half plane containing $(1, 1)$.

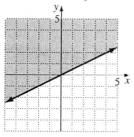

3. $x^2 + y^2 \geq 16$

Graph $x^2 + y^2 = 16$ as a solid circle with radius 4 and center $(0, 0)$.

Test $(0, 0)$:

$(0)^2 + (0)^2 \geq 16?$

$0 \geq 16$ false

Shade the half plane not containing $(0, 0)$.

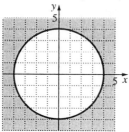

4. $x + 2y > 4$
     $2x - 3y \leq -6$

Begin by graphing $x + 2y = 4$ as a dashed line by using its x-intercept, $(4, 0)$, and its y-intercept $(0, 2)$. Since $(0, 0)$ makes the

inequality $x + 2y > 4$ false, shade the half-plane not containing $(0, 0)$. Graph $2x - 3y = -6$ as a solid line by graphing its x-intercept, $(-3, 0)$, and its y-intercept $(0, 2)$. Since $(0, 0)$ makes the inequality $2x - 3y \leq -6$ false, shade the half-plane not containing $(0, 0)$. The solution set of the system is the intersection of the above half-planes, and is indicated as the shaded region in the following graph.

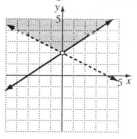

5. $y \geq x^2 - 4$
     $x + y \leq 2$

Begin by graphing $y = x^2 - 4$ as a solid parabola with vertex $(0, -4)$ and x-intercepts $(-2, 0)$ and $(2, 0)$. Since $(0, 0)$ makes the inequality $y \geq x^2 - 4$ true, shade the half-plane containing $(0, 0)$. Graph $x + y = 2$ as a solid line by using its x-intercept, $(2, 0)$, and its y-intercept $(0, 2)$. Since $(0, 0)$ makes the inequality $x + y \leq 2$ true, shade the half-plane containing $(0, 0)$. The solution set of the system is the intersection of the above half-planes, and is indicated as the shaded region in the following graph.

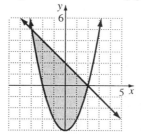

6. $x + y < 2$
$-2 \le x < 1$
$y > -3$
Begin by graphing $x + y = 2$ as a dashed line by using its x-intercept, $(2, 0)$, and its y-intercept $(0, 2)$. Since $(0, 0)$ makes the inequality $x + y < 2$ true, shade the half-plane containing $(0, 0)$. Graph $x = -2$ as a solid vertical line and $x = 1$ as a dashed vertical line. Since $(0, 0)$ makes the inequality $-2 \le x < 1$ true, shade the region between the two vertical lines. Graph $y = -3$ as a dashed horizontal line. Since $(0, 0)$ makes the inequality $y > -3$ true, shade the half-plane containing $(0, 0)$. The solution set of the system is the intersection of the above half-planes, and is indicated as the shaded region in the following graph.

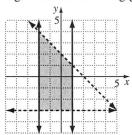

7. Answers may vary.

Exercise Set 8.5

1. $x + 2y \le 8$
Graph $x + 2y = 8$ as a solid line using its x-intercept, $(8, 0)$, and its y-intercept, $(0, 4)$.
Test $(0, 0)$:
$0 + 2(0) \le 8$?
$0 \le 8$ true
Shade the half-plane containing $(0, 0)$.

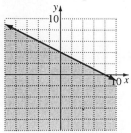

3. $x - 2y > 10$
Graph $x - 2y = 10$ as a dashed line using its x-intercept, $(10, 0)$, and its y-intercept, $(0, -5)$.
Test $(0, 0)$:
$0 - 2(0) > 10$?
$0 > 10$ false
Shade the half-plane not containing $(0, 0)$.

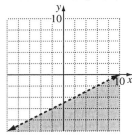

5. $y \le \dfrac{1}{3}x$

Graph $y = \dfrac{1}{3}x$ as a solid line using its slope, $\dfrac{1}{3}$, and its y-intercept $(0, 0)$.
Test $(1, 1)$:
$1 \le \dfrac{1}{3}(1)$?
$1 \le \dfrac{1}{3}$ false
Shade the half-plane not containing $(1, 1)$.

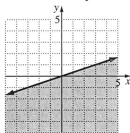

7. $y > 2x - 1$

Graph $y = 2x - 1$ as a dashed line using its

x-intercept, $\left(\dfrac{1}{2}, 0\right)$ and its y-intercept,

$(0, -1)$.

Test $(0,0)$:

$0 > 2(0) - 1$?

$0 > -1$ true

Shade the half-plane containing $(0, 0)$.

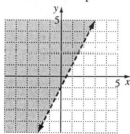

9. $x \le 1$

Graph $x = 1$ as a solid vertical line.

Test $(0, 0)$:

$0 \le 1$ true

Shade the half-plane containing $(0, 0)$.

11. $y > 1$

Graph $y = 1$ as a dashed horizontal line.

Test $(0, 0)$:

$0 > 1$ false

Shade the half-plane not containing $(0, 0)$.

13. $x^2 + y^2 \le 1$

Graph $x^2 + y^2 = 1$ as a solid circle with

radius 1 and center $(0, 0)$.

Test $(0, 0)$:

$(0)^2 + (0)^2 \le 1$?

$\qquad 0 \le 1$ true

Shade the half-plane containing $(0, 0)$.

15. $x^2 + y^2 > 25$

Graph $x^2 + y^2 = 25$ as a dashed circle with

radius 5 and center $(0, 0)$.

Test $(0, 0)$:

$(0)^2 + (0)^2 > 25$?

$\qquad 0 > 25$ false

Shade the half-plane not containing $(0, 0)$.

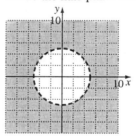

17. $y < x^2 - 1$

Graph $y = x^2 - 1$ as a dashed parabola with vertex $(0, -1)$ and x-intercepts $(1, 0)$ and $(-1, 0)$.
Test $(0, 0)$:
$0 < (0)^2 - 1$?
$0 < -1$ false
Shade the half-plane not containing $(0, 0)$.

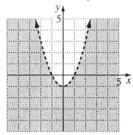

19. $y \geq x^2 - 9$

Graph $y = x^2 - 9$ as a solid parabola with vertex $(0, -9)$ and x-intercepts $(3, 0)$ and $(-3, 0)$.
Test $(0, 0)$:
$0 \geq (0)^2 - 9$?
$0 \geq -9$ true
Shade the half-plane containing $(0, 0)$.

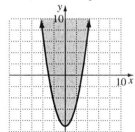

21. $y > 2^x$

Graph $y = 2^x$ as a dashed exponential function with base 2 that passes through the point $(0, 1)$.
Test $(0, 0)$:
$0 > 2^0$?
$0 > 1$ false
Shade the half-plane not containing $(0, 0)$.

23. $3x + 6y \leq 6$
$2x + y \leq 8$

Begin by graphing $3x + 6y = 6$ as a solid line using its x-intercept, $(2, 0)$, and its y-intercept, $(0, 1)$. Since $(0, 0)$ makes the inequality $3x + 6y \leq 6$ true, shade the half-plane containing $(0, 0)$. Graph $2x + y = 8$ as a solid line using its x-intercept, $(4, 0)$, and its y-intercept, $(0, 8)$. Since $(0, 0)$ makes the inequality $2x + y \leq 8$ true, shade the half-plane containing $(0, 0)$. The solution set of the system is the intersection of the above shaded half-planes, and is shown as the shaded region in the following graph.

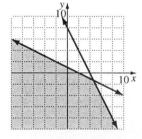

25. $2x - 5y \leq 10$
$3x - 2y > 6$

Begin by graphing $2x - 5y = 10$ as a solid line using its x-intercept, $(5, 0)$, and its y-intercept, $(0, -2)$. Since $(0, 0)$ makes the inequality $2x - 5y \leq 10$ true, shade the half-plane containing $(0, 0)$. Graph $3x - 2y = 6$ as a dashed line using its x-intercept, $(2, 0)$, and its y-intercept, $(0, -3)$. Since $(0, 0)$ makes the inequality $3x - 2y > 6$ false, shade the half-plane containing $(0, 0)$. The solution set of the system is the intersection of the above shaded half-planes, and is shown as the shaded region in the following graph.

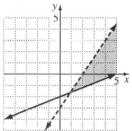

27. $y > 2x - 3$
$y < -x + 6$

Begin by graphing $y = 2x - 3$ as a dashed line using its slope, 2, and its y-intercept, $(0, -3)$. Since $(0, 0)$ makes the inequality $y > 2x - 3$ true, shade the half-plane containing $(0, 0)$. Graph $y = -x + 6$ as a dashed line using its slope, -1, and its y-intercept, $(0, 6)$. Since $(0, 0)$ makes the inequality $y < -x + 6$ true, shade the half-plane containing $(0, 0)$. The solution set of the system is the intersection of the above shaded half-planes, and is shown as the shaded region in the following graph.

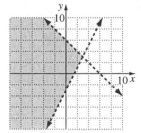

29. $x + 2y \leq 4$
$y \geq x - 3$

Begin by graphing $x + 2y = 4$ as a solid line using its x-intercept, $(4, 0)$, and its y-intercept, $(0, 2)$. Since $(0, 0)$ makes the inequality $x + 2y \leq 4$ true, shade the half-plane containing $(0, 0)$. Graph $y = x - 3$ as a solid line using its slope, 1, and its y-intercept, $(0, -3)$. Since $(0, 0)$ makes the inequality $y \geq x - 3$ true, shade the half-plane containing $(0, 0)$. The solution set of the system is the intersection of the above shaded half-planes, and is shown as the shaded region in the following graph.

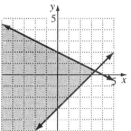

31. $x \leq 2$
$y \geq -1$

Begin by graphing $x = 2$ as a solid vertical line . Since $(0, 0)$ makes the inequality $x \leq 2$ true, shade the half-plane containing $(0, 0)$. Graph $y = 1$ as a solid horizontal line. Since $(0, 0)$ makes the inequality $y \geq -1$ true, shade the half-plane containing $(0, 0)$. The solution set of the system is the intersection of the above shaded half-planes, and is shown as the shaded region in the following graph.

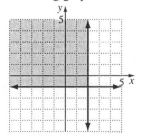

33. $-2 \le x < 5$

Graph $x = -2$ as a solid vertical line and $x = 5$ as a dashed vertical line. Since $(0, 0)$ makes the inequality $-2 \le x < 5$ true, shade the region between the two lines.

35. $x - y \le 1$
$x \ge 2$

Begin by graphing $x - y = 1$ as a solid line using its x-intercept, $(1, 0)$, and its y-intercept $(0, -1)$. Since $(0, 0)$ makes the inequality $x - y \le 1$ true, shade the half-plane containing $(0, 0)$. Graph $x = 2$ as a solid horizontal line. Since $(0, 0)$ makes the inequality $x \ge 2$ false, shade the half-plane not containing $(0, 0)$. The solution set of the system is the intersection of the above shaded half-planes, and is shown as the shaded region in the following graph.

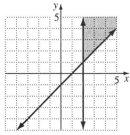

37. $x + y > 4$
$x + y < -1$

Begin by graphing $x + y = 4$ as a dashed line using its x-intercept, $(4, 0)$, and its y-intercept $(0, 4)$. Since $(0, 0)$ makes the inequality $x + y > 4$ false, shade the half-plane not containing $(0, 0)$. Graph $x + y = -1$ as a dashed line using its x-intercept, $(-1, 0)$, and its y-intercept,

$(0, -1)$. Since $(0, 0)$ makes the inequality $x + y < -1$ false, shade the half-plane not containing $(0, 0)$. The solution set of the system is the intersection of the above half-planes. Since these half-planes do not intersect the system has no solution.

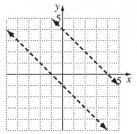

39. $x + y > 4$
$x + y > -1$

Begin by graphing $x + y = 4$ as a dashed line using its x-intercept, $(4, 0)$, and its y-intercept, $(0, 4)$. Since $(0, 0)$ makes the inequality $x + y > 4$ false, shade the half-plane not containing $(0, 0)$. Graph $x + y = -1$ as a dashed line using its x-intercept, $(-1, 0)$, and its y-intercept, $(0, -1)$. Since $(0, 0)$ makes the inequality $x + y > -1$ true, shade the half-plane containing $(0, 0)$. The solution set of the system is the intersection of the above half-planes, and is shown as the shaded region in the following graph.

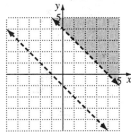

41. $y \geq x^2 - 1$
$x - y \geq -1$

Begin by graphing $y = x^2 - 1$ as a solid parabola with vertex $(0, -1)$ and x-intercepts, $(-1, 0)$, and $(1, 0)$. Since $(0, 0)$ makes the inequality $y \geq x^2 - 1$ true, shade the half-plane containing $(0, 0)$. Graph $x - y = -1$ as a solid line using its x-intercept, $(-1, 0)$, and its y-intercept, $(0, 1)$. Since $(0, 0)$ makes the inequality $x - y \geq -1$ true, shade the half-plane containing $(0, 0)$. The solution set of the system is the intersection of the above half-planes, and is shown as the shaded region in the following graph.

43. $x^2 + y^2 \leq 16$
$x + y > 2$

Begin by graphing $x^2 + y^2 = 16$ as a solid circle with radius 4 and center, $(0, 0)$. Since $(0, 0)$ makes the inequality $x^2 + y^2 \leq 16$ true, shade the half-plane containing $(0, 0)$. Graph $x + y = 2$ as a dashed line using its x-intercept, $(2, 0)$, and its y-intercept, $(0, 2)$. Since $(0, 0)$ makes the inequality $x + y > 2$ false, shade the half-plane not containing

$(0, 0)$. The solution set of the system is the intersection of the above half-planes, and is shown as the shaded region in the following graph.

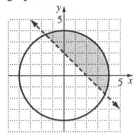

45. $x^2 + y^2 > 1$
$x^2 + y^2 < 4$

Begin by graphing $x^2 + y^2 = 1$ as a dashed circle with radius 1 and center, $(0, 0)$. Since $(0, 0)$ makes the inequality $x^2 + y^2 > 1$ false, shade the half-plane not containing $(0, 0)$. Graph $x^2 + y^2 = 4$ as a dashed circle with radius 2 and center $(0, 0)$. Since $(0, 0)$ makes the inequality $x^2 + y^2 < 4$ true, shade the half-plane containing $(0, 0)$. The solution set of the system is the intersection of the above half-planes, and is shown as the shaded region in the following graph.

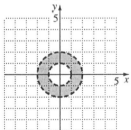

47. $x - y \le 2$
     $x \ge -2$
     $y \le 3$

Begin by graphing $x - y = 2$ as a solid line using its x-intercept, $(2, 0)$, and its y-intercept, $(0, -2)$. Since $(0, 0)$ makes the inequality $x - y \le 2$ true, shade the half-plane containing $(0, 0)$. Graph $x = -2$ as a solid vertical line. Since $(0, 0)$ makes the inequality $x \ge -2$ true, shade the half-plane containing $(0, 0)$. Graph $y = 3$ as a solid horizontal line. Since $(0, 0)$ makes the inequality $y \le 3$ true, shade the half-plane containing $(0, 0)$. The solution set of the system is the intersection of the above half-planes, and is shown as the shaded region in the following graph.

49. $x \ge 0$
     $y \ge 0$
     $2x + 5y \le 10$
     $3x + 4y \le 12$

Since $x \ge 0$ and $y \ge 0$ the solution to the system lies in the first quadrant. Graph $2x + 5y = 10$ as a solid line using its x-intercept, $(5, 0)$, and its y-intercept, $(0, 2)$. Since $(0, 0)$ makes the inequality $2x + 5y \le 10$ true, shade the half-plane containing $(0, 0)$. Graph $3x + 4y = 12$ as a solid line by using its x-intercept, $(4, 0)$, and its y-intercept, $(0, 3)$. Since $(0, 0)$ makes the inequality $3x + 4y \le 12$ true, shade the half-plane containing $(0, 0)$. The solution set of the system is the intersection of the above

half-planes which lies in the first quadrant, and is shown as the shaded region in the following graph.

51. $3x + y \le 6$
     $2x - y \le -1$
     $x \ge -2$
     $y \le 4$

Begin by graphing $3x + y = 6$ as a solid line using its x-intercept, $(2, 0)$, and its y-intercept, $(0, 6)$. Since $(0, 0)$ makes the inequality $3x + y \le 6$ true, shade the half-plane containing $(0, 0)$. Graph $2x - y = -1$ as a solid line using its x-intercept, $\left(-\dfrac{1}{2}, 0\right)$, and its y-intercept, $(0, 1)$. Since $(0, 0)$ makes the inequality $2x - y \le -1$ false, shade the half-plane not containing $(0, 0)$. Graph $x = -2$ as a solid vertical line. Since $(0, 0)$ makes the inequality $x \ge -2$ true, shade the half-plane containing $(0, 0)$. Graph $y = 4$ as a solid horizontal line. Since $(0, 0)$ makes the inequality $y \le 4$ true, shade the half-plane containing $(0, 0)$. The solution set of the system is the intersection of the above half-planes, and is shown as the shaded region in the following graph.

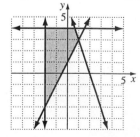

53. Answers may vary.

55. no

57. $7w - 25h \geq -800$
$w - 5h \leq -170$

59. $5T - 7P \leq 70$

61. $50x + 150y > 2000$
Graph $50x + 150y$ as a dashed line using its
x-intercept, $(40, 0)$, and its y-intercept,
$\left(0, \dfrac{40}{3}\right).$
Test $(0, 0)$:
$50(0) + 150(0) > 2000\,?$
$\qquad\qquad 0 > 2000$ false
Shade the half-plane not containing $(0, 0)$.

Ordered pairs may vary.

63. $x =$ amount invested at high risk.
$y =$ amount invested at high risk.
$x + y \leq 15,000$
$x \geq 2000$
$y \geq 3x$
$x \geq 0$
$y \geq 0$
Since $x \geq 0$ and $y \geq 0$ the solution set to the
system lies in the first quadrant. Graph
$x + y = 15,000$ as a solid line using its
x-intercept, $(15,000, 0)$, and its y-intercept,
$(0, 15,000)$. Since $(0, 0)$ makes the

inequality $x + y \leq 15,000$ true, shade the
half-plane containing $(0, 0)$. Graph $y = 3x$
as a solid line by using its slope, 3, and its y-
intercept, $(0, 0)$. Since $(1, 1)$ makes the
inequality $y \geq 3x$ false, shade the half-plane
not containing $(0, 0)$. Graph $x = 2000$ as a
solid vertical line. Since $(0, 0)$ makes the
inequality $x \geq 2000$ false, shade the half-
plane not containing $(0, 0)$. The solution set
of the system is the intersection of the above
half-planes, and is shown as the shaded
region in the following graph.

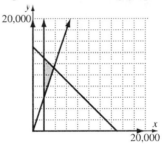

65.–69. Answers may vary.

71.

73. $y \geq x^2 - 4$

75. Answers may vary.

77. Exercise 23

Exercise 25

Exercise 27

Exercise 29

Exercise 31

79. $x^2 + y^2 \le 9$

$y < x^2$

81. $|x + y| \le 3$ is equivalent to $-3 \le x + y \le 3$, and $|y| \le z$ is equivalent to $-2 \le y \le 2$, so the system is equivalent to

$x + y \le 3$

$x + y \ge -3$

$\quad y \le 2$

$\quad y \ge -2$

Section 8.6

Check Point Exercises

1.

The total daily profit	is	the number of book shelves times the profit per bookshelf	plus	the number of desks times the profit per desk.
(z)	=	(x) · (25)	+	(y) · (55)

$z = 25x + 55y$

2.

The number of bookshelves	plus desks	the number of more than	is not	80.
(x)	+(y)	$\le$		80

$x + y \le 80$

584

3. Let x represent the number of bookshelves and y represent the number of desks.
between 30 and 80 bookselves: $30 \leq x \leq 80$
at least 10 and no more than 30 desks:
$10 \leq y \leq 30$
objective function: $z = 25x + 55y$
constraints: $x + y \leq 80$
$\qquad\qquad\quad 30 \leq x \leq 80$
$\qquad\qquad\quad 10 \leq y \leq 30$

4. We must maximize $z = 25x + 55y$ subject to the constraints
$x + y \leq 80$
$30 \leq x \leq 80$
$10 \leq y \leq 30$
Because x(the number of bookshelves) and y(the number of desks) must be nonnegative, graph the system of inequalitites in quadrant I and its boundary only. To graph the inequality $x + y \leq 80$, graph the equation $x + y = 80$ as a solid line with x-intercept (80, 0) and y-intercept (0, 80). The test point (0, 0) satisfies the inequality so shade the region containing (0, 0). To graph the inequality $30 \leq x \leq 80$, graph the equations $x = 30$ and $x = 80$ as solid vertical lines and shade the region between these lines. To graph the inequality $10 \leq y \leq 30$, graph the equations $y = 10$ and $y = 30$ as solid horizontal lines and shade the region between these lines. The system of inequalities representing the constraints is shown where all shaded regions overlap.

The lines $x = 30$ and $y = 10$ intersect at (30, 10).
The lines $x = 30$ and $y = 10$ intersect at (30, 30).
Use the substitution method to find where $x + y = 80$ and $y = 10$ intersect.

$x + y = 80$
$x + 10 = 80$
$\qquad x = 70$
So the intersection point is (70, 10).
Use the substitution method to find where $x + y = 80$ and $y = 30$ intersect.
$x + y = 80$
$x + 30 = 80$
$\qquad x = 50$
So the intersection point is (50, 30).
Evaluate the objective function
$z = 25x + 55y$ at the four corner points of the region found above.
(30, 10): $25(30) + 55(10) = 1300$
(30, 30): $25(30) + 55(30) = 2400$
(50, 30): $25(50) + 55(30) = 2900$
(70, 10): $25(70) + 55(10) = 2300$
The maximum value of z is 2900 and this occurs when $x = 50$ and $y = 30$. This means 50 bookshelves and 30 desks should be manufactured per day. The maximum profit is $2900.

5. objective function: $z = 3x + 5y$
constraints: $x \geq 0,\ y \geq 0$
$\qquad\qquad\quad x + y \geq 1$
$\qquad\qquad\quad x + y \leq 6$

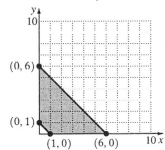

Evaluate the objective function at the four vertices of the region shown:
(1, 0): $3(1) + 5(0) = 3$
(0, 1): $3(0) + 5(1) = 5$
(0, 6): $3(0) + 5(6) = 30$
(6, 0): $3(6) + 5(0) = 18$
The maximum value of z is 30 and this occurs when $x = 0$ and $y = 6$.

Exercise Set 8.6

1. $z = 5x + 6y$

(1, 2): $5(1) + 6(2) = 5 + 12 = 17$
(2, 10): $5(2) + 6(10) = 10 + 60 = 70$
(7, 5): $5(7) + 6(5) = 35 + 30 = 65$
(8, 3): $5(8) + 6(3) = 40 + 18 = 58$
The maximum value is $z = 70$; the minimum value is $z = 17$.

3. $z = 40x + 50y$

(0, 0): $40(0) + 50(0) = 0 + 0 = 0$
(0, 8): $40(0) + 50(8) = 0 + 400 = 400$
(4, 9): $40(4) + 50(9) = 160 + 450 = 610$
(8, 0): $40(8) + 50(0) = 320 + 0 = 320$
The maximum value is $z = 610$; the minimum value is $z = 0$.

5. $z = 2x + 3y$
$x \geq 0, y \geq 0$
$3x + y \leq 6$
$2x + 3y \leq 12$

a.

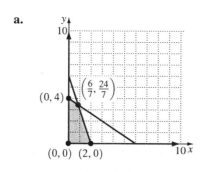

b. (0, 0): $z = 2(0) + 3(0) = 0$
(0, 4): $z = 2(0) + 3(4) = 12$
$\left(\dfrac{6}{7}, \dfrac{24}{7}\right): z = 2\left(\dfrac{6}{7}\right) + 3\left(\dfrac{24}{7}\right)$
$= \dfrac{12}{7} + \dfrac{72}{7} = \dfrac{84}{7} = 12$
$(2, 0): z = 2(2) + 3(0) = 4$

c. The maximum value is 12
at $x = 0$ and $y = 4$ and at $x = \dfrac{6}{7}$
and $y = \dfrac{24}{7}$.

7. $z = 4x + y$
$x \geq 0, y \geq 0$
$2x + 3y \leq 12$
$x + y \geq 3$

a.

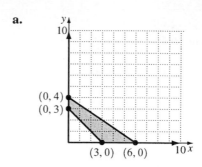

b. (0, 4): $z = 4(0) + 4 = 4$
(0, 3): $z = 4(0) + 3 = 3$
(3, 0): $z = 4(3) + 0 = 12$
(6, 0): $z = 4(6) + 0 = 24$

c. The maximum value is 24 at $x = 6$ and $y = 0$.

9. $z = 3x - 2y$
$1 \leq x \leq 5$
$y \geq 2$
$x - y \geq -3$

a.

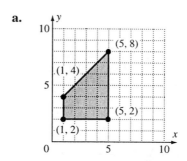

b. (1, 2): $z = 3(1) - 2(2) = -1$
(1, 4): $z = 3(1) - 2(4) = -5$
(5, 8): $z = 3(5) - 2(8) = -1$
(5, 2): $z = 3(5) - 2(2) = 11$

c. Maximum value is 11 at $x = 5$ and $y = 2$.

11. $z = 4x + 2y$
$x \geq 0, y \geq 0$
$2x + 3y \leq 12$
$3x + 2y \leq 12$
$x + y \geq 2$

a.

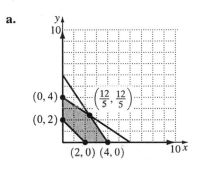

b. $(0, 4)$: $z = 4(0) + 2(4) = 8$
$(0, 2)$: $z = 4(0) + 2(2) = 4$
$(2, 0)$: $z = 4(2) + 2(0) = 8$
$(4, 0)$: $z = 4(4) + 2(0) = 16$
$\left(\dfrac{12}{5}, \dfrac{12}{5}\right)$: $z = 4\left(\dfrac{12}{5}\right) + 2\left(\dfrac{12}{5}\right)$
$\qquad\qquad = \dfrac{48}{5} + \dfrac{24}{5} = \dfrac{72}{5}$

c. The maximum value is 16 at $x = 4$ and $y = 0$.

13. $z - 10x + 12y$
$x \geq 0, y \geq 0$
$x + y \leq 7$
$2x + y \leq 10$
$2x + 3y \leq 18$

a.

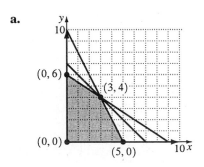

b. $(0, 6)$: $z = 10(0) + 12(6) = 72$
$(0, 0)$: $z = 10(0) + 12(0) = 0$
$(5, 0)$: $z = 10(5) + 12(0) = 50$
$(3, 4)$: $z = 10(3) + 12(4) =$
$\qquad\qquad = 30 + 48 = 78$

c. The maximum value is 78 at $x = 3$ and $y = 4$.

15. a. $z = 125x + 200y$

b. $x \leq 450$
$y \leq 200$
$600x + 900y \leq 360{,}000$

c. Simplify the third inequality by dividing by 300 to get $2x + 3y \leq 1200$.

d. $(0, 0)$: $125(0) + 200(0) = 0 + 0 = 0$
$(0, 200)$: $125(0) + 200(200)$
$\qquad\qquad = 0 + 40{,}000 = 40{,}000$
$(300, 200)$: $125(300) + 200(200)$
$\qquad\qquad = 37{,}500 + 40{,}000 = 77{,}500$
$(450, 100)$: $125(450) + 200(100)$
$\qquad\qquad = 56{,}250 + 20{,}000 = 76{,}250$
$(450, 0)$: $125(450) + 200(0)$
$\qquad\qquad = 56{,}250 + 0 = 56{,}250$

e. The television manufacturer will make the greatest profit by manufacturing <u>300</u> console televisions each month and <u>200</u> wide-screen televisions each month. The maximum monthly profit is <u>$77,500</u>.

17. Let x = number of model A bicycles and
y = number of model B bicycles.
The constraints are
$5x + 4y \leq 200$
$2x + 3y \leq 108$
Graph these inequalities in the first quadrant,
since x and y cannot be negative.

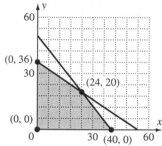

The quantity to be maximized is the profit,
which is $25x + 15y$.
(0, 0): $25(0) + 15(0) = 0 + 0 = 0$
(0, 36): $25(0) + 15(36) = 0 + 540 = 540$
(24, 20): $25(24) + 15(20) = 600 + 300 = 900$
(40, 0): $25(40) + 15(0) = 1000 + 0 = 1000$
40 model A bicycles and no model B
bicycles should be produced.

19. Let x = the number of cartons of food and
y = the number of cartons of clothing.
The constraints are:
$50x + 5y \leq 18{,}000$ or $10x + y \leq 3600$
$30x + 20y \leq 12{,}000$ or $3x + 2y \leq 1200$
Graph these inequalities in the first quadrant,
since x and y cannot be negative.

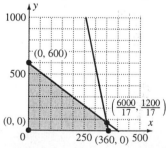

The quantity to be maximized is the number
of people helped, which is $5x + 6y$.
(0, 0): $5(0) + 6(0) = 0 + 0 = 0$
(0, 600): $5(0) + 6(600) = 0 + 3600 = 3600$

$$\left(\frac{6000}{17}, \frac{1200}{17}\right): 5\left(\frac{6000}{17}\right) + 6\left(\frac{1200}{17}\right)$$
$$= \frac{30{,}000}{17} + \frac{7200}{17}$$
$$= \frac{37{,}200}{17} \approx 2188$$

(360, 0): $5(360) + 6(0) = 1800 + 0 = 1800$
No cartons of food and 600 cartons of
clothing should be shipped. This will help
3600 people.

21. Let x = number of students attending and
y = number of parents attending.
The constraints are
$x + y \leq 150$
$\quad 2x \geq y$
or
$\quad x + y \leq 150$
$2x - y \geq 0$
Graph these inequalities in the first quadrant,
since x and y cannot be negative.

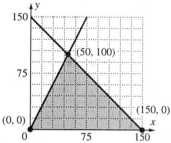

The quantity to be maximized is the amount
of money raised, which is $x + 2y$.
(0, 0): $0 + 2(0) = 0 + 0 = 0$
(50, 100): $50 + 2(100) = 50 + 200 = 250$
(150, 0): $150 + 2(0) = 150 + 0 = 150$
50 students and 100 parents should attend.

23. Let x = number of Boeing 727s, y = number of Falcon 20s.
Maximize $z = x + y$ with the following constraints:
$1400x + 500y \le 35,000$ or $14x + 5y \le 350$
$42,000x + 6000y \ge 672,000$ or
$7x + y \ge 112$
$x \le 20$
$x \ge 0, y \ge 0$

$(16, 0): z = 16$
$(20, 0): z = 20$
$(20, 14): z = 34$
$(10, 42): z = 52$
Federal Express should have purchased 10 Boeing 727s and 42 Falcon 20s.

25.–27. Answers may vary.

29. $z = 6x + 8y$
$x \ge 0, y \ge 0$
$x + 2y \le 6$ or $y \le -0.5x + 3$

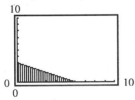

$(6, 0): 6(6) + 8(0) = 36$
$(0, 3): 6(0) + 8(3) = 24$
Maximum value is 36.

31. $z = 9x + 14y$
$x \ge 0, y \ge 0$
$2x + y \le 10$ or $y \le -2x + 10$
$2x + 3y \le 18$ or $y \le -\dfrac{2}{3}x + 6$

$(3, 4): 9(3) + 14(4) = 83$
$(5, 0): 9(5) + 14(0) = 45$
$(0, 6): 9(0) + 14(6) = 84$
Maximum value is 84.

33. Let x = amount invested in stocks and y = amount invested in bonds.
The constraints are:
$x + y \le 10,000$
$y \ge 3000$
$x \ge 2000$
$y \ge x$
Graph these inequalities in the first quadrant, since x and y cannot be negative.

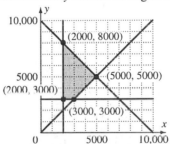

The quantity to be maximized is the return on the investment, which is $0.12x + 0.08y$.
(2000, 3000):
$0.12(2000) + 0.08(3000) = 240 + 240 = 480$
(2000, 8000):
$0.12(2000) + 0.08(8000) = 240 + 640 = 880$
(5000, 5000):
$0.12(5000) + 0.08(5000) = 600 + 400 = 1000$
(3000, 3000):
$0.12(3000) + 0.08(3000) = 360 + 240 = 600$
The greatest return occurs when $5000 is invested in stocks and $5000 is invested in bonds.

Review Exercises

1. $$y = 4x + 1$$
$$3x + 2y = 13$$
Substitute $4x + 1$ for y in the second equation:
$$3x + 2(4x + 1) = 13$$
$$3x + 8x + 2 = 13$$
$$11x = 11$$
$$x = 1$$
$$y = 4(1) + 1 = 5$$
The solution set is $\{(1, 5)\}$.

2. $x + 4y = 14$
$2x - y = 1$
Multiply the second equation by 4 and add to the first equation.
$$x + 4y = 14$$
$$\underline{8x - 4y = 4}$$
$$9x = 18$$
$$x = 2$$
$$2(2) - y = 1$$
$$-y = -3$$
$$y = 3$$
The solution set is $\{(2, 3)\}$.

3. $5x + 3y = 1$
$3x + 4y = -6$
Multiply the first equation by 4 and the second equation by -3.
Then add.
$$20x + 12y = 4$$
$$\underline{-9x - 12y = 18}$$
$$11x = 22$$
$$x = 2$$
$$5(2) + 3y = 1$$
$$3y = -9$$
$$y = -3$$
The solution set is $\{(2, -3)\}$.

4. $2y - 6x = 7$
$3x - y = 9$
The second equation can be written as
$y = 3x - 9$.

Substitute:
$$2(3x - 9) - 6x = 7$$
$$6x - 18 - 6x = 7$$
$$-18 = 7$$
Since this is false, the system has no solution.
The solution set is the empty set, $\varnothing$.

5. $4x - 8y = 16$
$3x - 6y = 12$
Divide the first equation by 4 and the second equation by 3.
$x - 2y = 4$
$x - 2y = 4$
Since these equations are identical, the system
ihas an infinite number of solutions.
The solution set is $\left\{(x, y) \mid 4x - 8y = 16\right\}$ or
$\left\{(x, y) \mid 3x - 6y = 12\right\}$.

6. No, $(-1, 3)$ is not a solution to $2x + y = -5$.
$2(-1) + 3 = 1 \neq -5$

7. $x =$ mg of cholesterol in one ounce of shrimp
$y =$ mg of cholesterol in one ounce of scallops
$3x + 2y = 156$
$5x + 3y = 255$
Multiply the first equation by -3 and multiply the second equation by 2.
Add the resulting equations together.
$$-9x - 6y = -468$$
$$\underline{10x + 6y = 510}$$
$$x = 42$$
$$3(42) + 2y = 156$$
$$126 + 2y = 156$$
$$2y = 30$$
$$y = 15$$
$$3(42) + 2y = 156$$
$$126 + 2y = 156$$
$$2y = 30$$
$$y = 15$$
Shrimp: 42 mg of cholesterol per ounce
Scallops: 15 mg of cholesterol per ounce

8. x = number of apples
y = number of avocados
$$100x + 350y = 1000$$
$$24x + 14y = 100$$

$$100x + 350y = 1000$$
$$\underline{-600x - 350y = -2500}$$
$$-500x = -1500$$
$$x = 3$$
$$100(3) + 350y = 1000$$
$$350y = 700$$
$$y = 2$$

3 apples and 2 avocados supply 1000 calories and 100 grams of carbohydrates.

9.
$$N = -60p + 100$$
$$N = 4p + 200$$
$$-60p + 1000 = 4p + 200$$
$$800 = 64p$$
$$p = 12.5$$
$$N = 4(12.5) + 200 = 250$$

250 copies can be supplied and sold for $12.50 each.

10.
$$2x - y + z = 1 \quad (1)$$
$$3x - 3y + 4z = 5 \quad (2)$$
$$4x - 2y + 3z = 4 \quad (3)$$
Eliminate y from (1) and (2) by multiplying (1) by -3 and adding the result to (2).
$$-6x + 3y - 3z = -3$$
$$\underline{3x - 3y + 4z = 5}$$
$$-3x + z = 2 \quad (4)$$
Eliminate y from (1) and (3) by multiplying (1) by -2 and adding the result to (3).
$$-4x + 2y - 2z = -2$$
$$\underline{4x - 2y + 3z = 4}$$
$$z = 2$$
Substituting $z = 2$ into (4), we get:
$$-3x + 2 = 2$$
$$-3x = 0$$
$$x = 0$$
Substituting $x = 0$ and $z = 2$ into (1), we have:
$$2(0) - y + 2 = 1$$
$$-y = -1$$
$$y = 1$$
The solution set is $\{(0, 1, 2)\}$.

11.
$$x + 2y - z = 5 \quad (1)$$
$$2x - y + 3z = 0 \quad (2)$$
$$2y + z = 1 \quad (3)$$
Eliminate x from (1) and (2) by multiplying (1) by -2 and adding the result to (2).
$$-2x - 4y + 2z = -10$$
$$\underline{2x - y + 3z = 0}$$
$$-5y + 5z = -10$$
$$y - z = 2 \quad (4)$$
Adding (3) and (4), we get:
$$2y + z = 1$$
$$\underline{y - z = 2}$$
$$3y = 3$$
$$y = 1$$
Substituting $y = 1$ into (3), we have:
$$2(1) + z = 1$$
$$z = -1$$
Substituting $y = 1$ and $z = -1$ into (1), we obtain:
$$x + 2(1) - (-1) = 5$$
$$x + 3 = 5$$
$$x = 2$$
The solution set is $\{(2, 1, -1)\}$.

12. $y = ax^2 + bx + c$
$$(1, 4): 4 = a + b + c \quad (1)$$
$$(3, 20): 20 = 9a + 3b + c \quad (2)$$
$$(-2, 25): 25 = 4a - 2b + c \quad (3)$$
Multiply (1) by -1 and add to (2).
$$20 = 9a + 3b + c$$
$$\underline{-4 = -a - b - c}$$
$$16 = 8a + 2b$$
$$8 = 4a + b$$
$$8 = 4a + b \quad (4)$$
Multiply (1) by -1 and add to (3).
$$25 = 4a - 2b + c$$
$$\underline{-4 = -a - b - c}$$
$$21 = 3a - 3b$$
$$7 = a - b \quad (5)$$
Add (4) and (5).
$$8 = 4a + b$$
$$\underline{7 = a - b}$$
$$15 = 5a$$
$$a = 3$$

$$8 = 4(3) + b$$
$$b = -4$$
$$3 - 4 + c = 4$$
$$c = 5$$

Hence, the quadratic function is
$$y = 3x^2 - 4x + 5.$$

13.
$x + y + z = 0.45$	(1)
$x = y + 0.01$	(2)
$x = 2z - 0.12$	(3)

Rewrite (2) as $y = x - 0.01$, then substitute into (1).
$$x + x - 0.01 + z = 0.45$$
$$2x + z = 0.46$$

Substitute (3) into the above equation.
$$2(2z - 0.12) + z = 0.46$$
$$4z - 0.24 + z = 0.46$$
$$5z = 0.70$$
$$z = 0.14$$
$$x = 2(0.14) - 0.12 = 0.16$$
$$y = 0.16 - 0.01 = 0.15$$

Japan: 16%
Germany: 15%
France: 14%

14. Substitute the ordered pairs into $y = ax^2 + bx + c$, solve the resulting system for a, b, and c. Then substitute these values into the equation to form a quadratic model.

15. $\dfrac{x}{(x-3)(x+2)} = \dfrac{A}{x-3} + \dfrac{B}{x+2}$
$$x = A(x + 2) + B(x - 3)$$
$$= (A + B)x + (2A - 3B)$$
$$A + B = 1$$
$$2A - 3B = 0$$

Multiply first equation by 3, then add to second equation.
$$3A + 3B = 3$$
$$2A - 3B = 0$$
$$\overline{\quad 5A = 3 \quad}$$
$$A = \frac{3}{5}, \ B = \frac{2}{5}$$

$$\dfrac{x}{(x-3)(x+2)} = \dfrac{3}{5(x-3)} + \dfrac{2}{5(x+2)}$$

16. $\dfrac{11x - 2}{x^2 - x - 12} = \dfrac{11x - 2}{(x-4)(x+3)} = \dfrac{A}{x-4} + \dfrac{B}{x+3}$
$$11x - 2 = A(x + 3) + B(x - 4)$$
$$= Ax + 3A + Bx - 4B$$
$$= (A + B)x + (3A - 4B)$$
$$A + B = 11$$
$$3A - 4B = -2$$

Multiply first equation by 4, then add to second equation.
$$3A - 4B = -2$$
$$4A + 4B = 44$$
$$\overline{\quad 7A = 42 \quad}$$
$$A = 6, \ B = 5$$

$$\dfrac{11x - 2}{x^2 - x - 12} = \dfrac{6}{x-4} + \dfrac{5}{x+3}$$

17. $\dfrac{4x^2-3x-4}{x^3+x^2-2x}=\dfrac{4x^2-3x-4}{x(x+2)(x-1)}=\dfrac{A}{x}+\dfrac{B}{x+2}+\dfrac{C}{x-1}$

$$4x^2-3x-4=A(x+2)(x-1)+Bx(x-1)+Cx(x+2)$$
$$=A(x^2+x-2)+Bx^2-Bx+Cx^2+2Cx$$
$$=Ax^2+Ax-2A+Bx^2-Bx+Cx^2+2Cx$$
$$=(A+B+C)x^2+(A-B+2C)x-2A$$

$$A+B+C=4$$
$$A-B+2C=-3$$
$$-2A=-4$$
$$A=2$$
$$B+C=2$$
$$\underline{-B+2C=-5}$$
$$3C=-3$$
$$C=-1$$
$$B-1=2$$
$$B=3$$

$$\dfrac{4x^2-3x-4}{x^3+x^2-2x}=\dfrac{2}{x}+\dfrac{3}{x+2}-\dfrac{1}{x-1}$$

18. $\dfrac{2x+1}{(x-2)^2}=\dfrac{A}{x-2}+\dfrac{B}{(x-2)^2}$

$$2x+1=A(x-2)+B=Ax-2A+B$$
$$A=2$$
$$-2A+B=1$$
$$-2(2)+B=1$$
$$B=5$$

$$\dfrac{2x+1}{(x-2)^2}=\dfrac{2}{x-2}+\dfrac{5}{(x-2)^2}$$

19. $\dfrac{2x-6}{(x-1)(x-2)^2} = \dfrac{A}{x-1} + \dfrac{B}{x-2} + \dfrac{C}{(x-2)^2}$

$2x - 6 = A(x-2)^2 + B(x-1)(x-2) + C(x-1)$

$\qquad = A(x^2 - 4x + 4) + B(x^2 - 3x + 2) + C(x-1)$

$\qquad = Ax^2 - 4Ax + 4A + Bx^2 - 3Bx + 2B + Cx - C$

$\qquad = (A+B)x^2 + (-4A - 3B + C)x + (4A + 2B - C)$

$\qquad A + B = 0$

$-4A - 3B + C = 2$

$\underline{\quad 4A + 2B - C = -6 \quad}$

$\qquad\qquad -B = -4$

$\qquad\qquad\quad B = 4$

$\qquad\qquad\quad A = -4$

$4(-4) + 2(4) - C = -6$

$\qquad -16 + 8 - C = -6$

$\qquad\quad -C - 8 = -6$

$\qquad\qquad -C = 2$

$\qquad\qquad\quad C = -2$

$\dfrac{2x-6}{(x-1)(x-2)^2} = -\dfrac{4}{x-1} + \dfrac{4}{x-2} - \dfrac{2}{(x-2)^2}$

20. $\dfrac{3x}{(x-2)(x^2+1)} = \dfrac{A}{x-2} + \dfrac{Bx+C}{x^2+1}$

$3x = A(x^2+1) + (Bx+C)(x-2) = Ax^2 + A + Bx^2 - 2Bx + Cx - 2C$

$\quad = (A+B)x^2 + (-2B+C)x - (2C-A)$

$\quad A + B = 0$

$-2B + C = 3$

$\;2C - A = 0$

$\qquad A = 2C$

$B + 2C = 0$

$\underline{4B - 2C = -6}$

$\qquad 5B = -6$

$\qquad\quad B = -\dfrac{6}{5}$

$\qquad\quad A = \dfrac{6}{5}$

$\qquad\quad C = \dfrac{6}{10} = \dfrac{3}{5}$

$\dfrac{3x}{(x-2)(x^2+1)} = \dfrac{6}{5(x-2)} + \dfrac{-6x+3}{5(x^2+1)}$

21. $\dfrac{7x^2 - 7x + 23}{(x-3)(x^2+4)} = \dfrac{A}{x-3} + \dfrac{Bx+C}{x^2+4}$

$$7x^2 - 7x + 23 = A(x^2+4) + (Bx+C)(x-3)$$

$$= Ax^2 + 4A + Bx^2 - 3Bx + Cx - 3C$$

$$= (A+B)x^2 + (-3B+C)x + (4A-3C)$$

$A + B = 7$

$-3B + C = -7$

$4A - 3C = 23$

$3A + 3B = 21$

$\underline{-3B + C = -7}$

$\ \ 3A + C = 14$

$9A + 3C = 42$

$\underline{4A - 3C = 23}$

$\ \ \ 13A = 65$

$\ \ \ \ \ A = 5$

$\ \ 5 + B = 7$

$\ \ \ \ \ \ B = 7 - 5 = 2$

$-3(2) + C = -7$

$\ \ \ \ \ \ C = -7 + 6 = -1$

$$\dfrac{7x^2 - 7x + 23}{(x-3)(x^2+4)} = \dfrac{5}{(x-3)} + \dfrac{2x-1}{(x^2+4)}$$

22. $\dfrac{x^3}{(x^2+4)^2} = \dfrac{Ax+B}{x^2+4} + \dfrac{Cx+D}{(x^2+4)^2}$

$$x^3 = (Ax+B)(x^2+4) + Cx + D$$

$$= Ax^3 + 4Ax + Bx^2 + 4B + Cx + D$$

$$= Ax^3 + Bx^2 + (4A+C)x + (4B+D)$$

$\ \ \ A = 1$

$\ \ \ B = 0$

$4A + C = 0$

$4B + D = 0$

$\ \ \ \ \ C = -4$

$\ \ 0 + D = 0, D = 0$

$$\dfrac{x^2}{(x^2+4)^2} = \dfrac{x}{x^2+4} - \dfrac{4x}{(x^2+4)^2}$$

23. $\dfrac{4x^3 + 5x^2 + 7x - 1}{(x^2 + x + 1)^2} = \dfrac{Ax + B}{x^2 + x + 1} + \dfrac{Cx + D}{(x^2 + x + 1)^2}$

$4x^3 + 5x^2 + 7x - 1$

$= (Ax + B)(x^2 + x + 1) + Cx + D$

$= Ax^3 + Ax^2 + Ax + Bx^2 + Bx + B + Cx + D$

$= Ax^3 + (A + B)x^2 (A + B + C)x + (B + D)$

$\quad\quad A = 4$

$\quad A + B = 5$

$A + B + C = 7$

$\quad\quad B + D = -1$

$\quad 4 + B = 5, B = 1$

$4 + 1 + C = 7, C = 2$

$\quad 1 + D = -1, D = -2$

$\dfrac{4x^3 + 5x^2 + 7x - 1}{(x^2 + x + 1)^2} = \dfrac{4x + 1}{x^2 + x + 1} + \dfrac{2x - 2}{(x^2 + x + 1)^2}$

24. $\quad\quad\quad 5y = x^2 - 1$

$\quad\quad\quad\quad x - y = 1$

$\quad\quad\quad\quad\quad y = x - 1$

$\quad\quad\quad 5(x - 1) = x^2 - 1$

$\quad\quad\quad 5x - 5 = x^2 - 1$

$\quad\quad x^2 - 5x + 4 = 0$

$\quad (x - 4)(x - 1) = 0$

$\quad\quad\quad\quad\quad x = 4, 1$

If $x = 4, y = 4 - 1 = 3$.

If $x = 1, y = 1 - 1 = 0$.

The solution set is $\{(4, 3), (1, 0)\}$.

25. $y = x^2 + 2x + 1$

$\quad\quad x + y = 1$

$\quad\quad\quad y = 1 - x$

$\quad 1 - x = x^2 + 2x + 1$

$x^2 + 3x = 0$

$x(x + 3) = 0$

$\quad\quad\quad x = 0, -3$

If $x = 0, y = 1 - 0 = 1$.

If $x = -3, y = 1 - (-3) = 4$.

The solution set is $\{(0, 1), (-3, 4)\}$.

26.
$$x^2 + y^2 = 2$$
$$x + y = 0$$
$$x = -y$$
$$(-y)^2 + y^2 = 2$$
$$2y^2 = 2$$
$$y^2 = 1$$
$$y = 1, -1$$
If $y = 1, x = -1$.
If $y = -1, x = 1$.
The solution set is $\{(1, -1), (-1, 1)\}$.

27.
$$2x^2 + y^2 = 24$$
$$x^2 + y^2 = 15$$

$$\begin{array}{r} 2x^2 + y^2 = 24 \\ -x^2 - y^2 = -15 \\ \hline x^2 = 9 \end{array}$$
$$x = 3, -3$$
If $x = 3, 3^2 + y^2 = 15, y^2 = 6$ and $y = \pm\sqrt{6}$.
If $x = -3, y = +\sqrt{6}$.
The solution set is
$$\left\{ \left(3, \sqrt{6}\right), \left(3, -\sqrt{6}\right), \left(-3, \sqrt{6}\right), \left(-3, -\sqrt{6}\right) \right\}.$$

28.
$$xy - 4 = 0$$
$$y - x = 0$$
$$y = x$$
$$xy = 4$$
$$x^2 = 4$$
$$x = 2, -2$$
If $x = 2, y = 2$.
If $x = -2, y = -2$.
The solution set is $\{(2, 2), (-2, -2)\}$.

29.
$$y^2 = 4x$$
$$x - 2y + 3 = 0$$
$$x = \frac{y^2}{4}$$
$$\frac{y^2}{4} - 2y + 3 = 0$$
$$y^2 - 8y + 12 = 0$$
$$(y - 6)(y - 2) = 0$$
$$y = 6, 2$$
If $y = 6, x = \frac{36}{4} = 9$.
If $y = 2, x = \frac{4}{4} = 1$.
The solution set is $\{(9, 6), (1, 2)\}$.

30.
$$x^2 + y^2 = 10$$
$$y = x + 2$$
$$x^2 + (x + 2)^2 = 10$$
$$x^2 + x^2 + 4x + 4 - 10 = 0$$
$$2x^2 + 4x - 6 = 0$$
$$x^2 + 2x - 3 = 0$$
$$(x + 3)(x - 1) = 0$$
$$x = -3, 1$$
If $x = -3, y = -3 + 2 = -1$.
If $x = 1, y = 1 + 2 = 3$.
The solution set is $\{(-3, -1), (1, 3)\}$.

31.
$$xy = 1$$
$$y = 2x + 1$$
$$x(2x + 1) = 1$$
$$2x^2 + x - 1 = 0$$
$$(2x - 1)(x + 1) = 0$$
$$x = \frac{1}{2}, -1$$
If $x = \frac{1}{2}, y = 2\left(\frac{1}{2}\right) + 1 = 2$.
If $x = -1, y = 2(-1) + 1 = -1$.
The solution set is $\left\{ \left(\frac{1}{2}, 2\right), (-1, -1) \right\}$.

32.
$$x + y + 1 = 0$$
$$x^2 + y^2 + 6y - x = -5$$
$$x = -y - 1$$
$$(-y-1)^2 + y^2 + 6y - (-y-1) + 5 = 0$$
$$y^2 + 2y + 1 + y^2 + 6y + y + 1 + 5 = 0$$
$$2y^2 + 9y + 7 = 0$$
$$(2y+7)(y+1) = 0$$
$$y = -\frac{7}{2}, -1$$

If $y = -\frac{7}{2}, x = \frac{7}{2} - 1 = \frac{5}{2}$.

If $y = -1, x = 1 - 1 = 0$.

The solution set is $\left\{\left(\frac{5}{2}, -\frac{7}{2}\right), (0, -1)\right\}$.

33. $x^2 + y^2 = 13$
$$x^2 - y = 7$$
$$x^2 + y^2 = 13$$
$$\underline{-x^2 + y = -7}$$
$$y^2 + y = 6$$
$$y^2 + y - 6 = 0$$
$$(y+3)(y-2) = 0$$
$$y = -3, 2$$

If $y = -3, x^2 + 3 = 7$

$x^2 = 4, x = 2, -2$

If $y = 2, x^2 - 2 = 7, x^2 = 9, x = 3, -3$.

The solution set is

$\{(2, -3), (-2, -3), (3, 2), (-3, 2)\}$.

34. $2x^2 + 3y^2 = 21$
$$3x^2 - 4y^2 = 23$$
$$8x^2 + 12y^2 = 84$$
$$\underline{9x^2 - 12y^2 = 69}$$
$$17x^2 = 153$$
$$x^2 = \frac{153}{17} = 9$$
$$x = 3, -3$$

If $x = 3, 2(3)^2 + 3y^2 = 21$.

$3y^2 = 21 - 18 = 3$

$y^2 = 1, y = 1, -1$

If $x = -3, y = 1, -1$.

The solution set is

$\{(3,1), (3,-1), (-3,1), (-3,-1)\}$.

35. $2L + 2W = 26$
$$LW = 40$$
$$L = \frac{40}{W}$$
$$2\left(\frac{40}{W}\right) + 2W = 26$$
$$\frac{80}{W} + 2W = 26$$
$$80 + 2W^2 = 26W$$
$$2W^2 - 26W + 80 = 0$$
$$W^2 - 13W + 40 = 0$$
$$(W-8)(W-5) = 0$$
$$W = 8, 5$$

If $W = 5, L = \frac{40}{5} = 8$

The dimensions are 8 m by 5 m.

36.
$$xy = 6$$
$$y = \frac{6}{x}$$
$$2x + y = 8$$
$$2x + \frac{6}{x} = 8$$
$$2x^2 + 6 = 8x$$
$$2x^2 - 8x + 6 = 0$$
$$x^2 - 4x + 3 = 0$$
$$(x-1)(x-3) = 0$$
$$x = 1, 3$$

If $x = 1, y = 6$.

If $x = 3, y = 2$.

The solution set is $\{(1, 6), (3, 2)\}$.

37. $x^2 + y^2 = 2900$
$4x + 2y = 240$
$2x + y = 120$
$\qquad y = 120 - 2x$

$\qquad\qquad\qquad x^2 + (120 - 2x)^2 = 2900$

$x^2 + 14,400 - 480x + 4x^2 - 2900 = 0$

$\qquad\qquad 5x^2 - 480x + 11,500 = 0$

$\qquad\qquad\qquad x^2 - 96x + 2300 = 0$

$\qquad\qquad\qquad (x - 46)(x - 50) = 0$

$\qquad\qquad\qquad\qquad\qquad x = 46, 50$

If $x = 46$, $y = 120 - 2(46) = 28$.
If $x = 50$, $y = 120 - 2(50) = 20$.
$x = 46$ ft and $y = 28$ ft or $x = 50$ ft and $y = 20$ ft

38. $3x - 4y > 12$

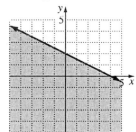

39. $y \leq -\dfrac{1}{2}x + 2$

40. $x < -2$

41. $y \geq 3$

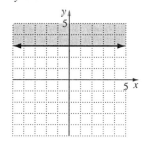

42. $x^2 + y^2 > 4$

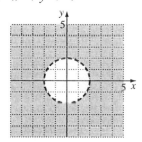

43. $y \leq x^2 - 1$

44. $y \leq 2^x$

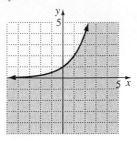

45. $3x + 2y \geq 6$
$2x + y \geq 6$

46. $2x - y \geq 4$
$x + 2y < 2$

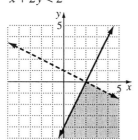

47. $y < x$
$y \leq 2$

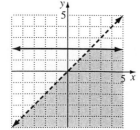

48. $y \leq x$
$2x + 5y \leq 10$

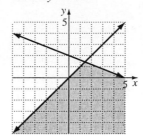

49. $0 \leq x \leq 3$
$y > 2$

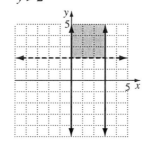

50. $2x + y < 4$
$2x + y > 6$

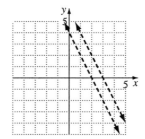

No solution

51. $x^2 + y^2 \leq 16$
$x + y < 2$

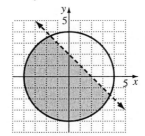

600

52. $x^2 + y^2 \le 9$
    $y < -3x + 1$

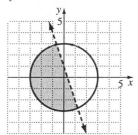

53. $y > x^2$
    $x + y < 6$
    $y < x + 6$

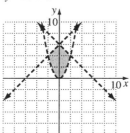

54. $x \ge 0, y \ge 0$
    $2x + 3y < 12$
    $3x + y \le 6$

55. $z = 2x + 3y$
    $(2,2): z = 2(2) + 3(2) = 10$
    $(4,0): z = 2(4) + 3(0) = 8$
    $\left(\dfrac{1}{2}, \dfrac{1}{2}\right): z = 2\left(\dfrac{1}{2}\right) + 3\left(\dfrac{1}{2}\right) = \dfrac{5}{2}$
    $(1,0): z = 2(1) + 3(0) = 2$
The maximum value is 10 and the minimum value is 2.

56. $z = 2x + 3y$
    $x \ge 0, y \ge 0$
    $x + y \le 8$
    $3x + 2y \ge 6$

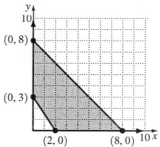

$(0,8): z = 2(0) + 3(8) = 24$
$(8,0): z = 2(8) + 3(0) = 16$
$(0,3): z = 2(0) + 3(3) = 9$
$(2,0): z = 2(2) + 3(0) = 6$
Maximum value is 24.

57. $z = x + 4y$
    $0 \le x \le 5$
    $0 \le y \le 7$
    $x + y \ge 3$

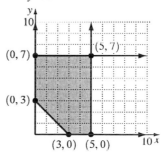

$(0,3): z = 0 + 4(3) = 12$
$(3,0): z = 3 + 4(0) = 3$
$(0,7): z = 0 + 4(7) = 28$
$(5,0): z = 5 + 4(0) = 5$
$(5,7): z = 5 + 4(7) = 33$
Maximum value is 33.

58. $z = 5x + 6y$

$x \geq 0, \; y \geq 0, \; y \leq x$

$2x + y \leq 12$

$2x + 3y > 6$

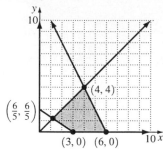

$(3, 0): z = 5(3) + 6(0) = 15$

$(6, 0): z = 5(6) + 6(0) = 30$

$\left(\dfrac{6}{5}, \dfrac{6}{5}\right): z = 5\left(\dfrac{6}{5}\right) + 6\left(\dfrac{6}{5}\right) = \dfrac{66}{5} = 13.2$

$(4, 4): 5(4) + 6(4) = 44$

The maximum value is 44.

59. a. $z = 500x + 350y$

b. $x + y \leq 200$

$x \geq 10$

$y \geq 80$

c.

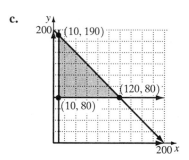

d.

Vertex	Objective Function
	$z = 500x + 350y$
$(10, 80)$	$z = 500(10) + 350(80)$
	$= 33,000$
$(10, 190)$	$z = 500(10) + 350(190)$
	$= 71,500$
$(120, 80)$	$z = 500(120) + 350(80)$
	$= 88,000$

e. The company will make the greatest profit by producing 120 units of writing paper and 80 units of newsprint each day. The maximum daily profit is $88,000.

60. Let $x =$ number of model A tents produced and
$y =$ number of model B tents produced.
The constraints are:
$0.9x + 1.8y \leq 864$
$0.8x + 1.2y \leq 672$
$\qquad x \geq 0$
$\qquad y \geq 0$

The vertices of the region are $(0, 0)$, $(0, 480)$, $(480, 240)$, and $(840, 0)$.
The objective is to maximize $25x + 40y$.
$(0, 0): 25(0) + 40(0) = 0 + 0 = 0$
$(0, 480): 25(0) + 40(480) = 0 + 19,200 = 19,200$
$(480, 240): 25(480) + 40(240) = 12,000 + 9600$
$\qquad\qquad = 21,600$
$(840, 0): 25(840) + 40(0) = 21,000 + 0 = 21,000$
The manufacturer should make 480 of model A and 240 of model B.

Chapter 8 Test

1. $x = y + 4$

$3x + 7y = -18$

Substitute $y + 4$ for x into second equation.

$3(y + 4) + 7y = -18$

$3y + 12 + 7y = -18$

$\qquad 10y = -30$

$\qquad\quad y = -3$

$\qquad x = -3 + 4 = 1$

The solution set to the system is $\{(1, -3)\}$.

2. $2x + 5y = -2$

$3x - 4y = 20$

Multiply the first equation by 3 and the second equation by -2 and add the result.

$6 + 15y = -6$

$\underline{-6x + 8y = -40}$

$23y = -46$

$y = -2$

Substitute $y = -2$ into the first equation:

$2x + 5(-2) = -2$

$2x - 10 = -2$

$2x = 8$

$x = 4$

The solution to the system is $\{(4, -2)\}$.

3. $x + y + z = 6$ (1)

$3x + 4y - 7z = 1$ (2)

$2x - y + 3z = 5$ (3)

Eliminate x by multiplying (1) by -3 and adding the result to (2) and by multiplying (1) by -2 and adding the result to (3).

$-3x - 3y - 3z = -18$

$\underline{3x + 4y - 7z = 1}$

$y - 10z = -17$ (4)

$-2x - 2y - 2z = -12$

$\underline{2x - y + 3z = 5}$

$-3y + z = -7$ (5)

Multiply (4) by 3 and add the result to (5) to eliminate y.

$3y - 30z = -51$

$\underline{-3y + z = -7}$

$-29z = -58$

$z = 2$

Substitute $z = 2$ into (5).

$-3y + 2 = -7$

$-3y = -9$

$y = 3$

Substitute $z = 2$ and $y = 3$ into (1).

$x + 3 + 2 = 6$

$x = 1$

The solution to the system is $\{(1, 3, 2)\}$.

4. $x^2 + y^2 = 25$

$x + y = 1$

$y = 1 - x$

Substitute $1 - x$ for y in the first equation.

$x^2 + (1 - x)^2 = 25$

$x^2 + 1 - 2x + x^2 = 25$

$2x^2 - 2x - 24 = 0$

$x^2 - x - 12 = 0$

$(x - 4)(x + 3) = 0$

$x = 4, -3$

If $x = 4$, $y = 1 - 4 = -3$.

If $x = -3$, $y = 1 - (-3) = 4$.

The solution set is $\{(4, -3), (-3, 4)\}$.

5. $2x^2 - 5y^2 = -2$

$3x^2 + 2y^2 = 35$

Multiply first equation by 2 and the second equation by 5. Then add.

$4x^2 - 10y^2 = -4$

$\underline{15x^2 + 10y^2 = 175}$

$19x^2 = 171$

$x^2 = 9$

$x = 3, -3$

If $x = 3$, $2(3)^2 - 5y^2 = -2$.

$18 - 5y^2 = -2$

$-5y^2 = -20$

$y^2 = 4$

$y = 2, -2$

If $x = -3$, $y = -2$.

The solution to the system is

$\{(3, 2), (3, -2), (-3, 2), (-3, -2)\}$

6. $\dfrac{x}{(x+1)(x^2+9)} = \dfrac{A}{x+1} + \dfrac{Bx+C}{x^2+9}$

$x = A(x^2 + 9) + (Bx + C)(x + 1)$

$\quad = Ax^2 + 9A + Bx^2 + Bx + Cx + C$

$\quad = (A + B)x^2 + (B + C)x + (9A + C)$

$A + B = 0 \rightarrow A = -B$

$B + C = 1$

$9A + C = 0$

$-9B + C = 0$

$\underline{9B - C = 0}$

$\underline{B + C = 1}$

$10B = 1$

$B = \dfrac{1}{10}$

$A = -\dfrac{1}{10}$

$$\frac{1}{10} + C = 1, \quad C = \frac{9}{10}$$

$$\frac{x}{(x+1)(x^2+9)} = \frac{-1}{10(x+1)} + \frac{x+9}{10(x^2+9)}$$

7. $x - 2y < 8$

8. $x \geq 0, y \geq 0$
$3x + y \leq 9$
$2x + 3y \geq 6$

9. $x^2 + y^2 > 1$
$x^2 + y^2 < 4$

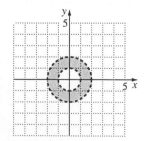

10. $y \leq 1 - x^2$
$x^2 + y^2 \leq 9$

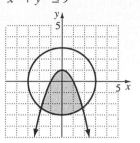

11. $z = 3x + 5y$
$x \geq 0, y \geq 0$
$x + y \leq 6$
$x \geq 2$

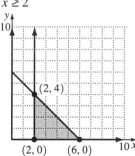

$(2,0): z = 3(2) + 5(0) = 6$
$(6,0): z = 3(6) + 5(0) = 18$
$(2,4): z = 3(2) + 5(4) = 26$
Maximum value is 26.

12. Let x = price of orchestra ticket, y = price of mezzanine ticket.
$$4x + 3y = 134$$
$$5x + 2y = 143$$
$$8x + 6y = 268$$
$$\underline{-15x - 6y = -429}$$
$$-7x = -161$$
$$x = 23$$
$$4(23) + 3y = 134$$
$$3y = 134 - 92 = 42$$
$$y = 14$$
An orchestra ticket costs \$23 and a mezzanine ticket costs \$14.

13.
$$N = 1000 - 20P$$
$$N = 250 + 5p$$
$$1000 - 20p = 250 + 5p$$
$$750 = 25p$$
$$p = 30$$
$$N = 250 + 5(30) = 400$$
400 units will be supplied and sold for $30 each.

14. $y = ax^2 + bx + c$
$(-1, -2): -2 = a - b + c$
$(2, 1): 1 = 4a + 2b + c$
$(-2, 1): 1 = 4a - 2b + c$

$4a + 2b + c = 1$
$$\underline{-4a + 2b - c = -1}$$
$$4b = 0$$
$$b = 0$$

$a + c = -2$
$4a + c = 1$
$$\underline{-a - c = 2}$$
$$3a = 3$$
$$a = 1$$
$a + c = -2$
$c = -3$

The quadratic function is $y = x^2 - 3$.

15. $2x + y = 39$
$xy = 180$
$y = 39 - 2x$
$$x(39 - 2x) = 180$$
$$39x - 2x^2 = 180$$
$$2x^2 - 39x + 180 = 0$$
$$(2x - 15)(x - 12) = 0$$
$$x = \frac{15}{2}, 12$$

If $x = \frac{15}{2}, \frac{15}{2}y = 180$ and $y = 24$.
If $x = 12, 12y = 180$ and $y = 15$.
The dimensions are 7.5 ft by 24 ft or 12 ft by 15 ft

16. Let x = regular, y = deluxe.
objective function: $z = 200x + 250y$
constraints: $x \geq 50, y \geq 75$
$$x + y \leq 150$$

$(50, 75): z = 200(50) + 250(75) = 28,750$
$(50, 100): z = 200(50) + 250(100) = 35,000$
$(75, 75): z = 200(75) + 250(75) = 33,750$
For a maximum profit of $35,000 a week, the company should manufacture 50 regular and 100 deluxe jet skis

Cumulative Review Exercises (Chapters 1–8)

1. $\sqrt{x^2 - 3x} = 2x - 6$
$$x^2 - 3x = 4x^2 - 24x + 36$$
$$3x^2 - 21x + 36 = 0$$
$$x^2 - 7x + 12 = 0$$
$$(x - 3)(x - 4) = 0$$
$$x = 3, 4$$
The solution set is $\{3, 4\}$.

2. $4x^2 = 8x - 7$
$4x^2 - 8x + 7 = 0$
$$x = \frac{8 \pm \sqrt{64 - 112}}{8} = \frac{8 \pm \sqrt{-48}}{8}$$
$$= \frac{8 \pm 4\sqrt{3}i}{8} = \frac{2 \pm \sqrt{3}i}{2}$$
The solution set is $\left\{ \frac{2 + i\sqrt{3}}{2}, \frac{2 - i\sqrt{3}}{2} \right\}$.

3. $\left| \frac{x}{3} + 2 \right| < 4$

$$-4 < \frac{x}{3} + 2 < 4$$
$$-6 < \frac{x}{3} < 2$$
$$-18 < x < 6$$
The solution is $\{x \mid -18 < x < 6\}$ or $(-18, 6)$.

4.
$$\frac{x+5}{x-1} > 2$$
$$\frac{x+5}{x-1} - 2 > 0$$
$$\frac{x+5-2(x-1)}{x-1} > 0$$
$$\frac{x+5-2x+2}{x-1} > 0$$
$$\frac{-x+7}{x-1} > 0$$

$\frac{-x+7}{x-1} = 0$ when $x = 7$ and is undefined
when
$x = 1$.
Test $x = 0$:
$$\frac{0+5}{0-1} > 2 ?$$
$$\frac{5}{-1} > 2 ?$$
$$-5 \not> 2$$
Test $x = 2$:
$$\frac{2+5}{2-1} > 2 ?$$
$$\frac{7}{1} > 2 ?$$
$$7 > 2$$
Test $x = 8$:
$$\frac{8+5}{8-1} > 2 ?$$
$$\frac{13}{7} > 2 ?$$
$$\frac{13}{7} \not> \frac{14}{7}$$
The solution is $\left\{ x \mid 1 < x < 7 \right\}$ or $(1,7)$..

5. $2x^3 + x^2 - 13x + 6 = 0$
$f(x) = 2x^3 + x^2 - 13x + 6$ has 2 sign
changes: 2 or 0 positive real roots.
$f(-x) = -2x^3 + x^2 + 13x + 6$ has 1 sign
change: 1 negative real root.
p: ±1, ±2, ±3, ±6
q: ±1, ±2
$\frac{p}{q}$: ±1, ±$\frac{1}{2}$, ±2, ±3, ±$\frac{3}{2}$, ±6

$$
\begin{array}{r|rrrr}
-3 & 2 & 1 & -13 & 6 \\
   &   & -6 & 15 & -6 \\
\hline
   & 2 & -5 & 2 & 0 \\
\end{array}
$$
$$2x^3 + x^2 - 13x + 6 = (x+3)(2x^2 - 5x + 2)$$
$$= (x+3)(2x-1)(x-2)$$
$$x = -3, \ x = \frac{1}{2}, \ x = 2$$
The solution set is $\left\{ -3, \frac{1}{2}, 2 \right\}$.

6. $6x - 3(5x + 2) = 4(1 - x)$
$$6x - 15x - 6 = 4 - 4x$$
$$-9x - 6 = 4 - 4x$$
$$-5x = 10$$
$$x = -2$$
The solution set is $\{-2\}$.

7. $\log (x+3) + \log x = 1$
$$\log x(x+3) = 1$$
$$x(x+3) = 10$$
$$x^2 + 3x - 10 = 0$$
$$(x+5)(x-2) = 0$$
$$x = -5 \text{ or } x = 2$$
$$x = -5 \text{ is extraneous.}$$
$$x = 2$$
The solution set is $\{2\}$.

8. $3^{x+2} = 11$
$$\log_3 3^{x+2} = \log_3 11$$
$$x + 2 = \log_3 11$$
$$x = -2 + \log_3 11$$
$$x = -2 + \frac{\log 11}{\log 3} \approx 0.18$$
The solution set is $\left\{ -2 + \log_3 11 \right\}$.

9. $f(x) = (x+2)^2 - 4$
vertex: $(-2, -4)$
y-intercept:
$$f(0) = (0+2)^2 - 4 = 0$$
x-intercepts:
$$(x+2)^2 - 4 = 0$$
$$x^2 + 4x + 4 - 4 = 0$$
$$x^2 + 4x = 0$$
$$x(x+4) = 0$$
$$x = 0, x - 4$$

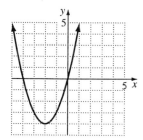

10. $2x - 3y \le 6$

11. $y = 3^{x-2}$

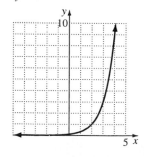

12. $f(x) = \dfrac{x^2 - x - 6}{x + 1}$
vertical asymptote: $x = -1$
horizontal asymptote: $m > n$, none

x-intercepts:
$$x^2 - x - 6 = 0$$
$$(x-3)(x+2) = 0$$
$$x = 3, x = -2$$
y-intercept:
$$f(0) = \dfrac{0^2 - 0 - 6}{0 + 1} = -6$$

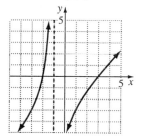

13. $\log_2(8x^5) = \log_2 8 + \log_2 x^5$
$\qquad\qquad = 3 + 5\log_2 x$

14. $A = Pe^{rt}$
$$18,000 = 6000e^{10r}$$
$$3 = e^{10r}$$
$$\ln 3 = \ln e^{10r}$$
$$\ln 3 = 10r$$
$$r = \dfrac{\ln 3}{10} \approx 0.1099$$
$$10.99\%$$

15. $f(x) = 7x - 3$
$$x = 7y - 3$$
$$x + 3 = 7y$$
$$y = \dfrac{1}{7}x + \dfrac{3}{7}$$
$$f^{-1}(x) = \dfrac{1}{7}x + \dfrac{3}{7}$$

16. $f(x) = 7x - 3, g(x) = 3x - 7$
$g(f(x)) = 3(7x - 3) - 7 = 21x - 9 - 7 = 21x - 16$

17. Answers may vary.

18. $3x - y = -2$
$2x^2 - y = 0$
Solve the first equation for y.

$y = 3x + 2$

Substitute the expression $3x + 2$ for y in the second equation and solve for x.

$$2x^2 - (3x + 2) = 0$$
$$2x^2 - 3x - 2 = 0$$
$$x = \frac{3 \pm \sqrt{9 + 16}}{4} = \frac{3 \pm 5}{4}$$
$$x = \frac{3 + 5}{4} = 2 \quad \text{or} \quad x = \frac{3 - 5}{4} = -\frac{1}{2}$$

If $x = 2, y = 3(2) + 2 = 8$.

If $x = -\frac{1}{2}, y = 3\left(-\frac{1}{2}\right) + 2 = \frac{1}{2}$.

The solution set is $\left\{(2, 8), \left(-\frac{1}{2}, \frac{1}{2}\right)\right\}$.

19.
$$L = 2W + 1$$
$$LW = 36$$
$$W(2W + 1) = 36$$
$$2W^2 + W - 36 = 0$$
$$(2W + 9)(W - 4) = 0$$
$$W = -\frac{9}{2} \text{ or } 4$$

Length cannot be negative. If $W = 4, 4L = 36$,
$L = 9$. The dimensions are 4 m by 9 m.

20. $f(x) = 0.1x^2 - 3x + 22$
$$f(90) = 0.1(90)^2 - 3(90) + 22$$
$$= 810 - 270 + 22$$
$$= 562$$

A plane with an initial landing speed of 90 feet per second needs 562 feet to land. There is a problem since 550 feet is not enough.

21. $\sec\theta - \cos\theta = \dfrac{1}{\cos\theta} - \cos\theta$
$$= \frac{1 - \cos^2\theta}{\cos\theta}$$
$$= \frac{\sin^2\theta}{\cos\theta}$$
$$= \frac{\sin\theta}{\cos\theta} \cdot \sin\theta$$
$$= \tan\theta \cdot \sin\theta$$

22. $\tan x + \tan y = \dfrac{\sin x}{\cos x} + \dfrac{\sin y}{\cos y}$
$$= \frac{\sin x \cdot \cos y + \sin y \cdot \cos x}{\cos x \cdot \cos y}$$
$$= \frac{\sin(x + y)}{\cos x \cdot \cos y}$$

23.
$$\sin\theta = \tan\theta$$
$$\sin\theta = \frac{\sin\theta}{\cos\theta}$$
$$\sin\theta - \frac{\sin\theta}{\cos\theta} = 0$$
$$\sin\theta\left(1 - \frac{1}{\cos\theta}\right) = 0$$
$$\sin\theta = 0 \quad \text{or} \quad 1 - \frac{1}{\cos\theta} = 0$$
$$\theta = 0, \pi \quad \text{or} \quad 1 = \frac{1}{\cos\theta}$$
$$\cos\theta = 1$$
$$\theta = 0$$

The solutions in the interval $[0, 2\pi)$ are 0 and π.

24.
$$2 + \cos 2\theta = 3\cos\theta$$
$$2 + (2\cos^2\theta - 1) = 3\cos\theta$$
$$2\cos^2\theta + 1 = 3\cos\theta$$
$$2\cos^2\theta - 3\cos\theta + 1 = 0$$
$$(2\cos\theta - 1)(\cos\theta - 1) = 0$$
$$2\cos\theta - 1 = 0 \quad \text{or} \quad \cos\theta - 1 = 0$$
$$2\cos\theta = 1 \qquad\qquad \cos\theta = 1$$
$$\cos\theta = \frac{1}{2}$$
$$\theta = \frac{\pi}{3}, \frac{5\pi}{3} \quad \text{or} \quad \theta = 0$$

The solutions in the interval $[0, 2\pi)$ are

$0, \dfrac{\pi}{3},$ and $\dfrac{5\pi}{3}$.

25.
$$\frac{b}{\sin B} = \frac{a}{\sin A}$$
$$\frac{b}{\sin 75°} = \frac{20}{\sin 12°}$$
$$b = \frac{20\sin 75°}{\sin 12°} \approx 92.9$$

Chapter 9

Check Point Exercises

1. $\begin{bmatrix} 1 & -1 & 1 & | & 8 \\ 0 & 1 & -12 & | & -15 \\ 0 & 0 & 1 & | & 1 \end{bmatrix} \rightarrow \begin{matrix} 1x - 1y + 1z = 8 \\ 0x + 1y - 12z = -15 \\ 0x + 0y + 1z = 1 \end{matrix}$

$x - y + z = 8$
$y - 12z = -15$
$z = 1$

Solve for y by back-substitution.
$y - 12(1) = -15$
$y - 12 = -15$
$y = -3$

Use back substitution for x.
$x - (-3) + 1 = 8$
$x + 4 = 8$
$x = 4$

The solution set for the system is $\{(4, -3, 1)\}$.

2. **a.** The notation $R_1 \leftrightarrow R_2$ means to interchange the elements in row 1 and row 2. This results in the row-equivalent matrix
$\begin{bmatrix} 1 & 6 & -3 & | & 7 \\ 4 & 12 & -20 & | & 8 \\ 3 & -2 & 1 & | & -9 \end{bmatrix}$.

   b. The notation $\frac{1}{4}R_1$ means to multiply each element in row 1 by $\frac{1}{4}$. This results in the row-equivalent matrix

   $\begin{bmatrix} \frac{1}{4}(4) & \frac{1}{4}(12) & \frac{1}{4}(-20) & | & \frac{1}{4}(8) \\ 1 & 6 & -3 & | & 7 \\ -3 & -2 & 1 & | & -9 \end{bmatrix} = \begin{bmatrix} 1 & 3 & -5 & | & 2 \\ 1 & 6 & -3 & | & 7 \\ -3 & -2 & 1 & | & -9 \end{bmatrix}$

   c. The notation $3R_2 + R_3$ means to add 3 times the elements in row 2 to the corresponding elements in row 3. Replace the elements in row 3 by these sums. First, we find 3 times the elements in row 2: $3(1) = 3$, $3(6) = 18$, $3(-3) = -9$, $3(7) = 21$. Now we add these products to the corresponding elements in row 3. This results in the row equivalent matrix

   $\begin{bmatrix} 4 & 12 & -20 & | & 8 \\ 1 & 6 & -3 & | & 7 \\ -3+3=0 & -2+18=16 & 1-9=-8 & | & -9+21=12 \end{bmatrix} = \begin{bmatrix} 4 & 12 & -20 & | & 8 \\ 1 & 6 & -3 & | & 7 \\ 0 & 16 & -8 & | & 12 \end{bmatrix}$.

3. $2x + y + 2z = 18$ $\begin{bmatrix} 2 & 1 & 2 & | & 18 \\ 1 & -1 & 2 & | & 9 \\ 1 & 2 & -1 & | & 6 \end{bmatrix}$
    $x - y + 2z = 9 \rightarrow$
    $x + 2y - z = 6$

Interchange row 1 with row 2 to get 1 in the top position of the first column.

$\begin{bmatrix} 1 & -1 & 2 & | & 9 \\ 2 & 1 & 2 & | & 18 \\ 1 & 2 & -1 & | & 6 \end{bmatrix}$

Multiply the first row by –2 and add these products to row 2.

$\begin{bmatrix} 1 & -1 & 2 & | & 9 \\ 2 + -2 = 0 & 1 + 2 = 3 & 2 + -4 = -2 & | & -18 + 18 = 0 \\ 1 & 2 & -1 & | & 6 \end{bmatrix} = \begin{bmatrix} 1 & -1 & 2 & | & 9 \\ 0 & 3 & -2 & | & 0 \\ 1 & 2 & -1 & | & 6 \end{bmatrix}$

Next, multiply the top row by –1 and add these products to row 3.

$\begin{bmatrix} 1 & -1 & 2 & | & 9 \\ 0 & 3 & -2 & | & 0 \\ 1 + -1 = 0 & 2 + 1 = 3 & -1 - 2 = -3 & | & 6 - 9 = -3 \end{bmatrix} = \begin{bmatrix} 1 & -1 & 2 & | & 9 \\ 0 & 3 & -2 & | & 0 \\ 0 & 3 & -3 & | & -3 \end{bmatrix}$

Next, to obtain a 1 in the second row, second column, multiply 3 by its reciprocal, $\frac{1}{3}$. Therefore, we multiply all the numbers in the second row by $\frac{1}{3}$ to get

$\begin{bmatrix} 1 & -1 & 2 & | & 9 \\ 0 & 1 & -\frac{2}{3} & | & 0 \\ 0 & 3 & -3 & | & -3 \end{bmatrix}$.

Next, to obtain a 0 in the third row, second column, multiply the second row by –3 and add the products to row three. The resulting matrix is

$\begin{bmatrix} 1 & -1 & 2 & | & 9 \\ 0 & 1 & -\frac{2}{3} & | & 0 \\ 0 & 0 & -1 & | & -3 \end{bmatrix}$.

To get 1 in the third row, third column, multiply –1 by its reciprocal, –1. Multiply all numbers in the third row by –1 to obtain the resulting matrix

$\begin{bmatrix} 1 & -1 & 2 & | & 9 \\ 0 & 1 & -\frac{2}{3} & | & 0 \\ 0 & 0 & 1 & | & 3 \end{bmatrix}$.

The system represented by this matrix is:

$x - y + 2z = 9$

$y - \dfrac{2}{3}z = 0$

$z = 3$

Use back substitution to find y and x.

$y - \frac{2}{3}(3) = 0$ $x - 2 + 6 = 9$

$y - 2 = 0$ $x + 4 = 9$

$y = 2$ $x = 5$

The solution set for the original system is $\{(5, 2, 3)\}$.

4. $x - 3y - 2z + w = -3$
$2x - 7y - z + 2w = 1$
$3x - 7y - 3z + 3w = -5$
$5x + y + 4z - 2w = 18$

The augmented matrix is
$$\begin{bmatrix} 1 & -3 & -2 & 1 & | & -3 \\ 2 & -7 & -1 & 2 & | & 1 \\ 3 & -7 & -3 & 3 & | & -5 \\ 5 & 1 & 4 & -2 & | & 18 \end{bmatrix}.$$

Multiply the top row by –2 and add the products to the second row. Multiply the top row by –3 and add the products to the third row. Multiply the top row by –5 and add the products to the fourth row. The resulting matrix is
$$\begin{bmatrix} 1 & -3 & -2 & 1 & | & -3 \\ 0 & -1 & 3 & 0 & | & 7 \\ 0 & 2 & 3 & 0 & | & 4 \\ 0 & 16 & 14 & -7 & | & 33 \end{bmatrix}.$$

Next, multiply the second row by –1 to obtain a 1 in the second row, second column.
$$\begin{bmatrix} 1 & -3 & -2 & 1 & | & -3 \\ 0 & 1 & -3 & 0 & | & -7 \\ 0 & 2 & 3 & 0 & | & 4 \\ 0 & 16 & 14 & -7 & | & 33 \end{bmatrix}$$

Next, multiply the second row by –2 and add the products to the third row. Multiply the second row by –16 and add the products to the fourth row. The resulting matrix is
$$\begin{bmatrix} 1 & -3 & -2 & 1 & | & -3 \\ 0 & 1 & -3 & 0 & | & -7 \\ 0 & 0 & 9 & 0 & | & 18 \\ 0 & 0 & 62 & -7 & | & 145 \end{bmatrix}.$$

Next, multiply the third row by $\frac{1}{9}$ to obtain a 1 in the third row, third column. The resulting matrix is
$$\begin{bmatrix} 1 & -3 & -2 & 1 & | & -3 \\ 0 & 1 & -3 & 0 & | & -7 \\ 0 & 0 & 1 & 0 & | & 2 \\ 0 & 0 & 62 & -7 & | & 145 \end{bmatrix}.$$

Multiply the third row by –62 and add the products to the fourth row to obtain the resulting matrix
$$\begin{bmatrix} 1 & -3 & -2 & 1 & | & -3 \\ 0 & 1 & -3 & 0 & | & -7 \\ 0 & 0 & 1 & 0 & | & 2 \\ 0 & 0 & 0 & -7 & | & 21 \end{bmatrix}.$$

Multiply the fourth row by $-\frac{1}{7}$, the reciprocal of –7. The resulting matrix is
$$\begin{bmatrix} 1 & -3 & -2 & 1 & | & -3 \\ 0 & 1 & -3 & 0 & | & -7 \\ 0 & 0 & 1 & 0 & | & 2 \\ 0 & 0 & 0 & 1 & | & -3 \end{bmatrix}.$$

The system of linear equations corresponding to the resulting matrix is
$x - 3y - 2z + w = -3$
$\quad\quad y - 3z \quad\quad = -7$
$\quad\quad\quad\quad z \quad\quad = 2$
$\quad\quad\quad\quad\quad w = -3$

Using back-substitution solve for x and y.
$\quad\quad y - 6 = -7$
$\quad\quad\quad\quad y = -1$
$x + 3 - 4 - 3 = -3$
$\quad\quad x + 4 = -3$
$\quad\quad x - 4 = -3$
$\quad\quad\quad\quad x = 1$

The solution set is $\{(1, -1, 2, -3)\}$.

5. The matrix obtained in 2*a* will be the starting point.

$$\begin{bmatrix} 1 & 6 & -3 & | & 7 \\ 4 & 12 & -20 & | & 8 \\ -3 & -2 & 1 & | & -9 \end{bmatrix}$$

First, multiply the first row by −4 and add the products to the second row. Multiply the first row by 3 and add the products to the third row. The resulting matrix is

$$\begin{bmatrix} 1 & 6 & -3 & | & 7 \\ 0 & -12 & -8 & | & -20 \\ 0 & 16 & -8 & | & 12 \end{bmatrix}.$$

Next, multiply the second row by $-\frac{1}{12}$ to obtain a 1 in the second row, second column.

$$\begin{bmatrix} 1 & 6 & -3 & | & 7 \\ 0 & 1 & \frac{2}{3} & | & \frac{5}{3} \\ 0 & 16 & -8 & | & 12 \end{bmatrix}.$$

Next, multiply the second row by −16 and add products to the third row.

$$\begin{bmatrix} 1 & 6 & -3 & | & 7 \\ 0 & 1 & \frac{2}{3} & | & \frac{5}{3} \\ 0 & 0 & -\frac{56}{3} & | & -\frac{44}{3} \end{bmatrix}.$$

Next, multiply the third row by $-\frac{3}{56}$ to obtain 1 in the third row, third column.

$$\begin{bmatrix} 1 & 6 & -3 & | & 7 \\ 0 & 1 & \frac{2}{3} & | & \frac{5}{3} \\ 0 & 0 & 1 & | & \frac{11}{14} \end{bmatrix}.$$

Next, multiply the second row by −6 and add products to the first row to obtain a 0 in the first row, second column.

$$\begin{bmatrix} 1 & 0 & -7 & | & -3 \\ 0 & 1 & \frac{2}{3} & | & \frac{5}{3} \\ 0 & 0 & 1 & | & \frac{11}{14} \end{bmatrix}.$$

Next, multiply the third row by $-\frac{2}{3}$ and add the products to the second row. Multiply the third row by 7 and add the products to the first row. The resulting matrix is

$$\begin{bmatrix} 1 & 0 & 0 & | & \frac{5}{2} \\ 0 & 1 & 0 & | & \frac{8}{7} \\ 0 & 0 & 1 & | & \frac{11}{14} \end{bmatrix}.$$

This matrix corresponds to $x = \dfrac{5}{2}$, $y = \dfrac{8}{7}$ and $z = \dfrac{11}{14}$. The solution set is

$$\left\{ \left(\frac{5}{2}, \frac{8}{7}, \frac{11}{14} \right) \right\}.$$

Exercise Set 9.1

1. $\begin{bmatrix} 2 & 1 & 2 & | & 2 \\ 3 & -5 & -1 & | & 4 \\ 1 & -2 & -3 & | & -6 \end{bmatrix}$

3. $\begin{bmatrix} 1 & -1 & 1 & | & 8 \\ 0 & 1 & -12 & | & -15 \\ 0 & 0 & 1 & | & 1 \end{bmatrix}$

5. $\begin{bmatrix} 5 & -2 & -3 & | & 0 \\ 1 & 1 & 0 & | & 5 \\ 2 & 0 & -3 & | & 4 \end{bmatrix}$

7. $\begin{bmatrix} 2 & 5 & -3 & 1 & | & 2 \\ 0 & 3 & 1 & 0 & | & 4 \\ 1 & -1 & 5 & 0 & | & 9 \\ 5 & -5 & -2 & 0 & | & 1 \end{bmatrix}$

9. $5x + 3z = -11$
$y - 4z = 12$
$7x + 2y = 3$

11.
$$x + y + 4z + w = 3$$
$$-x + y - z = 7$$
$$2x + 5w = 11$$
$$12z + 4w = 5$$

13.
$$x - 4z = 5$$
$$y - 12z = 13$$
$$z = -\frac{1}{2}$$
$$y - 12\left(-\frac{1}{2}\right) = 13$$
$$y + 6 = 13$$
$$y = 7$$
$$x - 4\left(-\frac{1}{2}\right) = 5$$
$$x + 2 = 5$$
$$x = 3$$

The solution set is $\left\{\left(3,\ 7,\ -\frac{1}{2}\right)\right\}$.

15.
$$\begin{bmatrix} 1 & \frac{1}{2} & 1 & \frac{11}{2} \\ 0 & 1 & \frac{3}{2} & 7 \\ 0 & 0 & 1 & 4 \end{bmatrix}$$
$$x + \frac{1}{2}y + z = \frac{11}{2}$$
$$y + \frac{3}{2}z = 7$$
$$z = 4$$
$$y + \frac{3}{2}(4) = 7$$
$$y + 6 = 7$$
$$y = 1$$
$$x + \frac{1}{2}(1) + 4 = \frac{11}{2}$$
$$x + \frac{9}{2} = \frac{11}{2}$$
$$x = \frac{11}{2} - \frac{9}{2}$$
$$x = 1$$

The solution set is $\{(1, 1, 4)\}$.

17.
$$\begin{bmatrix} 1 & -1 & 1 & 1 & 3 \\ 0 & 1 & -2 & -1 & 0 \\ 0 & 0 & 1 & 6 & 17 \\ 0 & 0 & 0 & 1 & 3 \end{bmatrix}$$
$$x - y + z + w = 3$$
$$y - 2z - w = 0$$
$$z + 6w = 17$$
$$w = 3$$
$$z + 6(3) = 17$$
$$z + 18 = 17$$
$$z = -1$$
$$y - 2(-1) - (3) = 0$$
$$y + 2 - 3 = 0$$
$$y = 1$$
$$x - (1) + (-1) + (3) = 3$$
$$x - 2 + 3 = 3$$
$$x + 1 = 3$$
$$x = 2$$

The solution set is $\{(2, 1, -1, 3)\}$.

19.
$$\begin{bmatrix} 2\left(\frac{1}{2}\right) & -6\left(\frac{1}{2}\right) & 4\left(\frac{1}{2}\right) & 10\left(\frac{1}{2}\right) \\ 1 & 5 & -5 & 0 \\ 3 & 0 & 4 & 7 \end{bmatrix} \frac{1}{2}R_1$$
$$\begin{bmatrix} 1 & -3 & 2 & 5 \\ 1 & 5 & -5 & 0 \\ 3 & 0 & 4 & 7 \end{bmatrix}$$

21. $\begin{bmatrix} 1 & -3 & 2 & 0 \\ -3(1)+3 & -3(-3)+1 & -3(2)+-1 & -3(0)+7 \\ 2 & -2 & 1 & 3 \end{bmatrix} -3R_1 + R_2$

$\begin{bmatrix} 1 & -3 & 2 & 0 \\ 0 & 10 & -7 & 7 \\ 2 & -2 & 1 & 3 \end{bmatrix}$

23. $\begin{bmatrix} 1 & -1 & 1 & 1 & 3 \\ 0 & 1 & -2 & -1 & 0 \\ 2 & 0 & 3 & 4 & 11 \\ 5 & 1 & 2 & 4 & 6 \end{bmatrix} \begin{matrix} \\ \\ -2R_1 + R_3 \\ -5R_1 + R_4 \end{matrix}$

$\begin{bmatrix} 1 & -1 & 1 & 1 & 3 \\ 0 & 1 & -2 & -1 & 0 \\ -2(1)+2 & -2(-1)+0 & -2(1)+3 & -2(1)+4 & -2(3)+11 \\ -5(1)+5 & -5(-1)+1 & -5(1)+2 & -5(1)+4 & -5(3)+6 \end{bmatrix} = \begin{bmatrix} 1 & -1 & 1 & 1 & 3 \\ 0 & 1 & -2 & -1 & 0 \\ 0 & 2 & 1 & 2 & 5 \\ 0 & 6 & -3 & -1 & -9 \end{bmatrix}$

25. $\begin{bmatrix} 1 & -1 & 1 & 8 \\ 2 & 3 & -1 & -2 \\ 3 & -2 & -9 & 9 \end{bmatrix}$

$\begin{bmatrix} 1 & -1 & 1 & 8 \\ -2(1)+2 & -2(-1)+3 & -2(1)-1 & -2(8)-2 \\ -3(1)+3 & -3(-1)-2 & -3(1)-9 & -3(8)+9 \end{bmatrix}$

$\begin{bmatrix} 1 & -1 & 1 & 8 \\ 0 & 5 & -3 & -18 \\ 0 & 1 & -12 & -15 \end{bmatrix}$

$\begin{bmatrix} 1 & -1 & 1 & 8 \\ 0\left(\frac{1}{5}\right) & 1\left(\frac{1}{5}\right) & -3\left(\frac{1}{5}\right) & -18\left(\frac{1}{5}\right) \\ 0 & 1 & -12 & -15 \end{bmatrix}$

$\begin{bmatrix} 1 & -1 & 1 & 8 \\ 0 & 1 & -\frac{3}{5} & -\frac{18}{5} \\ 0 & 1 & -12 & -15 \end{bmatrix}$

27.

$$x + y - z = -2$$
$$2x - y + z = 5$$
$$-x + 2y + 2z = 1$$

$$\begin{bmatrix} 1 & 1 & -1 & \vline & -2 \\ 2 & -1 & 1 & \vline & 5 \\ -1 & 2 & 2 & \vline & 1 \end{bmatrix} -2R_1 + R_2$$

$$\begin{bmatrix} 1 & 1 & -1 & \vline & -2 \\ 0 & -3 & 3 & \vline & 9 \\ -1 & 2 & 2 & \vline & 1 \end{bmatrix} 1R_1 + R_3$$

$$\begin{bmatrix} 1 & 1 & -1 & \vline & -2 \\ 0 & -3 & 3 & \vline & 9 \\ 0 & 3 & 1 & \vline & -1 \end{bmatrix} -\tfrac{1}{3}R_2$$

$$\begin{bmatrix} 1 & 1 & -1 & \vline & -2 \\ 0 & 1 & -1 & \vline & -3 \\ 0 & 3 & 1 & \vline & -1 \end{bmatrix} -3R_2 + R_3$$

$$= \begin{bmatrix} 1 & 1 & -1 & \vline & -2 \\ 0 & 1 & -1 & \vline & -3 \\ 0 & 0 & 4 & \vline & 8 \end{bmatrix}$$

$$4z = 8$$
$$z = 2$$
$$y - z = -3$$
$$y - 2 = -3$$
$$y = -1$$
$$x + y - z = -2$$
$$x - 1 - 2 = -2$$
$$x - 3 = -2$$
$$x = 1$$

The solution set is $\{(1, -1, 2)\}$.

29.

$$x + 3y = 0$$
$$x + y + z = 1$$
$$3x - y - z = 11$$

$$\begin{bmatrix} 1 & 3 & 0 & \vline & 0 \\ 1 & 1 & 1 & \vline & 1 \\ 3 & -1 & -1 & \vline & 11 \end{bmatrix} -1R_1 + R_2$$

$$\begin{bmatrix} 1 & 3 & 0 & \vline & 0 \\ 0 & -2 & 1 & \vline & 1 \\ 3 & -1 & -1 & \vline & 11 \end{bmatrix} -3R_1 + R_3$$

$$\begin{bmatrix} 1 & 3 & 0 & \vline & 0 \\ 0 & -2 & 1 & \vline & 1 \\ 0 & -10 & -1 & \vline & 11 \end{bmatrix} -\tfrac{1}{2}R_2$$

$$\begin{bmatrix} 1 & 3 & 0 & \vline & 0 \\ 0 & 1 & -\tfrac{1}{2} & \vline & -\tfrac{1}{2} \\ 0 & -10 & -1 & \vline & 11 \end{bmatrix} 10R_2 + R_3$$

$$\begin{bmatrix} 1 & 3 & 0 & \vline & 0 \\ 0 & 1 & -\tfrac{1}{2} & \vline & -\tfrac{1}{2} \\ 0 & 0 & -6 & \vline & 6 \end{bmatrix} -\tfrac{1}{6}R_3$$

$$\begin{bmatrix} 1 & 3 & 0 & \vline & 0 \\ 0 & 1 & -\tfrac{1}{2} & \vline & -\tfrac{1}{2} \\ 0 & 0 & 1 & \vline & -1 \end{bmatrix}$$

$$z = -1$$
$$y - \tfrac{1}{2}z = -\tfrac{1}{2}$$
$$y - \tfrac{1}{2}(-1) = -\tfrac{1}{2}$$
$$y + \tfrac{1}{2} = -\tfrac{1}{2}$$
$$y = -1$$
$$x + 3y = 0$$
$$x + 3(-1) = 0$$
$$x = 3$$

The solution set is $\{(3, -1, -1)\}$.

31. $2x + 2y + 7z = -1$

$2x + y + 2z = 2$

$4x + 6y + z = 15$

$$\begin{bmatrix} 2 & 2 & 7 & | & -1 \\ 2 & 1 & 2 & | & 2 \\ 4 & 6 & 1 & | & 15 \end{bmatrix} \frac{1}{2}R_1$$

$$\begin{bmatrix} 1 & 1 & \frac{7}{2} & | & -\frac{1}{2} \\ 2 & 1 & 2 & | & 2 \\ 4 & 6 & 1 & | & 15 \end{bmatrix} -2R_1 + R_2$$

$$\begin{bmatrix} 1 & 1 & \frac{7}{2} & | & -\frac{1}{2} \\ 0 & -1 & -5 & | & 3 \\ 4 & 6 & 1 & | & 15 \end{bmatrix} -4R_1 + R_3$$

$$\begin{bmatrix} 1 & 1 & \frac{7}{2} & | & -\frac{1}{2} \\ 0 & -1 & -5 & | & 3 \\ 0 & 2 & -13 & | & 17 \end{bmatrix} -1R_2$$

$$\begin{bmatrix} 1 & 1 & \frac{7}{2} & | & -\frac{1}{2} \\ 0 & 1 & 5 & | & -3 \\ 0 & 2 & -13 & | & 17 \end{bmatrix} -2R_2 + R_3$$

$$\begin{bmatrix} 1 & 1 & \frac{7}{2} & | & -\frac{1}{2} \\ 0 & 1 & 5 & | & -3 \\ 0 & 0 & -23 & | & 23 \end{bmatrix} -\frac{1}{23}R_3$$

$$\begin{bmatrix} 1 & 1 & \frac{7}{2} & | & -\frac{1}{2} \\ 0 & 1 & 5 & | & -3 \\ 0 & 0 & 1 & | & -1 \end{bmatrix}$$

$z = -1$

$y + 5z = -3$

$y + 5(-1) = -3$

$y - 5 = -3$

$y = 2$

$x + y + \dfrac{7}{2}z = -\dfrac{1}{2}$

$x + 2 + \dfrac{7}{2}(-1) = -\dfrac{1}{2}$

$x - \dfrac{3}{2} = -\dfrac{1}{2}$

$x = 1$

The solution set is $\{(1, 2, -1)\}$.

33. $x + y + z + w = 4$

$2x + y - 2z - w = 0$

$x - 2y - z - 2w = -2$

$3x + 2y + z + 3w = 4$

$$\begin{bmatrix} 1 & 1 & 1 & 1 & | & 4 \\ 2 & 1 & -2 & -1 & | & 0 \\ 1 & -2 & -1 & -2 & | & -2 \\ 3 & 2 & 1 & 3 & | & 4 \end{bmatrix} -2R_1 + R_2$$

$$\begin{bmatrix} 1 & 1 & 1 & 1 & | & 4 \\ 0 & -1 & -4 & -3 & | & -8 \\ 1 & -2 & -1 & -2 & | & -2 \\ 3 & 2 & 1 & 3 & | & 4 \end{bmatrix} -1R_1 + R_3$$

$$\begin{bmatrix} 1 & 1 & 1 & 1 & | & 4 \\ 0 & -1 & -4 & -3 & | & -8 \\ 0 & -3 & -2 & -3 & | & -6 \\ 3 & 2 & 1 & 3 & | & 4 \end{bmatrix} -3R_1 + R_4$$

$$\begin{bmatrix} 1 & 1 & 1 & 1 & | & 4 \\ 0 & -1 & -4 & -3 & | & -8 \\ 0 & -3 & -2 & -3 & | & -6 \\ 0 & -1 & -2 & 0 & | & -8 \end{bmatrix} -1R_2$$

$$\begin{bmatrix} 1 & 1 & 1 & 1 & | & 4 \\ 0 & 1 & 4 & 3 & | & 8 \\ 0 & -3 & -2 & -3 & | & -6 \\ 0 & -1 & -2 & 0 & | & -8 \end{bmatrix} 3R_2 + R_3$$

$$\begin{bmatrix} 1 & 1 & 1 & 1 & | & 4 \\ 0 & 1 & 4 & 3 & | & 8 \\ 0 & 0 & 10 & 6 & | & 18 \\ 0 & -1 & -2 & 0 & | & -8 \end{bmatrix} 1R_2 + R_4$$

$$\begin{bmatrix} 1 & 1 & 1 & 1 & | & 4 \\ 0 & 1 & 4 & 3 & | & 8 \\ 0 & 0 & 10 & 6 & | & 18 \\ 0 & 0 & 2 & 3 & | & 0 \end{bmatrix} \frac{1}{10}R_3$$

$$\begin{bmatrix} 1 & 1 & 1 & 1 & | & 4 \\ 0 & 1 & 4 & 3 & | & 8 \\ 0 & 0 & 1 & \frac{3}{5} & | & \frac{9}{5} \\ 0 & 0 & 2 & 3 & | & 0 \end{bmatrix} -2R_3 + R_4$$

$$\begin{bmatrix} 1 & 1 & 1 & 1 & | & 4 \\ 0 & 1 & 4 & 3 & | & 8 \\ 0 & 0 & 1 & \frac{3}{5} & | & \frac{9}{5} \\ 0 & 0 & 0 & \frac{9}{5} & | & -\frac{18}{5} \end{bmatrix} \frac{5}{9} R_4$$

$$\begin{bmatrix} 1 & 1 & 1 & 1 & | & 4 \\ 0 & 1 & 4 & 3 & | & 8 \\ 0 & 0 & 1 & \frac{3}{5} & | & \frac{9}{5} \\ 0 & 0 & 0 & 1 & | & -2 \end{bmatrix}$$

$$w = -2$$
$$z + \frac{3}{5}w = \frac{9}{5}$$
$$z + \frac{3}{5}(-2) = \frac{9}{5}$$
$$z - \frac{6}{5} = \frac{9}{5}$$
$$z = 3$$
$$y + 4z + 3w = 8$$
$$y + 4(3) + 3(-2) = 8$$
$$y + 6 = 8$$
$$y = 2$$
$$x + y + z + w = 4$$
$$x + 2 + 3 + (-2) = 4$$
$$x + 3 = 4$$
$$x - 1$$

The solution set is $\{(1, 2, 3, -2)\}$.

35.
$$3x - 4y + z + w = 9$$
$$x + y - z - w = 0$$
$$2x + y + 4z - 2w = 3$$
$$-x + 2y + z \quad 3w = 3$$

$$\begin{bmatrix} 3 & -4 & 1 & 1 & | & 9 \\ 1 & 1 & -1 & -1 & | & 0 \\ 2 & 1 & 4 & -2 & | & 3 \\ -1 & 2 & 1 & -3 & | & 3 \end{bmatrix} R_1 \leftrightarrow R_2$$

$$\begin{bmatrix} 1 & 1 & -1 & -1 & | & 0 \\ 3 & -4 & 1 & 1 & | & 9 \\ 2 & 1 & 4 & -2 & | & 3 \\ -1 & 2 & 1 & -3 & | & 3 \end{bmatrix} -3R_1 + R_2$$

$$\begin{bmatrix} 1 & 1 & -1 & -1 & | & 0 \\ 0 & -7 & 4 & 4 & | & 9 \\ 2 & 1 & 4 & -2 & | & 3 \\ -1 & 2 & 1 & -3 & | & 3 \end{bmatrix} -2R_1 + R_3$$

$$\begin{bmatrix} 1 & 1 & -1 & -1 & | & 0 \\ 0 & -7 & 4 & 4 & | & 9 \\ 0 & -1 & 6 & 0 & | & 3 \\ -1 & 2 & 1 & -3 & | & 3 \end{bmatrix} 1R_1 + R_4$$

$$\begin{bmatrix} 1 & 1 & -1 & -1 & | & 0 \\ 0 & -7 & 4 & 4 & | & 9 \\ 0 & -1 & 6 & 0 & | & 3 \\ 0 & 3 & 0 & -4 & | & 3 \end{bmatrix} R_2 \leftrightarrow R_3$$

$$\begin{bmatrix} 1 & 1 & -1 & -1 & | & 0 \\ 0 & -1 & 6 & 0 & | & 3 \\ 0 & -7 & 4 & 4 & | & 9 \\ 0 & 3 & 0 & -4 & | & 3 \end{bmatrix} -R_2$$

$$\begin{bmatrix} 1 & 1 & -1 & -1 & | & 0 \\ 0 & 1 & -6 & 0 & | & -3 \\ 0 & -7 & 4 & 4 & | & 9 \\ 0 & 3 & 0 & -4 & | & 3 \end{bmatrix} 7R_2 + R_3$$

$$\begin{bmatrix} 1 & 1 & -1 & -1 & | & 0 \\ 0 & 1 & -6 & 0 & | & -3 \\ 0 & 0 & -38 & 4 & | & -12 \\ 0 & 3 & 0 & -4 & | & 3 \end{bmatrix} -3R_2 + R_4$$

$$\begin{bmatrix} 1 & 1 & -1 & -1 & | & 0 \\ 0 & 1 & -6 & 0 & | & -3 \\ 0 & 0 & -38 & 4 & | & -12 \\ 0 & 0 & 18 & -4 & | & 12 \end{bmatrix} -\frac{1}{38} R_3$$

$$\begin{bmatrix} 1 & 1 & -1 & -1 & | & 0 \\ 0 & 1 & -6 & 0 & | & -3 \\ 0 & 0 & 1 & -\frac{2}{19} & | & \frac{6}{19} \\ 0 & 0 & 18 & -4 & | & 12 \end{bmatrix} -18R_3 + R_4$$

$$\begin{bmatrix} 1 & 1 & -1 & -1 & | & 0 \\ 0 & 1 & -6 & 0 & | & -3 \\ 0 & 0 & 1 & -\frac{2}{19} & | & \frac{6}{19} \\ 0 & 0 & 0 & -\frac{40}{19} & | & \frac{120}{19} \end{bmatrix} -\frac{19}{40} R_4$$

$$\begin{bmatrix} 1 & 1 & -1 & -1 & | & 0 \\ 0 & 1 & -6 & 0 & | & -3 \\ 0 & 0 & 1 & -\frac{2}{19} & | & \frac{6}{19} \\ 0 & 0 & 0 & 1 & | & -3 \end{bmatrix}$$

$w = -3$

$$z - \frac{2}{19}w = \frac{6}{19}$$

$$z - \frac{2}{19}(-3) = \frac{6}{19}$$

$$z + \frac{6}{19} = \frac{6}{19}$$

$$z = 0$$

$$y - 6z = -3$$

$$y - 6(0) = -3$$

$$y = -3$$

$$x + y - z - w = 0$$

$$x - 3 - 0 + 3 = 0$$

$$x = 0$$

The solution set is $\{(0, -3, 0, -3)\}$.

37.　$2x + 3y - z - w = -3$

$$2x - y - 3z + 2w = -5$$

$$x - y + z - w = -4$$

$$3x - 2y + z + w = 0$$

$$\begin{bmatrix} 2 & 3 & -1 & -1 & | & -3 \\ 2 & -1 & -3 & 2 & | & -5 \\ 1 & -1 & 1 & -1 & | & -4 \\ 3 & -2 & 1 & 1 & | & 0 \end{bmatrix} R_1 \leftrightarrow R_3$$

$$\begin{bmatrix} 1 & -1 & 1 & -1 & | & -4 \\ 2 & -1 & -3 & 2 & | & -5 \\ 2 & 3 & -1 & -1 & | & -3 \\ 3 & -2 & 1 & 1 & | & 0 \end{bmatrix} -2R_1 + R_2$$

$$\begin{bmatrix} 1 & -1 & 1 & -1 & | & -4 \\ 0 & 1 & -5 & 4 & | & 3 \\ 2 & 3 & -1 & -1 & | & -3 \\ 3 & -2 & 1 & 1 & | & 0 \end{bmatrix} -2R_1 + R_3$$

$$\begin{bmatrix} 1 & -1 & 1 & -1 & | & -4 \\ 0 & 1 & -5 & 4 & | & 3 \\ 0 & 5 & -3 & 1 & | & 5 \\ 3 & -2 & 1 & 1 & | & 0 \end{bmatrix} -3R_1 + R_4$$

$$\begin{bmatrix} 1 & -1 & 1 & -1 & | & -4 \\ 0 & 1 & -5 & 4 & | & 3 \\ 0 & 5 & -3 & 1 & | & 5 \\ 0 & 1 & -2 & 4 & | & 12 \end{bmatrix} -5R_2 + R_3$$

$$\begin{bmatrix} 1 & -1 & 1 & -1 & | & -4 \\ 0 & 1 & -5 & 4 & | & 3 \\ 0 & 0 & 22 & -19 & | & -10 \\ 0 & 1 & -2 & 4 & | & 12 \end{bmatrix} -1R_2 + R_4$$

$$\begin{bmatrix} 1 & -1 & 1 & -1 & | & -4 \\ 0 & 1 & -5 & 4 & | & 3 \\ 0 & 0 & 22 & -19 & | & -10 \\ 0 & 0 & 3 & 0 & | & 9 \end{bmatrix} \frac{1}{22}R_3$$

$$\begin{bmatrix} 1 & -1 & 1 & -1 & | & -4 \\ 0 & 1 & -5 & 4 & | & 3 \\ 0 & 0 & 1 & -\frac{19}{22} & | & -\frac{5}{11} \\ 0 & 0 & 3 & 0 & | & 9 \end{bmatrix} -3R_3 + R_4$$

$$\begin{bmatrix} 1 & -1 & 1 & -1 & | & -4 \\ 0 & 1 & -5 & 4 & | & 3 \\ 0 & 0 & 1 & -\frac{19}{22} & | & -\frac{5}{11} \\ 0 & 0 & 0 & \frac{57}{22} & | & \frac{114}{11} \end{bmatrix} \frac{22}{57}R_4$$

$$\begin{bmatrix} 1 & -1 & 1 & -1 & | & -4 \\ 0 & 1 & -5 & 4 & | & 3 \\ 0 & 0 & 1 & -\frac{19}{22} & | & -\frac{5}{11} \\ 0 & 0 & 0 & 1 & | & 4 \end{bmatrix}$$

$w = 4$

$$z - \frac{19}{22}w = -\frac{5}{11}$$

$$z - \frac{19}{22}(4) = -\frac{5}{11}$$

$$z - \frac{76}{22} = -\frac{5}{11}$$

$$22z - 76 = -10$$

$$22z = 66$$

$$z = 3$$

$$y - 5z + 4w = 3$$
$$y - 5(3) + 4(4) = 3$$
$$y - 15 + 16 = 3$$
$$y + 1 = 3$$
$$y = 2$$
$$x - y + z - w = -4$$
$$x - 2 + 3 - 4 = -4$$
$$x - 3 = -4$$
$$x = -1$$

The solution set is $\{(-1, 2, 3, 4)\}$.

39.
$$2x_1 - 2x_2 + 3x_3 - x_4 = 12$$
$$x_1 + 2x_2 - x_3 + 2x_4 - x_5 = -7$$
$$x_1 + x_3 - x_4 - 5x_5 = 5$$
$$-x_1 + x_2 - x_3 - 2x_4 - 3x_5 = 0$$
$$x_1 - x_2 \quad - x_4 + x_5 = 4$$

$$\left[\begin{array}{ccccc|c} 2 & -2 & 3 & -1 & 0 & 12 \\ 1 & 2 & -1 & 2 & -1 & -7 \\ 1 & 0 & 1 & -1 & -5 & 5 \\ -1 & 1 & -1 & -2 & -3 & 0 \\ 1 & -1 & 0 & -1 & 1 & 4 \end{array}\right] R_1 \leftrightarrow R_5$$

$$\left[\begin{array}{ccccc|c} 1 & -1 & 0 & -1 & 1 & 4 \\ 1 & 2 & -1 & 2 & -1 & -7 \\ 1 & 0 & 1 & -1 & -5 & 5 \\ -1 & 1 & -1 & -2 & -3 & 0 \\ 2 & -2 & 3 & -1 & 0 & 12 \end{array}\right] \begin{array}{l} \\ -1R_1 + R_2 \\ -1R_1 + R_3 \\ 1R_1 + R_4 \\ -2R_1 + R_5 \end{array}$$

$$\left[\begin{array}{ccccc|c} 1 & -1 & 0 & -1 & 1 & 4 \\ 0 & 3 & -1 & 3 & -2 & -11 \\ 0 & 1 & 1 & 0 & -6 & 1 \\ 0 & 0 & -1 & -3 & -2 & 4 \\ 0 & 0 & 3 & 1 & -2 & 4 \end{array}\right] R_2 \leftrightarrow R_3$$

$$\left[\begin{array}{ccccc|c} 1 & -1 & 0 & -1 & 1 & 4 \\ 0 & 1 & 1 & 0 & -6 & 1 \\ 0 & 3 & -1 & 3 & -2 & -11 \\ 0 & 0 & -1 & -3 & -2 & 4 \\ 0 & 0 & 3 & 1 & -2 & 4 \end{array}\right] \begin{array}{l} 1R_2 + R_1 \\ -3R_2 + R_3 \\ \\ \\ \end{array}$$

$$\left[\begin{array}{ccccc|c} 1 & 0 & 1 & -1 & -5 & 5 \\ 0 & 1 & 1 & 0 & -6 & 1 \\ 0 & 0 & -4 & 3 & 16 & -14 \\ 0 & 0 & -1 & -3 & -2 & 4 \\ 0 & 0 & 3 & 1 & -2 & 4 \end{array}\right] R_3 \leftrightarrow R_4$$

$$\left[\begin{array}{ccccc|c} 1 & 0 & 1 & -1 & -5 & 5 \\ 0 & 1 & 1 & 0 & -6 & 1 \\ 0 & 0 & -1 & -3 & -2 & 4 \\ 0 & 0 & -4 & 3 & 16 & -14 \\ 0 & 0 & 3 & 1 & -2 & 4 \end{array}\right] -R_3$$

$$\left[\begin{array}{ccccc|c} 1 & 0 & 1 & -1 & -5 & 5 \\ 0 & 1 & 1 & 0 & -6 & 1 \\ 0 & 0 & 1 & 3 & 2 & -4 \\ 0 & 0 & -4 & 3 & 16 & -14 \\ 0 & 0 & 3 & 1 & -2 & 4 \end{array}\right] \begin{array}{l} -1R_3 + R_1 \\ -1R_3 + R_2 \\ \\ 4R_3 + R_4 \\ -3R_3 + R_5 \end{array}$$

$$\left[\begin{array}{ccccc|c} 1 & 0 & 0 & -4 & -7 & 9 \\ 0 & 1 & 0 & -3 & -8 & 5 \\ 0 & 0 & 1 & 3 & 2 & -4 \\ 0 & 0 & 0 & 15 & 24 & -30 \\ 0 & 0 & 0 & -8 & -8 & 16 \end{array}\right] R_4 \leftrightarrow R_5$$

$$\left[\begin{array}{ccccc|c} 1 & 0 & 0 & -4 & -7 & 9 \\ 0 & 1 & 0 & -3 & -8 & 5 \\ 0 & 0 & 1 & 3 & 2 & -4 \\ 0 & 0 & 0 & -8 & -8 & 16 \\ 0 & 0 & 0 & 15 & 24 & -30 \end{array}\right] -\tfrac{1}{8}R_4$$

$$\left[\begin{array}{ccccc|c} 1 & 0 & 0 & -4 & -7 & 9 \\ 0 & 1 & 0 & -3 & -8 & 5 \\ 0 & 0 & 1 & 3 & 2 & -4 \\ 0 & 0 & 0 & 1 & 1 & -2 \\ 0 & 0 & 0 & 15 & 24 & -30 \end{array}\right] \begin{array}{l} 4R_4 + R_1 \\ 3R_4 + R_2 \\ -3R_4 + R_3 \\ \\ -15R_4 + R_5 \end{array}$$

$$\begin{bmatrix} 1 & 0 & 0 & 0 & -3 & | & 1 \\ 0 & 1 & 0 & 0 & -5 & | & -1 \\ 0 & 0 & 1 & 0 & -1 & | & 2 \\ 0 & 0 & 0 & 1 & 1 & | & -2 \\ 0 & 0 & 0 & 0 & 9 & | & 0 \end{bmatrix} \frac{1}{9} R_5$$

$$\begin{bmatrix} 1 & 0 & 0 & 0 & -3 & | & 1 \\ 0 & 1 & 0 & 0 & -5 & | & -1 \\ 0 & 0 & 1 & 0 & -1 & | & 2 \\ 0 & 0 & 0 & 1 & 1 & | & -2 \\ 0 & 0 & 0 & 0 & 1 & | & 0 \end{bmatrix} \begin{matrix} -3R_5 + R_1 \\ 5R_5 + R_2 \\ 1R_5 + R_3 \\ -1R_5 + R_4 \end{matrix}$$

$$\begin{bmatrix} 1 & 0 & 0 & 0 & 0 & | & 1 \\ 0 & 1 & 0 & 0 & 0 & | & -1 \\ 0 & 0 & 1 & 0 & 0 & | & 2 \\ 0 & 0 & 0 & 1 & 0 & | & -2 \\ 0 & 0 & 0 & 0 & 1 & | & 0 \end{bmatrix}$$

$x_1 = 1, \; x_2 = -1, \; x_3 = 2, \; x_4 = -2, \; x_5 = 0$

The solution set is $\{(1, -1, 2, -2, 0)\}$.

41. a. $344 = a(1)^2 + b(1) + c$

$344 = a + b + c$

$480 = a(5)^2 + b(5) + c$

$480 = 25a + 5b + c$

$740 = a(10)^2 + b(10) + c$

$740 = 100a + 10b + c$

$a + b + c = 344$

$25a + 5b + c = 480$

$100a + 10b + c = 740$

$$\begin{bmatrix} 1 & 1 & 1 & | & 344 \\ 25 & 5 & 1 & | & 480 \\ 100 & 10 & 1 & | & 740 \end{bmatrix} \begin{matrix} -25R_1 + R_2 \\ -100R_1 + R_3 \end{matrix}$$

$$\begin{bmatrix} 1 & 1 & 1 & | & 344 \\ 0 & -20 & -24 & | & -8120 \\ 0 & -90 & -99 & | & -33660 \end{bmatrix} \begin{matrix} -\frac{1}{20}R_2 \\ -\frac{1}{90}R_3 \end{matrix}$$

$$\begin{bmatrix} 1 & 1 & 1 & | & 344 \\ 0 & 1 & \frac{6}{5} & | & 406 \\ 0 & 1 & \frac{11}{10} & | & 374 \end{bmatrix} 1R_2 + R_3$$

$$\begin{bmatrix} 1 & 1 & 1 & | & 344 \\ 0 & 1 & \frac{6}{5} & | & 406 \\ 0 & 0 & -\frac{1}{10} & | & -32 \end{bmatrix} -10R_3$$

$$\begin{bmatrix} 1 & 1 & 1 & | & 344 \\ 0 & 1 & \frac{6}{5} & | & 406 \\ 0 & 0 & 1 & | & 320 \end{bmatrix}$$

$a + b + c = 344$

$b + \dfrac{6}{5}c = 406$

$c = 320$

$b + \dfrac{6}{5}(320) = 406$

$b + 384 = 406$

$b = 22$

$a + 22 + 320 = 344$

$a = 2$

The solution set is $\{(2, 22, 320)\}$.

b. $y = 2x^2 + 22x + 320$

$x = 2010 - 1980 = 30$

$y = 2(30)^2 + 22(30) + 320$

$y = 1800 + 660 + 320$

$y = 2780$

c. Answers may vary.

43. Let $x =$ under 30 age group

Let $y = 30$–49 age group

Let $z = 50$ and over age group

$x + z = y + 2$

$2z = x - 3$

$x + y + z = 100$

$x + y + z = 100$

$x - y + z = 2$

$-x + 2z = -3$

$$\begin{bmatrix} 1 & 1 & 1 & | & 100 \\ 1 & -1 & 1 & | & 2 \\ -1 & 0 & 2 & | & -3 \end{bmatrix} \begin{matrix} -1R_1 + R_2 \\ 1R_1 + R_3 \end{matrix}$$

$$\begin{bmatrix} 1 & 1 & 1 & | & 100 \\ 0 & -2 & 0 & | & -98 \\ 0 & 1 & 3 & | & 97 \end{bmatrix} -\frac{1}{2}R_2$$

$$\begin{bmatrix} 1 & 1 & 1 & | & 100 \\ 0 & 1 & 0 & | & 49 \\ 0 & 1 & 3 & | & 97 \end{bmatrix} -1R_2 + R_3$$

$$\begin{bmatrix} 1 & 1 & 1 & | & 100 \\ 0 & 1 & 0 & | & 49 \\ 0 & 0 & 3 & | & 48 \end{bmatrix} \begin{matrix} -1R_2 + R_1 \\ \\ \frac{1}{3}R_3 \end{matrix}$$

$$\begin{bmatrix} 1 & 0 & 1 & | & 51 \\ 0 & 1 & 0 & | & 49 \\ 0 & 0 & 1 & | & 16 \end{bmatrix} -1R_3 + R_1$$

$$\begin{bmatrix} 1 & 0 & 0 & | & 35 \\ 0 & 1 & 0 & | & 49 \\ 0 & 0 & 1 & | & 16 \end{bmatrix}$$

$x = 35;\ y = 49;\ z = 16$
50 and over—16%
30–49—49%
under 30—35%

45. Let $x =$ Food A
Let $y =$ Food B
Let $z =$ Food C

$$\begin{aligned} 40x + 200y + 400z &= 660 \\ 5x + 2y + 4z &= 25 \\ 30x + 10y + 300z &= 425 \\ 2x + 10y + 20z &= 33 \\ 5x + 2y + 4z &= 25 \\ 6x + 2y + 60z &= 85 \end{aligned}$$

$$\begin{bmatrix} 2 & 10 & 20 & | & 33 \\ 5 & 2 & 4 & | & 25 \\ 6 & 2 & 60 & | & 85 \end{bmatrix} \frac{1}{2}R_1$$

$$\begin{bmatrix} 1 & 5 & 10 & | & \frac{33}{2} \\ 5 & 2 & 4 & | & 25 \\ 6 & 2 & 60 & | & 85 \end{bmatrix} -5R_1 + R_2$$

$$\begin{bmatrix} 1 & 5 & 10 & | & \frac{33}{2} \\ 0 & -23 & -46 & | & -\frac{115}{2} \\ 6 & 2 & 60 & | & 85 \end{bmatrix} -6R_1 + R_3$$

$$\begin{bmatrix} 1 & 5 & 10 & | & \frac{33}{2} \\ 0 & -23 & -46 & | & -\frac{115}{2} \\ 0 & -28 & 0 & | & -14 \end{bmatrix} -\frac{1}{23}R_2$$

$$\begin{bmatrix} 1 & 5 & 10 & | & \frac{33}{2} \\ 0 & 1 & 2 & | & \frac{5}{2} \\ 0 & -28 & 0 & | & -14 \end{bmatrix} 28R_2 + R_3$$

$$\begin{bmatrix} 1 & 5 & 10 & | & \frac{33}{2} \\ 0 & 1 & 2 & | & \frac{5}{2} \\ 0 & 0 & 56 & | & 56 \end{bmatrix} \frac{1}{56}R_3$$

$$\begin{bmatrix} 1 & 5 & 10 & | & \frac{33}{2} \\ 0 & 1 & 2 & | & \frac{5}{2} \\ 0 & 0 & 1 & | & 1 \end{bmatrix}$$

$$z = 1$$
$$y + 2z = \frac{5}{2}$$
$$y + 2 = \frac{5}{2}$$
$$2y + 4 = 5$$
$$2y = 1$$
$$y = \frac{1}{2}$$

$$x + 5y + 10z = \frac{33}{2}$$
$$x + \frac{5}{2} + 10 = \frac{33}{2}$$
$$2x + 5 + 20 = 33$$
$$2x + 25 = 33$$
$$2x = 8$$
$$x = 4$$

4 ounces of Food A
$\dfrac{1}{2}$ ounce of Food B
1 ounce of Food C

47.–53. Answers may vary.

55. Exercise 27

Exercise 29

Exercise 31

Exercise 33

Exercise 35

```
][[1,1,-1,-1,0][2
,1,4,-2,3][-1,2,
1,-3,3]])▶Frac
[[1  -4/3  1/3  …
 [0 1    10/11  …
 [0 0    1      …
 [0 0    0      …
```

$$\begin{bmatrix} 1 & 1 & 1 & 1 & 5 \\ -1 & 1 & -1 & 1 & -7 \\ -8 & 4 & -2 & 1 & -13 \\ 0 & 0 & 0 & 1 & -3 \end{bmatrix} \begin{matrix} \\ R_1 + R_2 \\ 8R_1 + R_3 \\ \\ \end{matrix}$$

$$\begin{bmatrix} 1 & 1 & 1 & 1 & 5 \\ 0 & 2 & 0 & 2 & -2 \\ 0 & 12 & 6 & 9 & 27 \\ 0 & 0 & 0 & 1 & -3 \end{bmatrix} \begin{matrix} \\ \\ \frac{1}{2}R_2 \\ \\ \end{matrix}$$

$$\begin{bmatrix} 1 & 1 & 1 & 1 & 5 \\ 0 & 1 & 0 & 1 & -1 \\ 0 & 12 & 6 & 9 & 27 \\ 0 & 0 & 0 & 1 & -3 \end{bmatrix} \begin{matrix} \\ -1R_2 + R_1 \\ -12R_2 + R_3 \\ \\ \end{matrix}$$

$$\begin{bmatrix} 1 & 0 & 1 & 0 & 6 \\ 0 & 1 & 0 & 1 & -1 \\ 0 & 0 & 6 & -3 & 39 \\ 0 & 0 & 0 & 1 & -3 \end{bmatrix} \begin{matrix} \\ \\ \frac{1}{6}R_3 \\ -R_4 + R_2 \end{matrix}$$

$$\begin{bmatrix} 1 & 0 & 1 & 0 & 6 \\ 0 & 1 & 0 & 0 & 2 \\ 0 & 0 & 1 & \frac{-1}{2} & \frac{13}{2} \\ 0 & 0 & 0 & 1 & -3 \end{bmatrix} \begin{matrix} \frac{1}{2}R_4 + R_3 \\ \\ \\ \end{matrix}$$

$$\begin{bmatrix} 1 & 0 & 1 & 0 & 6 \\ 0 & 1 & 0 & 0 & 2 \\ 0 & 0 & 1 & 0 & 5 \\ 0 & 0 & 0 & 1 & -3 \end{bmatrix} \begin{matrix} \\ \\ -R_3 + R_1 \\ \\ \end{matrix}$$

$$\begin{bmatrix} 1 & 0 & 0 & 0 & 1 \\ 0 & 1 & 0 & 0 & 2 \\ 0 & 0 & 1 & 0 & 5 \\ 0 & 0 & 0 & 1 & -3 \end{bmatrix}$$

$a = 1$
$b = 2$
$c = 5$
$d = -3$
$y = x^3 + 2x^2 + 5x - 3$

57. $y = ax^3 + bx^2 + cx + d$
$-3 = a(0)^3 + b(0)^2 + c(0) + d$
$-3 = d$
$5 = a + b + c + d$
$-7 = a(-1)^3 + b(-1)^2 + c(-1) + d$
$-7 = -a + b - c + d$
$-13 = a(-2)^3 + b(-2)^2 + c(-2) + d$
$-13 = -8a + 4b - 2c + d$
$a + b + c + d = 5$
$-a + b - c + d = -7$
$-8a + 4b - 2c + d = -13$
$d = -3$

Section 9.2

Check Point Exercises

1. $\begin{aligned} x - 2y - z &= 5 \\ 2x - 3y - z &= 0 \\ 3x - 4y - z &= 1 \end{aligned} \rightarrow \left[\begin{array}{ccc|c} 1 & -2 & -1 & -5 \\ 2 & -3 & -1 & 0 \\ 3 & -4 & -1 & 1 \end{array}\right]$

$\left[\begin{array}{ccc|c} 1 & -2 & -1 & -5 \\ 2 & -3 & -1 & 0 \\ 3 & -4 & -1 & 1 \end{array}\right] \begin{array}{l} -2R_1 + R_2 \\ -3R_1 + R_3 \end{array}$

$\left[\begin{array}{ccc|c} 1 & -2 & -1 & -5 \\ 0 & 1 & 1 & 10 \\ 0 & 2 & 2 & 16 \end{array}\right] -2R_2 + R_3$

$\left[\begin{array}{ccc|c} 1 & -2 & -1 & -5 \\ 0 & 1 & -1 & -10 \\ 0 & 0 & 0 & -4 \end{array}\right]$

$0x + 0y + 0z = -4$ This equation can never be a true statement. Consequently, the system has no solution. The solution set is $\varnothing$, the empty set.

2. $\begin{aligned} x - 2y - z &= 5 \\ 2x - 5y + 3z &= 16 \\ x - 3y + 4z &= 1 \end{aligned} \rightarrow \left[\begin{array}{ccc|c} 1 & -2 & -1 & 5 \\ 2 & -5 & 3 & 6 \\ 1 & -3 & 4 & 1 \end{array}\right]$

$\left[\begin{array}{ccc|c} 1 & -2 & -1 & 5 \\ 2 & -5 & 3 & 6 \\ 1 & -3 & 4 & 1 \end{array}\right] \begin{array}{l} -2R_1 + R_2 \\ -1R_1 + R_3 \end{array}$

$\left[\begin{array}{ccc|c} 1 & -2 & -1 & 5 \\ 0 & -1 & 5 & -4 \\ 0 & -1 & 5 & -4 \end{array}\right] -1R_2$

$\left[\begin{array}{ccc|c} 1 & -2 & -1 & 5 \\ 0 & 1 & -5 & 4 \\ 0 & -1 & 5 & -4 \end{array}\right] 1R_2 + R_3$

$\left[\begin{array}{ccc|c} 1 & -2 & -1 & 5 \\ 0 & 1 & -5 & 4 \\ 0 & 0 & 0 & 0 \end{array}\right]$

$0x + 0y + 0z = 0$ or $0 = 0$

This equation, $0x + 0y + 0z = 0$ is *dependent* on the other two equations. Thus, it can be dropped from the system which can now be expressed in the form

$\left[\begin{array}{ccc|c} 1 & -2 & -1 & 5 \\ 0 & 1 & -5 & 4 \end{array}\right]$

The original system is equivalent to the system

$\begin{aligned} x - 2y - z &= 5 \\ y - 5z &= 4 \end{aligned}$

Solve for x and y in terms of z.

$y = 5z + 4$

Use back-substitution for y in the previous equation.

$\begin{aligned} x - 2(5z + 4) - z &= 5 \\ x - 10z - 8 - z &= 5 \\ x &= 11z + 13 \end{aligned}$

Finally, letting $z = t$ (or any letter of your choice), the solutions to the system are all of the form $x = 11t + 13$, $y = 5t + 4$, $z = t$, where t is a real number. The solution set of the system with dependent equations can be written as $\{(11t + 13,\ 5t + 4,\ t)\}$.

3. $\begin{aligned} x + 2y + 3z &= 70 \\ x + y + z &= 60 \end{aligned} \rightarrow \left[\begin{array}{ccc|c} 1 & 2 & 3 & 70 \\ 1 & 1 & 1 & 60 \end{array}\right]$

$\left[\begin{array}{ccc|c} 1 & 2 & 3 & 70 \\ 1 & 1 & 1 & 60 \end{array}\right] -1R_1 + R_2$

$\left[\begin{array}{ccc|c} 1 & 2 & 3 & 70 \\ 0 & -1 & -2 & -10 \end{array}\right] -1R_2$

$\left[\begin{array}{ccc|c} 1 & 2 & 3 & 70 \\ 0 & 1 & 2 & 10 \end{array}\right] \rightarrow \begin{aligned} x + 2y + 3z &= 70 \\ y + 2z &= 10 \end{aligned}$

Express x and y in terms of z using back-substitution.

$\begin{aligned} y &= -2z + 10 \\ x + 2(-2z + 10) + 3z &= 70 \\ x - 4z + 20 + 3z &= 70 \\ x &= z + 50 \end{aligned}$

With $z = t$, the ordered solution (x, y, z) enables us to express the system's solution set as $\{(t + 50,\ -2t + 10,\ t)\}$.

4. a. I_1: $10 + 5 = 15$ cars enter I_1, and $x + w$ cars leave I_1, then $x + w = 15$.
I_2: $20 + 10 = 30$ cars enter I_2 and $x + y$ cars leave I_2, then $x + y = 30$.
I_3: $15 + 30 = 45$ cars enter I_3 and $y + z$ cars leave I_3, then $y + z = 45$.
I_4: $10 + 20 = 30$ cars enter I_4 and $z + w$ cars leave I_4, then $z + w = 30$.
The system of equations that describes this situation is given by
$$x + w = 15$$
$$x + y = 30$$
$$y + z = 45$$
$$z + w = 30.$$

b. $\begin{bmatrix} 1 & 0 & 0 & 1 & | & 15 \\ 1 & 1 & 0 & 0 & | & 30 \\ 0 & 1 & 1 & 0 & | & 45 \\ 0 & 0 & 1 & 1 & | & 30 \end{bmatrix} -1R_2 + R_2$

$\begin{bmatrix} 1 & 0 & 0 & 1 & | & 15 \\ 0 & 1 & 0 & -1 & | & 15 \\ 0 & 1 & 1 & 0 & | & 45 \\ 0 & 0 & 1 & 1 & | & 30 \end{bmatrix} -1R_2 + R_3$

$\begin{bmatrix} 1 & 0 & 0 & 1 & | & 15 \\ 0 & 1 & 0 & -1 & | & 15 \\ 0 & 0 & 1 & 1 & | & 30 \\ 0 & 0 & 1 & 1 & | & 30 \end{bmatrix} -1R_3 + R_4$

$\begin{bmatrix} 1 & 0 & 0 & 1 & | & 15 \\ 0 & 1 & 0 & -1 & | & 15 \\ 0 & 0 & 1 & 1 & | & 30 \\ 0 & 0 & 0 & 0 & | & 0 \end{bmatrix}$

$$x + w = 15$$
$$y - w = 15$$
$$z + w = 30$$

The last row of the matrix shows that the system has dependent equations and infinitely many solutions.
Let w be any real number.
Express x, y and z in terms of w:
$$x = 15 - w$$
$$y = 15 + w$$
$$z = 30 - w$$

With $w = t$, the ordered solution (x, y, z, w) enables us to express the system's solution set as
$$\{(15 - t, 15 + t, 30 - t, t)\}$$

c. Because $w = t$, we replace 10 for t in the system's ordered solution:
$(15 - t, 15 + t, 30 - t, t)$
$= (15 - 10, 15 + 10, 30 - 10, 10)$
$= (5, 25, 20, 10)$
Thus, $x = 5$, $y = 25$, $z = 20$.
With construction, this means that to keep traffic flowing, 5 cars per minute must be routed between I_1, and I_2, 25 cars per minute between I_2 and I_3 and 20 cars per minute between I_3 and I_4.

Exercise Set 9.2

1. $\begin{bmatrix} 5 & 12 & 1 & | & 10 \\ 2 & 5 & 2 & | & -1 \\ 1 & 2 & -3 & | & 5 \end{bmatrix} R_1 \leftrightarrow R_3$

$\begin{bmatrix} 1 & 2 & -3 & | & 5 \\ 2 & 5 & 2 & | & -1 \\ 5 & 12 & 1 & | & 10 \end{bmatrix} \begin{matrix} -2R_1 + R_2 \\ -5R_1 + R_3 \end{matrix}$

$\begin{bmatrix} 1 & 2 & -3 & | & 5 \\ 0 & 1 & 8 & | & -11 \\ 0 & 2 & 16 & | & -15 \end{bmatrix} -2R_2 + R_3$

$\begin{bmatrix} 1 & 2 & 3 & | & 5 \\ 0 & 1 & 8 & | & -11 \\ 0 & 0 & 0 & | & 7 \end{bmatrix}$

From the last row, we see that the system has no solution. The solution set is $\varnothing$, the empty set.

3. $\begin{bmatrix} 5 & 8 & -6 & | & 14 \\ 3 & 4 & -2 & | & 8 \\ 1 & 2 & -2 & | & 3 \end{bmatrix} R_1 \leftrightarrow R_3$

$\begin{bmatrix} 1 & 2 & -2 & | & 3 \\ 3 & 4 & -2 & | & 8 \\ 5 & 8 & -6 & | & 14 \end{bmatrix} \begin{matrix} -3R_1 + R_2 \\ -5R_1 + R_3 \end{matrix}$

$$\begin{bmatrix} 1 & 2 & -2 & | & 3 \\ 0 & -2 & 4 & | & -1 \\ 0 & -2 & 4 & | & -1 \end{bmatrix} -1R_2 + R_3$$

$$\begin{bmatrix} 1 & 2 & -2 & | & 3 \\ 0 & -2 & 4 & | & -1 \\ 0 & 0 & 0 & | & 0 \end{bmatrix} -\frac{1}{2}R_2$$

$$\begin{bmatrix} 1 & 2 & -2 & | & 3 \\ 0 & 1 & -2 & | & \frac{1}{2} \\ 0 & 0 & 0 & | & 0 \end{bmatrix}$$

$$x + 2y - 2z = 3$$

The system $\quad y - 2z = \dfrac{1}{2}\quad$ has no unique

solution. Express x and y in terms of z:

$$y = 2z + \frac{1}{2}$$

$$x + 2\left(2z + \frac{1}{2}\right) - 2z = 3$$

$$x + 4z + 1 - 2z = 3$$

$$x + 2z + 1 = 3$$

$$x = -2z + 2$$

With $z = t$, the complete solution to the

system is $\left\{\left(-2t + 2,\ 2t + \dfrac{1}{2},\ t\right)\right\}$.

5. $\begin{bmatrix} 3 & 4 & 2 & | & 3 \\ 4 & -2 & -8 & | & -4 \\ 1 & 1 & -1 & | & 3 \end{bmatrix} R_1 \leftrightarrow R_3$

$$\begin{bmatrix} 1 & 1 & -1 & | & 3 \\ 4 & -2 & -8 & | & -4 \\ 3 & 4 & 2 & | & 3 \end{bmatrix} \begin{matrix} -4R_1 + R_2 \\ -3R_1 + R_3 \end{matrix}$$

$$\begin{bmatrix} 1 & 1 & -1 & | & 3 \\ 0 & -6 & -4 & | & -16 \\ 0 & 1 & 5 & | & -6 \end{bmatrix} R_2 \leftrightarrow R_3$$

$$\begin{bmatrix} 1 & 1 & -1 & | & 3 \\ 0 & 1 & 5 & | & -6 \\ 0 & -6 & -4 & | & -16 \end{bmatrix} 6R_2 + R_3$$

$$\begin{bmatrix} 1 & 1 & 1 & | & 3 \\ 0 & 1 & 5 & | & -6 \\ 0 & 0 & 26 & | & -52 \end{bmatrix} \frac{1}{26}R_3$$

$$\begin{bmatrix} 1 & 1 & -1 & | & 3 \\ 0 & 1 & 5 & | & -6 \\ 0 & 0 & 1 & | & -2 \end{bmatrix}$$

This corresponds to the system

$$x + y - z = 3$$
$$y + 5z = -6$$
$$z = -2$$

Use back-substitution to find the values of x and y:

$$y + 5(-2) = -6$$
$$y - 10 = -6$$
$$y = 4$$
$$x + 4 + 2 = 3$$
$$x + 6 = 3$$
$$x = -3$$

The solution to the system is $\{(-3,\ 4,\ -2)\}$.

7. $\begin{bmatrix} 8 & 5 & 11 & | & 30 \\ -1 & -4 & 2 & | & 3 \\ 2 & -1 & 5 & | & 12 \end{bmatrix} R_1 \leftrightarrow R_2$

$$\begin{bmatrix} -1 & -4 & 2 & | & 3 \\ 8 & 5 & 11 & | & 30 \\ 2 & -1 & 5 & | & 12 \end{bmatrix} -1R_1$$

$$\begin{bmatrix} 1 & 4 & -2 & | & -3 \\ 8 & 5 & 11 & | & 30 \\ 2 & -1 & 5 & | & 12 \end{bmatrix} \begin{matrix} -8R_1 + R_2 \\ -2R_1 + R_3 \end{matrix}$$

$$\begin{bmatrix} 1 & 4 & -2 & | & -3 \\ 0 & -27 & 27 & | & 54 \\ 0 & -9 & 9 & | & 18 \end{bmatrix} -\frac{1}{27}R_2$$

$$\begin{bmatrix} 1 & 4 & -2 & | & -3 \\ 0 & 1 & -1 & | & -2 \\ 0 & -9 & 9 & | & 18 \end{bmatrix} 9R_2 + R_3$$

$$\begin{bmatrix} 1 & 4 & -2 & | & -3 \\ 0 & 1 & -1 & | & -2 \\ 0 & 0 & 0 & | & 0 \end{bmatrix}$$

The system $\begin{array}{l} x + 4y - 2z = -3 \\ y - z = -2 \end{array}$ has no unique

solution. Express x and y in terms of z:
$y = -2 + z$
$x + 4(-2 + z) - 2z = -3$
$x - 8 + 4z - 2z = -3$
$x - 8 + 2z = -3$
$x = 5 - 2z$
With $z = t$, the complete solution to the
system is $\{(5 - 2t, -2 + t, t)\}$.

9.

$$\left[\begin{array}{cccc|c} 1 & -2 & -1 & -3 & -9 \\ 1 & 1 & -1 & 0 & 0 \\ 3 & 4 & 0 & 1 & 6 \\ 0 & 2 & -2 & 1 & 3 \end{array}\right] \begin{array}{l} -1R_1 + R_2 \\ -3R_1 + R_3 \end{array}$$

$$\left[\begin{array}{cccc|c} 1 & -2 & -1 & -3 & -9 \\ 0 & 3 & 0 & 3 & 9 \\ 0 & 10 & 3 & 10 & 33 \\ 0 & 2 & -2 & 1 & 3 \end{array}\right] \tfrac{1}{3}R_2$$

$$\left[\begin{array}{cccc|c} 1 & -2 & -1 & -3 & -9 \\ 0 & 1 & 0 & 1 & 3 \\ 0 & 10 & 3 & 10 & 33 \\ 0 & 2 & -2 & 1 & 3 \end{array}\right] \begin{array}{l} -10R_2 + R_3 \\ -2R_2 + R_4 \end{array}$$

$$\left[\begin{array}{cccc|c} 1 & -2 & -1 & -3 & -9 \\ 0 & 1 & 0 & 1 & 3 \\ 0 & 0 & 3 & 0 & 3 \\ 0 & 0 & -2 & -1 & -3 \end{array}\right] \tfrac{1}{3}R_3$$

$$\left[\begin{array}{cccc|c} 1 & -2 & -1 & -3 & -9 \\ 0 & 1 & 0 & 1 & 3 \\ 0 & 0 & 1 & 0 & 1 \\ 0 & 0 & -2 & -1 & -3 \end{array}\right] 2R_3 + R_4$$

$$\left[\begin{array}{cccc|c} 1 & -2 & -1 & -3 & -9 \\ 0 & 1 & 0 & 1 & 3 \\ 0 & 0 & 1 & 0 & 1 \\ 0 & 0 & 0 & -1 & -1 \end{array}\right] -1R_4$$

$$\left[\begin{array}{cccc|c} 1 & -2 & -1 & -3 & -9 \\ 0 & 1 & 0 & 1 & 3 \\ 0 & 0 & 1 & 0 & 1 \\ 0 & 0 & 0 & 1 & 1 \end{array}\right]$$

This corresponds to the system
$$\begin{array}{l} x - 2y - z - 3w = -9 \\ y + w = 3 \\ z = 1 \\ w = 1 \end{array}$$
Use back-substitution to find the values of
x and y:
$y + 1 = 3$
$\quad y = 2$
$x - 2(2) - 1 - 3(1) = -9$
$\quad\quad x - 4 - 1 - 3 = -9$
$\quad\quad\quad\quad x - 8 = -9$
$\quad\quad\quad\quad\quad x = -1$
The solution to the system is $\{(-1, 2, 1, 1)\}$.

11.

$$\left[\begin{array}{cccc|c} 2 & 1 & -1 & 0 & 3 \\ 1 & -3 & 2 & 0 & -4 \\ 3 & 1 & -3 & 1 & 1 \\ 1 & 2 & -4 & -1 & -2 \end{array}\right] R_1 \leftrightarrow R_2$$

$$\left[\begin{array}{cccc|c} 1 & -3 & 2 & 0 & -4 \\ 2 & 1 & -1 & 0 & 3 \\ 3 & 1 & -3 & 1 & 1 \\ 1 & 2 & -4 & -1 & -2 \end{array}\right] \begin{array}{l} -2R_1 + R_2 \\ -3R_1 + R_3 \\ -1R_1 + R_4 \end{array}$$

$$\left[\begin{array}{cccc|c} 1 & -3 & 2 & 0 & -4 \\ 0 & 7 & -5 & 0 & 11 \\ 0 & 10 & -9 & 1 & 13 \\ 0 & 5 & -6 & -1 & 2 \end{array}\right] \tfrac{1}{7}R_2$$

$$\left[\begin{array}{cccc|c} 1 & -3 & 2 & 0 & -4 \\ 0 & 1 & -\tfrac{5}{7} & 0 & \tfrac{11}{7} \\ 0 & 10 & -9 & 1 & 13 \\ 0 & 5 & -6 & -1 & 2 \end{array}\right] \begin{array}{l} -10R_2 + R_3 \\ -5R_2 + R_4 \end{array}$$

$$\left[\begin{array}{cccc|c} 1 & -3 & 2 & 0 & -4 \\ 0 & 1 & -\tfrac{5}{7} & 0 & \tfrac{11}{7} \\ 0 & 0 & -\tfrac{13}{7} & 1 & -\tfrac{19}{7} \\ 0 & 0 & -\tfrac{17}{7} & -1 & -\tfrac{41}{7} \end{array}\right] -\tfrac{7}{13}R_3$$

$$\left[\begin{array}{cccc|c} 1 & -3 & 2 & 0 & -4 \\ 0 & 1 & -\tfrac{5}{7} & 0 & \tfrac{11}{7} \\ 0 & 0 & 1 & -\tfrac{7}{13} & \tfrac{19}{13} \\ 0 & 0 & -\tfrac{17}{7} & -1 & -\tfrac{41}{7} \end{array}\right] \tfrac{17}{7}R_3 + R_4$$

$$\begin{bmatrix} 1 & -3 & 2 & 0 & -4 \\ 0 & 1 & -\frac{5}{7} & 0 & \frac{11}{7} \\ 0 & 0 & 1 & -\frac{7}{13} & \frac{19}{13} \\ 0 & 0 & 0 & -\frac{30}{13} & -\frac{30}{13} \end{bmatrix} -\frac{13}{30}R_4$$

$$\begin{bmatrix} 1 & -3 & 2 & 0 & -4 \\ 0 & 1 & -\frac{5}{7} & 0 & \frac{11}{7} \\ 0 & 0 & 1 & -\frac{7}{13} & \frac{19}{13} \\ 0 & 0 & 0 & 1 & 1 \end{bmatrix}$$

This corresponds to the system

$$x - 3y + 2z = -4$$
$$y - \frac{5}{7}z = \frac{11}{7}$$
$$z - \frac{7}{13}w = \frac{19}{13}$$
$$w = 1$$

Use back-substitution to find the values of x, y, and z:

$$z - \frac{7}{13} = \frac{19}{13}$$
$$z = 2$$
$$y - \frac{5}{7}(2) = \frac{11}{7}$$
$$y - \frac{10}{7} = \frac{11}{7}$$
$$y = 3$$
$$x - 3(3) + 2(2) = 4$$
$$x - 9 + 4 = -4$$
$$x - 5 = -4$$
$$x = 1$$

The solution to the system is $\{(1, 3, 2, 1)\}$.

13.
$$\begin{bmatrix} 1 & -3 & 1 & -4 & 4 \\ -2 & 1 & 2 & 0 & -2 \\ 3 & -2 & 1 & -6 & 2 \\ -1 & 3 & 2 & -1 & -6 \end{bmatrix} \begin{matrix} 2R_1 + R_2 \\ -3R_1 + R_3 \\ R_1 + R_4 \end{matrix}$$

$$\begin{bmatrix} 1 & -3 & 1 & -4 & 4 \\ 0 & -5 & 4 & -8 & 6 \\ 0 & 7 & -2 & 6 & -10 \\ 0 & 0 & 3 & -5 & -2 \end{bmatrix} -\frac{1}{5}R_2$$

$$\begin{bmatrix} 1 & -3 & 1 & -4 & 4 \\ 0 & 1 & -\frac{4}{5} & \frac{8}{5} & -\frac{6}{5} \\ 0 & 7 & -2 & 6 & -10 \\ 0 & 0 & 3 & -5 & -2 \end{bmatrix} -7R_2 + R_3$$

$$\begin{bmatrix} 1 & -3 & 1 & -4 & 4 \\ 0 & 1 & -\frac{4}{5} & \frac{8}{5} & -\frac{6}{5} \\ 0 & 0 & \frac{18}{5} & -\frac{26}{5} & -\frac{8}{5} \\ 0 & 0 & 3 & -5 & -2 \end{bmatrix} \frac{5}{18}R_3$$

$$\begin{bmatrix} 1 & -3 & 1 & -4 & 4 \\ 0 & 1 & -\frac{4}{5} & \frac{8}{5} & -\frac{6}{5} \\ 0 & 0 & 1 & -\frac{13}{9} & -\frac{4}{9} \\ 0 & 0 & 3 & -5 & -2 \end{bmatrix} -3R_3 + R_4$$

$$\begin{bmatrix} 1 & -3 & 1 & -4 & 4 \\ 0 & 1 & -\frac{4}{5} & \frac{8}{5} & -\frac{6}{5} \\ 0 & 0 & 1 & -\frac{13}{9} & -\frac{4}{9} \\ 0 & 0 & 0 & -\frac{2}{3} & -\frac{2}{3} \end{bmatrix} -\frac{3}{2}R_4$$

$$\begin{bmatrix} 1 & -3 & 1 & -4 & 4 \\ 0 & 1 & -\frac{4}{5} & \frac{8}{5} & -\frac{6}{5} \\ 0 & 0 & 1 & -\frac{13}{9} & -\frac{4}{9} \\ 0 & 0 & 0 & 1 & 1 \end{bmatrix}$$

This corresponds to the system

$$x - 3y + z - 4w = 4$$
$$y - \frac{4}{5}z + \frac{8}{5}w = -\frac{6}{5}$$
$$z - \frac{13}{9}w = -\frac{4}{9}$$
$$w = 1$$

Use back-substitution to find the values of x, y, and z:

$$z - \frac{13}{9} = -\frac{4}{9}$$
$$z = 1$$
$$y - \frac{4}{5} + \frac{8}{5} = -\frac{6}{5}$$
$$y + \frac{4}{5} = -\frac{6}{5}$$
$$y = -2$$
$$x - 3(-2) + 1 - 4 = 4$$
$$x + 6 - 3 = 4$$
$$x = 1$$

The solution to the system is $\{(1, -2, 1, 1)\}$.

15. $\begin{bmatrix} 2 & 1 & -1 & | & 2 \\ 3 & 3 & -2 & | & 3 \end{bmatrix} \frac{1}{2}R_1$

$\begin{bmatrix} 1 & \frac{1}{2} & -\frac{1}{2} & | & 1 \\ 3 & 3 & -2 & | & 3 \end{bmatrix} -3R_1 + R_2$

$\begin{bmatrix} 1 & \frac{1}{2} & -\frac{1}{2} & | & 1 \\ 0 & \frac{3}{2} & -\frac{1}{2} & | & 0 \end{bmatrix} \frac{2}{3}R_2$

$\begin{bmatrix} 1 & \frac{1}{2} & -\frac{1}{2} & | & 1 \\ 0 & 1 & -\frac{1}{3} & | & 0 \end{bmatrix}$

The system $x + \dfrac{1}{2}y - \dfrac{1}{2}z = 1$ has no unique

$\qquad\qquad\qquad y - \dfrac{1}{3}z = 0$

solution. Express x and y in terms of z:

$y = \dfrac{1}{3}z$

$x + \dfrac{1}{2}\left(\dfrac{1}{3}z\right) - \dfrac{1}{2}z = 1$

$x + \dfrac{1}{6}z - \dfrac{1}{2}z = 1$

$x - \dfrac{1}{3}z = 1$

$x = 1 + \dfrac{1}{3}z$

With $z = t$, the complete solution to the

system is $\left\{\left(1 + \dfrac{1}{3}t, \dfrac{1}{3}t, t\right)\right\}$.

17. The system $\begin{array}{c} x + 2y + 3z = 5 \\ y - 5z = 0 \end{array}$ has no unique

solution. Express x and y in terms of z:
$y = 5z$
$x + 2(5z) + 3z = 5$
$\quad x + 10z + 3z = 5$
$\qquad\qquad x = -13z + 5$
With $z = t$, the complete solution to the
system is $\{(-13t + 5, 5t, t)\}$.

19. $\begin{bmatrix} 1 & 1 & -2 & | & 2 \\ 3 & -1 & -6 & | & -7 \end{bmatrix} -3R_1 + R_2$

$\begin{bmatrix} 1 & 1 & -2 & | & 2 \\ 0 & -4 & 0 & | & -13 \end{bmatrix} -\frac{1}{4}R_2$

$\begin{bmatrix} 1 & 1 & -2 & | & 2 \\ 0 & 1 & 0 & | & \frac{13}{4} \end{bmatrix}$

$\qquad\qquad x + y - 2z = 2$

The system $\qquad\qquad y = \dfrac{13}{4}$ has no unique

solution. Express x in terms of z:

$x + \dfrac{13}{4} - 2z = 2$

$\qquad x = 2z - \dfrac{5}{4}$

With $z = t$, the complete solution to the

system is $\left\{\left(2t - \dfrac{5}{4}, \dfrac{13}{4}, t\right)\right\}$.

21. $\begin{bmatrix} 1 & 1 & -1 & 1 & | & -2 \\ 2 & -1 & 2 & -1 & | & 7 \\ -1 & 2 & 1 & 2 & | & -1 \end{bmatrix} \begin{array}{l} -2R_1 + R_2 \\ 1R_1 + R_3 \end{array}$

$\begin{bmatrix} 1 & 1 & -1 & 1 & | & -2 \\ 0 & -3 & 4 & -3 & | & 11 \\ 0 & 3 & 0 & 3 & | & -3 \end{bmatrix} R_2 \leftrightarrow R_3$

$\begin{bmatrix} 1 & 1 & -1 & 1 & | & -2 \\ 0 & 3 & 0 & 3 & | & -3 \\ 0 & -3 & 4 & -3 & | & 11 \end{bmatrix} \frac{1}{3}R_2$

$\begin{bmatrix} 1 & 1 & -1 & 1 & | & -2 \\ 0 & 1 & 0 & 1 & | & -1 \\ 0 & -3 & 4 & -3 & | & 11 \end{bmatrix} 3R_2 + R_3$

$\begin{bmatrix} 1 & 1 & -1 & 1 & | & -2 \\ 0 & 1 & 0 & 1 & | & -1 \\ 0 & 0 & 4 & 0 & | & 8 \end{bmatrix} \frac{1}{4}R_3$

$\begin{bmatrix} 1 & 1 & -1 & 1 & | & -2 \\ 0 & 1 & 0 & 1 & | & -1 \\ 0 & 0 & 1 & 0 & | & 2 \end{bmatrix}$

The system $\begin{aligned} x+y-z+w&=-2 \\ y+w&=-1 \\ z&=2 \end{aligned}$ has no unique

solution. Express x and y in terms of w:

$y = -w - 1$

$x + (-w - 1) - 2 + w = -2$

$x - w + 1 - 2 + w = -2$

$x = 1$

With $w = t$, the complete solution to the system is $\{(1, -t - 1, 2, t)\}$.

23. $\begin{bmatrix} 1 & 2 & 3 & -1 & | & 7 \\ 0 & 2 & -3 & 1 & | & 4 \\ 1 & -4 & 1 & 0 & | & 3 \end{bmatrix} -1R_1 + R_3$

$\begin{bmatrix} 1 & 2 & 3 & -1 & | & 7 \\ 0 & 2 & -3 & 1 & | & 4 \\ 0 & -6 & -2 & 1 & | & -4 \end{bmatrix} \frac{1}{2}R_2$

$\begin{bmatrix} 1 & 2 & 3 & -1 & | & 7 \\ 0 & 1 & -\frac{3}{2} & \frac{1}{2} & | & 2 \\ 0 & -6 & -2 & 1 & | & -4 \end{bmatrix} 6R_2 + R_3$

$\begin{bmatrix} 1 & 2 & 3 & -1 & | & 7 \\ 0 & 1 & -\frac{3}{2} & \frac{1}{2} & | & 2 \\ 0 & 0 & -11 & 4 & | & 8 \end{bmatrix} -\frac{1}{11}R_3$

$\begin{bmatrix} 1 & 2 & 3 & -1 & | & 7 \\ 0 & 1 & -\frac{3}{2} & \frac{1}{2} & | & 2 \\ 0 & 0 & 1 & -\frac{4}{11} & | & -\frac{8}{11} \end{bmatrix}$

The system $\begin{aligned} x+2y+3z-w&=7 \\ y-\frac{3}{2}z+\frac{1}{2}w&=2 \\ z-\frac{4}{11}w&=-\frac{8}{11} \end{aligned}$ has no

unique solution. Express x, y, and z in terms of w:

$z = \frac{4}{11}w - \frac{8}{11}$

$y - \frac{3}{2}\left(\frac{4}{11}w - \frac{8}{11}\right) + \frac{1}{2}w = 2$

$y - \frac{6}{11}w + \frac{12}{11} + \frac{1}{2}w = 2$

$y - \frac{1}{22}w + \frac{12}{11} = 2$

$y = \frac{1}{22}w + \frac{10}{11}$

$x + 2\left(\frac{1}{22}w + \frac{10}{11}\right) + 3\left(\frac{4}{11}w - \frac{8}{11}\right) - w = 7$

$x + \frac{1}{11}w + \frac{20}{11} + \frac{12}{11}w - \frac{24}{11} - w = 7$

$x + \frac{2}{11}w - \frac{4}{11} = 7$

$x = -\frac{2}{11}w + \frac{81}{11}$

With $w = t$, the complete solution to the system is

$$\left\{\left(-\frac{2}{11}t + \frac{81}{11}, \frac{1}{22}t + \frac{10}{11}, \frac{4}{11}t - \frac{8}{11}, t\right)\right\}.$$

25. $z + 12 = x + 6$

27. $\begin{aligned} x - y &= 4 \\ x - z &= 6 \\ y - z &= 2 \end{aligned}$

$\begin{bmatrix} 1 & -1 & 0 & | & 4 \\ 1 & 0 & -1 & | & 6 \\ 0 & 1 & -1 & | & 2 \end{bmatrix} -1R_1 + R_2$

$\begin{bmatrix} 1 & -1 & 0 & | & 4 \\ 0 & -1 & 1 & | & -2 \\ 0 & 1 & -1 & | & 2 \end{bmatrix} -1R_2$

$\begin{bmatrix} 1 & -1 & 0 & | & 4 \\ 0 & 1 & -1 & | & 2 \\ 0 & 1 & -1 & | & 2 \end{bmatrix} \begin{aligned} -1R_2 + R_3 \\ 1R_2 + R_1 \end{aligned}$

$\begin{bmatrix} 1 & 0 & -1 & | & 6 \\ 0 & 1 & -1 & | & 2 \\ 0 & 0 & 0 & | & 0 \end{bmatrix}$

The system has no unique solution. Express x and y in terms of z:

$x - z = 6$

$y - z = 2$

$x = z + 6$

$y = z + 2$

With $z = t$, the complete solution to the system is $\{(t + 6, t + 2, t)\}$.

29. **a.** From left to right along Palm Drive, then along Sunset Drive, we get the equations

$$x + w = 200 + 180 = 380;$$
$$x + y = 400 + 200 = 600;$$
$$w + 70 = z + 20 \text{ or } z - w = 50;$$
$$z + 200 = y + 30 \text{ or } y - z = 170.$$

The system is

$x + w = 380$

$x + y = 600$

$z - w = 50$

$y - z = 170$

b.
$$\begin{bmatrix} 1 & 0 & 0 & 1 & | & 380 \\ 0 & 1 & 0 & -1 & | & 220 \\ 0 & 0 & 1 & -1 & | & 50 \\ 0 & 1 & -1 & 0 & | & 170 \end{bmatrix} -1R_2 + R_4$$

$$\begin{bmatrix} 1 & 0 & 0 & 1 & | & 380 \\ 0 & 1 & 0 & -1 & | & 220 \\ 0 & 0 & 1 & -1 & | & 50 \\ 0 & 0 & -1 & 1 & | & -50 \end{bmatrix} 1R_3 + R_4$$

$$\begin{bmatrix} 1 & 0 & 0 & 1 & | & 380 \\ 0 & 1 & 0 & -1 & | & 220 \\ 0 & 0 & 1 & -1 & | & 50 \\ 0 & 0 & 0 & 0 & | & 0 \end{bmatrix}$$

$$x + w = 380$$

The system $y - w = 220$ has no unique

$$z - w = 50$$

solution. Express x and y and z in terms of w:

$x = 380 - w$

$y = 220 + w$

$z = 50 + w$

With $w = t$, the complete solution to the system is $\{(380 - t, 220 + t, 50 + t, t)\}$.

c. Letting $w = 50$, the solution is $x = 330$, $y = 270$, $z = 100$, $w = 50$.

31. Let x = the amount of Food 1, y = the amount of Food 2, and z = the amount of Food 3, in ounces. The amount of vitamin A is $20x + 30y + 10z$; the amount of iron is $20x + 10y + 10z$; the amount of calcium is $10x + 10y + 30z$.

a. Not having Food 1 means that all x terms are left out. The vitamin A requirement can then be represented by $30y + 10z = 220$; the iron requirement is $10y + 10z = 180$; the calcium requirement is $10y + 30z = 340$. The corresponding system is

$30y + 10z = 220$

$10y + 10z = 180$

$10y + 30z = 340$.

Dividing all of the numbers by 10, the matrix for this system is

$$\begin{bmatrix} 3 & 1 & | & 22 \\ 1 & 1 & | & 18 \\ 1 & 3 & | & 34 \end{bmatrix} R_1 \leftrightarrow R_2$$

$$\begin{bmatrix} 1 & 1 & | & 18 \\ 3 & 1 & | & 22 \\ 1 & 3 & | & 34 \end{bmatrix} \begin{matrix} -3R_1 + R_2 \\ -1R_1 + R_3 \end{matrix}$$

$$\begin{bmatrix} 1 & 1 & | & 18 \\ 0 & -2 & | & -32 \\ 0 & 2 & | & 16 \end{bmatrix} 1R_2 + R_3$$

$$\begin{bmatrix} 1 & 1 & | & 18 \\ 0 & -2 & | & -32 \\ 0 & 0 & | & -16 \end{bmatrix}.$$

From the last row, we see that the system has no solution, so there is no way to satisfy these dietary requirements with no Food 1 available.

b. With Food 1 available, and dropping the vitamin A requirement, the system is

$20x + 10y + 10z = 180$

$10x + 10y + 30z = 340$.

Dividing all of the numbers by 10, the matrix for this system is

$$\begin{bmatrix} 2 & 1 & 1 & | & 18 \\ 1 & 1 & 3 & | & 34 \end{bmatrix} R_1 \leftrightarrow R_2$$

$$\begin{bmatrix} 1 & 1 & 3 & | & 34 \\ 2 & 1 & 1 & | & 18 \end{bmatrix} -2R_1 + R_2$$

$$\begin{bmatrix} 1 & 1 & 3 & | & 34 \\ 0 & -1 & -5 & | & -50 \end{bmatrix} -1R_2$$

$$\begin{bmatrix} 1 & 1 & 3 & | & 34 \\ 0 & 1 & 5 & | & 50 \end{bmatrix}.$$

The system $\begin{array}{l} x + y + 3z = 34 \\ y + 5z = 50 \end{array}$ has no

unique solution. Express x and y in terms of z:
$y = -5z + 50$
$x + (-5z + 50) + 3z = 34$
$\quad x - 2z + 50 = 34$
$\qquad\qquad x = 2z - 16$
Now we can choose a value for z, i.e., an amount of Food 3, and find the corresponding values of x and y. Note that negative amounts of food are not realistic, so $z \geq 0$, $y = -5z + 50 \geq 0$, and $x - 2z - 16 \geq 0$. These conditions are equivalent to $8 \leq z \leq 10$.
Using $z = 8$ and $z = 10$, two possibilities are 0 ounces of Food 1, 10 ounces of Food 2, and 8 ounces of Food 3 or 4 ounces of Food 1, 0 ounces of Food 2, and 10 ounces of Food 3. (Other answers are possible.)

33.–35. Answers may vary.

37. $\begin{bmatrix} 1 & 3 & 1 & | & a^2 \\ 2 & 5 & 2a & | & 0 \\ 1 & 1 & a^2 & | & -9 \end{bmatrix} \begin{array}{l} -2R_1 + R_2 \\ -1R_1 + R_3 \end{array}$

$$\begin{bmatrix} 1 & 3 & 1 & | & a^2 \\ 0 & -1 & 2a-2 & | & -2a^2 \\ 0 & -2 & a^2-1 & | & -9-a^2 \end{bmatrix} -1R_2$$

$$\begin{bmatrix} 1 & 3 & 1 & | & a^2 \\ 0 & 1 & 2-2a & | & 2a^2 \\ 0 & -2 & a^2-1 & | & -9-a^2 \end{bmatrix} 2R_2 + R_3$$

$$\begin{bmatrix} 1 & 3 & 1 & | & a^2 \\ 0 & 1 & 2-2a & | & 2a^2 \\ 0 & 0 & a^2-4a+3 & | & -9+3a^2 \end{bmatrix}$$

The system will be inconsistent when
$a^2 - 4a + 3 = 0$ but $-9 + 3a^2 \neq 0$.
$a^2 - 4a + 3 = (a-1)(a-3) = 0$ when $a = 1$ or
$a = 3$. $-9 + 3a^2 = 0$ when $a = \pm\sqrt{3}$.
Thus, the system is inconsistent when $a = 1$ or $a = 3$.

Section 9.3

Check Point Exercises

1. a. The matrix $A = \begin{bmatrix} 5 & -2 \\ -3 & \pi \\ 1 & 6 \end{bmatrix}$ has 3 rows

and 2 columns, so it is of order 3×2.

   b. The element a_{12} is in the first row and second column. Thus, $a_{12} = -2$. The element a_{31} is in the third row and first column. Thus, $a_{31} = 1$.

2. a. $\begin{bmatrix} -4 & 3 \\ 7 & -6 \end{bmatrix} + \begin{bmatrix} 6 & -3 \\ 2 & -4 \end{bmatrix}$

$= \begin{bmatrix} -4+6 & 3+(-3) \\ 7+2 & -6+(-4) \end{bmatrix} = \begin{bmatrix} 2 & 0 \\ 9 & -10 \end{bmatrix}$

   b. $\begin{bmatrix} 5 & 4 \\ -3 & 7 \\ 0 & 1 \end{bmatrix} - \begin{bmatrix} -4 & 8 \\ 6 & 0 \\ -5 & 3 \end{bmatrix}$

$= \begin{bmatrix} 5-(-4) & 4-8 \\ -3-6 & 7-0 \\ 0-(-5) & 1-3 \end{bmatrix}$

$= \begin{bmatrix} 9 & -4 \\ -9 & 7 \\ 5 & -2 \end{bmatrix}$

3. a. $-6B = -6\begin{bmatrix} -1 & -2 \\ 8 & 5 \end{bmatrix}$

$= \begin{bmatrix} -6(-1) & -6(-2) \\ -6(8) & -6(5) \end{bmatrix}$

$= \begin{bmatrix} -6 & 12 \\ -48 & -30 \end{bmatrix}$

b.

$3A + 2B = \begin{bmatrix} -4 & 1 \\ 3 & 0 \end{bmatrix} + 2\begin{bmatrix} -1 & -2 \\ 8 & 5 \end{bmatrix}$

$= \begin{bmatrix} 3(-4) & 3(1) \\ 3(3) & 3(0) \end{bmatrix} + \begin{bmatrix} 2(-1) & 2(-2) \\ 2(8) & 2(5) \end{bmatrix}$

$= \begin{bmatrix} -12 & 3 \\ 9 & 0 \end{bmatrix} + \begin{bmatrix} -2 & -4 \\ 16 & 10 \end{bmatrix}$

$= \begin{bmatrix} -12+(-2) & 3+(-4) \\ 9+16 & 0+10 \end{bmatrix}$

$= \begin{bmatrix} -14 & -1 \\ 25 & 10 \end{bmatrix}$

4. Given $A = \begin{bmatrix} 1 & 3 \\ 2 & 5 \end{bmatrix}$ and $B = \begin{bmatrix} 4 & 6 \\ 1 & 0 \end{bmatrix}$,

$AB = \begin{bmatrix} 1 & 3 \\ 2 & 5 \end{bmatrix}\begin{bmatrix} 4 & 6 \\ 1 & 0 \end{bmatrix}$

$= \begin{bmatrix} 1(4)+3(1) & 1(6)+3(0) \\ 2(4)+5(1) & 2(6)+5(0) \end{bmatrix}$

$= \begin{bmatrix} 7 & 6 \\ 13 & 12 \end{bmatrix}.$

5. If $A = \begin{bmatrix} 2 & 0 & 4 \end{bmatrix}$ and $B = \begin{bmatrix} 1 \\ 3 \\ 7 \end{bmatrix}$, then

$AB = \begin{bmatrix} 2 & 0 & 4 \end{bmatrix}\begin{bmatrix} 1 \\ 3 \\ 7 \end{bmatrix}$

$= \begin{bmatrix} 2(1)+0(3)+4(7) \end{bmatrix}$

$= \begin{bmatrix} 2+0+28 \end{bmatrix}$

$= \begin{bmatrix} 30 \end{bmatrix}$

and $BA = \begin{bmatrix} 1 \\ 3 \\ 7 \end{bmatrix}\begin{bmatrix} 2 & 0 & 4 \end{bmatrix}$

$= \begin{bmatrix} 1(2) & 1(0) & 1(4) \\ 3(2) & 3(0) & 3(4) \\ 7(2) & 7(0) & 7(4) \end{bmatrix}$

$= \begin{bmatrix} 2 & 0 & 4 \\ 6 & 0 & 12 \\ 14 & 0 & 28 \end{bmatrix}.$

6. a.
$$\begin{bmatrix} 1 & 3 \\ 0 & 2 \end{bmatrix}\begin{bmatrix} 2 & 3 & -1 & 6 \\ 0 & 5 & 4 & 1 \end{bmatrix} = \begin{bmatrix} 1(2)+3(0) & 1(3)+3(5) & 1(-1)+3(4) & 1(6)+3(1) \\ 0(2)+2(0) & 0(3)+2(5) & 0(-1)+2(4) & 0(6)+2(1) \end{bmatrix} = \begin{bmatrix} 2 & 18 & 11 & 9 \\ 0 & 10 & 8 & 2 \end{bmatrix}$$

b.
$$\begin{bmatrix} 2 & 3 & -1 & 6 \\ 0 & 5 & 4 & 1 \end{bmatrix}\begin{bmatrix} 1 & 3 \\ 0 & 2 \end{bmatrix}$$

The number of columns in the first matrix does not equal the number of rows in the second matrix. Thus, the product of these two matrcies is undefined.

7. Because the *T* is dark gray and the background is light gray, a digital photograph of Figure 6.7 can be represented by the matrix

$$\begin{bmatrix} 2 & 2 & 2 \\ 1 & 2 & 1 \\ 1 & 2 & 1 \end{bmatrix}.$$

We can make the *T* light gray by decreasing each 2 in the above matrix to 1. We can make the background black by increasing each 1 in the matrix to 3. This is accomplished using the following matrix addition.

$$\begin{bmatrix} 2 & 2 & 2 \\ 1 & 2 & 1 \\ 1 & 2 & 1 \end{bmatrix} + \begin{bmatrix} -1 & -1 & -1 \\ 2 & -1 & 2 \\ 2 & -1 & 2 \end{bmatrix} = \begin{bmatrix} 1 & 1 & 1 \\ 3 & 1 & 3 \\ 3 & 1 & 3 \end{bmatrix}.$$

8. The gas station's total sales is represented in the first column of the product matrix

$$\begin{bmatrix} 836 & 117.40 \\ 791 & 111.80 \\ 921 & 129.70 \end{bmatrix}.$$

The gas station's total sales for Monday, Tuesday, and Wednesday is $836 + 791 + 921$ or $2548.

Exercise Set 9.3

1. a. 2×3

b. a_{32} does not exist (*A* only has 2 rows).
$a_{23} = -1$

3. a. 3×4

b. $a_{32} = \dfrac{1}{2}$; $a_{23} = -6$

5. $\begin{bmatrix} x \\ 4 \end{bmatrix} = \begin{bmatrix} 6 \\ y \end{bmatrix}$
$x = 6$
$y = 4$

7. $\begin{bmatrix} x & 2y \\ z & 9 \end{bmatrix} = \begin{bmatrix} 4 & 12 \\ 3 & 9 \end{bmatrix}$

$x = 4$

$2y = 12$

$y = 6$

$z = 3$

9. **a.** $A + B = \begin{bmatrix} 4+5 & 1+9 \\ 3+0 & 2+7 \end{bmatrix} = \begin{bmatrix} 9 & 10 \\ 3 & 9 \end{bmatrix}$

b. $A - B = \begin{bmatrix} 4-5 & 1-9 \\ 3-0 & 2-7 \end{bmatrix} = \begin{bmatrix} -1 & -8 \\ 3 & -5 \end{bmatrix}$

c. $-4A = \begin{bmatrix} -16 & -4 \\ -12 & -8 \end{bmatrix}$

d. $3A + 2B = \begin{bmatrix} 12+10 & 3+18 \\ 9+0 & 6+14 \end{bmatrix} = \begin{bmatrix} 22 & 21 \\ 9 & 20 \end{bmatrix}$

11. **a.** $A + B = \begin{bmatrix} 1+2 & 3+(-1) \\ 3+3 & 4+(-2) \\ 5+0 & 6+1 \end{bmatrix} = \begin{bmatrix} 3 & 2 \\ 6 & 2 \\ 5 & 7 \end{bmatrix}$

b. $A - B = \begin{bmatrix} 1-2 & 3-(-1) \\ 3-3 & 4-(-2) \\ 5-0 & 6-1 \end{bmatrix} = \begin{bmatrix} -1 & 4 \\ 0 & 6 \\ 5 & 5 \end{bmatrix}$

c. $-4A = \begin{bmatrix} -4 & -12 \\ -12 & -16 \\ -20 & -24 \end{bmatrix}$

d. $3A + 2B = \begin{bmatrix} 3+4 & 9-2 \\ 9+6 & 12-4 \\ 15+0 & 18+2 \end{bmatrix} = \begin{bmatrix} 7 & 7 \\ 15 & 8 \\ 15 & 20 \end{bmatrix}$

13. **a.** $A + B = \begin{bmatrix} 2+(-5) \\ -4+3 \\ 1+(-1) \end{bmatrix} = \begin{bmatrix} -3 \\ -1 \\ 0 \end{bmatrix}$

b. $A - B = \begin{bmatrix} 2-(-5) \\ -4-3 \\ 1-(-1) \end{bmatrix} = \begin{bmatrix} 7 \\ -7 \\ 2 \end{bmatrix}$

c. $-4A = \begin{bmatrix} -8 \\ 16 \\ -4 \end{bmatrix}$

d. $3A + 2B = \begin{bmatrix} 6-10 \\ -12+6 \\ 3-2 \end{bmatrix} = \begin{bmatrix} -4 \\ -6 \\ 1 \end{bmatrix}$

15. **a.** $A + B = \begin{bmatrix} 2+6 & -10+10 & -2+(-2) \\ 14+0 & 12+(-12) & 10+(-4) \\ 4+(-5) & -2+2 & 2+(-2) \end{bmatrix}$

$= \begin{bmatrix} 8 & 0 & -4 \\ 14 & 0 & 6 \\ -1 & 0 & 0 \end{bmatrix}$

b. $A - B = \begin{bmatrix} 2-6 & -10-10 & -2-(-2) \\ 14-0 & 12-(-12) & 10-(-4) \\ 4-(-5) & -2-2 & 2-(-2) \end{bmatrix}$

$= \begin{bmatrix} -4 & -20 & 0 \\ 14 & 24 & 14 \\ 9 & -4 & 4 \end{bmatrix}$

c. $-4A = \begin{bmatrix} -8 & 40 & 8 \\ -56 & -48 & -40 \\ -16 & 8 & -8 \end{bmatrix}$

d. $3A + 2B = \begin{bmatrix} 6+12 & -30+20 & -6-4 \\ 42+0 & 36-24 & 30-8 \\ 12-10 & -6+4 & 6-4 \end{bmatrix}$

$= \begin{bmatrix} 18 & -10 & -10 \\ 42 & 12 & 22 \\ 2 & -2 & 2 \end{bmatrix}$

17. a. $AB = \begin{bmatrix} 1 & 3 \\ 5 & 3 \end{bmatrix}\begin{bmatrix} 3 & -2 \\ -1 & 6 \end{bmatrix}$

$= \begin{bmatrix} (1)(3)+(3)(-1) & (1)(-2)+(3)(6) \\ (5)(3)+(3)(-1) & (5)(-2)+(3)(6) \end{bmatrix}$

$= \begin{bmatrix} 3-3 & -2+18 \\ 15-3 & -10+18 \end{bmatrix}$

$= \begin{bmatrix} 0 & 16 \\ 12 & 8 \end{bmatrix}$

b. $BA = \begin{bmatrix} 3 & -2 \\ -1 & 6 \end{bmatrix}\begin{bmatrix} 1 & 3 \\ 5 & 3 \end{bmatrix}$

$= \begin{bmatrix} (3)(1)+(-2)(5) & (3)(3)+(-2)(3) \\ (-1)(1)+(6)(5) & (-1)(3)+(6)(3) \end{bmatrix}$

$= \begin{bmatrix} 3-10 & 9-6 \\ -1+30 & -3+18 \end{bmatrix}$

$= \begin{bmatrix} -7 & 3 \\ 29 & 15 \end{bmatrix}$

19. a. $AB = \begin{bmatrix} 1 & 2 & 3 & 4 \end{bmatrix}\begin{bmatrix} 1 \\ 2 \\ 3 \\ 4 \end{bmatrix}$

$= [(1)(1)+(2)(2)+(3)(3)+(4)(4)]$
$= [1+4+9+16] = [30]$

b.

$BA = \begin{bmatrix} 1 \\ 2 \\ 3 \\ 4 \end{bmatrix}\begin{bmatrix} 1 & 2 & 3 & 4 \end{bmatrix}$

$= \begin{bmatrix} (1)(1) & (1)(2) & (1)(3) & (1)(4) \\ (2)(1) & (2)(2) & (2)(3) & (2)(4) \\ (3)(1) & (3)(2) & (3)(3) & (3)(4) \\ (4)(1) & (4)(2) & (4)(3) & (4)(4) \end{bmatrix}$

$= \begin{bmatrix} 1 & 2 & 3 & 4 \\ 2 & 4 & 6 & 8 \\ 3 & 6 & 9 & 12 \\ 4 & 8 & 12 & 16 \end{bmatrix}$

21. a. $AB = \begin{bmatrix} 1 & -1 & 4 \\ 4 & -1 & 3 \\ 2 & 0 & -2 \end{bmatrix} \begin{bmatrix} 1 & 1 & 0 \\ 1 & 2 & 4 \\ 1 & -1 & 3 \end{bmatrix}$

$$= \begin{bmatrix} (1)(1)+(-1)(1)+(4)(1) & (1)(1)+(-1)(2)+(4)(-1) & (1)(0)+(-1)(4)+(4)(3) \\ (4)(1)+(-1)(1)+(3)(1) & (4)(1)+(-1)(2)+(3)(-1) & (4)(0)+(-1)(4)+(3)(3) \\ (2)(1)+(0)(1)+(-2)(1) & (2)(1)+(0)(2)+(-2)(-1) & (2)(0)+(0)(4)+(-2)(3) \end{bmatrix}$$

$$= \begin{bmatrix} 1-1+4 & 1-2-4 & 0-4+12 \\ 4-1+3 & 4-2-3 & 0-4+9 \\ 2+0-2 & 2+0+2 & 0+0-6 \end{bmatrix}$$

$$= \begin{bmatrix} 4 & -5 & 8 \\ 6 & -1 & 5 \\ 0 & 4 & -6 \end{bmatrix}$$

b. $BA = \begin{bmatrix} 1 & 1 & 0 \\ 1 & 2 & 4 \\ 1 & -1 & 3 \end{bmatrix} \begin{bmatrix} 1 & -1 & 4 \\ 4 & -1 & 3 \\ 2 & 0 & -2 \end{bmatrix}$

$$= \begin{bmatrix} (1)(1)+(1)(4)+(0)(2) & (1)(-1)+(1)(-1)+(0)(0) & (1)(4)+(1)(3)+(0)(-2) \\ (1)(1)+(2)(4)+(4)(2) & (1)(-1)+(2)(-1)+(4)(0) & (1)(4)+(2)(3)+(4)(-2) \\ (1)(1)+(-1)(4)+(3)(2) & (1)(-1)+(-1)(-1)+(3)(0) & (1)(4)+(-1)(3)+(3)(-2) \end{bmatrix}$$

$$= \begin{bmatrix} 1+4+0 & -1-1+0 & 4+3+0 \\ 1+8+8 & -1-2+0 & 4+6-8 \\ 1-4+6 & -1+1+0 & 4-3-6 \end{bmatrix}$$

$$= \begin{bmatrix} 5 & -2 & 7 \\ 17 & -3 & 2 \\ 3 & 0 & -5 \end{bmatrix}$$

23. a. $AB = \begin{bmatrix} 4 & 2 \\ 6 & 1 \\ 3 & 5 \end{bmatrix} \begin{bmatrix} 2 & 3 & 4 \\ -1 & -2 & 0 \end{bmatrix}$

$$= \begin{bmatrix} (4)(2)+(2)(-1) & (4)(3)+(2)(-2) & (4)(4)+(2)(0) \\ (6)(2)+(1)(-1) & (6)(3)+(1)(-2) & (6)(4)+(1)(0) \\ (3)(2)+(5)(-1) & (3)(3)+(5)(-2) & (3)(4)+(5)(0) \end{bmatrix}$$

$$= \begin{bmatrix} 8-2 & 12-4 & 16+0 \\ 12-1 & 18-2 & 24+0 \\ 6-5 & 9-10 & 12+0 \end{bmatrix}$$

$$= \begin{bmatrix} 6 & 8 & 16 \\ 11 & 16 & 24 \\ 1 & -1 & 12 \end{bmatrix}$$

b. $BA = \begin{bmatrix} 2 & 3 & 4 \\ -1 & -2 & 0 \end{bmatrix} \begin{bmatrix} 4 & 2 \\ 6 & 1 \\ 3 & 5 \end{bmatrix} = \begin{bmatrix} (2)(4)+(3)(6)+(4)(3) & (2)(2)+(3)(1)+(4)(5) \\ (-1)(4)+(-2)(6)+(0)(3) & (-1)(2)+(-2)(1)+(0)(5) \end{bmatrix}$

$$= \begin{bmatrix} 8+18+12 & 4+3+20 \\ -4-12+0 & -2-2+0 \end{bmatrix}$$

$$= \begin{bmatrix} 38 & 27 \\ -16 & -4 \end{bmatrix}$$

25. a. $AB = \begin{bmatrix} 2 & -3 & 1 & -1 \\ 1 & 1 & -2 & 1 \end{bmatrix} \begin{bmatrix} 1 & 2 \\ -1 & 1 \\ 5 & 4 \\ 10 & 5 \end{bmatrix}$

$$= \begin{bmatrix} (2)(1)+(-3)(-1)+(1)(5)+(-1)(10) & (2)(2)+(-3)(1)+(1)(4)+(-1)(5) \\ (1)(1)+(1)(-1)+(-2)(5)+(1)(10) & (1)(2)+(1)(1)+(-2)(4)+(1)(5) \end{bmatrix}$$

$$= \begin{bmatrix} 2+3+5-10 & 4-3+4-5 \\ 1-1-10+10 & 2+1-8+5 \end{bmatrix}$$

$$= \begin{bmatrix} 0 & 0 \\ 0 & 0 \end{bmatrix}$$

b. $BA = \begin{bmatrix} 1 & 2 \\ -1 & 1 \\ 5 & 4 \\ 10 & 5 \end{bmatrix} \begin{bmatrix} 2 & -3 & 1 & -1 \\ 1 & 1 & -2 & 1 \end{bmatrix}$

$$= \begin{bmatrix} (1)(2)+(2)(1) & (1)(-3)+(2)(1) & (1)(1)+(2)(-2) & (1)(-1)+(2)(1) \\ (-1)(2)+(1)(1) & (-1)(-3)+(1)(1) & (-1)(1)+(1)(-2) & (-1)(-1)+(1)(1) \\ (5)(2)+(4)(1) & (5)(-3)+(4)(1) & (5)(1)+(4)(-2) & (5)(-1)+(4)(1) \\ (10)(2)+(5)(1) & (10)(-3)+(5)(1) & (10)(1)+(5)(-2) & (10)(-1)+(5)(1) \end{bmatrix}$$

$$= \begin{bmatrix} 2+2 & -3+2 & 1-4 & -1+2 \\ -2+1 & 3+1 & -1-2 & 1+1 \\ 10+4 & -15+4 & 5-8 & -5+4 \\ 20+5 & -30+5 & 10-10 & -10+5 \end{bmatrix}$$

$$= \begin{bmatrix} 4 & -1 & -3 & 1 \\ -1 & 4 & -3 & 2 \\ 14 & -11 & -3 & -1 \\ 25 & -25 & 0 & -5 \end{bmatrix}$$

27. $4B - 3C = \begin{bmatrix} 20 & 4 \\ -8 & -8 \end{bmatrix} - \begin{bmatrix} 3 & -3 \\ -3 & 3 \end{bmatrix} = \begin{bmatrix} 20-3 & 4-(-3) \\ -8-(-3) & -8-3 \end{bmatrix} = \begin{bmatrix} 17 & 7 \\ -5 & -11 \end{bmatrix}$

29. $BC + CB = \begin{bmatrix} 5-1 & -5+1 \\ -2+2 & 2-2 \end{bmatrix} + \begin{bmatrix} 5+2 & 1+2 \\ -5-2 & -1-2 \end{bmatrix} = \begin{bmatrix} 4 & -4 \\ 0 & 0 \end{bmatrix} + \begin{bmatrix} 7 & 3 \\ -7 & -3 \end{bmatrix} = \begin{bmatrix} 11 & -1 \\ -7 & -3 \end{bmatrix}$

31. $A - C$ is not defined because A is 3×2 and C is 2×2.

33. $A(BC) = \begin{bmatrix} 4 & 0 \\ -3 & 5 \\ 0 & 1 \end{bmatrix} \begin{bmatrix} 5-1 & -5+1 \\ -2+2 & 2-2 \end{bmatrix} = \begin{bmatrix} 4 & 0 \\ -3 & 5 \\ 0 & 1 \end{bmatrix} \begin{bmatrix} 4 & -4 \\ 0 & 0 \end{bmatrix} = \begin{bmatrix} 16+0 & -16+0 \\ -12+0 & 12+0 \\ 0+0 & 0+0 \end{bmatrix} = \begin{bmatrix} 16 & -16 \\ -12 & 12 \\ 0 & 0 \end{bmatrix}$

35. $\begin{bmatrix} 1 & 3 & 1 \\ 3 & 3 & 3 \\ 1 & 3 & 1 \end{bmatrix} + \begin{bmatrix} -1 & -1 & -1 \\ -1 & -1 & -1 \\ -1 & -1 & -1 \end{bmatrix} = \begin{bmatrix} 0 & 2 & 0 \\ 2 & 2 & 2 \\ 0 & 2 & 0 \end{bmatrix}$

37. $\begin{bmatrix} 1 & 3 & 1 \\ 3 & 3 & 3 \\ 1 & 3 & 1 \end{bmatrix} + \begin{bmatrix} 1 & -2 & 1 \\ -2 & -2 & -2 \\ 1 & -2 & 1 \end{bmatrix} = \begin{bmatrix} 2 & 1 & 2 \\ 1 & 1 & 1 \\ 2 & 1 & 2 \end{bmatrix}$

39. a. $A = \begin{bmatrix} 0 & 3 & 0 \\ 0 & 3 & 0 \\ 0 & 3 & 0 \end{bmatrix}$

   b. $B = \begin{bmatrix} 1 & 0 & 1 \\ 1 & 0 & 1 \\ 1 & 0 & 1 \end{bmatrix}$

41. a. $AB = \begin{bmatrix} 0.15 & 0.25 & 0.20 & 0.10 \\ 0.35 & 0.40 & 0.35 & 0.70 \\ 0.50 & 0.35 & 0.45 & 0.20 \end{bmatrix} \begin{bmatrix} 820 & 640 \\ 950 & 1020 \\ 680 & 720 \\ 930 & 910 \end{bmatrix} = \begin{bmatrix} 589.5 & 586 \\ 1556 & 1521 \\ 1234.5 & 1183 \end{bmatrix}$

   b. AB represents the distribution of students by gender and state of health. On this campus, there are 1521 females who are sick.

   c. There are 1235 male carriers.

43. a. System 1: The midterm and final both count for 50% of the course grade. System 2: The midterm counts for 30% of the course grade and the final counts for 70%

b. $AB = \begin{bmatrix} 84 & 87.2 \\ 79 & 81 \\ 90 & 88.4 \\ 73 & 68.6 \\ 69 & 73.4 \end{bmatrix}$

System 1 grades are listed first (if different).
Student 1: B; Student 2: C or B;
Student 3: A or B; Student 4: C or D;
Student 5: D or C

45.–57. Answers may vary.

59. $AB = \begin{bmatrix} 0 & -1 \\ 1 & 0 \end{bmatrix}\begin{bmatrix} 1 & 0 \\ 0 & -1 \end{bmatrix} = \begin{bmatrix} 0 & 1 \\ 1 & 0 \end{bmatrix}$

$-BA = \begin{bmatrix} 1 & 0 \\ 0 & -1 \end{bmatrix}\begin{bmatrix} 0 & -1 \\ 1 & 0 \end{bmatrix} = -\begin{bmatrix} 0 & -1 \\ -1 & 0 \end{bmatrix} = \begin{bmatrix} 0 & 1 \\ 1 & 0 \end{bmatrix}$

$AB = -BA$ so they are anticommutative.

Section 9.4

Check Point Exercises

1. We must show that: $AB = I_2 = \begin{bmatrix} 1 & 0 \\ 0 & 1 \end{bmatrix}$, and

$BA = I_2 = \begin{bmatrix} 1 & 0 \\ 0 & 1 \end{bmatrix}$.

$AB = \begin{bmatrix} 2 & 1 \\ 1 & 1 \end{bmatrix}\begin{bmatrix} 1 & -1 \\ -1 & 2 \end{bmatrix}$

$= \begin{bmatrix} 2(1) + 1(-1) & 2(-1) + 1(2) \\ 1(1) + 1(-1) & 1(-1) + 1(2) \end{bmatrix}$

$= \begin{bmatrix} 1 & 0 \\ 0 & 1 \end{bmatrix}$

$BA = \begin{bmatrix} 1 & -1 \\ -1 & 2 \end{bmatrix}\begin{bmatrix} 2 & 1 \\ 1 & 1 \end{bmatrix}$

$= \begin{bmatrix} 1(2) + -1(1) & 1(1) + -1(1) \\ -1(2) + 2(1) & -1(1) + 2(1) \end{bmatrix}$

$= \begin{bmatrix} 1 & 0 \\ 0 & 1 \end{bmatrix}$

Both products (AB and BA) give the multiplicative identity matrix, I_2. Thus, B is the mulpilicative inverse of A.

2. Let us denote the multiplicative inverse of A by $A^{-1} = \begin{bmatrix} x & y \\ z & w \end{bmatrix}$. Because A is a 2×2 matrix, we use the equation $AA^{-1} = I_2$ to find values for x, y, z and w.

$\begin{bmatrix} 5 & 7 \\ 2 & 3 \end{bmatrix}\begin{bmatrix} x & y \\ z & w \end{bmatrix} = \begin{bmatrix} 1 & 0 \\ 0 & 1 \end{bmatrix}$

$\begin{bmatrix} 5x + 7z & 5y + 7w \\ 2x + 3z & 2y + 3w \end{bmatrix} = \begin{bmatrix} 1 & 0 \\ 0 & 1 \end{bmatrix}$

$5x + 7z = 1$ and $5y + 7w = 0$

$2x + 3z = 0 \qquad 2y + 3w = 1$

Each of these systems can be solved using the addition method.
Multiply by -2:
$5x + 7z = 1 \rightarrow -10x - 14z = -2$
Multiply by 5:
$\underline{2x + 3z = 0 \rightarrow 10x + 15z = 0}$
$z = -2$
Use back substitution: $x = 3$
Multiply by -2:
$5y + 7w = 0 \rightarrow -10y - 14w = 0$
Multiply by 5:
$\underline{2y + 3w = 1 \rightarrow 10y + 15w = 5}$
$w = 5$
Use back substitution: $y = -7$
Using these values, we have
$A^{-1} = \begin{bmatrix} x & y \\ z & w \end{bmatrix} = \begin{bmatrix} 3 & -7 \\ -2 & 5 \end{bmatrix}.$

3. $A^{-1} = \dfrac{1}{ad-bc}\begin{bmatrix} d & -b \\ -c & a \end{bmatrix}$

$= \dfrac{1}{3(1)-(-2)(-1)}\begin{bmatrix} 1 & -(-2) \\ -(-1) & 3 \end{bmatrix}$

$= \dfrac{1}{3-2}\begin{bmatrix} 1 & 2 \\ 1 & 3 \end{bmatrix}$

$= \dfrac{1}{1}\begin{bmatrix} 1 & 2 \\ 1 & 3 \end{bmatrix}$

$= \begin{bmatrix} 1 & 2 \\ 1 & 3 \end{bmatrix}$

4. The augmented matrix $\begin{bmatrix} A \mid I_3 \end{bmatrix}$ is

$\left[\begin{array}{ccc|ccc} 1 & 0 & 2 & 1 & 0 & 0 \\ -1 & 2 & 3 & 0 & 1 & 0 \\ 1 & -1 & 0 & 0 & 0 & 1 \end{array}\right].$

Perform row transformations on $\begin{bmatrix} A \mid I_3 \end{bmatrix}$ to obtain a matrix of the form $\begin{bmatrix} I_3 \mid B \end{bmatrix}$.

$\left[\begin{array}{ccc|ccc} 1 & 0 & 2 & 1 & 0 & 0 \\ 1 & 2 & 3 & 0 & 1 & 0 \\ 1 & -1 & 0 & 0 & 0 & 1 \end{array}\right] 1R_1 + R_2$

$= \left[\begin{array}{ccc|ccc} 1 & 0 & 2 & 1 & 0 & 0 \\ 0 & 2 & 5 & 1 & 1 & 0 \\ 1 & -1 & 0 & 0 & 0 & 1 \end{array}\right] -1R_1 + R_3$

$= \left[\begin{array}{ccc|ccc} 1 & 0 & 2 & 1 & 0 & 0 \\ 0 & 2 & 5 & 1 & 1 & 0 \\ 0 & -1 & -2 & -1 & 0 & 1 \end{array}\right] \dfrac{1}{2}R_2$

$= \left[\begin{array}{ccc|ccc} 1 & 0 & 2 & 1 & 0 & 0 \\ 0 & 1 & \frac{5}{2} & \frac{1}{2} & \frac{1}{2} & 0 \\ 0 & -1 & -2 & -1 & 0 & 1 \end{array}\right] R_2 + R_3$

$= \left[\begin{array}{ccc|ccc} 1 & 0 & 2 & 1 & 0 & 0 \\ 0 & 1 & \frac{5}{2} & \frac{1}{2} & \frac{1}{2} & 0 \\ 0 & 0 & \frac{1}{2} & -\frac{1}{2} & \frac{1}{2} & 1 \end{array}\right] 2R_3$

$= \left[\begin{array}{ccc|ccc} 1 & 0 & 2 & 1 & 0 & 0 \\ 0 & 1 & \frac{5}{2} & \frac{1}{2} & \frac{1}{2} & 0 \\ 0 & 0 & 1 & -1 & 1 & 2 \end{array}\right] \begin{array}{l} -2R_3 + R_1 \\ -\frac{5}{2}R_3 + R_2 \end{array}$

$= \left[\begin{array}{ccc|ccc} 1 & 0 & 0 & 3 & -2 & -4 \\ 0 & 1 & 0 & 3 & -2 & -5 \\ 0 & 0 & 1 & 1 & 1 & 2 \end{array}\right]$

Thus, the multiplicative inverse of A is

$A^{-1} = \begin{bmatrix} 3 & -2 & -4 \\ 3 & -2 & -5 \\ -1 & 1 & 2 \end{bmatrix}.$

5. The linear system can be written as $AX = B$.

$\begin{bmatrix} 1 & 0 & 2 \\ -1 & 2 & 3 \\ 1 & -1 & 0 \end{bmatrix}\begin{bmatrix} x \\ y \\ z \end{bmatrix} = \begin{bmatrix} 6 \\ -5 \\ 6 \end{bmatrix}.$

$X = A^{-1}B = \begin{bmatrix} 3 & -2 & -4 \\ 3 & -2 & -5 \\ -1 & 1 & 2 \end{bmatrix}\begin{bmatrix} 6 \\ -5 \\ 6 \end{bmatrix}$

$= \begin{bmatrix} 3(6) + -2(-5) + -4(6) \\ 3(6) + -2(-5) + -5(6) \\ -1(6) + 1(-5) + 2(6) \end{bmatrix}$

$= \begin{bmatrix} 18 + 10 - 24 \\ 18 + 10 - 30 \\ -6 - 5 + 12 \end{bmatrix} = \begin{bmatrix} 4 \\ -2 \\ 1 \end{bmatrix}$

Thus, $x = 4$, $y = -2$, and $z = 1$. The solution set is $\{(4, -2, 1)\}$.

6. The numerical representation of the word BASE is 2, 1, 19, 5. The 2×2 matrix formed is $\begin{bmatrix} 2 & 19 \\ 1 & 5 \end{bmatrix}$.

$\begin{bmatrix} -2 & -3 \\ 3 & 4 \end{bmatrix}\begin{bmatrix} 2 & 19 \\ 1 & 5 \end{bmatrix}$

$= \begin{bmatrix} -2(2) + -3(1) & -2(19) + -3(5) \\ 3(2) + 4(1) & 3(19) + 4(5) \end{bmatrix}$

$= \begin{bmatrix} -4 - 3 & -38 - 15 \\ 6 + 4 & 57 + 20 \end{bmatrix} = \begin{bmatrix} -7 & -53 \\ 10 & 77 \end{bmatrix}$

The encoded message is $-7, 10, -53, 77$.

7. Use the multiplicative inverse of the coding matrix. It is $\begin{bmatrix} 4 & 3 \\ -3 & -2 \end{bmatrix}$.

$$\begin{bmatrix} 4 & 3 \\ -3 & -2 \end{bmatrix} \begin{bmatrix} -7 & -53 \\ 10 & 77 \end{bmatrix}$$

$$= \begin{bmatrix} 4(-7)+3(10) & 4(-53)+3(77) \\ -3(-7)+-2(10) & -3(-53)+-2(77) \end{bmatrix} = \begin{bmatrix} -28+30 & -212+231 \\ 21-20 & 159-154 \end{bmatrix} = \begin{bmatrix} 2 & 19 \\ 1 & 5 \end{bmatrix}$$

The numbers are 2, 1, 19, and 5. Using letters, the decoded message is BASE.

Exercise Set 9.4

1. $A = \begin{bmatrix} 4 & -3 \\ -5 & 4 \end{bmatrix} \quad B = \begin{bmatrix} 4 & 3 \\ 5 & 4 \end{bmatrix}$

$$AB = \begin{bmatrix} 16-15 & 12-12 \\ -20+20 & -15+16 \end{bmatrix} = \begin{bmatrix} 1 & 0 \\ 0 & 1 \end{bmatrix}$$

$$BA = \begin{bmatrix} 16-15 & -12+12 \\ 20-20 & -15+16 \end{bmatrix} = \begin{bmatrix} 1 & 0 \\ 0 & 1 \end{bmatrix}$$

Since $AB = I_2 \ BA = I_2, \ B = A^{-1}$.

3. $AB = \begin{bmatrix} 8+0 & -16+0 \\ -2+0 & 4+3 \end{bmatrix} = \begin{bmatrix} 8 & -16 \\ -2 & 7 \end{bmatrix}$

$$BA = \begin{bmatrix} 8+4 & 0+12 \\ 0+1 & 0+3 \end{bmatrix} = \begin{bmatrix} 12 & 12 \\ 1 & 3 \end{bmatrix}$$

If B is the multiplicative inverse of A, both products (AB and BA) will be the multiplicative identity matrix, I_2. Therefore, B is not the multiplicative inverse of A. That is, $B \neq A^{-1}$.

5. $AB = \begin{bmatrix} -2+3 & -4+4 \\ \frac{3}{2}-\frac{3}{2} & 3-2 \end{bmatrix} = \begin{bmatrix} 1 & 0 \\ 0 & 1 \end{bmatrix}$

$$BA = \begin{bmatrix} -2+3 & 1-1 \\ -6+6 & 3-2 \end{bmatrix} = \begin{bmatrix} 1 & 0 \\ 0 & 1 \end{bmatrix}$$

Since $AB = I_2$ and $BA = I_2, \ B = A^{-1}$.

7. $A = \begin{bmatrix} 0 & 1 & 0 \\ 0 & 0 & 1 \\ 1 & 0 & 0 \end{bmatrix}$ $B = \begin{bmatrix} 0 & 0 & 1 \\ 1 & 0 & 0 \\ 0 & 1 & 0 \end{bmatrix}$

$AB = \begin{bmatrix} 0+1+0 & 0+0+0 & 0+0+0 \\ 0+0+0 & 0+0+1 & 0+0+0 \\ 0+0+0 & 0+0+0 & 1+0+0 \end{bmatrix} = \begin{bmatrix} 1 & 0 & 0 \\ 0 & 1 & 0 \\ 0 & 0 & 1 \end{bmatrix}$

$BA = \begin{bmatrix} 0+0+1 & 0+0+0 & 0+0+0 \\ 0+0+0 & 1+0+0 & 0+0+0 \\ 0+0+0 & 0+0+0 & 0+1+0 \end{bmatrix} = \begin{bmatrix} 1 & 0 & 0 \\ 0 & 1 & 0 \\ 0 & 0 & 1 \end{bmatrix}$

Since $AB = I_3$ and $BA = I_3$, $B = A^{-1}$.

9. $AB = \begin{bmatrix} \frac{7}{2}-1-\frac{3}{2} & -3+0+3 & \frac{1}{2}+1-\frac{3}{2} \\ \frac{7}{2}-\frac{3}{2}-2 & -3+0+4 & \frac{1}{2}+\frac{3}{2}-2 \\ \frac{7}{2}-2-\frac{3}{2} & -3+0+3 & \frac{1}{2}+2-\frac{3}{2} \end{bmatrix} = \begin{bmatrix} 1 & 0 & 0 \\ 0 & 1 & 0 \\ 0 & 0 & 1 \end{bmatrix}$

$BA = \begin{bmatrix} \frac{7}{2}-3+\frac{1}{2} & 7-9+2 & \frac{21}{2}-12+\frac{3}{2} \\ -\frac{1}{2}+0+\frac{1}{2} & -1+0+2 & -\frac{3}{2}+0+\frac{3}{2} \\ -\frac{1}{2}+1-\frac{1}{2} & -1+3-2 & -\frac{3}{2}+4-\frac{3}{2} \end{bmatrix} = \begin{bmatrix} 1 & 0 & 0 \\ 0 & 1 & 0 \\ 0 & 0 & 1 \end{bmatrix}$

Since $AB = I_3$ and $BA = I_3$, $B = A^{-1}$.

11. $AB = \begin{bmatrix} 0+0+0+1 & 0+0-2+2 & 0+0+0+0 & 0+0-2+2 \\ -1+0+0+1 & -2+0+1+2 & 0+0+0+0 & -3+0+1+2 \\ 0+0+0+0 & 0+1-1+0 & 0+1+0+0 & 0+1-1+0 \\ 1+0+0-1 & 2+0+0-2 & 0+0+0+0 & 3+0+0-2 \end{bmatrix} = \begin{bmatrix} 1 & 0 & 0 & 0 \\ 0 & 1 & 0 & 0 \\ 0 & 0 & 1 & 0 \\ 0 & 0 & 0 & 1 \end{bmatrix}$

$BA = \begin{bmatrix} 0-2+0+3 & 0+0+0+0 & -2+2+0+0 & 1+2+0-3 \\ 0-1+0+1 & 0+0+1+0 & 0+1-1+0 & 0+1+0-1 \\ 0-1+0+1 & 0+0+0+0 & 0+1+0+0 & 0+1+0-1 \\ 0-2+0+2 & 0+0+0+0 & -2+2+0+0 & 1+2+0-2 \end{bmatrix} = \begin{bmatrix} 1 & 0 & 0 & 0 \\ 0 & 1 & 0 & 0 \\ 0 & 0 & 1 & 0 \\ 0 & 0 & 0 & 1 \end{bmatrix}$

Since $AB = I_4$ and $BA = I_4$, $B = A^{-1}$.

13. $ad - bc = (2)(2) - (3)(-1) = 4 + 3 = 7$

$A^{-1} = \frac{1}{7}\begin{bmatrix} 2 & -3 \\ 1 & 2 \end{bmatrix} = \begin{bmatrix} \frac{2}{7} & -\frac{3}{7} \\ \frac{1}{7} & \frac{2}{7} \end{bmatrix}$

$AA^{-1} = \begin{bmatrix} \frac{4}{7}+\frac{3}{7} & -\frac{6}{7}+\frac{6}{7} \\ -\frac{2}{7}+\frac{2}{7} & \frac{3}{7}+\frac{4}{7} \end{bmatrix} = \begin{bmatrix} 1 & 0 \\ 0 & 1 \end{bmatrix}$

$A^{-1}A = \begin{bmatrix} \frac{4}{7}+\frac{3}{7} & \frac{6}{7}-\frac{6}{7} \\ \frac{2}{7}-\frac{2}{7} & \frac{3}{7}+\frac{4}{7} \end{bmatrix} = \begin{bmatrix} 1 & 0 \\ 0 & 1 \end{bmatrix}$

15. $ad - bc = (3)(2) - (-1)(-4) = 6 - 4 = 2$

$$A^{-1} = \frac{1}{2}\begin{bmatrix} 2 & 1 \\ 4 & 3 \end{bmatrix} = \begin{bmatrix} 1 & \frac{1}{2} \\ 2 & \frac{3}{2} \end{bmatrix}$$

$$AA^{-1} = \begin{bmatrix} 3-2 & \frac{3}{2}-\frac{3}{2} \\ -4+4 & -\frac{4}{2}+\frac{6}{2} \end{bmatrix} = \begin{bmatrix} 1 & 0 \\ 0 & 1 \end{bmatrix}$$

$$A^{-1}A = \begin{bmatrix} 3-\frac{4}{2} & -1+\frac{2}{2} \\ 6-\frac{12}{2} & -2+\frac{6}{2} \end{bmatrix} = \begin{bmatrix} 1 & 0 \\ 0 & 1 \end{bmatrix}$$

17. $ad - bc = (10)(1) - (-2)(-5) = 10 - 10 = 0$
Since division by zero is undefined, A does
not have an inverse.

For Exercises 19–23, verification that $AA^{-1} = I$
and $A^{-1}A = I$ is left to the student.

19.
$$\left[\begin{array}{ccc|ccc} 2 & 2 & -1 & 1 & 0 & 0 \\ 0 & 3 & -1 & 0 & 1 & 0 \\ -1 & -2 & 1 & 0 & 0 & 1 \end{array}\right] R_1 \leftrightarrow R_3$$

$$\left[\begin{array}{ccc|ccc} -1 & -2 & 1 & 0 & 0 & 1 \\ 0 & 3 & -1 & 0 & 1 & 0 \\ 2 & 2 & -1 & 1 & 0 & 0 \end{array}\right] -1R_1$$

$$\left[\begin{array}{ccc|ccc} 1 & 2 & 1 & 0 & 0 & 1 \\ 0 & 3 & -1 & 0 & 1 & 0 \\ 2 & 2 & -1 & 1 & 0 & 0 \end{array}\right] -2R_1 + R_3$$

$$\left[\begin{array}{ccc|ccc} 1 & 2 & -1 & 0 & 0 & -1 \\ 0 & 3 & -1 & 0 & 1 & 0 \\ 0 & -2 & 1 & 1 & 0 & 2 \end{array}\right] \frac{1}{3}R_2$$

$$\left[\begin{array}{ccc|ccc} 1 & 2 & -1 & 0 & 0 & -1 \\ 0 & 1 & -\frac{1}{3} & 0 & \frac{1}{3} & 0 \\ 0 & -2 & 1 & 1 & 0 & 2 \end{array}\right] \begin{array}{l} -2R_2 + R_1 \\ 2R_2 + R_3 \end{array}$$

$$\left[\begin{array}{ccc|ccc} 1 & 0 & -\frac{1}{3} & 0 & -\frac{2}{3} & -1 \\ 0 & 1 & -\frac{1}{3} & 0 & \frac{1}{3} & 0 \\ 0 & 0 & \frac{1}{3} & 1 & \frac{2}{3} & 2 \end{array}\right] \begin{array}{l} 1R_3 + R_1 \\ 1R_2 + R_1 \end{array}$$

$$\left[\begin{array}{ccc|ccc} 1 & 0 & 0 & 1 & 0 & 1 \\ 0 & 1 & 0 & 1 & 1 & 2 \\ 0 & 0 & \frac{1}{3} & 1 & \frac{2}{3} & 2 \end{array}\right] 3R_3$$

$$\left[\begin{array}{ccc|ccc} 1 & 0 & 0 & 1 & 0 & 1 \\ 0 & 1 & 0 & 1 & 1 & 2 \\ 0 & 0 & 1 & 3 & 2 & 6 \end{array}\right]$$

$$A^{-1} = \begin{bmatrix} 1 & 0 & 1 \\ 1 & 1 & 2 \\ 3 & 2 & 6 \end{bmatrix}$$

21.
$$\left[\begin{array}{ccc|ccc} 5 & 0 & 2 & 1 & 0 & 0 \\ 2 & 2 & 1 & 0 & 1 & 0 \\ -3 & 1 & -1 & 0 & 0 & 1 \end{array}\right] \frac{1}{5}R_1$$

$$\left[\begin{array}{ccc|ccc} 1 & 0 & \frac{2}{5} & \frac{1}{5} & 0 & 0 \\ 2 & 2 & 1 & 0 & 1 & 0 \\ -3 & 1 & -1 & 0 & 0 & 1 \end{array}\right] \begin{array}{l} -2R_1 + R_2 \\ 3R_1 + R_3 \end{array}$$

$$\left[\begin{array}{ccc|ccc} 1 & 0 & \frac{2}{5} & \frac{1}{5} & 0 & 0 \\ 0 & 2 & \frac{1}{5} & -\frac{2}{5} & 1 & 0 \\ 0 & 1 & \frac{1}{5} & \frac{3}{5} & 0 & 1 \end{array}\right] R_2 \leftrightarrow R_3$$

$$\left[\begin{array}{ccc|ccc} 1 & 0 & \frac{2}{5} & \frac{1}{5} & 0 & 0 \\ 0 & 1 & \frac{1}{5} & \frac{3}{5} & 0 & 1 \\ 0 & 2 & \frac{1}{5} & -\frac{2}{5} & 1 & 0 \end{array}\right] -2R_2 + R_3$$

$$\left[\begin{array}{ccc|ccc} 1 & 0 & \frac{2}{5} & \frac{1}{5} & 0 & 0 \\ 0 & 1 & \frac{1}{5} & \frac{3}{5} & 0 & 1 \\ 0 & 0 & -\frac{1}{5} & -\frac{8}{5} & 1 & -2 \end{array}\right] \begin{array}{l} 2R_3 + R_1 \\ 1R_3 + R_2 \end{array}$$

$$\left[\begin{array}{ccc|ccc} 1 & 0 & 0 & -3 & 2 & -4 \\ 0 & 1 & 0 & -1 & 1 & -1 \\ 0 & 0 & -\frac{1}{5} & -\frac{8}{5} & 1 & -2 \end{array}\right] -5R_3$$

$$\left[\begin{array}{ccc|ccc} 1 & 0 & 0 & -3 & 2 & -4 \\ 0 & 1 & 0 & -1 & 1 & -1 \\ 0 & 0 & 1 & 8 & -5 & 10 \end{array}\right]$$

$$A^{-1} = \begin{bmatrix} -3 & 2 & -4 \\ -1 & 1 & -1 \\ 8 & -5 & 10 \end{bmatrix}$$

23. $\begin{bmatrix} 1 & 0 & 0 & 0 & | & 1 & 0 & 0 & 0 \\ 0 & -1 & 0 & 0 & | & 0 & 1 & 0 & 0 \\ 0 & 0 & 3 & 0 & | & 0 & 0 & 1 & 0 \\ 1 & 0 & 0 & 1 & | & 0 & 0 & 0 & 1 \end{bmatrix} -1R_1 + R_4$

$\begin{bmatrix} 1 & 0 & 0 & 0 & | & 1 & 0 & 0 & 0 \\ 0 & -1 & 0 & 0 & | & 0 & 1 & 0 & 0 \\ 0 & 0 & 3 & 0 & | & 0 & 0 & 1 & 0 \\ 0 & 0 & 0 & 1 & | & -1 & 0 & 0 & 1 \end{bmatrix} -1R_2$

$\begin{bmatrix} 1 & 0 & 0 & 0 & | & 1 & 0 & 0 & 0 \\ 0 & 1 & 0 & 0 & | & 0 & -1 & 0 & 0 \\ 0 & 0 & 3 & 0 & | & 0 & 0 & 1 & 0 \\ 0 & 0 & 0 & 1 & | & -1 & 0 & 0 & 1 \end{bmatrix} \frac{1}{3}R_3$

$\begin{bmatrix} 1 & 0 & 0 & 0 & | & 1 & 0 & 0 & 0 \\ 0 & 1 & 0 & 0 & | & 0 & -1 & 0 & 0 \\ 0 & 0 & 1 & 0 & | & 0 & 0 & \frac{1}{3} & 0 \\ 0 & 0 & 0 & 1 & | & -1 & 0 & 0 & 1 \end{bmatrix}$

$A^{-1} = \begin{bmatrix} 1 & 0 & 0 & 0 \\ 0 & -1 & 0 & 0 \\ 0 & 0 & \frac{1}{3} & 0 \\ -1 & 0 & 0 & 1 \end{bmatrix}$

25. $\begin{bmatrix} 6 & 5 \\ 5 & 4 \end{bmatrix}\begin{bmatrix} x \\ y \end{bmatrix} = \begin{bmatrix} 13 \\ 10 \end{bmatrix}$

27. $\begin{bmatrix} 1 & 3 & 4 \\ 1 & 2 & 3 \\ 1 & 4 & 3 \end{bmatrix}\begin{bmatrix} x \\ y \\ z \end{bmatrix} = \begin{bmatrix} -3 \\ -2 \\ -6 \end{bmatrix}$

29. $4x - 7y = -3$
$2x - 3y = 1$

31. $2x - z = 6$
$3y = 9$
$x + y = 5$

33. a. $\begin{bmatrix} 2 & 6 & 6 \\ 2 & 7 & 6 \\ 2 & 7 & 7 \end{bmatrix}\begin{bmatrix} x \\ y \\ z \end{bmatrix} = \begin{bmatrix} 8 \\ 10 \\ 9 \end{bmatrix}$

b. $\begin{bmatrix} \frac{7}{2} & 0 & -3 \\ -1 & 1 & 0 \\ 0 & -1 & 1 \end{bmatrix}\begin{bmatrix} 8 \\ 10 \\ 9 \end{bmatrix} = \begin{bmatrix} 28+0-27 \\ -8+10+0 \\ 0-10+9 \end{bmatrix} = \begin{bmatrix} 1 \\ 2 \\ -1 \end{bmatrix}$

The solution set is $\{(1, 2, -1)\}$.

35. a. $\begin{bmatrix} 1 & -1 & 1 \\ 0 & 2 & -1 \\ 2 & 3 & 0 \end{bmatrix}\begin{bmatrix} x \\ y \\ z \end{bmatrix} = \begin{bmatrix} 8 \\ -7 \\ 1 \end{bmatrix}$

b. $\begin{bmatrix} 3 & 3 & -1 \\ -2 & -2 & 1 \\ -4 & -5 & 2 \end{bmatrix}\begin{bmatrix} 8 \\ -7 \\ 1 \end{bmatrix}$

$= \begin{bmatrix} 24-21-1 \\ -16+14+1 \\ -32+35+2 \end{bmatrix} = \begin{bmatrix} 2 \\ -1 \\ 5 \end{bmatrix}$

The solution set is $\{(2, -1, 5)\}$.

37. a. $\begin{bmatrix} 1 & -1 & 2 & 0 \\ 0 & 1 & -1 & 1 \\ -1 & 1 & -1 & 2 \\ 0 & -1 & 1 & -2 \end{bmatrix}\begin{bmatrix} x \\ y \\ z \\ w \end{bmatrix} = \begin{bmatrix} -3 \\ 4 \\ 2 \\ -4 \end{bmatrix}$

b. $\begin{bmatrix} 0 & 0 & -1 & -1 \\ 1 & 4 & 1 & 3 \\ 1 & 2 & 1 & 2 \\ 0 & -1 & 0 & -1 \end{bmatrix}\begin{bmatrix} -3 \\ 4 \\ 2 \\ -4 \end{bmatrix}$

$= \begin{bmatrix} 0+0-2+4 \\ -3+16+2-12 \\ -3+8+2-8 \\ 0-4+0+4 \end{bmatrix} = \begin{bmatrix} 2 \\ 3 \\ -1 \\ 0 \end{bmatrix}$

The solution set is $\{(2, 3, -1, 0)\}$.

39. The numerical equivalent of HELP is
8, 5, 12, 16.

$$\begin{bmatrix} 4 & -1 \\ -3 & 1 \end{bmatrix}\begin{bmatrix} 8 \\ 5 \end{bmatrix} = \begin{bmatrix} 27 \\ -19 \end{bmatrix},$$

$$\begin{bmatrix} 4 & -1 \\ -3 & 1 \end{bmatrix}\begin{bmatrix} 12 \\ 16 \end{bmatrix} = \begin{bmatrix} 32 \\ -20 \end{bmatrix}$$

The encoded message is 27, −19, 32, −20.

$$\begin{bmatrix} 1 & 1 \\ 3 & 4 \end{bmatrix}\begin{bmatrix} 27 \\ -19 \end{bmatrix} = \begin{bmatrix} 8 \\ 5 \end{bmatrix}, \begin{bmatrix} 1 & 1 \\ 3 & 4 \end{bmatrix}\begin{bmatrix} 32 \\ -20 \end{bmatrix} = \begin{bmatrix} 12 \\ 16 \end{bmatrix}$$

The decoded message is 8, 5, 12, 16 or HELP.

41.
$$\begin{bmatrix} 1 & -1 & 0 \\ 3 & 0 & 2 \\ -1 & 0 & -1 \end{bmatrix}\begin{bmatrix} 19 & 4 & 1 \\ 5 & 0 & 19 \\ 14 & 3 & 8 \end{bmatrix}$$

$$= \begin{bmatrix} 19-5+0 & 4+0+0 & 1-19+0 \\ 57+0+28 & 12+0+6 & 3+0+16 \\ -19+0-14 & -4+0-3 & -1+0-8 \end{bmatrix}$$

$$= \begin{bmatrix} 14 & 4 & -18 \\ 85 & 18 & 19 \\ -33 & -7 & -9 \end{bmatrix}$$

The encoded message is 14, 85, −33, 4, 18, −7, −18, 19, −9.

$$\begin{bmatrix} 0 & 1 & 2 \\ -1 & 1 & 2 \\ 0 & -1 & -3 \end{bmatrix}\begin{bmatrix} 14 & 4 & -18 \\ 85 & 18 & 19 \\ -33 & -7 & -9 \end{bmatrix}$$

$$= \begin{bmatrix} 0+85-66 & 0+18-14 & 0+19-18 \\ -14+85-66 & -4+18-14 & 18+19-18 \\ 0-85+99 & 0-18+21 & 0-19+27 \end{bmatrix}$$

$$= \begin{bmatrix} 19 & 4 & 1 \\ 5 & 0 & 19 \\ 14 & 3 & 8 \end{bmatrix}$$

The decoded message is 19, 5, 14, 4, 0, 3, 1, 19, 8 or SEND_CASH.

43.–51. Answers may vary.

53. Enter the matrix $\begin{bmatrix} 3 & -1 \\ -2 & 1 \end{bmatrix}$ as $[A]$,
then use $[A]^{-1}$.
$$[A]^{-1} = \begin{bmatrix} 1 & 1 \\ 2 & 3 \end{bmatrix}$$
Verify this result by showing that
$[A][A]^{-1} = I_2$ and $[A]^{-1}[A] = I_2$.

55. Enter the matrix $\begin{bmatrix} -2 & 1 & -1 \\ -5 & 2 & -1 \\ 3 & -1 & 1 \end{bmatrix}$
as $[A]$, then use $[A]^{-1}$.
$$[A]^{-1} = \begin{bmatrix} 1 & 0 & 1 \\ 2 & 1 & 3 \\ -1 & 1 & 1 \end{bmatrix}$$
Verify this result by showing that
$[A][A]^{-1} = I_3$ and $[A]^{-1}[A] = I_3$.

57. Enter the matrix $\begin{bmatrix} 7 & -3 & 0 & 2 \\ -2 & 1 & 0 & -1 \\ 4 & 0 & 1 & -2 \\ -1 & 1 & 0 & -1 \end{bmatrix}$ as $[A]$,
then use $[A]^{-1}$. $[A]^{-1} = \begin{bmatrix} 0 & -1 & 0 & 1 \\ -1 & -5 & 0 & 3 \\ -2 & -4 & 1 & -2 \\ -1 & -4 & 0 & 1 \end{bmatrix}$
Verify this result by showing that
$[A][A]^{-1} = I_4$ and $[A]^{-1}[A] = I_4$.

For Exercises 59–63, enter the matrix A as [A] and the matrix B as [B] in your graphing utility, then calculate $[A]^{-1}[B]$ to find X.

59. The system is $AX = B$ where

$$A = \begin{bmatrix} 1 & -1 & 1 \\ 4 & 2 & 1 \\ 4 & -2 & 1 \end{bmatrix}, \ X = \begin{bmatrix} x \\ y \\ z \end{bmatrix}, \text{ and } B = \begin{bmatrix} -6 \\ 9 \\ -3 \end{bmatrix}.$$

$X = \begin{bmatrix} 2 \\ 3 \\ -5 \end{bmatrix}$, so the solution to the system is

$\{(2, 3, -5)\}$.

61. The system is $AX = B$ where

$$A = \begin{bmatrix} 3 & -2 & 1 \\ 4 & -5 & 3 \\ 2 & -1 & 5 \end{bmatrix}, \ X = \begin{bmatrix} x \\ y \\ z \end{bmatrix}, \text{ and } B = \begin{bmatrix} -2 \\ -9 \\ -5 \end{bmatrix}.$$

$X = \begin{bmatrix} 1 \\ 2 \\ -1 \end{bmatrix}$ so the solution to the system is

$\{(1, 2, -1)\}$.

63. The system is $AX = B$ where

$$A = \begin{bmatrix} 1 & 0 & -3 & 0 & 1 \\ 0 & 1 & 0 & 1 & 0 \\ 0 & 0 & 1 & 0 & 1 \\ 1 & 1 & -1 & 4 & 0 \\ 1 & 1 & 1 & 1 & 1 \end{bmatrix}, \ X = \begin{bmatrix} x \\ y \\ z \\ w \\ v \end{bmatrix}, \text{ and }$$

$B = \begin{bmatrix} -3 \\ -1 \\ 7 \\ -8 \\ 8 \end{bmatrix}$. $X = \begin{bmatrix} 2 \\ 1 \\ 3 \\ -2 \\ 4 \end{bmatrix}$, so the solution to the

system is $\{(2, 1, 3, -2, 4)\}$.

65. Answers may vary.

67. a. False; only square matrices have inverses.

b. False; $\begin{bmatrix} 3 & 6 \\ 2 & 4 \end{bmatrix}$ does not have an inverse since $(3)(4) - (6)(2) = 12 - 12 = 0$ and division by zero is undefined.

c. True; $\begin{bmatrix} 1 & 2 \\ 2 & 3 \end{bmatrix} + \begin{bmatrix} 2 & 4 \\ 0 & 1 \end{bmatrix} = \begin{bmatrix} 3 & 6 \\ 2 & 4 \end{bmatrix}$ and

$\begin{bmatrix} 1 & 2 \\ 2 & 3 \end{bmatrix}^{-1} = \begin{bmatrix} -3 & 2 \\ 2 & -1 \end{bmatrix}$,

$\begin{bmatrix} 2 & 4 \\ 0 & 1 \end{bmatrix}^{-1} = \begin{bmatrix} \frac{1}{2} & -2 \\ 0 & 1 \end{bmatrix}$ while $\begin{bmatrix} 3 & 6 \\ 2 & 4 \end{bmatrix}$

does not have an inverse. [See part (b).]

d. False; to solve the matrix equation for X, multiply the inverse of A and B $(A^{-1}B)$ provided the inverse of A exists.

(c) is true.

69. Answers may vary.

71. Using the statement before exercises 13–18, we want to find values for a such that
$(1)(4) - (a + 1)(a - 2) = 0$.
$(1)(4) - (a+1)(a-2) = 4 - (a^2 - a - 2)$
$\quad = -a^2 + a + 6$
$0 = -a^2 + a + 6$
$0 = a^2 - a - 6$
$0 = (a - 3)(a + 2)$
$a = 3, -2$

Section 9.5

Check Point Exercises

1. a. $\begin{vmatrix} 10 & 9 \\ 6 & 5 \end{vmatrix} = 10 \cdot 5 - 6 \cdot 9 = 50 - 54 = -4$

b. $\begin{vmatrix} 4 & 3 \\ -5 & -8 \end{vmatrix} = 4 \cdot (-8) - (-5) \cdot (3)$
$\quad = -32 + 15$
$\quad = -17$

2. $5x + 4y = 12$
$3x - 6y = 24$

$$D = \begin{vmatrix} 5 & 4 \\ 3 & -6 \end{vmatrix} = 5 \cdot (-6) - 3 \cdot 4$$
$$= -30 - 12 = -42$$

$$D_x = \begin{vmatrix} 12 & 4 \\ 24 & -6 \end{vmatrix} = 12(-6) - 24(4)$$
$$= -72 - 96 = -168$$

$$D_y = \begin{vmatrix} 5 & 12 \\ 3 & 24 \end{vmatrix} = 5(24) - 3(12)$$
$$= 120 - 36 = 84$$

Thus, $x = \dfrac{D_x}{D} = \dfrac{-168}{-42} = 4$

$$y = \frac{D_y}{D} = \frac{84}{-42} = -2$$

The solution set is $\{(4, -2)\}$.

3. $\begin{vmatrix} 2 & 1 & 7 \\ -5 & 6 & 0 \\ -4 & 3 & 1 \end{vmatrix}$

The minor for 2 is $\begin{vmatrix} 6 & 0 \\ 3 & 1 \end{vmatrix}$.

The minor for -5 is $\begin{vmatrix} 1 & 7 \\ 3 & 1 \end{vmatrix}$.

The minor for -4 is $\begin{vmatrix} 1 & 7 \\ 6 & 0 \end{vmatrix}$.

$$\begin{vmatrix} 2 & 1 & 7 \\ -5 & 6 & 0 \\ -4 & 3 & 1 \end{vmatrix} = 2\begin{vmatrix} 6 & 0 \\ 3 & 1 \end{vmatrix} - (-5)\begin{vmatrix} 1 & 7 \\ 3 & 1 \end{vmatrix} - 4\begin{vmatrix} 1 & 7 \\ 6 & 0 \end{vmatrix}$$

$$= 2(6 \cdot 1 - 3 \cdot 0) + 5(1 \cdot 1 - 3 \cdot 7) - 4(1 \cdot 0 - 6 \cdot 7)$$
$$= 2(6 - 0) + 5(1 - 21) - 4(0 - 42)$$
$$= 12 - 100 + 168$$
$$= 80$$

4. $\begin{vmatrix} 6 & 4 & 0 \\ -3 & -5 & 3 \\ 1 & 2 & 0 \end{vmatrix} = 0\begin{vmatrix} -3 & -5 \\ 1 & 2 \end{vmatrix} - 3\begin{vmatrix} 6 & 4 \\ 1 & 2 \end{vmatrix} + 0\begin{vmatrix} 6 & 4 \\ -3 & -5 \end{vmatrix}$

$$= 0 - 3(6 \cdot 2 - 1 \cdot 4) + 0$$
$$= -3(12 - 4)$$
$$= -3(8)$$
$$= -24$$

5. $3x - 2y + z = 16$
    $2x + 3y - z = -9$
    $x + 4y + 3z = 2$

$$D = \begin{vmatrix} 3 & -2 & 1 \\ 2 & 3 & -1 \\ 1 & 4 & 3 \end{vmatrix}; \quad D_x = \begin{vmatrix} 16 & -2 & 1 \\ -9 & 3 & -1 \\ 2 & 4 & 3 \end{vmatrix}; \quad D_y = \begin{vmatrix} 3 & 16 & 1 \\ 2 & -9 & -1 \\ 1 & 2 & 3 \end{vmatrix}; \quad D_z = \begin{vmatrix} 3 & -2 & 16 \\ 2 & 3 & -9 \\ 1 & 4 & 2 \end{vmatrix}$$

$$D = \begin{vmatrix} 3 & -2 & 1 \\ 2 & 3 & -1 \\ 1 & 4 & 3 \end{vmatrix} = 3\begin{vmatrix} 3 & -1 \\ 4 & 3 \end{vmatrix} - 2\begin{vmatrix} -2 & 1 \\ 4 & 3 \end{vmatrix} + 1\begin{vmatrix} -2 & 1 \\ 3 & -1 \end{vmatrix}$$

$= 3[(3) \cdot 3 - 4 \cdot (-1)] - 2[(-2) \cdot 3 - 4 \cdot 1] + 1[(-2) \cdot (-1) - (3) \cdot 1]$

$= 3(9 + 4) - 2(-6 - 4) + 1(2 - 3)$

$= 39 + 20 - 1$

$= 58$

$$D_x = \begin{vmatrix} 16 & -2 & 1 \\ -9 & 3 & -1 \\ 2 & 4 & 3 \end{vmatrix} = 1\begin{vmatrix} -9 & 3 \\ 2 & 4 \end{vmatrix} - (-1)\begin{vmatrix} 16 & -2 \\ 2 & 4 \end{vmatrix} + 3\begin{vmatrix} 16 & -2 \\ -9 & 3 \end{vmatrix}$$

$= 1[(-9) \cdot 4 - 2 \cdot (3)] + 1[16 \cdot 4 - 2(-2)] + 3[16 \cdot (3) - (-9) \cdot (-2)]$

$= 1(-36 - 6) + 1(64 + 4) + 3(48 - 18)$

$= -42 + 68 + 90$

$= 116$

$$D_y = \begin{vmatrix} 3 & 16 & 1 \\ 2 & -9 & -1 \\ 1 & 2 & 3 \end{vmatrix} = 3\begin{vmatrix} -9 & -1 \\ 2 & 3 \end{vmatrix} - 2\begin{vmatrix} 16 & 1 \\ 2 & 3 \end{vmatrix} + 1\begin{vmatrix} 16 & 1 \\ -9 & -1 \end{vmatrix}$$

$= 3[(-9) \cdot 3 - 2 \cdot (-1)] - 2[16 \cdot 3 - 2 \cdot 1] + 1[16(-1) - (-9) \cdot 1]$

$= 3(-27 + 2) - 2(48 - 2) + 1(-16 + 9)$

$= -75 - 92 - 7$

$= -174$

$$D_z = \begin{vmatrix} 3 & -2 & 16 \\ 2 & 3 & -9 \\ 1 & 4 & 2 \end{vmatrix} = 3\begin{vmatrix} 3 & -9 \\ 4 & 2 \end{vmatrix} - 2\begin{vmatrix} -2 & 16 \\ 4 & 2 \end{vmatrix} + 1\begin{vmatrix} -2 & 16 \\ 3 & -9 \end{vmatrix}$$

$= 3[(3)2 - 4(-9)] - 2[(-2)2 - 4 \cdot 16] + 1[(-2)(-9) - (3) \cdot 16]$

$= 3(6 + 36) - 2(-4 - 64) + 1(18 - 48)$

$= 126 + 136 - 30$

$= 232$

$x = \dfrac{D_x}{D} = \dfrac{116}{58} = 2$

$y = \dfrac{D_y}{D} = \dfrac{-174}{58} = -3$

$z = \dfrac{D_z}{D} = \dfrac{232}{58} = 4$

The solution to the system is $\{(2, -3, 4)\}$.

6. $|A| = \begin{vmatrix} 0 & 4 & 0 & -3 \\ -1 & 1 & 5 & 2 \\ 1 & -2 & 0 & 6 \\ 3 & 0 & 0 & 1 \end{vmatrix} = (-1)^{2+3} 5 \begin{vmatrix} 0 & 4 & -3 \\ 1 & -2 & 6 \\ 3 & 0 & 1 \end{vmatrix} = -5 \begin{vmatrix} 0 & 4 & -3 \\ 1 & -2 & 6 \\ 3 & 0 & 1 \end{vmatrix}$

Evaluate the third-order determinant to get $|A| = -5(50) = -250$.

Exercise Set 9.5

1. $\begin{vmatrix} 5 & 7 \\ 2 & 3 \end{vmatrix} = 5 \cdot 3 - 2 \cdot 7 = 15 - 14 = 1$

3. $\begin{vmatrix} -4 & 1 \\ 5 & 6 \end{vmatrix} = (-4)6 - 5 \cdot 1 = -24 - 5 = -29$

5. $\begin{vmatrix} -7 & 14 \\ 2 & -4 \end{vmatrix} = (-7)(-4) - 2(14) = 28 - 28 = 0$

7. $\begin{vmatrix} -5 & -1 \\ 2 & 7 \end{vmatrix} = (-5)(-7) - (-2)(-1) = 35 - 2 = 33$

9. $\begin{vmatrix} \frac{1}{2} & \frac{1}{2} \\ \frac{1}{8} & -\frac{3}{4} \end{vmatrix} = \frac{1}{2}\left(-\frac{3}{4}\right) - \frac{1}{8} \cdot \frac{1}{2} = -\frac{3}{8} - \frac{1}{16} = -\frac{7}{16}$

11. $D = \begin{vmatrix} 1 & 1 \\ 1 & -1 \end{vmatrix} = -1 - 1 = -2$

$D_x = \begin{vmatrix} 7 & 1 \\ 3 & -1 \end{vmatrix} = -7 - 3 = -10$

$D_y = \begin{vmatrix} 1 & 7 \\ 1 & 3 \end{vmatrix} = 3 - 7 = -4$

$x = \dfrac{D_x}{D} = \dfrac{-10}{-2} = 5$

$y = \dfrac{D_y}{D} = \dfrac{-4}{-2} = 2$

The solution set is $\{(5, 2)\}$.

13. $D = \begin{vmatrix} 12 & 3 \\ 2 & -3 \end{vmatrix} = -36 - 6 = -42$

$D_x = \begin{vmatrix} 15 & 3 \\ 13 & -3 \end{vmatrix} = -45 - 39 = -84$

$D_y = \begin{vmatrix} 12 & 15 \\ 2 & 13 \end{vmatrix} = 156 - 30 = 126$

$x = \dfrac{D_x}{D} = \dfrac{-84}{-42} = 2$

$y = \dfrac{D_y}{D} = \dfrac{126}{-42} = -3$

The solution set is $\{(2, -3)\}$.

15. $D = \begin{vmatrix} 4 & -5 \\ 2 & 3 \end{vmatrix} = 12 - (-10) = 22$

$D_x = \begin{vmatrix} 17 & -5 \\ 3 & 3 \end{vmatrix} = 51 - (-15) = 66$

$D_y = \begin{vmatrix} 4 & 17 \\ 2 & 3 \end{vmatrix} = 12 - 34 = -22$

$x = \dfrac{D_x}{D} = \dfrac{66}{22} = 3$

$y = \dfrac{D_y}{D} = \dfrac{-22}{22} = -1$

The solution set is $\{(3, -1)\}$.

17. $D = \begin{vmatrix} 1 & 2 \\ 5 & 10 \end{vmatrix} = 10 - 10 = 0$

$D_x = \begin{vmatrix} 3 & 2 \\ 15 & 10 \end{vmatrix} = 30 - 30 = 0$

$D_y = \begin{vmatrix} 1 & 3 \\ 5 & 15 \end{vmatrix} = 15 - 15 = 0$

Because all 3 determinants equal zero, the system is dependent.

19. $D = \begin{vmatrix} 3 & -4 \\ 2 & 2 \end{vmatrix} = 6 - (-8) = 14$

$D_x = \begin{vmatrix} 4 & -4 \\ 12 & 2 \end{vmatrix} = 8 - (-48) = 56$

$D_y = \begin{vmatrix} 3 & 4 \\ 2 & 12 \end{vmatrix} = 36 - 8 = 28$

$x = \dfrac{D_x}{D} = \dfrac{56}{14} = 4$

$y = \dfrac{D_y}{D} = \dfrac{28}{14} = 2$

The solution set is $\{(4, 2)\}$.

21. $D = \begin{vmatrix} 2 & -3 \\ 5 & 4 \end{vmatrix} = 8 - (-15) = 23$

$D_x = \begin{vmatrix} 2 & -3 \\ 51 & 4 \end{vmatrix} = 8 - (-153) = 161$

$D_y = \begin{vmatrix} 2 & 2 \\ 5 & 51 \end{vmatrix} = 102 - 10 = 92$

$x = \dfrac{D_x}{D} = \dfrac{161}{23} = 7$

$y = \dfrac{D_y}{D} = \dfrac{92}{23} = 4$

The solution set is $\{(7, 4)\}$.

23. $D = \begin{vmatrix} 3 & 3 \\ 2 & 2 \end{vmatrix} = 6 - 6 = 0$

$D_x = \begin{vmatrix} 2 & 3 \\ 3 & 2 \end{vmatrix} = 4 - 9 = -5$

$D_y = \begin{vmatrix} 3 & 2 \\ 2 & 3 \end{vmatrix} = 9 - 4 = 5$

Because $D = 0$ but D_x and $D_y \neq 0$, the system is inconsistent.

25. $D = \begin{vmatrix} 3 & 4 \\ 5 & 3 \end{vmatrix} = 9 - 20 = -11$

$D_x = \begin{vmatrix} 16 & 4 \\ 12 & 3 \end{vmatrix} = 48 - 48 = 0$

$D_y = \begin{vmatrix} 3 & 16 \\ 5 & 12 \end{vmatrix} = 36 - 80 = -44$

$x = \dfrac{D_x}{D} = \dfrac{0}{-11} = 0$

$y = \dfrac{D_y}{D} = \dfrac{-44}{-11} = 4$

The solution set is $\{(0, 4)\}$.

27. $\begin{vmatrix} 3 & 0 & 0 \\ 2 & 1 & -5 \\ -2 & 5 & -1 \end{vmatrix} = 3\begin{vmatrix} 1 & -5 \\ 5 & -1 \end{vmatrix} - 0\begin{vmatrix} 2 & -5 \\ -2 & -1 \end{vmatrix} + 0\begin{vmatrix} 2 & 1 \\ -2 & 5 \end{vmatrix}$

$= 3[(1)(-1) - (5)(-5)]$
$= 3(-1 + 25)$
$= 3(24)$
$= 72$

29. $\begin{vmatrix} 3 & 1 & 0 \\ -3 & 4 & 0 \\ -1 & 3 & -5 \end{vmatrix} = 0\begin{vmatrix} -3 & 4 \\ -1 & 3 \end{vmatrix} - 0\begin{vmatrix} 3 & 1 \\ -1 & 3 \end{vmatrix} + (-5)\begin{vmatrix} 3 & 1 \\ -3 & 4 \end{vmatrix}$

$= -5[3 \cdot 4 - (-3)(1)]$
$= -5(12 + 3)$
$= -5(15)$
$= -75$

31. $\begin{vmatrix} 1 & 1 & 1 \\ 2 & 2 & 2 \\ -3 & 4 & -5 \end{vmatrix} = \begin{vmatrix} 2 & 2 \\ 4 & -5 \end{vmatrix} - \begin{vmatrix} 2 & 2 \\ -3 & -5 \end{vmatrix} + \begin{vmatrix} 2 & 2 \\ -3 & 4 \end{vmatrix}$

$= (-10 - 8) - [-10 - (-6)] + [8 - (-6)]$
$= -18 - (-4) + 14$
$= 0$

33. $D = \begin{vmatrix} 1 & 1 & 1 \\ 2 & -1 & 1 \\ -1 & 3 & -1 \end{vmatrix}$

$= \begin{vmatrix} -1 & 1 \\ 3 & -1 \end{vmatrix} - \begin{vmatrix} 2 & 1 \\ -1 & -1 \end{vmatrix} + \begin{vmatrix} 2 & -1 \\ -1 & 3 \end{vmatrix}$

$= (1 - 3) - [-2 - (-1)] + (6 - 1)$
$= -2 - (-1) + 5 = -2 + 1 + 5 = 4$

$D_x = \begin{vmatrix} 0 & 1 & 1 \\ -1 & -1 & 1 \\ -8 & 3 & -1 \end{vmatrix} = (-1)\begin{vmatrix} -1 & 1 \\ -8 & -1 \end{vmatrix} + \begin{vmatrix} -1 & -1 \\ -8 & 3 \end{vmatrix}$

$= (-1)[1 - (-8)] + (-3 - 8) = (-1)(9) - 11$
$= -20$

$D_y = \begin{vmatrix} 1 & 0 & 1 \\ 2 & -1 & 1 \\ -1 & -8 & -1 \end{vmatrix} = \begin{vmatrix} -1 & 1 \\ -8 & -1 \end{vmatrix} + \begin{vmatrix} 2 & -1 \\ -1 & -8 \end{vmatrix}$

$= 1 - (-8) + (-16 - 1) = 1 + 8 - 17 = -8$

$D_z = \begin{vmatrix} 1 & 1 & 0 \\ 2 & -1 & -1 \\ -1 & 3 & -8 \end{vmatrix} = 1\begin{vmatrix} -1 & -1 \\ 3 & -8 \end{vmatrix} - 1\begin{vmatrix} 2 & -1 \\ -1 & -8 \end{vmatrix}$

$= 8 - (-3) - 1(-16 - 1) = 11 + 17 = 28$

$x = \dfrac{D_x}{D} = \dfrac{-20}{4} = 5$

$y = \dfrac{D_y}{D} = \dfrac{-8}{4} = -2$

$z = \dfrac{D_z}{D} = \dfrac{28}{4} = 7$

The solution to the system is $\{(-5, -2, 7)\}$.

35. $D = \begin{vmatrix} 4 & -5 & -6 \\ 1 & -2 & -5 \\ 2 & -1 & 0 \end{vmatrix} = 2\begin{vmatrix} -5 & -6 \\ -2 & -5 \end{vmatrix} - (-1)\begin{vmatrix} 4 & -6 \\ 1 & -5 \end{vmatrix}$

$= 2(25 - 12) + [-20 - (-6)] = 2(13) + (-14)$

$= 26 - 14 = 12$

$D_x = \begin{vmatrix} -1 & -5 & -6 \\ -12 & -2 & -5 \\ 7 & -1 & 0 \end{vmatrix}$

$= 7\begin{vmatrix} -5 & -6 \\ -2 & -5 \end{vmatrix} - (-1)\begin{vmatrix} -1 & -6 \\ -12 & -5 \end{vmatrix}$

$= 7(25 - 12) + (5 - 72) = 7(13) - 67$

$= 91 - 67 = 24$

$D_y = \begin{vmatrix} 4 & -1 & -6 \\ 1 & -12 & -5 \\ 2 & 7 & 0 \end{vmatrix} = 2\begin{vmatrix} -1 & -6 \\ -12 & -5 \end{vmatrix} - 7\begin{vmatrix} 4 & -6 \\ 1 & -5 \end{vmatrix}$

$= 2(5 - 72) - 7[-20 - (-6)]$

$= 2(-67) - 7(-14) = -134 + 98 = -36$

$D_z = \begin{vmatrix} 4 & -5 & -1 \\ 1 & -2 & -12 \\ 2 & -1 & 7 \end{vmatrix}$

$= 4\begin{vmatrix} -2 & -12 \\ -1 & 7 \end{vmatrix} - (-5)\begin{vmatrix} 1 & -12 \\ 2 & 7 \end{vmatrix} + (-1)\begin{vmatrix} 1 & -2 \\ 2 & -1 \end{vmatrix}$

$= 4(-14 - 12) + 5[7 - (-24)] - [-1 - (-4)]$

$= 4(-26) + 5(31) - (3) = -104 + 155 - 3 = 48$

$x = \dfrac{D_x}{D} = \dfrac{24}{12} = 2, \ y = \dfrac{D_y}{D} = \dfrac{-36}{12} = -3,$

$z = \dfrac{D_z}{D} = \dfrac{48}{12} = 4$

The solution set is $\{(2, -3, 4)\}$.

37. $D = \begin{vmatrix} 1 & 1 & 1 \\ 1 & -2 & 1 \\ 1 & 3 & 2 \end{vmatrix} = 1\begin{vmatrix} -2 & 1 \\ 3 & 2 \end{vmatrix} - 1\begin{vmatrix} 1 & 1 \\ 1 & 2 \end{vmatrix} + 1\begin{vmatrix} 1 & -2 \\ 1 & 3 \end{vmatrix}$

$= -4 - 3 - (2 - 1) + [3 - (-2)]$

$= -7 - 1 + 5 = -3$

$D_x = \begin{vmatrix} 4 & 1 & 1 \\ 7 & -2 & 1 \\ 4 & 3 & 2 \end{vmatrix} = 4\begin{vmatrix} -2 & 1 \\ 3 & 2 \end{vmatrix} - 1\begin{vmatrix} 7 & 1 \\ 4 & 2 \end{vmatrix} + 1\begin{vmatrix} 7 & -2 \\ 4 & 3 \end{vmatrix}$

$= 4(-4 - 3) - (14 - 4) + [21 - (-8)]$

$= 4(-7) - 10 + 29 = -28 + 19 = -9$

$D_y = \begin{vmatrix} 1 & 4 & 1 \\ 1 & 7 & 1 \\ 1 & 4 & 2 \end{vmatrix} = 1\begin{vmatrix} 7 & 1 \\ 4 & 2 \end{vmatrix} - 1\begin{vmatrix} 4 & 1 \\ 4 & 2 \end{vmatrix} + 1\begin{vmatrix} 4 & 1 \\ 7 & 1 \end{vmatrix}$

$= 14 - 4 - (8 - 4) + (4 - 7) = 10 - 4 - 3 = 3$

$D_z = \begin{vmatrix} 1 & 1 & 4 \\ 1 & -2 & 7 \\ 1 & 3 & 4 \end{vmatrix} = 1\begin{vmatrix} -2 & 7 \\ 3 & 4 \end{vmatrix} - 1\begin{vmatrix} 1 & 4 \\ 3 & 4 \end{vmatrix} + 1\begin{vmatrix} 1 & 4 \\ -2 & 7 \end{vmatrix}$

$= -8 - 21 - (4 - 12) + [7 - (-8)]$

$= -29 + 8 + 15 = -6$

$x = \dfrac{D_x}{D} = \dfrac{-9}{-3} = 3, \ y = \dfrac{D_y}{D} = \dfrac{3}{-3} = -1,$

$z = \dfrac{D_z}{D} = \dfrac{-6}{-3} = 2$

The solution set is $\{(3, -1, 2)\}$.

39. $D = \begin{vmatrix} 1 & 0 & 2 \\ 0 & 2 & -1 \\ 2 & 3 & 0 \end{vmatrix} = \begin{vmatrix} 2 & -1 \\ 3 & 0 \end{vmatrix} + 2\begin{vmatrix} 0 & 2 \\ 2 & 3 \end{vmatrix}$

$= 0 - (-3) + 2(0 - 4) = 3 - 8 = -5$

$D_x = \begin{vmatrix} 4 & 0 & 2 \\ 5 & 2 & -1 \\ 13 & 3 & 0 \end{vmatrix} = 4\begin{vmatrix} 2 & -1 \\ 3 & 0 \end{vmatrix} + 2\begin{vmatrix} 5 & 2 \\ 13 & 3 \end{vmatrix}$

$= 4[0 - (-3)] + 2(15 - 26)$

$= 4(3) + 2(-11) = 12 - 22 = -10$

$D_y = \begin{vmatrix} 1 & 4 & 2 \\ 0 & 5 & -1 \\ 2 & 13 & 0 \end{vmatrix} = \begin{vmatrix} 5 & -1 \\ 13 & 0 \end{vmatrix} + 2\begin{vmatrix} 4 & 2 \\ 5 & -1 \end{vmatrix}$

$= 0 - (-13) + 2(-4 - 10)$

$= 13 + 2(-14) = 13 - 28 = -15$

$D_z = \begin{vmatrix} 1 & 0 & 4 \\ 0 & 2 & 5 \\ 2 & 3 & 13 \end{vmatrix} = \begin{vmatrix} 2 & 5 \\ 3 & 13 \end{vmatrix} + 4\begin{vmatrix} 0 & 2 \\ 2 & 3 \end{vmatrix}$

$= 26 - 15 + 4(0 - 4) = 11 + 4(-4)$

$= 11 - 16 = -5$

$x = \dfrac{D_x}{D} = \dfrac{-10}{-5} = 2, \ y = \dfrac{D_y}{D} = \dfrac{-15}{-5} = 3,$

$z = \dfrac{D_z}{D} = \dfrac{-5}{-5} = 1$

The solution set is $\{(2, 3, 1)\}$.

41. $\begin{vmatrix} 4 & 2 & 8 & -7 \\ -2 & 0 & 4 & 1 \\ 5 & 0 & 0 & 5 \\ 4 & 0 & 0 & -1 \end{vmatrix} = -2\begin{vmatrix} -2 & 4 & 1 \\ 5 & 0 & 5 \\ 4 & 0 & -1 \end{vmatrix} + 0\begin{vmatrix} 4 & 8 & -7 \\ 5 & 0 & 5 \\ 4 & 0 & -1 \end{vmatrix} - 0\begin{vmatrix} 4 & 8 & -7 \\ -2 & 4 & 1 \\ 4 & 0 & -1 \end{vmatrix} + 0\begin{vmatrix} 4 & 8 & -7 \\ -2 & 4 & 1 \\ 5 & 0 & 5 \end{vmatrix}$

$$= (-2)\left[(-4)\begin{vmatrix} 5 & 5 \\ 4 & -1 \end{vmatrix} + 0\begin{vmatrix} -2 & 1 \\ 4 & -1 \end{vmatrix} - 0\begin{vmatrix} -2 & 1 \\ 5 & 5 \end{vmatrix} \right]$$

$$= (-2)(-4)[5(-1) - 4 \cdot 5]$$
$$= 8(-5 - 20)$$
$$= 8(-25)$$
$$= -200$$

43. $\begin{vmatrix} -2 & -3 & 3 & 5 \\ 1 & -4 & 0 & 0 \\ 1 & 2 & 2 & -3 \\ 2 & 0 & 1 & 1 \end{vmatrix}$

$$= -1\begin{vmatrix} -3 & 3 & 5 \\ 2 & 2 & -3 \\ 0 & 1 & 1 \end{vmatrix} + (-4)\begin{vmatrix} -2 & 3 & 5 \\ 1 & 2 & -3 \\ 2 & 1 & 1 \end{vmatrix} - 0\begin{vmatrix} -2 & -3 & 5 \\ 1 & 2 & -3 \\ 2 & 0 & 1 \end{vmatrix} + 0\begin{vmatrix} -2 & -3 & 3 \\ 1 & 2 & 2 \\ 2 & 0 & 1 \end{vmatrix}$$

$$= (-1)\left[0\begin{vmatrix} 3 & 5 \\ 2 & -3 \end{vmatrix} - 1\begin{vmatrix} -3 & 5 \\ 2 & -3 \end{vmatrix} + 1\begin{vmatrix} -3 & 3 \\ 2 & 2 \end{vmatrix} \right] - 4\left[2\begin{vmatrix} 3 & 5 \\ 2 & -3 \end{vmatrix} - 1\begin{vmatrix} -2 & 5 \\ 1 & -3 \end{vmatrix} + 1\begin{vmatrix} -2 & 3 \\ 1 & 2 \end{vmatrix} \right]$$

$$= (-1)\{(-1)[(-3)(-3) - 2 \cdot 5] + [(-3)(2) - 2 \cdot 3]\} - 4\{2[3(-3) - 2 \cdot 5] - [(-2)(-3) - 1 \cdot 5] + [(-2)(2) - 1 \cdot 3]\}$$
$$= (-1)[(-1)(9 - 10) + (-6 - 6)] - 4[2(-9 - 10) - (6 - 5) + (-4 - 3)]$$
$$= (-1)[(-1)(-1) - 12] - 4[2(-19) - 1 - 7]$$
$$= (-1)(1 - 12) - 4(-38 - 8)$$
$$= (-1)(-11) - 4(-46)$$
$$= 11 + 184$$
$$= 195$$

45. a. Area $= \pm\dfrac{1}{2}\begin{vmatrix} 3 & -5 & 1 \\ 2 & 6 & 1 \\ -3 & 5 & 1 \end{vmatrix} = \pm\dfrac{1}{2}\begin{vmatrix} 3 & -5 & 1 \\ -1 & 11 & 0 \\ -6 & 10 & 0 \end{vmatrix} = \pm\dfrac{1}{2}\begin{vmatrix} -1 & 11 \\ -6 & 10 \end{vmatrix} = \pm\dfrac{1}{2}[-10 - (-66)] = \pm\dfrac{1}{2}(56) = 28$

The area is 28 square units.

b.

The slope of the line through (3, –5) and (–3, 5) is $m = \dfrac{5-(-5)}{-3-3} = \dfrac{10}{-6} = -\dfrac{5}{3}$.

The equation of the line is $y-(-5) = -\dfrac{5}{3}(x-3)$ or $y = -\dfrac{5}{3}x$.

The line perpendicular to $y = -\dfrac{5}{3}x$ through (2, 6) has equation $y-6 = \dfrac{3}{5}(x-2)$ or $y = \dfrac{3}{5}x + \dfrac{24}{5}$.

These lines intersect where $-\dfrac{5}{3}x = \dfrac{3}{5}x + \dfrac{24}{5}$.

$$-\dfrac{24}{5} = \dfrac{34}{15}x$$

$$-\dfrac{36}{17} = x \text{ and } y = -\dfrac{5}{3}\left(-\dfrac{36}{17}\right) = \dfrac{60}{17}$$

Using the side connecting (3, –5) and

(–3, 5) as the base, the height is the distance from (2, 6) to $\left(-\dfrac{36}{17}, \dfrac{60}{17}\right)$.

$$b = \sqrt{[3-(-3)]^2 + (-5-5)^2} = \sqrt{36+100} = \sqrt{136} = 2\sqrt{34}$$

$$h = \sqrt{\left[2-\left(-\dfrac{36}{17}\right)\right]^2 + \left(6 - \dfrac{60}{17}\right)^2} = \sqrt{\dfrac{4900}{289} + \dfrac{1764}{289}} = \dfrac{14\sqrt{34}}{17}$$

$$\dfrac{1}{2}bh = \dfrac{1}{2}\left(2\sqrt{34}\right)\left(\dfrac{14\sqrt{34}}{17}\right)$$

$$= \dfrac{14(34)}{17}$$

$$= 14(2)$$

$$= 28 \text{ square units}$$

47. $\begin{vmatrix} 3 & -1 & 1 \\ 0 & -3 & 1 \\ 12 & 5 & 1 \end{vmatrix} = \begin{vmatrix} 3 & -1 & 1 \\ -3 & -2 & 0 \\ 9 & 6 & 0 \end{vmatrix}$

$$= \begin{vmatrix} -3 & -2 \\ 9 & 6 \end{vmatrix}$$

$$= -18 - (-18)$$

$$= 0$$

Yes, the points are collinear.

49.

$$\begin{vmatrix} x & y & 1 \\ 3 & -5 & 1 \\ -2 & 6 & 1 \end{vmatrix} = x \begin{vmatrix} -5 & 1 \\ 6 & 1 \end{vmatrix} - y \begin{vmatrix} 3 & 1 \\ -2 & 1 \end{vmatrix} + \begin{vmatrix} 3 & -5 \\ -2 & 6 \end{vmatrix}$$

$$= x(-5-6) - y[3-(-2)] + (18-10)$$
$$= -11x - 5y + 8$$

The equation of the line is $-11x - 5y + 8 = 0$. The equation of the line in slope-intercept form is

$$y = -\frac{11}{5}x + \frac{8}{5}.$$

51.–57. Answers may vary.

59. Exercise 1 and 3

```
det([[5,7][2,3]]
)
                 1
det([[-4,1][5,6]
])
               -29
■
```

Exercises 5 and 7

```
det([[-7,14][2,-
4]])
                 0
det([[-5,-1][-2,
-7]])
                33
```

Exercise 9

```
det([[1/2,1/2][1
/8,-3/4]])▶Frac
              -7/16
■
```

61. Input the matrix as $[A]$, then use $\det[A]$ to find the determinant.

$$\begin{vmatrix} 8 & 2 & 6 & -1 & 0 \\ 2 & 0 & -3 & 4 & 7 \\ 2 & 1 & -3 & 6 & -5 \\ -1 & 2 & 1 & 5 & -1 \\ 4 & 5 & -2 & 3 & -8 \end{vmatrix} = 13,200$$

63. a. $\begin{vmatrix} a & a \\ 0 & a \end{vmatrix} = a^2 - 0 = a^2$

b. $\begin{vmatrix} a & a & a \\ 0 & a & a \\ 0 & 0 & a \end{vmatrix} = a \begin{vmatrix} a & a \\ 0 & a \end{vmatrix} - 0 + 0$

$$= a\left(a^2\right)$$
$$= a^3$$

c. $\begin{vmatrix} a & a & a & a \\ 0 & a & a & a \\ 0 & 0 & a & a \\ 0 & 0 & 0 & a \end{vmatrix} = a \begin{vmatrix} a & a & a \\ 0 & a & a \\ 0 & 0 & a \end{vmatrix} - 0 + 0 - 0$

$$= a\left(a^3\right)$$
$$= a^4$$

d. Each determinant has zeros below the main diagonal and a's everywhere else.

e. Each determinant equals a raised to the power equal to the order of the determinant.

65. The sign of the value is changed when 2 columns are interchanged in a 2nd order determinant.

Review Exercises

1. $x + y + 3z = 12$
$\quad\quad y - 2z = -4$
$\quad\quad\quad\quad z = 3$

$y - 2(3) = -4$
$\quad y - 6 = -4$
$\quad\quad\quad y = 2$

$x + 2 + 3(3) = 12$
$\quad\quad x + 11 = 12$
$\quad\quad\quad\quad x = 1$
The solution to the system is $\{(1, 2, 3)\}$.

2. $x - 2z + 2w = 1$
$\quad y + z - w = 0$
$\quad\quad z - \dfrac{7}{3}w = -\dfrac{1}{3}$
$\quad\quad\quad\quad w = 1$

$z - \dfrac{7}{3}(1) = -\dfrac{1}{3}$
$z - \dfrac{7}{3} = -\dfrac{1}{3}$
$z = \dfrac{6}{3}$
$z = 2$

$y + 2 - 1 = 0$
$\quad y + 1 = 0$
$\quad\quad\quad y = -1$

$x - 2(2) + 2(1) = 1$
$\quad\quad\quad x - 2 = 1$
$\quad\quad\quad\quad\quad x = 3$
The solution to the system is $\{(3, -1, 2, 1)\}$.

3. $\begin{bmatrix} 1 & 2 & 2 & | & 2 \\ 0 & 1 & -1 & | & 2 \\ 0 & 5 & 4 & | & 1 \end{bmatrix} -5R_2 + R_3$

$\begin{bmatrix} 1 & 2 & 2 & | & 2 \\ 0 & 1 & -1 & | & 2 \\ 0 & 0 & 9 & | & -9 \end{bmatrix}$

4. $\begin{bmatrix} 2 & -2 & 1 & | & -1 \\ 1 & 2 & -1 & | & 2 \\ 6 & 4 & 3 & | & 5 \end{bmatrix} \dfrac{1}{2}R_1$

$\begin{bmatrix} 1 & -1 & \frac{1}{2} & | & -\frac{1}{2} \\ 1 & 2 & -1 & | & 2 \\ 6 & 4 & 3 & | & 5 \end{bmatrix}$

5. $\begin{bmatrix} 1 & 2 & 3 & | & -5 \\ 2 & 1 & 1 & | & 1 \\ 1 & 1 & -1 & | & 8 \end{bmatrix} \begin{matrix} -2R_1 + R_2 \\ -1R_1 + R_3 \end{matrix}$

$\begin{bmatrix} 1 & 2 & 3 & | & -5 \\ 0 & -3 & -5 & | & 11 \\ 0 & -1 & -4 & | & 13 \end{bmatrix} R_2 \leftrightarrow R_3$

$$\begin{bmatrix} 1 & 2 & 3 & | & -5 \\ 0 & -1 & -4 & | & 13 \\ 0 & -3 & -5 & | & 11 \end{bmatrix} -1R_2$$

$$\begin{bmatrix} 1 & 2 & 3 & | & -5 \\ 0 & 1 & 4 & | & -13 \\ 0 & -3 & -5 & | & 11 \end{bmatrix} 3R_2 + R_3$$

$$\begin{bmatrix} 1 & 2 & 3 & | & -5 \\ 0 & 1 & 4 & | & -13 \\ 0 & 0 & 7 & | & -28 \end{bmatrix} \tfrac{1}{7}R_3$$

$$\begin{bmatrix} 1 & 2 & 3 & | & -5 \\ 0 & 1 & 4 & | & -13 \\ 0 & 0 & 1 & | & -4 \end{bmatrix} -2R_2 + R_1$$

$$\begin{bmatrix} 1 & 0 & -5 & | & 21 \\ 0 & 1 & 4 & | & -13 \\ 0 & 0 & 1 & | & -4 \end{bmatrix} \begin{matrix} 5R_3 + R_1 \\ \\ -4R_3 + R_2 \end{matrix}$$

$$\begin{bmatrix} 1 & 0 & 0 & | & 1 \\ 0 & 1 & 0 & | & 3 \\ 0 & 0 & 1 & | & -4 \end{bmatrix}$$

The solution set is $\{(1, 3, -4)\}$.

6. $$\begin{bmatrix} 1 & -2 & 1 & | & 0 \\ 0 & 1 & -3 & | & -1 \\ 0 & 2 & 5 & | & -2 \end{bmatrix} -2R_2 + R_3$$

$$\begin{bmatrix} 1 & -2 & 1 & | & 0 \\ 0 & 1 & -3 & | & -1 \\ 0 & 0 & 11 & | & 0 \end{bmatrix} \tfrac{1}{11}R_3$$

$$\begin{bmatrix} 1 & -2 & 1 & | & 0 \\ 0 & 1 & -3 & | & -1 \\ 0 & 0 & 1 & | & 0 \end{bmatrix} 2R_2 + R_1$$

$$\begin{bmatrix} 1 & 0 & -5 & | & -2 \\ 0 & 1 & -3 & | & -1 \\ 0 & 0 & 1 & | & 0 \end{bmatrix} \begin{matrix} 3R_3 + R_2 \\ 5R_3 + R_1 \end{matrix}$$

$$\begin{bmatrix} 1 & 0 & 0 & | & -2 \\ 0 & 1 & 0 & | & -1 \\ 0 & 0 & 1 & | & 0 \end{bmatrix}$$

$x = -2; y = -1; z = 0$
The solution set is $\{(-2, -1, 0)\}$.

7. $$\begin{bmatrix} 3 & 5 & -8 & 5 & | & -8 \\ 1 & 2 & -3 & 1 & | & -7 \\ 2 & 3 & -7 & 3 & | & -11 \\ 4 & 8 & -10 & 7 & | & -10 \end{bmatrix} R_1 \leftrightarrow R_2$$

$$\begin{bmatrix} 1 & 2 & -3 & 1 & | & -7 \\ 3 & 5 & -8 & 5 & | & -8 \\ 2 & 3 & -7 & 3 & | & -11 \\ 4 & 8 & -10 & 7 & | & -10 \end{bmatrix} \begin{matrix} -3R_1 + R_2 \\ -2R_1 + R_3 \\ -4R_1 + R_4 \end{matrix}$$

$$\begin{bmatrix} 1 & 2 & -3 & 1 & | & -7 \\ 0 & -1 & 1 & 2 & | & 13 \\ 0 & -1 & -1 & 1 & | & 3 \\ 0 & 0 & 2 & 3 & | & 18 \end{bmatrix} -1R_2$$

$$\begin{bmatrix} 1 & 2 & -3 & 1 & | & -7 \\ 0 & 1 & -1 & -2 & | & -13 \\ 0 & -1 & -1 & 1 & | & 3 \\ 0 & 0 & 2 & 3 & | & 18 \end{bmatrix} \begin{matrix} -2R_2 + R_1 \\ 1R_2 + R_3 \end{matrix}$$

$$\begin{bmatrix} 1 & 0 & -1 & 5 & | & 19 \\ 0 & 1 & -1 & -2 & | & -13 \\ 0 & 0 & -2 & -1 & | & -10 \\ 0 & 0 & 2 & 3 & | & 18 \end{bmatrix} -\tfrac{1}{2}R_3$$

$$\begin{bmatrix} 1 & 0 & -1 & 5 & | & 19 \\ 0 & 1 & -1 & -2 & | & -13 \\ 0 & 0 & 1 & \tfrac{1}{2} & | & 5 \\ 0 & 0 & 2 & 3 & | & 18 \end{bmatrix} \begin{matrix} 1R_3 + R_1 \\ 1R_3 + R_2 \\ -2R_3 + R_4 \end{matrix}$$

$$\begin{bmatrix} 1 & 0 & 0 & \tfrac{11}{2} & | & 24 \\ 0 & 1 & 0 & -\tfrac{3}{2} & | & -8 \\ 0 & 0 & 1 & \tfrac{1}{2} & | & 5 \\ 0 & 0 & 0 & 2 & | & 8 \end{bmatrix} \tfrac{1}{2}R_4$$

$$\begin{bmatrix} 1 & 0 & 0 & \tfrac{11}{2} & | & 24 \\ 0 & 1 & 0 & -\tfrac{3}{2} & | & -8 \\ 0 & 0 & 1 & \tfrac{1}{2} & | & 5 \\ 0 & 0 & 0 & 1 & | & 4 \end{bmatrix} \begin{matrix} -\tfrac{11}{2}R_4 + R_1 \\ \tfrac{3}{2}R_4 + R_2 \\ -\tfrac{1}{2}R_4 + R_3 \end{matrix}$$

$$\begin{bmatrix} 1 & 0 & 0 & 0 & | & 2 \\ 0 & 1 & 0 & 0 & | & -2 \\ 0 & 0 & 1 & 0 & | & 3 \\ 0 & 0 & 0 & 1 & | & 4 \end{bmatrix}$$

The solution set is $\{(2, -2, 3, 4)\}$.

8. a. The function must satisfy:

$98 = 4a = 2b + c$
$138 = 16a + 4b + c$
$162 = 100a + 10b + c.$

$$\begin{bmatrix} 4 & 2 & 1 & | & 98 \\ 16 & 4 & 1 & | & 138 \\ 100 & 10 & 1 & | & 162 \end{bmatrix} \frac{1}{4}R_1$$

$$\begin{bmatrix} 1 & \frac{1}{2} & \frac{1}{4} & | & \frac{49}{2} \\ 16 & 4 & 1 & | & 138 \\ 100 & 10 & 1 & | & 162 \end{bmatrix} \begin{matrix} -16R_1 + R_2 \\ \\ -100R_1 + R_3 \end{matrix}$$

$$\begin{bmatrix} 1 & \frac{1}{2} & \frac{1}{4} & | & \frac{49}{2} \\ 0 & -4 & -3 & | & -254 \\ 0 & -40 & -24 & | & -2288 \end{bmatrix} -\frac{1}{4}R_2$$

$$\begin{bmatrix} 1 & \frac{1}{2} & \frac{1}{4} & | & \frac{49}{2} \\ 0 & 1 & \frac{3}{4} & | & \frac{127}{2} \\ 0 & -40 & -24 & | & -2288 \end{bmatrix} 40R_2 + R_3$$

$$\begin{bmatrix} 1 & \frac{1}{2} & \frac{1}{4} & | & \frac{49}{2} \\ 0 & 1 & \frac{3}{4} & | & \frac{127}{2} \\ 0 & 0 & 6 & | & 252 \end{bmatrix} \frac{1}{6}R_3$$

$$\begin{bmatrix} 1 & \frac{1}{2} & \frac{1}{4} & | & \frac{49}{2} \\ 0 & 1 & \frac{3}{4} & | & \frac{127}{2} \\ 0 & 0 & 1 & | & 42 \end{bmatrix} \begin{matrix} -\frac{1}{4}R_3 + R_1 \\ \\ -\frac{3}{4}R_3 + R_2 \end{matrix}$$

$$\begin{bmatrix} 1 & \frac{1}{2} & 0 & | & 14 \\ 0 & 1 & 0 & | & 32 \\ 0 & 0 & 1 & | & 42 \end{bmatrix} -\frac{1}{2}R_3 + R_1$$

$$\begin{bmatrix} 1 & 0 & 0 & | & -2 \\ 0 & 1 & 0 & | & 32 \\ 0 & 0 & 1 & | & 42 \end{bmatrix}$$

The function is $y = -2x^2 + 32x + 42$
and $a = -2$, $b = 32$ and $c = 42$.

b. $y = -2x^2 + 32x + 42$ is a parabola.
The maximum occurs when
$$x = \frac{-32}{2(-2)} = \frac{-32}{-4} = 8.$$

The air pollution level is a maximum 8
hours after 6 A.M., which is 2 P.M.
When $x = 8$, $y = -2(64) + 32(8) + 42$
$\qquad\qquad = -128 + 256 + 42.$
$\qquad\qquad = 170.$
The maximum level is 170 parts per
million.

9. $$\begin{bmatrix} 2 & -3 & 1 & | & 1 \\ 1 & -2 & 3 & | & 2 \\ 3 & -4 & -1 & | & 1 \end{bmatrix} R_1 \leftrightarrow R_2$$

$$\begin{bmatrix} 1 & -2 & 3 & | & 2 \\ 2 & -3 & 1 & | & 1 \\ 3 & -4 & -1 & | & 1 \end{bmatrix} \begin{matrix} -2R_1 + R_2 \\ \\ -3R_1 + R_3 \end{matrix}$$

$$\begin{bmatrix} 1 & -2 & 3 & | & 2 \\ 0 & 1 & -5 & | & -3 \\ 0 & 2 & -10 & | & -5 \end{bmatrix} -2R_2 + R_3$$

$$\begin{bmatrix} 1 & -2 & 3 & | & 2 \\ 0 & 1 & -5 & | & -3 \\ 0 & 0 & 0 & | & 1 \end{bmatrix}$$

From the last line, we see that the system has
no solution. Thus, the solution set is $\varnothing$.

10. $$\begin{bmatrix} 1 & -3 & 1 & | & 1 \\ -2 & 1 & 3 & | & -7 \\ 1 & -4 & 2 & | & 0 \end{bmatrix} \begin{matrix} 2R_1 + R_2 \\ \\ -1R_1 + R_3 \end{matrix}$$

$$\begin{bmatrix} 1 & -3 & 1 & | & 1 \\ 0 & -5 & 5 & | & -5 \\ 0 & -1 & 1 & | & -1 \end{bmatrix} -\frac{1}{5}R_2$$

$$\begin{bmatrix} 1 & -3 & 1 & | & 1 \\ 0 & 1 & -1 & | & 1 \\ 0 & -1 & 1 & | & -1 \end{bmatrix} 1R_2 + R_3$$

$$\begin{bmatrix} 1 & -3 & 1 & | & 1 \\ 0 & 1 & -1 & | & 1 \\ 0 & 0 & 0 & | & 0 \end{bmatrix}$$

The system $\begin{array}{l} x - 3y + z = 1 \\ y - z = 1 \end{array}$ has no unique

solution. Express x and y in terms of z:
$y = z + 1$
$x - 3(z + 1) + z = 1$
$\quad x - 3z - 3 + z = 1$
$\qquad\qquad x = 2z + 4$
With $z = t$, the complete solution to the
system is $\{(2t + 4, t + 1, t)\}$.

11. $\begin{bmatrix} 1 & 4 & 3 & -6 & | & 5 \\ 1 & 3 & 1 & -4 & | & 3 \\ 2 & 8 & 7 & -5 & | & 11 \\ 2 & 5 & 0 & -6 & | & 4 \end{bmatrix} \begin{matrix} -1R_1 + R_2 \\ -2R_1 + R_3 \\ -2R_1 + R_4 \end{matrix}$

$\begin{bmatrix} 1 & 4 & 3 & -6 & | & 5 \\ 0 & -1 & -2 & 2 & | & -2 \\ 0 & 0 & 1 & 7 & | & 1 \\ 0 & -3 & -6 & 6 & | & -6 \end{bmatrix} -1R_2$

$\begin{bmatrix} 1 & 4 & 3 & -6 & | & 5 \\ 0 & 1 & 2 & -2 & | & 2 \\ 0 & 0 & 1 & 7 & | & 1 \\ 0 & -3 & -6 & 6 & | & -6 \end{bmatrix} 3R_2 + R_4$

$\begin{bmatrix} 1 & 4 & 3 & -6 & | & 5 \\ 0 & 1 & 2 & -2 & | & 2 \\ 0 & 0 & 1 & 7 & | & 1 \\ 0 & 0 & 0 & 0 & | & 0 \end{bmatrix}$

The system $\begin{array}{l} x_1 + 4x_2 + 3x_3 - 6x_4 = 5 \\ x_2 + 2x_3 - 2x_4 = 2 \\ x_3 + 7x_4 = 1 \end{array}$

does not have a unique solution.
Express x_1, x_2, and x_3 in terms of x_4:
$x_3 = -7x_4 + 1$
$x_2 + 2(-7x_4 + 1) - 2x_4 = 2$
$\quad x_2 - 14x_4 + 2 - 2x_4 = 2$
$\qquad\qquad x_2 = 16x_4$
$x_1 + 4(16x_4) + 3(-7x_4 + 1) - 6x_4 = 5$
$\quad x_1 + 64x_4 - 21x_4 + 3 - 6x_4 = 5$
$\qquad\qquad\qquad x_1 = -37x_4 + 2$
With $x_4 = t$, the complete solution to the
system is $\{(-37t + 2, 16t, -7t + 1, t)\}$.

12. $\begin{bmatrix} 2 & 3 & -5 & | & 15 \\ 1 & 2 & -1 & | & 4 \end{bmatrix} R_1 \leftrightarrow R_2$

$\begin{bmatrix} 1 & 2 & -1 & | & 4 \\ 2 & 3 & -5 & | & 15 \end{bmatrix} -2R_1 + R_2$

$\begin{bmatrix} 1 & 2 & -1 & | & 4 \\ 0 & -1 & -3 & | & 7 \end{bmatrix} -1R_2$

$\begin{bmatrix} 1 & 2 & -1 & | & 4 \\ 0 & 1 & 3 & | & -7 \end{bmatrix}$

The system $\begin{array}{l} x + 2y - z = 4 \\ y + 3z = -7 \end{array}$ has no unique

solution. Express x and y in terms of z:
$y = -3z - 7$
$x + 2(-3z - 7) - z = 4$
$\quad x - 6z - 14 - z = 4$
$\qquad\qquad x = 7z + 18$
With $z = t$, the complete solution to the
system is $\{(7t + 18, -3t - 7, t)\}$.

13. a. $350 + 400 = x + z$
$450 + z = y + 700$
$x + y = 300 + 200$
or
$x + z = 750$
$y \quad z = 250$
$x + y = 500$

b. $\begin{bmatrix} 1 & 0 & 1 & | & 750 \\ 0 & 1 & -1 & | & -250 \\ 1 & 1 & 0 & | & 500 \end{bmatrix} -1R_1 + R_3$

$\begin{bmatrix} 1 & 0 & 1 & | & 750 \\ 0 & 1 & -1 & | & -250 \\ 0 & 1 & -1 & | & -250 \end{bmatrix} -1R_2 + R_3$

$\begin{bmatrix} 1 & 0 & 1 & | & 750 \\ 0 & 1 & -1 & | & -250 \\ 0 & 0 & 0 & | & 0 \end{bmatrix}$

The system $\begin{array}{l} x + z = 750 \\ y - z = -250 \end{array}$ has no unique

solution.
Express x and y in terms of z:
$y = z - 250$
$x = -z + 750$

With $z = t$, the complete solution to the system is $\{(-t + 750, t - 250, t)\}$.

c. $x = -400 + 750 = 350$
$y = 400 - 250 = 150$

14. $2x = -10$
$x = -5$
$y + 7 = 13$
$y = 6$
$z = 6$
$x = -5; y = 6; z = 6$

15. $A + D = \begin{bmatrix} 2-2 & -1+3 & 2+1 \\ 5+3 & 3-2 & -1+4 \end{bmatrix} = \begin{bmatrix} 0 & 2 & 3 \\ 8 & 1 & 3 \end{bmatrix}$

16. $2B = \begin{bmatrix} 2(0) & 2(-2) \\ 2(3) & 2(2) \\ 2(1) & 2(-5) \end{bmatrix} = \begin{bmatrix} 0 & -4 \\ 6 & 4 \\ 2 & -10 \end{bmatrix}$

17. $D - A = \begin{bmatrix} -2-2 & 3+1 & 1-2 \\ 3-5 & -2-3 & 4+1 \end{bmatrix}$
$= \begin{bmatrix} -4 & 4 & -1 \\ -2 & -5 & 5 \end{bmatrix}$

18. Not possible since B is 3×2 and C is 3×3.

19. $3A + 2D = \begin{bmatrix} 6 & -3 & 6 \\ 15 & 9 & -3 \end{bmatrix} + \begin{bmatrix} -4 & 6 & 2 \\ 6 & -4 & 8 \end{bmatrix} = \begin{bmatrix} 2 & 3 & 8 \\ 21 & 5 & 5 \end{bmatrix}$

20. $-2A + 4D = \begin{bmatrix} -4 & 2 & -4 \\ -10 & -6 & 2 \end{bmatrix} + \begin{bmatrix} -8 & 12 & 4 \\ 12 & -8 & 16 \end{bmatrix} = \begin{bmatrix} -12 & 14 & 0 \\ 2 & -14 & 18 \end{bmatrix}$

21. $-5(A + D) = -5\left(\begin{bmatrix} 0 & 2 & 3 \\ 8 & 1 & 3 \end{bmatrix} \right) = \begin{bmatrix} 0 & -10 & -15 \\ -40 & -5 & -15 \end{bmatrix}$

22. $AB = \begin{bmatrix} 0-3+2 & -4-2-10 \\ 0+9-1 & -10+6+5 \end{bmatrix} = \begin{bmatrix} -1 & -16 \\ 8 & 1 \end{bmatrix}$

23. $BA = \begin{bmatrix} 0-10 & 0-6 & 0+2 \\ 6+10 & -3+6 & 6-2 \\ 2-25 & -1-15 & 2+5 \end{bmatrix} = \begin{bmatrix} -10 & -6 & 2 \\ 16 & 3 & 4 \\ -23 & -16 & 7 \end{bmatrix}$

24. $BD = \begin{bmatrix} 0-6 & 0+4 & 0-8 \\ -6+6 & 9-4 & 3+8 \\ -2-15 & 3+10 & 1-20 \end{bmatrix} = \begin{bmatrix} -6 & 4 & -8 \\ 0 & 5 & 11 \\ -17 & 13 & -19 \end{bmatrix}$

25. $DB = \begin{bmatrix} 0+9+1 & 4+6-5 \\ 0-6+4 & -6-4-20 \end{bmatrix} = \begin{bmatrix} 10 & 5 \\ -2 & -30 \end{bmatrix}$

26. Not possible since AB is 2×2 and BA is 3×3.

27. $(A-D)C = \begin{bmatrix} 4 & -4 & 1 \\ 2 & 5 & -5 \end{bmatrix} \begin{bmatrix} 1 & 2 & 3 \\ -1 & 1 & 2 \\ -1 & 2 & 1 \end{bmatrix} = \begin{bmatrix} 4+4-1 & 8-4+2 & 12-8+1 \\ 2-5+5 & 4+5-10 & 6+10-5 \end{bmatrix} = \begin{bmatrix} 7 & 6 & 5 \\ 2 & -1 & 11 \end{bmatrix}$

28. $B(AC) = \begin{bmatrix} 0 & -2 \\ 3 & 2 \\ 1 & -5 \end{bmatrix} \begin{bmatrix} 2+1-2 & 4-1+4 & 6-2+2 \\ 5-3+1 & 10+3-2 & 15+6-1 \end{bmatrix}$

$= \begin{bmatrix} 0 & -2 \\ 3 & 2 \\ 1 & -5 \end{bmatrix} \begin{bmatrix} 1 & 7 & 6 \\ 3 & 11 & 20 \end{bmatrix}$

$= \begin{bmatrix} 0-6 & 0-22 & 0-40 \\ 3+6 & 21+22 & 18+40 \\ 1-15 & 7-55 & 6-100 \end{bmatrix}$

$= \begin{bmatrix} -6 & -22 & -40 \\ 9 & 43 & 58 \\ -14 & -48 & -94 \end{bmatrix}$

29. $\begin{bmatrix} 2 & 1 & 1 \\ 2 & 1 & 1 \\ 2 & 2 & 2 \end{bmatrix}$

30. $B = \begin{bmatrix} 1 & -1 & -1 \\ 1 & -1 & -1 \\ 1 & 1 & 1 \end{bmatrix}$

31. a. $AB = \begin{bmatrix} 192,000+84,000+84,000 & 228,000+105,000+111,000 \\ 340,000+96,000+140,000 & 380,000+120,000+185,000 \\ 112,000+24,000+42,000 & 133,000+30,000+55,500 \end{bmatrix} = \begin{bmatrix} 360,000 & 444,000 \\ 556,000 & 685,000 \\ 178,000 & 218,500 \end{bmatrix}$

   b. The rows of AB correspond to the outlets, the columns represent the wholesale and retail prices. The entries tell how much value in wholesale or retail is at each outlet.

    c. $360,000

    d. $685,000

    e. Profit = retail price − wholesale price = $218,500 − $178,000 = $40,500

32. $AB = \begin{bmatrix} 8-7 & -14+21 \\ 4-4 & -7+12 \end{bmatrix} = \begin{bmatrix} 1 & 7 \\ 0 & 5 \end{bmatrix}$

$BA = \begin{bmatrix} 8-7 & 28-28 \\ -2+3 & -7+12 \end{bmatrix} = \begin{bmatrix} 1 & 0 \\ 1 & 5 \end{bmatrix}$

If B is the multiplicative inverse of A, both products (AB and BA) will be the multiplicative identity matrix, I_2. Therefore, B is not the multiplicative inverse of A. That is, $B \neq A^{-1}$.

33. $AB = \begin{bmatrix} 1+0+0 & 0+0+0 & 0+0+0 \\ 0+0+0 & 0+8-7 & 0+14-14 \\ 0+0+0 & 0-4+4 & 0-7+8 \end{bmatrix} = \begin{bmatrix} 1 & 0 & 0 \\ 0 & 1 & 0 \\ 0 & 0 & 1 \end{bmatrix}$

$BA = \begin{bmatrix} 1+0+0 & 0+0+0 & 0+0+0 \\ 0+0+0 & 1+8-7 & 0-28+28 \\ 0+0+0 & 0+2-2 & 0-7+8 \end{bmatrix} = \begin{bmatrix} 1 & 0 & 0 \\ 0 & 1 & 0 \\ 0 & 0 & 1 \end{bmatrix}$

Since $AB = I_3$ and $BA = I_3$, $B = A^{-1}$.

34. $A^{-1} = \dfrac{1}{3-2} \begin{bmatrix} 3 & 1 \\ 2 & 1 \end{bmatrix}$

$= 1 \begin{bmatrix} 3 & 1 \\ 2 & 1 \end{bmatrix}$

$= \begin{bmatrix} 3 & 1 \\ 2 & 1 \end{bmatrix}$

$AA^{-1} = \begin{bmatrix} 1 & -1 \\ -2 & 3 \end{bmatrix} \begin{bmatrix} 3 & 1 \\ 2 & 1 \end{bmatrix}$

$= \begin{bmatrix} 3-2 & 1-1 \\ -6+6 & -2+3 \end{bmatrix}$

$= \begin{bmatrix} 1 & 0 \\ 0 & 1 \end{bmatrix}$

$A^{-1}A = \begin{bmatrix} 3 & 1 \\ 2 & 1 \end{bmatrix} \begin{bmatrix} 1 & -1 \\ -2 & 3 \end{bmatrix}$

$= \begin{bmatrix} 3-2 & 3+3 \\ 2-2 & -2+3 \end{bmatrix}$

$= \begin{bmatrix} 1 & 0 \\ 0 & 1 \end{bmatrix}$

35. $A^{-1} = \dfrac{1}{0-5}\begin{bmatrix} 3 & -1 \\ -5 & 0 \end{bmatrix}$

$\qquad = \dfrac{-1}{5}\begin{bmatrix} 3 & -1 \\ -5 & 0 \end{bmatrix}$

$\qquad = \begin{bmatrix} -\frac{3}{5} & \frac{1}{5} \\ 1 & 0 \end{bmatrix}$

$AA^{-1} = \begin{bmatrix} 0 & 1 \\ 5 & 3 \end{bmatrix}\begin{bmatrix} -\frac{3}{5} & \frac{1}{5} \\ 1 & 0 \end{bmatrix}$

$\qquad = \begin{bmatrix} 0+1 & 0+0 \\ -3+3 & 1+0 \end{bmatrix}$

$\qquad = \begin{bmatrix} 1 & 0 \\ 0 & 1 \end{bmatrix}$

$A^{-1}A = \begin{bmatrix} -\frac{3}{5} & \frac{1}{5} \\ 1 & 0 \end{bmatrix}\begin{bmatrix} 0 & 1 \\ 5 & 3 \end{bmatrix}$

$\qquad = \begin{bmatrix} 0+1 & -\frac{3}{5}+\frac{3}{5} \\ 0+0 & 1+0 \end{bmatrix}$

$\qquad = \begin{bmatrix} 1 & 0 \\ 0 & 1 \end{bmatrix}$

36. $\left[\begin{array}{ccc|ccc} 1 & 0 & -2 & 1 & 0 & 0 \\ 2 & 1 & 0 & 0 & 1 & 0 \\ 1 & 0 & -3 & 0 & 0 & 1 \end{array}\right]\begin{array}{l} \\ -2R_1 + R_2 \\ -1R_1 + R_3 \end{array}$

$\left[\begin{array}{ccc|ccc} 1 & 0 & -2 & 1 & 0 & 0 \\ 0 & 1 & 4 & -2 & 1 & 0 \\ 0 & 0 & -1 & -1 & 0 & 1 \end{array}\right]\begin{array}{l} \\ \\ -1R_3 \end{array}$

$\left[\begin{array}{ccc|ccc} 1 & 0 & -2 & 1 & 0 & 0 \\ 0 & 1 & 4 & -2 & 1 & 0 \\ 0 & 0 & 1 & 1 & 0 & -1 \end{array}\right]\begin{array}{l} 2R_3 + R_1 \\ \\ -4R_3 + R_2 \end{array}$

$\left[\begin{array}{ccc|ccc} 1 & 0 & 0 & 3 & 0 & -2 \\ 0 & 1 & 0 & -6 & 1 & 4 \\ 0 & 0 & 1 & 1 & 0 & -1 \end{array}\right]$

$$A^{-1} = \begin{bmatrix} 3 & 0 & -2 \\ -6 & 1 & 4 \\ 1 & 0 & -1 \end{bmatrix}$$

$$AA^{-1} = \begin{bmatrix} 1 & 0 & -2 \\ 2 & 1 & 0 \\ 1 & 0 & -3 \end{bmatrix}\begin{bmatrix} 3 & 0 & -2 \\ -6 & 1 & 4 \\ 1 & 0 & -1 \end{bmatrix}$$

$$= \begin{bmatrix} 3+0-2 & 0+0+0 & -2+0+2 \\ 6-6+0 & 0+1+0 & -4+4+0 \\ 3+0-3 & 0+0+0 & -2+0+3 \end{bmatrix}$$

$$= \begin{bmatrix} 1 & 0 & 0 \\ 0 & 1 & 0 \\ 0 & 0 & 1 \end{bmatrix}$$

$$A^{-1}A = \begin{bmatrix} 3 & 0 & -2 \\ -6 & 1 & 4 \\ 1 & 0 & -1 \end{bmatrix}\begin{bmatrix} 1 & 0 & -2 \\ 2 & 1 & 0 \\ 1 & 0 & -3 \end{bmatrix}$$

$$= \begin{bmatrix} 3+0-2 & 0+0+0 & -6+0+6 \\ -6+2+4 & 0+1+0 & 12+0-12 \\ 1+0-1 & 0+0+0 & -2+0+3 \end{bmatrix}$$

$$= \begin{bmatrix} 1 & 0 & 0 \\ 0 & 1 & 0 \\ 0 & 0 & 1 \end{bmatrix}$$

37. $\left[\begin{array}{ccc|ccc} 1 & 3 & -2 & 1 & 0 & 0 \\ 4 & 13 & -7 & 0 & 1 & 0 \\ 5 & 16 & -8 & 0 & 0 & 1 \end{array}\right]\begin{array}{l} -4R_1 + R_2 \\ -5R_1 + R_3 \end{array}$

$\left[\begin{array}{ccc|ccc} 1 & 3 & -2 & 1 & 0 & 0 \\ 0 & 1 & 1 & -4 & 1 & 0 \\ 0 & 1 & 2 & -5 & 0 & 1 \end{array}\right]\begin{array}{l} -1R_2 + R_3 \\ -3R_2 + R_1 \end{array}$

$\left[\begin{array}{ccc|ccc} 1 & 0 & -5 & 13 & -3 & 0 \\ 0 & 1 & 1 & -4 & 1 & 0 \\ 0 & 0 & 1 & -1 & -1 & 1 \end{array}\right]\begin{array}{l} -1R_3 + R_2 \\ 5R_3 + R_1 \end{array}$

$\left[\begin{array}{ccc|ccc} 1 & 0 & 0 & 8 & -8 & 5 \\ 0 & 1 & 0 & -3 & 2 & -1 \\ 0 & 0 & 1 & -1 & -1 & 1 \end{array}\right]$

$$A^{-1} = \begin{bmatrix} 8 & -8 & 5 \\ -3 & 2 & -1 \\ -1 & -1 & 1 \end{bmatrix}$$

$$AA^{-1} = \begin{bmatrix} 1 & 3 & -2 \\ 4 & 13 & -7 \\ 5 & 16 & -8 \end{bmatrix} \begin{bmatrix} 8 & -8 & 5 \\ -3 & 2 & -1 \\ -1 & -1 & 1 \end{bmatrix} = \begin{bmatrix} 8-9+2 & -8+6+2 & 5-3-2 \\ 32-39+7 & -32+26+7 & 20-13-7 \\ 40-48+8 & -40+32+8 & 25-16-8 \end{bmatrix} = \begin{bmatrix} 1 & 0 & 0 \\ 0 & 1 & 0 \\ 0 & 0 & 1 \end{bmatrix}$$

$$A^{-1}A = \begin{bmatrix} 8 & -8 & 5 \\ -3 & 2 & -1 \\ -1 & -1 & -1 \end{bmatrix} \begin{bmatrix} 1 & 3 & -2 \\ 4 & 13 & -7 \\ 5 & 16 & -8 \end{bmatrix} = \begin{bmatrix} 8-32+25 & 24-104+80 & -16+56-40 \\ -3+8-5 & -9+26-16 & 6-14+8 \\ -1-4+5 & -3-13+16 & 2+7-8 \end{bmatrix} = \begin{bmatrix} 1 & 0 & 0 \\ 0 & 1 & 0 \\ 0 & 0 & 1 \end{bmatrix}$$

38. a. $\begin{bmatrix} 1 & 1 & 2 \\ 0 & 1 & 3 \\ 3 & 0 & -2 \end{bmatrix} \begin{bmatrix} x \\ y \\ z \end{bmatrix} = \begin{bmatrix} 7 \\ -2 \\ 0 \end{bmatrix}$.

b. $A^{-1}B = \begin{bmatrix} -2 & 2 & 1 \\ 9 & -8 & -3 \\ -3 & 3 & 1 \end{bmatrix} \begin{bmatrix} 7 \\ -2 \\ 0 \end{bmatrix} = \begin{bmatrix} -14-4+0 \\ 63+16+0 \\ -21-6+0 \end{bmatrix} = \begin{bmatrix} -18 \\ 79 \\ -27 \end{bmatrix}$

The solution to the system is $\{(-18, 79, -27)\}$.

39. a. $\begin{bmatrix} 1 & -1 & 2 \\ 0 & 1 & -1 \\ 1 & 0 & 2 \end{bmatrix} \begin{bmatrix} x \\ y \\ z \end{bmatrix} = \begin{bmatrix} 12 \\ -5 \\ 10 \end{bmatrix}$

b.

$$A^{-1}B = \begin{bmatrix} 2 & 2 & -1 \\ -1 & 0 & 1 \\ -1 & -1 & 1 \end{bmatrix} \begin{bmatrix} 12 \\ -5 \\ 10 \end{bmatrix} = \begin{bmatrix} 24-10-10 \\ -12+10 \\ -12+5+10 \end{bmatrix} = \begin{bmatrix} 4 \\ -2 \\ 3 \end{bmatrix}$$

The solution to the system is $\{(4, -2, 3)\}$.

40. R U L E has a numerical equivalent of 18, 21, 12, 5.
$$\begin{bmatrix} 3 & 2 \\ 4 & 3 \end{bmatrix} \begin{bmatrix} 18 & 12 \\ 21 & 5 \end{bmatrix} = \begin{bmatrix} 54+42 & 36+10 \\ 72+63 & 48+15 \end{bmatrix} = \begin{bmatrix} 96 & 46 \\ 135 & 63 \end{bmatrix}$$
The encoded message is 96, 135, 46, 63.

$$\begin{bmatrix} 3 & -2 \\ -4 & 3 \end{bmatrix} \begin{bmatrix} 96 & 46 \\ 135 & 63 \end{bmatrix} = \begin{bmatrix} 288-270 & 138-126 \\ -384+405 & -184+189 \end{bmatrix} = \begin{bmatrix} 18 & 12 \\ 21 & 5 \end{bmatrix}$$
The decoded message is 18, 21, 12, 5 or RULE.

41. $\begin{vmatrix} 3 & 2 \\ -1 & 5 \end{vmatrix} = 15-(-2) = 17$

42. $\begin{vmatrix} -2 & -3 \\ -4 & -8 \end{vmatrix} = 16 - 12 = 4$

43. $\begin{vmatrix} 2 & 4 & -3 \\ 1 & -1 & 5 \\ -2 & 4 & 0 \end{vmatrix} = -2\begin{vmatrix} 4 & -3 \\ -1 & 5 \end{vmatrix} - 4\begin{vmatrix} 2 & -3 \\ 1 & 5 \end{vmatrix} + 0\begin{vmatrix} 2 & 4 \\ 1 & -1 \end{vmatrix}$

$= -2(20 - 3) - 4[10 - (-3)] + 0$
$= -2(17) - 4(13)$
$= -34 - 52$
$= -86$

44. $\begin{vmatrix} 4 & 7 & 0 \\ -5 & 6 & 0 \\ 3 & 2 & -4 \end{vmatrix} = 4\begin{vmatrix} 6 & 0 \\ 2 & -4 \end{vmatrix} + 5\begin{vmatrix} 7 & 0 \\ 2 & -4 \end{vmatrix} + 3\begin{vmatrix} 7 & 0 \\ 6 & 0 \end{vmatrix}$

$= 4(-24 - 0) + 5(-28 - 0) + 3(0 - 0)$
$= 4(-24) + 5(-28) + 0$
$= -236$

45. $\begin{vmatrix} 1 & 1 & 0 & 2 \\ 0 & 3 & 2 & 1 \\ 0 & -2 & 4 & 0 \\ 0 & 3 & 0 & 1 \end{vmatrix} = \begin{vmatrix} 3 & 2 & 1 \\ -2 & 4 & 0 \\ 3 & 0 & 1 \end{vmatrix}$

$= 3\begin{vmatrix} 2 & 1 \\ 4 & 0 \end{vmatrix} + \begin{vmatrix} 3 & 2 \\ -2 & 4 \end{vmatrix}$
$= 3(0 - 4) + [12 - (-4)]$
$= 3(-4) + 16$
$= -12 + 16$
$= 4$

46. $\begin{vmatrix} 2 & 2 & 2 & 2 \\ 0 & 2 & 2 & 2 \\ 0 & 0 & 2 & 2 \\ 0 & 0 & 0 & 2 \end{vmatrix} = 2\begin{vmatrix} 2 & 2 & 2 \\ 0 & 2 & 2 \\ 0 & 0 & 2 \end{vmatrix}$

$= 2(2)\begin{vmatrix} 2 & 2 \\ 0 & 2 \end{vmatrix}$
$= 2(2)(4)$
$= 16$

47. $D = \begin{vmatrix} 1 & -2 \\ 3 & 2 \end{vmatrix} = 2 - (-6) = 2 + 6 = 8$

$D_x = \begin{vmatrix} 8 & -2 \\ -1 & 2 \end{vmatrix} = 16 - 2 = 14$

$D_y = \begin{vmatrix} 1 & 8 \\ 3 & -1 \end{vmatrix} = -1 - 24 = -25$

$x = \dfrac{D_x}{D} = \dfrac{14}{8} = \dfrac{7}{4}, \ y = \dfrac{D_y}{D} = \dfrac{-25}{8} = -\dfrac{25}{8}$

The solution to the system is $\left\{ \left(\dfrac{7}{4}, -\dfrac{25}{8} \right) \right\}$.

48. $D = \begin{vmatrix} 7 & 2 \\ 2 & 1 \end{vmatrix} = 7 - 4 = 3$

$D = \begin{vmatrix} 7 & 2 \\ 2 & 1 \end{vmatrix} = 7 - 4 = 3$

$D_x = \begin{vmatrix} 0 & 2 \\ -3 & 1 \end{vmatrix} = 0 - (-6) = 6$

$D_y = \begin{vmatrix} 7 & 0 \\ 2 & -3 \end{vmatrix} = -21 - 0 = -21$

$x = \dfrac{D_x}{D} - \dfrac{6}{3} - 2$

$y = \dfrac{D_y}{D} = \dfrac{-21}{3} = -7$

The solution to the system is $\{(2, -7)\}$.

49. $D = \begin{vmatrix} 1 & 2 & 2 \\ 2 & 4 & 7 \\ -2 & -5 & -2 \end{vmatrix}$

$= \begin{vmatrix} 1 & 2 & 2 \\ 0 & 0 & 3 \\ 0 & -1 & 2 \end{vmatrix}$

$= \begin{vmatrix} 0 & 3 \\ -1 & 2 \end{vmatrix}$

$= 0 - (-3)$

$= 3$

$D_x = \begin{vmatrix} 5 & 2 & 2 \\ 19 & 4 & 7 \\ 8 & -5 & -2 \end{vmatrix}$

$= 5 \begin{vmatrix} 4 & 7 \\ -5 & -2 \end{vmatrix} - 2 \begin{vmatrix} 19 & 7 \\ 8 & -2 \end{vmatrix} + 2 \begin{vmatrix} 19 & 4 \\ 8 & -5 \end{vmatrix}$

$= 5[-8 - (-35)] - 2(-38 - 56) + 2(-95 - 32)$

$= 5(27) - 2(-94) - 2(127)$

$= 135 + 188 - 254$

$= 69$

$D_y = \begin{vmatrix} 1 & 5 & 2 \\ 2 & 19 & 7 \\ -2 & 8 & -2 \end{vmatrix}$

$= \begin{vmatrix} 1 & 5 & 2 \\ 0 & 9 & 3 \\ 0 & 18 & 2 \end{vmatrix}$

$= \begin{vmatrix} 9 & 3 \\ 18 & 2 \end{vmatrix}$

$= 18 - 54$

$= -36$

$D_z = \begin{vmatrix} 1 & 2 & 5 \\ 2 & 4 & 19 \\ -2 & -5 & 8 \end{vmatrix}$

$= \begin{vmatrix} 1 & 2 & 5 \\ 0 & 0 & 9 \\ 0 & -1 & 18 \end{vmatrix}$

$= \begin{vmatrix} 0 & 9 \\ -1 & 18 \end{vmatrix}$

$= 0 - (-9)$

$= 9$

$x = \dfrac{D_x}{D} = \dfrac{69}{3} = 23, \ y = \dfrac{D_y}{D} = \dfrac{-36}{3} = -12,$

$z = \dfrac{D_z}{D} = \dfrac{9}{3} = 3$

The solution to the system is $\{(23, -12, 3)\}$.

50. $D = \begin{vmatrix} 2 & 1 & 0 \\ 0 & 1 & -2 \\ 3 & 0 & -2 \end{vmatrix}$

$= 2\begin{vmatrix} 1 & -2 \\ 0 & -2 \end{vmatrix} + 3\begin{vmatrix} 1 & 0 \\ 1 & -2 \end{vmatrix}$

$= 2(-2-0) + 3(-2-0)$

$= 2(-2) + 3(-2)$

$= -4 - 6$

$= -10$

$D_x = \begin{vmatrix} -4 & 1 & 0 \\ 0 & 1 & -2 \\ -11 & 0 & -2 \end{vmatrix}$

$= -1\begin{vmatrix} 0 & -2 \\ -11 & -2 \end{vmatrix} + 1\begin{vmatrix} -4 & 0 \\ -11 & -2 \end{vmatrix}$

$= -1(0-22) + 1(8-0)$

$= 22 + 8$

$= 30$

$D_y = \begin{vmatrix} 2 & -4 & 0 \\ 0 & 0 & -2 \\ 3 & -11 & -2 \end{vmatrix}$

$= 2\begin{vmatrix} 0 & -2 \\ -11 & -2 \end{vmatrix} + 3\begin{vmatrix} -4 & 0 \\ 0 & -2 \end{vmatrix}$

$= 2(0-22) + 3(8-0)$

$= 2(-22) + 3(8)$

$= -44 + 24$

$= -20$

$D_z = \begin{vmatrix} 2 & 1 & -4 \\ 0 & 1 & 0 \\ 3 & 0 & -11 \end{vmatrix}$

$= 2\begin{vmatrix} 1 & 0 \\ 0 & -11 \end{vmatrix} + 3\begin{vmatrix} 1 & -4 \\ 1 & 0 \end{vmatrix}$

$= 2(-11-0) + 3(0+4)$

$= 2(-11) + 3(+4) = -22 + 12$

$= -10$

$x = \dfrac{D_x}{D} = \dfrac{30}{-10} = -3$

$y = \dfrac{D_y}{D} = \dfrac{-20}{-10} = 2$

$z = \dfrac{D_z}{D} = \dfrac{-10}{-10} = 1$

The solution to the system is $\{(-3, 2, 1)\}$.

51. The quadratic function must satisfy
$f(20) = 400 = 400a + 20b + c$
$f(40) = 150 = 1600a + 40b + c$
$f(60) = 400 = 3600a + 60b + c$

$D = \begin{vmatrix} 400 & 20 & 1 \\ 1600 & 40 & 1 \\ 3600 & 60 & 1 \end{vmatrix}$

$= (400)(20)\begin{vmatrix} 1 & 1 & 1 \\ 4 & 2 & 1 \\ 9 & 3 & 1 \end{vmatrix}$

$= 8000\begin{vmatrix} 1 & 1 & 1 \\ 3 & 1 & 0 \\ 8 & 2 & 0 \end{vmatrix}$

$= 8000\begin{vmatrix} 3 & 1 \\ 8 & 2 \end{vmatrix}$

$= 8000(6-8)$

$= 8000(-2)$

$= -16,000$

$D_a = \begin{vmatrix} 400 & 20 & 1 \\ 150 & 40 & 1 \\ 400 & 60 & 1 \end{vmatrix}$

$= (50)(20)\begin{vmatrix} 8 & 1 & 1 \\ 3 & 2 & 1 \\ 8 & 3 & 1 \end{vmatrix}$

$= 1000\begin{vmatrix} 8 & 1 & 1 \\ -5 & 1 & 0 \\ 0 & 2 & 0 \end{vmatrix}$

$= 1000\begin{vmatrix} -5 & 1 \\ 0 & 2 \end{vmatrix}$

$= 1000(-10-0)$

$= -10,000$

$$D_b = \begin{vmatrix} 400 & 400 & 1 \\ 1600 & 150 & 1 \\ 3600 & 400 & 1 \end{vmatrix}$$

$$= (400)(50)\begin{vmatrix} 1 & 8 & 1 \\ 4 & 3 & 1 \\ 9 & 8 & 1 \end{vmatrix}$$

$$= 20,000\begin{vmatrix} 1 & 8 & 1 \\ 3 & -5 & 0 \\ 8 & 0 & 0 \end{vmatrix}$$

$$= 20,000\begin{vmatrix} 3 & -5 \\ 8 & 0 \end{vmatrix}$$

$$= 20,000[0-(-40)]$$
$$= 20,000(40)$$
$$= 800,000$$

$$D_c = \begin{vmatrix} 400 & 20 & 400 \\ 1600 & 40 & 150 \\ 3600 & 60 & 400 \end{vmatrix}$$

$$= (400)(20)(50)\begin{vmatrix} 1 & 1 & 8 \\ 4 & 2 & 3 \\ 9 & 3 & 8 \end{vmatrix}$$

$$= 400,000\begin{vmatrix} 1 & 0 & 0 \\ 4 & -2 & -29 \\ 2 & -6 & -64 \end{vmatrix}$$

$$= 400,000\begin{vmatrix} -2 & -29 \\ -6 & -64 \end{vmatrix}$$

$$= 400,000(128-174)$$
$$= 400,000(-46)$$
$$= -18,400,000$$

$$a = \frac{D_a}{D} = \frac{-10,000}{-16,000} = \frac{5}{8},$$

$$b = \frac{D_b}{D} = \frac{800,000}{-16,000} = -50,$$

$$c = \frac{D_c}{D} = \frac{-18,400,000}{-16,000} = 1150$$

The model is $f(x) = \frac{5}{8}x^2 - 50x + 1150$.

$$f(30) = \frac{5}{8}(900) - 50(30) + 1150$$
$$= 562.5 - 1500 + 1150$$
$$= 212.5$$
$$f(50) = \frac{5}{8}(2500) - 50(50) + 1150$$
$$= 1562.8 - 2500 + 1150$$
$$= 212.5$$

30- and 50-year-olds are involved in an average of 212.5 automobile accidents per day.

Chapter 9 Test

1. $\begin{bmatrix} 1 & 2 & -1 & | & -3 \\ 2 & -4 & 1 & | & -7 \\ -2 & 2 & -3 & | & 4 \end{bmatrix} \begin{matrix} -2R_1 + R_2 \\ \\ 2R_1 + R_3 \end{matrix}$

$\begin{bmatrix} 1 & 2 & -1 & | & -3 \\ 0 & -8 & 3 & | & -1 \\ 0 & 6 & -5 & | & -2 \end{bmatrix} -\frac{1}{8}R_2$

$\begin{bmatrix} 1 & 2 & -1 & | & -3 \\ 0 & 1 & -\frac{3}{8} & | & \frac{1}{8} \\ 0 & 6 & -5 & | & -2 \end{bmatrix} -6R_2 + R_3$

$\begin{bmatrix} 1 & 2 & -1 & | & -3 \\ 0 & 1 & -\frac{3}{8} & | & \frac{1}{8} \\ 0 & 0 & -\frac{11}{4} & | & -\frac{11}{4} \end{bmatrix} -\frac{4}{11}R_3$

$\begin{bmatrix} 1 & 2 & -1 & | & -3 \\ 0 & 1 & -\frac{3}{8} & | & \frac{1}{8} \\ 0 & 0 & 1 & | & 1 \end{bmatrix}$

$$x + 2y - z = -3$$
$$y - \frac{3}{8}z = \frac{1}{8}$$
$$z = 1$$

Using back substitution,

$y - \frac{3}{8}(1) = \frac{1}{8}$ and $x + 2\left(\frac{1}{2}\right) - 1 = -3$.

$\qquad y = \frac{1}{2} \qquad\qquad x + 1 - 1 = -3$

$\qquad\qquad\qquad\qquad x = -3$

The solution to the system is $\left\{\left(-3, \frac{1}{2}, 1\right)\right\}$.

2. $\begin{bmatrix} 1 & -2 & 1 & | & 2 \\ 2 & -1 & -1 & | & 1 \end{bmatrix} -2R_1 + R_2$

$\begin{bmatrix} 1 & -2 & 1 & | & 2 \\ 0 & 3 & -3 & | & -3 \end{bmatrix} \frac{1}{3}R_2$

$\begin{bmatrix} 1 & -2 & 1 & | & 2 \\ 0 & 1 & -1 & | & -1 \end{bmatrix}$

The system $\begin{aligned} x - 2y + z &= 2 \\ y - z &= -1 \end{aligned}$ has no unique solution. Express x and y in terms of z:

$y = z - 1$
$x - 2(z - 1) + z = 2$
$\quad x - 2z + 2 + z = 2$
$\qquad\qquad\qquad x = z$

With $z = t$, the complete solution to the system is $\{(t, t - 1, t)\}$.

3. $2B + 3C = \begin{bmatrix} 2 & -2 \\ 4 & 2 \end{bmatrix} + \begin{bmatrix} 3 & 6 \\ -3 & 9 \end{bmatrix} = \begin{bmatrix} 5 & 4 \\ 1 & 11 \end{bmatrix}$

4. $AB = \begin{bmatrix} 3+2 & -3+1 \\ 1+0 & -1+0 \\ 2+2 & -2+1 \end{bmatrix} = \begin{bmatrix} 5 & -2 \\ 1 & -1 \\ 4 & -1 \end{bmatrix}$

5. $C^{-1} = \dfrac{1}{(1)(3)-(2)(-1)}\begin{bmatrix} 3 & -2 \\ 1 & 1 \end{bmatrix} = \dfrac{1}{3+2}\begin{bmatrix} 3 & -2 \\ 1 & 1 \end{bmatrix} = \begin{bmatrix} \frac{3}{5} & -\frac{2}{5} \\ \frac{1}{5} & \frac{1}{5} \end{bmatrix}$

6. $BC = \begin{bmatrix} 1+1 & 2-3 \\ 2-1 & 4+3 \end{bmatrix} = \begin{bmatrix} 2 & -1 \\ 1 & 7 \end{bmatrix}$

$BC - 3B = \begin{bmatrix} 2 & -1 \\ 1 & 7 \end{bmatrix} - \begin{bmatrix} 3 & -3 \\ 6 & 3 \end{bmatrix} = \begin{bmatrix} -1 & 2 \\ -5 & 4 \end{bmatrix}$

7. $AB = \begin{bmatrix} -3+14-10 & 2-8+6 & 0+2-2 \\ -6+21-15 & 4-12+9 & 0+3-3 \\ -3-7+10 & 2+4-6 & 0-1+2 \end{bmatrix} = \begin{bmatrix} 1 & 0 & 0 \\ 0 & 1 & 0 \\ 0 & 0 & 1 \end{bmatrix} = I_3$

$BA = \begin{bmatrix} -3+4+0 & -6+6+0 & -6+6+0 \\ 7-8+1 & 14-12-1 & 14-12-2 \\ -5+6-1 & -10+9+1 & -10+9+2 \end{bmatrix} = \begin{bmatrix} 1 & 0 & 0 \\ 0 & 1 & 0 \\ 0 & 0 & 1 \end{bmatrix} = I_3$

8. a. $\begin{bmatrix} 3 & 5 \\ 2 & -3 \end{bmatrix} \begin{bmatrix} x \\ y \end{bmatrix} = \begin{bmatrix} 9 \\ -13 \end{bmatrix}$

b. $A^{-1} = \dfrac{1}{(3)(-3)-(5)(2)} \begin{bmatrix} -3 & -5 \\ -2 & 3 \end{bmatrix}$

$= \dfrac{1}{-19} \begin{bmatrix} -3 & -5 \\ -2 & 3 \end{bmatrix} = \begin{bmatrix} \frac{3}{19} & \frac{5}{19} \\ \frac{2}{19} & -\frac{3}{19} \end{bmatrix}$

c. $A^{-1}B = \begin{bmatrix} \frac{3}{19} & \frac{5}{19} \\ \frac{2}{19} & -\frac{3}{19} \end{bmatrix} \begin{bmatrix} 9 \\ -13 \end{bmatrix} = \begin{bmatrix} \frac{27}{19} - \frac{65}{19} \\ \frac{18}{19} + \frac{39}{19} \end{bmatrix} = \begin{bmatrix} -2 \\ 3 \end{bmatrix}$

The solution to the system is $\{(-2, 3)\}$.

9. $\begin{vmatrix} 4 & -1 & 3 \\ 0 & 5 & -1 \\ 5 & 2 & 4 \end{vmatrix} = 4 \begin{vmatrix} 5 & -1 \\ 2 & 4 \end{vmatrix} + 5 \begin{vmatrix} -1 & 3 \\ 5 & -1 \end{vmatrix}$

$= 4[20 - (-2)] + 5(1 - 15)$
$= 4(22) + 5(-14)$
$= 88 - 70$
$= 18$

10. $D = \begin{vmatrix} 3 & 1 & -2 \\ 2 & 7 & 3 \\ 4 & -3 & -1 \end{vmatrix} = 3 \begin{vmatrix} 7 & 3 \\ -3 & -1 \end{vmatrix} - 1 \begin{vmatrix} 2 & 3 \\ 4 & -1 \end{vmatrix} - 2 \begin{vmatrix} 2 & 7 \\ 4 & -3 \end{vmatrix}$

$= 3[-7 - (-9)] - 1(-2 - 12) - 2(-6 - 28)$
$= 3(2) - 1(-14) - 2(-34)$
$= 6 + 14 + 68$
$= 88$

$D_x = \begin{vmatrix} -3 & 1 & -2 \\ 9 & 7 & 3 \\ 7 & -3 & -1 \end{vmatrix} = -3 \begin{vmatrix} 7 & 3 \\ -3 & -1 \end{vmatrix} - 1 \begin{vmatrix} 9 & 3 \\ 7 & -1 \end{vmatrix} - 2 \begin{vmatrix} 9 & 7 \\ 7 & -3 \end{vmatrix}$

$= -3[-7 - (-9)] - 1(-9 - 21) - 2(-27 - 49)$
$= -3(2) - 1(-30) - 2(-76)$
$= -6 + 30 + 152$
$= 176$

$x = \dfrac{D_x}{D} = \dfrac{176}{88} = 2$

Cumulative Review Exercises (Chapters 1–9)

1. $2x^2 = 4 - x$

$2x^2 + x - 4 = 0$

$x = \dfrac{-1 \pm \sqrt{1^2 - 4(2)(-4)}}{2(2)}$

$x = \dfrac{-1 \pm \sqrt{1 - 32}}{4}$

$x = \dfrac{-1 \pm \sqrt{33}}{4}$

The solution set is $\left\{ \dfrac{-1 + \sqrt{33}}{4}, \dfrac{-1 - \sqrt{33}}{4} \right\}$.

2. $5x + 8 \le 7(1 + x)$

$5x + 8 \le 7 + 7x$

$-2x \le -1$

$x \ge \dfrac{1}{2}$

The solution set is $\left\{ x \,\middle|\, x \ge \dfrac{1}{2} \right\}$ or $\left[\dfrac{1}{2}, \infty \right)$.

3. $\sqrt{2x+4} - \sqrt{x+3} - 1 = 0$

$\sqrt{2x+4} = \sqrt{x+3} + 1$

$2x + 4 = x + 3 + 2\sqrt{x+3} + 1$

$x = 2\sqrt{x+3}$

$x^2 = 4(x+3)$

$x^2 = 4x + 12$

$x^2 - 4x - 12 = 0$

$(x-6)(x+2) = 0$

$x = 6$ or $x = -2$

$x = -2$ is an extraneous solution. The solution set is $\{6\}$.

4. $3x^3 + 8x^2 - 15x + 4 = 0$

$p = \pm 1, \pm 2, \pm 4$

$q = \pm 1, \pm 3$

$\dfrac{p}{q} = \pm 1, \pm \dfrac{1}{3}, \pm 2, \pm \dfrac{2}{3}, \pm 4, \pm \dfrac{4}{3}$

$$
\begin{array}{r|rrrr}
-4 & 3 & 8 & -15 & 4 \\
   &   & -12 & 16 & -4 \\
\hline
   & 3 & -4 & 1 & 0
\end{array}
$$

$(x+4)(3x^2 - 4x + 1) = 0$

$(x+4)(3x-1)(x-1) = 0$

$x = -4, \quad x = \dfrac{1}{3}, \quad x = 1$

The solution set is $\left\{ 4, \dfrac{1}{3}, 1 \right\}$.

5. $e^{2x} - 14e^x + 45 = 0 \quad le + t = e^x$

$t^2 - 14t + 45 = 0$

$(t-5)(t-9) = 0$

$t = 5 \quad t = 9$

$e^x = 5 \quad e^x = 9$

$\ln e^x = \ln 5 \quad \ln e^x = \ln 9$

$x = e^x = \ln 5 \quad x = \ln 9$

The solution set is $\{\ln 5, \ln 9\}$.

6. $\log_3 x + \log_3(x+2) = 1$

$\log_3 x^2 + 2x = 1$

$3^1 = x^2 + 2x$

$x^2 + 2x - 3 = 0$

$(x-1)(x+3) = 0$

$x = 1, \quad x = -3$

$x = -3$ is an extraneous solution. The solution set is $\{1\}$.

7.

$$
\left[\begin{array}{rrr|r}
1 & -1 & 1 & 17 \\
2 & 3 & 1 & 8 \\
-4 & 1 & 5 & -2
\end{array} \right]
\begin{array}{l}
\\ -2R_1 + R_2 \\ 4R_1 + R_3
\end{array}
$$

$$
\left[\begin{array}{rrr|r}
1 & -1 & 1 & 17 \\
0 & 5 & -1 & -26 \\
0 & -3 & 9 & 66
\end{array} \right]
\begin{array}{l}
\\ -\frac{1}{3}R_3 \\ \\
\end{array}
$$

$$
\left[\begin{array}{rrr|r}
1 & -1 & 1 & 17 \\
0 & 1 & -3 & -22 \\
0 & 5 & -1 & -26
\end{array} \right]
\begin{array}{l}
\\ -5R_2 + R_3 \\ 1R_2 + R_1
\end{array}
$$

$$
\left[\begin{array}{rrr|r}
1 & 0 & -2 & -5 \\
0 & 1 & -3 & -22 \\
0 & 0 & 14 & 84
\end{array} \right]
\begin{array}{l}
\\ \\ \frac{1}{14}R_3
\end{array}
$$

$$
\left[\begin{array}{rrr|r}
1 & 0 & -2 & -5 \\
0 & 1 & -3 & -22 \\
0 & 0 & 1 & 6
\end{array} \right]
\begin{array}{l}
\\ 3R_3 + R_2 \\ 2R_3 + R_1
\end{array}
$$

$$\begin{bmatrix} 1 & 0 & 0 & 7 \\ 0 & 1 & 0 & -4 \\ 0 & 0 & 1 & 6 \end{bmatrix}$$

$x = 7 \quad y = -4 \quad z = 6$

The solution set is $\{(7, -4, 6)\}$.

8. $D = \begin{vmatrix} 1 & -2 & 1 \\ 2 & 1 & -1 \\ 3 & 2 & -2 \end{vmatrix}$

$= 1\begin{vmatrix} 1 & -1 \\ 2 & -2 \end{vmatrix} - 2\begin{vmatrix} -2 & 1 \\ 2 & -2 \end{vmatrix} + 3\begin{vmatrix} -2 & 1 \\ 1 & 1 \end{vmatrix}$

$= 1(-2 + 2) - 2(4 - 2) + 3(2 - 1)$

$= 0 - 4 + 3$

$= -1$

$D_y = \begin{vmatrix} 1 & 7 & 1 \\ 2 & 0 & -1 \\ 3 & -2 & -2 \end{vmatrix} = 7\begin{vmatrix} 2 & -1 \\ 3 & -2 \end{vmatrix} - 2\begin{vmatrix} 1 & 1 \\ 2 & -1 \end{vmatrix}$

$= 7(-4 + 3) - 2(-1 - 2)$

$= -7 + 6 = 1$

$y = \dfrac{D_y}{D} = \dfrac{1}{-1} = -1$

$y = -1$

9. $y = \sqrt{4x - 7}$

$x = \sqrt{4y - 7}$

$x^2 = 4y - 7$

$x^2 + 7 - 4y$

$\dfrac{x^2 + 7}{4} = y$

$f^{-1}(x) = \dfrac{x^2 + 7}{4} \ (x \ge 0)$

10. $f(x) = \dfrac{x}{x^2 - 16}$

$f(0) = \dfrac{0}{-16} = 0$

y-intercept at 0

$0 = \dfrac{x}{x^2 - 16}$

$0 = x$

x-intercept at 0

$f(x) = \dfrac{x}{(x + 4)(x - 4)}$

vertical asymptotes at 4, –4

horizontal asymptote at 0

11. $f(x) = 4x^4 - 4x^3 - 25x^2 + x + 6$

2	4	4	–25	1	6
		–8	24	2	–6
3	4	–12	–1	3	0
		12	0	–3	
	4	0	–1	0	

$f(x) = (x + 2)(x - 3)(4x^2 - 1)$

$f(x) = (x + 2)(x - 3)(2x + 1)(2x - 1)$

12. $y = \log_2 x$

$2^y = x$

x	y
1	0
2	1
$\frac{1}{2}$	-1

$y = \log_2(x+1)$

Shift the graph of $y = \log_2{}^x$ left one unit.

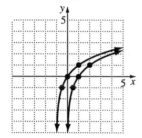

13. a. $A = A_0 e^{kt}$

$450 = 900 e^{k(40)}$

$\dfrac{1}{2} = e^{40k}$

$\ln\left(\dfrac{1}{2}\right) = 40k$

$k = \dfrac{\ln \frac{1}{2}}{40} \approx -0.017$

$A = A_0 e^{-0.017t}$

b. $A = 900 e^{-0.017(10)}$

$A = 900 e^{-0.17}$

$A \approx 759.30$ grams

14. $\begin{bmatrix} 1 & -1 & 0 \\ 2 & 1 & 3 \end{bmatrix} \begin{bmatrix} 4 & -1 \\ 2 & 0 \\ 1 & 1 \end{bmatrix} = \begin{bmatrix} 4-2+0 & -1+0+0 \\ 8+2+3 & -2+0+3 \end{bmatrix}$

$= \begin{bmatrix} 2 & -1 \\ 13 & 1 \end{bmatrix}$

15. $\dfrac{3x^2+17x-38}{(x-3)(x-2)(x+2)} = \dfrac{A}{x-3} + \dfrac{B}{x-2} + \dfrac{C}{x+2}$

$3x^2+17x-38$
$= A(x^2-4) + B(x^2-x-6) + C(x^2-5x+6)$

$3x^2+17x-38$
$= Ax^2-4A+Bx^2-Bx-6B+Cx^2-5Cx+6c$

$3x^2+17x-38$
$= (A+B+C)x^2+(-B-5C)x-(4A+6B-6C)$

$A+B+C = 3$
$-B-5C = 17$
$4A+6B-6C = 38$

$\begin{bmatrix} 1 & 1 & 1 & | & 3 \\ 0 & -1 & -5 & | & 17 \\ 4 & 6 & -6 & | & 38 \end{bmatrix} -4R_1+R_3$

$\begin{bmatrix} 1 & 1 & 1 & | & 3 \\ 0 & -1 & -5 & | & 17 \\ 0 & 2 & -10 & | & 26 \end{bmatrix} -1R_2$

$\begin{bmatrix} 1 & 1 & 1 & | & 3 \\ 0 & 1 & 5 & | & -17 \\ 0 & 2 & -10 & | & 26 \end{bmatrix} \begin{matrix} -2R_2+R_3 \\ -1R_2+R_1 \end{matrix}$

$\begin{bmatrix} 1 & 0 & -4 & | & 20 \\ 0 & 1 & 5 & | & -17 \\ 0 & 0 & -20 & | & 60 \end{bmatrix} -\frac{1}{20}R_3$

$\begin{bmatrix} 1 & 0 & -4 & | & 20 \\ 0 & 1 & 5 & | & -17 \\ 0 & 0 & 1 & | & -3 \end{bmatrix} \begin{matrix} -5R_3+R_2 \\ 4R_3+R_1 \end{matrix}$

$\begin{bmatrix} 1 & 0 & 0 & | & 8 \\ 0 & 1 & 0 & | & -2 \\ 0 & 0 & 1 & | & -3 \end{bmatrix}$

$A = 8$
$B = -2$
$C = -3$

$\dfrac{3x^2+17x-38}{(x-3)(x-2)(x+2)} = \dfrac{8}{x-3} + \dfrac{-2}{x-2} + \dfrac{-3}{x+2}$

16. $y = -\dfrac{2}{3}x - 1$

x	y
0	−1
3	−3
−3	1

17. $3x - 5y < 15$
$-5y < -3x + 15$
$y > \dfrac{3}{5}x - 3$

18. $f(x) = x^2 - 2x - 3$
$f(x) = (x^2 - 2x + 1) - 3 - 1$
$f(x) = (x - 1)^2 - 4$

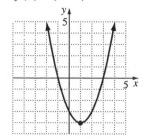

19. $(x - 1)^2 + (y + 1)^2 = 9$
center $(1, -1)$
radius $= 3$

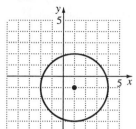

20.

$$
\begin{array}{r|rrrr}
2 & 1 & 0 & -6 & 4 \\
  &   & 2 & 4 & -4 \\
\hline
  & 1 & 2 & -2 & 0
\end{array}
$$

$\dfrac{x^3 - 6x + 4}{x - 2} = x^2 + 2x - 2$

21. $y = 2\sin 2\pi x, \quad 0 \le x \le 2$
Amplitude: $|A| = |2| = 2$
Period: $\dfrac{2\pi}{B} = \dfrac{2\pi}{2\pi} = 1$
x-intercepts:
$(0, 0), \left(\dfrac{1}{2}, 0\right), (1, 0), \left(\dfrac{3}{2}, 0\right), (2, 0)$

22. $\cos\left[\tan^{-1}\left(-\dfrac{4}{3}\right)\right]$

If $\tan\theta = -\dfrac{4}{3}$, θ lies in quadrant IV.

$\tan\theta = -\dfrac{4}{3} = \dfrac{y}{x} = \dfrac{-4}{3}$

$r = \sqrt{(3)^2 + (-4)^2} = \sqrt{9+16} = \sqrt{25} = 5$

$\cos\left[\tan^{-1}\left(-\dfrac{4}{3}\right)\right] = \dfrac{x}{r} = \dfrac{3}{5}$

23. $\dfrac{\cos 2x}{\cos x - \sin x} = \dfrac{\cos^2 x - \sin^2 x}{\cos x - \sin x}$

$\qquad\qquad = \dfrac{(\cos x - \sin x)(\cos x + \sin x)}{\cos x - \sin x}$

$\qquad\qquad = \cos x + \sin x$

24. $\quad\cos^2 x + \sin x + 1 = 0$

$\quad(1 - \sin^2 x) + \sin x + 1 = 0$

$\qquad -\sin^2 x + \sin x + 2 = 0$

$\qquad\quad \sin^2 x - \sin x - 2 = 0$

$\quad(\sin x - 2)(\sin x + 1) = 0$

$\sin x - 2 = 0 \quad\text{or}\quad \sin x + 1 = 0$

$\qquad \sin x = 2 \qquad\qquad \sin x = -1$

$\text{no solution} \quad\text{or}\qquad x = \dfrac{3\pi}{2}$

The solution in the interval $[0, 2\pi)$ is $\dfrac{3\pi}{2}$.

25. $4\mathbf{w} - 5\mathbf{v} = 4(-7\mathbf{i} + 3\mathbf{j}) - 5(-6\mathbf{i} + 5\mathbf{j})$

$\qquad\qquad = -28\mathbf{i} + 12\mathbf{j} + 30\mathbf{i} - 25\mathbf{j}$

$\qquad\qquad = 2\mathbf{i} - 13\mathbf{j}$

Chapter 10

Section 10.1

Check Point Exercises

1. $\dfrac{x^2}{36} + \dfrac{y^2}{9} = 1$

$a^2 = 36,\ a = 6$

$b^2 = 9,\ b = 3$

$c^2 = a^2 - b^2 = 36 - 9 = 27$

$c = \sqrt{27} = 3\sqrt{3}$

The foci are located at

$(-3\sqrt{3},\ 0)$ and $(3\sqrt{3},\ 0)$.

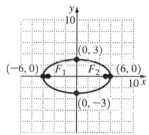

2. $16x^2 + 9y^2 = 144$

$\dfrac{16x^2}{144} + \dfrac{9y^2}{144} = \dfrac{144}{144}$

$\dfrac{x^2}{9} + \dfrac{y^2}{16} = 1$

$a^2 = 16,\ a = 4$

$b^2 = 9,\ b = 3$

$c^2 = a^2 - b^2 = 16 - 9 = 7$

$c = \sqrt{7}$

The foci are located at

$(0,\ -\sqrt{7})$ and $(0,\ \sqrt{7})$.

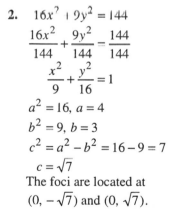

3. $c^2 = 4,\ a^2 = 9$

$b^2 = a^2 - c^2 = 9 - 4 = 5$

$\dfrac{x^2}{9} + \dfrac{y^2}{5} = 1$

4. $\dfrac{(x+1)^2}{9} + \dfrac{(y-2)^2}{4} = 1$

$a^2 = 9,\ a = 3$

$b^2 = 4,\ b = 2$

center at $(-1,\ 27)$

$c^2 = a^2 - b^2 = 9 - 4 = 5$

$c = \sqrt{5}$

The foci are located at

$(-1 - \sqrt{5},\ 2)$ and $(-1 + \sqrt{5},\ 2)$.

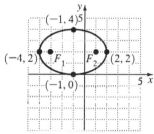

5. $a = 20,\ b = 10$

$\dfrac{x^2}{400} + \dfrac{y^2}{100} = 1$

Let $x = 6$

$\dfrac{6^2}{400} + \dfrac{y^2}{100} = 1$

$400\left(\dfrac{36}{400} + \dfrac{y^2}{100}\right) = 400(1)$

$36 + 4y^2 = 400$

$4y^2 = 364$

$y^2 = 91$

$y = \sqrt{91} \approx 9.54$

Yes, the truck needs only 9 feet so it will clear.

Exercise Set 10.1

1. $\dfrac{x^2}{16} + \dfrac{y^2}{4} = 1$

$a^2 = 16,\ a = 4$

$b^2 = 4,\ b = 2$

$c^2 = a^2 - b^2 = 16 - 4 = 12$

$\quad c = \sqrt{12} = 2\sqrt{3}$

The foci are located at $(-2\sqrt{3},\ 0)$ and $(2\sqrt{3},\ 0)$.

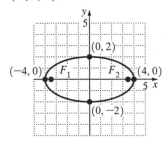

3. $\dfrac{x^2}{9} + \dfrac{y^2}{36} = 1$

$a^2 = 36,\ a = 6$

$b^2 = 9,\ b = 3$

$c^2 = a^2 - b^2 = 36 - 9 = 27$

$\quad c = \sqrt{27} = 3\sqrt{3}$

The foci are located at $(0,\ -3\sqrt{3})$ and $(0,\ 3\sqrt{3})$.

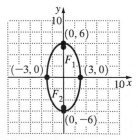

5. $\dfrac{x^2}{25} + \dfrac{y^2}{64} = 1$

$a^2 = 64,\ a = 8$

$b^2 = 25,\ b = 5$

$c^2 = a^2 - b^2 = 64 - 25 = 39$

$\quad c = \sqrt{39}$

The foci are located at $(0,\ -\sqrt{39})$ and $(0,\ \sqrt{39})$.

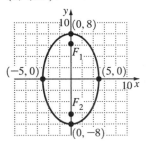

7. $\dfrac{x^2}{49} + \dfrac{y^2}{81} = 1$

$a^2 = 81,\ a = 9$

$b^2 = 49,\ b = 7$

$c^2 = a^2 - b^2 = 81 - 49 = 32$

$\quad c = \sqrt{32} = 4\sqrt{2}$

The foci are located at $(0,\ -4\sqrt{2})$ and $(0,\ 4\sqrt{2})$.

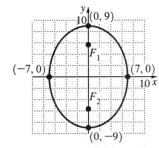

9. $25x^2 + 4y^2 = 100$

$$\frac{25x^2}{100} + \frac{4y^2}{100} = \frac{100}{100}$$

$$\frac{x^2}{4} + \frac{y^2}{25} = 1$$

$a^2 = 25,\ a = 5$

$b^2 = 4,\ b = 2$

$c^2 = a^2 = b^2 = 25 - 4 = 21$

The foci are located at $(0, -\sqrt{21})$ and $(0, \sqrt{21})$.

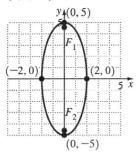

11. $4x^2 + 16y^2 = 64$

$$\frac{4x^2}{64} + \frac{16y^2}{64} = \frac{64}{64}$$

$$\frac{x^2}{16} + \frac{y^2}{4} = 1$$

$a^2 = 16,\ a = 4$

$b^2 = 4,\ b = 2$

$c^2 = a^2 - b^2 = 16 - 4 = 12$

$c = \sqrt{12} = 2\sqrt{3}$

The foci are located at $(-2\sqrt{3},\ 0)$ and $(2\sqrt{3},\ 0)$.

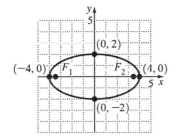

13. $25x^2 + 9y^2 = 225$

$$\frac{25x^2}{225} + \frac{9y^2}{225} = \frac{225}{225}$$

$$\frac{x^2}{9} + \frac{y^2}{25} = 1$$

$a^2 = 25,\ a = 5$

$b^2 = 9,\ b = 3$

$c^2 = a^2 - b^2 = 25 - 9 = 16$

$c = 4$

The foci are located at $(0, 4)$ and $(0, -4)$.

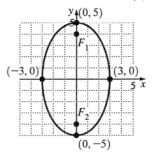

15. $x^2 + 2y^2 = 8$

$$\frac{x^2}{8} + \frac{2y^2}{8} = \frac{8}{8}$$

$$\frac{x^2}{8} + \frac{y^2}{4} = 1$$

$a^2 = 8,\ a = \sqrt{8} = 2\sqrt{2}$

$b^2 = 4,\ b = 2$

$c^2 = a^2 - b^2 = 8 - 4 = 4$

$c = 2$

The foci are located at $(2, 0)$ and $(-2, 0)$.

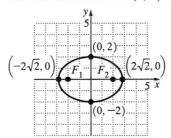

17. $a^2 = 4$, $b^2 = 1$, center at $(0, 0)$

$$\frac{x^2}{4} + \frac{y^2}{1} = 1$$

$$c^2 = a^2 - b^2 = 4 - 1 = 3$$

$$c = \sqrt{3}$$

The foci are at $(-\sqrt{3}, 0)$ and $(\sqrt{3}, 0)$.

19. $a^2 = 4$, $b^2 = 1$,

center: $(0, 0)$

$$\frac{x^2}{1} + \frac{y^2}{4} = 1$$

$$c^2 = a^2 - b^2 = 4 - 1 = 3$$

$$c = \sqrt{3}$$

The foci are at $(0, \sqrt{3})$ and $(0, -\sqrt{3})$.

21. $c^2 = 25$, $a^2 = 64$

$$b^2 = a^2 - c^2 = 64 - 25 = 39$$

$$\frac{x^2}{64} + \frac{y^2}{39} = 1$$

23. $c^2 = 16$, $a^2 = 49$

$$b^2 = a^2 - c^2 = 49 - 16 = 33$$

$$\frac{x^2}{33} + \frac{y^2}{49} = 1$$

25. $c^2 = 4$, $b^2 = 9$

$$a^2 = b^2 + c^2 = 9 + 4 = 13$$

$$\frac{x^2}{13} + \frac{y^2}{9} = 1$$

27. $2a = 8$, $a = 4$, $a^2 = 16$

$2b = 4$, $b = 2$, $b^2 = 4$

$$\frac{x^2}{16} + \frac{y^2}{4} = 1$$

29. $2a = 10$, $a = 5$, $a^2 = 25$

$2b = 4$, $b = 2$, $b^2 = 4$

$$\frac{x^2}{4} + \frac{y^2}{25} = 1$$

31. $\dfrac{(x-2)^2}{9} + \dfrac{(y-1)^2}{4} = 1$

$a^2 = 9$, $a = 3$

$b^2 = 4$, $b = 2$

center: $(2, 1)$

$$c^2 = a^2 - b^2 = 9 - 4 = 5$$

$$c = \sqrt{5}$$

The foci are at $(2 - \sqrt{5}, 1)$ and $(2 + \sqrt{5}, 1)$.

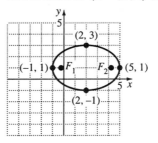

33. $(x+3)^2 + 4(y-2)^2 = 16$

$$\frac{(x+3)^2}{16} + \frac{4(y-2)^2}{16} = \frac{16}{16}$$

$$\frac{(x+3)^2}{16} + \frac{(y-2)^2}{4} = 1$$

$a^2 = 16$, $a = 4$

$b^2 = 4$, $b = 2$

center: $(-3, 2)$

$$c^2 = a^2 - b^2 = 16 - 4 = 12$$

$$c = \sqrt{12} = 2\sqrt{3}$$

The foci are at $(-3 - 2\sqrt{3}, 2)$ and $(-3 + 2\sqrt{3}, 2)$.

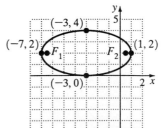

35. $\dfrac{(x-4)^2}{9} + \dfrac{(y+2)^2}{25} = 1$

$a^2 = 25, \ a = 5$

$b^2 = 9, \ b = 3$

center: $(4, -2)$

$c^2 = a^2 - b^2 = 25 - 9 = 16$

$\quad c = 4$

The foci are at $(4, 2)$ and $(4, -6)$.

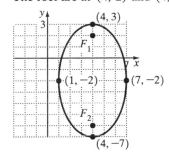

37. $\dfrac{x^2}{25} + \dfrac{(y-2)^2}{36} = 1$

$a^2 = 36, \ a = 6$

$b^2 = 25, \ b = 5$

center: $(0, 2)$

$c^2 = a^2 - b^2 = 36 - 25 = 11$

$\quad c = \sqrt{11}$

The foci are at $(0, \, 2+\sqrt{11})$ and

$(0, \, 2-\sqrt{11})$.

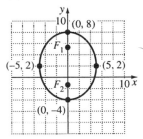

39. $\dfrac{(x+3)^2}{9} + (y-2)^2 = 1$

$a^2 = 9, \ a = 3$

$b^2 = 1, \ b = 1$

center: $(-3, 2)$

$c^2 = a^2 - b^2 = 9 - 1 = 8$

$\quad c = \sqrt{8} = 2\sqrt{2}$

The foci are at $(-3 - 2\sqrt{2}, \ 2)$ and

$(-3 + 2\sqrt{2}, \ 2)$.

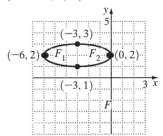

41. $9(x-1)^2 + 4(y+3)^2 = 36$

$\dfrac{9(x-1)^2}{36} + \dfrac{4(y+3)^2}{36} = \dfrac{36}{36}$

$\dfrac{(x-1)^2}{4} + \dfrac{(y+3)^2}{9} = 1$

$a^2 = 9, \ a = 3$

$b^2 = 4, \ b = 2$

center: $(1, -3)$

$c^2 = a^2 - b^2 = 9 - 4 = 5$

$\quad c = \sqrt{5}$

The foci are at $(1, \, -3+\sqrt{5})$ and

$(1, \, -3-\sqrt{5})$.

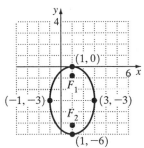

43. $9x^2 + 25y^2 - 36x + 50y - 164 = 0$

$$(9x^2 - 36x) + (25y^2 + 50y) = 164$$

$$9(x^2 - 4x) + 25(y^2 + 2y) = 164$$

$$9(x^2 - 4x + 4) + 25(y^2 + 2y + 1)$$
$$= 164 + 36 + 25$$

$$9(x - 2)^2 + 25(y + 1)^2 = 225$$

$$\frac{9(x-2)^2}{225} + \frac{25(y+1)^2}{225} = \frac{225}{225}$$

$$\frac{(x-2)^2}{25} + \frac{(y+1)^2}{9} = 1$$

center: $(2, -1)$
$a^2 = 25,\ a = 5$
$b^2 = 9,\ b = 3$
$c^2 = a^2 - b^2 = 25\ - 9 = 16$
$c = 4$

The foci are at $(-2, -1)$ and $(6, -1)$.

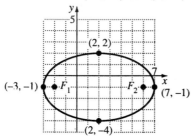

45. $9x^2 + 16y^2 - 18x + 64y - 71 = 0$

$$(9x^2 - 18x) + (16y^2 + 64y) = 71$$
$$9(x^2 - 2x) + 16(y^2 + 4y) = 71$$
$$9(x^2 - 2x + 1) + 16(y^2 + 4y + 4)$$
$$= 71 + 9 + 64$$

$$9(x-1)^2 + 16(y+2)^2 = 144$$

$$\frac{9(x-1)^2}{144} + \frac{16(y+2)^2}{144} = \frac{144}{144}$$

$$\frac{(x-1)^2}{16} + \frac{(y+2)^2}{9} = 1$$

center: $(1, -2)$
$a^2 = 16,\ a = 4$
$b^2 = 9,\ b = 3$
$c^2 = a^2 -\ b^2 = 16 - 9 = 7$
$c = \sqrt{7}$

The foci are at
$(1 - \sqrt{7}, -2)$ and $(1 + \sqrt{7}, -2)$.

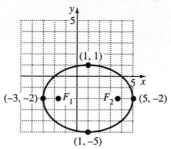

47. $4x^2 + y^2 + 16x - 6y - 39 = 0$

$$(4x^2 + 16x) + (y^2 - 6y) = 39$$

$$4(x^2 + 4x) + (y^2 - 6y) = 39$$

$$4(x^2 + 4x + 4) + (y^2 - 6y + 9) = 39 + 16 + 9$$

$$4(x + 2)^2 + (y - 3)^2 = 64$$

$$\frac{4(x+2)^2}{64} + \frac{(y-3)^2}{64} = \frac{64}{64}$$

$$\frac{(x+2)^2}{16} + \frac{(y-3)^2}{64} = 1$$

center: $(-2, 3)$
$a^2 = 64,\ a = 8$
$b^2 = 16,\ b = 4$
$c^2 = a^2 - b^2 = 64 - 16 = 48$
$c = \sqrt{48} = 4\sqrt{3}$

The foci are at $(-2, 3 + 4\sqrt{3})$ and
$(-2, 3 - 4\sqrt{3})$.

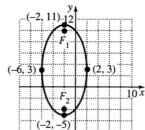

49. $a = 15, b = 10$

$$\frac{x^2}{225} + \frac{y^2}{100} = 1$$

Let $x = 4$

$$\frac{4^2}{225} + \frac{y^2}{100} = 1$$

$$900\left(\frac{16}{225} + \frac{y^2}{100}\right) = 900(1)$$

$$64 + 9y^2 = 900$$

$$9y^2 = 836$$

$$y = \sqrt{\frac{836}{9}} \approx 9.64$$

Yes, the truck only needs 7 feet so it will clear.

51. a. $a = 48, a^2 = 2304$
$b = 23, b^2 = 529$

$$\frac{x^2}{2304} + \frac{y^2}{529} = 1$$

b. $c^2 = a^2 - b^2 = 2304 - 529 = 1775$

$c = \sqrt{1775} \approx 42.13$

He situated his desk about 42 feet from the center of the ellipse, along the major axis.

53.–57. Answers may vary.

59. Exercise 1

Exercise 3

Exercise 5

Exercise 7

Exercise 9

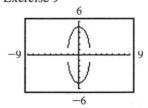

61. Exercise 43

$$25y^2 + 50y + 9x^2 - 36x - 164 = 0$$

$$y = \frac{-50 \pm \sqrt{(50)^2 - 4(25)(9x^2 - 36x - 164)}}{2(25)}$$

$$= \frac{-50 \pm \sqrt{2500 - 900x^2 + 3600x - 16,400}}{50}$$

$$= \frac{-50 \pm \sqrt{-900x^2 + 3600x + 18,900}}{50}$$

$$= \frac{-50 \pm \sqrt{900\left(-x^2 + 2x + 21\right)}}{50}$$

$$= \frac{-50 \pm 30\sqrt{-x^2 + 4x + 21}}{50}$$

$$y = \frac{-5 \pm 3\sqrt{-x^2 + 4x + 21}}{5}$$

63. $a = 6,\ a^2 = 36$

$$\frac{x^2}{b^2} + \frac{y^2}{36} = 1$$

When $x = 2$ and $y = -4$,

$$\frac{2^2}{b^2} + \frac{(-4)^2}{36} = 1$$

$$\frac{4}{b^2} + \frac{16}{36} = 1$$

$$\frac{4}{b^2} = \frac{5}{9}$$

$$36 = 5b^2$$

$$b^2 = \frac{36}{5}$$

$$\frac{x^2}{\frac{36}{5}} + \frac{y^2}{36} = 1$$

65. The large circle has radius 5 with center $(0, 0)$. Its equation is $x^2 + y^2 = 25$. The small circle has radius 3 with center $(0, 0)$. Its equation is $x^2 + y^2 = 9$.

Section 10.2

Check Point Exercises

1. a. $a^2 = 25,\ a = 5$
vertices: $(5, 0)$ and $(-5, 0)$
$b^2 = 16$
$c^2 = a^2 + b^2 = 25 + 16 = 41$
$c = \sqrt{41}$
The foci are at $(\sqrt{41}, 0)$ and $(-\sqrt{41}, 0)$.

b. $a^2 = 25,\ a = 5$
vertices: $(0, 5)$ and $(0, -5)$
$b^2 = 16$
$c^2 = a^2 + b^2 = 25 + 16 = 41$
$c = \sqrt{41}$
The foci are at $(0, \sqrt{41})$ and $(0, -\sqrt{41})$.

2. $a = 3,\ c = 5$
$b^2 = c^2 - a^2 = 25 - 9 = 16$
$$\frac{y^2}{9} - \frac{x^2}{16} = 1$$

3. $\dfrac{x^2}{36} - \dfrac{y^2}{9} = 1$
$a^2 = 36,\ a = 6$
The vertices are $(6, 0)$ and $(-6, 0)$.
$b^2 = 9,\ b = 3$

asymptotes: $y = \pm\dfrac{b}{a}x = \pm\dfrac{3}{6}x = \pm\dfrac{1}{2}x$
$c^2 = a^2 + b^2 = 36 + 9 = 45$
$c = \sqrt{45} = 3\sqrt{5}$
The foci are at $(-3\sqrt{5}, 0)$ and $(3\sqrt{5}, 0)$.

4. $y^2 - 4x^2 = 4$

$$\frac{y^2}{4} - \frac{4x^2}{4} = \frac{4}{4}$$

$$\frac{y^2}{4} - x^2 = 1$$

$a^2 = 4,\ a = 2$

The vertices are $(0, 2)$ and $(0, -2)$.

$b^2 = 1,\ b = 1$

asymptotes: $y = \pm \dfrac{a}{b} x = \pm 2x$

$c^2 = a^2 + b^2 = 4 + 1 = 5$

$c = \sqrt{5}$

The foci are at $(0, \sqrt{5})$ and $(0, -\sqrt{5})$.

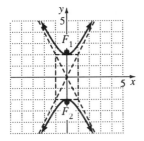

5. $\dfrac{(x-3)^2}{4} - \dfrac{(y-1)^2}{1} = 1$

center at $(3, 1)$

$a^2 = 4,\ a = 2$

$b^2 = 1,\ b = 1$

The vertices are $(1, 1)$ and $(5, 1)$.

asymptotes: $y - 1 = \pm \dfrac{1}{2}(x - 3)$

$c^2 = a^2 + b^2 = 4 + 1 = 5$

$c = \sqrt{5}$

The foci are at $(3 - \sqrt{5}, 1)$ and $(3 + \sqrt{5}, 1)$.

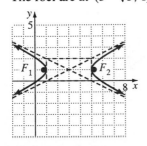

6. $c = 5280$

$2a = 3300,\ a = 1650$

$b^2 = c^2 - a^2 = 5280^2 - 1650^2 = 25,155,900$

The explosion occurred somewhere at the right branch of the hyperbola given by

$$\frac{x^2}{2,722,500} - \frac{y^2}{25,155,900} = 1.$$

Exercise Set 10.2

1. $a^2 = 4,\ a = 2$

The vertices are $(2, 0)$ and $(-2, 0)$.

$b^2 = 1$

$c^2 = a^2 + b^2 = 4 + 1 = 5$

$c = \sqrt{5}$

The foci are located at $(\sqrt{5}, 0)$ and $(-\sqrt{5}, 0)$.

graph (b)

3. $a^2 = 4,\ a = 2$

The vertices are $(0, 2)$ and $(0, -2)$.

$b^2 = 1$

$c^2 = a^2 + b^2 = 4 + 1 = 5$

$c = \sqrt{5}$

The foci are located at $(0, \sqrt{5})$ and $(0, -\sqrt{5})$.

graph (a)

5. $a = 1,\ c = 3$

$b^2 = c^2 - a^2 = 9 - 1 = 8$

$$y^2 - \frac{x^2}{8} = 1$$

7. $a = 3,\ c = 4$

$b^2 = c^2 - a^2 = 16 - 9 = 7$

$$\frac{x^2}{9} - \frac{y^2}{7} = 1$$

9. $\dfrac{x^2}{9} - \dfrac{y^2}{25} = 1$

$a^2 = 9, a = 3$

$b^2 = 25, b = 5$

vertices: $(3, 0)$ and $(-3, 0)$

asymptotes: $y = \pm\dfrac{b}{a}x = \pm\dfrac{5}{3}x$

$c^2 = a^2 + b^2 = 9 + 25 = 34$

$c = \sqrt{34}$ on x-axis

The foci are at $(\sqrt{34}, 0)$ and $(-\sqrt{34}, 0)$.

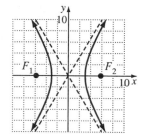

11. $\dfrac{x^2}{100} - \dfrac{y^2}{64} = 1$

$a^2 = 100, a = 10$

$b^2 = 64, b = 8$

vertices: $(10, 0)$ and $(-10, 0)$

asymptotes: $y = \pm\dfrac{b}{a}x = \pm\dfrac{8}{10}x$

or $y = \pm\dfrac{4}{5}x$

$c^2 = a^2 + b^2 = 100 + 64 = 164$

$c = \sqrt{164} = 2\sqrt{41}$ on x-axis

The foci are at $(2\sqrt{41}, 0)$ and $(-2\sqrt{41}, 0)$.

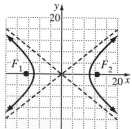

13. $\dfrac{y^2}{16} - \dfrac{x^2}{36} = 1$

$a^2 = 16, a = 4$

$b^2 = 36, b = 6$

vertices: $(0, 4)$ and $(0, -4)$

asymptotes: $y = \pm\dfrac{a}{b}x = \pm\dfrac{4}{6}x$

or $y = \pm\dfrac{2}{3}x$

$c^2 = a^2 + b^2 = 16 + 36 = 52$

$c = \sqrt{52} = 2\sqrt{13}$ on y-axis

The foci are at $(0, 2\sqrt{13})$ and $(0, -2\sqrt{13})$.

15. $\dfrac{y^2}{36} - \dfrac{x^2}{25} = 1$

$a^2 = 36, a = 6$

$b^2 = 25, b = 5$

vertices: $(0, 6)$ and $(0, -6)$

asymptotes: $y = \pm\dfrac{a}{b}x = \pm\dfrac{6}{5}x$

$c^2 = a^2 + b^2 = 36 + 25 = 61$

$c = \sqrt{61}$ on y-axis

The foci are at $(0, \sqrt{61})$ and $(0, -\sqrt{61})$.

17. $9x^2 - 4y^2 = 36$

$$\frac{9x^2}{36} - \frac{4y^2}{36} = \frac{36}{36}$$

$$\frac{x^2}{4} - \frac{y^2}{9} = 1$$

$a^2 = 4,\ a = 2$

$b^2 = 9,\ b = 3$

vertices: $(2, 0)$ and $(-2, 0)$

asymptotes: $y = \pm\frac{b}{a}x = \pm\frac{3}{2}x$

$c^2 = a^2 + b^2 = 4 + 9 = 13$

$c = \sqrt{13}$ on x-axis

The foci are at $(\sqrt{13},\ 0)$ and $(-\sqrt{13},\ 0)$.

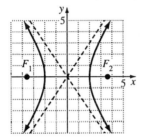

19. $9y^2 - 25x^2 = 225$

$$\frac{9y^2}{225} - \frac{25x^2}{225} - \frac{225}{225}$$

$$\frac{y^2}{25} - \frac{x^2}{9} = 1$$

$a^2 = 25,\ a = 5$

$b^2 = 9,\ b = 3$

vertices: $(0, 5)$ and $(0, -5)$

asymptotes: $y = \pm\frac{a}{b}x = \pm\frac{5}{3}x$

$c^2 = a^2 + b^2 = 25 + 9 = 34$

$c = \sqrt{34}$ on y-axis

The foci are at $(0, \sqrt{34})$ and $(0, -\sqrt{34})$.

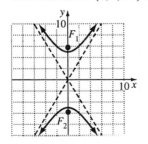

21. $4x^2 = 4 + y^2$

$$4x^2 - y^2 = 4$$

$$\frac{4x^2}{4} - \frac{y^2}{4} = \frac{4}{4}$$

$$x^2 - \frac{y^2}{4} = 1$$

$a^2 = 1,\ a = 1$

$b^2 = 4,\ b = 2$

vertices: $(1, 0)$ and $(-1, 0)$

asymptotes: $y = \pm\frac{b}{a}x = \pm 2x$

$c^2 = a^2 + b^2 = 1 + 4 = 5$

$c = \sqrt{5}$ on x-axis

The foci are at $(\sqrt{5},\ 0)$ and $(-\sqrt{5},\ 0)$.

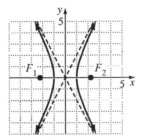

23. $a - 3,\ b - 5$

$$\frac{x^2}{9} - \frac{y^2}{25} = 1$$

25. $a = 2,\ b = 3$

$$\frac{y^2}{4} - \frac{x^2}{9} = 1$$

27. $\dfrac{(x+4)^2}{9} - \dfrac{(y+3)^2}{16} = 1$

center: $(-4, -3)$

$a^2 = 9$, $a = 3$

$b^2 = 16$, $b = 4$

vertices: $(-7, -3)$ and $(-1, -3)$

asymptotes: $y + 3 = \pm\dfrac{4}{3}(x + 4)$

$c^2 = a^2 + b^2 = 9 + 16 = 25$

$c = \pm 5$ parallel to x-axis

The foci are at $(-9, -3)$ and $(1, -3)$.

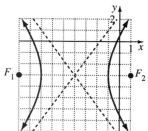

29. $\dfrac{(x+3)^2}{25} - \dfrac{y^2}{16} = 1$

center: $(-3, 0)$

$a^2 = 25$, $a = 5$

$b^2 = 16$, $b = 4$

vertices: $(2, 0)$ and $(-8, 0)$

asymptotes: $y = \pm\dfrac{4}{5}(x + 3)$

$c^2 = a^2 + b^2 = 25 + 16 = 41$

$c = \sqrt{41}$

The foci are at $(-3 + \sqrt{41}, 0)$ and $(-3 - \sqrt{41}, 0)$.

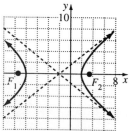

31. $\dfrac{(y+2)^2}{4} - \dfrac{(x-1)^2}{16} = 1$

center: $(1, -2)$

$a^2 = 4$, $a = 2$

$b^2 = 16$, $b = 4$

vertices: $(1, 0)$ and $(1, -4)$

asymptotes: $y + 2 = \pm\dfrac{1}{2}(x - 1)$

$c^2 = a^2 + b^2 = 4 + 16 = 20$

$c = \sqrt{20} = 2\sqrt{5}$ parallel to y-axis

The foci are at $(1, -2 + 2\sqrt{5})$ and $(1, -2 - 2\sqrt{5})$.

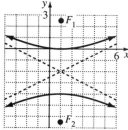

33. $(x-3)^2 - 4(y+3)^2 = 4$

$$\frac{(x-3)^2}{4} - \frac{4(y+3)^2}{4} = \frac{4}{4}$$

$$\frac{(x-3)^2}{4} - (y+3)^2 = 1$$

center: $(3, -3)$

$a^2 = 4,\ a = 2$

$b^2 = 1,\ b = 1$

vertices: $(1, -3)$ and $(5, -3)$

asymptotes: $y + 3 = \pm\dfrac{1}{2}(x-3)$

$c^2 = a^2 + b^2 = 4 + 1 = 5$

$c = \sqrt{5}$

The foci are at $(3+\sqrt{5},\ -3)$ and $(3-\sqrt{5},\ -3)$.

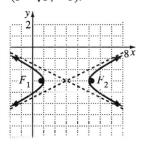

35. $(x-1)^2 - (y-2)^2 = 4$

$$\frac{(x-1)^2}{4} - \frac{(y-2)^2}{4} = 1$$

center: $(1, 2)$

$a^2 = 4,\ a = 2$

$b^2 = 4,\ b = 2$

vertices: $(-1, 2)$ and $(3, 2)$

asymptotes: $y - 2 = \pm(x - 1)$

$c^2 = a^2 + b^2 = 4 + 4 = 8$

$c = \sqrt{8} = 2\sqrt{2}$ parallel to y-axis

The foci are at $(1+2\sqrt{2},\ 2)$ and $(1-2\sqrt{2},\ 2)$.

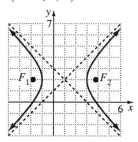

37. $x^2 - y^2 - 2x - 4y - 4 = 0$

$(x^2 - 2x) - (y^2 + 4y) = 4$

$(x^2 - 2x + 1) - (y^2 + 4y + 4) = 4 + 1 - 4$

$(x-1)^2 - (y+2)^2 = 1$

center: $(1, -2)$

$a^2 = 1,\ a = 1$

$b^2 = 1,\ b = 1$

$c^2 = a^2 + b^2 = 1 + 1 = 2$

$c = \sqrt{2}$

The foci are at $(1+\sqrt{2},\ -2)$ and $(1-\sqrt{2},\ -2)$.

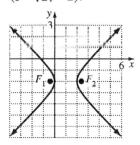

39. $16x^2 - y^2 + 64x - 2y + 67 = 0$

$(16x^2 + 64x) - (y^2 + 2y) = -67$

$16(x^2 + 4x + 4) - (y^2 + 2y + 1)$

$$= -67 + 64 - 1$$

$$16(x + 2)^2 - (y + 1)^2 = -4$$

$$\frac{16(x + 2)^2}{-4} - \frac{(y + 1)^2}{-4} = \frac{-4}{-4}$$

$$\frac{(y + 1)^2}{4} - \frac{(x + 2)^2}{\frac{1}{4}} = 1$$

center: $(-2, -1)$

$a^2 = 4$, $a = 2$

$b^2 = \dfrac{1}{4}$, $b = \dfrac{1}{2}$

$c^2 = a^2 + b^2 = 4 + \dfrac{1}{4} = \dfrac{17}{4}$

$c = \sqrt{\dfrac{17}{4}} = \sqrt{4.25}$

The foci are at $\left(-2, -1 + \sqrt{4.25}\right)$ and

$\left(-2, -1 - \sqrt{4.25}\right)$.

41. $4x^2 - 9y^2 - 16x + 54y - 101 = 0$

$(4x^2 - 16x) - (9y^2 - 54y) = 101$

$4(x^2 - 4x + 4) - 9(y^2 - 6y + 9)$

$$= 101 + 16 - 81$$

$$4(x - 2)^2 - 9(y - 3)^2 = 36$$

$$\frac{(x - 2)^2}{9} - \frac{(y - 3)^2}{4} = 1$$

center: $(2, 3)$

$a^2 = 9$, $a = 3$

$b^2 = 4$, $b = 2$

$c^2 = a^2 + b^2 = 9 + 4 = 13$

$c = \sqrt{13}$

The foci are at $(2 + \sqrt{13}, 3)$ and

$(2 - \sqrt{13}, 3)$.

43. $4x^2 - 25y^2 - 32x + 164 = 0$

$(4x^2 - 32x) - 25y^2 = -164$

$4(x^2 - 8x + 16) - 25y^2 = -164 + 64$

$4(x - 4)^2 - 25y^2 = -100$

$$\frac{4(x - 4)^2}{-100} - \frac{25y^2}{-100} = \frac{-100}{-100}$$

$$\frac{y^2}{4} - \frac{(x - 4)^2}{25} = 1$$

center: $(4, 0)$

$a^2 = 4$, $a = 2$

$b^2 = 25$, $b = 5$

$c^2 = a^2 + b^2 = 4 + 25 = 29$

$c = \sqrt{29}$

The foci are at $(4, \sqrt{29})$ and $(4, -\sqrt{29})$.

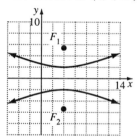

45. $|d_2 - d_1| = 2a = (2\text{ s})(1100\text{ ft / s}) = 2200\text{ ft}$

$a = 1100$ ft

$2c = 5280$ ft, $c = 2640$ ft

$b^2 = c^2 - a^2 = (2640)^2 - (1100)^2$

$$= 5,759,600$$

$$\frac{x^2}{(1100)^2} - \frac{y^2}{5,759,600} = 1$$

$$\frac{x^2}{1,210,000} - \frac{y^2}{5,759,600} = 1$$

If M_1 is located 2640 feet to the right of the origin on the x-axis, the explosion is located on the right branch of the hyperbola given by the equation above.

47. $625y^2 - 400x^2 = 250,000$

$$\frac{625y^2}{250,000} - \frac{400x^2}{250,000} = \frac{250,000}{250,000}$$

$$\frac{y^2}{400} - \frac{x^2}{625} = 1$$

$a^2 = 400$, $a = \sqrt{400} = 20$

$2a = 40$

The houses are 40 yards apart at their closest point.

49.–55.   Answers may vary.

57.   Exercise 27

Exercise 29

Exercise 31

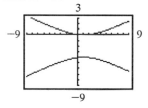

59. $\dfrac{x^2}{4} - \dfrac{y^2}{9} = 0$

$$y^2 = \frac{9}{4}x^2$$

$$y = \pm\frac{3}{2}x$$

No; in general, the graph is two intersecting lines.

61. $4x^2 - 6xy + 2y^2 - 3x + 10y - 6 = 0$

$2y^2 + (10 - 6x)y + (4x^2 - 3x - 6) = 0$

$$y = \frac{6x - 10 \pm \sqrt{(10 - 6x)^2 - 8(4x^2 - 3x - 6)}}{4}$$

$$y = \frac{6x - 10 \pm \sqrt{4(x^2 - 24x + 37)}}{4}$$

$$y = \frac{3x - 5 \pm \sqrt{x^2 - 24x + 37}}{2}$$

The *xy*-term rotates the hyperbola. Separation of terms into ones containing only *x* or only *y* would be impossible.

63. a.   False; one branch of the hyperbola

$\dfrac{x^2}{a^2} - \dfrac{y^2}{b^2} = 1$ will not pass the vertical line test, so will not define *y* as a function of *x*.

     b.   False; none of the points on the asymptotes satisfy the hyperbola's equation, since the hyperbola never touches its asymptotes.

     c.   True; $y = -\dfrac{2}{3}x$ is one of the asymptotes of the hyperbola and they will not intersect.

     d.   False; for example, $\dfrac{x^2}{4} - \dfrac{y^2}{4} = 1$ and

$\dfrac{y^2}{4} - \dfrac{x^2}{4} = 1$ each have asymptotes

$y = \pm x$, but are different hyperbolas.

(c) is true.

65. The center is at the midpoint of the line segment joining the vertices, so it is located at (5, 0). The standard form is:

$$\frac{(y-k)^2}{a^2} - \frac{(x-h)^2}{b^2} = 1$$

$(h, k) = (5, 0)$, and $a = 6$, so $a^2 = 36$.

$$\frac{y^2}{36} - \frac{(x-5)^2}{b^2} = 1.$$

Substitute $x = 0$ and $y = 9$:

$$\frac{9^2}{36} - \frac{(0-5)^2}{b^2} = 1$$

$$-\frac{25}{b^2} = -\frac{5}{4}$$

$$-100 = -5b^2$$

$$b^2 = 20$$

Standard form: $\dfrac{y^2}{36} - \dfrac{(x-5)^2}{20} = 1$

Section 10.3

Check Point Exercises

1. $y^2 = 8x$
$4p = 8, \ p = 2$
focus: (2, 0)
directrix: $x = -2$

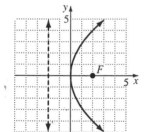

2. $x^2 = -12y$
$4p = -12, \ p = 3$
focus: (0, –3)
directrix: $y = 3$

3. $p = 8$
$y^2 = 4 \cdot 8x$
$y^2 = 32x$

4. $(x-2)^2 = 4(y+1)$
$4p = 4, \ p = 1$
vertex: (2, –1)
focus: (2, 0)
directrix: $y = -2$

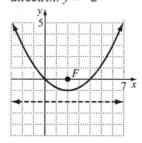

5. $y^2 + 2y + 4x - 7 = 0$
$$y^2 + 2y = -4x + 7$$
$$y^2 + 2y + 1 = -4x + 7 + 1$$
$$(y+1)^2 = -4(x-2)$$
$4p = -4, \ p = -1$
vertex: (2, –1)
focus: (1, –1)
directrix: $x = 3$

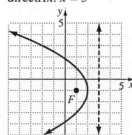

6. $x^2 = 4py$

Let $x = 3$ and $y = 4$.

$$3^2 = 4p \cdot 4$$
$$9 = 16p$$
$$p = \frac{9}{16}$$
$$x^2 = \frac{9}{4}y$$

The light should be placed at $\left(0, \dfrac{9}{16}\right)$ or $\dfrac{9}{16}$ inch above the vertex.

Exercise Set 10.3

1. $y^2 = 4x$
$4p = 4$, $p = 1$
vertex: $(0, 0)$
focus: $(1, 0)$
directrix: $x = -1$
graph (c)

3. $x^2 = -4y$
$4p = -4$, $p = -1$
vertex: $(0, 0)$
focus: $(0, -1)$
directrix: $y = 1$
graph (b)

5. $y^2 = 16x$
$4p = 16$, $p = 4$
vertex: $(0, 0)$
focus: $(4, 0)$
directrix: $x = -4$

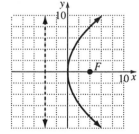

7. $y^2 = -8x$
$4p = -8$, $p = -2$
vertex: $(0, 0)$
focus: $(-2, 0)$
directrix: $x = 2$

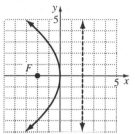

9. $x^2 = 12y$
$4p = 12$, $p = 3$
vertex: $(0, 0)$
focus: $(0, 3)$
directrix: $y = -3$

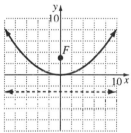

11. $x^2 = -16y$
$4p = -16$, $p = -4$
vertex: $(0, 0)$
focus: $(0, -4)$
directrix: $y = 4$

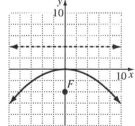

13. $y^2 - 6x = 0$

$y^2 = 6x$

$4p = 6,\ p = \dfrac{6}{4} = \dfrac{3}{2}$

vertex: $(0, 0)$

focus: $\left(\dfrac{3}{2}, 0\right)$

directrix: $x = -\dfrac{3}{2}$

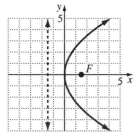

15. $p = 7,\ 4p = 28$

$y^2 = 28x$

17. $p = -5,\ 4p = -20$

$y^2 = -20x$

19. $p = 15,\ 4p = 60$

$x^2 = 60y$

21. $p = -25,\ 4p = -100$

$x^2 = -100y$

23. $(y - 1)^2 = 4(x - 1)$

$4p = 4,\ p = 1$

vertex: $(1, 1)$

focus: $(2, 1)$

directrix: $x = 0$

graph (c)

25. $(x + 1)^2 = -4(y + 1)$

$4p = -4,\ p = -1$

vertex: $(-1, -1)$

focus: $(-1, -2)$

directrix: $y = 0$

graph (d)

27. $(x - 2)^2 = 8(y - 1)$

$4p = 8,\ p = 2$

vertex: $(2, 1)$

focus: $(2, 3)$

directrix: $y = -1$

29. $(x + 1)^2 = -8(y + 1)$

$4p = -8,\ p = -2$

vertex: $(-1, -1)$

focus: $(-1, -3)$

directrix: $y = 1$

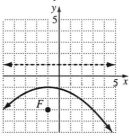

31. $(y + 3)^2 = 12(x + 1)$

$4p = 12,\ p = 3$

vertex: $(-1, -3)$

focus: $(2, -3)$

directrix: $x = -4$

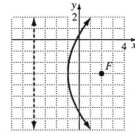

33. $(y + 1)^2 = -8x$
$\qquad (y + 1)^2 = -8(x - 0)$
$\qquad 4p = -8, \, p = -2$
$\qquad$ vertex: $(0, -1)$
$\qquad$ focus: $(-2, -1)$
$\qquad$ directrix: $x = 2$

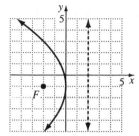

35. $x^2 - 2x - 4y + 9 = 0$
$\qquad\qquad x^2 - 2x = 4y - 9$
$\qquad x^2 - 2x + 1 = 4y - 9 + 1$
$\qquad\quad (x - 1)^2 = 4y - 8$
$\qquad\quad (x - 1)^2 = 4(y - 2)$
$\qquad 4p = 4, \, p = 1$
$\qquad$ vertex: $(1, 2)$
$\qquad$ focus: $(1, 3)$
$\qquad$ directrix: $y = 1$

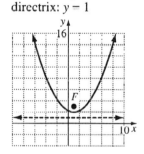

37. $y^2 - 2y + 12x - 35 = 0$
$\qquad\qquad y^2 - 2y = -12x + 35$
$\qquad y^2 - 2y + 1 = -12x + 35 + 1$
$\qquad\quad (y - 1)^2 = -12x + 36$
$\qquad\quad (y - 1)^2 = -12(x - 3)$
$\qquad 4p = -12, \, p = -3$
$\qquad$ vertex: $(3, 1)$
$\qquad$ focus: $(0, 1)$
$\qquad$ directrix: $x = 6$

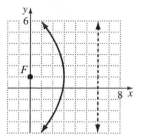

39. $x^2 + 6x - 4y + 1 = 0$
$\qquad\qquad x^2 + 6x = 4y - 1$
$\qquad x^2 + 6x + 9 = 4y - 1 + 9$
$\qquad\quad (x + 3)^2 = 4(y + 2)$
$\qquad 4p = 4, \, p = 1$
$\qquad$ vertex: $(-3, -2)$
$\qquad$ focus: $(-3, -1)$
$\qquad$ directrix: $y = -3$

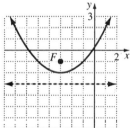

41. $x^2 = 4py$
$\qquad 2^2 = 4p(1)$
$\qquad\; 4 = 4p$
$\qquad\; p = 1$
The light bulb should be placed 1 inch above the vertex.

43. $x^2 = 4py$
$\qquad 6^2 = 4p(2)$
$\qquad 36 = 8p$
$\qquad p = \dfrac{36}{8} = \dfrac{9}{2} = 4.5$
The receiver should be located 4.5 feet from the base of the dish.

45. $x^2 = 4py$

$(640)^2 = 4p(160)$

$$p = \frac{(640)^2}{640} = 640$$

$$x = 640 - 200 = 440$$

$(440)^2 = 4(640)y$

$$y = \frac{(440)^2}{4(640)} = 75.625$$

The height is 75.625 meters.

47. $x^2 = 4py$

$$\left(\frac{200}{2}\right)^2 = 4p(-50)$$

$$\frac{10,000}{-50} = 4p$$

$$4p = -200$$

$$x^2 = -200y$$

$(30)^2 = -200y$

$$y = \frac{900}{-200} = -4.5$$

(height of bridge) $- 50 - 4.5 = 45.5$ feet.
Yes, the boat will clear the arch.

49.–53. Answers may vary.

55. Exercise 27

Exercise 29

Exercise 31

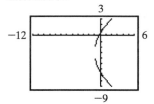

57. $y^2 + 10y - x + 25 = 0$

$y^2 + 10y + (-x + 25) = 0$

$$y = \frac{-10 \pm \sqrt{10^2 - 4(-x + 25)}}{2}$$

$$y = \frac{-10 \pm \sqrt{4x}}{2}$$

$$y = -5 \pm \sqrt{x}$$

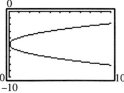

59. $x^2 + 2\sqrt{3}\,xy + 3y^2 + 8\sqrt{3}\,x - 8y + 32 = 0$

$3y^2 + (2\sqrt{3}\,x - 8)y + (x^2 + 8\sqrt{3}\,x + 32) = 0$

$$y = \frac{-(2\sqrt{3}x - 8) \pm \sqrt{(2\sqrt{3}x - 8)^2 - 12(x^2 + 8\sqrt{3}x + 32)}}{6}$$

$$y = \frac{-2\sqrt{3}x + 8 \pm \sqrt{-128\sqrt{3}x - 320}}{6}$$

$$y = \frac{-2\sqrt{3}x + 8 \pm 8\sqrt{-2\sqrt{3}x - 5}}{6}$$

$$y = \frac{-\sqrt{3}x + 4 \pm 4\sqrt{-2\sqrt{3}x - 5}}{3}$$

61. $p = 6, 4p = 24$

$x^2 = 24y$

$10^2 = 24y$

$y = \dfrac{100}{24} = \dfrac{25}{6}$

The dish should have a depth of $\dfrac{25}{6}$ feet.

Section 10.4

Check Point Exercises

1. **a.** $A = 3$ and $C = 2$.
   $AC = 3(2) = 6$. Since $A \neq C$ and $AC > 0$, the graph is an ellipse.

   b. $A = 1$ and $C = 1$. Since $A = C$, the graph is a circle.

   c. $A = 0$ and $C = 1$. Since $AC = 0$, the graph is a parabola.

   d. $A = 9$ and $C = -16$. Since $AC < 0$, the graph is a hyperbola.

2. $x = x'\cos 45° - y'\sin 45° = x'\left(\dfrac{\sqrt{2}}{2}\right) - y'\left(\dfrac{\sqrt{2}}{2}\right) = \dfrac{\sqrt{2}}{2}(x' - y')$

$y = x'\sin 45° + y'\cos 45° = x'\left(\dfrac{\sqrt{2}}{2}\right) + y'\left(\dfrac{\sqrt{2}}{2}\right) = \dfrac{\sqrt{2}}{2}(x' + y')$

Substitute into the equation: $xy = 2$

$$\left[\dfrac{\sqrt{2}}{2}(x' - y')\right]\left[\dfrac{\sqrt{2}}{2}(x' + y')\right] = 2$$

$$\dfrac{1}{2}\left(x'^2 - y'^2\right) = 2$$

$$\dfrac{x'^2}{4} - \dfrac{y'^2}{4} = 1$$

$\theta = 45°$

3. $2x^2 + \sqrt{3}xy + y^2 - 2 = 0$

Step 1

$A = 2, B = \sqrt{3},$ and $C = 1$.

$\cot 2\theta = \dfrac{A - C}{B} = \dfrac{2 - 1}{\sqrt{3}} = \dfrac{1}{\sqrt{3}} = \dfrac{\sqrt{3}}{3}$

Step 2

Since $\cot 2\theta = \dfrac{\sqrt{3}}{3}, 2\theta = 60°.$ Thus, $\theta = 30°$.

Step 3

$x = x'\cos 30° - y'\sin 30° = x'\left(\dfrac{\sqrt{3}}{2}\right) - y'\left(\dfrac{1}{2}\right) = \dfrac{\sqrt{3}x' - y'}{2}$

$y = x'\sin 30° + y'\cos 30° = x'\left(\dfrac{1}{2}\right) + y'\left(\dfrac{\sqrt{3}}{2}\right) = \dfrac{x' + \sqrt{3}y'}{2}$

Step 4
Substitute into the equation:

$2x^2 + \sqrt{3}xy + y^2 - 2 = 0$

$$2\left(\frac{\sqrt{3}x' - y'}{2}\right)^2 + \sqrt{3}\left(\frac{\sqrt{3}x' - y'}{2}\right)\left(\frac{x' + \sqrt{3}y'}{2}\right) + \left(\frac{x' + \sqrt{3}y'}{2}\right)^2 - 2 = 0$$

$$2\left(\frac{3x'^2 - 2\sqrt{3}x'y' + y'^2}{4}\right) + \sqrt{3}\left(\frac{\sqrt{3}x'^2 + 2x'y' - \sqrt{3}y'^2}{4}\right) + \frac{x'^2 + 2\sqrt{3}x'y' + 3y'^2}{4} = 2$$

$$6x'^2 - 4\sqrt{3}x'y' + 2y'^2 + 3x'^2 + 2\sqrt{3}x'y' - 3y'^2 + x'^2 + 2\sqrt{3}x'y' + 3y'^2 = 8$$

$$10x'^2 + 2y'^2 = 8$$

$$\frac{10x'^2}{8} + \frac{2y'^2}{8} = \frac{8}{8}$$

$$\frac{x'^2}{\frac{4}{5}} + \frac{y^2}{4} = 1$$

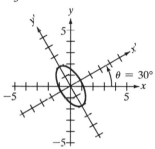

$\theta = 30°$

4. $4x^2 - 4xy + y^2 - 8\sqrt{5}x - 16\sqrt{5}y = 0$

Step 1:
$A = 4, B = -4,$ and $C = 1.$

$$\cot 2\theta = \frac{A - C}{B} = \frac{4 - 1}{-4} = \frac{-3}{4}$$

Step 2: Since θ is always acute, and $\cot 2\theta$ is negative, 2θ is in quadrant II.
    The third side of the right tiangle is found using the Pythagorean theorem:

$$(-3)^2 + 4^2 = r^2$$
$$25 = r^2$$
$$r = 5$$

So, $\cos 2\theta = \dfrac{\text{adjacent}}{\text{hypotenuse}} = \dfrac{-3}{5}.$

$$\sin\theta = \sqrt{\frac{1 - \cos 2\theta}{2}} = \sqrt{\frac{1 - \left(-\frac{3}{5}\right)}{2}} = \sqrt{\frac{8}{10}} = \sqrt{\frac{4}{5}} = \frac{2\sqrt{5}}{5} \text{ and}$$

$$\cos\theta = \sqrt{\frac{1 + \cos 2\theta}{2}} = \sqrt{\frac{1 + \left(-\frac{3}{5}\right)}{2}} = \sqrt{\frac{1}{5}} = \frac{\sqrt{5}}{5}$$

Step 3:

$$x = x'\cos\theta - y'\sin\theta = x'\left(\frac{\sqrt{5}}{5}\right) - y'\left(\frac{2\sqrt{5}}{5}\right) = \sqrt{5}\left(\frac{x'-2y'}{5}\right)$$

$$y = x'\sin\theta + y'\cos\theta = x'\left(\frac{2\sqrt{5}}{5}\right) + y'\left(\frac{\sqrt{5}}{5}\right) = \sqrt{5}\left(\frac{2x'+y'}{5}\right)$$

Step 4: Substitute into the equation: $4x^2 - 4xy + y^2 - 8\sqrt{5}x - 16\sqrt{5}y = 0$

$$4\left[\sqrt{5}\left(\frac{x'-2y'}{5}\right)\right]^2 - 4\left[\sqrt{5}\left(\frac{x'-2y'}{5}\right)\right]\left[\sqrt{5}\left(\frac{2x'+y'}{5}\right)\right] + \left[\sqrt{5}\left(\frac{2x'+y'}{5}\right)\right]^2 - 8\sqrt{5}\left[\sqrt{5}\left(\frac{x'-2y'}{5}\right)\right]$$

$$-16\sqrt{5}\left[\sqrt{5}\left(\frac{2x'+y'}{5}\right)\right] = 0$$

$$20\left(\frac{x'^2 - 4x'y' + 4y'^2}{25}\right) - 20\left(\frac{2x'^2 - 3x'y' - 2y'^2}{25}\right) + 5\left(\frac{4x'^2 + 4x'y' + y'^2}{25}\right) - 40\left(\frac{x'-2y'}{5}\right)$$

$$-80\left(\frac{2x'+y'}{5}\right) = 0$$

Multiply both sides by 25:

$$20x'^2 - 80x'y' + 80y'^2 - 40x'^2 + 60x'y' + 40y'^2 + 20x'^2 + 20x'y' + 5y'^2 - 200x' + 400y'$$
$$-800x' - 400y' = 0$$

$$125y'^2 - 1000x' = 0$$

$$y'^2 - 8x' = 0$$

Step 5: This is a parabola, since it has only the y' squared.

$$y'^2 - 8x' = 0$$

$$y'^2 = 8x'$$

The vertex of the parabola, relative to the $x'y'$ system, is (0, 0). Using a calculator to solve

$\sin\theta = \dfrac{2\sqrt{5}}{5}$, we find $\theta = \sin^{-1}\left(\dfrac{2\sqrt{5}}{5}\right) \approx 63°$. Rotate the axes through approximately 63°.

5. $3x^2 - 2\sqrt{3}xy + y^2 + 2x + 2\sqrt{3}y = 0$

   $A = 3, B = -2\sqrt{3}$, and $C = 1$.

   $B^2 - 4AC = \left(-2\sqrt{3}\right)^2 - 4(3)(1) = 12 - 12 = 0$

   Because $B^2 - 4AC = 0$, the graph of the equation is a parabola.

Exercise Set 10.4

1. $A = 0$ and $C = 1$. Since $AC = 0$, the graph is a parabola.

3. $A = 4$ and $C = -9$. Since $AC = -36 < 0$, the graph is a hyperbola.

5. $A = 4$ and $C = 4$. Since $A = C$, the graph is a circle.

7. $A = 100$ and $C = -7$. Since $AC = -700 < 0$, the graph is a hyperbola.

9. $x = x' \cos 45^\circ - y' \sin 45^\circ = x'\left(\dfrac{\sqrt{2}}{2}\right) - y'\left(\dfrac{\sqrt{2}}{2}\right) = \dfrac{\sqrt{2}}{2}(x' - y')$

   $y = x' \sin 45^\circ + y' \cos 45^\circ = x'\left(\dfrac{\sqrt{2}}{2}\right) + y'\left(\dfrac{\sqrt{2}}{2}\right) = \dfrac{\sqrt{2}}{2}(x' + y')$

   Substitute into the equation: $xy = -1$

   $$\left[\dfrac{\sqrt{2}}{2}(x' - y')\right]\left[\dfrac{\sqrt{2}}{2}(x' + y')\right] = -1$$

   $$\dfrac{1}{2}\left(x'^2 - y'^2\right) = -1$$

   $$\dfrac{y'^2}{2} - \dfrac{x'^2}{2} = 1$$

11. $x = x' \cos 45^\circ - y' \sin 45^\circ = x'\left(\dfrac{\sqrt{2}}{2}\right) - y'\left(\dfrac{\sqrt{2}}{2}\right) = \dfrac{\sqrt{2}}{2}(x' - y')$

    $y = x' \sin 45^\circ + y' \cos 45^\circ = x'\left(\dfrac{\sqrt{2}}{2}\right) + y'\left(\dfrac{\sqrt{2}}{2}\right) = \dfrac{\sqrt{2}}{2}(x' + y')$

    Substitute into the equation: $x^2 - 4xy + y^2 - 3 = 0$

    $$\left[\dfrac{\sqrt{2}}{2}(x' - y')\right]^2 - 4\left[\dfrac{\sqrt{2}}{2}(x' - y')\right]\left[\dfrac{\sqrt{2}}{2}(x' + y')\right] + \left[\dfrac{\sqrt{2}}{2}(x' + y')\right]^2 - 3 = 0$$

    $$\dfrac{1}{2}(x' - y')^2 - 4\left[\dfrac{1}{2}\left(x'^2 - y'^2\right)\right] + \dfrac{1}{2}(x' + y')^2 = 3$$

    $$\dfrac{1}{2}\left(x'^2 - 2x'y' + y'^2\right) - 2x'^2 + 2y'^2 + \dfrac{1}{2}\left(x'^2 + 2x'y' + y'^2\right) = 3$$

    $$\dfrac{1}{2}x'^2 - x'y' + \dfrac{1}{2}y'^2 - 2x'^2 + 2y'^2 + \dfrac{1}{2}x'^2 + x'y' + \dfrac{1}{2}y'^2 = 3$$

    $$-x'^2 + 3y'^2 = 3$$

    $$\dfrac{-x'^2}{3} + \dfrac{3y'^2}{3} = \dfrac{3}{3}$$

    $$\dfrac{y'^2}{1} - \dfrac{x'^2}{3} = 1$$

13. $x = x' \cos 30° - y' \sin 30° = x'\left(\dfrac{\sqrt{3}}{2}\right) - y'\left(\dfrac{1}{2}\right) = \dfrac{\sqrt{3}x' - y'}{2}$

$y = x' \sin 30° + y' \cos 30° = x'\left(\dfrac{1}{2}\right) + y'\left(\dfrac{\sqrt{3}}{2}\right) = \dfrac{x' + \sqrt{3}y'}{2}$

Substitute into the equation: $23x^2 + 26\sqrt{3}xy - 3y^2 - 144 = 0$

$$23\left(\dfrac{\sqrt{3}x' - y'}{2}\right)^2 + 26\sqrt{3}\left(\dfrac{\sqrt{3}x' - y'}{2}\right)\left(\dfrac{x' + \sqrt{3}y'}{2}\right) - 3\left(\dfrac{x' + \sqrt{3}y'}{2}\right)^2 = 144$$

$$23\left(\dfrac{3x'^2 - 2\sqrt{3}x'y' + y'^2}{4}\right) + 26\sqrt{3}\left(\dfrac{\sqrt{3}x'^2 + 2x'y' - \sqrt{3}y'^2}{4}\right) - 3\left(\dfrac{x'^2 + 2\sqrt{3}x'y' + 3y'^2}{4}\right) = 144$$

$$69x'^2 - 46\sqrt{3}x'y' + 23y'^2 + 78x'^2 + 52\sqrt{3}x'y' - 78y'^2 - 3x'^2 - 6\sqrt{3}x'y' - 9y'^2 = 576$$

$$144x'^2 - 64y'^2 = 576$$

$$\dfrac{144x'^2}{576} - \dfrac{64y'^2}{576} = \dfrac{576}{576}$$

$$\dfrac{x'^2}{4} - \dfrac{y'^2}{9} = 1$$

15. $x^2 + xy + y^2 - 10 = 0$
$A = 1, B = 1,$ and $C = 1.$

$\cot 2\theta = \dfrac{A - C}{B} = \dfrac{1 - 1}{1} = 0$

$2\theta = 90°$

$\theta = 45°$

$x = x' \cos 45° - y' \sin 45° = x'\left(\dfrac{\sqrt{2}}{2}\right) - y'\left(\dfrac{\sqrt{2}}{2}\right) = \dfrac{\sqrt{2}}{2}(x' - y')$

$y = x' \sin 45° + y' \cos 45° = x'\left(\dfrac{\sqrt{2}}{2}\right) + y'\left(\dfrac{\sqrt{2}}{2}\right) = \dfrac{\sqrt{2}}{2}(x' + y')$

17. $3x^2 - 10xy + 3y^2 - 32 = 0$
$A = 3, B = -10,$ and $C = 3.$

$\cot 2\theta = \dfrac{A - C}{B} = \dfrac{3 - 3}{-10} = 0$

$2\theta = 90°$

$\theta = 45°$

$x = x' \cos 45° - y' \sin 45° = x'\left(\dfrac{\sqrt{2}}{2}\right) - y'\left(\dfrac{\sqrt{2}}{2}\right) = \dfrac{\sqrt{2}}{2}(x' - y')$

$y = x' \sin 45° + y' \cos 45° = x'\left(\dfrac{\sqrt{2}}{2}\right) + y'\left(\dfrac{\sqrt{2}}{2}\right) = \dfrac{\sqrt{2}}{2}(x' + y')$

19. $11x^2 + 10\sqrt{3}xy + y^2 - 4 = 0$

$A = 11, B = 10\sqrt{3},$ and $C = 1.$

$\cot 2\theta = \dfrac{A - C}{B} = \dfrac{11 - 1}{10\sqrt{3}} = \dfrac{10}{10\sqrt{3}} = \dfrac{1}{\sqrt{3}} = \dfrac{\sqrt{3}}{3}$

$2\theta = 60°$

$\theta = 30°$

$x = x' \cos 30° - y' \sin 30°$

$x = x'\left(\dfrac{\sqrt{3}}{2}\right) - y'\left(\dfrac{1}{2}\right)$

$x = \dfrac{\sqrt{3}x' - y'}{2}$

$y = x' \sin 30° + y' \cos 30°$

$y = x'\left(\dfrac{1}{2}\right) + y'\left(\dfrac{\sqrt{3}}{2}\right)$

$y = \dfrac{x' + \sqrt{3}y'}{2}$

21. $10x^2 + 24xy + 17y^2 - 9 = 0$

$A = 10, B = 24,$ and $C = 17.$

$\cot 2\theta = \dfrac{A - C}{B} = \dfrac{10 - 17}{24} = \dfrac{-7}{24}$

Since θ is always acute, and $\cot 2\theta$ is negative, 2θ is in quadrant II.
The third side of the right triangle is found by using the Pythagorean theorem:

$(-7)^2 + 24^2 = r^2$

$625 = r^2$

$r = 25$

So, $\cos 2\theta = \dfrac{-7}{25}.$

$\sin \theta = \sqrt{\dfrac{1 - \cos 2\theta}{2}} = \sqrt{\dfrac{1 - \left(\frac{-7}{25}\right)}{2}} = \dfrac{4}{5}$ and

$\cos \theta = \sqrt{\dfrac{1 + \cos 2\theta}{2}} = \sqrt{\dfrac{1 + \left(\frac{-7}{25}\right)}{2}} = \dfrac{3}{5}$

$x = x' \cos \theta - y' \sin \theta$

$x = x'\left(\dfrac{3}{5}\right) - y'\left(\dfrac{4}{5}\right)$

$x = \dfrac{3x' - 4y'}{5}$

$y = x' \sin \theta + y' \cos \theta$

$y = x'\left(\dfrac{4}{5}\right) + y'\left(\dfrac{3}{5}\right)$

$y = \dfrac{4x' + 3y'}{5}$

23. $x^2 + 4xy - 2y^2 - 1 = 0$

$A = 1, B = 4,$ and $C = -2.$

$\cot 2\theta = \dfrac{A - C}{B} = \dfrac{1 - (-2)}{4} = \dfrac{3}{4}$

Since θ is always acute, and $\cot 2\theta$ is positive, 2θ is in quadrant I.
The third side of the right triangle is found using the Pythagorean theorem:

$3^2 + 4^2 = r^2$

$25 = r^2$

$r = 5$

So, $\cos 2\theta = \dfrac{3}{5}.$

$\sin \theta = \sqrt{\dfrac{1 - \cos 2\theta}{2}} = \sqrt{\dfrac{1 - \frac{3}{5}}{2}} = \dfrac{\sqrt{5}}{5}$ and

$\cos \theta = \sqrt{\dfrac{1 + \cos 2\theta}{2}} = \sqrt{\dfrac{1 + \frac{3}{5}}{2}} = \dfrac{2\sqrt{5}}{5}$

$x = x' \cos \theta - y' \sin \theta$

$x = x'\left(\dfrac{2\sqrt{5}}{5}\right) - y'\left(\dfrac{\sqrt{5}}{5}\right)$

$x = \sqrt{5}\left(\dfrac{2x' - y'}{5}\right)$

$y = x' \sin \theta + y' \cos \theta$

$y = x'\left(\dfrac{\sqrt{5}}{5}\right) + y'\left(\dfrac{2\sqrt{5}}{5}\right)$

$y = \sqrt{5}\left(\dfrac{x' + 2y'}{5}\right)$

25. $34x^2 - 24xy + 41y^2 - 25 = 0$

$A = 34, B = -24,$ and $C = 41.$

$$\cot 2\theta = \frac{A-C}{B} = \frac{34-41}{-24} = \frac{-7}{-24} = \frac{7}{24}$$

Since θ is always acute, and $\cot 2\theta$ is positive, 2θ is in quadrant I.

The third side of the right triangle is found using the Pythagorean theorem:

$$7^2 + 24^2 = r^2$$
$$625 = r^2$$
$$r = 25$$

So, $\cos 2\theta = \dfrac{7}{25}.$

$$\sin\theta = \sqrt{\frac{1-\cos 2\theta}{2}} = \sqrt{\frac{1-\frac{7}{25}}{2}} = \frac{3}{5} \text{ and } \cos\theta = \sqrt{\frac{1+\cos 2\theta}{2}} = \sqrt{\frac{1+\frac{7}{25}}{2}} = \frac{4}{5}$$

$$x = x'\cos\theta - y'\sin\theta = x'\left(\frac{4}{5}\right) - y'\left(\frac{3}{5}\right) = \frac{4x'-3y'}{5}$$

$$y = x'\sin\theta + y'\cos\theta = x'\left(\frac{3}{5}\right) + y'\left(\frac{4}{5}\right) = \frac{3x'+4y'}{5}$$

27. a. From Exercise 15,

$$x = \frac{\sqrt{2}}{2}(x'-y') \text{ and } y = \frac{\sqrt{2}}{2}(x'+y').$$

Substitute into the equation: $x^2 + xy + y^2 - 10 = 0$

$$\left[\frac{\sqrt{2}}{2}(x'-y')\right]^2 + \left[\frac{\sqrt{2}}{2}(x'-y')\right]\left[\frac{\sqrt{2}}{2}(x'+y')\right] + \left[\frac{\sqrt{2}}{2}(x'+y')\right]^2 - 10 = 0$$

$$\frac{1}{2}\left(x'^2 - 2x'y' + y'^2\right) + \frac{1}{2}\left(x'^2 - y'^2\right) + \frac{1}{2}\left(x'^2 + 2x'y' + y'^2\right) = 10$$

Multiply both sides by 2.

$$x'^2 - 2x'y' + y'^2 + x'^2 - y'^2 + x'^2 + 2x'y' + y'^2 = 20$$

$$3x'^2 + y'^2 = 20$$

b. $\dfrac{x'^2}{\frac{20}{3}} + \dfrac{y'^2}{20} = 1$

c.

$\theta = 45°$

29. a. From Exercise 17, $x = \dfrac{\sqrt{2}}{2}(x' - y')$ and $y = \dfrac{\sqrt{2}}{2}(x' + y')$.

Substitute into the equation: $3x^2 - 10xy + 3y^2 - 32 = 0$

$$3\left[\frac{\sqrt{2}}{2}(x'-y')\right]^2 - 10\left[\frac{\sqrt{2}}{2}(x'-y')\right]\left[\frac{\sqrt{2}}{2}(x'+y')\right] + 3\left[\frac{\sqrt{2}}{2}(x'+y')\right]^2 - 32 = 0$$

$$3\left[\frac{1}{2}\left(x'^2 - 2x'y' + y'^2\right)\right] - 10\left[\frac{1}{2}\left(x'^2 - y'^2\right)\right] + 3\left[\frac{1}{2}\left(x'^2 + 2x'y' + y'^2\right)\right] = 32$$

Multiply both sides by 2.

$$3x'^2 - 6x'y' + 3y'^2 - 10x'^2 + 10y'^2 + 3x'^2 + 6x'y' + 3y'^2 = 64$$
$$-4x'^2 + 16y'^2 = 64$$

b. $\dfrac{y'^2}{4} - \dfrac{x'^2}{16} = 1$

c.

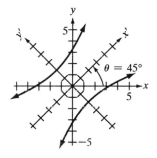

31. a. From Exercise 19,

$$x = \frac{\sqrt{3}x' - y'}{2} \text{ and } y = \frac{x' + \sqrt{3}y'}{2}.$$

Substitute into the equation: $11x^2 + 10\sqrt{3}xy + y^2 - 4 = 0$

$$11\left(\frac{\sqrt{3}x' - y'}{2}\right)^2 + 10\sqrt{3}\left(\frac{\sqrt{3}x' - y'}{2}\right)\left(\frac{x' + \sqrt{3}y'}{2}\right) + \left(\frac{x' + \sqrt{3}y'}{2}\right)^2 - 4 = 0$$

$$11\left(\frac{3x'^2 - 2\sqrt{3}x'y' + y'^2}{4}\right) + 10\sqrt{3}\left(\frac{\sqrt{3}x'^2 + 2x'y' - \sqrt{3}y'^2}{4}\right) + \frac{x'^2 + 2\sqrt{3}x'y' + 3y'^2}{4} = 4$$

Multiply both sides by 4:

$$33x'^2 - 22\sqrt{3}x'y' + 11y'^2 + 30x'^2 + 20\sqrt{3}x'y' - 30y'^2 + x'^2 + 2\sqrt{3}x'y' + 3y'^2 = 16$$
$$64x'^2 - 16y'^2 = 16$$

b. $\dfrac{x'^2}{\frac{1}{4}} - \dfrac{y'^2}{1} = 1$

c.

33. a.   From Exercise 21, $x = \dfrac{3x' - 4y'}{5}$ and $y = \dfrac{4x' + 3y'}{5}$.

Substitute into the equation: $10x^2 + 24xy + 17y^2 - 9 = 0$

$$10\left(\frac{3x' - 4y'}{5}\right)^2 + 24\left(\frac{3x' - 4y'}{5}\right)\left(\frac{4x' + 3y'}{5}\right) + 17\left(\frac{4x' + 3y'}{5}\right)^2 - 9 = 0$$

$$10\left(\frac{9x'^2 - 24x'y' + 16y'^2}{25}\right) + 24\left(\frac{12x'^2 - 7x'y' - 12y'^2}{25}\right) + 17\left(\frac{16x'^2 + 24x'y' + 9y'^2}{25}\right) = 9$$

Multiply both sides by 25:

$90x'^2 - 240x'y' + 160y'^2 + 288x'^2 - 168x'y' - 288y'^2 + 272x'^2 + 408x'y' + 153y'^2 = 225$

$650x'^2 + 25y'^2 = 225$

b. $\dfrac{x'^2}{\frac{9}{26}} + \dfrac{y'^2}{9} = 1$

c.

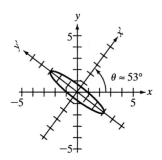

The axes are rotated by $\theta = \sin^{-1}\left(\dfrac{4}{5}\right) \approx 53°$.

35. a. From Exercise 23,
$$x = \sqrt{5}\left(\frac{2x'-y'}{5}\right) \text{ and } y = \sqrt{5}\left(\frac{x'+2y'}{5}\right).$$
Substitute into the equation: $x^2 + 4xy - 2y^2 - 1 = 0$

$$\left[\sqrt{5}\left(\frac{2x'-y'}{5}\right)\right]^2 + 4\left[\sqrt{5}\left(\frac{2x'-y'}{5}\right)\right]\left[\sqrt{5}\left(\frac{x'+2y'}{5}\right)\right] - 2\left[\sqrt{5}\left(\frac{x'+2y'}{5}\right)\right]^2 = 1$$

$$5\left(\frac{4x'^2 - 4x'y' + y'^2}{25}\right) + 20\left(\frac{2x'^2 + 3x'y' - 2y'^2}{25}\right) - 10\left(\frac{x'^2 + 4x'y' + 4y'^2}{25}\right) = 1$$

Multiply both sides by 25:
$$20x'^2 - 20x'y' + 5y'^2 + 40x'^2 + 60x'y' - 40y'^2 - 10x'^2 - 40x'y' - 40y'^2 = 25$$
$$50x'^2 - 75y'^2 = 25$$

b. $\dfrac{x'^2}{\frac{1}{2}} - \dfrac{y'^2}{\frac{1}{3}} = 1$

c.

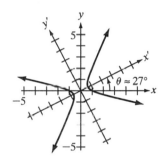

The axes are rotated by $\theta = \sin^{-1}\left(\dfrac{\sqrt{5}}{5}\right) \approx 27°$.

37. a. From Exercise 25,
$$x = \frac{4x'-3y'}{5} \text{ and } y = \frac{3x'+4y'}{5}.$$
Substitute into the equation: $34x^2 - 24xy + 41y^2 - 25 = 0$

$$34\left(\frac{4x'-3y'}{5}\right)^2 - 24\left(\frac{4x'-3y'}{5}\right)\left(\frac{3x'+4y'}{5}\right) + 41\left(\frac{3x'+4y'}{5}\right)^2 = 25$$

$$34\left(\frac{16x'^2 - 24x'y' + 9y'^2}{25}\right) - 24\left(\frac{12x'^2 + 7x'y' - 12y'^2}{25}\right) + 41\left(\frac{9x'^2 + 24x'y' + 16y'^2}{25}\right) = 25$$

Multiply both sides by 25:
$$544x'^2 - 816x'y' + 306y'^2 - 288x'^2 - 168x'y' + 288y'^2 + 369x'^2 + 984x'y' + 656y'^2 = 625$$
$$625x'^2 + 1250y'^2 = 625$$

b.
$$\frac{625x'^2 + 1250y'^2}{625} = \frac{625}{625}$$
$$\frac{x'^2}{1} + \frac{y'^2}{\frac{1}{2}} = 1$$

c.

The axes are rotated by $\theta = \sin^{-1}\left(\frac{3}{5}\right) \approx 37°$.

39. $5x^2 - 2xy + 5y^2 - 12 = 0$
$A = 5, B = -2,$ and $C = 5$.
$B^2 - 4AC = (-2)^2 - 4(5)(5) = -96$.
Since $B^2 - 4AC < 0$, the graph is an ellipse or a circle.

41. $24x^2 + 16\sqrt{3}xy + 8y^2 - x + \sqrt{3}y - 8 = 0$
$A = 24, B = 16\sqrt{3},$ and $C = 8$.
$B^2 - 4AC = \left(16\sqrt{3}\right)^2 - 4(24)(8) = 768 - 768 = 0$
Since $B^2 - 4AC = 0$, the graph is a parabola.

43. $23x^2 + 26\sqrt{3}xy - 3y^2 - 144 = 0$
$A = 23, B = 26\sqrt{3},$ and $C = -3$.
$B^2 - 4AC = \left(26\sqrt{3}\right)^2 - 4(23)(-3) = 2028 + 276 = 2304$
Since $B^2 - 4AC > 0$, the graph is a hyperbola.

45.–49. Answers may vary.

51. $A = 7, B = 8, C = 1, D = 0, E = 0,$ and $F = -1$.

Graph $y_1 = \dfrac{-8x + \sqrt{64x^2 - 4\left(7x^2 - 1\right)}}{2}$ and $y_2 = \dfrac{-8x - \sqrt{64x^2 - 4\left(7x^2 - 1\right)}}{2}$.

53. $A = 3$, $B = -6$, $C = 3$, $D = 10$, $E = -8$, and $F = -2$.

Graph $y_1 = \dfrac{-(-6x-8) + \sqrt{(-6x-8)^2 - 12(3x^2 + 10x - 2)}}{6}$ and

$y_2 = \dfrac{-(-6x-8) - \sqrt{(-6x-8)^2 - 12(3x^2 + 10x - 2)}}{6}$.

55. $A = 1$, $B = 4$, $C = 4$, $D = 10\sqrt{5}$, $E = 0$, and $F = -9$.

Graph $y_1 = \dfrac{-4x + \sqrt{16x^2 - 16(x^2 + 10\sqrt{5}x - 9)}}{8}$ and $y_2 = \dfrac{-4x - \sqrt{16x^2 - 16(x^2 + 10\sqrt{5}x - 9)}}{8}$.

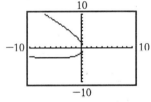

57. $A = 3$, $B = 2$, and $C = 3$.

$\cot 2\theta = \dfrac{A - C}{B} = \dfrac{3 - 3}{2} = 0$

$2\theta = 90°$

$\theta = 45°$

$x = x' \cos 45° - y' \sin 45° = x'\left(\dfrac{\sqrt{2}}{2}\right) - y'\left(\dfrac{\sqrt{2}}{2}\right) = \dfrac{\sqrt{2}}{2}(x' - y')$

$y = x' \sin 45° + y' \cos 45° = x'\left(\dfrac{\sqrt{2}}{2}\right) + y'\left(\dfrac{\sqrt{2}}{2}\right) = \dfrac{\sqrt{2}}{2}(x' + y')$

Substitute into the equation: $3x^2 - 2xy + 3y^2 + 2 = 0$

$3\left[\dfrac{\sqrt{2}}{2}(x' - y')\right]^2 - 2\left[\dfrac{\sqrt{2}}{2}(x' - y')\right]\left[\dfrac{\sqrt{2}}{2}(x' + y')\right] + 3\left[\dfrac{\sqrt{2}}{2}(x' + y')\right]^2 + 2 = 0$

$\dfrac{3}{2}\left(x'^2 - 2x'y' + y'^2\right) - \left(x'^2 - y'^2\right) + \dfrac{3}{2}\left(x'^2 + 2x'y' + y'^2\right) = -2$

Multiply both sides by 2:

$$3x'^2 - 6x'y' + 3y'^2 - 2x'^2 + 2y'^2 + 3x'^2 + 6x'y' + 3y'^2 = -4$$

$$4x'^2 + 8y'^2 = -4$$

$$\frac{4x'^2 + 8y'^2}{-4} = \frac{-4}{-4}$$

$$-x'^2 - 2y'^2 = 1$$

There are no solutions to this equation since the left side of the equation is negative or 0 for all values of x' and y'. Thus, there are no points on the graph of this equation, just as one hand clapping makes no sound.

59.
$$A' = A\cos^2\theta + B\sin\theta\cos\theta + C\sin^2\theta$$
$$C' = A\sin^2\theta - B\sin\theta\cos\theta + C\cos^2\theta$$
$$A' + C' = A\cos^2\theta + B\sin\theta\cos\theta + C\sin^2\theta + A\sin^2\theta - B\sin\theta\cos\theta + C\cos^2\theta$$
$$= A\left(\cos^2\theta + \sin^2\theta\right) + B(\sin\theta\cos\theta - \sin\theta\cos\theta) + C\left(\sin^2\theta + \cos^2\theta\right)$$
$$= A(1) + B(0) + C(1)$$
$$= A + C$$

Section 10.5

Check Point Exercises

1.

t	$x = t^2 + 1$	$y = 3t$	(x, y)
-2	$(-2)^2 + 1 = 5$	$3(-2) = -6$	$(5, -6)$
-1	$(-1)^2 + 1 = 2$	$3(-1) = -3$	$(2, -3)$
0	$0^2 + 1 = 1$	$3(0) = 0$	$(1, 0)$
1	$1^2 + 1 = 2$	$3(1) = 3$	$(2, 3)$
2	$2^2 + 1 = 5$	$3(2) = 6$	$(5, 6)$

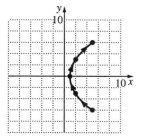

2. $x = \sqrt{t} \;\Rightarrow\; t = x^2$

Using $t = x^2$ and $y = 2t - 1$, $y = 2x^2 - 1$.
Since $t \geq 0$, x is nonnegative.

3. $x = 6\cos t$ and $y = 4\sin t$, $\pi \le t \le 2\pi$

$\dfrac{x}{6} = \cos t$ $\qquad$ $\dfrac{y}{4} = \sin t$

Square and add the equations:

$$\dfrac{x^2}{36} = \cos^2 t$$

$$+ \quad \dfrac{y^2}{16} = \sin^2 t$$

$$\dfrac{x^2}{36} + \dfrac{y^2}{16} = \cos^2 t + \sin^2 t$$

$$\dfrac{x^2}{36} + \dfrac{y^2}{16} = 1$$

Since t is in the interval $[\pi,\ 2\pi]$, we use

$t = \pi$, $t = \dfrac{3\pi}{2}$, and $t = 2\pi$:

$t = \pi$: $\quad x = 6\cos\pi = -6$

$\qquad\qquad y = 4\sin\pi = 0$

$t = \dfrac{3\pi}{2}$: $\ x = 6\cos\dfrac{3\pi}{2} = 0$

$\qquad\qquad y = 4\sin\dfrac{3\pi}{2} = -4$

$t = 2\pi$: $\quad x = 6\cos 2\pi = 6$

$\qquad\qquad y = 4\cos 2\pi = 0$

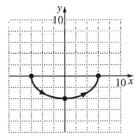

4. $y = x^2 - 25$

Let $x = t$. Then $y = t^2 - 25$.

The parametric equations are $x = t$ and $y = t^2 - 25$.

Exercise Set 10.5

1. $x = 3 - 5(1) = -2$

$\ y = 4 + 2(1) = 6$;

$\quad (-2,\ 6)$

3. $x = 2^2 + 1 = 5$

$\ y = 5 - 2^3 = 5 - 8 = -3$;

$\quad (5,\ -3)$

5. $x = 4 + 2\cos\dfrac{\pi}{2} = 4 + 2(0) = 4$

$\ y = 3 + 5\sin\dfrac{\pi}{2} = 3 + 5(1) = 8$;

$\quad (4,\ 8)$

7. $x = (60\cos 30°)(2) = \left(60 \cdot \dfrac{\sqrt{3}}{2}\right)(2) = 60\sqrt{3}$

$\ y = 5 + (60\sin 30°)(2) - 16(2)^2$

$\quad = 5 + \left(60 \cdot \dfrac{1}{2}\right)(2) - 16 \cdot 4$

$\quad = 5 + 60 - 64 = 1$;

$\quad \left(60\sqrt{3},\ 1\right)$

9.

t	$x = t + 2$	$y = t^2$	(x, y)
-2	$-2 + 2 = 0$	$(-2)^2 = 4$	$(0,\ 4)$
-1	$-1 + 2 = 1$	$(-1)^2 = 1$	$(1,\ 1)$
0	$0 + 2 = 2$	$0^2 = 0$	$(2,\ 0)$
1	$1 + 2 = 3$	$1^2 = 1$	$(3,\ 1)$
2	$2 + 2 = 4$	$2^2 = 4$	$(4,\ 4)$

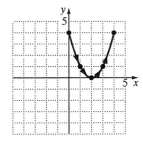

11.

t	$x = t - 2$	$y = 2t + 1$	(x, y)
−2	$-2 - 2 = -4$	$2(-2) + 1 = -3$	$(-4, -3)$
−1	$-1 - 2 = -3$	$2(-1) + 1 = -1$	$(-3, -1)$
0	$0 - 2 = -2$	$2(0) + 1 = 1$	$(-2, 1)$
1	$1 - 2 = -1$	$2(1) + 1 = 3$	$(-1, 3)$
2	$2 - 2 = 0$	$2(2) + 1 = 5$	$(0, 5)$
3	$3 - 2 = 1$	$2(3) + 1 = 7$	$(1, 7)$

13.

t	$x = t + 1$	$y = \sqrt{t}$	(x, y)
0	$0 + 1 = 1$	$\sqrt{0} = 0$	$(1, 0)$
1	$1 + 1 = 2$	$\sqrt{1} = 1$	$(2, 1)$
4	$4 + 1 = 5$	$\sqrt{4} = 2$	$(5, 2)$
9	$9 + 1 = 10$	$\sqrt{9} = 3$	$(10, 3)$

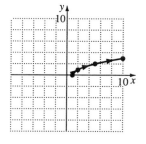

15.

t	$x = \cos t$	$y = \sin t$	(x, y)
0	$\cos 0 = 1$	$\sin 0 = 0$	$(1, 0)$
$\dfrac{\pi}{2}$	$\cos \dfrac{\pi}{2} = 0$	$\sin \dfrac{\pi}{2} = 1$	$(0, 1)$
π	$\cos \pi = -1$	$\sin \pi = 0$	$(-1, 0)$
$\dfrac{3\pi}{2}$	$\cos \dfrac{3\pi}{2} = 0$	$\sin \dfrac{3\pi}{2} = -1$	$(0, -1)$
2π	$\cos 2\pi = 1$	$\sin 2\pi = 0$	$(1, 0)$

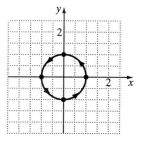

17.

t	$x = t^2$	$y = t^3$	(x, y)
−2	$(-2)^2 = 4$	$(-2)^3 = -8$	$(4, -8)$
−1	$(-1)^2 = 1$	$(-1)^3 = -1$	$(1, -1)$
0	$0^2 = 0$	$0^3 = 0$	$(0, 0)$
1	$1^2 = 1$	$1^3 = 1$	$(1, 1)$
2	$2^2 = 4$	$2^3 = 8$	$(4, 8)$

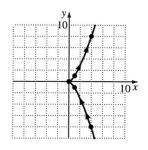

19.

t	$x = 2t$	$y = |t - 1|$	(x, y)
−2	$2(-2) = -4$	$|-2 - 1| = 3$	$(-4, 3)$
−1	$2(-1) = -2$	$|-1 - 1| = 2$	$(-2, 2)$
0	$2(0) = 0$	$|0 - 1| = 1$	$(0, 1)$
1	$2(1) = 2$	$|1 - 1| = 0$	$(2, 0)$
2	$2(2) = 4$	$|2 - 1| = 1$	$(4, 1)$

21. $x = t \Rightarrow y = 2x$

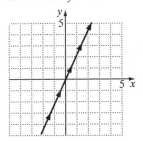

23. $x = 2t - 4$

$\dfrac{x + 4}{2} = t$

Substitute into y:

$y = 4\left(\dfrac{x + 4}{2}\right)^2 = (x + 4)^2$

$y = (x + 4)^2$

25. $x = \sqrt{t}$

$x^2 = t$

Substitute into y:

$y = x^2 - 1$

Since $t \geq 0$ in $x = \sqrt{t}$, $x \geq 0$.

27. $x = 2\sin t$ and $y = 2\cos t$

$\dfrac{x}{2} = \sin t$ $\dfrac{y}{2} = \cos t$

Square and add the equations:

$\dfrac{x^2}{4} = \sin^2 t$

$+ \quad \dfrac{y^2}{4} = \cos^2 t$

$\dfrac{x^2}{4} + \dfrac{y^2}{4} = \sin^2 t + \cos^2 t$

$\dfrac{x^2}{4} + \dfrac{y^2}{4} = 1$

$x^2 + y^2 = 4$

The circle centered at (0, 0) with radius 2.

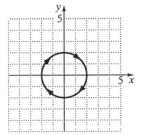

29. $x = 1 + 3\cos t$ and $y = 2 + 3\sin t$

$\dfrac{x - 1}{3} = \cos t$ $\dfrac{y - 2}{3} = \sin t$

Square and add the equations:

$\dfrac{(x - 1)^2}{9} = \cos^2 t$

$+ \quad \dfrac{(y - 2)^2}{9} = \sin^2 t$

$\dfrac{(x - 1)^2}{9} + \dfrac{(y - 2)^2}{9} = \cos^2 t + \sin^2 t$

$\dfrac{(x - 1)^2}{9} + \dfrac{(y - 2)^2}{9} = 1$

$(x - 1)^2 + (y - 2)^2 = 9$

This is a circle centered at (1, 2) with radius 3.

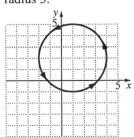

31. $x = 2\cos t$ and $y = 3\sin t$

$\dfrac{x}{2} = \cos t$ $\dfrac{y}{3} = \sin t$

Square and add the equations:

$$\dfrac{x^2}{4} = \cos^2 t$$

$$+ \quad \dfrac{y^2}{9} = \sin^2 t$$

$$\overline{\dfrac{x^2}{4} + \dfrac{y^2}{9} = \cos^2 t + \sin^2 t}$$

$$\dfrac{x^2}{4} + \dfrac{y^2}{9} = 1$$

This is an ellipse centered at $(0, 0)$.

33. $x = 1 + 3\cos t$ and $y = -1 + 2\sin t$

$\dfrac{x-1}{3} = \cos t$ $\dfrac{y+1}{2} = \sin t$

Square and add the equations:

$$\dfrac{(x-1)^2}{9} = \cos^2 t$$

$$+ \quad \dfrac{(y+1)^2}{4} = \sin^2 t$$

$$\overline{\dfrac{(x-1)^2}{9} + \dfrac{(y+1)^2}{4} = \cos^2 t + \sin^2 t}$$

$$\dfrac{(x-1)^2}{9} + \dfrac{(y+1)^2}{4} = 1$$

Since $0 \le t \le \pi$, $-1 \le \cos t \le 1$ and

$0 \le \sin t \le 1$. Thus, $-1 \le \dfrac{x-1}{3} \le 1$ and

$0 \le \dfrac{y+1}{2} \le 1$. Hence, $-2 \le x \le 4$ and

$-1 \le y \le 1$. This is the upper half of an ellipse centered at $(-1, 1)$.

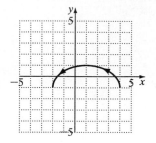

35. $x = \sec t$ and $y = \tan t$

Square and subtract the equations:

$$x^2 = \sec^2 t$$

$$- \quad (y^2 = \tan^2 t)$$

$$\overline{x^2 - y^2 = \sec^2 t - \tan^2 t}$$

$$x^2 - y^2 = 1$$

This is a hyperbola centered at $(0, 0)$.

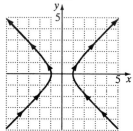

37. $x = t^2 + 2$ and $y = t^2 - 2$

$x - 2 = t^2$

Substitute $x - 2$ into $y = t^2 - 2$ for t^2:

$y = (x - 2) - 2$

$y = x - 4$

Since $t^2 \ge 0$ for all t, $x \ge 2$ and $y \ge -2$.

39. $x = 2^t$ and $y = 2^{-t}$

$$y = \left(2^t\right)^{-1}$$

Substitute x in $y = \left(2^t\right)^{-1}$ for 2^t:

$$y = (x)^{-1}$$
$$y = \frac{1}{x}$$

Since $t \geq 0$, $x \geq 1$ and $y \geq 0$.

41. $x = h + r\cos t$ and $y = k + r\sin t$

$$\frac{x - h}{r} = \cos t \qquad\qquad \frac{y - k}{r} = \sin t$$

Square and add the equations:

$$\frac{(x - h)^2}{r^2} = \cos^2 t$$

$$+ \quad \frac{(y - k)^2}{r^2} = \sin^2 t$$

$$\overline{\frac{(x - h)^2}{r^2} + \frac{(y - k)^2}{r^2} = \cos^2 t + \sin^2 t}$$

$$\frac{(x - h)^2}{r^2} + \frac{(y - k)^2}{r^2} = 1$$

$$(x - h)^2 + (y - k)^2 = r^2$$

43. $x = h + a\sec t$ and $y = k + b\tan t$

$$\frac{x - h}{a} = \sec t \qquad\qquad \frac{y - k}{b} = \tan t$$

Square and subtract the equations:

$$\frac{(x - h)^2}{a^2} = \sec^2 t$$

$$- \quad \left(\frac{(y - k)^2}{b^2} = \tan^2 t \right)$$

$$\overline{\frac{(x - h)^2}{a^2} - \frac{(y - k)^2}{b^2} = \sec^2 t - \tan^2 t}$$

$$\frac{(x - h)^2}{a^2} - \frac{(y - k)^2}{b^2} = 1$$

45. $h = 3$, $k = 5$, and $r = 6$

$x = h + r\cos t$ and $y = k + r\sin t$

$x = 3 + 6\cos t$ $y = 5 + 6\sin t$

47. $h = -2$, $k = 3$, $a = 5$, $b = 2$

$x = h + a\cos t$ and $y = k + b\sin t$

$x = -2 + 5\cos t$ $y = 3 + 2\sin t$

49. $h = 0$, $k = 0$, $a = 4$, $c = 6$

$$c^2 = a^2 + b^2$$
$$6^2 = 4^2 + b^2$$
$$36 - 16 = b^2$$
$$b = \sqrt{20} = 2\sqrt{5}$$

$x = h + a\sec t$ and $y = k + b\tan t$

$x = 0 + 4\sec t$ $y = 0 + 2\sqrt{5}\tan t$

$x = 4\sec t$ $y = 2\sqrt{5}\tan t$

51. $x_1 = -2$, $y_1 = 4$, $x_2 = 1$, $y_2 = 7$

$x = x_1 + t(x_2 - x_1)$ and $y = y_1 + t(y_2 - y_1)$

$x = -2 + t(1 - (-2))$ $y = 4 + t(7 - 4)$

$x = -2 + 3t$ $y = 4 + 3t$

53.–55. Answers may vary.

57. a.

b.

c.

d.

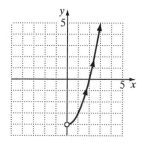

Explanations of how the curves differ from each other may vary.

59. a. $x = (180\cos 40°)t$

$y = 3 + (180\sin 40°)t - 16t^2$

b. After 1 second:

$x = (180\cos 40°) \cdot 1 \approx 137.9$ feet in distance

$y = 3 + (180\sin 40°)1 - 16 \cdot 1^2 \approx 102.7$ feet in height

After 2 seconds:

$x = (180\cos 40°) \cdot 2 \approx 275.8$ feet in distance

$y = 3 + (180\sin 40°) \cdot 2 - 16 \cdot 2^2 \approx 170.4$ feet in height

After 3 seconds:

$x = (180\cos 40°) \cdot 3 \approx 413.7$ feet in distance

$y = 3 + (180\sin 40°) \cdot 3 - 16 \cdot 3^2 \approx 206.1$ feet in height

The points on the curve are (137.9, 102.7), (275.8, 170.4), (413.7, 206.1).

c. The ball is no longer in flight when its height above ground is zero:

$0 = 3 + (180\sin 40°)t - 16t^2$

$0 = -16t^2 + (180\sin 40°)t + 3$

$t = \dfrac{-(180\sin 40°) \pm \sqrt{(180\sin 40°)^2 - 4 \cdot (-16)(3)}}{2(-16)}$

$t \approx -.03$ or $t \approx 7.3$

Since we cannot use the negative time, the ball hits the ground at $t \approx 7.3$ seconds.

The total horizontal distance is: $x = (180\cos 40°) \cdot (7.3) \approx 1006.6$ feet

d. Answers may vary.

61.–65. Answers may vary.

67. Exercise 9

Exercise 11

Exercise 13

Exercise 15

Exercise 17

69.

71.

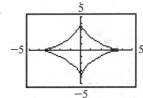

In Exercises 73-75, use the equations:
$x = (v_0 \cos\theta)t$ and $y = h + (v_0 \sin\theta)t - 16t^2$
where v_0 is the initial velocity, θ is the angle from horizontal, h is the height above the ground, and t is the time, in seconds.

73. $x = (200\cos 55°)t$ and
$y = (200\sin 55°)t - 16t^2$

Window: $[-100, 1500] \times [-100, 500]$
The maximum height is 419.4 feet at a time of 5.1 seconds. The range of the projective is 1174.6 feet horizontally. It hits the ground at 10.2 seconds.

75. **a.** $x = (140\cos 22°)t$ and
$y = 5 + (140\sin 22°)t - 16t^2$

b.

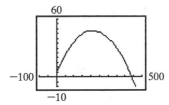

Window: $[-100, 500] \times [-10, 60]$

c. The maximum height is 48.0 feet. It occurs at 1.6 seconds.

d. The ball is in the air for 3.4 seconds.

e. The ball travels 437.5 feet.

77. $x = 3\sin t$ and $y = 3\cos t$

Section 10.6

Check Point Exercises

1. Graph $r = \dfrac{4}{2 - \cos\theta}$.

   Step 1: Divide numerator and denominator by 2 to write the equation in standard form:

   $$r = \frac{2}{1 - \frac{1}{2}\cos\theta}$$

   Step 2: $e = \dfrac{1}{2}$ and $ep = \dfrac{1}{2}\, p = 2$, so $p = 4$.

   Since $e < 1$, the graph is an ellipse.

   Step 3: The graph has symmetry with respect to the polar axis. One focus is at the pole and the directrix is $x = -4$.

   Find the vertices by selecting $\theta = 0$ and $\theta = \pi$: $(4, 0)$ and $\left(\dfrac{4}{3}, \pi\right)$.

   Sketch the upper half by plotting some points, then use the symmetry of the graph to sketch the lower half.

   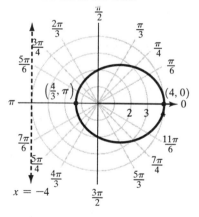

2. Graph $r = \dfrac{8}{4 + 4\sin\theta}$.

   Step 1: Divide numerator and denominator by 4 to write the equation in standard form:

   $$r = \frac{2}{1 + \sin\theta}$$

   Step 2: $e = 1$ and $ep = 1\; p = 2$, so $p = 2$.

   Since $e = 1$, the graph is parabola.

   Step 3: The graph has symmetry with respect to $\theta = \dfrac{\pi}{2}$. The focus is at the pole and the directrix is $y = 2$. Since the vertex is on the line $\theta = \dfrac{\pi}{2}$ (y-axis) the vertex is at $\left(1, \dfrac{\pi}{2}\right)$. To find the intercepts on the polar axis, select $\theta = 0$ and $\theta = \pi$: $(2, 0)$ and $(2, \pi)$.

   Sketch the right half by plotting some points, then use symmetry to sketch the left half.

   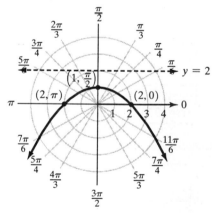

3. Graph $r = \dfrac{9}{3 - 9\cos\theta}$.

Step 1: Divide numerator and denominator by 3 to write the equation in standard form:

$$r = \frac{3}{1 - 3\cos\theta}$$

Step 2: $e = 3$ and $ep = 3p = 3$, so $p = 1$. Since $e > 1$, the graph is a hyperbola.

Step 3: The graph is symmetric with respect to the polar axis. One focus is at the pole and the directrix is at $x = -1$. The transverse axis is horizontal and the vertices lie on the polar axis. Find them by selecting $\theta = 0$ and $0 = \pi$:

$$\left(-\frac{3}{2}, 0\right) \text{ and } \left(\frac{3}{4}, \pi\right).$$

Sketch the upper half of the hyperbola by plotting some points, then use symmetry to sketch the lower half.

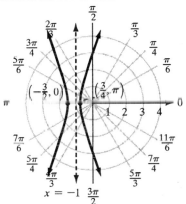

Exercise Set 10.6

1. $r = \dfrac{3}{1 + \sin\theta}$

$e = 1$ and $ep = 3$, so $p = 3$.

a. The graph is a parabola.

b. The directrix is 3 units above the pole, at $y = 3$.

3. $r = \dfrac{6}{3 - 2\cos\theta}$

Divide numerator and denominator

by 3: $r = \dfrac{2}{1 - \frac{2}{3}\cos\theta}$.

$e = \dfrac{2}{3}$ and $ep = 2$, so $p = 3$.

a. The graph is an ellipse.

b. The directrix is 3 units to the left of the pole, at $x = -3$.

5. $r = \dfrac{8}{2 + 2\sin\theta}$

Divide numerator and denominator

by 2: $r = \dfrac{4}{1 + \sin\theta}$.

$e = 1$ and $ep = 4$, so $p = 4$.

a. The graph is a parabola.

b. The directrix is 4 units above the pole, at $y = 4$.

7. $r = \dfrac{12}{2 - 4\cos\theta}$

Divide numerator and denominator

by 2: $r = \dfrac{6}{1 - 2\cos\theta}$.

$e = 2$ and $ep = 6$, so $p = 3$.

a. The graph is a hyperbola.

b. The directrix is 3 units to the left of the pole, at $x = -3$.

9. $r = \dfrac{1}{1 + \sin\theta}$

$e = 1$ and $ep = 1$, so $p = 1$.

Since $e = 1$, the graph is a parabola. It is symmetric with respect to the y-axis and has a directrix at $y = 1$. The vertex is at $\left(\dfrac{1}{2}, \dfrac{\pi}{2}\right)$.

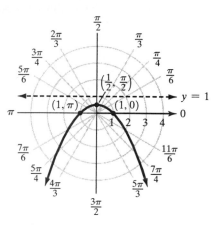

11. $r = \dfrac{2}{1 - \cos\theta}$

$e = 1$ and $ep = 2$, so $p = 2$.

Since $e = 1$, the graph is a parabola. It is symmetric with respect to the polar axis and has a directrix at $x = -2$. The vertex is at $(1, \pi)$.

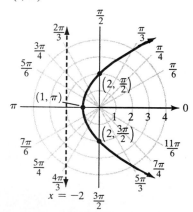

13. $r = \dfrac{12}{5 + 3\cos\theta}$

Write in standard form:

$r = \dfrac{\dfrac{12}{5}}{1 + \dfrac{3}{5}\cos\theta}$

$e = \dfrac{3}{5}$ and $ep = \dfrac{12}{5}$, so $p = 4$. Since $e < 1$, the graph is an ellipse. It is symmetric with respect to the polar axis and has a directrix at $x = 4$.

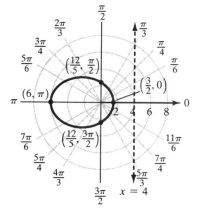

15. $r = \dfrac{6}{2 - 2\sin\theta}$

Write in standard form: $r = \dfrac{3}{1 - \sin\theta}$

$e = 1$ and $ep = 3$, so $p = 3$. Since $e = 1$, the graph is a parabola. It is symmetric with respect to the y-axis and has a directrix at $y = -3$. The vertex is at $\left(\dfrac{3}{2}, \dfrac{3\pi}{2}\right)$.

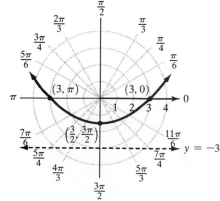

17. $r = \dfrac{8}{2 - 4\cos\theta}$

Write in standard form:

$r = \dfrac{4}{1 - 2\cos\theta}$

$e = 2$ and $ep = 4$, so $p = 2$. Since $e > 1$, the graph is a hyperbola. It is symmetric with respect to the polar axis and it has a directrix at $x = -2$. The transverse axis is horizontal and the vertices lie on the polar axis

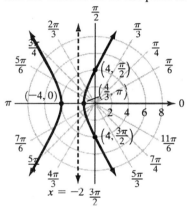

19. $r = \dfrac{12}{3 - 6\cos\theta}$

Write in standard form:

$r = \dfrac{4}{1 - 2\cos\theta}$

$e = 2$ and $ep = 4$, so $p = 2$. Since $e > 2$, the graph is a hyperbola. It is symmetric with respect to the polar axis and has a directrix at $x = -2$. The transverse axis is horizontal and the vertices lie on the polar axis

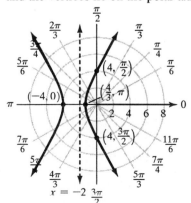

21. The shortest distance from the sun occurs on the positive *y*-axis, at $\theta = \dfrac{\pi}{2}$.

When $\theta = \dfrac{\pi}{2}$, $r = \dfrac{1.069}{1 + 0.967\sin\frac{\pi}{2}} = \dfrac{1.069}{1.967}$

≈ 0.54 astronomical units or about 51 million miles.

23. His greatest distance from Earth's center occured when $\theta = 0$:

$r = \dfrac{4090.76}{1 - 0.0076\cos 0} = \dfrac{4090.76}{0.9924}$

≈ 4122 miles from the center of the earth. Assuming the earth to be perfectly spherical, he was $4122 - 3960 = 162$ miles from the surface of the earth.

25.–29. Answers may vary.

31. Exercise 9

Exercise 11

Exercise 13

Exercise 15

Exercise 17

33. Write the equation in standard form:

$$r = \frac{3}{1 + \frac{5}{4}\sin\theta}$$

Since $e = \dfrac{5}{4} > 1$, the graph is a hyperbola.

35.

The graph appears to be rotated counter-clockwise through an angle of $\dfrac{\pi}{4}$ radians.

37. Mercury: $r = \dfrac{\left(1 - 0.2056^2\right)\left(36.0 \times 10^6\right)}{1 - 0.2056\cos\theta}$

Earth: $r = \dfrac{\left(1 - 0.0167^2\right)\left(92.96 \times 10^6\right)}{1 - 0.0167\cos\theta}$

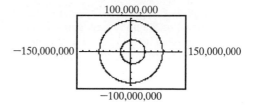

$r: -150,000,000 - 150,000,000$
$y: -100,000,000, -100,000,000$
Answers may vary.

39. Since the equation is an ellipse with a vertex at (4, 0), the polar axis is the major axis.

Since $\dfrac{PF}{PD} = e$, then at the point (4, 0),

$\dfrac{4}{x} = \dfrac{1}{2}$, where x is the distance between the point (4, 0) and the directrix. Thus, $x = 8$ and the distance between the point (4, 0) and the directrix is 8. The directrix is either $x = -4$ or $x = 12$. There are two polar equations that meet the given conditions. If the directrix is $x = -4$,

$$r = \frac{\frac{1}{2}(4)}{1 - \frac{1}{2}\cos\theta} = \frac{2}{1 - \frac{1}{2}\cos\theta}.$$

If the directrix is $x = 12$,

$$r = \frac{\frac{1}{2}(12)}{1 + \frac{1}{2}\cos\theta} = \frac{6}{1 + \frac{1}{2}\cos\theta}.$$

41. $r = \dfrac{1}{2 - 2\cos\theta}$

Write the equation in standard form:

$r = \dfrac{\frac{1}{2}}{1 - \cos\theta}$

Since $e = 1$, the graph is a parabola.
Write in rectangular coordinates:

$r = \dfrac{\frac{1}{2}}{1 - \cos\theta}$

$r(1 - \cos\theta) = \dfrac{1}{2}$

$r - r\cos\theta = \dfrac{1}{2}$

              Distributive property

$r = r\cos\theta + \dfrac{1}{2}$

$r = x + \dfrac{1}{2}$

       Substitution: $x = r\cos\theta$

$r^2 = \left(x + \dfrac{1}{2}\right)^2$

       Square both sides

$x^2 + y^2 = \left(x + \dfrac{1}{2}\right)^2$

       Substitution: $r^2 = x^2 + y^2$

$x^2 + y^2 = x^2 + x + \dfrac{1}{4}$

$y^2 = x + \dfrac{1}{4}$

Review Exercises

1. $\dfrac{x^2}{36} + \dfrac{y^2}{25} = 1$

$a^2 = 36,\ a = 6$
$b^2 = 25,\ b = 5$
$c^2 = a^2 - b^2 = 36 - 25 = 11$
$c = \sqrt{11}$
The foci are at $(\sqrt{11},\ 0)$ and $(-\sqrt{11},\ 0)$.

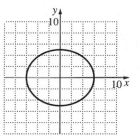

2. $\dfrac{y^2}{25} + \dfrac{x^2}{16} = 1$

$a^2 = 25,\ a = 5$
$b^2 = 16,\ b = 4$
$c^2 = a^2 - b^2 = 25 - 16 = 9$
$c = 3$
The foci are at $(0,\ 3)$ and $(0,\ -3)$.

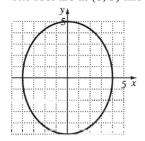

3. $4x^2 + y^2 = 16$

$\dfrac{4x^2}{16} + \dfrac{y^2}{16} = \dfrac{16}{16}$

$\dfrac{x^2}{4} + \dfrac{y^2}{16} = 1$

$b^2 = 4,\ b = 2$
$a^2 = 16,\ a = 4$
$c^2 = a^2 - b^2 = 16 - 4 = 12$
$c = \sqrt{12} = 2\sqrt{3}$
The foci are at $(0,\ 2\sqrt{3})$ and $(0,\ -2\sqrt{3})$.

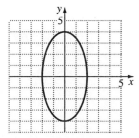

4. $4x^2 + 9y^2 = 36$

$$\frac{4x^2}{36} + \frac{9y^2}{36} = \frac{36}{36}$$

$$\frac{x^2}{9} + \frac{y^2}{4} = 1$$

$a^2 = 9,\ a = 3$

$b^2 = 4,\ b = 2$

$c^2 = a^2 - b^2 = 9 - 4 = 5,\ c = \sqrt{5}$

The foci are at $(\sqrt{5}, 0)$ and $(-\sqrt{5}, 0)$.

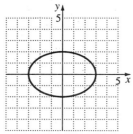

5. $\dfrac{(x-1)^2}{16} + \dfrac{(y+2)^2}{9} = 1$

$a^2 = 16\ a = 4$

$b^2 = 9\ b = 3$

$c^2 = 16 - 9 = 7,\ c = \sqrt{7}$

center: $(1, -2)$

The foci are at

$(1 + \sqrt{7},\ -2)$ and $(1 - \sqrt{7},\ -2)$.

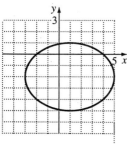

6. $\dfrac{(x+1)^2}{9} + \dfrac{(y-2)^2}{16} = 1$

$a^2 = 16,\ a = 4$

$b^2 = 9,\ b = 3$

$c^2 = a^2 - b^2 = 16 - 9 = 7,\ c = \sqrt{7}$

center: $(-1, 2)$

The foci are at $(-1,\ 2 + \sqrt{7})$ and

$(-1,\ 2 - \sqrt{7})$.

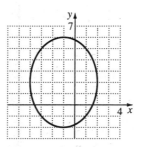

7. $4x^2 + 9y^2 + 24x - 36y + 36 = 0$

$4x^2 + 24x + 9y^2 - 36y = -36$

$4(x^2 + 6x + 9) + 9(y^2 - 4y + 4)$

$= -36 + 36 + 36$

$= 4(x + 3)^2 + 9(y - 2)^2 = 36$

$$\frac{(x+3)^2}{9} + \frac{(y-2)^2}{4} = 1$$

$c^2 = a^2 - b^2 = 5,\ c = \sqrt{5}$

center: $(-3, 2)$

The foci are at $(-3 + \sqrt{5},\ 2)$ and

$(-3 - \sqrt{5},\ 2)$.

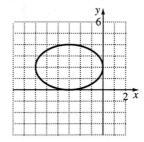

8. $9x^2 + 4y^2 - 18x + 8y - 23 = 0$

$9x^2 - 18x + 4y^2 + 8y = 23$

$9(x^2 - 2x + 1) + 4(y^2 + 2y + 1) = 23 + 9 + 4$

$9(x - 1)^2 + 4(y + 1)^2 = 36$

$$\frac{(x-1)^2}{4} + \frac{(y+1)^2}{9} = 1$$

$c^2 = a^2 - b^2 = 9 - 4 = 5, \ c = \sqrt{5}$

center: $(1, -1)$

The foci are at $(1, -1 + \sqrt{5})$ and

$(1, -1 - \sqrt{5})$.

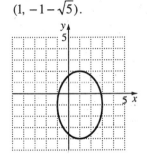

9. $c = 4, c^2 = 16$

$a = 5, a^2 = 25$

$b^2 = a^2 - c^2 = 25 - 16 = 9$

$$\frac{x^2}{25} + \frac{y^2}{9} = 1$$

10. $c = 3, c^2 = 9$

$a = 6, a^2 = 36$

$b^2 = a^2 - c^2 = 36 - 9 = 27$

$$\frac{x^2}{27} + \frac{y^2}{36} = 1$$

11. $2a = 12, a = 6, a^2 = 36$

$2b = 4, b = 2, b^2 = 4$

$$\frac{x^2}{36} + \frac{y^2}{4} = 1$$

12. $2a = 20, a = 10, a^2 = 100$

$b = 6, b^2 = 36$

$$\frac{x^2}{100} + \frac{y^2}{36} = 1$$

13. $2a = 50, a = 25$

$b = 15$

$$\frac{x^2}{625} + \frac{y^2}{225} = 1$$

Let $x = 14$.

$$\frac{(14)^2}{625} + \frac{y^2}{225} = 1$$

$$y^2 = 225\left(1 - \frac{196}{625}\right)$$

$y \approx 15(0.8285) \approx 12.4 > 12$

Yes, the truck can drive under the archway.

14. The hit ball will collide with the other ball.

15. $\dfrac{x^2}{16} - y^2 = 1$

$c^2 = a^2 + b^2 = 16 + 1 = 17, \ c = \sqrt{17}$

The foci are at $(\sqrt{17}, 0)$ and $(-\sqrt{17}, 0)$.

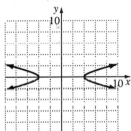

16. $\dfrac{y^2}{16} - x^2 = 1$

$c^2 = a^2 + b^2 = 16 + 1 = 17$

$c = \sqrt{17}$

The foci are at $(0, \sqrt{17})$ and $(0, -\sqrt{17})$.

17. $9x^2 - 16y^2 = 144$

$$\frac{x^2}{16} - \frac{y^2}{9} = 1$$

$c^2 = a^2 + b^2 = 16 + 9 = 25, c = 5$

The foci are at $(5, 0)$ and $(-5, 0)$.

18. $4y^2 - x^2 = 16$

$$\frac{y^2}{4} - \frac{x^2}{16} = 1$$

$c^2 = a^2 + b^2 = 4 + 16 = 20$

$c = \sqrt{20} = 2\sqrt{5}$

The foci are at $(0, 2\sqrt{5})$ and $(0, -2\sqrt{5})$.

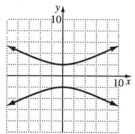

19. $\dfrac{(x-2)^2}{25} - \dfrac{(y+3)^2}{16} = 1$

$c^2 = a^2 + b^2 = 25 + 16 = 41, c = \sqrt{41}$

center: $(2, -3)$

The foci are at

$(2 + \sqrt{41}, -3)$ and $(2 - \sqrt{41}, -3)$.

20. $\dfrac{(y+2)^2}{25} - \dfrac{(x-3)^2}{16} = 1$

$c^2 = a^2 + b^2 = 25 + 16 = 41, \ c = \sqrt{41}$

center: $(3, -2)$

The foci are at

$(3, -2 + \sqrt{41})$ and $(3, -2 - \sqrt{41})$.

21. $y^2 - 4y - 4x^2 + 8x - 4 = 0$

$(y^2 - 4y + 4) - 4(x^2 - 2x + 1) = 4 + 4 - 4$

$(y - 2)^2 - 4(x - 1)^2 = 4$

$$\frac{(y-2)^2}{4} - (x-1)^2 = 1$$

$c^2 = a^2 + b^2 = 4 + 1 = 5, \ c = \sqrt{5}$

center: $(1, 2)$

The foci are at $(1, 2 + \sqrt{5})$ and $(1, 2 - \sqrt{5})$.

22. $x^2 - y^2 - 2x - 2y - 1 = 0$
$x^2 - 2x - y^2 - 2y = 1$
$(x^2 - 2x + 1) - (y^2 + 2y + 1) = 1 + 1 - 1$
$(x - 1)^2 - (y + 1)^2 = 1$
$c^2 = a^2 + b^2 = 1 + 1 = 2,\ c = \sqrt{2}$

center: $(1, -1)$
The foci are at
$(1 + \sqrt{2},\ -1)$ and $(1 - \sqrt{2},\ -1)$.

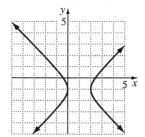

23. $c = 4,\ c^2 = 16$
$a = 2,\ a^2 = 4$
$b^2 = c^2 - a^2 = 16 - 4 = 12$

$$\frac{y^2}{4} - \frac{x^2}{12} = 1$$

24. $c = 8,\ c^2 = 64$
$a = 3,\ a^2 = 9$
$b^2 = c^2 - a^2 = 64 - 9 = 55$

$$\frac{x^2}{9} - \frac{y^2}{55} = 1$$

25. If the foci are at $(0, -2)$ and $(0, 2)$, then
$c = 2$. If the vertices are at $(0, -3)$ and $(0, 3)$
then $a = 3$. This is not possible since c must
be greater than a.

26. foci: $(\pm100, 0)$, $c = 100$

$$|d_1 - d_2| = \left(0.186\frac{\text{mi}}{\mu\text{s}}\right)(500\mu\text{s}) = 93 \text{ mi} = 2a$$

$$a = \frac{93}{2}$$

$$b^2 = c^2 - a^2 = (100)^2 - \left(\frac{93}{2}\right)^2 = 7837.75$$

$$\frac{x^2}{\left(\frac{93}{2}\right)^2} - \frac{y^2}{7837.75} = 1$$

$$\frac{x^2}{2162.25} - \frac{y^2}{7837.75} = 1$$

27. $y^2 = 8x$
$4p = 8,\ p = 2$
vertex: $(0, 0)$
focus: $(2, 0)$
directrix: $x = -2$

28. $x^2 + 16y = 0$
$$x^2 = -16y$$
$4p = -16$
$p = -4$
vertex: $(0, 0)$
focus: $(0, -4)$
directrix: $y = 4$

29. $(y - 2)^2 = -16x$
$4p = -16$
$p = -4$
vertex: $(0, 2)$
focus: $(-4, 2)$
directrix: $x = 4$

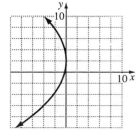

30. $(x-4)^2 = 4(y+1)$

$4p = 4,\ p = 1$

vertex: $(4, -1)$

focus: $(4, 0)$

directrix: $y = -2$

31. $x^2 + 4y = 4$

$x^2 = -4y + 4$

$x^2 = -4\,(y - 1)$

$4p = -4,\ p = -1$

vertex: $(0, 1)$

focus: $(0, 0)$

directrix: $y = 2$

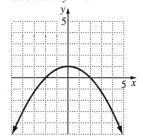

32. $y^2 - 4x - 10y + 21 = 0$

$y^2 - 10y = 4x - 21$

$y^2 - 10y + 25 = 4x - 21 + 25$

$(y - 5)^2 = 4(x + 1)$

$4p = 4,\ p = 1$

vertex: $(-1, 5)$

focus: $(0, 5)$

directrix: $x = -2$

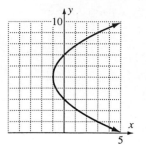

33. $x^2 - 4x - 2y = 0$

$x^2 - 4x = 2y$

$(x^2 - 4x + 4) = 2y + 4$

$(x - 2)^2 = 2(y + 2)$

$4p = 2,\ p = \dfrac{1}{2}$

vertex: $(2, -2)$

focus: $\left(2, -\dfrac{3}{2}\right)$

directrix: $y = -\dfrac{5}{2}$

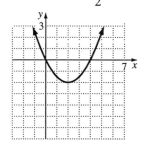

34. $p = 12$

$y^2 = 48x$

35. $p = -11$

$x^2 = -44y$

36. $x^2 = 4py$

$(6)^2 = 4p(3)$

$p = 3$

$x^2 = 12y$

Place the light 3 inches from the vertex at $(0, 3)$.

37. $x^2 = 4py$

$(1750)^2 = 4p(316)$

$4p \approx 9691$

$x^2 = 9691y$

Let $x = 1750 - 1000 = 750$.

$y = \dfrac{x^2}{9691} = \dfrac{(750)^2}{9691} \approx 58$

The height is approximately 58 feet.

38. $x^2 = 4py$

$(150)^2 = 4p(44)$

$22{,}500 = 176p$

$p \approx 128$

The receiver should be placed approximately 128 feet from the base of the dish.

39. $A = 0$, $C = 1$.

$AC = 0$, so the graph is a parabola.

40. $A = 1$, $C = 16$.

$AC = 16 > 0$ and $A \neq C$, so the graph is an ellipse.

41. $A = 16$, $C = 9$.

$AC = 16 \cdot 9 = 144 > 0$ and $A \neq C$, so the graph is an ellipse.

42. $A = 4$, $C = -9$.

$AC = 4(-9) = 36 < 0$, so the graph is a hyperbola.

43. $A = 5$, $B = 2\sqrt{3}$, $C = 3$.

$B^2 - 4AC = \left(2\sqrt{3}\right)^2 - 4(5)(3) = 12 - 60 = -48$

Since $B^2 - 4AC < 0$, the graph is an ellipse or a circle.

44. $A = 5$, $B = -8$, $C = 7$.

$B^2 - 4AC = (-8)^2 - 4(5)(7) = 64 - 140 = -76$.

Since $B^2 - 4AC < 0$, the graph is an ellipse or a circle.

45. $A = 1$, $B = 6$, $C = 9$.

$B^2 - 4AC = 6^2 - 4(1)(9) = 36 - 36 = 0$.

Since $B^2 - 4AC = 0$, the graph is a parabola.

46. $A = 1$, $B = -2$, $C = 3$.

$B^2 - 4AC = (-2)^2 - 4(1)(3) = 4 - 12 = -8$

Since $B^2 - 4AC < 0$, the graph is an ellipse or a circle.

47. $xy - 4 = 0$

    a. $A = 0$, $B = 1$, $C = 0$.

$$\cot 2\theta = \frac{A - C}{B} = \frac{0 - 0}{1} = 0$$
$$2\theta = 90°$$
$$\theta = 45°$$

$$x = x' \cos 45° - y' \sin 45° = x'\left(\frac{\sqrt{2}}{2}\right) - y'\left(\frac{\sqrt{2}}{2}\right) = \frac{\sqrt{2}}{2}(x' - y')$$

$$y = x' \sin 45° + y' \cos 45° = x'\left(\frac{\sqrt{2}}{2}\right) + y'\left(\frac{\sqrt{2}}{2}\right) = \frac{\sqrt{2}}{2}(x' + y')$$

Substitute into the equation: $xy - 4 = 0$

$$\left[\frac{\sqrt{2}}{2}(x' - y')\right]\left[\frac{\sqrt{2}}{2}(x' - y')\right] - 4 = 0$$
$$\frac{1}{2}\left(x'^2 - y'^2\right) - 4 = 0$$
$$x'^2 - y'^2 = 8$$

    b. $\dfrac{x'^2}{8} - \dfrac{y'^2}{8} = 1$

    c.

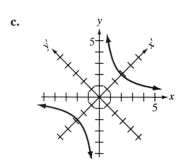

48. $x^2 + xy + y^2 - 1 = 0$

   a. $A = 1, B = 1, C = 1.$

$$\cot 2\theta = \frac{A - C}{B} = \frac{1-1}{1} = \frac{0}{1} = 0$$
$$2\theta = 90°$$
$$\theta = 45°$$

$$x = x' \cos 45° - y' \sin 45° = \frac{\sqrt{2}}{2}(x' - y')$$

$$y = x' \sin 45° + y' \cos 45° = \frac{\sqrt{2}}{2}(x' + y')$$

Substitute into the equation: $x^2 + xy + y^2 - 1 = 0$

$$\left[\frac{\sqrt{2}}{2}(x' - y')\right]^2 + \left[\frac{\sqrt{2}}{2}(x' - y')\right]\left[\frac{\sqrt{2}}{2}(x' + y')\right] + \left[\frac{\sqrt{2}}{2}(x' + y')\right]^2 - 1 = 0$$

$$\frac{1}{2}\left(x'^2 - 2x'y' + y'^2\right) + \frac{1}{2}\left(x'^2 - y'^2\right) + \frac{1}{2}\left(x'^2 + 2x'y' + y'^2\right) = 1$$

Multiply both sides by 2 and simplify: $3x'^2 + y'^2 = 2$

   b. $\dfrac{x'^2}{\frac{2}{3}} + \dfrac{y'^2}{2} = 1$

   c.

49. $4x^2 + 10xy + 4y^2 - 9 = 0$

    a. $A = 4$, $B = 10$, $C = 4$.

$$\cot 2\theta = \frac{A-C}{B} = \frac{4-4}{10} = \frac{0}{10} = 0$$

$$2\theta = 90°$$
$$\theta = 45°$$

$$x = x'\cos 45° - y'\sin 45° = \frac{\sqrt{2}}{2}(x' - y')$$

$$y = x'\sin 45° + y'\cos 45° = \frac{\sqrt{2}}{2}(x' + y')$$

Substitute into the equation: $4x^2 + 10xy + 4y^2 - 9 = 0$

$$4\left[\frac{\sqrt{2}}{2}(x'-y')\right]^2 + 10\left[\frac{\sqrt{2}}{2}(x'-y')\right]\left[\frac{\sqrt{2}}{2}(x'+y')\right] + 4\left[\frac{\sqrt{2}}{2}(x'+y')\right]^2 - 9 = 0$$

$$4 \cdot \frac{1}{2}\left(x'^2 - 2x'y' + y'^2\right) + 10 \cdot \frac{1}{2}\left(x'^2 - y'^2\right) + 4 \cdot \frac{1}{2}\left(x'^2 + 2x'y' + y'^2\right) = 9$$

Multiply both sides by 2 and simplify: $18x'^2 - 2y'^2 = 18$

    b. $\dfrac{x'^2}{1} - \dfrac{y'^2}{9} = 1$

    c.

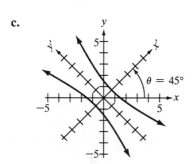

50. $6x^2 - 6xy + 14y^2 - 45 = 0$

    a. $A = 6,\ B = -6\ C = 14$

$$\cot 2\theta = \frac{A-C}{B} = \frac{6-14}{-6} = \frac{-8}{-6} = \frac{4}{3}$$

Since θ is always acute, and $\cot 2\theta$ is positive, 2θ lies in quadrant I. The third side of the right triangle is found using the Pythagorean Theorem.

$$4^2 + 3^2 = r^2$$
$$r = 5$$

So, $\cos 2\theta = \dfrac{4}{5}$.

$$\sin \theta = \sqrt{\frac{1 - \cos 2\theta}{2}} = \sqrt{\frac{1 - \frac{4}{5}}{2}} = \frac{\sqrt{10}}{10} \text{ and } \cos \theta = \sqrt{\frac{1 + \cos 2\theta}{2}} = \sqrt{\frac{1 + \frac{4}{5}}{2}} = \frac{3\sqrt{10}}{10}.$$

So, $x = x'\cos\theta - y'\sin\theta = x'\left(\dfrac{3\sqrt{10}}{10}\right) - y'\left(\dfrac{\sqrt{10}}{10}\right) = \dfrac{\sqrt{10}}{10}(3x' - y')$

and $y = x'\sin\theta - y'\cos\theta = x'\left(\dfrac{\sqrt{10}}{10}\right) + y'\left(\dfrac{3\sqrt{10}}{10}\right) = \dfrac{\sqrt{10}}{10}(x' + 3y')$.

Substitute into the equation: $6x^2 - 6xy + 14y^2 - 45 = 0$

$$6\left[\frac{\sqrt{10}}{10}(3x' - y')\right]^2 - 6\left[\frac{\sqrt{10}}{10}(3x' - y')\right]\left[\frac{\sqrt{10}}{10}(x' + 3y')\right] + 14\left[\frac{\sqrt{10}}{10}(x' + 3y')\right]^2 - 45 = 0$$

$$6\left[\frac{1}{10}\left(9x'^2 - 6x'y' + y'^2\right)\right] - 6\left[\frac{1}{10}\left(3x'^2 + 8x'y' - 3y'^2\right)\right] + 14\left[\frac{1}{10}\left(x'^2 + 6x'y' + 9y'^2\right)\right] = 45$$

Multiply both sides by 10 and simplify: $50x'^2 + 150y'^2 = 450$

    b. $\dfrac{x'^2}{9} + \dfrac{y'^2}{3} = 1$

    c.

The axes are rotated by $\theta = \sin^{-1}\left(\dfrac{\sqrt{10}}{10}\right) \approx 18°$.

51. $x^2 + 2\sqrt{3}xy + 3y^2 - 12\sqrt{3}x + 12y = 0$

$A = 1, \; B = 2\sqrt{3}, \; C = 3$

$\cot 2\theta = \dfrac{A - C}{B} = \dfrac{1 - 3}{2\sqrt{3}} = \dfrac{-2}{2\sqrt{3}} = \dfrac{-\sqrt{3}}{3}$

$\quad 2\theta = 120°$

$\quad\; \theta = 60°$

$x = x' \cos 60° - y' \sin 60° = x'\left(\dfrac{1}{2}\right) - y'\left(\dfrac{\sqrt{3}}{2}\right) = \dfrac{1}{2}\left(x' - \sqrt{3}y'\right)$

and $\; y = x' \sin 60° + y' \cos 60° = x'\left(\dfrac{\sqrt{3}}{2}\right) + y'\left(\dfrac{1}{2}\right) = \dfrac{1}{2}\left(\sqrt{3}x' + y'\right)$

Substitute into the equation: $x^2 + 2\sqrt{3}xy + 3y^2 - 12\sqrt{3}x + 12y = 0$

$\left[\dfrac{1}{2}\left(x' - \sqrt{3}y'\right)\right]^2 + 2\sqrt{3}\left[\dfrac{1}{2}\left(x' - \sqrt{3}y'\right)\right]\left[\dfrac{1}{2}\left(\sqrt{3}x' + y'\right)\right] + 3\left[\dfrac{1}{2}\left(\sqrt{3}x' + y'\right)\right]^2 - 12\sqrt{3}\left[\dfrac{1}{2}\left(x' - \sqrt{3}y'\right)\right]$

$+ 12\left[\dfrac{1}{2}\left(\sqrt{3}x' + y'\right)\right] = 0$

$\dfrac{1}{4}\left(x'^2 - 2\sqrt{3}x'y' + 3y'^2\right) + 2\sqrt{3} \cdot \dfrac{1}{4}\left(\sqrt{3}x'^2 - 2x'y' - \sqrt{3}y'^2\right) + 3 \cdot \dfrac{1}{4}\left(3x'^2 + 2\sqrt{3}x'y' + y'^2\right) - 6\sqrt{3}x' + 18y'$

$+ 6\sqrt{3}x' + 6y' = 0$

Multiply both sides by 4 and simplify: $16x'^2 + 96y' = 0$

b. $\quad 16x'^2 = -96y'$

$\qquad\; x'^2 = -6y'$

c.

$\theta = 60°$

734

52. $x = 2t - 1$ and $y = 1 - t; \; -\infty < t < \infty$

$$\frac{x+1}{2} = t$$

Substitute into y: $y = 1 - \left(\frac{x+1}{2}\right)$

$$y = -\frac{1}{2}x + \frac{1}{2}$$

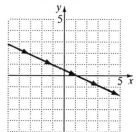

53. $x = t^2$ and $y = t - 1; \; -1 \le t \le 3$

$$y + 1 = t$$

Substitute into x:

$$x = (y+1)^2$$

$$(y+1)^2 = x$$

$$0 \le x \le 9, \; -2 \le y \le 2$$

54. $x = 4t^2$ and $y = t + 1; \; -\infty < t < \infty$

$$y - 1 = t$$

Substitute into x:

$$x = 4(y-1)^2$$

$$\frac{1}{4}x = (y-1)^2$$

$$(y-1)^2 = \frac{1}{4}x$$

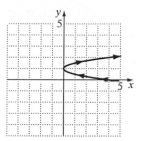

55. $x = 4\sin t, \; y = 3\cos t; \; 0 \le t < \pi$

$$\frac{x}{4} = \sin t \qquad \frac{y}{3} = \cos t$$

Square and add the equations:

$$\frac{x^2}{16} = \sin^2 t$$

$$+ \quad \frac{y^2}{9} = \cos^2 t$$

$$\overline{\qquad\qquad\qquad\qquad}$$

$$\frac{x^2}{16} + \frac{y^2}{9} = \sin^2 t + \cos^2 t$$

$$\frac{x^2}{16} + \frac{y^2}{9} = \sin^2 t + \cos^2 t$$

$$\frac{x^2}{16} + \frac{y^2}{9} = 1$$

$$0 \le x \le 4, \quad -3 \le y \le 3$$

56. $x = 3 + 2\cos t, \; y = 1 + 2\sin t; \; 0 \le t < 2\pi$

$$\frac{x-3}{2} = \cos t \qquad \frac{y-1}{2} = \sin t$$

Square and add the equations:

$$\frac{(x-3)^2}{4} = \cos^2 t$$

$$+ \quad \frac{(y-1)^2}{4} = \sin^2 t$$

$$\overline{\frac{(x-3)^2}{4} + \frac{(y-1)^2}{4} = \cos^2 t + \sin^2 t}$$

$$\frac{(x-3)^2}{4} + \frac{(y-1)^2}{4} = 1$$

or $(x-3)^2 + (y-1)^2 = 4$

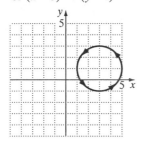

57. $x = 3\sec t, \; y = 3\tan t; \; 0 \le t \le \dfrac{\pi}{4}$

$$\frac{x}{3} = \sec t \qquad \frac{y}{3} = \tan t$$

Square and subtract the equations:

$$\frac{x^2}{9} = \sec^2 t$$

$$- \left(\frac{y^2}{9} = \tan^2 t \right)$$

$$\overline{\frac{x^2}{9} - \frac{y^2}{9} = \sec^2 t - \tan^2 t}$$

$$\frac{x^2}{9} - \frac{y^2}{9} = 1$$

$3 \le x \le 3\sqrt{2}, \; 0 \le y \le 3$

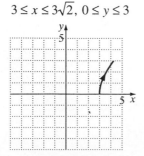

58. Answers may vary.

59. a. $x = (100\cos 40°)t$

       $y = 6 + (100\sin 40°)t - 16t^2$

b.   After 1 second:

$x = (100\cos 40°) \cdot 1$

   ≈ 76.6 feet in distance

$y = 6 + (100\sin 40°) \cdot 1 - 16(1)^2$

   ≈ 54.3 feet in height

After 2 seconds:

$x = (100\cos 40°) \cdot 2$

   ≈ 153.2 feet in distance

$y = 6 + (100\sin 40°) \cdot 2 - 16(2)^2$

   ≈ 70.6 feet in height

After 3 seconds:

$x = (100\cos 40°) \cdot 3$

   ≈ 229.8 feet in distance

$y = 6 + (100\sin 40°) \cdot 3 - 16(3)^2$

   ≈ 54.8 feet in height

c. $0 = 6t(100\sin 40°)t - 16t^2$

Using the quadratic formula with

$a = -16, \; b = 100\sin 40°, \;$ and $c = 6$,

$$t = \frac{-100\sin 40° \pm \sqrt{(100\sin 40°)^2 - 4(-16)(6)}}{2(-16)}$$

$t \approx -0.1$ or $t \approx 4.1$

Since t cannot be negative, we discard

$t \approx -0.1$.

At

$t \approx 4.1, \; x = (100\cos 40°)(4.1) \approx 314.1$

The ball is in flight for 4.1 seconds. It travels a total horizontal distance of 314.1 feet.

d.

The ball is at its maximum height at 2.0 seconds. The maximum height is 70.6 feet.

60. a. $r = \dfrac{4}{1 - \sin\theta}$

    b. $e = 1$ and $ep = 4$, so $p = 4$. Since $e = 1$, the graph is a parabola.

    c.

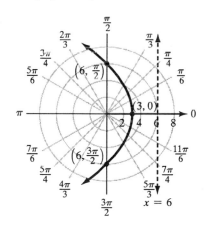

61. a. $r = \dfrac{6}{1 + \cos\theta}$

    b. $e = 1$ and $ep = 6$, so $p = 6$. Since $e = 1$, the graph is a parabola.

    c.

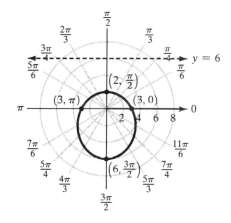

62. a.   Divide numerator and denominator by 2:

$$r = \dfrac{3}{1 + \frac{1}{2}\sin\theta}$$

    b. $e = \dfrac{1}{2}$ and $ep = 3$, so $p = 6$. Since $e < 1$, the graph is an ellipse.

    c.

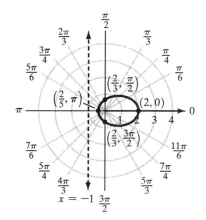

63. a.   Divide the numerator and denominator by 3:

$$r = \dfrac{\frac{2}{3}}{1 - \frac{2}{3}\cos\theta}$$

    b. $e = \dfrac{2}{3}$ and $ep = \dfrac{2}{3}$, so $p = 1$. Since $e < 1$, the graph is an ellipse.

    c.

64. a. Divide the numerator and denominator by 3:

$$r = \frac{2}{1 + 2\sin\theta}$$

b. $e = 2$ and $ep = 2$, so $p = 1$. Since $e > 1$, the graph is a hyperbola.

c.

65. a. Divide the numerator and denominator by 4:

$$r = \frac{2}{1 + 4\cos\theta}$$

b. $e = 4$ and $ep = 2$, so $p = \frac{1}{2}$. Since $e > 1$, the graph is a hyperbola.

c.

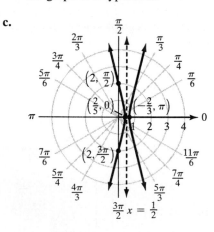

Chapter 10 Test

1. $9x^2 - 4y^2 = 36$

$$\frac{x^2}{4} - \frac{y^2}{9} = 1$$

$c^2 = a^2 + b^2 = 4 + 9 = 13$, $c = \sqrt{13}$

hyperbola

The foci are at $\left(\sqrt{13}, 0\right)$ and $\left(-\sqrt{13}, 0\right)$.

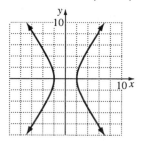

2. $x^2 = -8y$

$4p = -8$, $p = -2$

parabola

vertex: $(0, 0)$

focus: $(0, -2)$

directrix: $y = 2$

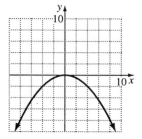

3. $\dfrac{(x+2)^2}{25} + \dfrac{(y-5)^2}{9} = 1$

The center is at (–2, 5).

$c^2 = a^2 - b^2 = 25 - 9 = 16$, $c = 4$

ellipse

The foci are at (–6, 5) and (2, 5).

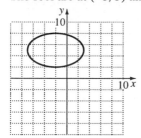

4. $\qquad 4x^2 - y^2 + 8x + 2y + 7 = 0$

$\left(4x^2 + 8x\right) - \left(y^2 - 2y\right) = -7$

$4\left(x^2 + 2x + 1\right) - \left(y^2 - 2y + 1\right) = -7 + 4 - 1$

$4(x+1)^2 - (y-1)^2 = -4$

$(y-1)^2 - 4(x+1)^2 = 4$

$\dfrac{(y-1)^2}{4} - (x+1)^2 = 1$

$c^2 = a^2 + b^2 = 4 + 1 = 5$, $c = \sqrt{5}$

The center is at (1, 1).

hyperbola

The foci are at $\left(-1, 1+\sqrt{5}\right)$ and $\left(-1, 1-\sqrt{5}\right)$.

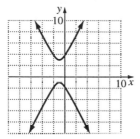

5. $(x+5)^2 = 8(y-1)$

$4p = 8$, $p = 2$

parabola

vertex: (–5, 1)

focus: (–5, 3)

directrix: $y = -1$

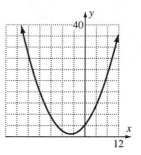

6. $c = 7$, $c^2 = 49$

$a = 10$, $a^2 = 100$

$b^2 = a^2 - c^2 = 100 - 49 = 51$

$\dfrac{x^2}{100} + \dfrac{y^2}{51} = 1$

7. $c = 10$, $c^2 = 100$

$a = 7$, $a^2 = 49$

$b^2 = c^2 - a^2 = 100 - 49 = 51$

$\dfrac{y^2}{49} - \dfrac{x^2}{51} = 1$

8. $p = 50$

$y^2 = 4px$

$y^2 = 200x$

9. $b = 24$, $b^2 = 576$

$2a = 80$, $a = 40$, $a^2 = 1600$

$c^2 = a^2 - b^2 = 1600 - 576 = 1024$

$c = \sqrt{1024} = 32$

The two people should each stand 32 feet from the center of the room, along the major axis.

10. a. $x^2 = 4py$

when $x = \pm 3$, $y = 3$

$9 = 4p(3)$

$3 = 4p$

$\dfrac{3}{4} = p$

$x^2 = 3y$

b. focus: $\left(0, \dfrac{3}{4}\right)$

The light is placed $\dfrac{3}{4}$ inch above the vertex.

11. $A = 1$, $C = 9$

$AC = 1 \cdot 9 = 9 > 0$, so the graph is an ellipse.

12. $A = 1$, $B = 1$, $C = 1$

$B^2 - 4AC = 1^2 - 4(1)(1) = -3$.

Since $B^2 - 4AC < 0$, the graph is an ellipse or circle.

13. $7x^2 - 6\sqrt{3}xy + 13y^2 - 16 = 0$

$A = 7$, $B = -6\sqrt{3}$, $C = 13$

$\cot 2\theta = \dfrac{A - C}{B} = \dfrac{7 - 13}{-6\sqrt{3}}$

$\qquad = \dfrac{-6}{-6\sqrt{3}} = \dfrac{1}{\sqrt{3}} = \dfrac{\sqrt{3}}{3}$

$2\theta = 60°$

$\theta = 30°$

14. $x = t^2$, $\quad y = t - 1$; $-\infty < t < \infty$

$\qquad y + 1 = t$

Substitute into x:

$\qquad x = (y + 1)^2$

$(y + 1)^2 = x$

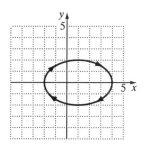

15. $\qquad x = 1 + 3\sin t$, $\quad y = 2\cos t$; $0 \le t < 2\pi$

$\dfrac{x - 1}{3} = \sin t \qquad \dfrac{y}{2} = \cos t$

Square and add the equations:

$\dfrac{(x - 1)^2}{9} = \sin^2 t$

$+ \qquad \dfrac{y^2}{4} = \cos^2 t$

$\rule{4cm}{0.4pt}$

$\dfrac{(x - 1)^2}{9} + \dfrac{y^2}{4} = \sin^2 t + \cos^2 t$

$\dfrac{(x - 1)^2}{9} + \dfrac{y^2}{4} = 1$

16. $r = \dfrac{2}{1 - \cos\theta}$

$e = 1$ and $ep = 2$, so $p = 2$.

Since $e = 1$, the graph is a parabola.

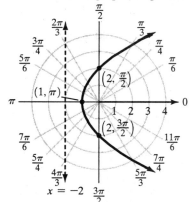

17. $r = \dfrac{4}{2 + \sin\theta}$

Divide the numerator and denominator by 2:

$r = \dfrac{2}{1 + \dfrac{1}{2}\sin\theta}$

$e = \dfrac{1}{2}$ and $ep = 2$, so $p = 4$. Since $e < 1$, the graph is an ellipse.

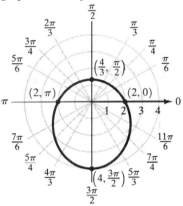

Cumulative Review Exercises (Chapters 1–10)

1. $2(x - 3) + 5x = 8(x - 1)$
$2x - 6 + 5x = 8x - 8$
$7x - 6 = 8x - 8$
$-x = -2$
$x = 2$
The solution set is $\{2\}$.

2. $-3(2x - 4) > 2(6x - 12)$
$-6x + 12 > 12x - 24$
$-18x > -36$
$x < 2$
The solution set is $\{x \mid x < 2\}$.

3. $x - 5 = \sqrt{x + 7}$
$(x - 5)^2 = x + 7$
$x^2 - 10x + 25 = x + 7$
$x^2 - 11x + 18 = 0$
$(x - 2)(x - 9) = 0$
$x = 2 \text{ or } x = 9$
The solution $x = 2$ is extraneous, so the only solution is $x = 9$.
The solution set is $\{9\}$.

4. $(x - 2)^2 = 20$
$x - 2 = \pm\sqrt{20}$
$x - 2 = \pm 2\sqrt{5}$
$x = 2 \pm 2\sqrt{5}$
The solution set is $\left\{2 + 2\sqrt{5},\, 2 - 2\sqrt{5}\right\}$.

5. $|2x - 1| \geq 7$
$2x - 1 \geq 7 \quad \text{or} \quad 2x - 1 \leq -7$
$\quad 2x \geq 8 \qquad\qquad 2x \leq -6$
$\quad\; x \geq 4 \quad \text{or} \qquad x \leq -3$
The solution set is $\left\{x \mid x \leq -3 \text{ or } x \geq 4\right\}$

6. $3x^3 + 4x^2 - 7x + 2 = 0$
$p : \pm 1, \pm 2$
$q : \pm 1, \pm 3$
$\dfrac{p}{q} : \pm 1,\ \pm 2,\ \pm\dfrac{1}{3},\ \pm\dfrac{2}{3}$
Let $f(x) = 3x^3 + 4x^2 - 7x + 2$.
Evaluate f at the possible rational zeros to find $f\left(\dfrac{2}{3}\right) = 0$.

$\dfrac{2}{3}$	3	4	–7	2
		2	4	–2
	3	6	–3	0

$\left(x - \dfrac{2}{3}\right)(3x^2 + 6x - 3) = 0$
$(3x - 2)(x^2 + 2x - 1) = 0$
$x = \dfrac{2}{3} \text{ or } x = \dfrac{-2 \pm \sqrt{(2)^2 - 4(1)(-1)}}{2}$
$x = \dfrac{-2 \pm \sqrt{8}}{2}$
$x = -1 \pm \sqrt{2}$
The solution set is $\left\{\dfrac{2}{3},\, -1 + \sqrt{2},\, -1 - \sqrt{2}\right\}$.

7. $\log_2(x+1) + \log_2(x-1) = 3$

$\qquad \log_2(x^2 - 1) = 3$

$\qquad\quad x^2 - 1 = 2^3$

$\qquad\qquad x^2 = 9$

$\qquad\qquad\quad x = \pm 3$

$x = -3$ is not a solution of the original equation. The solution set is $\{3\}$.

8. $3x + 4y = 2$

$\;2x + 5y = -1$

$\quad 6x + 8y = 4$

$-6x - 15y = 3$

$\overline{\qquad\quad -7y = 7}$

$\qquad\qquad\quad y = -1$

$3x + 4(-1) = 2$

$\qquad\quad 3x = 6$

$\qquad\qquad x = 2$

The solution set is $\{(2, -1)\}$.

9. $2x^2 - y^2 = -8$

$\quad x - y - 6$

$\quad x - y = 6$

$\qquad x = y + 6$

$\quad x^2 = (y+6)^2 = y^2 + 12y + 36$

Substitute into first equation.

$2(y^2 + 12y + 36) - y^2 = -8$

$2y^2 + 24y + 72 - y^2 = -8$

$\quad y^2 + 24y + 80 = 0$

$\quad (y+4)(y+20) = 0$

$\qquad y = -4 \text{ or } y = -20$

$\qquad x = 2 \qquad x = -14$

The solution set is $\{(2, -4), (-14, -20)\}$.

10. Set up the augmented matrix and use Gauss-Jordan reduction.

$$\begin{bmatrix} 1 & -1 & 1 & | & 17 \\ -4 & 1 & 5 & | & -2 \\ 2 & 3 & 1 & | & 8 \end{bmatrix}$$

$$\begin{bmatrix} 1 & -1 & 1 & | & 17 \\ 0 & -3 & 9 & | & 66 \\ 0 & 5 & -1 & | & -26 \end{bmatrix} \begin{matrix} \\ 4R_1 + R_2 \\ -2R_1 + R_3 \end{matrix}$$

$$\begin{bmatrix} 1 & -1 & 1 & | & 17 \\ 0 & 1 & -3 & | & -22 \\ 0 & 5 & -1 & | & -26 \end{bmatrix} -\frac{1}{3}R_2$$

$$\begin{bmatrix} 1 & 0 & -2 & | & -5 \\ 0 & 1 & -3 & | & -22 \\ 0 & 0 & 14 & | & 84 \end{bmatrix} \begin{matrix} R_2 + R_1 \\ \\ -5R_2 + R_3 \end{matrix}$$

$$\begin{bmatrix} 1 & 0 & -2 & | & -5 \\ 0 & 1 & -3 & | & -22 \\ 0 & 0 & 1 & | & 6 \end{bmatrix} \frac{1}{14}R_3$$

$$\begin{bmatrix} 1 & 0 & 0 & | & 7 \\ 0 & 1 & 0 & | & -4 \\ 0 & 0 & 1 & | & 6 \end{bmatrix} \begin{matrix} 2R_3 + R_1 \\ 3R_3 + R_2 \\ \\ \end{matrix}$$

$x = 7, y = -4, z = 6$

The solution set is $\{(7, -4, 6)\}$.

11. $f(x) = (x-1)^2 - 4$

Parabola with vertex at $(1, -4)$.

12. $\dfrac{x^2}{9} + \dfrac{y^2}{4} = 1$

Ellipse with center at $(0, 0)$ and vertices at $(3, 0)$ and $(-3, 0)$.

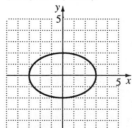

13. $5x + y \le 10$ $\qquad$ $y \ge \dfrac{1}{4}x + 2$

$\qquad$ $y \le -5x + 10$

Graph with solid line $y = -5x + 10$ and

$y = \dfrac{1}{4}x + 2$. Shade the region which is

below the line $y = -5x + 10$ and above the

line $y = \dfrac{1}{4}x + 2$. Then dash the solid lines

that do not contain the solution set.

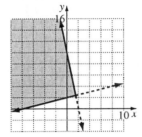

14. a. $p: \pm 1, \pm 3$

$q: \pm 1, \pm 2, \pm 4, \pm 8, \pm 16, \pm 32$

$\dfrac{p}{q}: \pm 1, \pm 3, \pm \dfrac{1}{2}, \pm \dfrac{3}{2}, \pm \dfrac{1}{4}, \pm \dfrac{3}{4}, \pm \dfrac{1}{8},$

$\pm \dfrac{3}{8}, \pm \dfrac{1}{16}, \pm \dfrac{3}{16}, \pm \dfrac{1}{32}, \pm \dfrac{3}{32}$

b. $x = 1$ appears to be a root.

$$
\begin{array}{r|rrrr}
1 & 32 & -52 & 17 & 3 \\
 & & 32 & -20 & -3 \\
\hline
 & 32 & -20 & -3 & 0
\end{array}
$$

$32x^3 - 52x^2 + 17x + 3 = 0$

$(x - 1)(32x^2 - 20x - 3) = 0$

$(x - 1)(4x - 3)(8x + 1) = 0$

$x = 1$ or $x = \dfrac{3}{4}$ or $x = -\dfrac{1}{8}$

The solution set is $\left\{ -\dfrac{1}{8}, \dfrac{3}{4}, 1 \right\}$.

15. a. The graph shows that the value is constant in the interval 1980–1990.

b. The graph shows that the value is increasing in the interval 1990–2025.

c. The graph shows that the value is decreasing in the interval 1950–1980.

d. Since the values are approximately 98, a constant function that approximately models the data is $f(x) = 98$.

e. The scale is not uniformly spaced.

16. $f(x) = x^2 - 4, g(x) = x + 2$

$(g \circ f)(x) = g\left(x^2 - 4\right) = \left(x^2 - 4\right) + 2 = x^2 - 2$

17. $\log_5 \dfrac{x^3 \sqrt{y}}{125} = \log_5 x^3 \sqrt{y} - \log_5 125$

$= \log_5 x^3 + \log_5 \sqrt{y} - 3$

$= 3 \log_5 x + \dfrac{1}{2} \log_5 y - 3$

18. $m = \dfrac{y_2 - y_1}{x_2 - x_1} = \dfrac{8 - (-4)}{-5 - 1} = \dfrac{12}{-6} = -2$

$y - y_1 = m(x - x_1)$

$y + 4 = -2(x - 1)$

$y = -2x - 2$

19. Let R = the cost of a rental at Rent a Truck and let A = the cost of a rental at Ace Truck Rentals.

$R = 39 + 0.16m$

$A = 25 + 0.24m$

where m is the number of miles.

$39 + 0.16m = 25 + 0.24m$

$14 = 0.08m$

$m = 175$

$R = 39 + 0.16(175) = 67$

The cost will be the same when the number of miles driven is 175 miles. The cost will be $67.

20. Let x = the age of Richard Nixon,

$x + 2$ = the age of Thomas Jefferson, and

$x + 4$ = the age of James Madison. Then:

$x + x + 2 + x + 4 = 249$

$3x + 6 = 249$

$3x = 243$

$x = 81$

Richard Nixon lived 81 years, Thomas Jefferson lived 83 years, and James Madison lived 85 years.

21. $\dfrac{\csc\theta - \sin\theta}{\sin\theta} = \dfrac{\dfrac{1}{\sin\theta} - \sin\theta}{\sin\theta} \cdot \dfrac{\sin\theta}{\sin\theta}$

$= \dfrac{1 - \sin^2\theta}{\sin^2\theta}$

$= \dfrac{\cos^2\theta}{\sin^2\theta}$

$= \left(\dfrac{\cos\theta}{\sin\theta}\right)^2$

$= \cot^2\theta$

22. $y = 2\cos(2x + \pi)$
   $A = 2,\ B = 2,\ C = -\pi$
   Amplitude: $|A| = |2| = 2$
   Period: $\dfrac{2\pi}{B} = \dfrac{2\pi}{2} = \pi$
   Phase Shift: $\dfrac{C}{B} = \dfrac{-\pi}{2} = -\dfrac{\pi}{2}$
   $(0, -2), \left(\dfrac{\pi}{4}, 0\right), \left(\dfrac{\pi}{2}, 2\right), \left(\dfrac{3\pi}{4}, 0\right), (\pi, -2)$

23. $(\mathbf{v}\cdot\mathbf{w})\mathbf{w} = \big[(3\mathbf{i} - 6\mathbf{j})\cdot(\mathbf{i} + \mathbf{j})\big](\mathbf{i} + \mathbf{j})$
   $= \big[3(1) - 6(1)\big](\mathbf{i} + \mathbf{j})$
   $= (3 - 6)(\mathbf{i} + \mathbf{j})$
   $= -3(\mathbf{i} + \mathbf{j})$
   $= -3\mathbf{i} - 3\mathbf{j}$

24. $\sin 2\theta = \sin\theta,\ 0 \le \theta < 2\pi$
            $2\sin\theta\cos\theta = \sin\theta$
        $2\sin\theta\cos\theta - \sin\theta = 0$
          $\sin\theta(2\cos\theta - 1) = 0$
   $\sin\theta = 0$ or $2\cos\theta - 1 = 0$
   $\theta = 0,\ \pi$ $2\cos\theta = 1$
                  $\cos\theta = \dfrac{1}{2}$
                  $\theta = \dfrac{\pi}{3},\ \dfrac{5\pi}{3}$

The solutions in the interval $[0,\ 2\pi)$ are 0,
π, $\dfrac{\pi}{3}$, and $\dfrac{5\pi}{3}$.

25. $A + B + C = 180°$
      $64° + 72° + C = 180°$
        $136° + C = 180°$
            $C = 44°$

   $\dfrac{b}{\sin B} = \dfrac{a}{\sin A}$

   $\dfrac{b}{\sin 72°} = \dfrac{13.6}{\sin 64°}$

   $b = \dfrac{13.6\sin 72°}{\sin 64°} \approx 14.4$

   $\dfrac{c}{\sin C} = \dfrac{a}{\sin A}$

   $\dfrac{c}{\sin 44°} = \dfrac{13.6}{\sin 64°}$

   $c = \dfrac{13.6\sin 44°}{\sin 64°} \approx 10.5$

The solution is $C = 44°$, $b \approx 14.4$, and $c \approx 10.5$.

Chapter 11

Section 11.1

Check Point Exercises

1. a. $a_n = 2n + 5$
$a_1 = 2(1) + 5 = 7$
$a_2 = 2(2) + 5 = 9$
$a_3 = 2(3) + 5 = 11$
$a_4 = 2(4) + 5 = 13$
The first four terms are 7, 9, 11, and 13.

b. $a_n = \dfrac{(-1)^n}{2^n + 1}$

$a_1 = \dfrac{(-1)^1}{2^1 + 1} = \dfrac{-1}{3} = -\dfrac{1}{3}$

$a_2 = \dfrac{(-1)^2}{2^2 + 1} = \dfrac{1}{5}$

$a_3 = \dfrac{(-1)^3}{2^3 + 1} = \dfrac{-1}{9} = -\dfrac{1}{9}$

$a_4 = \dfrac{(-1)^4}{2^4 + 1} = \dfrac{1}{17}$

The first four terms are $-\frac{1}{3}, \frac{1}{5}, -\frac{1}{9}$, and $\frac{1}{17}$.

2. $a_1 = 3$ and $a_n = 2a_{n-1} + 5$ for $n \geq 2$
$a_2 = 2a_1 + 5$
$\quad = 2(3) + 5 = 11$
$a_3 = 2a_2 + 5$
$\quad = 2(11) + 5 = 27$
$a_4 = 2a_3 + 5$
$\quad = 2(27) + 5 = 59$
The first four terms are 3, 11, 27, and 59.

3. $u_n = \dfrac{20}{(n+1)!}$

$a_1 = \dfrac{20}{(1+1)!} = \dfrac{20}{2!} = 10$

$a_2 = \dfrac{20}{(2+1)!} = \dfrac{20}{3!} = \dfrac{20}{6} = \dfrac{10}{3}$

$a_3 = \dfrac{20}{(3+1)!} = \dfrac{20}{4!} = \dfrac{20}{24} = \dfrac{5}{6}$

$a_4 = \dfrac{20}{(4+1)!} = \dfrac{20}{5!} = \dfrac{20}{120} = \dfrac{1}{6}$

The first four terms are $10, \frac{10}{3}, \frac{5}{6}$, and $\frac{1}{6}$.

4. a. $\dfrac{14!}{2! \, 12!} = \dfrac{14 \cdot 13 \cdot 12!}{2! \, 12!} = \dfrac{14 \cdot 13}{2 \cdot 1} = 91$

b. $\dfrac{n!}{(n-1)!} = \dfrac{n \cdot (n-1)!}{(n-1)!} = n$

5. a. $\displaystyle\sum_{i=1}^{6} 2i^2$
$= 2(1)^2 + 2(2)^2 + 2(3)^2$
$\quad + 2(4)^2 + 2(5)^2 + 2(6)^2$
$= 2 + 8 + 18 + 32 + 50 + 72$
$= 182$

b. $\displaystyle\sum_{k=3}^{5} \left(2^k - 3\right)$
$= \left(2^3 - 3\right) + \left(2^4 - 3\right) + \left(2^5 - 3\right)$
$= (8 - 3) + (16 - 3) + (32 - 3)$
$= 5 + 13 + 29$
$= 47$

c. $\displaystyle\sum_{i=1}^{5} 4 = 4 + 4 + 4 + 4 + 4 = 20$

6. a. The sum has nine terms, each of the form i^2, starting at $i = 1$ and ending at $i = 9$.

$1^2 + 2^2 + 3^2 + \cdots + 9^2 = \displaystyle\sum_{i=1}^{9} i^2$

b. The sum has n terms, each of the form $\frac{1}{2^{i-1}}$, starting at $i = 1$ and ending at $i = n$.

$1 + \dfrac{1}{2} + \dfrac{1}{4} + \dfrac{1}{8} + \cdots + \dfrac{1}{2^{n-1}} = \displaystyle\sum_{i=1}^{n} \dfrac{1}{2^{i-1}}$

Exercise Set 11.1

1. $a_n = 3n + 2$
   $a_1 = 3(1) + 2 = 5$
   $a_2 = 3(2) + 2 = 8$
   $a_3 = 3(3) + 2 = 11$
   $a_4 = 3(4) + 2 = 14$
   The first four terms are 5, 8, 11, and 14.

3. $a_n = 3^n$
   $a_1 = 3^1 = 3$
   $a_2 = 3^2 = 9$
   $a_3 = 3^3 = 27$
   $a_4 = 3^4 = 81$
   The first four terms are 3, 9, 27, and 81.

5. $a_n = (-3)^n$
   $a_1 = (-3)^1 = -3$
   $a_2 = (-3)^2 = 9$
   $a_3 = (-3)^3 = -27$
   $a_4 = (-3)^4 = 81$
   The first four terms are –3, 9, –27, and 81.

7. $a_n = (-1)^n (n + 3)$
   $a_1 = (-1)^1 (1 + 3) = -4$
   $a_2 = (-1)^2 (2 + 3) = 5$
   $a_3 = (-1)^3 (3 + 3) = -6$
   $a_4 = (-1)^4 (4 + 3) = 7$
   The first four terms are –4, 5, –6, and 7.

9. $a_n = \dfrac{2n}{n + 4}$
   $a_1 = \dfrac{2(1)}{1 + 4} = \dfrac{2}{5}$
   $a_2 = \dfrac{2(2)}{2 + 4} = \dfrac{4}{6} = \dfrac{2}{3}$
   $a_3 = \dfrac{2(3)}{3 + 4} = \dfrac{6}{7}$
   $a_4 = \dfrac{2(4)}{4 + 4} = \dfrac{8}{8} = 1$
   The first four terms are $\frac{2}{5}, \frac{2}{3}, \frac{6}{7},$ and 1.

11. $a_n = \dfrac{(-1)^{n+1}}{2^n - 1}$
    $a_1 = \dfrac{(-1)^{1+1}}{2^1 - 1} = \dfrac{1}{1} \quad n = 1$
    $a_2 = \dfrac{(-1)^{2+1}}{2^2 - 1} = -\dfrac{1}{3}$
    $a_3 = \dfrac{(-1)^{3+1}}{2^3 - 1} = \dfrac{1}{7}$
    $a_4 = \dfrac{(-1)^{4+1}}{2^4 - 1} = -\dfrac{1}{15}$
    The first four terms are $1, -\frac{1}{3}, \frac{1}{7},$ and $-\frac{1}{15}$.

13. $a_1 = 7$ and $a_n = a_{n-1} + 5$ for $n \geq 2$
    $a_2 = a_1 + 5 = 7 + 5 = 12$
    $a_3 = a_2 + 5 = 12 + 5 = 17$
    $a_4 = a_3 + 5 = 17 + 5 = 22$
    The first four terms are 7, 12, 17, and 22.

15. $a_1 = 3$ and $a_n = 4a_{n-1}$ for $n \geq 2$
    $a_2 = 4a_1 = 4(3) = 12$
    $a_3 = 4a_2 = 4(12) = 48$
    $a_4 = 4a_3 = 4(48) = 192$
    The first four terms are 3, 12, 48, and 192.

17. $a_1 = 4$ and $a_n = 2a_{n-1} + 3$
    $a_2 = 2(4) + 3 = 11$
    $a_3 = 2(11) + 3 = 25$
    $a_4 = 2(25) + 3 = 53$
    The first four terms are 4, 11, 25, and 53.

19. $a_n = \dfrac{n^2}{n!}$
    $a_1 = \dfrac{1^2}{1!} = 1$
    $a_2 = \dfrac{2^2}{2!} = 2$
    $a_3 = \dfrac{3^2}{3!} = \dfrac{9}{6} = \dfrac{3}{2}$
    $a_4 = \dfrac{4^2}{4!} = \dfrac{16}{24} = \dfrac{2}{3}$
    The first four terms are $1, \ 2, \ \frac{3}{2},$ and $\frac{2}{3}$.

21. $a_n = 2(n+1)!$
$a_1 = 2(1+1)! = 2(2) = 4$
$a_2 = 2(2+1)! = 2(6) = 12$
$a_3 = 2(3+1)! = 2(24) = 48$
$a_4 = 2(4+1)! = 2(120) = 240$
The first four terms are 4, 12, 48, and 240.

23. $\dfrac{17!}{15!} = \dfrac{17 \cdot 16 \cdot 15!}{15!} = 17 \cdot 16 = 272$

25. $\dfrac{16!}{2! \cdot 14!} = \dfrac{16 \cdot 15 \cdot 14!}{2! 14!} = \dfrac{16 \cdot 15}{2 \cdot 1} = \dfrac{8 \cdot 15}{1} = 120$

27. $\dfrac{(n+2)!}{n!} = \dfrac{(n+2)(n+1)n!}{n!} = (n+2)(n+1)$

29. $\displaystyle\sum_{i=1}^{6} 5i = 5 \cdot 1 + 5 \cdot 2 + 5 \cdot 3 + 5 \cdot 4 + 5 \cdot 5 + 5 \cdot 6$
$\qquad = 5 + 10 + 15 + 20 + 25 + 30$
$\qquad = 105$

31. $\displaystyle\sum_{i=1}^{4} 2i^2 = 2 \cdot 1^2 + 2 \cdot 2^2 + 2 \cdot 3^2 + 2 \cdot 4^2$
$\qquad = 2 + 8 + 18 + 32$
$\qquad = 60$

33. $\displaystyle\sum_{k=1}^{5} k(k+4) = 1(5) + 2(6) + 3(7) + 4(8) + 5(9)$
$\qquad = 5 + 12 + 21 + 32 + 45$
$\qquad = 115$

35. $\displaystyle\sum_{i=1}^{4} \left(\dfrac{-1}{2}\right)^i$
$= \left(-\dfrac{1}{2}\right)^1 + \left(-\dfrac{1}{2}\right)^2 + \left(-\dfrac{1}{2}\right)^3 + \left(-\dfrac{1}{2}\right)^4$
$= -\dfrac{1}{2} + \dfrac{1}{4} + -\dfrac{1}{8} + \dfrac{1}{16}$
$= -\dfrac{5}{16}$

37. $\displaystyle\sum_{i=5}^{9} 11 = 11 + 11 + 11 + 11 + 11 = 55$

39. $\displaystyle\sum_{i=0}^{4} \dfrac{(-1)^i}{i!}$
$= \dfrac{(-1)^0}{0!} + \dfrac{(-1)^1}{1!} + \dfrac{(-1)^2}{2!} + \dfrac{(-1)^3}{3!} + \dfrac{(-1)^4}{4!}$
$= 1 - 1 + \dfrac{1}{2} - \dfrac{1}{6} + \dfrac{1}{24}$
$= \dfrac{9}{24} = \dfrac{3}{8}$

41. $\displaystyle\sum_{i=1}^{5} \dfrac{i!}{(i-1)!} = \dfrac{1!}{0!} + \dfrac{2!}{1!} + \dfrac{3!}{2!} + \dfrac{4!}{3!} + \dfrac{5!}{4!}$
$\qquad = 1 + 2 + 3 + 4 + 5 = 15$

43. $1^2 + 2^2 + 3^2 + \cdots + 15^2 = \displaystyle\sum_{i=1}^{15} i^2$

45. $2 + 2^2 + 2^3 + 2^4 + \cdots + 2^{11} = \displaystyle\sum_{i=1}^{11} 2^i$

47. $1 + 2 + 3 + \cdots + 30 = \displaystyle\sum_{i=1}^{30} i$

49. $\dfrac{1}{2} + \dfrac{2}{3} + \dfrac{3}{4} + \cdots + \dfrac{14}{14+1} = \displaystyle\sum_{i=1}^{14} \dfrac{i}{i+1}$

51. $4 + \dfrac{4^2}{2} + \dfrac{4^3}{3} + \cdots + \dfrac{4^n}{n} = \displaystyle\sum_{i=1}^{n} \dfrac{4^i}{i}$

53. $1 + 3 + 5 + \cdots + (2n-1) = \displaystyle\sum_{i=1}^{n} (2i-1)$

55. $5 + 7 + 9 + 11 + \cdots + 31$
Possible answer: $\displaystyle\sum_{k=1}^{14} (2k+3)$

57. $5 + 7 + 9 + 11 + \cdots + 31$
Possible answer: $\displaystyle\sum_{k=0}^{12} ar^k$

59. $a + (a+d) + (a+2d) + \cdots + (a+nd)$

Possible answer: $\displaystyle\sum_{k=0}^{n}(a+kd)$

61. a. $\displaystyle\sum_{i=2}^{7}a_i$

$= 470 + 588 + 735 + 800 + 920 + 1100$

$= 4613$

This represents the total number of home-educated children in the U.S. from 1992 to 1997, in thousands.

b. $\dfrac{1}{6}\displaystyle\sum_{i=2}^{7}a_i = \dfrac{4613}{6} \approx 769$

This represents the average number of children home-educated each year from 1992 to 1997, in thousands.

63. $a_n = 0.16n^2 - 1.04n + 7.39$

$a_1 = 0.16(1)^2 - 1.04(1) + 7.39 = 6.51$

$a_2 = 0.16(2)^2 - 1.04(2) + 7.39 = 5.95$

$a_3 = 0.16(3)^2 - 1.04(3) + 7.39 = 5.71$

$a_4 = 0.16(4)^2 - 1.04(4) + 7.39 = 5.79$

$a_5 = 0.16(5)^2 - 1.04(5) + 7.39 = 6.19$

$\displaystyle\sum_{i=1}^{5}a_i = 6.51 + 5.95 + 5.71 + 5.79 + 6.19 = 30.15$

Americans spent a total of $30.15 billion on recreational boating from 1991 through 1995.

65. $a_n = 6000\left(1 + \dfrac{0.06}{4}\right)^n$, $n = 1, 2, 3, \ldots$

$a_{20} = 6000\left(1 + \dfrac{0.06}{4}\right)^{20} \approx 8081.13$

After five years, the balance is $8081.13.

67.–73. Answers may vary.

75. $\dfrac{200!}{198!} = 39,800$

77. $\dfrac{20!}{300} = 8,109,673,360,588,800$

79. $\dfrac{54!}{(54-3)!\,3!} = 24,804$

81. Exercise 29

Exercise 31

Exercise 33

Exercise 35

Exercise 37

83. $a_n = \dfrac{n}{n+1}$

As n gets larger, a_n approaches 1.

85. $a_n = \dfrac{2n^2 + 5n - 7}{n^3}$

As n gets larger, a_n approaches 0.

87. a. False; $\dfrac{n!}{(n-1)!} = \dfrac{n \cdot (n-1)!}{(n-1)!} = n$

b. True

c. False; $\displaystyle\sum_{i=1}^{2} (-1)^i 2^i = -2 + 4 = 2$

d. False;

$$a_1 b_1 + a_2 b_2 \neq (a_1 + a_2) + (b_1 + b_2)$$

(b) is true.

Section 11.2

Check Point Exercises

1. $a_1 = 100$, $a_n = a_{n-1} - 30$
$a_2 = a_1 - 30 = 100 - 30 = 70$
$a_3 = a_2 - 30 = 70 - 30 = 40$
$a_4 = a_3 - 30 = 40 - 30 = 10$
$a_5 = a_4 - 30 = 10 - 30 = -20$
The first five terms are 100, 70, 40, 10, and –20.

2. $a_1 = 6$, $d = -5$
To find the ninth term, a_9, replace n in the formula with 9, a_1 with 6, and d with –5.
$a_n = a_1 + (n-1)d$
$a_9 = 6 + (9-1)(-5)$
$\quad = 6 + 8(-5)$
$\quad = 6 + (-40)$
$\quad = -34$

3. a. The amounts spent can be expressed by the following arithmetic sequence:
12,808, 15,158, 17,508
In this sequence, a_1, the first term, represents the amount spent in 1984.

Each subsequent year, this amount increases by \$2350, so $d = 2350$. Thus, the nth term of the sequence that describes the amount spent n years after 1983 is:
$a_n = a_1 + (n-1)d$
$a_n = 12,808 + (n-1)2350$
$a_n = 12,808 + 2350n - 2350$
$a_n = 2350n + 10,458$

b. The year 2010 is 27 years after 1983. So substitute 27 for n in $a_n = 2350n + 10,458$.
$a_{27} = 2350(27) + 10,458 = 73,908$
In 2010, U.S. travelers will spend \$73,908 million in other countries.

4. 3, 6, 9, 12, ...
To find the sum of the first 15 terms, S_{15}, replace n in the formulas with 15.
$$S_n = \frac{n}{2}(a_1 + a_n)$$
$$S_{15} = \frac{15}{2}(a_1 + a_{15})$$
Use the formula for the general term of a sequence to find a_{15}. The common difference, d, is 3, and the first term, a_1, is 3.
$a_n = a_1 + (n-1)d$
$a_{15} = 3 + (15-1)(3)$
$\quad = 3 + 14(3)$
$\quad = 3 + 42$
$\quad = 45$
Thus, $S_{15} = \frac{15}{2}(3 + 45) = \frac{15}{2}(48) = 360$.

5. $\displaystyle\sum_{i=1}^{30} (6i - 11) = (6 \cdot 1 - 11) + (6 \cdot 2 - 11)$
$\qquad\qquad\qquad + (6 \cdot 3 - 11) + \cdots + (6 \cdot 30 - 11)$
$\qquad\qquad\qquad = -5 + 1 + 7 + \cdots + 169$
So the first term, a_1, is –5; the common difference, d, is $1 - (-5) = 6$; the last term, a_{30}, is 169. Substitute $n = 30$, $a_1 = -5$, and $a_{30} = 169$ in the formula $S_n = \frac{n}{2}(a_1 + a_n)$.
$S_{30} = \frac{30}{2}(-5 + 169) = 15(164) = 2460$
Thus, $\displaystyle\sum_{i=1}^{30} (6i - 11) = 2460$

6. Find the sum of the arithmetic sequence whose first term corresponds to costs in 2001 and whose last term corresponds to costs in 2010. Because the model describes costs n years after 2000, $n = 1$ describes the year 2001 and $n = 10$ describes the year 2010.

$$a_n = 1800n + 49{,}730$$
$$a_1 = 1800 \cdot 1 + 49{,}730 = 51{,}530$$
$$a_{10} = 1800 \cdot 10 + 49{,}730 = 67{,}730$$

To find the sum of the costs for all 10 years, find the sum of the ten terms of the arithmetic sequence
51,530, 53,330, . . . , 67,730.
There are 10 terms with first term 51,530 and last term 67,730 so $n = 10$, $a_1 = 51{,}530$, and $a_{10} = 67{,}730$.

$$S_n = \frac{n}{2}(a_1 + a_n)$$
$$S_{10} = \frac{10}{2}(51{,}530 + 67{,}730) = 5(119{,}260)$$
$$= 596{,}300$$

The total cost for the ten-year period is \$596,300.

Exercise Set 11.2

1. $a_1 = 200$, $d = 20$
The first six terms are 200, 220, 240, 260, 280, and 300.

3. $a_1 = -7$, $d = 4$
The first six terms are −7, −3, 1, 5, 9, and 13.

5. $a_1 = 300$, $d = -90$
The first six terms are 300, 210, 120, 30, −60, and −150.

7. $a_1 = \dfrac{5}{2}, \ d = -\dfrac{1}{2}$
The first six terms are $\dfrac{5}{2}, 2, \dfrac{3}{2}, 1, \dfrac{1}{2}$, and 0.

9. $a_n = a_{n-1} + 6$, $a_1 = -9$
The first six terms are −9, −3, 3, 9, 15, and 21.

11. $a_n = a_{n-1} - 10$, $a_1 = 30$
The first six terms are 30, 20, 10, 0, −10, and −20.

13. $a_n = a_{n-1} - 0.4$, $a_1 = 1.6$
The first six terms are 1.6, 1.2, 0.8, 0.4, 0, and −0.4.

15. $a_1 = 13$, $d = -4$
$$a_n = 13 + (n-1)4$$
$$a_6 = 13 + 5(4) = 13 + 20 = 33$$

17. $a_1 = 7$, $d = 5$
$$a_n = 7 + (n-1)2$$
$$a_{50} = 7 + 49(5) = 252$$

19. $a_1 = -40$, $d = 5$
$$a_n = -40 + (n-1)5$$
$$a_{200} = -40 + (199)5 = 955$$

21. $a_1 = 35$, $d = -3$
$$a_n = 35 - 3(n-1)$$
$$a_{60} = 35 - 3(59) = -142$$

23. 1, 5, 9, 13, …
$$d = 5 - 1, \ = 4$$
$$a_n = 1 + (n-1)4 = 1 + 4n - 4$$
$$a_n = 4n - 3$$
$$a_{20} = 4(20) - 3 = 77$$

25. 7, 3, −1, −5, …
$$d = 3 - 7 = -4$$
$$a_n = 7 + (n-1)(-4) = 7 - 4n + 4$$
$$a_n = 11 - 4n$$
$$a_{20} = 11 - 4(20) = -69$$

27. $a_1 = 9$, $d = 2$
$$a_n = 9 + (n-1)(2)$$
$$a_n = 7 + 2n$$
$$a_{20} = 7 + 2(20) = 47$$

29. $a_1 = -20$, $d = -4$
$$a_n = -20 + (n-1)(-4)$$
$$a_n = -20 - 4n + 4$$
$$a_n = -16 - 4n$$
$$a_{20} = -16 - 4(20) = -96$$

31. $a_n = a_{n-1} + 3, \ a_1 = 4$
$d = 3$
$a_n = 4 + (n-1)(3)$
$a_n = 1 + 3n$
$a_{20} = 1 + 3(20) = 61$

33. $a_n = a_{n-1} - 10, \ a_1 = 30, \ d = -10$
$a_n = 30 - 10(n-1) = 30 - 10n + 10$
$a_n = 40 - 10n$
$a_{20} = 40 - 10(20) = -160$

35. $4, \ 10, \ 16, \ 22, \ \ldots$
$d = 10 - 4 = 6$
$a_n = 4 + (n-1)(6)$
$a_{20} = 4 + (19)(6) = 118$
$S_{20} = \dfrac{20}{2}(4 + 118) = 1220$

37. $-10, \ -6, \ -2, \ 2, \ \ldots$
$d = -6 - (-10) = -6 + 10 = 4$
$a_n = -10 + (n-1)4$
$a_{50} = -10 + (49)4 = 186$
$S_{50} = \dfrac{50}{2}(-10 + 186) = 4400$

39. $1 + 2 + 3 + 4 + \cdots + 100$
$S_{100} - \dfrac{100}{2}(1 + 100) = 5050$

41. $2 + 4 + 6 + \cdots + 120$
$S_{60} = \dfrac{60}{2}(2 + 120) = 3660$

43.   even integers between 21 and 45;
$22 + 24 + 26 + \cdots + 144$
$S_{12} = \dfrac{12}{2}(22 + 44) = 396$

45. $\displaystyle\sum_{i=1}^{17}(5i + 3)$
$= (5 + 3) + (10 + 3) + (15 + 3) + \cdots + (85 + 3)$
$= 8 + 13 + 18 + \cdots + 88$
$S_{17} = \dfrac{17}{2}(8 + 88) = 816$

47. $\displaystyle\sum_{i=1}^{30}(-3i + 5)$
$= (-3 + 5) + (-6 + 5) + (-9 + 5) + \cdots$
$\quad + (-90 + 5)$
$= 2 - 1 - 4 - \cdots - 85$
$S_{30} = \dfrac{30}{2}(2 - 85) = -1245$

49. $\displaystyle\sum_{i=1}^{100} 4i = 4 + 8 + 12 + \cdots + 400$
$S_{100} = \dfrac{100}{2}(4 + 400) = 20,200$

51. a. $a_n = 126{,}424, \ d = 1265$
$a_n = 126{,}424 + (n-1)(1265)$
$a_n = 125{,}159 + 1265n$

    b. $n = 2005 - 1989 = 16$
$a_{16} = 125{,}159 + 1265(16) = 145{,}399$
In 2005, there will be 145,399 thousand employees.

53.   Company A:
$a_n = 24{,}000 + (n-1)(1600)$
$a_{10} = 24{,}000 + 9(1600) = \$38{,}400$
Company B:
$a_n = 28{,}000 + (n-1)(1000)$
$a_{10} = 28{,}000 + 9(1000) = \$37{,}000$
Company A will pay \$1400 more.

55. a. $a_1 = 3.78, \ d = 0.576$
$a_n = 3.78 + (n-1)(0.576)$
$a_n = 3.204 + 0.576n$

    b. $a_1 = 3.78$
$a_{41} = 3.204 + 0.576(41) = 26.82$
$S_{41} = \dfrac{41}{2}(3.78 + 26.82) = 627.3$
The total amount is 627.3 million tons.

57. $a_n = 33{,}000 + (n-1)(2500)$
$a_{10} = 33{,}000 + 9(2500) = 55{,}500$
$S_n = \dfrac{10}{2}(33{,}000 + 55{,}500) = 442{,}500$
The total ten year salary is \$442,500.

59. $a_n = 30 + (n-1)2$

$a_{26} = 30 + (25)2 = 80$

$S_{26} = \dfrac{26}{2}(30 + 80) = 1430$

The theater has 1430 seats.

61.–65. Answers may vary.

67. Answers may vary for Exercises 45, 47, and 49:

Exercise 45

```
sum(seq(5X+3,X,1
,17,1))
              816
```

Exercise 47

```
sum(seq(-3X+5,X,
1,30,1))
            -1245
```

Exercise 49

```
sum(seq(4X,X,1,1
00,1))
            20200
```

69. 21,700, 23,172, 24,644, 26,166, ..., 314,628

$d = 23,172 - 21,700 = 1472$

$314,628 = 1472n + 20,228$

$1472n = 294,400$

$n = 200$

It is the 200th term.

71. $1 + 3 + 5 + \cdots + (2n-1)$

$S_n = \dfrac{n}{2}(1 + 2n - 1)$

$= \dfrac{n}{2}(2n)$

$= n^2$

Section 11.3

Check Point Exercises

1. $a_1 = 12, r = \dfrac{1}{2}$

$a_2 = 12\left(\dfrac{1}{2}\right)^1 = 6$

$a_3 = 12\left(\dfrac{1}{2}\right)^2 = \dfrac{12}{4} = 3$

$a_4 = 12\left(\dfrac{1}{2}\right)^3 = \dfrac{12}{8} = \dfrac{3}{2}$

$a_5 = 12\left(\dfrac{1}{2}\right)^4 = \dfrac{12}{16} = \dfrac{3}{4}$

$a_6 = 12\left(\dfrac{1}{2}\right)^5 = \dfrac{12}{32} = \dfrac{3}{8}$

The first six terms are $12, 6, 3, \dfrac{3}{2}, \dfrac{3}{4}, \text{and } \dfrac{3}{8}$.

2. $a_1 = 5, r = -3$

$a_n = 5r^{n-1}$

$a_7 = 5(-3)^{7-1} = 5(-3)^6 = 5(729) = 3645$

The seventh term is 3645.

3. 3, 6, 12, 24, 48, ...

$r = \dfrac{6}{3} = 2, a_1 = 3$

$a_n = 3(2)^{n-1}$

$a_8 = 3(2)^{8-1} = 3(2)^7 = 3(128) = 384$

The eighth term is 384.

4. $a_1 = 2, r = \dfrac{-6}{2} = -3$

$S_n = \dfrac{a_1(1 - r^r)}{1 - r}$

$S_9 = \dfrac{2\left(1 - (-3)^9\right)}{1 - (-3)} = \dfrac{2(19,684)}{4} = 9842$

The sum of the first nine terms is 9842.

5. $\sum_{i=1}^{8} 2 \cdot 3^i$

$a_1 = 2 \cdot (3)^1 = 6, \; r = 3$

$S_n = \dfrac{a_1(1 - r^n)}{1 - r}$

$S_8 = \dfrac{6\left(1 - 3^8\right)}{1 - 3} = \dfrac{6(-6560)}{-2} = 19,680$

Thus, $\sum_{i=1}^{8} 2 \cdot 3^i = 19,680$.

6. $a_1 = 30,000, \; r = 1.06$

$S_n = \dfrac{a_1(1 - r^n)}{1 - r}$

$S_{30} = \dfrac{30,000\left(1 - (1.06)^{30}\right)}{1 - 1.06} \approx 2,371,746$

The total lifetime salary is $2,371,746.

7. $A = P\dfrac{\left(1 + \frac{r}{n}\right)^{nt} - 1}{\frac{r}{n}}$

$P = 3000, \; r = 0.10, \; n = 1, \; t = 40$

$A = 3000 \dfrac{(1 + 0.10)^{40} - 1}{0.10} \approx 1,327,778$

The value of the IRA will be $1,327,778.

8. $3 + 2 + \dfrac{4}{3} + \dfrac{8}{9} + \cdots$

$a_1 = 3, \; r = \dfrac{2}{3}$

$S = \dfrac{a_1}{1 - r}$

$S = \dfrac{3}{1 - \frac{2}{3}} = \dfrac{3}{\frac{1}{3}} = 9$

The sum of this infinite geometric series is 9.

9. $0.\overline{9} = 0.9999\ldots = \dfrac{9}{10} + \dfrac{9}{100} + \dfrac{9}{1000} + \cdots$

$a_1 = \dfrac{9}{10}, \; r = \dfrac{1}{10}$

$S = \dfrac{\frac{9}{10}}{1 - \frac{1}{10}} = \dfrac{\frac{9}{10}}{\frac{9}{10}} = 1$

An equivalent fraction for $0.\overline{9}$ is 1.

10. $a_1 = 1000(0.8) = 800, \; r = 0.8$

$S = \dfrac{800}{1 - 0.8} = 4000$

The total amount spent is $4000.

Exercise Set 11.3

1. $a_1 = 5, \; r = 3$
The first five terms are 5, 15, 45, 135, and 405.

3. $a_1 = 20, \; r = \dfrac{1}{2}$
The first five terms are 20, 10, 5, $\frac{5}{2}$, and $\frac{5}{4}$.

5. $a_n = -4a_{n-1}, \; a_1 = 10$
The first five terms are 10, -40, 160, -640, and 2560.

7. $a_n = -5a_{n-1}, \; a_1 = -6$
The first five terms are -6, 30, -150, 750, and -3750.

9. $a_1 = 6, \; r = 2$
$a_n = 6 \cdot 2^{n-1}$
$a_8 = 6 \cdot 2^7 = 768$

11. $a_1 = 5, \; r = -2$
$a_n = 5 \cdot (-2)^{n-1}$
$a_{12} = 5 \cdot (-2)^{11} = -10,240$

13. $a_1 = 1000, \quad r = -\dfrac{1}{2}$

$a_n = 1000\left(-\dfrac{1}{2}\right)^{n-1}$

$a_{40} = 1000\left(-\dfrac{1}{2}\right)^{39}$

≈ 0.000000002

15. $a_1 = 1,000,000, \quad r = 0.1$

$a_n = 1,000,000(0.1)^{n-1}$

$a_8 = 1,000,000(0.1)^7 = 0.1$

17. 3, 12, 48, 192, . . .

$r = \dfrac{12}{3} = 4$

$a_n = 3(4)^{n-1}$

$a_7 = 3(4)^6 = 12,288$

19.   18, 6, 2, $\dfrac{2}{3}$, . . .

$r = \dfrac{6}{18} = \dfrac{1}{3}$

$a_n = 18\left(\dfrac{1}{3}\right)^{n-1}$

$a_7 = 18\left(\dfrac{1}{3}\right)^6 = \dfrac{2}{81}$

21. 1.5, –3, 6, –12, . . .

$r = \dfrac{6}{-3} = -2$

$a_n = 1.5(-2)^{n-1}$

$a_7 = 1.5(-2)^6 = 96$

23. 0.0004, –0.004, 0.04, –0.4, . . .

$r = \dfrac{-0.004}{0.0004} = -10$

$a_n = 0.0004(-10)^{n-1}$

$a_7 = 0.0004(-10)^6 = 400$

25. 2, 6, 18, 54, . . .

$r = \dfrac{6}{2} = 3$

$S_{12} = \dfrac{2\left(1-3^{12}\right)}{1-3} = \dfrac{2(-531,440)}{-2} = 531,440$

27. 3, –6, 12, –24, . . .

$r = \dfrac{-6}{3} = -2$

$S_{11} = \dfrac{3\left[1-(-2)^{11}\right]}{1-(-2)} = \dfrac{3(2049)}{3} = 2049$

29. $-\dfrac{3}{2}, \;\; 3, \;\; -6, \;\; 12, \ldots$

$r = \dfrac{3}{\frac{-3}{2}} = -2$

$S_{14} = \dfrac{-\frac{3}{2}\left[1-(-2)^{14}\right]}{1-(-2)} = \dfrac{-\frac{3}{2}(-16,383)}{3} = \dfrac{16,383}{2}$

31. $\displaystyle\sum_{i=1}^{8} 3^i$

$r = 3, \quad a_1 = 3$

$S_8 = \dfrac{3\left(1-3^8\right)}{1-3} = \dfrac{3(-6560)}{-2} = 9840$

33. $\displaystyle\sum_{i=1}^{10} 5\cdot 2^i$

$r = 2, \quad a_1 = 10$

$S_{10} = \dfrac{10\left(1-2^{10}\right)}{1-2} = \dfrac{10(-1023)}{-1} = 10,230$

35. $\displaystyle\sum_{i=1}^{6}\left(\dfrac{1}{2}\right)^{i+1}$

$r = \dfrac{1}{2}, \quad a_1 = \dfrac{1}{4}$

$S_6 = \dfrac{\dfrac{1}{4}\left(1-\left(\dfrac{1}{2}\right)^6\right)}{1-\dfrac{1}{2}} = \dfrac{\dfrac{1}{4}\left(\dfrac{63}{64}\right)}{\dfrac{1}{2}} = \dfrac{63}{128}$

37. $1 + \dfrac{1}{3} + \dfrac{1}{9} + \dfrac{1}{27} + \cdots$

$r = \dfrac{1}{3}$

$S_\infty = \dfrac{1}{1 - \frac{1}{3}} = \dfrac{1}{\frac{2}{3}} = \dfrac{3}{2}$

39. $3 + \dfrac{3}{4} + \dfrac{3}{4^2} + \dfrac{3}{4^3} + \cdots$

$r = \dfrac{1}{4}$

$S_\infty = \dfrac{3}{1 - \frac{1}{4}} = \dfrac{3}{\frac{3}{4}} = 4$

41. $1 - \dfrac{1}{2} - \dfrac{1}{4} - \dfrac{1}{8} + \cdots$

$r = -\dfrac{1}{2}$

$S_\infty = \dfrac{1}{1 - \left(-\frac{1}{2}\right)} = \dfrac{1}{\frac{3}{2}} = \dfrac{2}{3}$

43. $\displaystyle\sum_{i=1}^{\infty} 8(-0.3)^{i-1} = 8 - 2.4 + \cdots$

$r = -0.3$

$S_\infty = \dfrac{8}{1 - (-0.3)} = \dfrac{8}{1.3} \approx 6.15385$

45. $0.\overline{5} = \dfrac{5}{10} + \dfrac{5}{100} + \dfrac{5}{1000} + \dfrac{5}{10,000} + \cdots$

$r = \dfrac{1}{10}$

$S_\infty = \dfrac{\frac{5}{10}}{1 - \frac{1}{10}} = \dfrac{\frac{5}{10}}{\frac{9}{10}} = \dfrac{5}{9}$

47. $0.\overline{47} = \dfrac{47}{100} + \dfrac{47}{10,000} + \dfrac{47}{1,000,000} + \cdots$

$r = \dfrac{1}{100}$

$S_\infty = \dfrac{\frac{47}{100}}{1 - \frac{1}{100}} = \dfrac{\frac{47}{100}}{\frac{99}{100}} = \dfrac{47}{99}$

49. $0.\overline{257} = \dfrac{257}{1000} + \dfrac{257}{10^6} + \dfrac{257}{10^9} + \cdots$

$r = \dfrac{1}{1000}$

$S_\infty = \dfrac{\frac{257}{1000}}{1 - \frac{1}{1000}} = \dfrac{\frac{257}{1000}}{\frac{999}{1000}} = \dfrac{257}{999}$

51. $a_n = n + 5$

arithmetic, $d = 1$

53. $a_n = 2^n$

geometric, $r = 2$

55. $a_n = n^2 + 5$

neither

57. $1, 2, 4, 8, \ldots$

$r = 2$

$a_n = 2^{n-1}$

$a_{15} = 2^{14} = \$16,384$

59. $a_1 = 3,000,000$

$r = 1.04$

$a_n = 3,000,000(1.04)^{n-1}$

$a_7 = 3,000,000(1.04)^6 = \$3,795,957$

61. a. $\dfrac{1996}{1995} \Rightarrow \dfrac{21.36}{20.60} \approx 1.04$

$\dfrac{1997}{1996} \Rightarrow \dfrac{22.19}{21.36} \approx 1.04$

$\dfrac{1998}{1997} \Rightarrow \dfrac{23.02}{22.19} \approx 1.04$

The population is increasing geometrically with $r = 1.04$.

b. $a_n = 20.6(1.04)^{n-1}$

c. $2005 - 1994 = 11$

$a_{11} = 20.6(1.04)^{10}$

≈ 30.49

In 2005, Iraq will have a population of 30.49 million.

63. $1, 2, 4, 8, \ldots$

$r = 2$

$S_{15} = \dfrac{1(1 - 2^{15})}{1 - 2} = 32{,}767$

The total savings is \$32,767.

65. $a_1 = 24{,}000, \ r = 1.05$

$S_{20} = \dfrac{24{,}000\left[1 - (1.05)^{20}\right]}{1 - 1.05} = 793{,}582.90$

The total salary is \$793,582.90.

67. $20 + 0.9(20) + (0.9)^2(20) + \cdots$

$r = 0.9$

$S_{10} = \dfrac{20(1 - 0.9^{10})}{1 - 0.9} \approx 130.26$

The total length is 130.26 inches.

69. $A = 2500 \dfrac{(1 + 0.09)^{40} - 1}{0.09} \approx 844{,}706.11$

In 40 years, the value is \$844,706.11.

71. $A = 600 \dfrac{\left(1 + \frac{0.08}{4}\right)^{72} - 1}{\frac{0.08}{4}} \approx 94{,}834.21$

After 18 years, the value is \$94,834.21.

73. $6(0.6) + 6(0.6)^2 + 6(0.6)^3 + \cdots$

$r = 0.6$

$S_\infty = \dfrac{6(0.6)}{1 - 0.6} = 9$

The total economic impact is \$9 million.

75. $\frac{1}{4} + \frac{1}{16} + \frac{1}{64} + \cdots$

$r = \frac{1}{4}$

$S_\infty = \dfrac{\frac{1}{4}}{1 - \frac{1}{4}} = \dfrac{1}{4} \cdot \dfrac{4}{3} = \dfrac{1}{3}$

77.–83. Answers may vary.

85. Exercise 17

Exercise 19

Exercise 21

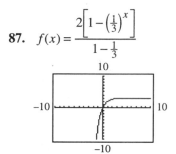

87. $f(x) = \dfrac{2\left[1 - \left(\frac{1}{3}\right)^x\right]}{1 - \frac{1}{3}}$

Horizontal asymptote at $y = 3$

$\displaystyle\sum_{n=0}^{\infty} 2\left(\tfrac{1}{3}\right)^n = \dfrac{2}{1 - \frac{1}{3}} = 3$

89. a. False; there is no common ratio.

b. False; the sum can be calculated exactly, since the series is geometric $\left(r = \tfrac{1}{2}\right)$.

c. False; $10 - 5 + \dfrac{5}{2} - \dfrac{5}{4} \cdots = \dfrac{10}{1 + \frac{1}{2}}$

d. True; $r = 0.5 = \tfrac{1}{2}$

(d) is true.

91. $1{,}000{,}000 = P \dfrac{\left(1 + \frac{0.1}{12}\right)^{360} - 1}{\frac{0.1}{12}}$

$1{,}000{,}000 \approx 2260.49P$

$P \approx 442.38$

You must deposit \$442.38 monthly.

Section 11.4

Check Point Exercises

1. a. S_1: $2 = 1(1+1)$

         S_k: $2 + 4 + 6 + \cdots + 2k = k(k+1)$

        S_{k+1}: $2 + 4 + 6 + \cdots + 2(k+1) = (k+1)(k+2)$

   b. S_1: $1^3 = \dfrac{1^2(1+1)^2}{4}$

         S_k: $1^3 + 2^3 + 3^3 + \cdots + k^3 = \dfrac{k^2(k+1)^2}{4}$

        S_{k+1}: $1^3 + 2^3 + 3^3 + \cdots + (k+1)^3 = \dfrac{(k+1)^2(k+2)^2}{4}$

2. S_1: $2 = 1(1+1)$

        $2 = 2$ is true.

     S_k: $2 + 4 + 6 + \cdots + 2k = k(k+1)$

    S_{k+1}: $2 + 4 + 6 + \cdots + 2k + 2(k+1) = (k+1)(k+2)$

Add $2(k+1)$ to both sides of S_k:

$2 + 4 + 6 + \cdots + 2k + 2(k+1) = k(k+1) + 2(k+1)$

Simplify the right-hand side:

$k(k+1) + 2(k+1) = (k+1)(k+2)$

If S_k is true, then S_{k+1} is true. The statement is true for all n.

3. S_1: $1^3 = \dfrac{1^2(1+1)^2}{4}$

        $1 = \dfrac{4}{4}$

        $1 = 1$ is true.

     S_k: $1^3 + 2^3 + 3^3 + \cdots + k^3 = \dfrac{k^2(k+1)^2}{4}$

    S_{k+1}: $1^3 + 2^3 + 3^3 + \cdots + k^3 + (k+1)^3 = \dfrac{(k+1)^2(k+2)^2}{4}$

Add $(k + 1)^3$ to both sides of S_k:

$$1^3 + 2^3 + 3^3 + \cdots + k^3 + (k+1)^3 = \frac{k^2(k+1)^2}{4} + (k+1)^3$$

Simplify the right hand side:

$$\frac{k^2(k+1)^2}{4} + (k+1)^3 = \frac{k^2(k+1)^2 + 4(k+1)^3}{4} = \frac{(k+1)^2\left[k^2 + 4(k+1)\right]}{4} = \frac{(k+1)^2(k^2 + 4k + 4)}{4}$$

$$= \frac{(k+1)^2(k+2)^2}{4}$$

If S_k is true, then S_{k+1} is true. The statement is true for all n.

4. S_1: 2 is a factor of $1^2 + 1 = 2$, since $2 = 2 \cdot 1$.
        S_k: 2 is a factor of $k^2 + k$
S_{k+1}: 2 is a factor of $(k+1)^2 + (k+1)$
Simplify:
$$(k+1)^2 + (k+1) = k^2 + 2k + 1 + k + 1$$
$$= k^2 + 3k + 2$$
$$= k^2 + k + 2k + 2$$
$$= (k^2 + k) + 2(k+1)$$

Because we assume S_k is true, we know 2 is a factor of $k^2 + k$. Since 2 is a factor of $2(k+1)$, we conclude 2 is a factor of the sum $(k^2 + k) + 2(k+1)$. If S_k is true, then S_{k+1} is true. The statement is true for all n.

Exercise Set 11.4

1. S_n: $1 + 3 + 5 + \cdots + (n-1) = n^2$
    S_1: $1 = 1^2$
        $1 = 1$ true

    S_2: $1 + 3 = 2^2$
            $4 = 4$ true

    S_3: $1 + 3 + 5 = 3^2$
                $9 = 9$ true

3. S_n: 2 is a factor of $n^2 - n$
    S_1: 2 is a factor of $1^2 - 1 = 0$
        $0 = 0 \cdot 2$ so 2 is a factor of 0 is true.

    S_2: 2 is a factor of $2^2 - 2 = 2$
        $2 = 1 \cdot 2$ so 2 is a factor of 2 is true.

    S_3: 2 is a factor of $3^2 - 3 = 6$
        $6 = 3 \cdot 2$ so 2 is a factor of 6 is true.

5. S_n: $4 + 8 + 12 + \cdots + 4n = 2n(n+1)$
        S_k: $4 + 8 + 12 + \cdots + 4k = 2k(k+1)$
S_{k+1}: $4 + 8 + 12 + \cdots + 4(k+1) = 2(k+1)(k+1+1)$
        $4 + 8 + 12 + \cdots + (4k+4) = 2(k+1)(k+2)$

7. S_n: $3 + 7 + 11 + \cdots + (4n-1) = n(2n+1)$
        S_k: $3 + 7 + 11 + \cdots + (4k-1) = k(2k+1)$
S_{k+1}: $3 + 7 + 11 + \cdots + [4(k+1)-1] = (k+1)[2(k+1)+1]$
        $3 + 7 + 11 + \cdots + (4k+3) = (k+1)(2k+3)$

9. S_n: 2 is a factor of $n^2 - n + 2$

     S_k: 2 is a factor of $k^2 - k + 2$

    S_{k+1}: 2 is a factor of $(k+1)^2 - (k+1) + 2$

         $k^2 + 2k + 1 - k - 1 + 2 = k^2 + k + 2$

    S_{k+1}: 2 is a factor of $k^2 + k + 2$.

11. S_1: $4 = 2(1)(1+1)$

        $4 = 2(2)$

        $4 = 4$ is true.

    S_k: $4 + 8 + 12 + \cdots + 4k = 2k(k+1)$

  S_{k+1}: $4 + 8 + 12 + \cdots + 4(k+1) = 2(k+1)(k+1+1)$

Add $4(k+1)$ to both sides of S_k:

$4 + 8 + 12 + \cdots + 4k + 4(k+1) = 2k(k+1) + 4(k+1)$

Simplify the right-hand side:

$= 2k(k+1) + 4(k+1) = (2k+4)(k+1)$

$= 2(k+2)(k+1)$

$= 2(k+1)(k+1+1)$

If S_k is true, then S_{k+1} is true. The statement is true for all n.

13. S_1: $1 = 1^2$

        $1 = 1$ is true.

    S_k: $1 + 3 + 5 + \cdots + (2k-1) = k^2$

  S_{k+1}: $1 + 3 + 5 + \cdots + (2k-1) + (2(k+1)-1) = (k+1)^2$

        $1 + 3 + 5 + \cdots + (2k-1) + (2k+1) = (k+1)^2$

Add $(2k+1)$ to both sides of S_k:

$1 + 3 + 5 + \cdots + (2k-1) + (2k+1) = k^2 + (2k+1)$

Simplify the right-hand side:

$= k^2 + (2k+1)$

$= (k+1)^2$

If S_k is true, then S_{k+1} is true. The statement is true for all n.

15. S_1: $3 = 1[2(1)+1]$

        $3 = 3$ is true.

    S_k: $3 + 7 + 11 + \cdots + (4k-1) = k(2k+1)$

  S_{k+1}: $3 + 7 + 11 + \cdots + (4k-1) + \left[4(k+1)-1\right] = (k+1)[2(k+1)+1]$

        $3 + 7 + 11 + \cdots + (4k-1) + (4k+3) = (k+1)(2k+3)$

Add $(4k+3)$ to both sides of S_k:

$3 + 7 + 11 + \cdots + (4k-1) + (4k-3) = k(2k+1) + 4(k+3)$

Simplify the right-hand side:

$= k(2k+1) + (4k+3) = 2k^2 + k + 4k + 3$

$= 2k^2 + 5k + 3$

$= (k+1)(2k+3)$

If S_k is true, then S_{k+1} is true. The statement is true for all n.

17. $S_1: 1 = 2^1 - 1$

$1 = 1$ is true.

$S_k: 1 + 2 + 2^2 + \cdots + 2^{k-1} = 2^k - 1$

$S_{k+1}: 1 + 2 + 2^2 + \cdots + 2^{k-1} + 2^{k+1-1} = 2^{k+1} - 1$

$1 + 2 + 2^2 + \cdots + 2^{k-1} + 2^k = 2^{k+1} - 1$

Add 2^k to both sides of S_k:

$1 + 2 + 2^2 + \cdots + 2^{k-1} + 2^k = 2^k + 2^k - 1$

Simplify the right-hand side:

$= 2^k + 2^k - 1 = 2\left(2^k\right) - 1$

$= 2^{k+1} - 1$

If S_k is true, then S_{k+1} is true. The statement is true for all n.

19. $S_1:\ 2 = 2^{1+1} - 2$

$2 = 4 - 2$

$2 = 2$ is true.

$S_k:\ 2 + 4 + 8 + \cdots + 2^k = 2^{k+1} - 2$

$S_{k+1}:\ 2 + 4 + 8 + \cdots + 2^k + 2^{k+1} = 2^{k+2} - 2$

Add 2^{k+1} to both sides of S_k:

$2 + 4 + 8 + \cdots + 2^k + 2^{k+1} = 2^{k+1} + 2^{k+1} - 2$

Simplify the right-hand side:

$= 2^{k+1} + 2^{k+1} - 1 = 2\left(2^{k+1}\right) - 2$

$= 2^{k+2} - 2$

If S_k is true, then S_{k+1} is true. The statement is true for all n.

21. $S_1:\ 1 \cdot 2 = \dfrac{1(1+1)(1+2)}{3}$

$2 = \dfrac{6}{3}$

$2 = 2$ is true.

$S_k:\ 1 \cdot 2 + 2 \cdot 3 + 3 \cdot 4 + \cdots + k(k+1) = \dfrac{k(k+1)(k+2)}{3}$

$S_{k+1}:\ 1 \cdot 2 + 2 \cdot 3 + 3 \cdot 4 + \cdots + k(k+1) + (k+1)(k+2) = \dfrac{(k+1)(k+2)(k+3)}{3}$

Add $(k+1)(k+2)$ to both sided of S_k:

$1 \cdot 2 + 2 \cdot 3 + 3 \cdot 4 + \cdots + k(k+1) + (k+1)(k+2) = \dfrac{k(k+1)(k+2)}{3} + (k+1)(k+2)$

Simplify the right-hand side:

$= \dfrac{k(k+1)(k+2)}{3} + (k+1)(k+2) = \dfrac{k(k+1)(k+2) + 3(k+1)(k+2)}{3}$

$= \dfrac{(k+1)(k+2)(k+3)}{3}$ `

If S_k is true, then S_{k+1} is true. The statement is true for all n.

23. S_1: $\dfrac{1}{1 \cdot 2} = \dfrac{1}{1+1}$

$\dfrac{1}{2} = \dfrac{1}{2}$ is true.

S_k: $\dfrac{1}{1 \cdot 2} + \dfrac{1}{2 \cdot 3} + \dfrac{1}{3 \cdot 4} + \cdots + \dfrac{1}{k(k+1)} = \dfrac{k}{k+1}$

S_{k+1}: $\dfrac{1}{1 \cdot 2} + \dfrac{1}{2 \cdot 3} + \dfrac{1}{3 \cdot 4} + \cdots + \dfrac{1}{k(k+1)} + \dfrac{1}{(k+1)(k+2)} = \dfrac{k+1}{k+2}$

Add $\dfrac{1}{(k+1)(k+2)}$ to both sides of S_k:

$\dfrac{1}{1 \cdot 2} + \dfrac{1}{2 \cdot 3} + \dfrac{1}{3 \cdot 4} + \cdots + \dfrac{1}{k(k+1)} + \dfrac{1}{(k+1)(k+2)} = \dfrac{k}{k+1} + \dfrac{1}{(k+1)(k+2)}$

Simplify the right-hand side:

$$\dfrac{k}{(k+1)} + \dfrac{1}{(k+1)(k+2)} = \dfrac{k(k+2)+1}{(k+1)(k+2)}$$

$$= \dfrac{k^2 + 2k + 1}{(k+1)(k+2)}$$

$$= \dfrac{(k+1)(k+1)}{(k+1)(k+2)}$$

$$= \dfrac{k+1}{k+2}$$

If S_k is true, then S_{k+1} is true. The statement is true for all n.

25. S_1: 2 is a factor of $1^2 - 1 = 0$, since $0 = 2 \cdot 0$.

S_k: 2 is a factor of $k^2 - k$

S_{k+1}: 2 is a factor of $(k+1)^2 - (k+1)$

$$(k+1)^2 - (k-1) = k^2 + 2k + 1 - k - 1$$

$$= k^2 + k$$

$$= k^2 - k + 2k$$

$$= (k^2 - k) + 2k$$

Because we assume S_k is true, we know 2 as a factor of $k^2 - k$. Since 2 is a factor of $2k$, we conclude 2 is factor of the sum $(k^2 + k) + 2k$. If S_k is true, then S_{k+1} is true. The statement is true for all n.

27. S_1: 6 is a factor of $1(1+1)(1+2) = 6$, since $6 = 6 \cdot 1$.

S_k: 6 is a factor of $k(k+1)(k+2)$

S_{k+1}: 6 is a factor of $(k+1)(k+2)(k+3)$

$(k+1)(k+2)(k+3) = k(k+1)(k+2) + 3(k+1)(k+2)$

Because we assume S_k is true, we know 6 as a factor of $k(k+1)(k+2)$. Since either $k+1$ or $k+2$ must be even, the product $(k+1)(k+2)$ is even. Thus 2 is a factor of $(k+1)(k+2)$, and we can conclude that 6 is factor of $3(k+1)(k+2)$ If S_k is true, then S_{k+1} is true.
The statement is true for all n.

29. $S_1: (ab)^1 = a^1 b^1$

$ab = ab$ is true.

$S_k: (ab)^k = a^k b^k$

$S_{k+1}: (ab)^{k+1} = a^{k+1} b^{k+1}$

Multiply both sides of S_k by ab:

$(ab)^k (ab) = a^k b^k (ab)$

$(ab)^{k+1} = a^{k+1} b^{k+1}$

If S_k is true, then S_{k+1} is true.

The statement is true for all n.

31. Answers may vary.

33. $n^2 > 2n + 1$ for $n \geq 3$

$S_3: 3^2 > 2 \cdot 3 + 1$

$9 > 7$

$S_k: k^2 > 2k + 1$ for $k \geq 3$

$S_{k+1}: (k+1)^2 > 2k + 3.$

Add $2k + 1$ to both sides of S_k.

$k^2 + (2k+1) > 2k + 1 + (2k+1)$

Write the left side of the inequalities as the square of a binomial and simplify the right side. $(k+1)^2 > 4k + 2$

Since $4k + 2 > 2k + 3$ for $k \geq 3$, we can

conclude that $(k+1)^2 > 4k + 2 > 2k + 3.$

By the transitive property,

$(k+1)^2 > 2k + 3$

$(k+1)^2 > 2(k+1) + 1$

If S_k is true, then S_{k+1} is true.

The statement is true for all n.

35. $S_1: \dfrac{1}{4} = \dfrac{1}{4}$

$S_2: \dfrac{1}{4} + \dfrac{1}{12} = \dfrac{2}{6} = \dfrac{1}{3}$

$S_3: \dfrac{1}{4} + \dfrac{1}{12} + \dfrac{1}{24} = \dfrac{3}{8}$

$S_4: \dfrac{1}{4} + \dfrac{1}{12} + \dfrac{1}{24} + \dfrac{1}{40} = \dfrac{4}{10} = \dfrac{2}{5}$

$S_5: \dfrac{1}{4} + \dfrac{1}{12} + \dfrac{1}{24} + \dfrac{1}{40} + \dfrac{1}{60} = \dfrac{5}{12}$

$S_n: \dfrac{1}{4} + \dfrac{1}{12} + \dfrac{1}{24} + \cdots + \dfrac{1}{2n(n+1)} = \dfrac{n}{2n+2}$

$S_k: \dfrac{1}{4} + \dfrac{1}{12} + \dfrac{1}{24} + \cdots + \dfrac{1}{2k(k+1)} = \dfrac{k}{2k+2}$

$S_{k+1}: \dfrac{1}{4} + \dfrac{1}{12} + \dfrac{1}{24} + \cdots$

$+ \dfrac{1}{2k(k+1)} + \dfrac{1}{2(k+1)(k+2)}$

$= \dfrac{k+1}{2k+4}$

Add $\dfrac{1}{2(k+1)(k+2)}$ to both sides of S_k:

$\dfrac{1}{4} + \dfrac{1}{12} + \dfrac{1}{24} + \cdots + \dfrac{1}{2k(k+1)} + \dfrac{1}{2(k+1)(k+2)}$

$= \dfrac{k}{2k+2} + \dfrac{1}{2(k+1)(k+2)}$

Simplify the right-hand side:

$\dfrac{k}{2k+2} + \dfrac{1}{2(k+1)(k+2)}$

$= \dfrac{k(k+2)+1}{2(k+1)(k+2)}$

$= \dfrac{k^2 + 2k + 1}{2(k+1)(k+2)}$

$= \dfrac{(k+1)^2}{2(k+1)(k+2)}$

$= \dfrac{k+1}{2k+4}$

If S_k is true, then S_{k+1} is true.

The conjecture is proven.

Section 11.5

Check Point Exercises

1. a. $\dbinom{6}{3} = \dfrac{6!}{3!(6-3)!} = \dfrac{6!}{3!3!} = \dfrac{5 \cdot 4}{1} = 20$

  b. $\dbinom{6}{0} = \dfrac{6!}{0!(6-0)!} = \dfrac{6!}{6!} = 1$

  c. $\dbinom{8}{2} = \dfrac{8!}{2!(8-2)!} = \dfrac{8!}{2!6!} = \dfrac{8 \cdot 7}{2} = 28$

  d. $\dbinom{3}{3} = \dfrac{3!}{3!(3-3)!} = \dfrac{3!}{3!0!} = \dfrac{3!}{3!} = 1$

2. $(x+1)^4 = \dbinom{4}{0}x^4 + \dbinom{4}{1}x^3 + \dbinom{4}{2}x^2 + \dbinom{4}{1}x + \dbinom{4}{0} = x^4 + 4x^3 + 6x^2 + 4x + 1$

3. $(x-2y)^5$

$$= \dbinom{5}{0}x^5(-2y)^0 + \dbinom{5}{1}x^4(-2y)^1 + \dbinom{5}{2}x^3(-2y)^2 + \dbinom{5}{3}x^2(-2y)^3 + \dbinom{5}{4}x(-2y)^4 + \dbinom{5}{5}x^0(-2y)^5$$

$$- x^5 - 5x^4(2y) + 10x^3(4y^2) - 10x^2(8y^3) + 5x(16y^4) - 32y^5$$

$$= x^5 - 10x^4y + 40x^3y^2 - 80x^2y^3 + 80xy^4 - 32y^5$$

4. $(2x+y)^9$

  fifth term $= \dbinom{9}{4}(2x)^5y^4 = \dfrac{9!}{4!5!}(32x^5)y^4 = 4032x^5y^4$

Exercise Set 11.5

1. $\dbinom{8}{3} = \dfrac{8!}{3!(8-3)!} = \dfrac{8 \cdot 7 \cdot 6}{3 \cdot 2 \cdot 1} = 56$

3. $\dbinom{12}{1} = \dfrac{12!}{1!11!} = 12$

5. $\dbinom{6}{6} = \dfrac{6!}{0!6!} = 1$

7. $\dbinom{100}{2} = \dfrac{100!}{2!98!} = \dfrac{100 \cdot 99}{2} = 4950$

9. $(x+2)^3 = \binom{3}{0}x^3 + \binom{3}{1}2x^2 + \binom{3}{2}4x + \binom{3}{3}8$

$\qquad = x^3 + 3x^2 \cdot 2 + 3x \cdot 4 + 8$

$\qquad = x^3 + 6x^2 + 12x + 8$

11. $(3x+y)^3 = \binom{3}{0}27x^3 + \binom{3}{1}9x^2y + \binom{3}{2}3xy^2 + \binom{3}{3}y^3$

$\qquad = 27x^3 + 27x^2y + 9xy^2 + y^3$

13. $(5x-1)^3 = \binom{3}{0}125x^3 - \binom{3}{1}25x^2 + \binom{3}{2}5x - \binom{3}{3}$

$\qquad = 125x^3 - 75x^2 + 15x - 1$

15. $(2x+1)^4 = \binom{4}{0}16x^4 - \binom{4}{1}8x^3 + \binom{4}{2}4x^2 + \binom{4}{3}2x + \binom{4}{4}$

$\qquad = 16x^4 + 32x^3 + 24x^2 + 8x + 1$

17. $(x^2+2y)^4 = \binom{4}{0}(x^2)^4 + \binom{4}{1}(x^2)^3(2y) + \binom{4}{2}(x^2)^2(2y)^2 + \binom{4}{3}(x^2)^1(2y)^3 + \binom{4}{4}(2y)^4$

$\qquad = 1(x^8) + 4(x^6)(2y) + 6(x^4)(4y^2) + 4x^2(8y^3) + 1(16y^4)$

$\qquad = x^8 + 8x^6y + 24x^4y^2 + 32x^2y^3 + 16y^4$

19. $(y-3)^4 = \binom{4}{0}y^4 + \binom{4}{1}y^3(-3) + \binom{4}{2}y^2(-3)^2 + \binom{4}{3}y(-3)^3 + \binom{4}{4}(-3)^4$

$\qquad = y^4 + 4(y^3)(-3) + 6(y^2)(9) + 4(y)(-27) + 81$

$\qquad = y^4 - 12y^3 + 54y^2 - 108y + 81$

21. $(2x^3-1)^4 = \binom{4}{0}(2x^3)^4 + \binom{4}{1}(2x^3)^3(-1) + \binom{4}{2}(2x^3)^2(-1)^2 + \binom{4}{3}(2x^3)(-1)^3 + \binom{4}{4}(-1)^4$

$\qquad = 16x^{12} - 4(8x^9) + 6(4x^6) - 4(2x^3) + 1$

$\qquad = 16x^{12} - 32x^9 + 24x^6 - 8x^3 + 1$

23. $(c+2)^5 = \binom{5}{0}c^5 + \binom{5}{1}c^4(2) + \binom{5}{2}c^3(2^2) + \binom{5}{3}c^2(2^3) + \binom{5}{4}c(2^4) + \binom{5}{5}(2^5)$

$\qquad = c^5 + 5c^4(2) + 10c^3(4) + 10c^2(8) + 5c(16) + 32$

$\qquad = c^5 + 10c^4 + 40c^3 + 80c^2 + 80c + 32$

25. $(x-1)^5 = \binom{5}{0}x^5 - \binom{5}{1}x^4 + \binom{5}{2}x^3 - \binom{5}{3}x^2 + \binom{5}{4}x - \binom{5}{5}$

$\qquad = x^5 - 5x^4 + 10x^3 - 10x^2 + 5x - 1$

27. $(x - 2y)^5 = \binom{5}{0}x^5 - \binom{5}{1}x^4(2y) + \binom{5}{2}x^3(2y)^2 - \binom{5}{3}x^2(2y)^3 + \binom{5}{4}x(2y)^4 - \binom{5}{5}(2y)^5$

$\qquad = x^5 - 10x^4 y + 40x^3 y^2 - 80x^2 y^3 + 80xy^4 - 32y^5$

29. $(2a + b)^6 = \binom{6}{0}(2a)^6 + \binom{6}{1}(2a)^5 b + \binom{6}{2}(2a)^4 b^2 + \binom{6}{3}(2a)^3 b^3 + \binom{6}{4}(2a)^2 b^4 + \binom{6}{5}(2a)b^5 + \binom{6}{6}b^6$

$\qquad = 64a^6 + 6\left(32a^5\right)b + 15\left(16a^4\right)b^2 + 20\left(8a^3\right)b^3 + 15\left(4a^2\right)b^4 + 6(2a)b^5 + b^6$

$\qquad = 64a^6 + 192a^5 b + 240a^4 b^2 + 160a^3 b^3 + 60a^2 b^4 + 12ab^5 + b^6$

31. $(x + 2)^8 = \binom{8}{0}x^8 + \binom{8}{1}2x^7 + \binom{8}{2}2^2 x^6 + \cdots$

$\qquad = x^8 + 16x^7 + 112x^6 + \cdots$

33. $(x - 2y)^{10} = \binom{10}{0}x^{10} - \binom{10}{1}x^9(2y) + \binom{10}{2}x^8(2y)^2 - \cdots$

$\qquad = x^{10} - 20x^9 y + 180x^8 y^2 - \cdots$

35. $\left(x^2 + 1\right)^{16} = \binom{16}{0}\left(x^2\right)^{16} + \binom{16}{1}\left(x^2\right)^{15} + \binom{16}{2}\left(x^2\right)^{14} + \cdots$

$\qquad = x^{32} + 16x^{30} + 120x^{28} + \cdots$

37. $\left(y^3 - 1\right)^{20} - \binom{20}{0}\left(y^3\right)^{20} \binom{20}{1}\left(y^3\right)^{19} + \binom{20}{2}\left(y^3\right)^{18} - \cdots$

$\qquad = y^{60} - 20y^{57} + 190y^{54} - \cdots$

39. $(2x + y)^6$

third term $= \binom{6}{2}(2x)^4(y)^2 = 15\left(16x^4 y^2\right) = 240x^4 y^2$

41. $(x - 1)^9$

fifth term $= \binom{9}{4}x^5(-1)^4 = 126x^5$

43. $\left(x^2 + y^3\right)^8$

sixth term $= \binom{8}{5}\left(x^2\right)^3\left(y^3\right)^5 = 56x^6 y^{15}$

45. $\left(x - \frac{1}{2}\right)^9$

fourth term $= \binom{9}{3}x^6\left(-\frac{1}{2}\right)^3 = 84x^6\left(-\frac{1}{8}\right) = -\frac{21}{2}x^6$

47. $f(t) = 0.002t^3 - 0.9t^2 + 1.27t + 6.76, \ 0 \le t \le 20$

$g(t) = f(t+10) = 0.002(t+10)^3 - 0.9(t+10)^2 + 1.27(t+10) + 6.76$

$(t+10)^3 = \binom{3}{0}t^3 + \binom{3}{1}t^2 \cdot 10 + \binom{3}{2}t \cdot 10^2 + \binom{3}{3}10^3 = t^3 + 30t^2 + 300t + 1000$

$(t+10)^2 = \binom{2}{0}t^2 + \binom{2}{1}t \cdot 10 + \binom{2}{2}10^2 = t^2 + 20t + 100$

$g(t) = 0.002\left(t^3 + 30t^2 + 300t + 1000\right) - 0.9\left(t^2 + 20t + 100\right) + 1.27(t+10) + 6.76$

$= 0.002t^3 + 0.06t^2 + 0.6t + 2 - 0.9t^2 - 18t - 90 + 1.27t + 12.7 + 6.76$

$= 0.002t^3 - 0.84t^2 - 16.13t - 68.54$

49.–57. Answers may vary.

59. Exercises 1 and 3   Exercises 5 and 7

```
8 nCr 3
              56
12 nCr 1
              12
■
```

```
6 nCr 6
               1
100 nCr 2
            4950
■
```

61. $f_1(x) = (x+1)^4$

$f_2(x) = x^4$

$f_3(x) = x^4 + 4x^3$

$f_4(x) = x^4 + 4x^3 + 6x^2$

$f_5(x) = x^4 + 4x^3 + 6x^2 + 4x$

$f_6(x) = x^4 + 4x^3 + 6x^2 + 4x + 1$

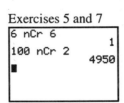

f_2, f_3, f_4, and f_5 are approaching $f_1 = f_6$.

63. $f_1(x) = (x-2)^4$

$= \binom{4}{0}x^4 + \binom{4}{1}x^3(-2) + \binom{4}{2}x^2(-2)^2 + \binom{4}{3}x(-2)^3 + \binom{4}{4}(-2)^4$

$= x^4 + 4x^3(-2) + 6x^2(4) + 4x(-8) + 16$

$= x^4 - 8x^3 + 24x^2 - 32x + 16$

65. Exercises 9, 11 and 13

Exercises 15 and 17

67. $\left(x^2 + x + 1\right)^3 = \left[x^2 + (x+1)\right]^3$

$$= \binom{3}{0}\left(x^2\right)^3 + \binom{3}{1}\left(x^2\right)^2(x+1) + \binom{3}{2}x^2(x+1)^2 + \binom{3}{3}(x+1)^3$$

$$= x^6 + 3x^4(x+1) + 3x^2\left(x^2 + 2x + 1\right) + x^3 + 3x^2 + 3x + 1$$

$$= x^6 + 3x^5 + 3x^4 + 3x^4 + 6x^3 + 3x^2 + x^3 + 3x^2 + 3x + 1$$

$$= x^6 + 3x^5 + 6x^4 + 7x^3 + 6x^2 + 3x + 1$$

69.
$$\binom{n}{r} = \frac{n!}{r!(n-r)!}$$

$$\binom{n}{n-r} = \frac{n!}{(n-r)!\left[n-(n-r)\right]!} = \frac{n!}{(n-r)!\,r!} = \binom{n}{r}$$

71. a. S_1: $(a+b)^1 = \binom{1}{0}a^1 + \binom{1}{1}a^{1-1}b = a + b$

    b. S_k: $(a+b)^k = \binom{k}{0}a^k + \binom{k}{1}a^{k-1}b + \binom{k}{2}a^{k-2}b^2 + \cdots + \binom{k}{k-1}ab^{k-1} + \binom{k}{k}b^k$

         S_{k+1}: $(a+b)^{k+1} = \binom{k+1}{0}a^{k+1} + \binom{k+1}{1}a^k b + \binom{k+1}{2}a^{k-1}b^2 + \cdots + \binom{k+1}{k}ab^k + \binom{k+1}{k+1}b^{k+1}$

c. $(a+b)(a+b)^k$

$$(a+b)^{k+1} = \binom{k}{0}a^{k+1} + \binom{k}{0}a^k b + \binom{k}{1}a^k b + \binom{k}{1}a^{k-1}b^2 + \binom{k}{2}a^{k-1}b^2 + \binom{k}{2}a^{k-2}b^3 + \cdots$$

$$+ \binom{k}{k-1}a^2 b^{k-1} + \binom{k}{k-1}ab^k + \binom{k}{k}ab^k + \binom{k}{k}b^{k+1}$$

d. $(a+b)^{k+1} = \binom{k}{0}a^{k+1} + \left[\binom{k}{0}+\binom{k}{1}\right]a^k b + \left[\binom{k}{1}+\binom{k}{2}\right]a^{k-1}b^2 + \left[\binom{k}{2}+\binom{k}{3}\right]a^{k-2}b^3 + \cdots$

$$+ \left[\binom{k}{k-1}+\binom{k}{k}\right]ab^k + \binom{k}{k}b^{k+1}$$

e. $(a+b)^{k+1} = \binom{k}{0}a^{k+1} + \binom{k+1}{1}a^k b + \binom{k+1}{2}a^{k-1}b^2 + \binom{k+1}{3}a^{k-2}b^3 + \cdots + \binom{k+1}{k}ab^k + \binom{k}{k}b^{k+1}$

f. $\binom{k}{0} = \binom{k+1}{0}$ because both equal 1. $\binom{k}{k} = \binom{k+1}{k+1}$ also because both equal 1.

$$S_{k+1}: (a+b)^{k+1} = \binom{k+1}{0}a^{k+1} + \binom{k+1}{1}a^k b + \binom{k+1}{2}a^{k-1}b^2 + \cdots + \binom{k+1}{k}ab^k + \binom{k+1}{k+1}b^{k+1}$$

Section 11.6

Check Point Exercises

1. We use the Fundamental Counting Principal to find the number of ways a one-topping pizza can be ordered. Multiply the number of choices for each of the three groups. $3 \cdot 4 \cdot 6 = 72$ pizzas
   There are 72 different ways of ordering a one-topping pizza.

2. We use the Fundamental Counting Principal to find the number of ways we can answer the questions. Multiply the number of choices, 3, for each of the six questions. $3 \cdot 3 \cdot 3 \cdot 3 \cdot 3 \cdot 3 = 3^6 = 729$ ways
   There are 729 ways of answering the questions.

3. We use the Fundamental Counting Principal to find the number of different license plates that can be manufactured. Multiply the number of different letters, 26, for the first two places and the number of different digits, 10, for the next three places. $26 \cdot 26 \cdot 10 \cdot 10 \cdot 10 = 26^2 \cdot 1000 = 676,000$ plates
   There are 676,000 different license plates possible.

4. Your group is choosing $r = 4$ officers from a group of $n = 7$ people. The order in which the officers are chosen matters because the four officers to be chosen have different responsibilities. Thus, we are looking for the number of permutations of 7 things taken 4 at a time.
   We use the formula $_nP_r = \dfrac{n!}{(n-r)!}$ with $n = 7$ and $r = 4$. $_7P_4 = \dfrac{7!}{(7-4)!} = \dfrac{7!}{3!} = 840.$
   Thus, there are·840 different ways of filling the four offices.

5. Because you are using all six of your books in every possible arrangement, you are arranging $r = 6$ books from a group of $n = 6$ books. Thus, we are looking for the number of permutations of 6 things taken 6 at a time. We use the formula

$$_nP_r = \frac{n!}{(n-r)!} \text{ with } n = 6 \text{ and } r = 6.$$

$$_6P_6 = \frac{6!}{(6-6)!} = \frac{6!}{0!} = 6! = 720.$$

There are 720 different possible permutations. Thus, you can arrange the books in 720 ways.

6. a. The order does not matter; this is a combination.

  b. Since what place each runner finishes matters, this is a permutation.

7. The order in which the four people are selected does not matter. This is a problem of selecting $r = 4$ people from a group of $n = 10$ people. We are looking for the number of combinations of 10 things taken 4 at a time. We use the formula

$$_nC_r = \frac{n!}{(n-r)! \; r!} \text{ with } n = 10 \text{ and } r = 4.$$

$$_{10}C_4 = \frac{10!}{(10-4)!4!} = \frac{10!}{6!4!} = \frac{10 \cdot 9 \cdot 8 \cdot 7 \cdot 6!}{6! \cdot 4 \cdot 3 \cdot 2 \cdot 1}$$

$$= \frac{10 \cdot 9 \cdot 8 \cdot 7}{4 \cdot 3 \cdot 2 \cdot 1} = 210$$

Thus, 210 committees of 4 people each can be found from 10 people at the conference on acupuncture.

8. Because the order in which the 4 cards are dealt does not matter, this is a problem involving combinations. We are looking for the number of combinations of $n = 16$ cards drawn $r = 4$ at a time. We use the formula

$$_nC_r = \frac{n!}{(n-r)! \; r!} \text{ with } n = 16 \text{ and } r = 4.$$

$$_{16}C_4 = \frac{16!}{(16-4)!4!} = \frac{16!}{12!4!} = \frac{16 \cdot 15 \cdot 14 \cdot 13 \cdot 12!}{12! \cdot 4 \cdot 3 \cdot 2 \cdot 1}$$

$$= 1820$$

Thus, there are 1820 different 4-card hands possible.

Exercise Set 11.6

1. $_9P_4 = \frac{9!}{5!} = 3024$

3. $_8P_5 = \frac{8!}{3!} = 8 \cdot 7 \cdot 6 \cdot 5 \cdot 4 = 6720$

5. $_6P_6 = \frac{6!}{0!} = 720$

7. $_8P_0 = \frac{8!}{8!} = 1$

9. $_9C_5 = \frac{9!}{4!5!} = \frac{9 \cdot 8 \cdot 7 \cdot 6}{4 \cdot 3 \cdot 2 \cdot 1} = \frac{3 \cdot 7 \cdot 6}{1} = 126$

11. $_{11}C_4 = \frac{11!}{7!4!} = \frac{11 \cdot 10 \cdot 9 \cdot 8}{4 \cdot 3 \cdot 2 \cdot 1} = \frac{11 \cdot 10 \cdot 3}{1} = 330$

13. $_7C_7 = \frac{7!}{0!7!} = 1$

15. $_5C_0 = \frac{5!}{5!0!} = 1$

17. combination; The order in which the volunteers are chosen does not matter.

19. permutation; The order of the letters matters because ABCD is not the same as BADC.

21. $9 \cdot 3 = 27$ ways

23. $2 \cdot 4 \cdot 5 = 40$ ways

25. $3^5 = 243$ ways

27. $8 \cdot 2 \cdot 9 = 144$ area codes

29. $5 \cdot 4 \cdot 3 \cdot 2 \cdot 1 \cdot 1 = 120$ ways

31. $1 \cdot 3 \cdot 2 \cdot 1 \cdot 1 = 6$ paragraphs

33. $_{10}P_3 = \frac{10!}{7!3!} = 10 \cdot 9 \cdot 8 = 720$ ways

35. $_{13}P_7 = \dfrac{13!}{6!} = 13 \cdot 12 \cdot 11 \cdot 10 \cdot 9 \cdot 8 \cdot 7$
$\qquad = 8,648,640 \text{ ways}$

37. $_6P_3 = \dfrac{6!}{3!} = 6 \cdot 5 \cdot 4 = 120 \text{ ways}$

39. $_9P_5 = \dfrac{9!}{4!} = 9 \cdot 8 \cdot 7 \cdot 6 \cdot 5 = 15,120 \text{ lineups}$

41. $_6C_3 = \dfrac{6!}{3!3!} = \dfrac{6 \cdot 5 \cdot 4}{3 \cdot 2 \cdot 1} = 20 \text{ ways}$

43. $_{12}C_4 = \dfrac{12!}{8!4!} = \dfrac{12 \cdot 11 \cdot 10 \cdot 9}{4 \cdot 3 \cdot 2 \cdot 1}$
$\qquad = 495 \text{ collections}$

45. $_{17}C_8 = \dfrac{17!}{9!8!} = \dfrac{17 \cdot 16 \cdot 15 \cdot 14 \cdot 13 \cdot 12 \cdot 11 \cdot 10}{8 \cdot 7 \cdot 6 \cdot 5 \cdot 4 \cdot 3 \cdot 2 \cdot 1}$
$\qquad = 24,310 \text{ groups}$

47. $_{49}C_6 = \dfrac{49!}{43!6!} = 13,983,816 \text{ selections}$

49. $_6P_4 = \dfrac{6!}{2!} = 6 \cdot 5 \cdot 4 \cdot 3 = 360 \text{ ways}$

51. $_{13}C_6 = \dfrac{13!}{7!6!} = \dfrac{13 \cdot 12 \cdot 11 \cdot 10 \cdot 9 \cdot 8}{6 \cdot 5 \cdot 4 \cdot 3 \cdot 2 \cdot 1}$
$\qquad = 1716 \text{ ways}$

53. $_{20}C_3 = \dfrac{20!}{17!3!} = \dfrac{20 \cdot 19 \cdot 18}{3 \cdot 2 \cdot 1} = 1140 \text{ ways}$

55. $_7P_4 = \dfrac{7!}{3!} = 840 \text{ passwords}$

57. $_{15}P_3 = \dfrac{15!}{12!} = 15 \cdot 14 \cdot 13 = 2730 \text{ cones}$

59.–65. Answers may vary.

67. Answers may vary.

Exercises 1 and 3

```
9 nPr 4
                 3024
8 nPr 5
                 6720
```

Exercises 5 and 7

```
6 nPr 6
                  720
8 nPr 0
                    1
■
```

69. a. False; the number of ways is $_{10}C_4$.

  b. False;
$$_nP_r = \frac{n!}{(n-r)!} > \frac{n!}{(n-r)!\,r!} = {_nC_r} \text{ if } r>1.$$

  c. True; $_7P_3 = \dfrac{7!}{4!} = 3! \dfrac{7!}{4!3!} = 3!\,_7C_3$

  d. False;
the number of ways is $20 \cdot 19 = {_{20}P_2}$.

  (c) is true.

71. $2 \cdot 6 \cdot 6 \cdot 2 = 144 \text{ numbers}$

Section 11.7

Check Point Exercises

1. $P(\text{seven hours sleep})$
$= \dfrac{\text{number of Americans who sleep 7 hours}}{\text{total number of Americans}}$
$= \dfrac{82.5}{275} = 0.3$
The empirical probability of randomly
selecting an American who gets seven hours
of sleep on a typical night is 0.3.

2. The sample space of equally likely outcomes is $S = \{1, 2, 3, 4, 5, 6\}$. There are six outcomes in the sample space, so $n(S) = 6$. The event of getting a number greater than 4 can be represented by $E = \{5, 6\}$. There are two outcomes in this event, so $n(E) = 2$. The probability of rolling a number greater than 4 is $P(E) = \dfrac{n(E)}{n(S)} = \dfrac{2}{6} = \dfrac{1}{3}$.

3. We have $n(S) = 36$. The phrase "getting a sum of 5" describes the event $E = \{(1, 4), (2, 3), (3, 2), (4, 1)\}$. This event has 4 outcomes, so $n(E) = 4$. Thus, the probability of getting a sum of 5 is

$$P(E) = \frac{n(E)}{n(S)} = \frac{4}{36} = \frac{1}{9}.$$

4. Let E be the event of being dealt a king. Because there are 4 kings in the deck, the event of being dealt a king can occur in 4 ways, i.e., $n(E) = 4$. With 52 cards in the deck, $n(S) = 52$. The probability of being dealt a king is $P(E) = \dfrac{n(E)}{n(S)} = \dfrac{4}{52} = \dfrac{1}{13}$.

5. Because the order of the six numbers does not matter, this is a situation involving combinations. With one lottery ticket, there is only one way of winning so $n(E) = 1$. Using the combinations formula

$${}_nC_r = \frac{n!}{(n-r)!\,r!} \text{ to find the number of}$$

outcomes in the sample space, we are selecting $r = 5$ numbers from a collection of $n = 30$ numbers.

$$\begin{aligned}
{}_{30}C_5 &= \frac{30!}{(30-5)!\,5!} = \frac{30!}{25!\,5!} \\
&= \frac{30 \cdot 29 \cdot 28 \cdot 27 \cdot 26 \cdot 25!}{25!\,5 \cdot 4 \cdot 3 \cdot 2 \cdot 1} \\
&= 142{,}506.
\end{aligned}$$

So $n(S) = 142{,}506$.
If a person buys one lottery ticket, the probability of winning is

$$\begin{aligned}
P(E) &= \frac{n(E)}{n(S)} = \frac{1}{142{,}506} \\
&\approx 0.00000702.
\end{aligned}$$

The probability of winning the state lottery is 0.00000702.

6. $P(\text{not winning}) = 1 - P(\text{winning})$

$$\begin{aligned}
&= 1 - \frac{1}{142{,}506} \\
&= \frac{142{,}505}{142{,}506} \approx 0.999993
\end{aligned}$$

The probability of not winning is about 0.999993.

7. We find the probability that either of these mutually exclusive events will occur by adding their individual probabilities.
$P(4 \text{ or } 5) = P(4) + P(5)$

$$= \frac{1}{6} + \frac{1}{6} = \frac{2}{6} = \frac{1}{3}$$

The probability of selecting a 4 or a 5 is $\frac{1}{3}$.

8. It is possible for the pointer to land on a number that is odd and less than 5. Two of the numbers, 1 and 3, are odd and less than 5. These events are not mutually exclusive. The probability of landing on a number that is odd and less than 5 is
$P(\text{odd or less than 5})$
$\quad P(\text{odd}) + P(\text{less than 5})$
$\quad - P(\text{odd and less than 5})$

$$\begin{aligned}
&= \frac{4}{8} + \frac{4}{8} - \frac{2}{8} \\
&= \frac{6}{8} = \frac{3}{4}
\end{aligned}$$

The probability that the pointer will stop on an odd number or a number less than 5 is $\frac{3}{4}$.

9. The group is comprised of 25 baboons. It is possible to select a baboon that enjoys picking fleas off of its neighbors that also screeches wildly. These events are not mutually exclusive.
$P(\text{picking or screeching})$
$= P(\text{picking}) + P(\text{screeching})$
$\quad - P(\text{picking and screeching})$

$$= \frac{18}{25} + \frac{16}{25} - \frac{10}{25} = \frac{24}{25}.$$

10. The wheel has 38 equally likely outcomes and 2 are green. Thus, the probability of a green occurring on a play is $\frac{2}{38}$, or $\frac{1}{19}$. The result that occurs on each play is independent of all previous results. Thus,
P (green and green)
$= P$ (green) $\cdot P$ (green)
$= \dfrac{1}{19} \cdot \dfrac{1}{19} = \dfrac{1}{361} \approx 0.003$.
The probability of green occurring on two consecutive plays is $\frac{1}{361}$.

11. If two or more events are independent, we can find the probability of them all occurring by multiplying the probabilities. The probability of a baby boy is $\frac{1}{2}$, so the probability of having four boys in a row is P (4 boys in a row)
$= \dfrac{1}{2} \cdot \dfrac{1}{2} \cdot \dfrac{1}{2} \cdot \dfrac{1}{2}$
$= \dfrac{1}{16}$.

Exercise Set 11.7

1. $P(2 \text{ people}) = \dfrac{29,780,000}{70,241,000} \approx 0.42$

3. $P(\text{African}) = \dfrac{761}{5926} \approx 0.13$

5. $P(R) = \dfrac{n(E)}{n(S)} = \dfrac{1}{6}$

7. $P(E) = \dfrac{n(E)}{n(S)} = \dfrac{3}{6} = \dfrac{1}{2}$

9. $P(E) = \dfrac{n(E)}{n(S)} = \dfrac{2}{6} = \dfrac{1}{3}$

11. $P(E) = \dfrac{n(E)}{n(S)} = \dfrac{4}{52} = \dfrac{1}{13}$

13. $P(E) = \dfrac{n(E)}{n(S)} = \dfrac{`12}{52} = \dfrac{3}{13}$

15. $P(E) = \dfrac{n(E)}{n(S)} = \dfrac{1}{4}$

17. $P(E) = \dfrac{n(E)}{n(S)} = \dfrac{7}{8}$

19. $P(E) = \dfrac{n(E)}{n(S)} = \dfrac{3}{36} = \dfrac{1}{12}$

21. Buying 1 ticket:
$P(E) = \dfrac{n(E)}{n(S)} = \dfrac{1}{{}_{51}C_6} = \dfrac{1}{18,009,460}$
Buying 100 tickets:
$P(E) = \dfrac{100}{18,009,460} = \dfrac{5}{900,473}$

23. **a.** ${}_{52}C_5 = \dfrac{52!}{47!5!}$
$= \dfrac{52 \cdot 51 \cdot 50 \cdot 49 \cdot 48}{5 \cdot 4 \cdot 3 \cdot 2 \cdot 1} = 2,598,960$

   b. ${}_{13}C_5 = \dfrac{13!}{8!5!} = \dfrac{13 \cdot 12 \cdot 11 \cdot 10 \cdot 9}{5 \cdot 4 \cdot 3 \cdot 2 \cdot 1} = 1287$

   c. $P(E) = \dfrac{n(E)}{n(S)} = \dfrac{1287}{2,598,960} \approx 0.0005$

25. $P(\text{under } 5) = \dfrac{18,987}{274,634}$
$P(\text{not under } 5) = 1 - P(\text{under } 5)$
$= \dfrac{255,647}{274,634} \approx 0.93$

27. $P(25 - 34) = \dfrac{37,233}{274,634}$
$P(\text{not } 25 - 34) = 1 - P(25 - 34)$
$= \dfrac{237,401}{274,634} \approx 0.86$

29. $P(E) = P(14 - 17) + P(18 - 24)$
$= \dfrac{15,752}{274,634} + \dfrac{26,258}{274,634}$
$= \dfrac{42,010}{274,634} \approx 0.15$

31. $P(E) = P(2) + P(3)$

$$= \frac{4}{52} + \frac{4}{52} = \frac{8}{52} = \frac{2}{13}$$

33. $P(E) = P(\text{even}) + P(\text{less than } 5)$
$\qquad - P(\text{even and less than } 5)$

$$= \frac{3}{6} + \frac{4}{6} - \frac{2}{6} = \frac{5}{6}$$

35. $P(E) = P(7) + P(\text{red}) - P(\text{red } 7)$

$$= \frac{4}{52} + \frac{26}{52} - \frac{2}{52} = \frac{28}{52} = \frac{7}{13}$$

37. $P(E) = P(\text{odd}) + P(\text{less than } 6)$
$\qquad - P(\text{odd and less than } 6)$

$$= \frac{4}{8} + \frac{5}{8} - \frac{3}{8} = \frac{6}{8} = \frac{3}{4}$$

39. $P(E)$
$= P(\text{professor}) + P(\text{male}) - P(\text{male professor})$

$$= \frac{19}{40} + \frac{22}{40} - \frac{8}{40} = \frac{33}{40}$$

41. $P(E) = P(2) \cdot P(3) = \frac{1}{6} \cdot \frac{1}{6} = \frac{1}{36}$

43. $P(E) = P(\text{even}) \cdot P(\text{greater than } 2)$

$$= \frac{3}{6} \cdot \frac{4}{6} = \frac{1}{2} \cdot \frac{2}{3} = \frac{1}{3}$$

45. $P(E) = \left(\frac{1}{2}\right)^6 = \frac{1}{64}$

47. a. $P(E) = \frac{1}{16} \cdot \frac{1}{16} = \frac{1}{256}$

b. $P(E) = \left(\frac{1}{16}\right)^3 = \frac{1}{4096}$

c. $P(E) = \left(\frac{15}{16}\right)^{10}$

d. $1 - \left(\frac{15}{16}\right)^{10}$

49.–59. Answers may vary.

Review Exercises

1. $a_n = 7n - 4$
$a_1 = 7 - 4 = 3$
$a_2 = 14 - 4 = 10$
$a_3 = 21 - 4 = 17$
$a_4 = 28 - 4 = 24$
The first four terms are 3, 10, 17, and 24.

2. $a_n = (-1)^n \dfrac{n+2}{n+1}$

$a_1 = (-1)^1 \dfrac{1+2}{1+1} = -\dfrac{3}{2}$

$a_2 = (-1)^2 \dfrac{2+2}{2+1} = \dfrac{4}{3}$

$a_3 = (-1)^3 \dfrac{3+2}{3+1} = -\dfrac{5}{4}$

$a_4 = (-1)^4 \dfrac{4+2}{4+1} = \dfrac{6}{5}$

The first four terms are $-\dfrac{3}{2}, \dfrac{4}{3}, -\dfrac{5}{4},$ and $\dfrac{6}{5}.$

3. $a_n = \dfrac{1}{(n-1)!}$

$a_1 = \dfrac{1}{0!} = 1$

$a_2 = \dfrac{1}{1!} = 1$

$a_3 = \dfrac{1}{2!} = \dfrac{1}{2}$

$a_4 = \dfrac{1}{3!} = \dfrac{1}{6}$

The first four terms are $1, 1, \dfrac{1}{2},$ and $\dfrac{1}{6}.$

4. $a_n = \dfrac{(-1)^{n+1}}{2^n}$

$a_1 = \dfrac{(-1)^2}{2^1} = \dfrac{1}{2}$

$a_2 = \dfrac{(-1)^3}{2^2} = -\dfrac{1}{4}$

$a_3 = \dfrac{(-1)^4}{2^3} = \dfrac{1}{8}$

$a_4 = \dfrac{(-1)^5}{2^4} = -\dfrac{1}{16}$

The first four terms are $\dfrac{1}{2}$, $-\dfrac{1}{4}$, $\dfrac{1}{8}$, and $-\dfrac{1}{16}$.

5. $a_1 = 9$ and $a_n = \dfrac{2}{3a_{n-1}}$

$a_1 = 9$

$a_2 = \dfrac{2}{3 \cdot 9} = \dfrac{2}{27}$

$a_3 = \dfrac{2}{3} \cdot \dfrac{27}{2} = \dfrac{54}{6} = 9$

$a_4 = \dfrac{2}{3 \cdot 9} = \dfrac{2}{27}$

The first four terms are 9, $\dfrac{2}{27}$, 9, and $\dfrac{2}{27}$.

6. $a_1 = 4$ and $a_n = 2a_{n-1} + 3$

$a_1 = 4$

$a_2 = 2 \cdot 4 + 3 = 8 + 3 = 11$

$a_3 = 2 \cdot 11 + 3 = 22 + 3 = 25$

$a_4 = 2 \cdot 25 + 3 = 50 + 3 = 53$

The first four terms are 4, 11, 25, and 53.

7. $\dfrac{40!}{4! \cdot 38!} = \dfrac{40 \cdot 39 \cdot 38!}{4 \cdot 3 \cdot 2 \cdot 1 \cdot 38!} = 65$

8. $\displaystyle\sum_{i=1}^{5} \left(2i^2 - 3\right) = (2 - 3) + \left(2 \cdot 2^2 - 3\right) + \left(2 \cdot 3^2 - 3\right) + \left(2 \cdot 4^2 - 3\right) + \left(2 \cdot 5^2 - 3\right)$

$= -1 + 5 + 15 + 29 + 47$

$= 95$

9. $\displaystyle\sum_{i=0}^{4}(-3)^{i+1}i!=(-1)^1 0!+(-1)^2 1!+(-1)^3 2!+(-1)^4 3!+(-1)^5 4!$

$$=-1+1-2+6-24$$
$$=-20$$

10. $\dfrac{1}{3}+\dfrac{2}{4}+\dfrac{3}{5}+\cdots+\dfrac{15}{17}=\displaystyle\sum_{i=1}^{15}\dfrac{i}{i+2}$

11. $4^3+5^3+6^3+\cdots+13^3=\displaystyle\sum_{i=1}^{10}(i+3)^3$

12. $a_1=7,\, d=4$
The first six terms are 7, 11, 15, 19, 23, and 27.

13. $a_1=-4,\, d=-5$
The first six terms are $-4,\,-9,\,-14,\,-19,\,-24,$ and -29.

14. $a_1=\dfrac{3}{2},\, d=-\dfrac{1}{2}$
The first six terms are $\dfrac{3}{2},\,1,\,\dfrac{1}{2},\,0,\,-\dfrac{1}{2},$ and -1.

15. $a_{n+1}=a_n+5,\, a_1=-2$
The first six terms are $-2,\,3,\,8,\,13,\,18,$ and 23.

16. $a_1=5,\, d=3$
$a_n=5+(n-1)3$
$a_6=5+(5)3=20$

17. $a_1=-8,\, d=-2$
$a_n=-8+(n-1)(-2)$
$a_{12}=-8+11(-2)=-30$

18. $a_1=14,\, d=-4$
$a_n=14+(n-1)(-4)$
$a_{14}=14+(13)(-4)=-38$

19. $-7,-3,1,5,\ldots$
$d=-3-(-7)=4$
$a_n=-7+(n-1)(4)$
$a_n=4n-11$
$a_{20}=4(20)-11$
$a_{20}=69$

20. $a_1 = 200, \, d = -20$

$a_n = 200 + (n-1)(-20)$

$a_n = 220 - 20n$

$a_{20} = 220 - 20(20)$

$a_{20} = -180$

21. $a_n = a_{n-1} - 5, \, a_1 = 3$

$d = -5$

$a_n = 3 + (n-1)(-5) = 3 - 5n + 5$

$a_n = 8 - 5n$

$a_{20} = 8 - 5(20) = -92$

22.   5, 12, 19, 26, ...

$d = 7$

$a_n = 5 + (n-1)(7)$

$a_{22} = 5 + 21(7) = 152$

$S_{22} = \dfrac{22}{2}(5 + 152) = 1727$

23. $-6, -3, 0, 3, ...$

$d = 3$

$a_n = -6 + (n-1)3$

$a_{15} = -6 + (14)3 = 36$

$S_{15} = \dfrac{15}{2}(-6 + 36) = 225$

24. $3 + 6 + 9 + \cdots + 300$

$S_{100} = \dfrac{100}{2}(3 + 300) = 15,150$

25. $\displaystyle\sum_{i=1}^{16}(3i + 2)$

$a_1 = 3 + 2 = 5$

$a_{16} = 3(16) + 2 = 50$

$S_{16} = \dfrac{16}{2}(5 + 50) = 440$

26. $\displaystyle\sum_{i=1}^{25}(-2i + 6)$

$a_1 = -2 + 6 = 4$

$a_{25} = -2(25) + 6 = -44$

$S_{25} = \dfrac{25}{2}(4 - 44) = -500$

27. $\displaystyle\sum_{i=1}^{30} -5i$

$a_1 = -5$

$a_{30} = -5(30) = -150$

$S_{30} = \dfrac{30}{2}(-5 - 150) = -2325$

28. a. $d = -0.4118$

$a_n = 1043.04 + (n-1)(-0.4118)$

$a_n = 1043.4518 - 0.4118n$

   b. $n = 2010 - 1910 = 100$

$a_{100} = 1043.4518 - 0.4118(90)$

$a = 1002.2718$

1002.2718 seconds

29. $a_n = 31,500 + (n-1)2300$

$a_{10} = 31,500 + (9)2300 = 52,200$

$S_{10} = \dfrac{10}{2}(31,500 + 52,200) = 418,500$

The total salary is \$418, 500.

30. $a_n = 25 + (n-1)$

$a_{35} = 25 + 34 = 59$

$S_{35} = \dfrac{35}{2}(25 + 59) = 1470$

There are 1470 seats.

31. $a_1 = 3, \, r = 2$

The first five terms are 3, 6, 12, 24, and 48.

32. $a_1 = \dfrac{1}{2}, \ r = \dfrac{1}{2}$

The first five terms are

$\dfrac{1}{2}, \dfrac{1}{4}, \dfrac{1}{8}, \dfrac{1}{16},$ and $\dfrac{1}{32}$.

33. $a_1 = 16, \ r = -\dfrac{1}{2}$

The first five terms are
$16, -8, 4, -2,$ and 1.

34. $a_n = -5a_{n-1}, \ a_1 = -1$

The first five terms are $-1, 5, -25, 125,$
and -625.

35. $a_1 = 2, \ r = 3$

$a_n = 2 \cdot 3^{n-1}$

$a_7 = 2 \cdot 3^6 = 1458$

36. $a_1 = 16, \ r = \dfrac{1}{2}$

$a_n = 16 \left(\dfrac{1}{2} \right)^{n-1}$

$a_6 = 16 \left(\dfrac{1}{2} \right)^5 = \dfrac{16}{32} = \dfrac{1}{2}$

37. $a_1 = -3, \ r = 2$

$a_n = -3 \cdot 2^{n-1}$

$a_5 = -3 \cdot 2^4 = -48$

38. $1, 2, 4, 8, \ldots$

$a_1 = 1, \ r = \dfrac{2}{1} = 2$

$a_n = 2^{n-1}$

$a_8 = 2^7 = 128$

39. $100, 10, 1, \dfrac{1}{10}, \ldots$

$a_1 = 100, \ r = \dfrac{10}{100} = \dfrac{1}{10}$

$a_n = 100 \left(\dfrac{1}{10} \right)^{n-1}$

$a_8 = 100 \left(\dfrac{1}{10} \right)^7 = \dfrac{1}{100,000}$

40. $12, -4, \dfrac{4}{3}, -\dfrac{4}{9}, \ldots$

$a_1 = 12, \ r = -\dfrac{4}{12} = -\dfrac{1}{3}$

$a_n = 12 \left(-\dfrac{1}{3} \right)^{n-1}$

$a_8 = 12 \left(-\dfrac{1}{3} \right)^7 = -\dfrac{4}{729}$

41. $5, -15, 45, -135, \ldots$

$r = \dfrac{-15}{5} = -3$

$S_{15} = \dfrac{5 \left[1 - (-3)^{15} \right]}{1 - (-3)} = 17,936,135$

42. $\dfrac{1}{3}, \dfrac{1}{9}, \dfrac{1}{27}, \dfrac{1}{81}, \ldots$

$r = \dfrac{1}{3}$

$S_7 = \dfrac{\frac{1}{3} \left[1 - \left(\frac{1}{3} \right)^7 \right]}{1 - \frac{1}{3}} = \dfrac{\frac{1}{3} \left(\frac{2186}{2187} \right)}{\frac{2}{3}} = \dfrac{1093}{2187}$

43. $\displaystyle\sum_{i=1}^{6} 5^i$

$r = 5, \ a_1 = 5$

$S_6 = \dfrac{5(1 - 5^6)}{1 - 5} = \dfrac{5(-15624)}{-4} = 19,530$

44. $\displaystyle\sum_{i=1}^{7} 3(-2)^i$

$a_1 = -6, \; r = -2$

$$S_7 = \frac{-6\left[1-(-2)^7\right]}{1-(-2)} = \frac{-6(129)}{3} = -258$$

45. $\displaystyle\sum_{i=1}^{5} 2\left(\tfrac{1}{4}\right)^{i-1}$

$a_1 = 2, \; r = \dfrac{1}{4}$

$$S_5 = \frac{2\left[1-\left(\tfrac{1}{4}\right)^5\right]}{1-\tfrac{1}{4}} = \frac{2\left(\tfrac{1023}{1024}\right)}{\tfrac{3}{4}} = \frac{341}{128}$$

46. $9 + 3 + 1 + \dfrac{1}{3} + \cdots$

$a_1 = 9, \; r = \dfrac{1}{3}$

$$S_\infty = \frac{9}{1-\tfrac{1}{3}} = \frac{9}{\tfrac{2}{3}} = 9 \cdot \frac{3}{2} = \frac{27}{2}$$

47. $2 - 1 + \dfrac{1}{2} - \dfrac{1}{4} + \cdots$

$a_1 = 2, \; r = -\dfrac{1}{2}$

$$S_\infty = \frac{2}{1-\left(-\tfrac{1}{2}\right)} = \frac{2}{\tfrac{3}{2}} = \frac{4}{3}$$

48. $-6 + 4 - \dfrac{8}{3} + \dfrac{16}{9} - \cdots$

$a_1 = -6, \; r = -\dfrac{2}{3}$

$$S_\infty = \frac{-6}{1-\left(-\tfrac{2}{3}\right)} = \frac{-6}{\tfrac{5}{3}} = -\frac{18}{5}$$

49. $\displaystyle\sum_{i=1}^{\infty} 5(0.8)^i = 4 + 3.2 + \cdots$

$r = 0.8$

$$S_\infty = \frac{4}{1-0.8} = 20$$

50. $0.\overline{6} = 0.6 + 0.06 + 0.006 + \cdots$

$a_1 = \dfrac{6}{10}, \; r = \dfrac{1}{10}$

$$S_\infty = \frac{\tfrac{6}{10}}{1-\tfrac{1}{10}} = \frac{\tfrac{6}{10}}{\tfrac{9}{10}} = \frac{6}{9} = \frac{2}{3}$$

51. $0.\overline{47} = 0.47 + 0.0047 + 0.000047 + \cdots$

$a_1 = \dfrac{47}{100}, \; r = \dfrac{1}{100}$

$$S_\infty = \frac{\tfrac{47}{100}}{1-\tfrac{1}{100}} = \frac{\tfrac{47}{100}}{\tfrac{99}{100}} = \frac{47}{99}$$

52. $a_1 = 32{,}000, \; r = 1.06$

$a_6 = 32{,}000(1.06)^5 \approx 42{,}823.22$

The sixth year salary is \$42,823.22.

$$S_6 = \frac{32{,}000\left(1-1.06^6\right)}{1-1.06} = \frac{32{,}000\left(1-1.06^6\right)}{-0.06}$$
$$\approx 223{,}210.19$$

The total salary paid is \$223,210.19.

53. $A = 200\dfrac{\left(1+\tfrac{0.1}{12}\right)^{18 \cdot 12}-1}{\tfrac{0.1}{12}} \approx 120{,}112.64$

You will save \$120,112.64.

54. $4(0.7) + 4(0.7)^2 + \cdots$

$r = 0.7$

$$S_\infty = \frac{4(0.7)}{1-0.7} = 9.\overline{3}$$

The total spending is $9\tfrac{1}{3}$ million.

55. S_1: $5 = \dfrac{5(1)(1+1)}{2}$

$\quad\quad 5 = \dfrac{5(2)}{2}$

$\quad\quad 5 = 5$ is true.

S_k: $5+10+15+\cdots+5k = \dfrac{5k(k+1)}{2}$

S_{k+1}: $5+10+15+\cdots+5k+5(k+1) = \dfrac{5(k+1)(k+2)}{2}$

Add $5(k+1)$ to both sides of S_k:

$5+10+15+\cdots+5k+5(k+1) = \dfrac{5k(k+1)}{2}+5(k+1)$

Simplify the right-hand side:

$\dfrac{5k(k+1)}{2}+5(k+1) = \dfrac{5k(k+1)+10(k+1)}{2} = \dfrac{(5k+10)(k+1)}{2}$

$\quad\quad = \dfrac{5(k+1)(k+2)}{2}$

If S_k is true, then S_{k+1} is true.
The statement is true for all n.

56. S_1: $1 = \dfrac{4^1-1}{3}$

$\quad\quad 1 = \tfrac{3}{3}$

$\quad\quad 1 = 1$ is true.

S_k: $1+4+4^2+\cdots+4^{k-1} = \dfrac{4^k-1}{3}$

S_{k+1}: $1+4+4^2+\cdots+4^{k-1}+4^k = \dfrac{4^{k+1}-1}{3}$

Add 4^k to both sides of S_k:

$1+4+4^2+\cdots+4^{k-1}+4^k = \dfrac{4^k-1}{3}+4^k$

Simplify the right-hand side:

$\dfrac{4^k-1}{3}+4^k = \dfrac{4^k-1+3\cdot4^k}{3} = \dfrac{4\cdot4^k-1}{3}$

$\quad\quad = \dfrac{4^{k+1}-1}{3}$

If S_k is true, then S_{k+1} is true. The statement is true for all n.

57. S_1: $2 = 2(1)^2$

$\quad\quad$ $2 = 2$ is true.

$\quad$ S_k: $2 + 6 + 10 + \cdots + (4k - 2) = 2k^2$

$\quad$ S_{k+1}: $2 + 6 + 10 + \cdots + (4k - 2) + (4k + 2) = 2(k + 1)^2$

$\quad$ Add $(4k + 2)$ to both sides of S_k:

$\quad\quad$ $2 + 6 + 10 + \cdots + (4k - 2) + (4k + 2) = 2k^2 + (4k + 2)$

$\quad$ Simplify the right-hand side:

$\quad\quad$ $2k^2 + 4k + 2 = 2(k^2 + 2k + 1)$

$\quad\quad\quad\quad\quad\quad\quad\; = 2(k + 1)^2$

$\quad$ If S_k is true, then S_{k+1} is true. The statement is true for all n.

58. S_1: $1 \cdot 3 = \dfrac{1(1+1)[2(1) + 7]}{6}$

$\quad\quad\quad$ $3 = \dfrac{2 \cdot 9}{6}$

$\quad\quad\quad$ $3 = \dfrac{18}{6}$

$\quad\quad\quad$ $3 = 3$ is true.

$\quad$ S_k: $\; 1 \cdot 3 + 2 \cdot 4 + 3 \cdot 5 + \cdots + k(k + 2) = \dfrac{k(k+1)(2k+7)}{6}$

$\quad$ S_{k+1}: $\; 1 \cdot 3 + 2 \cdot 4 + 3 \cdot 5 + \cdots + k(k + 2) + (k + 1)(k + 3) = \dfrac{(k+1)(k+2)(2k+9)}{6}$

$\quad$ Add $(k + 1)(k + 3)$ to both sides of S_k:

$\quad\quad$ $1 \cdot 3 + 2 \cdot 4 + 3 \cdot 5 + \cdots + k(k + 2) + (k + 1)(k + 3) = \dfrac{k(k+1)(2k+7)}{6} + (k+1)(k+3)$

$\quad$ Simplify the right-hand side:

$\quad\quad$ $= \dfrac{k(k+1)(2k+7)}{6} + (k+1)(k+3)$

$\quad\quad$ $= \dfrac{k(k+1)(2k+7) + 6(k+1)(k+3)}{6}$

$\quad\quad$ $= \dfrac{(k+1)[k(2k+7) + 6(k+3)]}{6}$

$\quad\quad$ $= \dfrac{(k+1)(2k^2 + 13k + 18)}{6}$

$\quad\quad$ $= \dfrac{(k+1)(k+2)(2k+9)}{6}$

$\quad$ If S_k is true, then S_{k+1} is true. The statement is true for all n.

59. S_1: 2 is a factor of $1^2 + 5(1) = 6$ since $6 = 2 \cdot 3$.

S_k: 2 is a factor of $k^2 + 5k$.

S_{k+1}: 2 is a factor of $(k+1)^2 + 5(k+1)$.

$$
\begin{aligned}
(k+1)^2 + 5(k+1) &= k^2 + 2k + 1 + 5k + 5 \\
&= k^2 + 7k + 6 \\
&= k^2 + 5k + 2(k+3) \\
&= \left(k^2 + 5k\right) + 2(k+3)
\end{aligned}
$$

Because we assume S_k is true, we know 2 is a factor of $k^2 + 5k$. Since 2 is a factor of $2(k+3)$, we conclude 2 is a factor of the sum $\left(k^2 + 5k\right) + 2(k+3)$. If S_k is true, then S_{k+1} is true. The statement is true for all n.

60. $\dbinom{11}{8} = \dfrac{11!}{3!8!} = \dfrac{11 \cdot 10 \cdot 9}{3 \cdot 2 \cdot 1} = 165$

61. $\dbinom{90}{2} = \dfrac{90!}{88!2!} = \dfrac{90 \cdot 89}{2 \cdot 1} = 4005$

62. $(2x+1)^3 = \dbinom{3}{0}(2x)^3 + \dbinom{3}{1}(2x)^2 \cdot 1 + \dbinom{3}{2}(2x)1^2 + \dbinom{3}{3}1^3 = 8x^3 + 3\left(4x^2\right) + 3(2x) + 1$

$\qquad = 8x^3 + 12x^2 + 6x + 1$

63. $\left(x^2 - 1\right)^4 = \dbinom{4}{0}\left(x^2\right)^4 + \dbinom{4}{1}\left(x^2\right)^3(-1) + \dbinom{4}{2}\left(x^2\right)^2(-1)^2 + \dbinom{4}{3}x^2(-1)^3 + \dbinom{4}{4}(-1)^4$

$\qquad = x^8 - 4x^6 + 6x^4 - 4x^2 + 1$

64. $(x+2y)^5 = \dbinom{5}{0}x^5 + \dbinom{5}{1}x^4(2y) + \dbinom{5}{2}x^3(2y)^2 + \dbinom{5}{3}x^2(2y)^3 + \dbinom{5}{4}x(2y)^4 + \dbinom{5}{5}(2y)^5$

$\qquad = x^5 + 5(2)x^4 y + 10(4)x^3 y^2 + 10(8)x^2 y^3 + 5(16)xy^4 + 32y^5$

$\qquad = x^5 + 10x^4 y + 40x^3 y^2 + 80x^2 y^3 + 80xy^4 + 32y^5$

65. $(x-2)^6 = \dbinom{6}{0}x^6 + \dbinom{6}{1}x^5(-2) + \dbinom{6}{2}x^4(-2)^2 + \dbinom{6}{3}x^3(-2)^3 + \dbinom{6}{4}x^2(-2)^4 + \dbinom{6}{5}x(-2)^5\dbinom{6}{6}(-2)^6$

$\qquad = x^6 + 6x^5(-2) + 15x^4(4) + 20x^3(-8) + 15x^2(16) + 6x(-32) + 64$

$\qquad = x^6 - 12x^5 + 60x^4 - 160x^3 + 240x^2 - 192x + 64$

66. $\left(x^2 + 3\right)^8 = \dbinom{8}{0}\left(x^2\right)^8 + \dbinom{8}{1}\left(x^2\right)^7 \cdot 3 + \dbinom{8}{2}\left(x^2\right)^6 \cdot 3^2 + \cdots$

$\qquad = x^{16} + 8x^{14} \cdot 3 + 28x^{12} \cdot 9 + \cdots$

$\qquad = x^{16} + 24x^{14} + 252x^{12} + \cdots$

67. $(x-3)^9$

$$= \binom{9}{0}x^9 + \binom{9}{1}x^8(-3) + \binom{9}{2}x^7(-3)^2 + \cdots$$

$$= x^9 + 9(-3)x^8 + 36(9)x^7 + \cdots$$

$$= x^9 - 27x^8 + 324x^7 - \cdots$$

68. $(x+2)^5$

fourth term $= \binom{5}{3}x^2(2)^3 = 10(8)x^2 = 80x^2$

69. $(2x-3)^6$

fifth term $= \binom{6}{4}(2x)^2(-3)^4 = 15(4x^2)(81)$

$$= 4860x^2$$

70. $_8P_3 = \dfrac{8!}{5!} = 8 \cdot 7 \cdot 6 = 336$

71. $_9P_5 = \dfrac{9!}{4!} = 9 \cdot 8 \cdot 7 \cdot 6 \cdot 5 = 15,120$

72. $_8C_3 = \dfrac{8!}{5!3!} = \dfrac{8 \cdot 7 \cdot 6}{3 \cdot 2 \cdot 1} = 56$

73. $_{13}C_{11} = \dfrac{13!}{2!11!} = \dfrac{13 \cdot 12}{2 \cdot 1} = 78$

74. $4 \cdot 5 = 20$ choices

75. $3^5 = 243$ possibilities

76. $_{15}P_4 = \dfrac{15!}{11!} = 15 \cdot 14 \cdot 13 \cdot 12 = 32,760$ ways

77. $_{20}C_4 = \dfrac{20!}{16!4!} = \dfrac{20 \cdot 19 \cdot 18 \cdot 17}{4 \cdot 3 \cdot 2 \cdot 1} = 4845$ ways

78. $_{20}C_3 = \dfrac{20!}{17!3!} = \dfrac{20 \cdot 19 \cdot 18}{3 \cdot 2 \cdot 1} = 1140$ sets

79. $_{20}P_4 = \dfrac{20!}{16!} = 20 \cdot 19 \cdot 18 \cdot 17$

$$= 116,280 \text{ ways}$$

80. $5! = 120$ ways

81. $P(E) = \dfrac{9,630,188}{31,878,234} \approx 0.302$

82. $P(E) = \dfrac{5,503,372}{19,128,261} \approx 0.288$

83. $P(E) = \dfrac{n(E)}{n(S)} = \dfrac{4}{6} = \dfrac{2}{3}$

84. $P(E) = \dfrac{2}{6} + \dfrac{2}{6} = \dfrac{4}{6} = \dfrac{2}{3}$

85. $P(E) = \dfrac{4}{52} + \dfrac{4}{52} = \dfrac{8}{52} = \dfrac{2}{13}$

86. $P(E) = \dfrac{4}{52} + \dfrac{26}{52} - \dfrac{2}{52} = \dfrac{28}{52} = \dfrac{7}{13}$

87. $P(\text{not yellow}) = 1 - P(\text{yellow}) = 1 - \dfrac{1}{6} = \dfrac{5}{6}$

88. $P(E) = \dfrac{3}{6} + \dfrac{3}{6} - \dfrac{1}{6} = \dfrac{5}{6}$

89. a. $P(E) = \dfrac{n(E)}{n(S)} = \dfrac{1}{_{20}C_5} = \dfrac{1}{15,504}$

b. $P(E) = \dfrac{100}{15,504} = \dfrac{25}{3876}$

90. $P(E) = \dfrac{70}{200} + \dfrac{140}{200} - \dfrac{50}{200} = \dfrac{160}{200} = \dfrac{4}{5}$

91. $P(E) = \dfrac{60}{200} + \dfrac{130}{200} - \dfrac{40}{200} = \dfrac{150}{200} = \dfrac{3}{4}$

92. $P(E) = \left(\dfrac{1}{2}\right)^5 = \dfrac{1}{32}$

93. a. $(0.2)^2 = 0.04$

b. $(0.2)^3 = 0.008$

c. $(1-0.2)^4 = (0.8)^4 = 0.4096$

Chapter 11 Test

1. $a_n = \dfrac{(-1)^{n+1}}{n^2}$

$a_1 = \dfrac{(-1)^2}{1^2} = 1$

$a_2 = \dfrac{(-1)^3}{2^2} = -\dfrac{1}{4}$

$a_3 = \dfrac{(-1)^4}{3^2} = \dfrac{1}{9}$

$a_4 = \dfrac{(-1)^5}{4^2} = -\dfrac{1}{16}$

$a_5 = \dfrac{(-1)^6}{5^2} = \dfrac{1}{25}$

The first five terms are

$1, -\dfrac{1}{4}, \dfrac{1}{9}, -\dfrac{1}{16},$ and $\dfrac{1}{25}$.

2. $\displaystyle\sum_{i=1}^{5}\left(i^2 + 10\right) = 11 + 14 + 19 + 26 + 35 = 105$

3. $\displaystyle\sum_{i=1}^{20}(3i - 1)$

$a_1 = 3 - 1 = 1$

$d = 3$

$a_n = -1 + (n-1)3$

$a_{20} = -1 + (19)3 = 56$

$S_{20} = \dfrac{20}{2}(-1 + 56) = 550$

4. $\displaystyle\sum_{i=1}^{15}(-2)^i$

$a_1 = -2, \ r = -2$

$S_{15} = \dfrac{-2\left[1 - (-2)^{15}\right]}{1 - (-2)} = -21,846$

5. $\dbinom{9}{2} = \dfrac{9!}{7!2!} = \dfrac{9 \cdot 8}{2 \cdot 1} = 36$

6. $_{10}P_3 = \dfrac{10!}{7!} = 10 \cdot 9 \cdot 8 = 720$

7. $_{10}C_3 = \dfrac{10!}{7!3!} = \dfrac{10 \cdot 9 \cdot 8}{3 \cdot 2 \cdot 1} = 120$

8. $\dfrac{2}{3} + \dfrac{3}{4} + \dfrac{4}{5} + \cdots + \dfrac{21}{22} = \displaystyle\sum_{i=1}^{20} \dfrac{i+1}{i+2}$

9. $4, 9, 14, 19, \ldots$

$a_1 = 4, \ d = 5$

$a_n = 4 + (n-1) \cdot 5 = 4 + 5n - 5$

$a_n = 5n - 1$

$a_{12} = 5(12) - 1 = 59$

10. $16, 4, 1, \dfrac{1}{4}, \ldots$

$a_1 = 16, \ r = \dfrac{1}{4}$

$a_n = 16\left(\dfrac{1}{4}\right)^{n-1}$

$a_{12} = 16\left(\dfrac{1}{4}\right)^{11} = \dfrac{1}{262,144}$

11. $7, -14, 28, -56, \ldots$

$a_1 = 7, \ r = -2$

$S_{10} = \dfrac{7\left[1 - (-2)^{10}\right]}{1 - (-2)} = \dfrac{7(-1023)}{3} = -2387$

12. $-7, -14, -21, -28, \ldots$

$a_1 = -7, \ d = -7$

$a_n = -7 + (n-1)(-7)$

$a_{10} = -7 + 9(-7) = -70$

$S_{10} = \dfrac{10}{2}(-7 - 70) = -385$

13. $4 + \dfrac{4}{2} + \dfrac{4}{2^2} + \dfrac{4}{2^3} + \cdots$

$r = \dfrac{1}{2}$

$S_{\infty} = \dfrac{4}{1 - \dfrac{1}{2}} = 8$

783

14. $a_1 = 30,000, \ r = 1.04$

$$S_8 = \frac{30,000\left[1 - (1.04)^8\right]}{1 - 1.04} \approx 276,426.79$$

The total salary is $276,426.79.

15. $S_1: 1 = \dfrac{1[3(1) - 1]}{2}$

$\qquad 1 = \dfrac{2}{2}$

$\qquad 1 = 1$ is true.

$S_k: 1 + 4 + 7 + \cdots + (3k - 2) = \dfrac{k(3k - 1)}{2}$

$S_{k+1}: \ 1 + 4 + 7 + \cdots + (3k - 2) + (3k + 1) = \dfrac{(k + 1)(3k + 2)}{2}$

Add $(3k + 1)$ to both sides of S_k:

$$1 + 4 + 7 + \cdots + (3k - 2) + (3k + 1) = \frac{k(3k - 1)}{2} + (3k + 1)$$

Simplify the right-hand side:

$$\frac{k(3k - 1)}{2} + (3k + 1) = \frac{k(3k - 1) + 2(3k + 1)}{2}$$

$$= \frac{3k^2 + 5k + 2}{2}$$

$$= \frac{(k + 1)(3k + 2)}{2}$$

If S_k is true, then S_{k+1} is true. The statement is true for all n.

16. $\left(x^2 - 1\right)^5 = \dbinom{5}{0}\left(x^2\right)^5 + \dbinom{5}{1}\left(x^2\right)^4(-1) + \dbinom{5}{2}\left(x^2\right)^3(-1)^2 + \dbinom{5}{3}\left(x^2\right)^2(-1)^3 + \dbinom{5}{4}x^2(-1)^4 + \dbinom{5}{5}(-1)^5$

$\qquad = x^{10} - 5x^8 + 10x^6 - 10x^4 + 5x^2 - 1$

17. $_{11}P_3 = \dfrac{11!}{8!} = 11 \cdot 10 \cdot 9 = 990$ ways

18. $_{10}C_4 = \dfrac{10!}{6! \, 4!} = \dfrac{10 \cdot 9 \cdot 8 \cdot 7}{4 \cdot 3 \cdot 2 \cdot 1} = 210$ sets

19.   Four digits are open: $10^4 = 10,000$

20. $_{15}C_6 = \dfrac{15!}{9! \, 6!} = \dfrac{15 \cdot 14 \cdot 13 \cdot 12 \cdot 11 \cdot 10}{6 \cdot 5 \cdot 4 \cdot 3 \cdot 2} = 5005$

$\qquad P(E) = \dfrac{50}{5005} = \dfrac{10}{1001}$

21. $P(E) = \dfrac{26}{52} + \dfrac{12}{52} - \dfrac{6}{52} = \dfrac{32}{52} = \dfrac{8}{13}$

22. $P(E) = \dfrac{25}{50} + \dfrac{20}{50} - \dfrac{15}{50} = \dfrac{30}{50} = \dfrac{3}{5}$

23. $P(E) = \left(\dfrac{1}{4}\right)^4 = \dfrac{1}{256}$

24. $P(E) = \dfrac{2}{8} \cdot \dfrac{2}{8} = \dfrac{1}{16}$

Cumulative Review Exercises (Chapters 1–11)

1. $-(x - 5) + 10 = 3(x + 2)$
$$-2x + 10 + 10 = 3x + 6$$
$$14 = 5x$$
$$x = \frac{14}{5}$$
The solution set is $\left\{\dfrac{14}{5}\right\}$.

2. $3x^2 - 6x + 2 = 0$
$$x = \frac{6 \pm \sqrt{36 - 24}}{6}$$
$$= \frac{6 \pm \sqrt{12}}{6}$$
$$= \frac{6 \pm 2\sqrt{3}}{6}$$
$$= \frac{3 \pm \sqrt{3}}{3}$$
The solution set is $\left\{\dfrac{3 + \sqrt{3}}{3}, \dfrac{3 - \sqrt{3}}{3}\right\}$.

3. $\log_2 x + \log_2 (2x - 3) = 1$
$$\log_2 x(2x - 3) = 1$$
$$x(2x - 3) = 2$$
$$2x^2 - 3x - 2 = 0$$
$$(2x + 1)(x - 2) = 0$$
$$2x + 1 = 0 \quad \text{or} \quad x - 2 = 0$$
$$x = -\frac{1}{2} \qquad\qquad x = 2$$

$x = -\dfrac{1}{2}$ does not check since $\log_2\left(-\dfrac{1}{2}\right)$
does not exist.
The solution set is $\{2\}$.

4. $x^{1/2} - 6x^{1/4} + 8 = 0$
Let $t = x^{1/4}$.
$$t^2 - 6t + 8 = 0$$
$$(t - 2)(t - 4) = 0$$
$$t - 2 = 0 \quad \text{or} \quad t - 4 = 0$$
$$t = 2 \qquad\qquad t = 4$$
$$x^{1/4} = 2 \qquad\qquad x^{1/4} = 4$$
$$x = 16 \qquad\qquad x = 256$$
The solution set is $\{16, 256\}$.

5. $\sqrt{2x + 4} - \sqrt{x + 3} - 1 = 0$
$$\left(\sqrt{2x + 4}\right)^2 = \left(\sqrt{x + 3} + 1\right)^2$$
$$2x + 4 = (x + 3) + 2\sqrt{x + 3} + 1$$
$$x = 2\sqrt{x + 3}$$
$$x^2 = 4(x + 3)$$
$$x^2 - 4x - 12 = 0$$
$$(x - 6)(x + 2) = 0$$
$$x - 6 = 0 \quad \text{or} \quad x + 2 = 0$$
$$x = 6 \qquad\qquad x = -2$$
$$x = -2 \text{ does not check.}$$
The solution set is $\{6\}$.

6. $|2x + 1| \leq 1$

$-1 \leq 2x + 1 \leq 1$

$-2 \leq 2x \leq 0$

$-1 \leq x \leq 0$ or $[-1, 0]$

The solution set is $\{x | -1 \leq x \leq 0\}$ or $[-1, 0]$.

7.
$$6x^2 - 6 < 5x$$
$$6x^2 - 5x - 6 < 0$$
$$6x^2 - 5x - 6 = 0$$
$$(3x + 2)(2x - 3) = 0$$
$$3x + 2 = 0 \text{ or } 2x - 3 = 0$$
$$x = -\frac{2}{3} \qquad x = \frac{3}{2}$$

The test intervals are $\left(-\infty, -\frac{2}{3}\right)$, $\left(-\frac{2}{3}, \frac{3}{2}\right)$, and $\left(\frac{3}{2}, \infty\right)$. Testing a point in each interval shows that the solution is $\left(-\frac{2}{3}, \frac{3}{2}\right)$.

8. $\dfrac{x-1}{x+3} \leq 0$

The test intervals are $(-\infty, -3)$, $(-3, 1)$ and $(1, \infty)$.

Testing a point in each interval shows that the solution is $(-3, 1]$.

9.
$$30e^{0.7x} = 240$$
$$e^{0.7x} = 8$$
$$\ln e^{0.7x} = \ln 8$$
$$0.7x = \ln 8$$
$$x = \frac{\ln 8}{0.7}$$

The solution set is $\left\{\dfrac{\ln 8}{0.7}\right\}$, approximately 2.9706.

10. $2x^3 + 3x^2 - 8x + 3 = 0$

p: ± 1, ± 3

q: ± 1, ± 2

$\dfrac{p}{q}$: ± 1, ± 3, $\pm \dfrac{1}{2}$, $\pm \dfrac{3}{2}$

$$
\begin{array}{r|rrrr}
1 & 2 & 3 & -8 & 3 \\
  &   & 2 & 5 & -3 \\
\hline
  & 2 & 5 & -3 & 0
\end{array}
$$

$(x - 1)(2x^2 + 5x - 3) = 0$

$(x - 1)(2x - 1)(x + 3) = 0$

$x = 1$ or $x = \dfrac{1}{2}$ or $x = -3$

The solution set is $\left\{-3, \dfrac{1}{2}, 1\right\}$.

11. $4x^2 + 3y^2 = 48$

$3x^2 + 2y^2 = 35$

Multiply equation 1 by -2.

Multiply equation 2 by 3.

$$-8x^2 - 6y^2 = -96$$
$$\underline{9x^2 + 6y^2 = 105}$$

Add: $\qquad x^2 = 9$

$\qquad\qquad x = \pm 3$

Let $x = -3$:

$$4(-3)^2 + 3y^2 = 48$$
$$36 + 3y^2 = 48$$
$$3y^2 = 12$$
$$y^2 = 4$$
$$y = \pm 2$$

Let $x = 3$:

$$4(3)^2 + 3y^2 = 48$$
$$36 + 3y^2 = 48$$
$$3y^2 = 12$$
$$y^2 = 4$$
$$y = \pm 2$$

The solution set is $\{(3, 2), (3, -2), (-3, 2), (-3, -2)\}$.

12.
$$x - 2y + z = 16$$
$$2x - y - z = 14$$
$$3x + 5y - 4z = -10$$

$$\begin{bmatrix} 1 & -2 & 1 & | & 16 \\ 0 & -1 & -1 & | & 14 \\ 3 & 5 & -4 & | & -10 \end{bmatrix} \begin{matrix} \\ -2R_1 + R_2 \\ -3R_1 + R_3 \end{matrix}$$

$$\begin{bmatrix} 1 & -2 & 1 & | & 16 \\ 0 & 3 & -3 & | & -18 \\ 0 & 11 & -7 & | & -58 \end{bmatrix} \begin{matrix} \\ \tfrac{1}{3}R_2 \\ \\ \end{matrix}$$

$$\begin{bmatrix} 1 & -2 & 1 & | & 16 \\ 0 & 1 & -1 & | & -6 \\ 0 & 11 & -7 & | & -58 \end{bmatrix} \begin{matrix} \\ 2R_2 + R_1 \\ -11R_2 + R_3 \end{matrix}$$

$$\begin{bmatrix} 1 & 0 & -1 & | & 4 \\ 0 & 1 & -1 & | & -6 \\ 0 & 0 & 4 & | & 8 \end{bmatrix} \begin{matrix} \\ \\ \tfrac{1}{4}R_3 \end{matrix}$$

$$\begin{bmatrix} 1 & 0 & -1 & | & 4 \\ 0 & 1 & -1 & | & -6 \\ 0 & 0 & 1 & | & 2 \end{bmatrix} \begin{matrix} R_3 + R_1 \\ R_2 + R_1 \\ \\ \end{matrix}$$

$$\begin{bmatrix} 1 & 0 & 0 & | & 6 \\ 0 & 1 & 0 & | & -4 \\ 0 & 0 & 1 & | & 2 \end{bmatrix} \begin{matrix} R_3 + R_1 \\ R_2 + R_1 \\ \\ \end{matrix}$$

The solution set is $\{(6, -4, 2)\}$.

13.
$$x - y = 1$$
$$x^2 - x - y = 1$$
Multiply $x - y = 1$ by -1, then add
$$-x + y = -1$$
$$\overline{\quad x^2 - x - y = 1\quad}$$
$$x^2 - 2x = 0$$
$$x(x - 2) = 0$$
$x = 0$ or $x = 2$
If $x = 0$, $-y = 1$ so $y = -1$.
If $x = 2$, $2 - y = 1$ so $y = 1$.
The solution set is $\{(0, -1), (2, 1)\}$.

14. $100x^2 + y^2 = 25$
$$4x^2 + \frac{y^2}{25} = 1$$
$$\frac{x^2}{\left(\frac{1}{4}\right)} + \frac{y^2}{25} = 1$$
Ellipse
Foci on the y-axis
$$a^2 = 25 \text{ and } b^2 = \frac{1}{4}, \text{ so } \frac{1}{4} = 25 - c^2.$$
$$c^2 = \frac{99}{4}$$
$$c = \frac{3\sqrt{11}}{2}$$
Foci: $\left(0, -\frac{3\sqrt{11}}{2}\right), \left(0, \frac{3\sqrt{11}}{2}\right)$

15. $4x^2 - 9y^2 - 16x + 54y - 29 = 0$

$$4(x^2 - 4x) - 9(y^2 - 6y) = 29$$

$$4(x^2 - 4x + 4) - 9(y^2 - 6y + 9) = 16 - 81 + 29$$

$$4(x-2)^2 - 9(y-3)^2 = -36$$

$$\frac{(y-3)^2}{4} - \frac{(x-2)^2}{9} = 1$$

Hyperbola with center at (2, 3)

Transverse axis vertical

$a^2 = 4$ and $b^2 = 9$, so $9 = c^2 - 4$.

$c^2 = 13$

$c = \sqrt{13}$

Foci: $\left(2, 3 - \sqrt{13}\right), \left(2, 3 + \sqrt{13}\right)$

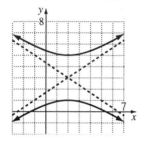

16. $f(x) = \dfrac{x^2 - 1}{x - 2}$

Symmetry:

$$f(-x) = \frac{x^2 - 1}{-x - 2}$$

No symmetry since $f(-x) \ne f(x)$ and $f(-x) \ne -f(-x)$.

x-intercepts:

$x^2 - 1 = 0$

    $x = \pm 1$

y-intercept:

$f(0) = \dfrac{1}{2}$

   $y = \dfrac{1}{2}$

Vertical asymptote:

$x - 2 = 0$

   $x = 2$

Horizontal asymptote:

$n > m$, so no horizontal asymptote.

Slant asymptote:

$n = m + 1$

$$f(x) = x + 2 + \frac{3}{x - 2}$$

    $y = x + 2$

17. $2x - y \ge 4$

     $x \le 2$

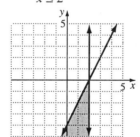

18. $f(x) = x^2 - 4x - 5$

$x = \dfrac{-b}{2a} = \dfrac{4}{2} = 2$

$f(2) = 2^2 - 8 - 5 = -9$

vertex: $(2, -9)$

x-intercepts:

$x^2 - 4x - 5 = 0$

$(x - 5)(x + 1) = 0$

$x = 5, -1$

y-intercept: $f(0) = -5$

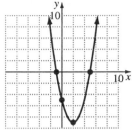

19. $y = \log_2 x$

20. $f(x) = \sqrt[3]{x + 4}$

$y = \sqrt[3]{x + 4}$

$x = \sqrt[3]{y + 4}$

$x^3 = y + 4$

$y = x^3 - 4$

$f^{-1}(x) = x^3 - 4$

21.

$AB - 4A = \begin{bmatrix} 4 & 2 \\ 1 & -1 \\ 0 & 5 \end{bmatrix} \begin{bmatrix} 2 & 4 \\ 3 & 1 \end{bmatrix} - 4 \begin{bmatrix} 4 & 2 \\ 1 & 1 \\ 0 & 5 \end{bmatrix}$

$= \begin{bmatrix} 14 & 18 \\ -1 & 3 \\ 15 & 5 \end{bmatrix} - \begin{bmatrix} 16 & 8 \\ 4 & -4 \\ 0 & 20 \end{bmatrix} = \begin{bmatrix} -2 & 10 \\ -5 & 7 \\ 15 & -15 \end{bmatrix}$

22. $\dfrac{2x^2 - 10x + 2}{(x - 2)(x^2 + 2x + 2)} = \dfrac{A}{x - 2} + \dfrac{Bx + C}{x^2 + 2x + 2}$

$2x^2 - 10x + 2$

$= A(x^2 + 2x + 2) + (Bx + C)(x - 2)$

$= Ax^2 + 2Ax + 2A + Bx^2 - 2Bx + Cx - 2C$

$= (A + B)x^2 + (2A - 2B + C)x + 2A - 2C$

Thus we have the following system of equations.

$A + B = 2$

$2A - 2B + C = -10$

$2A - 2C = 2$

Add twice the first equation to the second equation.

$2A + 2B = 4$

$\underline{2A - 2B + C = -10}$

$4A + C = -6$

Add twice the resulting equation to the third equation.

$8A + 2C = -12$

$\underline{2A - 2C = 2}$

$10A = -10$

$A = -1$

Back-substitute to find B and C.

$2(-1) - 2C = 2$

$-2 - 2C = 2$

$-2C = 4$

$C = -2$

$-1 + B = 2$

$B = 3$

We have the following partial fraction decomposition.

$\dfrac{-1}{x - 2} + \dfrac{3x - 2}{x^2 + 2x + 2}$

23. $(x^3 + 2y)^5 = \binom{5}{0}(x^3)^5 + \binom{5}{1}(x^3)^4(2y) + \binom{5}{2}(x^3)^3(2y)^2 + \binom{5}{3}(x^3)^2(2y)^3 + \binom{5}{4}(x^3)(2y)^4 + \binom{5}{5}(2y)^5$

$\qquad = x^{15} + 5x^{12}(2y) + 10x^9(4y^2) + 10x^6(8y^3) + 5x^3(16y^4) + 32y^5$

$\qquad = x^{15} + 10x^{12}y + 40x^9y^2 + 80x^6y^3 + 80x^3y^4 + 32y^5$

24. $\displaystyle\sum_{i=1}^{50}(4i - 25)$

$\qquad a_1 = 4(1) - 25 = -21$

$\qquad a_{50} = 4(50) - 25 = 175$

$\qquad S_{50} = \dfrac{50}{2}(-21 + 175) = 3850$

25. a. $m = \dfrac{171.1 - 119.4}{10 - 0} = 5.17$

$\qquad y - 119.4 = 5.17x$

b. $y = 5.17x + 119.4$

c. $\qquad\qquad 2000 - 1983 = 17$

$\qquad\qquad y = 5.17(17) + 119.4$

$\qquad\qquad\quad = 207.29$

207.29 billion pieces of mail

26. x = height of Empire State Building

y = height of World Trade Center

$y = 2x - 790$

$\dfrac{x + y}{2} = 980$

Substitute the first equation into the second:

$\dfrac{x + 2x - 790}{2} = 980$

$3x - 790 = 1960$

$\qquad 3x = 2750$

$\qquad x \approx 916.7$

$\qquad y \approx 1043.4$

The Empire State Building is about 916.7 feet tall and the World Trade Center is about 1043.4 feet tall.

27. $2L + 2W = 300$

$\qquad L = W + 50$

Rearrange the equations and add:

$L + W = 150$

$\underline{L - W = 50}$

$\quad 2L = 200$

$\qquad L = 100$

$\qquad W = 50$

length: 100 yards, width 50 yards

28. $10x + 12y = 42$
$\quad\ 5x + 10y = 29$
Multiply second equation by -2
and add:
$$\begin{aligned}
10x + 12y &= 42 \\
\underline{-10x - 20y} &= \underline{-58} \\
-8y &= -16 \\
y &= 2
\end{aligned}$$
Back substitute:
$$5x + 10(2) = 29$$
$$5x = 9$$
$$x = 1.8$$
pen: \$1.80, pad: \$2

29. $s(t) = -16t^2 + 80t + 96$

a. $-16t^2 + 80t + 96 = 0$
$\qquad\ t^2 - 5t - 6 = 0$
$\quad\ (t + 1)(t - 6) = 0$
$\qquad\qquad\quad t = -1 \text{ or } t = 6$
The ball will strike the ground after
6 seconds.

b. $t = \dfrac{-b}{2a} = \dfrac{-80}{-32} = \dfrac{5}{2}$ or 2.5
$S(2.5) = -16(2.5)^2 + 80(2.5) + 96 = 196$
The ball reaches a maximum height of
196 feet, 2.5 seconds after it is thrown.

30. $I = \dfrac{k}{R}$
$5 = \dfrac{k}{22}$
$k = 110$
$I = \dfrac{110}{10} = 11$
11 amperes

31. $d = 10\sin\dfrac{3\pi}{4}t$

a. $|a| = |10| = 10$
The maximum displacement is 10
inches.

b. $f = \dfrac{\omega}{2\pi} = \dfrac{\frac{3\pi}{4}}{2\pi} = \dfrac{3}{8}$
The frequency is $\dfrac{3}{8}$ cycle per second.

c. period $= \dfrac{2\pi}{\omega} = \dfrac{2\pi}{\frac{3\pi}{4}} = \dfrac{8}{3}$
The time required for one oscillation is
$\dfrac{8}{3}$ seconds.

32. $\tan x + \dfrac{1}{\tan x} = \dfrac{\sin x}{\cos x} + \dfrac{1}{\frac{\sin x}{\cos x}} = \dfrac{\sin x}{\cos x} + \dfrac{\cos x}{\sin x}$
$\qquad\qquad = \dfrac{\sin^2 x + \cos^2 x}{\cos x \cdot \sin x}$
$\qquad\qquad = \dfrac{1}{\cos x \cdot \sin x}$

33. $\dfrac{1 - \tan^2 x}{1 + \tan^2 x} = \dfrac{1 - \frac{\sin^2 x}{\cos^2 x}}{1 + \frac{\sin^2 x}{\cos^2 x}} \cdot \dfrac{\cos^2 x}{\cos^2 x}$
$\qquad\qquad = \dfrac{\cos^2 x - \sin^2 x}{\cos^2 x + \sin^2 x}$
$\qquad\qquad = \dfrac{\cos 2x}{1} = \cos 2x$

34. $y = -2\cos(3x - \pi)$
Amplitude: $|A| = |-2| = 2$
Period: $\dfrac{2\pi}{B} = \dfrac{2\pi}{3}$
Phase shift: $\dfrac{C}{B} = \dfrac{\pi}{3}$
$\left(\dfrac{\pi}{3}, -2\right), \left(\dfrac{\pi}{2}, 0\right), \left(\dfrac{2\pi}{3}, 2\right), \left(\dfrac{5\pi}{6}, 0\right),$
$(\pi, -2)$

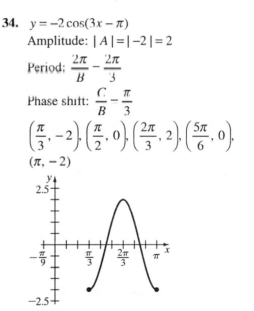

35. $4\cos^2 x = 3$

$\cos^2 x = \dfrac{3}{4}$

$\cos x = \pm\sqrt{\dfrac{3}{4}} = \pm\dfrac{\sqrt{3}}{2}$

$x = \dfrac{\pi}{6}, \dfrac{5\pi}{6}, \dfrac{7\pi}{6}, \dfrac{11\pi}{6}$

The solutions in the interval $[0, 2\pi)$ are

$\dfrac{\pi}{6}, \dfrac{5\pi}{6}, \dfrac{7\pi}{6}$, and $\dfrac{11\pi}{6}$.

36. $2\sin^2 x + 3\cos x - 3 = 0$

$2(1 - \cos^2 x) + 3\cos x - 3 = 0$

$2 - 2\cos^2 x + 3\cos x - 3 = 0$

$2\cos^2 x - 3\cos x + 1 = 0$

$(2\cos x - 1)(\cos x - 1) = 0$

$2\cos x - 1 = 0 \quad \text{or} \quad \cos x - 1 = 0$

$2\cos x = 1 \qquad\qquad \cos x = 1$

$\cos x = \dfrac{1}{2}$

$x = \dfrac{\pi}{3}, \dfrac{5\pi}{3} \quad \text{or} \qquad x = 0$

The solutions in the interval $[0, 2\pi)$ are

$0, \dfrac{\pi}{3}$, and $\dfrac{5\pi}{3}$.

37. $\cot\left[\cos^{-1}\left(-\dfrac{5}{6}\right)\right]$

If $\cos\theta = -\dfrac{5}{6}$, θ lies in quadrant II.

$\cos\theta = -\dfrac{5}{6} = \dfrac{x}{r} = \dfrac{-5}{6}$

$x^2 + y^2 = r^2$

$(-5)^2 + y^2 = 6^2$

$25 + y^2 = 36$

$y^2 = 11$

$\cot\left[\cos^{-1}\left(-\dfrac{5}{6}\right)\right] = \dfrac{x}{y} = \dfrac{-5}{\sqrt{11}} = -\dfrac{5\sqrt{11}}{11}$

38. $r = 1 + 2\cos\theta$
Check for symmetry:

Polar Axis	The Line $\theta = \dfrac{\pi}{2}$	The Pole
$r = 1 + 2\cos(-\theta)$	$-r = 1 + 2\cos(-\theta)$	$-r = 1 + 2\cos\theta$
$r = 1 + 2\cos\theta$	$r = -1 - 2\cos\theta$	$r = -1 - 2\cos\theta$

Graph is symmetric with respect to the polar axis.

θ	0	$\dfrac{\pi}{6}$	$\dfrac{\pi}{3}$	$\dfrac{\pi}{2}$	$\dfrac{2\pi}{3}$	$\dfrac{5\pi}{6}$	π
r	3	2.73	2	1	0	-0.73	-1

Use symmetry to obtain the graph.

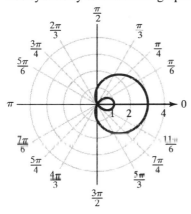

39. $\dfrac{b}{\sin B} = \dfrac{a}{\sin A}$

$\dfrac{32}{\sin B} = \dfrac{22}{\sin 34°}$

$\sin B = \dfrac{32 \sin 34°}{22} \approx 0.8134$

$B_1 \approx 54°, \ B_2 \approx 180° - 54° = 126°$

$C_1 = 180° - B_1 - A \approx 180° - 54° - 34° = 92°$

$C_2 = 180° - B_2 - A \approx 180° - 126° - 34° = 20°$

$\dfrac{c_1}{\sin C_1} = \dfrac{a}{\sin A}$

$\dfrac{c_1}{\sin 92°} = \dfrac{22}{\sin 34°}$

$c_1 = \dfrac{22 \sin 92°}{\sin 34°} \approx 39.3$

$\dfrac{c_2}{\sin C_2} = \dfrac{a}{\sin A}$

$\dfrac{c_2}{\sin 20°} = \dfrac{22}{\sin 34°}$

$c_2 = \dfrac{22 \sin 20°}{\sin 34°} \approx 13.5$

There are two triangles. In the first triangle, the solution is $B_1 \approx 54°$, $C_1 \approx 92°$, and $c_1 \approx 39.3$.

In the other triangle,
$B_2 \approx 126°$, $C_2 \approx 20°$, and $c_2 \approx 13.5$.

40. $x = \sin t, \ y = 1 + \cos^2 t, \ -\dfrac{\pi}{2} < t < \dfrac{\pi}{2}$

$y = 1 + \cos^2 t = 1 + (1 - \sin^2 t)$

$= 1 + (1 - x^2) = 2 - x^2$

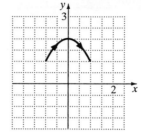